BUSINESS STATISTICS

BUSINESS STATISTICS

THIRD CANADIAN EDITION

NOREAN R.
SHARPE
Georgetown University

RICHARD D.
DE VEAUX
Williams College

PAUL F.
VELLEMAN
Cornell University

DAVID
WRIGHT
University of Ottawa

With contributions by David Bock

Pearson

EDITORIAL DIRECTOR: Claudine O'Donnell
ACQUISITIONS EDITOR: Jennifer Sutton
MARKETING MANAGER: Euan White
PROGRAM MANAGER: Emily Dill
PROJECT MANAGER: Pippa Kennard
MANAGER OF CONTENT DEVELOPMENT: Suzanne Schaan
DEVELOPMENTAL EDITOR: Katherine Goodes
MEDIA EDITOR: Nicole Mellow
MEDIA DEVELOPER: Kelli Cadet

PRODUCTION SERVICES: Cenveo® Publisher Services
PERMISSIONS PROJECT MANAGER: Shruti Jamadagni
TEXT AND PHOTO PERMISSION RESEARCH: Integra Publishing Services
INTERIOR DESIGNER: Anthony Leung
COVER DESIGNER: Anthony Leung
COVER IMAGE: Oleg Tovologuine/Shutterstock
VICE-PRESIDENT, CROSS MEDIA AND PUBLISHING SERVICES: Gary Bennett

Pearson Canada Inc., 26 Prince Andrew Place, Don Mills, Ontario M3C 2T8.

978-0-13-457760-9

2   17

Library and Archives Canada Cataloguing in Publication

Sharpe, Norean Radke, author
   Business statistics / Norean R. Sharpe, Richard D. De Veaux, Paul F. Velleman, David Wright.—Third Canadian edition.

Includes bibliographical references and index.
ISBN 978-0-13-457760-9 (llv)

   1. Commercial statistics—Textbooks. 2. Textbooks—I. Velleman, Paul F., 1949-, author II. Wright, David J. (David John), 1947-, author III. De Veaux, Richard D., author IV. Title.

HF1017.S43 2017   650.01'5195   C2016-906936-2

To my husband, Peter, for his patience and support
—*Norean*

To my family
—*Dick*

To my father, who taught me about ethical business practice
by his constant example as a small businessman and parent
—*Paul*

To Mina, Ramin, Leila, Norman, Rebecca, and Allison
—*David*

Meet the Authors

Norean Radke Sharpe (Ph.D. University of Virginia) has developed an international reputation as an educator, administrator, and consultant on assessment and accreditation. She is currently a professor at the McDonough School of Business at Georgetown University, where she is also Senior Associate Dean and Director of Undergraduate Programs. Prior to joining Georgetown, Norean taught Business Statistics and Operations Research courses to both undergraduate and MBA students for 14 years at Babson College. Before moving into business education, she taught Statistics for several years at Bowdoin College and conducted research at Yale University. Norean is co-author of the recent text, *A Casebook for Business Statistics: Laboratories for Decision Making*, and she has authored more than 30 articles—primarily in the areas of Statistics education and women in science. Norean currently serves as Associate Editor for the journal *Cases in Business, Industry, and Government Statistics*. Her scholarship focuses on business forecasting, Statistics education, and student learning. She is co-founder of the DOME Foundation, a nonprofit foundation that works to increase diversity and outreach in mathematics and engineering, and she currently serves on two other nonprofit boards in the Washington, D.C., area. Norean has been active in increasing the participation of women and underrepresented students in science and mathematics for several years and has two children of her own.

Richard D. De Veaux (Ph.D. Stanford University) is an internationally known educator, consultant, and lecturer. Dick has taught Statistics at a business school (Wharton), an engineering school (Princeton), and a liberal arts college (Williams). While at Princeton, he won a Lifetime Award for Dedication and Excellence in Teaching. Since 1994, he has taught at Williams College, although he returned to Princeton for the academic year 2006–2007 as the William R. Kenan Jr. Visiting Professor of Distinguished Teaching. He is currently the C. Carlisle and Margaret Tippit Professor of Statistics at Williams College. Dick holds degrees from Princeton University in Civil Engineering and Mathematics and from Stanford University in Dance Education and Statistics, where he studied with Persi Diaconis. His research focuses on the analysis of large data sets and data mining in science and industry. Dick has won both the Wilcoxon and Shewell awards from the American Society for Quality. He is an elected member of the International Statistics Institute (ISI) and a Fellow of the American Statistical Association (ASA). He currently serves on the board of directors of the ASA. Dick is also well known in industry, having consulted for such *Fortune* 500 companies as American Express, Hewlett-Packard, Alcoa, DuPont, Pillsbury, General Electric, and Chemical Bank. He was named the Statistician of the Year for 2008 by the Boston Chapter of the American Statistical Association for his contributions to teaching, research, and consulting. In his spare time he is an avid cyclist and swimmer. He also is the founder and bass player for the doo-wop group The Diminished Faculty, and is a frequent singer and soloist with various local choirs, including the Choeur Vittoria of Paris, France. Dick is the father of four children.

Paul F. Velleman (Ph.D. Princeton University) has an international reputation for innovative Statistics education. He designed the Data Desk® software package and is also the author and designer of the award-winning ActivStats® multimedia software, for which he received the EDUCOM Medal for innovative uses of computers in teaching Statistics and the ICTCM Award for Innovation in Using Technology in College Mathematics. He is the founder and CEO of Data Description, Inc. (www.datadesk.com), which supports both of these programs. He also developed the internet site *Data and Story Library* (DASL; lib.stat.cmu.edu/DASL/), which provides data sets for teaching Statistics. Paul co-authored (with David Hoaglin) the book *ABCs of Exploratory Data Analysis*. Paul teaches Statistics at Cornell University in the Department of Statistical Sciences and in the School of Industrial and Labor Relations, for which he has been awarded the MacIntyre Prize for Exemplary Teaching. His research often focuses on statistical graphics and data analysis methods. Paul is a Fellow of the American Statistical Association and of the American Association for the Advancement of Science. Paul's experience as a professor, entrepreneur, and business leader brings a unique perspective to the book. Richard De Veaux and Paul Velleman have authored successful books in the introductory college and AP High School market with David Bock, including *Intro Stats*, Fourth Edition (Pearson,

2014); *Stats: Modeling the World*, Fourth Edition (Pearson, 2015); and *Stats: Data and Models*, Third Edition (Pearson, 2012).

David Wright combines an Engineering Ph.D. from Cambridge University, UK, with his current position as Full Professor at the University of Ottawa's Telfer School of Management to provide a business perspective on new technology. Dr. Wright has taught in universities on three continents and has experience in government and in industry. In government, he has developed statistical models to evaluate the impact of industrial society on natural resource depletion. In industry, he has worked with telecommunications equipment vendors and network operators on the impact of new technology on business. His university teaching and research includes the economics of solar energy, business statistics, and the environmental impact of the ICT industry. He is cited in *Who's Who in the World, Who's Who in Canadian Business,* and *Who's Who in Science and Engineering.*

Brief Contents

Contents

Better Decisions. Better Results

The authors' unique blend of academic, consulting, industrial, government, and entrepreneurial experience brings a compelling, real-world edge to this book that will capture students' interest and equip them with skills for the future.

Analyzing Data and Communicating Results

Plan/Do/Report guided examples walk students through the steps of how to:

- **Plan** the problem, checking assumptions and conditions.

- **Do** the calculations.

- **Report** findings within a business context.

Reports are often presented in the form of a memo to model realistic business communications.

GUIDED EXAMPLE New York Stock Exchange Trading Volume

Are some months on the NYSE busier than others? Boxplots of the number of shares traded by month are a good way to see such patterns. We're interested not only in the centres, but also in the spreads. Are volumes equally variable from month to month, or are they more spread out in some months?

PLAN	Setup Identify the variable, report the time frame of the data, and state the objective.	We want to compare the daily volume of shares traded from month to month on the NYSE during 2006. The daily volume is quantitative and measured in number of shares.
DO	Mechanics Choose an appropriate display for the data.	We can partition the values by month and use side-by-side boxplots to compare the volume across months.
REPORT	Conclusion Report what you've learned about the data and any recommended action or analysis.	MEMO **Re: Research on the Trading Volume of the NYSE** We have examined the daily sales volume on the NYSE (number of shares traded) for each month of 2006. As the attached display shows, sales volume has lower median volume in March and August. The highest median trading activity is found in November. The variability of trading volume also shows a pattern. June and December have higher variability than the rest, and March has noticeably less variability. There were several unusually high-volume days that bear investigation and extremely low-volume days in July and November.

page 110

FOR EXAMPLE   Diamond prices

The price of a jewellery diamond depends on the 4 C's: carat weight, cut, clarity, and colour. Diamond colours are assigned letters from D, for colourless stones, through K, for increasingly more yellow stones. A K-colour stone is only faintly yellow and still considered jewellery quality. We've collected a sample of diamond prices from a website. Here's a scatterplot of *Price* vs. *Carat Weight* with points coloured according to *Colour*:

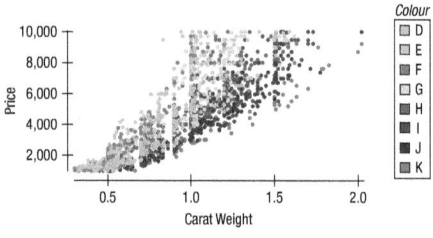

page 646

For Example—short, illustrative business examples have been added to most sections to solidify understanding of newly learned statistical methods and concepts.

The Latest Technology

- **Expanded coverage of the latest software** includes Excel® 2010, with screenshots and guidance on how to use Excel to perform statistical analysis.

Cases

Congratulations! You have now completed all seven chapters of Part I, "Exploring and Collecting Data." A comprehensive case study available online in MyStatLab draws together many of the topics you have learned in Part I. Here is a brief synopsis:

AIDS in Canada

How do we tell the difference between a few isolated cases of a new disease and the start of an epidemic? This case study puts you in the position of a manager at Health Canada, the Canadian Institute for Health Information, and/or the Public Health Agency of Canada when confronted by a new disease. It is based on real data that was available to such a person when AIDS was new and illustrates how to analyze unusual patterns and formats of data using the information from Part I of this book.

Learning Objectives

Chapter	1	2	3	4	5	6	7
Learning Objective	1	1, 2	1	1	5, 7	1, 2	1, 2, 3

Case Studies covering multiple chapters are provided at the end of Parts 1, 2, and 3 of the book, giving students experience working through an in-depth application using real data and scenarios from actual organizations.

page 204

MINI case studies Canadian Exports

Statistics on Canadian exports are used for a variety of purposes, from projecting Canada's foreign exchange earnings to planning capacity in Canadian ports. The file **ch05_MCSP_Canadian_Exports** contains monthly export data from Statistics Canada for three geographical areas. Statistics Canada calculates exports on a "Customs" basis and also on a "Balance of Payments" basis, and the file contains footnotes describing the difference.[6]

a) Draw time series graphs of this export data and identify any major differences between the "Customs" and "Balance of Payments" series.

b) Explain which basis of calculation, "Customs" or "Balance of Payments," would be appropriate for projecting Canada's foreign exchange earnings.

c) Explain which basis of calculation, "Customs" or "Balance of Payments," would be appropriate for planning capacity in Canadian ports.

d) Are there any exceptional periods during which exports in the three geographical areas have differed from overall trends?

Mini Case Studies at the end of each chapter ask students to investigate a question or make a business decision using real data. Students define the objective, plan the process, complete the analysis, and report their conclusion(s). Data are provided.

page 125

Better Statistical Thinking

ETHICS IN ACTION

Beth Ghazi owns Zenna's Café, an independent coffee shop located in a small city in Atlantic Canada. Since opening Zenna's in 2002, she has been steadily growing her business and now distributes her custom coffee blends to a number of regional restaurants and markets. She operates a microroaster that offers specialty-grade Arabica coffees recognized as some of the best in the area. In addition to providing the highest-quality coffees, Beth wants her business to be socially responsible. To that end, she pays fair prices to coffee farmers and donates profits to help charitable causes in Panama, Costa Rica, and Guatemala. She also encourages her employees to get involved in the local community. Recently, one of the well-known multinational coffeehouse chains announced plans to locate shops in her area. This chain is one of the few to offer Certified Free Trade coffee products and work toward social justice in the global community.

Consequently, Beth thought it might be a good idea for her to begin communicating Zenna's message of social responsibility to the public, but with an emphasis on its commitment to the local community. Three months ago, she began collecting data on the number of volunteer hours donated by her employees per week. She has a total of 12 employees, of whom 10 are full-time. Most

employees volunteered fewer than two hours per week, but Beth noticed that one part-time employee volunteered more than 20 hours per week. She discovered that her employees collectively volunteered an average of 15 hours per month (with a median of eight hours). She planned to report the average number and believed that most people would be impressed with Zenna's level of commitment to the local community.

Ethical Issue *The outlier in the data affects the average in a direction that benefits Beth Ghazi and Zenna's Café (related to Item C, ASA Ethical Guidelines; see Appendix C, the American Statistical Association's Ethical Guidelines for Statistical Practice, also available online at www.amstat.org/about/ethicalguidelines.cfm).*

Ethical solution *Beth's data are highly skewed. There is an outlier value (for a part-time employee) that pulls the average number of volunteer hours up. Reporting the average is misleading. In addition, there may be justification to eliminate the value, since it belongs to a part-time employee (and 10 of the 12 employees are full-time). It would be more ethical for Beth to (1) report the average but discuss the outlier value; (2) report the average for only full-time employees; or (3) report the median instead of the average.*

page 122

WHAT CAN GO WRONG?

* **Don't base your null hypotheses on what you see in the data.** You're not allowed to look at the data first and then adjust your null hypothesis so that it will be rejected. If your sample value turns out to be $\hat{p} = 51.8\%$ with a standard deviation of 1%, don't form a null hypothesis as $H_0: p = 49.8\%$, knowing that this will enable you to reject it. Your null hypothesis describes the "nothing interesting" or "nothing has changed" scenario and should not be based on the data you collect.

* **Don't base your alternative hypothesis on the data, either.** You should always think about the situation you're investigating and base your alternative hypothesis on that. Are you interested only in knowing whether something has *increased*? Then write a one-tail (upper tail) alternative. Or would you be equally interested in a change in either direction? Then you want a two-tailed alternative. You should decide whether to do a one- or two-tailed test based on what results would be of interest to you, not on what you might see in the data.

What Can Go Wrong? Sections near the end of each chapter help students detect common statistical errors and practise debunking misuses of statistics.

page 395

Ethics In Action boxes in every chapter teach students to identify challenging issues and propose ethically and statistically sound solutions. Questions are included for study and reflection.

Preface

The question that motivates a business student's study of Statistics is "How can I make better decisions?" As entrepreneurs and consultants, we know that in today's data-rich environment, knowledge of Statistics is essential to survive and thrive in the business world. But, as educators, we've seen a disconnect between the way Business Statistics is traditionally taught and the way it should be used in making business decisions. In *Business Statistics*, we try to narrow the gap between theory and practice by presenting relevant statistical methods that will empower business students to make effective, data-informed decisions.

Of course, students should come away from their Statistics course knowing how to think statistically and how to apply Statistics methods with modern technology. But they must also be able to communicate their analyses effectively to others. When asked about Statistics education, a group of CEOs from *Fortune* 500 companies recently said that although they were satisfied with the technical competence of students who had studied Statistics, they found the students' ability to communicate their findings to be woefully inadequate.

Our "Plan, Do, Report" rubric provides a structure for solving business problems that mimics the correct application of statistics to solving real business problems. Unlike many other books, we emphasize the often neglected thinking (Plan) and communication (Report) steps in problem solving in addition to the methodology (Do). This approach requires up-to-date, real-world examples and data. So we constantly strive to illustrate our lessons with current business issues and examples.

What's New in This Edition?

We've been delighted with the reaction to previous editions of *Business Statistics*. We continue to update examples and exercises so that the story we tell is always tied to the ways Statistics informs modern business practice.

More Use of Canadian Business Examples

We teach with real data whenever possible, so we've updated data throughout the book. New examples reflect current stories in the news and recent economic and business events. The Mini Case Studies have been updated with new data and new contexts.

Improved Pedagogical Features

- **Streamlined design.** Our goal has always been an extremely readable text. In this edition, the major theme of each chapter is more linear and easier to follow. Supporting material is clearly boxed, so students know where to focus their study efforts.
- **Reflecting the Changing World.** Since our previous edition, the world economies have changed with major impacts on business. We have updated many of our examples and exercises to reflect the current situation using recent data.
- **Precise Analysis and Precise Business Implications.** Statistics in practice means making smart decisions based on data. We've tightened our discussions to ensure that rigorous and precise statistical reasoning is applied to realistic business situations, and we then give precise interpretation of our results to support managerial decision making.
- **Learning Objectives.** Each chapter begins with a short list of learning objectives so that it is clear what you should master from this chapter. These objectives are referenced in the margins of the sections that address them and in the end-of-chapter section and chapter exercises.
- **Section Examples.** Almost every section of every chapter includes a focused example to illustrate and apply the concepts and methods discussed in that section.

- **Section Exercises.** Each chapter's exercises begin with single-concept exercises that target section topics. This makes it easier to check your understanding of each topic as you learn it.
- **Recent Data and New Examples.** We teach with real data whenever possible. To keep examples and exercises fresh, we've updated data throughout the book.
- **Chapter Summaries.** Our "What Have We Learned?" chapter summaries link back to the Learning Objectives stated at the start of the chapter so that you can see clearly when you have learned the key concepts in each chapter.
- **Statistical Case Studies.** Each chapter ends with a selection of Mini Case Studies, and there are more extensive cases found on MyStatLab for Parts 1, 2, and 3 of the text. Each part-ending case study covers material from multiple chapters.
- **Streamlined "Technology Help" Sections with Additional Excel Coverage.** Technology Help sections were updated to reflect changes in commercial software, and, when possible, Excel screen shots are included to illustrate the menu options available.

What *We Retained* in This Edition: Statistical Thinking

For all of the improvements, examples, and updates that are included in this edition of *Business Statistics*, we haven't lost sight of our original mission—to write a modern Business Statistics text that addresses the importance of *statistical thinking* when making business decisions and that acknowledges how Statistics is actually used in business.

Statistics is practised with technology. This insight informs everything, from our choice of forms for equations (favouring intuitive forms over calculation forms) to our extensive use of real data. But most important, understanding the value of technology allows us to focus on teaching statistical thinking rather than just calculation. The questions that motivate each of our hundreds of examples are geared not to the question "How do you find the answer?" but rather to the question "Does your data satisfy the necessary assumptions and how do you apply the result to a business situation?" This focus on statistical thinking ties the chapters of the book together.

Our Goal: Read This Book!

The best textbook in the world is of little value if it isn't read. Here are some of the ways we made *Business Statistics* more approachable:

- ***Readability.*** We strive for a conversational, approachable style, and we introduce anecdotes to maintain interest. While using the First Canadian Edition, instructors reported (to their amazement) that their students read ahead of their assignments voluntarily. Students write to tell us (to *their* amazement) that they actually enjoy the book.
- ***Focus on assumptions and conditions.*** More than any other textbook, *Business Statistics* emphasizes the need to verify assumptions when using statistical procedures. We emphasize this focus throughout the examples and exercises. We make every effort to provide templates that reinforce the practice of checking assumptions and conditions, rather than simply rushing through the computations. Business decisions have consequences. Blind calculations open the door to errors that could easily be avoided by taking the time to graph the data, check assumptions and conditions, and then check again that the results make sense.

- *Emphasis on graphing and exploring data.* Our consistent emphasis on the importance of displaying data is evident from the first chapters devoted to understanding data to the sophisticated model-building chapters at the end of the book. Examples often illustrate the value of examining data graphically, and the exercises reinforce this concept. Graphics reveal structures, patterns, and occasional anomalies that could otherwise go unnoticed. The sight of patterns displayed graphically often raises new questions and informs both the path of a resulting statistical analysis and the ensuing business decisions. The graphics that appear throughout the book also demonstrate that the simple structures that underlie even the most sophisticated statistical inferences are the same ones we look for in the simplest examples. That helps to tie the concepts of the book together to tell a coherent story.

- *Consistency.* Having taught the importance of plotting data and checking assumptions and conditions, we are careful to model that behaviour throughout the book. (Check the exercises in the chapters on multiple regression or time series and you'll find us still requiring and demonstrating the plots and checks that were introduced in the early chapters.) This consistency helps reinforce these fundamental principles and provides a familiar foundation for the more sophisticated topics.

Coverage

We were guided in our choice of topics by the GAISE (Guidelines for Assessment and Instruction in Statistics Education) Report, which emerged from extensive studies exploring how students best learn Statistics (**www.amstat.org/education/gaise/**). Those recommendations, now officially adopted and recommended by the American Statistical Association, urge (among other detailed suggestions) that Statistics education should achieve the following goals:

1. Emphasize statistical literacy and develop statistical thinking;
2. Use real data;
3. Stress conceptual understanding rather than mere knowledge of procedures;
4. Foster active learning;
5. Use technology for developing conceptual understanding and analyzing data; and
6. Use assessments to improve and evaluate student learning.

With respect to the order of topics, we followed the principle that a coherent introductory course should be designed so that concepts and methods fit together in a stepwise progression to provide a new understanding of how reasoning with data can uncover new and important truths. For example, we teach inference concepts with proportions *first* and then with means. Most students have had exposure to proportions through polls and advertising. And by starting with proportions, we can teach inference with the Normal model and then introduce inference for means with the Student's t distribution. We introduce the concepts of association, correlation, and regression *early* in *Business Statistics*. Our experience in the classroom shows that introducing these fundamental ideas early makes Statistics useful and relevant, even at the beginning of the course. Later in the semester, when we explore data through inference, it feels natural and logical to build on the fundamental concepts learned earlier.

Syllabus Flexibility

Many instructors prefer to teach topics in a different sequence than the one presented in the textbook. In order to assist you with your decision, Figure 1 is a diagram that illustrates the dependency among chapters.

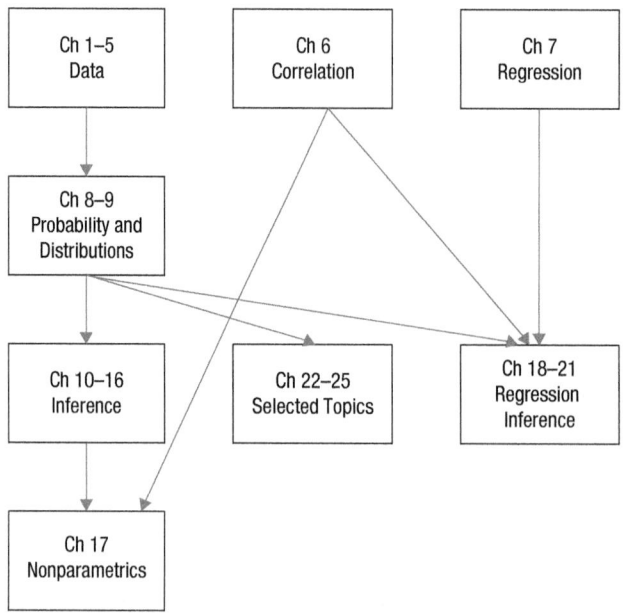

Figure 1   Visual map of the links between chapters

The subject of Business Statistics is sometimes taught in a single semester and other times taught over the course of two semesters. Table 1 offers one suggestion for the way in which chapters can be divided between two semesters.

Features

A textbook isn't just words on a page—instead, it's the cumulation of many features that form a big picture. The features in *Business Statistics* are designed to provide a real-world context for concepts, to help students to apply these concepts, to promote problem solving, and to integrate technology—all in the name of helping students to more readily identify the key themes the book is trying to teach.

	Core Topics				Optional Topics		
	Data	**Regression**	**Probability Distributions**	**Inference**	**Nonparametrics**	**Multiple Regression**	**Selected Topics**
First Semester	Ch 1–5	Ch 6–7	Ch 8–9				Ch 22–25
Second Semester		Ch 18–19		Ch 10–16	Ch 17	Ch 20–21	

Table 1   Chapter selection

Motivating Vignettes. Each chapter opens with a motivating vignette, often taken from the authors' consulting experiences. These descriptions of companies—such as Bell Canada, Sport Chek, Rogers, Intact Financial Corp., Ipsos Reid, PotashCorp of Saskatchewan, Canada's Wonderland, and Loblaw—enhance and illustrate the story of each chapter and show how and why statistical thinking is so vital to modern business decision making. We analyze data from or about the companies in the motivating vignettes throughout the chapter.

FOR EXAMPLE

For Examples. Nearly every section of every chapter includes a focused example that illustrates and applies the concepts or methods of that section. The best way to understand and remember a new theoretical concept or method is to see it applied in a real-world business context right away. That's what these examples do throughout the book.

PLAN

DO

REPORT

Step-by-Step Guided Examples. The answer to a statistical question is almost never just a number. Statistics is about understanding the world and making better decisions with data. To that end, some examples in each chapter are presented as Guided Examples. A thorough solution is modelled in the right column while commentary appears in the left column. The overall analysis follows our innovative **Plan, Do, Report** template. That template begins each analysis with a clear question about a business decision and an examination of the data available (**Plan**). It then moves to calculating the selected statistics (**Do**). Finally, it concludes with a **Report** that specifically addresses the question. To emphasize that our goal is to address the motivating question, we present the **Report** step as a business memo that summarizes the results in the context of the example and states a recommendation if the data are able to support one. To preserve the realism of the example, whenever it is appropriate we include limitations of the analysis or models in the concluding memo, as would be required when writing a report for management.

WHAT CAN GO WRONG?

What Can Go Wrong? Each chapter contains an innovative section called "What Can Go Wrong?" which highlights the most common statistical errors and the misconceptions about Statistics. The most common mistakes for the new user of Statistics involve misusing a method—*not* miscalculating a statistic. Most of the mistakes we discuss have been experienced by the authors in a business context or in a classroom situation. One of our goals is to arm students with the tools to detect statistical errors and to offer practice in debunking misuses of Statistics, whether intentional or not. In this spirit, some of our exercises probe how, and why, common errors tend to arise.

NOTATION ALERT

Notation Alert. Throughout this book, we emphasize the importance of clear communication. Proper notation is part of the vocabulary of Statistics, but it can be daunting. We all know that in Algebra, n can stand for any variable, so it may be surprising to learn that in Statistics, n is reserved for the sample size. Statisticians dedicate many letters and symbols for specific meanings (e.g., the letters b, e, n, p, q, r, s, t, and z, along with many Greek letters, all carry special connotations). Our "Notation Alerts" clarify which letters and symbols statisticians use and the purpose of each letter and symbol.

JUST CHECKING

Just Checking. It is easy to start nodding in agreement without really understanding, so we ask questions at points throughout the chapter. These questions are designed to conduct a quick check of whether or not students have properly understood a section; most involve very little calculation, and the answers are given in Appendix A. The questions can also be used to motivate class discussion.

Optional Math Box

Optional Math Boxes. In many chapters we present the mathematical underpinnings of the statistical methods and concepts. We set proofs, derivations, and justifications apart from the narrative in "Optional Math Boxes," so the underlying mathematics is available for those who want greater depth, but the text itself presents the logical development of the topic at hand using a minimal amount of mathematics.

ETHICS IN ACTION

Ethics in Action. Statistics involves more than simply plugging numbers into formulas; most statistical analyses require a fair amount of judgment. When faced with these sorts of important judgments, the best advice we can offer is to make an honest and ethical attempt to address the appropriate business issue. The chapter-specific *Ethics in Action* boxes illustrate some of the judgments needed when conducting statistical analyses, identify possible errors, link the issues to the American Statistical Association's Ethical Guidelines, and then propose ethically and statistically sound alternative approaches.

WHAT HAVE WE LEARNED?

Learning Objectives and What Have We Learned? Each chapter begins with a specific list of learning objectives and ends by relating the objectives to the chapter summary (i.e., the "What Have We Learned?" section). We review the concepts, define the terms introduced in the chapter, and list the skills that form the core message of the chapter. The "What Have We Learned?" sections make excellent study guides: the student who understands the concepts in the summary, knows the terms, and practises the skills correctly is better prepared to apply statistics to the world of business.

Technology Help

Technology Help. At the end of each chapter, we summarize what students can find in the most common software, often with annotated output. We then offer specific guidance for Excel, Minitab, SPSS, and JMP, formatted in easy-to-read sections. This advice is intended not to replace the documentation that accompanies the software, but rather to point the way and provide startup assistance.

Mini Case Studies. Each chapter includes Mini Case Studies that ask students to conduct an analysis based on a real business situation. Students define the objective, plan the process, complete the analysis, and report a conclusion. An ideal way for students to write up their work is the "Plan/Do/Report" format described above and used in each chapter. Data for the Mini Case Studies are available on the MyStatLab site and are formatted for use with various technologies.

Case Studies. Parts 1, 2, and 3 of the book have a Comprehensive Case Study on MyStatLab. Students are given realistically large data sets (also on the MyStatLab site) and challenged to respond to open-ended business questions using the data. Students have the opportunity to bring together methods they have learned in the chapters included in that part (and indeed, throughout the book) to address the issues raised. Students will be required to use a computer to manipulate the large data sets that accompany these Case Studies.

EXERCISES

Section Exercises. The Exercises for each chapter begin with a series of straightforward exercises targeted at the topics in each chapter section. This is the place to check understanding of specific topics. Because the exercises are labelled by section, turning back to the right part of the chapter to clarify a concept or review a method is easy.

Chapter Exercises. These exercises are designed to be more realistic than the Section Exercises and to lead to conclusions about practical management situations. The Chapter Exercises may combine concepts and methods from different sections. We've worked hard to make sure that they contain relevant, modern, and realistic business situations. Whenever possible, the data are on the MyStatLab site (always in a variety of formats) so they can be explored further. Often, we pair the exercises so that each odd-numbered exercise (with answers that appear at the end of the book) is followed by an even-numbered exercise on the same Statistics topic.

The exercises marked with a data set icon in the margin indicate that the data are provided on the MyStatLab site.

Data and Sources. Most of the data used in examples and exercises stem from real-world sources. Whenever possible, we present the original data as we collected it. Sometimes, due to concerns about confidentiality or privacy, we had to change the values of the data or the names of the variables slightly, always being careful to keep the context as realistic and true to life as possible. Whenever we can, we include references to internet data sources. As internet users know well, URLs often break as websites evolve. To minimize the impact of such changes, we point as high in the address tree as is practical, so it may be necessary to search down into a site to find the data. Moreover, the data online may change as more recent values become available. The data we use are usually posted on the MyStatLab site.

MyStatLab™ Online Course (access code required)
MyStatLab™ is a text-specific, easily customizable online course that integrates interactive multimedia instruction with textbook content.

- **Interactive homework exercises,** correlated to your textbook at the learning objective level, are algorithmically generated for unlimited practice and mastery. Most exercises are free-response and provide guided solutions, sample problems, and learning aids for extra help. StatCrunch, an online data analysis tool, is available with online homework and practice exercises.

- **Personalized homework** allows you to assign homework to meet the needs of your class. MyStatLab tailors the assignment for each student based on his or her test or quiz scores. Each student receives a homework assignment that contains only the problems he or she still needs to master.

- **A Personalized Study Plan,** generated when students complete a test or quiz or homework, indicates which topics have been mastered and links to tutorial exercises for topics students have not mastered. You can customize the Study Plan so that the topics available match your course content.

- **Multimedia learning aids,** such as videos and animations help students independently improve their understanding and performance. You can assign these multimedia learning aids as homework to help your students grasp the concepts. In addition, applets are also available to display statistical concepts in a graphical manner for classroom demonstration or independent use.

- **Pearson eText** The Pearson eText gives students access to their textbook anytime, anywhere. In addition to note taking, highlighting, and bookmarking, the Pearson eText offers interactive and sharing features. Instructors can share their comments or highlights, and students can add their own, creating a tight community of learners within the class.

- **StatCrunch.com** access is now included with MyStatLab. StatCrunch.com is the first web-based data analysis tool designed for teaching Statistics. Users can perform complex analyses, share data sets, and generate compelling reports. The vibrant online community offers more than 10,000 data sets for students to analyze.

- **Assignment Manager** lets you assign homework, quizzes, and tests that are automatically graded. Select just the right mix of questions from the MyStatLab exercise bank, instructor-created custom exercises, and/or TestGen test items.

- **Gradebook,** designed specifically for Mathematics and Statistics, automatically tracks students' results, allows you to stay on top of student performance, and gives you control over how to calculate final grades. You can also add offline (paper-and-pencil) grades to the gradebook.

- **MathXL Exercise Builder** allows you to create static and algorithmic exercises for your online assignments. You can use the library of sample exercises as an easy starting point

or use the Exercise Builder to edit any of the course-related exercises.

- **Excel Manual**
- **Minitab Manual**
- **SPSS Manual**
- **Ten Business Insight Videos** (concept videos) feature Deckers, Southwest Airlines, Starwood, and other companies and focus on statistical concepts as they pertain to the real world. Available with captioning, these 4- to 7-minute videos can be viewed from within the online MyStatLab course.

Instructor Supplements

Instructor's Resource Guide contains chapter-by-chapter comments on the major concepts, tips on presenting topics (and what to avoid), teaching examples, suggested assignments, basic exercises, and web links and lists of other resources. Available at http://catalogue.pearsoned.ca/pearsonhigheredca.

PowerPoint Lecture Slides. The PowerPoint package provides an outline to use in a lecture setting, presenting definitions, key concepts, and figures from the text. These slides are available at http://catalogue.pearsoned.ca/pearsonhigheredca.

Technology Resources

Data for exercises that are flagged with the data set icon in the margins of the text are available on the MyStatLab site formatted for Excel, JMP, Minitab, SPSS, and as text files suitable for these and virtually any other statistics software. The data sets can also be downloaded from the open-access Companion Website at www.pearsoncanada.ca/canadianstats.

StatCrunch™

MyStatLab includes a web-based statistical software, StatCrunch, within the online assessment platform so that students can easily analyze data sets from exercises and the text. In addition, MyStatLab includes access to www.StatCrunch.com, a website where users can access more than 13,000 shared data sets, conduct online surveys, perform complex analyses using the powerful statistical software, and generate compelling reports.

TestGen®

TestGen® (www.pearsoned.com/testgen) enables instructors to build, edit, print, and administer tests using a computerized bank of questions developed to cover all the objectives of the text. TestGen is algorithmically based, allowing instructors to create multiple but equivalent versions of the same question or test with the click of a button. Instructors can also modify test bank questions or add new questions. The software and testbank are available for download from Pearson Canada's online catalogue.

An Introduction to Statistics

LEARNING OBJECTIVES

In this chapter we show you how statistics is useful in business and why it will be increasingly in demand in the 21st century. After reading and studying this chapter, you should be able to:

❶ Identify the importance of understanding statistics

The graphs and tables shown here are the daily bread and butter of investment managers and stock brokers. They're full of "statistics." Obviously this kind of information is important to them, but is this what Statistics is all about? Well, yes and no. This page may contain a lot of facts, but as we'll see, Statistics is much more interesting and rich than building and assessing graphs and tables.

Most companies have large databases, but there's not much point in having all that information sitting there unless we can analyze it. In the 20th century, we figured out how to store information and index it so that we can retrieve the items we want. The focus in the 21st century is on analyzing this information and using it to make effective business decisions. The field of "data analytics" is worth hundreds of billions of dollars, and it's growing at about 10% per year;[1] much of that analysis is statistical.

As a manager, the decisions you make based on data will chart the future course of your organization. You'll want to be able to interpret the data that surrounds you and come to your own conclusions. And you'll find that studying Statistics is much more important and enjoyable than you thought.

---

[1]Special report: Managing information: Data, data everywhere. (2010, February 25). *The Economist.*

LO① 1.1 So What Is Statistics?

Statistics is the basis for the global economy of the 21st century. If you didn't expect that answer, or if it sounds a bit grandiose, consider this: The global economy has undergone several dramatic changes over the years, as illustrated in Figure 1.1.

1. *The agricultural revolution.* We produced more food by farming than by hunting and gathering.
2. *The 19th-century industrial revolution.* Factories and mass production gave us a vast array of consumer and industrial products.
3. *The 20th-century information revolution.* Technology gave us a diverse range of electronic products, made our industry more efficient, and greatly increased the amount of information at our disposal.

But how can we make sense of all the data produced by the information revolution? Enter the next stage.

4. *The 21st-century data analytics revolution.* With vast volumes of information on hand, the challenge for the 21st century is extracting meaning from it all—and a key way of doing so is through statistical analysis.

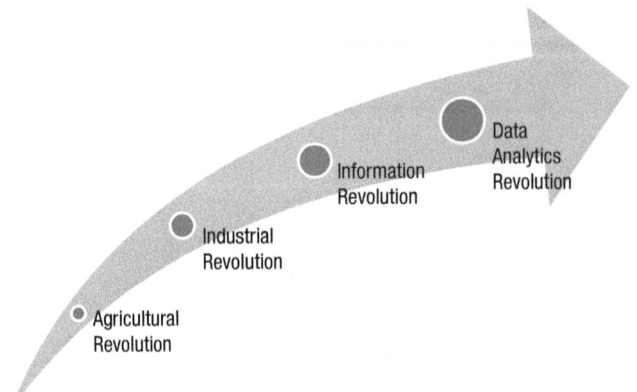

Figure 1.1 Revolutions in business.

It is the mark of a truly intelligent person to be moved by statistics.

—George Bernard Shaw

Q: What is Statistics?

A: Statistics is a way of reasoning, along with a collection of tools and methods, designed to help us understand the world.

Q: What are statistics?

A: Statistics (plural) are quantities calculated from data.

Q: So what is data?

A: You mean, "What *are* data?" *Data* is the plural form. The singular is *datum.*

Q: So what are data?

A: Data are values, along with their context.

Data analytics refers to the statistical analysis of large amounts of data in order to sift out the key information needed for corporate planning. Data analytics is becoming so powerful that some commentators claim it polarizes the labour market into "lousy and lovely jobs." And as *The Globe and Mail* put it, "The lovely jobs are why we should all enroll our children in statistics courses."[2]

Let's now look at some examples of what statistics can do for us. Most 20th-century applications of statistics continue to be important today, and some applications are new with the data analytics revolution of this century. So we'll start with the applications common to the 20th and 21st centuries, move on to what's new in this century, and then describe the cutting-edge applications that continue to be a challenge. As you read these examples, you can put them in context using Figure 1.2.

20th- and 21st-Century Statistics

Analyzing Large Amounts of Data

We've always used statistics to analyze both large and small amounts of data. We analyze large databases—for example, stock market and interest-rate data—for patterns that can identify what factors are associated with, say, an increase in share

---

[2]From The Globe and Mail by Chrystia Freeland. Published by The Globe and Mail Inc, © 2012.

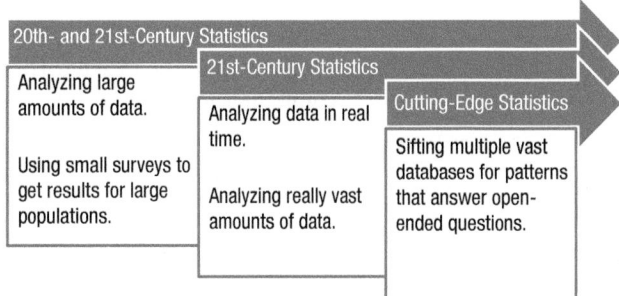

Figure 1.2　Trends in the use of statistical analysis.

prices or a lowering of interest rates. Similarly, retail firms like Loblaw and Future Shop analyze trends in retail sales, and insurance companies analyze trends in claims. We hope this text will empower *you* to draw conclusions from data and to make valid business decisions in response to such questions as

- Do aggressive, "high-growth" mutual funds really have higher returns than more conservative funds?
- Do your customers have common characteristics, and do they choose your products for similar reasons? And more importantly, are those characteristics the same among people who *aren't* your customers?
- What is the effect of advertising on sales?

Analyzing Small Amounts of Data

Drawing conclusions from small amounts of data is important, too. Indeed, one of the powers of statistical analysis is its ability to survey a small sample and generalize the results to a much larger population. (We talk more about sampling in Chapters 3 and 10, and the movement from the specific to the general is a theme we revisit throughout this book.) You've probably read media stories about the results of opinion polls based on relatively small samples, for instance, "A survey of 1000 adults has shown that 35% of Canadians believe this country should not invest in any more nuclear power plants." It's quite remarkable that the statisticians in the survey company can select just 1000 people to be representative of the country's entire population. These organizations use surveys to answer such questions as

- How many people will accept our credit card with certain new features?
- How many Canadians who vote for our political party support the legalization of marijuana?

Statistics was successful in addressing these questions during the 20th century and will continue to excel in these areas during the 21st century, as shown in Figure 1.2. Now let's look at what's new in this century.

21st-Century Statistics

Today we continue to use statistics the way we did in the previous century, but with two major differences. First, much of the analysis is performed in real time, the moment the data become available; and second, the amounts of data available to us are much larger than ever before.

Real-Time Analysis of Data

According to IBM, "The biggest leaps forward in the next several decades—in business, science, and society at large—will come from insights gleaned through perpetual, real-time analysis of data. . . . The new science of analytics must be core to every leader's thinking."[3]

One example of what IBM refers to as "real-time analysis of data" is the way companies look at sales data in order to analyze their market. In the 20th century, these companies collected sales data at the end of each month and compiled them into reports for each region of the global market. Then they held quarterly and annual sales and marketing meetings at which regional directors shared their sales information with one another in order to identify patterns and trends. But by the time this was done, the results were often out of date. Today, companies record sales data in a database right when the product is sold, whether at the cash register in a retail store or when a salesperson signs a multimillion-dollar deal for industrial equipment. Those data are incorporated into a statistical analysis of global market trends that is immediately accessible to directors and executives throughout the company. In short, companies are now able to apply statistics in real time so that their analysis is completely up to date.

Analyzing Vast Amounts of Data

Corporate executives are keen to find useful value in the massive amounts of data now available to them. Even small companies can afford large databases and the statistical-analysis software that comes with them. So for this 21st-century revolution we've coined the term "data analytics" in order to focus on how all that data can be analyzed. And it's Statistics that provides a major methodology to tackle the problem. Moreover, Statistics is no longer being left to the statisticians; rather, it has become an increasingly important part of management decision making at all levels. Everywhere you look, statistics are being used in corporate planning, and this is why a solid grounding in Statistics is important for all managers.

Here are three examples of the results of analyzing really vast databases:

- Facebook gets more advertising revenue as a result of its members' visiting the site more frequently and actively contributing to their pages. The popular social network therefore tracked its members' behaviour using statistical analysis of its huge database—and found that the best predictor of whether members would contribute to the site was knowing that their friends had contributed. As a result of this analysis, Facebook started informing its members of what their friends had been saying.
- Some airlines routinely overbook flights because not all passengers show up. This is a delicate balancing act. The airlines don't want to lose revenue by flying with empty seats, but on the other hand they don't want to annoy passengers who are turned away and have to compensate them financially. If the airlines could improve their estimates of "no-shows," they'd be able to fine-tune how much overbooking they can do. *On average* they know the percentage of no-shows, but what about each individual flight, with its particular mix of passengers? Which passengers are the type who don't show? Statistical analysis allows airlines to match everything they know about each passenger with the number of times that passenger has been a no-show in the past. As a result of statistical analysis, one airline found that the passengers most likely to show up are those who order vegetarian meals. Now airlines take into account how many vegetarians they have on board when figuring out how much to overbook a particular flight.

---

[3]IBM. (2010). Building a smarter planet: 2 in a series: On a smarter planet, answers are hidden in the data. Retrieved from http://www.ibm.com/smarterplanet/global/files/us__en_us__intelligence__Data_visualization_4_6.pdf

- Closer to home, what can the Canadian winter teach retailers? They already know that if a storm results in a power outage, people will need batteries and flashlights. But statisticians have also found a correlation between storm warnings and sales of Pop-Tarts—a quick and easy snack you can eat even when the power is out. Now some retailers watch the weather forecast when deciding how much of that product to stock.

The Cutting Edge

In the three cases above, we knew the questions we were asking:

- How can we predict whether members will contribute to Facebook?
- How can an airline predict no-shows?
- Which products sell more during winter storms?

But the real challenge comes when a corporate executive does *not* have a specific question in mind, and instead asks management: "How can we improve our way of doing business by making use of our vast database of information and perhaps linking to other publicly available databases?" These more open-ended questions challenge us to think outside the box and apply statistical thinking in unusual ways.

Here's an example of how Google uses its own enormous database, along with a database from the European Union, to do language translation. If you ask Google to translate a document, say, from Spanish to Hungarian, it doesn't look each word up in a dictionary, in part because a single word in one language has many alternatives in another language. Instead, Google compares each phrase with phrases that appear in professionally translated European Union documents. The Google processor uses statistics to assess the probability of various possible translations of your phrase in its context, and then chooses the most likely one. And Google doesn't use statistics merely for language translation—statistics are at the core of its business. It continuously updates its analysis that ranks search results, taking into account evolving patterns in the various links people click on. Moreover, Google web crawlers select sites to "crawl" based on statistical analysis that chooses the sites most likely to have changed since they were last crawled.

We can gain competitive advantage in the 21st century by thinking outside the box and applying the full range of statistical analysis at our disposal to the vast databases that organizations are adding to every minute of every day.

LO❶ 1.2

Economic value has moved from goods to services and to data and the statistical algorithms used to analyse them.

—BASED ON IT's A SMART WORLD: A SPECIAL REPORT ON SMART SYSTEMS

How Is Statistics Used in Management?

Statistical analysis is used to manage most public and private sector organizations, in just those areas that are popular with students in business schools: accounting, finance, marketing, and human resource planning.

Accounting

When a company's accounts are audited, the auditor often doesn't have the time to go through every item—for example, invoices. Instead, a "statistical audit" is conducted in which a representative sample of invoices is audited. The auditor then uses a statistical analysis of this sample to make valid conclusions about all the invoices to a required degree of accuracy. Chapters 11 to 17 are devoted to this topic, known as "statistical inference" since we are inferring a conclusion about all invoices from only a small sample of them.

Finance

A major element in financial planning is managing risk. If you can measure something, you can manage it, and Statistics provides many ways of measuring risk. When an investor is choosing among alternative investments, he or she needs measures of their riskiness as well as their expected return on investment. These are statistical measures that we'll deal with in this book.

Marketing

Marketing, particularly retail marketing, is largely based on statistical analysis of consumer purchasing patterns. Most of Part 3 of this book is about the concept of regression, meaning how one variable relates to others, which is used to figure out how spending on a product depends on age group, income level, gender, postal code, and many other factors. This enables marketers to design promotional campaigns focused on the appropriate target audience.

Human Resource Planning

Any large organization today has a certain mix of employees at different levels in the management hierarchy. But what will that mix look like in 5 to 10 years' time? Will we have too many senior managers or not enough? The answer depends on statistical analysis of past patterns of promotion, recruitment, retirements, transfers, and resignations. Some of these, for example promotion and recruitment, are under the organization's control, but retirements and resignations are decisions made by employees for which we can calculate probabilities from past records. Part 2 of this book deals in detail with probabilities. Putting all this together enables us to calculate a statistical forecast of the number of employees at different levels of the management pyramid in the future.

1.3   How Can I Learn Statistics?

This book can teach you Statistics, but teaching isn't the same as learning. The book does the teaching, but you need to be very proactive in doing the learning by putting into practice the concepts and methods the book teaches. That's why we've provided you with MyStatLab. It is essential to practise examples of each learning objective of each chapter on MyStatLab, which includes many tools to help you, like "Help me solve this."

A coach teaches a hockey player how to play, but the player really acquires those skills only by practice on the ice. You learn Statistics in the same way as a hockey player learns hockey. This book is the coach, and the end-of-chapter exercises and MyStatLab are the ice. Statistics is like most useful things in life: You must practise it to really learn it.

How Will This Book Help?

That is a fair question. Most likely, this book will not turn out to be what you expect. It emphasizes graphics and understanding rather than computation and formulas. Instead of learning how to plug numbers into formulas, you'll learn the process of model development and come to understand the limitations of both the data you analyze and the methods you use. Every chapter uses real data and real business scenarios so that you can see how to use data to make decisions.

Netflix offered a $1 million prize in a competition to improve the company's movie recommendation software, and statistics was the main tool used by the contestants.

Far too many scientists have only a shaky grasp of the statistical techniques they are using. They employ them as an amateur chef employs a cookbook, believing the recipes will work without understanding why. A more cordon bleu attitude . . . might lead to fewer statistical soufflés failing to rise.

—Sloppy Stats Shame Science
The Economist, June 3, 2004

This book includes numerous examples of the application of statistics in Canadian management situations. Canada is a major player internationally, and so to Canadian managers, international statistics are just as important as Canadian statistics. Our principal trading partner is, of course, the United States, so U.S. data are also of primary concern. Therefore, this book includes both U.S. and international business situations and data in addition to Canadian ones. You may choose a career in a Canadian company or in a multinational or in the public or nonprofit sectors. In that sense, this book mirrors the work environment of a typical Canadian business.

Graphs and Tables

Close your eyes and open this book at random. Is there a graph or table on the page? Do it again, say, 10 times. You probably saw data displayed in many ways, even near the back of the book and in the exercises. Graphs and tables help you understand what the data are saying. So each story and data set and every new statistical technique will come with graphics to help you understand both the methods and the data.

Optional Sections and Chapters

Some sections and chapters of this book are marked with an asterisk (*). These are optional, in the sense that subsequent material doesn't depend on them directly. We hope you'll read them anyway, as you did this section.

Getting Started

It's only fair to warn you: You can't get there by just reading the summaries. This book is different. It's not about memorizing definitions and learning equations. It's deeper than that. And much more interesting. But . . .
You have to read the book!

MINI case studies

Applications of Statistics in Business

Write one page describing an application of statistics in one of the functional areas of business (marketing, accounting, finance, . . .). Since this is Chapter 1, you are not expected to know which statistical method is appropriate. Instead, you should clearly state (i) the business problem to be solved, (ii) the data you expect to need in order to solve it, and (iii) the type of result that you might get from an analysis of those data. You can base your answer on an actual application of statistics by a specific organization or you can make up your own example.

Kristoffer Tripplaar/Alamy Stock Photo

2

Data

LEARNING OBJECTIVES

This chapter will show you how to probe data in order to understand it better. After reading and studying this chapter, you should be able to:

❶ Identify the context of your data

❷ Distinguish different types of data

Amazon.com

Amazon.com opened for business in July 1995, billing itself even then as "Earth's Biggest Bookstore," with an unusual business plan: Executives didn't plan to turn a profit for four to five years. Although some shareholders complained when the dot-com bubble burst, Amazon continued its slow, steady growth, becoming profitable for the first time in 2002. Since then, Amazon has remained profitable and has continued to grow.

It operates separate websites internationally, including the Canadian site Amazon.ca, which coordinates shipment from a fulfillment centre in Mississauga, Ontario. One key to Amazon's success is proprietary software that continuously analyzes data on past sales. Other businesses also use Amazon's unique analytical software. For instance, Sears Canada's website is powered by Amazon Services Canada and uses Amazon's software to track shopping patterns and other data. The results are used to give suggestions to Sears customers based on frequently purchased items and to provide comparison shopping among alternative brands.

Amazon R&D is constantly monitoring and revising its software to best serve customers and maximize sales performance. To make changes to the website, it experiments by collecting data and analyzing what works best. As Ronny Kohavi, former director of Data Mining and Personalization, said, "Data trumps intuition. Instead of using our intuition, we experiment on the live site and let our customers tell us what works for them."[1]

---

[1]Based on Amazon.com 2005 annual report; www.homegoodsonline.ca; www.sears.ca/gp/home.html. Accessed January 5, 2009.

8

The decision makers at Amazon.com recently stated, "Many of the important decisions we make at Amazon.com can be made with data. There is a right answer or a wrong answer, a better answer or a worse answer, and math tells us which is which. These are our favorite kinds of decisions."[2] It's clear that data analysis, forecasting, and statistical inference are at the core of the decision-making tools of Amazon.com.

Data is king at Amazon. Clickstream and purchase data are the crown jewels at Amazon. They help us build features to personalize the website experience.

—USED BY PERMISSION OF
RONNY KOHAVI.

Many years ago, store owners in small towns knew their customers personally. If you walked into the hobby shop, the owner might tell you about a new bridge that had come in for your Lionel train set. The tailor knew your dad's size, and the hairdresser knew how your mom liked her hair to be styled. There are still some stores like that around today, but we're increasingly likely to shop at large stores, by phone, or on the internet. Even so, when you phone an 800 number to buy new running shoes, customer service representatives may call you by your first name or ask about the socks you bought six weeks ago. Or the company may send an email in October offering new head warmers for winter running. That this same company can identify who you are, where you live, and the items you bought online—all without your even being asked to supply this information—is standard fare these days. How did the telephone sales representative know all these things about you?

The answer is data. Collecting data on customers, transactions, and sales lets companies track inventory and know what their customers prefer. These data can help businesses predict what their customers may buy in the future so that they'll know how much of each item to stock. And in connection with the earlier example, the store can use the data and what it learns from the data to improve customer service, mimicking the kind of personal attention a shopper experienced 50 years ago.

Companies use data to make decisions about other aspects of their business as well. By studying the past behaviour of customers and predicting their responses, they hope to better serve their customers and to compete more effectively. This process of using data, especially **transactional data** (data collected for recording a company's transactions), to make other decisions and predictions is sometimes called *data mining* or *predictive analytics*. The more general term **business analytics** (or sometimes simply *analytics*) describes *any* use of statistical analysis to drive business decisions from data, whether the purpose is predictive or simply descriptive.

LO❶ 2.1   ## What *Are* Data?

We bet you thought you knew this instinctively. Think about it for a minute. What exactly *do* we mean by **data**? Do data even have to be numbers? The amount of your last purchase in dollars is numerical data, but some data record names or other labels. The names in Amazon.com's database are regarded as data, but they are not numerical.

---

[2]From Amazon.com Annual Report. Published by amazon, © 2005.

THE FIVE W'S:
WHO
WHAT
WHEN
WHERE
WHY

Sometimes, data can have values that look like numerical values but are just numerals serving as labels. This can be confusing. For example, the ASIN (Amazon Standard Item Number) of a book may have a numerical value, such as 978-0321426592, but it's really just another *name* for the book *Business Statistics*.

Data values, no matter what kind, are useless without an understanding of their context. Newspaper journalists know that the lead paragraph of a good story should establish the "Five W's": *Who, What, When, Where,* and (if possible) *Why.* Often, they add *How* to the list as well. The situation is similar for statisticians. Answering these types of questions can provide a **context** for data values. The answers to the first two questions are essential. If you can't answer *Who* and *What,* you don't have data, and you don't have any useful information.

Table 2.1 shows an example of some of the data Amazon might collect:

10675489	B0000010AA	10.99	Chris G.	905	Quebec	15.98
Samuel P.	Nova Scotia	10783489	12837593	N	B000068ZVQ	15783947
Ontario	Katherine H.	16.99	Alberta	N	11.99	N
B000002BK9	902	Monique D.	Y	819	B0000015Y6	403

Table 2.1   An example of data with no context. It's impossible to say anything about what these values might mean without knowing their context.

Try to guess what the data in Table 2.1 represent. Why is that hard? Because these data have no *context.* We can make the meaning clear if we add the context of *Who* and *What* and organize the values into a **data table** such as the one in Table 2.2.

Purchase Order Number	Name	Ship to Province	Price	Area Code	Gift?	ASIN
10675489	Katherine H.	Alberta	10.99	403	N	B0000015Y6
10783489	Samuel P.	Nova Scotia	16.99	902	Y	B000002BK9
12837593	Chris G.	Quebec	15.98	819	N	B000068ZVQ
15783947	Monique D.	Ontario	11.99	905	N	B0000010AA

Table 2.2   Example of a data table. The variable names are in the top row. Typically, the *Who* of the table are found in the leftmost column.

Now we can see that the data in Table 2.2 represent four purchase records relating to orders from Amazon. The column titles tell *What* has been recorded. The rows tell us *Who.* But be careful. Look at all the variables to see *Who* the variables are about. Even if people are involved, they may not be the *Who* of the data. For example, the *Who* here are the purchase orders (not the people who made the purchases) because each row refers to a different purchase order, not necessarily a different *person.* A common place to find the *Who* of the table is the leftmost column. The other W's might have to come from the company's database administrator.[3]

In general, a row of a data table corresponds to an individual **case** about *Whom* (or about which—if they're not people) we record some characteristics. These cases go by different names, depending on the situation. An individual who answers a survey is referred to as a **respondent.** A person on whom we experiment is a **subject** or (in an attempt to acknowledge the importance of their role in the experiment) **participant,** but a company, website, or other inanimate subject is

---

[3]In database management, this kind of information is called "metadata," or data about data.

often called an **experimental unit**. In a database, a row is called a **record**—in this example, a purchase record. Perhaps the most generic term is *case*. In Table 2.2, the cases are the individual purchase orders.

Sometimes people refer to data values as *observations*, without being clear about the *Who*. Make sure you know the *Who* of the data, or you may not know what the data say. Each *characteristic* recorded about each individual or case is called a **variable**. These are usually shown as the columns of a data table, and they should have a name that identifies *What* has been measured. If the number of cases (*Who*) is smaller than the number of characteristics (*What*), we may interchange rows and columns so that *Who* is shown in columns and *What* is shown in rows.

A general term for a data table like this is a **spreadsheet**, a name that comes from bookkeeping ledgers of financial information. The data were typically spread across facing pages of a bound ledger, the book used by an accountant for keeping records of expenditures and sources of income. For the accountant, the columns were the types of expenses and income, and the cases were transactions, typically invoices or receipts.

Although data tables and spreadsheets are great for relatively small data sets, they're cumbersome for the complex data sets that companies must maintain on a day-to-day basis. And so various other architectures are used to store data, the most common being a relational database. In a **relational database**, two or more separate data tables are linked so that information can be merged across them. Each data table is a *relation* because it's about a specific set of cases with information about each of these cases for all (or at least most) of the variables ("fields" in database terminology). A table of customers, along with demographic information on each, is an example of such a relation. A data table with information about a different collection of cases is a different relation. For example, a data table of all the items sold by the company, including information on price, inventory, and past history, is a relation as well (as shown in Table 2.3). Finally, the day-to-day

Customers						
Customer Number	Name	City	Province	Postal Code	Customer Since	Gold Member
473859	Rahini, R.	Magog	QC	J1X SV8	2007	No
127389	Li, V.	Guelph	ON	N1K 2H9	2000	Yes
335682	Marstas, J.	Calgary	AB	T2E 0B9	2003	No

Items			
Product ID	Name	Price	Currently in Stock
SC5662	Silver Cane	43.50	Yes
TH2839	Top Hat	29.99	No
RS3883	Red Sequinned Shoes	35.00	Yes
...			

Transactions						
Transaction Number	Date	Customer Number	Product ID	Quantity	Shipping Method	Free Ship?
T23478923	9/15/17	473859	SC5662	1	UPS 2nd Day	N
T23478924	9/15/17	473859	TH2839	1	UPS 2nd Day	N
T63928934	10/22/17	335473	TH2839	3	UPS Ground	N
T72348299	12/22/17	127389	RS3883	1	FedEx Ovnt	Y

Table 2.3   A relational database shows all the relevant information for the three separate relations linked by customer and product numbers.

transactions may be held in a third database, in which each purchase of an item by a customer is listed as a case. In a relational database, these three relations can be linked. For example, you can look up a customer to see what he or she purchased, or look up an item to see which customers purchased it.

In statistics, all analyses are performed on a single data table. But often the data must be retrieved from a relational database. Retrieving data from these databases often requires specific expertise with that software. We'll assume that all data have been downloaded to a data table or spreadsheet, with variables listed as columns and cases listed as rows.

FOR EXAMPLE   **Credit card company: The variables and the Five W's**

Carly, the marketing manager at a credit card company, wants to know if an offer mailed three months ago has affected customers' use of their cards. To answer that, she asks the information technology department to assemble the following information for each customer: total spending on the card during the three months before the offer (*Pre Spending*); spending for three months after the offer (*Post Spending*); the customer's *Age* (by category); what kind of expenditure he or she made (*Segment*); if customers are enrolled in the website (*Enrol?*); what offer they were sent (*Offer*); and the amount each customer has spent on the card in his or her segment (*Segment Spend*). She gets a spreadsheet whose first six rows look like this:

ACCOUNT ID	PRE SPENDING	POST SPENDING	AGE	SEGMENT	ENROL?	OFFER	SEGMENT SPEND
393371	$2,698.12	$6,261.40	25-34	Travel/Ent	NO	None	$887.36
462715	$2,707.92	$3,397.22	45-54	Retail	NO	Gift Card	$5,062.55
433469	$800.51	$4,196.77	65+	Retail	NO	None	$673.80
462716	$3,459.52	$3,335.00	25-34	Services	Yes	Double Miles	$800.75
420605	$2,106.48	$5,576.83	35-44	Leisure	Yes	Double Miles	$3,064.81
473703	$2,603.92	$7,397.50	<25	Travel/Ent	Yes	Double Miles	$491.29

QUESTION   Identify the cases and the variables. Describe as many of the Five W's as you can for this data set.

ANSWER   The cases are individual customers of the credit card company. The data are from the internal records of the card company from the past six months (three months before and three months after an offer was sent to the customers). The variables include the account ID of the customer (*Account ID*) and the amount charged on the card before (*Pre Spending*) and after (*Post Spending*) the offer was sent out. Also included are the customer's *Age*, marketing *Segment*, whether they enrolled on the website (*Enrol?*), what offer they were sent (*Offer*), and how much they charged on the card in their marketing segment (*Segment Spend*).

LO❷   2.2   Variable Types

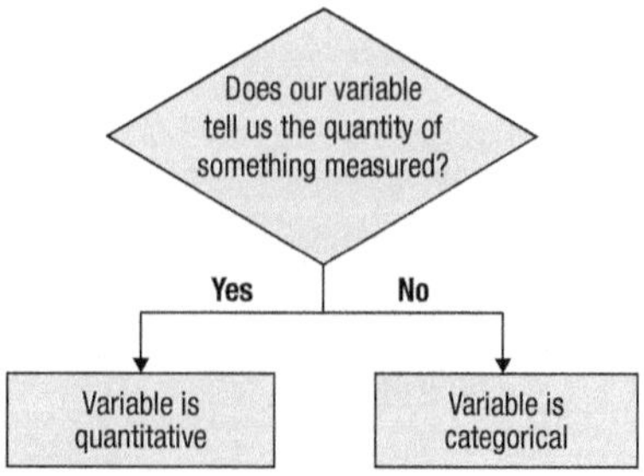

Figure 2.1   Variable types.

Variables play different roles, and knowing the variable's *type* is crucial to knowing what to do with it and what it can tell us. When a variable names categories and answers questions about how cases fall into those categories, we call it a **categorical variable**. When a variable has measured numerical values and the variable tells us about the quantity of what is measured, we call it a **quantitative variable**. (See Figure 2.1.) Classifying a variable as categorical or quantitative can help us decide what to do with a variable, but doing so is really more about what we hope to learn from a variable than about the variable itself. It's the questions we ask of a variable (the *Why* of our analysis) that shape how we think about it and how we treat it.

Descriptive responses to questions are often categories. For example, the responses to the questions "What type of mutual fund do you invest in?" and "What kind of advertising does your firm use?" yield categorical values. An important special case of categorical variables is one that has only two possible responses (usually "yes" or "no"), which arise naturally from questions like "Do you invest in the stock market?" and "Do you make online purchases from this website?"

Be careful, though. If you treat a variable as quantitative, be sure the values measure a quantity of something. For example, area codes are numbers, but do we use them that way? Is 204 plus 306 equal to 510? Of course, but that's irrelevant when we're speaking of area codes. We don't care that Manitoba (area code 204) plus Saskatchewan (306) equals Oakland, California (510). The numbers assigned to the area codes are codes that *categorize* the phone number into a geographical area. So we treat area code as a categorical variable.

Some quantitative variables are just numbers without units. For example, the number of visits to a website yesterday might be 5876. The number of Royal Bank of Canada shares traded on the Toronto Stock Exchange might be 5,675,876. These are numbers of website visits and shares traded without any units such as kilograms or centimetres. Other quantitative variables do have **units**, which tell how each value has been measured. Even more important, units such as yen, cubits, carats, angstroms, nanoseconds, kilometres per hour, or degrees Celsius tell us the *scale* of measurement. The units tell us how much of something we have or how far apart two values are. Without units, the values have no meaning. It does little good to be promised a raise of 5000 a year if you don't know whether it will be paid in euros, dollars, yen, or Estonian krooni.

Sometimes the type of variable is clear. Some variables can answer questions *only* about categories. If the values of a variable are words rather than numbers, it's a good bet that it's categorical. (Table 2.4 lists some examples of categorical variables.) But some variables can answer both kinds of questions. For example, Amazon could ask for your *Age* in years. That seems quantitative, and would be if Amazon staff want to know the average age of those customers who visit the website after 3:00 A.M. But suppose Amazon staff want to decide which music to offer in a special deal—Folk, Jazz, Hip Hop, or Reggae. Then asking you to specify your age based on the categories of Child, Teen, Adult, or Senior might be more useful. If it isn't clear whether to treat a variable as categorical or quantitative, think about *Why* you're looking at it and what you want it to tell you.

A typical course evaluation survey asks:

"How valuable do you think this course will be to you?"

1 = Not valuable; 2 = Slightly valuable; 3 = Moderately valuable; 4 = Extremely valuable.

Is this variable categorical or quantitative? Once again, we'll look to the *Why*. Instructors might simply count the number of students who gave each response for a course, treating *Educational Value* as a categorical variable. When they want to see whether the course is improving, they might treat the responses as the *Amount* of perceived value—in effect, treating the variable as quantitative.

Question	Categories or Responses
Do you invest in the stock market?	___Yes___No
What kind of advertising do you use?	___Magazines___Internet___Direct Mailings
I would recommend this course to another student.	___Strongly Disagree___ Slightly Disagree___ Slightly Agree___Strongly Agree
How satisfied are you with this product?	___Very Unsatisfied___Unsatisfied___Satisfied___Very Satisfied

Table 2.4   Some examples of categorical variables.

Shipping Method	Number of Purchases
Ground	20,345
Second-day air	7,890
Overnight	5,432

Table 2.5   A summary of the categorical variable *Shipping Method* that shows the counts, or number of cases, for each category.

Counts

In statistics, we often count things. When Amazon staff consider making a special offer of free shipping to customers, they might first analyze how purchases have been shipped in the recent past. They might start by counting the number of purchases shipped in each category: ground transportation, second-day air, and overnight air (see Table 2.5). Counting is a natural way to summarize the categorical variable *Shipping Method*. (Chapter 4 discusses summaries and displays of categorical variables more fully. Chapter 5 discusses quantitative variables, which require different summaries and displays.) So *every* time we see counts, does that mean the associated variable is categorical? Actually, no.

We also use counts to *measure* the amounts of things. How many songs are on your digital music player? How many classes are you taking this semester? To measure these quantities, we'd naturally count. The variables (*Songs, Classes*) are quantitative.

Identifiers

What's your student ID number? It may be numerical, but is it a quantitative variable? No, it doesn't measure the quantity of anything. Is it categorical? Yes, but a special kind. Look at how many categories there are and at how many individuals exist in each category. There are exactly as many categories as individuals, and only one individual in each category. While it's easy to count the totals for each category, it's not very interesting. Your student ID is an **identifier variable**. Amazon wants to know who you are when you sign into the Amazon website again and doesn't want to confuse you with some other customer. So it assigns you a unique identifier.

Identifier variables themselves don't tell us anything useful about the categories because we know there's exactly one individual in each. However, they're crucial in this era of large data sets because, by uniquely identifying the cases, identifier variables make it possible to combine data from different sources, protect confidentiality, and provide unique labels. Most company databases are, in fact, relational databases. The identifier is crucial to linking one data table to another in a relational database. The identifiers in Table 2.3 are the *Customer Number, Product ID*, and *Transaction Number*. Variables like *UPS Tracking Number, Social Insurance Number*, and Amazon's *ASIN* are other examples of identifiers.

You'll want to recognize when a variable is playing the role of an identifier so that you won't be tempted to analyze it. Knowing that Amazon's average ASIN value increased 10% from 2007 to 2008 doesn't really tell you anything—any more than analyzing any categorical variable as if it were quantitative would.

Be careful not to be inflexible in your typing of variables. Variables can play different roles, depending on the question we ask of them, and classifying variables rigidly into types can be misleading. For example, in its annual reports, Amazon refers to its database and looks at the variables *Sales* and *Year*. When analysts ask how many books Amazon sold in 2016, what role does *Year* play? There's only one row for 2016, and *Year* identifies it, so it plays the role of an identifier variable. In its role as an identifier, you might match other data from Amazon, or the economy in general, for the same year. But analysts also track sales growth over time. In this role, *Year* measures time. Now it's being treated as a quantitative variable. The difference lies in the consideration of the *Why* of our question.

Other Variable Types

A categorical variable that is used only to name a category is sometimes called a **nominal variable**. Sometimes all we want to know about a variable is the order of its values. For example, we may want to pick out the first, the last, or the middle value. In such cases, we can say that our variable is an **ordinal variable**. Values can be individually ordered (e.g., the ranks of employees based on the number of days they've worked for the company) or ordered in classes (e.g., Branch Office, Regional Office, Head Office). But the ordering always depends on our purpose. Are the categories Infant, Youth, Teen, Adult, and Senior ordinal? Well, if we're ordering data on age, they surely are. But if we're ordering (as Amazon might) on purchase volume, it's likely that either Teen or Adult will be the top group.

Some people differentiate quantitative variables according to whether their measured values have a defined value for zero. This is a technical distinction, and not usually one we'll need to make. (For example, it isn't correct to say that a temperature of 80°F is twice as hot as 40°F, because 0° is an arbitrary value. On the Celsius scale, those temperatures are 26.7°C and 4.44°C—a ratio of 6. Ratios aren't meaningful for temperatures in Celsius or Fahrenheit.) The term *interval scale* is sometimes applied to data such as these, and the term *ratio scale* is applied to measurements for which such ratios are appropriate.

Cross-Sectional and Time Series Data

The share price of the Royal Bank of Canada at the end of each day for the past year is an example of **time series data** because we're measuring the same variable at intervals over time. Time series are common in business. Typical measuring points are months, quarters, or years, but virtually any time interval is possible. Variables collected over time hold special challenges for statistical analysis, and Chapter 20 discusses these in more detail.

By contrast, most of the methods in this book are better suited to **cross-sectional data**, where several variables are measured at the same time point, as shown in Figure 2.2. For example, if we collect data on sales revenue, number of customers, and expenses totalled over the past month at each Starbucks location, this would be cross-sectional data. If we expanded our data collection process to include daily sales revenue and expenses over a time span of several months, we would now have a time series for sales and expenses. Because different methods are used to analyze these different types of data, it's important to be able to identify both time series and cross-sectional data sets.

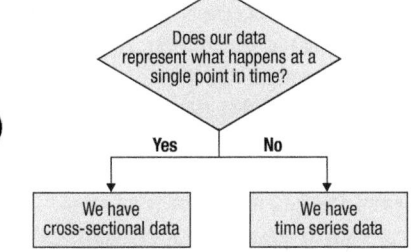

Figure 2.2   Cross-sectional and time series data.

Primary and Secondary Data

Data aren't just a bunch of numbers. There are subtle meanings attached to the numbers, so there's no point in doing detailed statistical analysis without understanding what each number includes and excludes.

Primary data are data we collect ourselves; for example, by standing outside a retail store and counting the number of people entering. We know exactly what we counted (e.g., whether we included children in strollers, or people who took one step inside, turned around, and came straight out). In the same way, staff who work at market research companies have a very clear idea of the meaning of the data they collect from surveys, since they themselves design the wording of every question in those surveys and conduct the interviews.

Many of us don't collect raw data this way. We mostly rely on *secondary* data— that is, data collected by another party, like Statistics Canada or the auditors of a company's accounts. In cases like these, it's very important to read all the guidelines and footnotes provided in order to get a precise idea of what the secondary data mean. See Understanding Your Data: "Canadian Unemployment Rate" to better understand the pitfalls associated with secondary data.

Data can be primary or secondary depending on who's using them, as shown in Figure 2.3. Let's take the case of a market research firm that surveys the market for a new wireless telecommunications technology and sells the results of its survey to a telecommunications equipment vendor. The survey

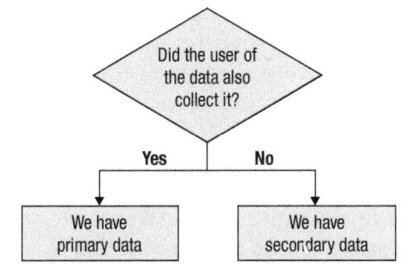

Figure 2.3   Primary and secondary data.

data are primary from the viewpoint of the market research firm, since it collected the data, but secondary from the viewpoint of the equipment vendor, since it's using data collected by another organization.

Understanding Your Data: Canadian Unemployment Rate

Most people think they understand what's meant by the "unemployment rate." You can do a quick test by telling someone that the unemployment rate is 7% and asking them what they think the employment rate is. Chances are they'll say 93%, so that the two numbers add up to 100%. As we write this, the Canadian unemployment rate is 7.3% and the employment rate, 61.1%. You can check the corresponding numbers by looking at Statistics Canada's latest release of the Labour Force Survey. Sanity checks, such as whether two numbers add up to 100%, lead us to probe exactly what the data represent.

If the unemployment rate is 7.3%, we need to ask: What is this number a percentage of? Statistics Canada's answer is that the number of people unemployed is 7.3% of the labour force. When it says the employment rate is 61.1%, it means that the number of people employed is 61.1% of the population. So unemployment rate and employment rate are percentages of different groups. No wonder the figures don't add up to 100%.

Let's probe a little further. What does Statistics Canada mean by "population"? Since we're interested in information about employment, it's no surprise that "population" doesn't include children under 15, since we don't allow child labour in Canada. But there are other exclusions as well: people serving in the Armed Forces, people living in institutions, and people living on First Nations reserves. Also, Nunavut, the Northwest Territories, and Yukon are excluded from national averages like the unemployment rate and are represented in their own territorial statistics instead.

Statistics Canada divides "population" into three groups: employed, unemployed, and not in the labour force. "Employed" sounds clear enough, but it's important to point out that the term *population* includes both full-time and part-time employees, plus people who are self-employed, but it does not include unpaid volunteers. Also, people can be "employed" even if not working, for example if they're on sick leave or vacation. Now, let's clarify the difference between "unemployed" and "not in the labour force." One key concept here is whether people are "available" for work—that is, they could have worked, if offered a suitable job (not just any job). The other key concept is whether people are "searching" for work. If someone is available for work, is searching for work, and is not working, then he or she is "unemployed." Otherwise, that person is "not in the labour force."

The deeper we probe, the more details we reveal about the complexity of data on the unemployment rate. There are plenty of exceptions to the rules given above, and you can find them in the *Guide to the Labour Force Survey*, which runs to about 30 pages plus the same again in appendices. One question you may have at the back of your mind is "What about students?" How are they categorized? In March, a full-time student "searching" for a summer job that begins in May is "not in the labour force," because he or she wasn't "available" to work in March. The same person, who is "searching" and "available" but not working in May, is regarded as "unemployed."

Source: Based on Guide to the Labour Force Survey, Catalogue no. 71-543-G

GUIDED EXAMPLE   Eskom

Gallo Images/Getty Images

Canada is rich in natural resources, which has resulted in a well-developed mining sector. Canadian mining companies also operate internationally, including Barrick Gold Corporation, IAM-Gold Corp., and First Quantum Minerals Ltd. in South Africa. The South African economy is largely driven by the global demand for commodities, which stimulates the country's own mining sector. South Africa has some of the deepest mines on the planet, and as demand increases, the mines need to be dug even deeper. Growth in mining demands electric power, and Eskom, the monopoly South African Government-owned power company, is hard-pressed to meet demand. Eskom, founded in 1923, is one of the top seven electric power utilities in the world in terms of generating capacity. The South African mining sector is particularly power-intensive, and Eskom also exports power to Zambia and Botswana, where the mining industry is important as well. Botswanan diamond mines account for 50% of the electricity consumption in that country.

Eskom needs to plan future generating capacity in conjunction with demand projections from its customers over the next 10 years. As VP of Strategic Planning for Eskom, you need to collect data available within Eskom, and also survey your current customers regarding their projected demand for electric power in megawatts (MW). Trends in demand from Eskom's current customers indicate that growth varies according to geographical region, within and outside of South Africa. Indicate what type of data you would collect, and whether they are quantitative or categorical, time series or cross-sectional.

PLAN	**Setup** State the objectives of the study.	To estimate electric power demand in megawatts from Eskom's customers over the next 10 years, divided among geographical regions.
DO	**Mechanics** Identify whom we're going to consult, and in which geographical regions. Identify which customers to consult.	We need to consult our customers as well as data sources internal to Eskom. We must include foreign demand and domestic demand in each geographic region of South Africa. The first task is therefore to obtain a list of current customers and select relevant variables for them. It's clear from the description of this guided example that Eskom has a few large customers. We're also told it's a monopoly; that is, it supplies all electric power in South Africa. Therefore it must also have medium-sized customers, such as office building owners, and small customers, such as residences. We need to estimate demand from all these customers, but that would be an enormous task. Instead we select just a sample from these customers.
REPORT	**Conclusion** State the conclusion in the context of the original objective.	Our report will consist of lists of customers, and for each customer several variables that represent the data we need to collect; for example: • Customer ID: Categorical (identifier) • Export or domestic: Categorical • Geographic region: Categorical • Current demand: Quantitative (MW) cross-sectional • Current growth rate: Quantitative (MW/year) cross-sectional • Demand over each of the next 10 years estimated by customer: Quantitative (MW) time series • Demand over each of the next 10 years estimated from internal sources: Quantitative (MW) time series

FOR EXAMPLE   Credit card company: The types of variables

QUESTION Before she can continue with her analysis, Carly (from For Example: "Credit Card Company: The variables and the Five W's") must classify each variable as being quantitative or categorical (or possibly both) and must identify whether the data are regarded as time series or cross-sectional. For quantitative variables, what are the units? For categorical variables, are they nominal or ordinal?

ANSWER

Account ID: categorical (nominal, identifier)

Pre Spending: quantitative (unit $)

Post Spending: quantitative (unit $)

Age: categorical (ordinal). Could be quantitative if we had more precise information.

Segment: categorical (nominal)

Enrol? categorical (nominal)

Offer: categorical (nominal)

Segment Spend: quantitative (unit $)

The data are cross-sectional. We don't have successive values of a single variable over time.

LO❶ **2.3** **Where, How, and When**

We must know *Who*, *What*, and *Why* to analyze data. Without knowing these three things, we don't have enough to start. Of course, we'd always like to know more about the data. The more we know, the more we'll understand. If possible, we'd like to know the *When* and *Where* of data as well. Values recorded in 1803 may mean something different from similar values recorded last year. Values measured in Tanzania may differ in meaning from similar measurements made in Mexico.

How the data are collected can make the difference between insight and nonsense. As we'll see later, data that come from a voluntary survey delivered via the internet are almost always worthless. Only people very interested in the topic will take the time to fill out the questionnaire. Statisticians have developed sound methods for collecting data from surveys and polls so that you can make inferences from the data you have at hand to the world at large. Chapter 3 discusses how to design a survey or poll to help ensure that the inferences you make are valid.

You may also collect data by performing an experiment in which you actively manipulate variables (called *factors*) to see what happens. For example, most of the "junk mail" credit card offers you receive are actually experiments done by marketing groups in those companies. They may make different versions of an offer to selected groups of customers to see which one works best before rolling out the winning idea to the entire customer base. Statisticians design and analyze the results of experiments like these.

Sometimes, the answer to the question you have may be found in data that someone, or more typically some organization, has already collected. Companies, nonprofit organizations, and government agencies collect a vast amount of data that is becoming increasingly easy to access via the internet, although some organizations may charge a fee for accessing or downloading their data. For example, Statistics Canada collects information on nearly every aspect of life in Canada, both social and economic (see www.statcan.gc.ca), as the European Union does for Europe (see ec.europa.eu/eurostat). International organizations such as the World Health Organization (www.who.int/en) and polling agencies such as Gallup (www.gallup.com) offer data on a variety of topics as well.

The first step of any data analysis is to know why you're examining the data (what you want to know), whom each row of your data table refers to, and what the variables (the columns of the table) record. These are the *Why*, the *Who*, and the *What*. Identifying them is a key part of the *Plan* step of any analysis. Make sure you know all three W's before you spend time analyzing the data.

JUST CHECKING

An insurance company that specializes in commercial property insurance has a separate database for its policies that involve churches and schools. Here's a small portion of that database:

Policy Number	Years Claim-free	Net Property Premium ($)	Net Liability Premium ($)	Total Property Value ($1000)	Median Age in Postal Code	School?	Territory	Coverage
4000174699	1	3107	503	1036	40	FALSE	SK580	BLANKET
8000571997	2	1036	261	748	42	FALSE	AB192	SPECIFIC
8000623296	1	438	353	344	30	FALSE	YT60	BLANKET
3000495296	1	582	339	270	35	TRUE	NU340	BLANKET
5000291199	4	993	357	218	43	FALSE	NL590	BLANKET
8000470297	2	433	622	108	31	FALSE	NS140	BLANKET
1000042399	4	2461	1016	1544	41	TRUE	NT20	BLANKET
4000554596	0	7340	1782	5121	44	FALSE	ON530	BLANKET

1 List as many of the Five W's as you can for this data set.

2 Classify each variable as to whether you think it should be treated as categorical or quantitative (or both); if quantitative, identify the units.

Answers are found in Appendix A.

WHAT CAN GO WRONG?

- **Don't label a variable as categorical or quantitative without thinking about the data and what they represent.** The same variable can sometimes take on different roles.

- **Don't assume that a variable is quantitative just because its values are numbers.** Categories are often given numerical labels. Don't let that fool you into thinking they measure the quantity of something. Look at the context.

- **Always be skeptical.** One reason to analyze data is to discover the truth. Even when you're told a context for the data, it may turn out that the truth is a bit (or even a lot) different. The context colours our interpretation of the data, so those who want to influence what you think may slant the context. A survey that seems to be about all students may, in fact, report just the opinions of those who visited a fan website. Also, the question that respondents answer may be posed in a way that influences their response.

ETHICS IN ACTION

Jim Hopler is operations manager for the local office of a top-ranked full-service brokerage firm. With increasing competition from both discount and online brokers, Jim's firm has redirected attention to attaining exceptional customer service through its client-facing staff, namely brokers. In particular, the firm wishes to emphasize the excellent advisory services provided by its brokers. Results from client surveys about the advice received from brokers at the local office revealed that 20% rated it poor, 5% rated it below average, 15% rated it average, 10% rated it above average, and 50% rated it outstanding. With corporate approval, Jim and his management team instituted several changes in an effort to provide the best possible advisory services at the local office. Their goal was to increase the percentage of clients who viewed their advisory services as outstanding. Surveys conducted after the changes were implemented showed the following results: 5% poor, 5% below average, 20% average, 40% above average, and 30% outstanding. In discussing these results, the management team expressed concern that the percentage of clients who considered their advisory services outstanding had fallen from 50% to 30%. One member of the team suggested an alternative way of summarizing the data. By coding the categories on a scale,

from 1 = poor to 5 = outstanding, and computing the average, they found that the average rating had increased from 3.65 to 3.85 as a result of the changes implemented. Jim was delighted to see that their changes were successful in improving the level of advisory services offered at the local office. In his report to corporate, he included only *average* ratings for the client surveys.

Ethical Issue *By taking an average, Jim is able to show improved customer satisfaction. However, the brokerage firm's goal was to increase the percentage of outstanding ratings. Jim redefined his study after the fact to support a position (related to Item A, ASA Ethical Guidelines; see Appendix C, the American Statistical Association's Ethical Guidelines for Statistical Practice, also available online at www.amstat.org/about/ethicalguidelines.cfm).*

Ethical Solution *Jim should report the percentages for each rating category. He can also report the average. He may wish to include in his report a discussion of what those different ways of looking at the data say and why they appear to differ. He may also want to explore with the survey participants the perceived differences between "above average" and "outstanding."*

WHAT HAVE WE LEARNED?

Learning Objectives

❶ We've learned that data are information gathered in a specific context.

- The Five W's help nail down the context: *Who, What, Why, Where, When.*
- We must know at least the *Who, What,* and *Why* to be able to say anything useful about the data. The *Who* are the *cases.* The *What* are the *variables.* A variable gives information about each of the cases. The *Why* helps us decide which way to treat the variables.

❷ Data can be divided into quantitative/categorical; cross-sectional/time series; and primary/secondary.
   We treat variables in two basic ways, as *categorical* or *quantitative.*

- Categorical variables identify a category for each case, including identifier variables that name each case.
- Quantitative variables record measurements or amounts of something.
- Sometimes we treat a variable as categorical or quantitative depending on what we want to learn from it, which means that some variables can't be labelled as one type or the other. That's an early hint that in Statistics we can't always categorize items precisely.

Terms

Business analytics	The process of using statistical analysis and modelling to drive business decisions.
Case	An individual about whom or which we have data.
Categorical variable	A variable that names categories (whether with words or numerals).
Context	The context ideally tells *Who* was measured, *What* was measured, *How* the data were collected, *Where* the data were collected, and *When* and *Why* the study was performed.
Cross-sectional data	Data taken from situations that are measured at a single time.
Data	Systematically recorded information, whether numbers or labels, together with its context.
Data table	An arrangement of data in which each row represents a case and each column represents a variable.
Experimental unit	An individual in a study for which or for whom data values are recorded. Human experimental units are usually called subjects or participants.
Identifier variable	A categorical variable that records a unique value for each case, used to name or identify it.
Nominal variable	The term "nominal" can be applied to data whose values are used only to name categories.
Ordinal variable	The term "ordinal" can be applied to data for which some kind of order is available but for which measured values are not available.
Participant	A human experimental unit. Also called a subject.
Quantitative variable	A variable in which the numbers are values of measured quantities.
Record	Information about an individual in a database.
Relational database	A database that stores and retrieves information. Within the database, information is kept in data tables that can be "related" to each other.
Respondent	Someone who answers, or responds to, a survey.
Spreadsheet	A layout that's designed for accounting and often used to store and manage data tables. Microsoft Excel is an example of a common spreadsheet program.
Subject	A human experimental unit. Also called a participant.
Time series data	Data measured over time. Usually the time intervals are equally spaced (e.g., every week, every quarter, or every year).
Transactional data	Data collected for recording a company's transactions.

Units	A quantity or amount adopted as a standard of measurement, such as dollars, hours, or grams.
Variable	A variable holds information about the same data for many cases.

Skills

Plan
- Be able to identify the *Who*, *What*, *When*, *Where*, *Why*, and *How* of data, or to recognize when some of this information has not been provided.
- Be able to identify the cases and variables in any data set.
- Know how to treat a variable as categorical or quantitative, depending on its use.

Report
- Be sure to describe a variable in terms of its *Who*, *What*, *When*, *Where*, *Why*, and *How* (and be prepared to remark when that information is not provided).

MINI case studies

Ottawa Senators

Canadians have been playing hockey since the 19th century. The National Hockey League (NHL) was founded in Montreal in 1917, with the Ottawa Senators as one of its founding members. Every fall, as the baseball season climaxes at the World Series, Canadians eagerly anticipate the start of hockey season in mid-October. In its 2005–06 season, the NHL adopted the shootout method to settle ties in regular-season games. The shootout is used to decide the winner if the game remains tied after five minutes of overtime. In the file **ch02_Ottawa_Senators** on MyStatLab, you can find data on shootout games, along with the results. What types of data are contained in the file? In particular, list the Five W's for those data, and classify the data according to whether they are primary/secondary, time series/cross-sectional, and categorical/quantitative, with an explanation included for your choice of classification.

Gene J. Puskar/AP Photo/The Canadian Press

Credit Card Company

Like all credit and charge card companies, this company makes money on each of its cardholders' transactions. Thus, its profitability is directly linked to card usage. To increase customer spending on its cards, the company sends many different offers to its cardholders, and market researchers analyze the results to see which offers yield the largest increases in the average amount charged.

On MyStatLab (in the file **ch02_MCSP_Credit_Card_Bank**) is a small part of a database like the one used by the researchers. For each customer, several variables appear in a spreadsheet.

Examine the data in the data file. List as many of the Five W's as you can for these data and classify each variable as categorical or quantitative. If a variable is quantitative, identify the units.

Inozemtsev Konstantin/Shutterstock

Canadian Immigrants

A Canadian immigrant, Anjali Gupta, and her Canadian-born friend, Bob Fisher, are celebrating at their high school graduation ceremony. They've both worked hard, achieved great grades, and been accepted into the Sauder School of Business at the University of British Columbia. Then Anjali draws Bob's attention to the data on unemployment rates in Statistics Canada's Labour Force Survey, summarized in the table below. "Going to university will really improve your chances of getting a job," she says to Bob, "but for me, a university degree doesn't make much difference. Canadian employers aren't in favour of hiring immigrants, even if they have a degree."

Which of the data below is Anjali referring to? How might the data be explained other than with the conclusion that "Canadian employers aren't in favour of hiring immigrants"?

What additional data do you suggest Statistics Canada collect in order to clarify this issue?

	UNEMPLOYMENT RATE (%)							
	LANDED IMMIGRANTS				BORN IN CANADA			
	HIGH SCHOOL		UNIVERSITY		HIGH SCHOOL		UNIVERSITY	
	MALE	FEMALE	MALE	FEMALE	MALE	FEMALE	MALE	FEMALE
2009	11.2	11.8	8.8	8.6	8.5	6.1	3.5	2.9
2010	9.9	10.3	8	9.2	7.8	6.2	3.7	3.4
2011	7.7	10	7.2	8.1	6.7	5.7	3.3	3.2
2012	7.8	8.8	7.7	8.1	6.2	6.1	3	3.1
2013	8.2	10	6.7	7.7	6.4	6.1	2.9	2.7

Source: Based loosely on Statistics Canada. (2014). Labour Force Survey. CANSIM Table 282-0106: Labour force characteristics by immigrant status of population aged 25 to 54, and by educational attainment.

Technology Help: Computer-Based Statistics Packages

Most often we find statistics on a computer using a program, or package, designed for that purpose. There are many different statistics packages, but they all do essentially the same things. If you understand what the computer needs to know to do what you want, and what it needs to show you in return, you can figure out the specific details of most packages pretty easily.

For example, in order to incorporate your data into a computer statistics package, you need to tell the computer:

- *Where to find the data.* This usually means directing the computer to a file stored on your computer's disk or to data in a database. Or it might just mean that you've copied the data from a spreadsheet program or internet site and it's currently on your computer's clipboard. Usually, the data should be in the form of a data table. Most computer statistics packages prefer the delimiter that marks the division between elements of a data table to be a tab character and the delimiter that marks the end of a case to be a return character.

- *Where to put the data.* (This is usually handled automatically.)

- *What to call the variables.* Some data tables have variable names as the first row of the data, and often statistics packages can take the variable names from the first row automatically.

EXERCISES

SECTION 2.1

1. A real estate agent collected information on some recent local home sales. The first six lines of the database appear below. The columns correspond to the house identification number, the community name, the property's number of acres, the year the house was built, the market value (in $), and the size of the living area (in square feet).

a) What does a row correspond to in this data table? How would you best describe its role: as a participant, subject, case, respondent, or experimental unit?
b) How many variables are measured in each row? **LO ❶**

HOUSE_ID	NEIGHBOURHOOD	ACRES	YR_BUILT	FULL_MARKET_VALUE	SFLA
413400536	Greenfield Manor	1.00	1967	100400	960
4128001474	Fort Amherst	0.09	1961	132500	906
412800344	Dublin	1.65	1993	140000	1620
4128001552	Granite Springs	0.33	1969	67100	900
412800352	Arcady	2.29	1955	190000	1224
413400322	Ormsbee	9.13	1997	126900	1056

2. A local bookstore is keeping a database of its customers in order to find out more about their spending habits so that the store can start to make personal recommendations based on past purchases. The table lists the first rows of the store's database.

a) What does a row correspond to in this data table? How would you best describe its role: as a participant, subject, case, respondent, or experimental unit?
b) How many variables are measured in each row? **LO ❶**

Transaction ID	Customer ID	Date	ISBN Number of Purchase	Price	Coupon?	Gift?	Quantity
29784320912	4J438	11/12/2017	345-23-2355	$29.95	N	N	1
26483589001	3K729	9/30/2017	983-83-2739	$16.99	N	N	1
26483589002	3K729	9/30/2017	102-65-2332	$9.95	Y	N	1
36429489305	3U034	12/5/2017	295-39-5884	$35.00	N	Y	1
36429489306	3U034	12/5/2017	183-38-2957	$79.95	N	Y	1

SECTION 2.2

3. Referring to the real estate data table of Exercise 1,

a) For each variable, would you describe it as primarily categorical or quantitative? If quantitative, what are the units? If categorical, is it ordinal or simply nominal?
b) Are these data a time series or cross-sectional? Explain briefly. **LO ❷**

4. Referring to the bookstore data table of Exercise 2,

a) For each variable, would you describe it as primarily categorical or quantitative? If quantitative, what are the units? If categorical, is it ordinal or simply nominal?
b) Are these data a time series or cross-sectional? Explain briefly. **LO ❷**

SECTION 2.3

5. For the real estate data of Exercise 1, do the data appear to have come from a designed survey or experiment? What concerns might you have about drawing conclusions from this data set? **LO ❶**

6. A student finds data on an internet site that contains financial information about selected companies. He plans to analyze the data and use the results to develop a stock investment strategy. What kind of data source is he using? What concerns might you have about drawing conclusions from this data set? **LO ❷**

CHAPTER EXERCISES

7. Canadian labour force. Referring to Understanding Your Data: "Canadian Unemployment Rate," classify the following people as "employed," "unemployed," or "not in the labour force":

a) Someone on vacation from a full-time job

b) Someone who is not working and has a job offer, but is trying to find a better offer

c) Someone who looked for work up to six months ago, but then gave up looking. **LO ❶**

8. Non-employment in Canada. In addition to "employed" and "unemployed," some economists identify a third category, "non-employed," consisting of people who may not be looking for a job but are available to work, if offered a job. The non-employment rate in member countries of the Organisation for Economic Co-operation and Development (OECD) increased between 2007 and 2014, particularly among young people, men, and low-skilled workers.

a) If the non-employment rate in Canada is 11.2%, what is that a percentage of? Refer to Understanding Your Data: "Canadian Unemployment Rate" for more information on this subject.

b) Does "non-employed" include people who are "unemployed"? **LO ❶**

For each description of data in Exercises 9 to 33, identify the Five W's, name the variables, specify for each variable whether its use indicates it should be treated as categorical or quantitative, and for any quantitative variable identify the units in which it was measured (or note that they weren't provided or that the variable doesn't have units). **LO ❶, ❷**

9. Domestic credit in Canada. A major factor influencing the rate of growth of a country's economy is the availability of credit for investment purposes. Domestic credit is the amount of credit given out by the Bank of Canada to Canadian commercial banks and to the Canadian government. In the 1950s, domestic credit (in $ billion) was about 50% of GDP (in $ billion) in industrialized countries, whereas it was around 20% in emerging countries. Today both figures are much higher, but it hasn't been a smooth ride from then until now. In order to investigate possible future trends, you collect data on domestic credit and GDP for Canada over a few recent years.

10. Oil spills. After several major ocean oil spills, oil tankers have been designed with thicker hulls and other structural improvements. The intention is to reduce the chance of an oil spill in the future, and if a spill does occur, to reduce the amount of oil spilled. Infoplease (www.infoplease.com) reports the date, the spillage amount, and the cause of puncture for 50 recent major oil spills from tankers and carriers.

11. Sales, part 1. A major Canadian company is interested in seeing how various promotional activities are related to domestic sales. Analysts decide to measure the money spent on different forms of advertising ($ thousand) and sales ($ million) on a monthly basis for the past three years.

12. Food store. A food retailer that specializes in selling organic food has decided to open a new store. To help determine the best location for the new store, researchers decide to examine data from existing stores, including weekly sales ($), town population (thousands), median age of town, median income of town ($), and whether the store sells wine and beer.

13. Sales, part 2. The company in Exercise 11 is also interested in the impact of national indicators on its sales. It decides to obtain measurements for the unemployment rate (%) and inflation rate (%) on a quarterly basis to compare with its quarterly sales ($ million) over the same time period.

14. Subway's menu. A listing posted by the Subway restaurant chain gives, for each of the sandwiches it sells, the type of meat in the sandwich, number of calories, and serving size in grams. The data might be used to assess the nutritional value of the different sandwiches.

15. MBA admissions, part 1. A business school is concerned with the recent drop in female students in its MBA program. It decides to collect data from the admissions office on each applicant, including the sex of each applicant, the age of each applicant, whether he or she was accepted, whether he or she attended, and the reason for not attending (if he or she did not attend). The school hopes to find commonalities among the female accepted students who decided not to attend the business program.

16. Climate. In a study appearing in the journal *Science*, a research team reports that plants in southern England are flowering earlier in the spring. Records of the first flowering dates for 385 species over a period of 47 years indicate that flowering has advanced by an average of 15 days per decade, an indication of climate warming, according to the authors.

17. MBA admissions, part 2. An internationally recognized MBA program in London intends to track the GPA of its MBA students and compares MBA performance with standardized test scores over the past five years.

18. Canadian schools. A provincial ministry of education requires local school boards to keep records on all students, recording age, days absent, current grade level, standardized test scores in reading and mathematics, and any disabilities or special educational needs the student may have.

19. Pharmaceutical firm. Scientists at a major pharmaceutical firm conducted an experiment to study the effectiveness of a herbal compound to treat the common cold. They exposed volunteers to a cold virus, then gave them either the herbal compound or a sugar solution known to have no effect on colds. Several days later the scientists assessed each patient's condition using a cold severity scale, ranging from 0 to 5. They found no evidence of benefits to the compound.

20. Startup company. A Canadian startup company is building a database of customers and sales information. For each customer, it records name, ID number, region of the country (1 = West, 2 = Prairies, 3 = North, 4 = Ontario, 5 = Quebec, 6 = Atlantic), date of last purchase, amount of purchase, and item purchased.

21. Cars. A survey of autos parked in executive and staff lots at a large company recorded the make, country of origin, type of vehicle (car, van, SUV, etc.), and age.

22. Canadian vineyards. Business analysts hoping to provide information helpful to grape growers compiled these data about vineyards: size (hectares), number of years in existence, province, varieties of grapes grown, average case price, gross sales, and profit percentage.

23. Environment. As research for an ecology class, university students in Alberta collect data on streams each year to study the impact of pollution on the environment. They record a number of biological, chemical, and physical variables, including the stream name, the substrate of the stream (limestone, shale, or mixed), the acidity of the water (pH), the temperature (°C), and the BCI (a numerical measure of biological diversity).

24. Canadian voters. The Gallup Poll conducted a representative telephone survey of 1180 Canadian voters. Among the reported results were the voter's region (East, West, Prairie, etc.), age, political party affiliation, whether the respondent owned any shares of stock, and the voter's attitude (on a scale of 1 to 5) toward unions.

25. CTA. The Canadian Transportation Agency (CTA) monitors airlines for adherence to safety regulations and customer service. For each flight, the carrier must report the type of aircraft, number of passengers, whether the flight departed and arrived on schedule, and any mechanical problems.

26. Mobile phones. In order to project the future of the mobile phone business, market analysts collect data on sales of mobile phones by major manufacturer in each country for each quarter of each year.

27. Canadian families. In order to investigate social trends, Statistics Canada collects data on family type (e.g., married-couple families, common-law-couple families, single-parent families) in the census every five years.

28. Canadian oil and gas production. Statistics Canada collects data on the value (in \$) and volume (in m^3) of crude oil, natural gas, and natural gas byproducts produced in Canada each year.

29. Overnight visitors to Canada. In order to provide information for the tourism industry, Statistics Canada collects data on overnight visitors to Canada according to the visitor's country of origin. Data is collected every year and includes the number of nights stayed in Canada and money spent while here.

30. Stock market. An online survey of students in a large MBA Statistics class in Toronto asked them to report their total personal investment in the stock market (\$), the total number of different stocks currently held, the total invested in mutual funds (\$), and the name of each mutual fund in which they have invested. The data were used in the aggregate for classroom illustrations.

31. Theme park sites. A study on the potential for developing theme parks in various locations throughout Europe in 2017 collects the following information: the country where the proposed site is located, the estimated cost to acquire the site (in euros), the size of population within a one-hour drive of the site, the size of the site (in hectares), and mass transportation available within five minutes of the site. The data will be presented to prospective developers.

32. Indy. The 2.5-mile (4-kilometre) Indianapolis Motor Speedway has been home to a race that takes place on Memorial Day nearly every year since 1911. Even during the first race there were controversies. Ralph Mulford was given the checkered flag first but took three extra laps just to make sure he'd completed 500 miles. When he finished, another driver, Ray Harroun, was being presented with the winner's trophy, and Mulford's protests were ignored. Harroun averaged 74.6 mph for the 500 miles. Here are the data for the first few, and three more recent, Indianapolis 500 races:

Year	Winner	Car	Time (h)	Speed	Car #
1911	Ray Harroun	Marmon Model 32	6.7022	74.602	32
1912	Joe Dawson	National	6.3517	78.719	8
1913	Jules Goux	Peugeot	6.5848	75.933	16
...					
...					
2010	Dario Franchitti	Dallara/Honda	3.0936	161.623	10
2011	Dan Wheldon	Dallara/Honda	2.9366	170.265	98
2012	Dario Franchitti	Dallara/Honda	2.9809	167.734	50

33. Kentucky Derby. The Kentucky Derby is a horse race that has been run every year since 1875 at Churchill Downs in Louisville, Kentucky. The race started as a 1.5-mile (2.4-kilometre) race, but in 1896 it was shortened to 1.25 miles because experts felt that three-year-old horses shouldn't run such a long race that early in the season. (It's been run in May every year but one—1901—when it took place on April 29.) The following table shows the data for the first few, and a few more recent, races:

Date	Kentucky Derby Winner	Margin (lengths)	Jockey	Winner's Payoff ($)	Duration (min:sec)	Track Condition
May 17, 1875	Aristides	2	O. Lewis	2850	2:37.75	Fast
May 15, 1876	Vagrant	2	B. Swim	2950	2:38.25	Fast
May 22, 1877	Baden-Baden	2	W. Walker	3300	2:38.00	Fast
May 1, 2010	Super Saver	2.75	Calvin Borel	2,000,000	2:04.45	Fast
May 7, 2011	Animal Kingdom	2.5	John R. Velazquez	2,000,000	2:02.04	Fast
May 5, 2012	I'll Have Another	1.5	Mario Gutierrez	2,000,000	2:01.83	Fast

When you organize data in a spreadsheet, it's important to lay it out as a data table. For each of the examples in Exercises 34 to 37, show how you would lay out the data. Indicate the headings of columns and what would be found in each row. **LO ❶**

34. Mortgages. For a study of mortgage loan performance: amount of the loan (in $), the name of the borrower.

35. Employee performance. Data collected to determine performance-based bonuses: employee ID, amount of average contract closed (in $), supervisor's rating (1–10), years with the company.

36. Company performance. Data collected for financial planning: weekly sales (in $), week (week number of the year), sales predicted by last year's plan (in $), difference between predicted sales and realized sales (in $).

37. Command performance. Data collected on investments in Broadway shows: number of investors, total invested (in $), name of the show, profit/loss (in $) after one year.

For the examples in Exercises 38 to 41, indicate whether the data are a time series or a cross-section. **LO ❷**

38. Car sales. Number of cars sold by each salesperson in a dealership in September.

39. Motorcycle sales. Number of motorcycles sold by a dealership in each month of last year.

40. Cross-sections. Average diameter of trees brought to a sawmill in each week of a year.

41. Series. Attendance at the third World Series game, recording the age of each fan.

42. Canadian immigrants. For the data given in Mini Case Study: "Canadian Immigrants,"

a) Identify the Five W's and also *How.*

b) Identify which data (if any) are

   i) Quantitative/categorical

   ii) Cross-sectional/time series

   iii) Primary/secondary **LO ❶, ❷**

43. Interpreting published data. Referring back to Understanding Your Data: "Canadian Unemployment Rate," many people are surprised that the employment rate and the unemployment rate don't add to 100%. How does that example change the way you interpret the statistics you read about in publications? Give an example of a website that states some statistics that may be ambiguous. **LO ❶**

Jacob Wackerhausen/E+/Getty Images

3

Surveys and Sampling

LEARNING OBJECTIVES

In this chapter we show you how to take samples that are representative of a larger population. After reading and studying this chapter, you should be able to:

❶ Identify different ways of selecting a representative sample

❷ Understand how to avoid bias

❸ Explain terms such as *population, sampling frame,* and *sample*

Angus Reid Strategies

Angus Reid Strategies is a Canadian market research firm that monitors the values, attitudes, and preferences of consumers. Angus Reid doesn't just phone people and ask their opinions; instead, much of the company's research is conducted over the internet so that the respondents can be shown images, streaming video, and 3D virtual environments. In this way respondents become more engaged than they would be with traditional telephone interviews, which in turn leads to a higher-quality survey with more accurate results.

One of Angus Reid's products is the Daily Omnibus, which allows business clients to pose questions one day and get a response from a representative sample of Canadians the next day. Angus Reid Strategies employs statisticians to ensure that the sample is *representative* of all regions of Canada. A representative sample is very important in ensuring that the results are valid nationwide. For instance, if we're designing a national marketing campaign for a new product, we may conduct a survey to investigate the product features most in demand. The population sample we survey must be representative of the whole country so that we can be sure the results apply to our national marketing campaign.

Angus Reid's statisticians also take other considerations into account when choosing the sample of respondents. Cost affects Angus Reid as it does all other market research companies, and the cost of conducting a survey is related to *how many* respondents participate in the survey. It's easy to get a representative sample of Canadians if we have a budget that will allow us to interview a million people. But do you think it could be done by interviewing just a thousand people? Angus Reid would answer yes. Its statisticians use just 1000 adult Canadians in its Daily Omnibus.[1]

How do the researchers at Angus Reid know that the responses they get reflect the real attitudes of consumers? After all, they don't poll entire populations, but they don't want to limit their conclusions to just the people they surveyed. Generalizing from the data at hand to the world at large is something that market researchers, investors, and pollsters do every day. To do it wisely, they need to follow three fundamental principles.

LO❶   3.1   **Three Principles of Sampling**

Principle 1: Examine a Part of the Whole

The first step is to draw a sample. We'd like to know about an entire **population** of individuals, but examining all of them is usually impractical, if not impossible. So we settle for examining a smaller group of individuals—a **sample**—selected from the population. For example, the whole of Canada is the population the Angus Reid researchers are interested in, but it's not practical, cost-effective, or feasible to survey the entire population. So they examine a sample selected from that population.

You take samples of a larger population every day. For example, if you want to know how the vegetable soup you're cooking for dinner tonight is going to taste, you try it. You certainly don't consume the whole pot. You trust that the taste will *represent* the flavour of the entire pot. The idea of tasting is that a small sample, if selected properly, can represent the entire population.

The Angus Reid Daily Omnibus is an example of a **sample survey**, designed to ask questions of a small group of people in the hope of learning something about the entire population. Most likely, you've never been selected to be part of an Angus Reid opinion poll. That's true of most people. So how can the pollsters claim that a sample is representative of the entire population? Professional researchers like those who run the Angus Reid survey work hard to ensure that the "taste"—the sample they take—represents the population fairly.

Selecting a sample to represent the population fairly is more difficult than it sounds. Polls or surveys most often fail because the sample fails to represent part of the population. The way the sample is drawn may overlook subgroups that are hard to find. For example, a telephone survey may get no responses from people with caller ID and may favour other groups, such as the retired or the homebound, who would be more likely to be near their phones when the interviewer calls. Sampling methods that over- or underemphasize some characteristics of the

> **The Five W's and Sampling**
>
> The population we are interested in is usually determined by the *Why* of our study. The participants or cases in the sample we draw from will be the *Who*. *When* and *How* we draw the sample may depend on what is practical. The questions we ask the participants provide the *What*.

---

[1]Based on Angus Reid Daily Omnibus: When You Need It Yesterday.

population are said to be biased. When a sample method is **biased**, the summary characteristics of the resulting samples will differ systematically from the corresponding characteristics of the population it is trying to represent. Conclusions based on biased samples are inherently flawed. There is usually no way to fix bias after the sample is drawn and no way to salvage useful information from it.

What are the basic techniques for making sure that a sample is representative? To make the sample as representative as possible, you might be tempted to handpick the individuals included in it. But the best strategy is to do something quite different: We should select individuals for the sample *at random*.

Principle 2: Randomize

Think back to our example of sampling vegetable soup. Suppose you add some salt to the pot. If you sample the soup from the top before stirring, you'll get the misleading idea that the whole pot is salty. If you sample from the bottom, you'll get the equally misleading idea that the whole pot is bland. But by stirring the soup, you *randomize* the amount of salt throughout the pot, making each spoonful more typical of the saltiness of the whole pot. Deliberate randomization is one of the great tools of statistics. (We'll discuss many aspects of randomness in Chapter 8.)

Randomization can protect against factors you aren't aware of, as well as those you know are in the data. Suppose that while you aren't looking a friend adds a handful of peas to the soup. The peas sink to the bottom of the pot, mixing with the other vegetables. If you don't randomize the soup by stirring, your test spoonful from the top won't include any peas. By stirring in the salt, you *also* randomize the peas throughout the pot, making your sample taste more typical of the overall pot *even though you didn't know the peas were there*. So, randomizing protects us by giving us a representative sample even for effects we were unaware of.

How do we "stir" people in our survey? We select them at random. Randomizing protects us from the influences of *all* the features of our population by making sure that, *on average*, the sample looks like the rest of the population.

We all think we know what it means for something to be random. Rolling dice, spinning dials, and shuffling cards all produce random outcomes. What's the most important aspect of the randomness in these games? It makes them fair.

Two things make **randomization** seem fair. First, nobody can guess the outcome before it happens. Second, when we want things to be fair, usually some underlying set of outcomes will be equally likely (although in many games, some combinations of outcomes are more likely than others). We'll soon see how to use randomness to ensure that the sample we draw is representative of the population we want to study.

Truly random values are surprisingly hard to get. Computers are a popular means of generating random numbers. But even though they often do a much better job than humans, computers can't generate truly random numbers either. Computers follow programs. Start a computer from the same place, and, all things being equal, it will follow the same path every time. So, numbers generated by a computer program are not truly random. Technically, "random" numbers generated by computer are *pseudorandom*. Fortunately, pseudorandom values are good enough for most purposes because they're virtually indistinguishable from truly random numbers.

- **Why not match the sample to the population?** Rather than randomizing, we could try to design our sample to include every possible relevant characteristic: income level, age, political affiliation, marital status, number of children, place of residence, etc. Clearly we couldn't possibly think of all the things that might be important, however. Even if we could, we wouldn't be able to match our sample to the population for all these characteristics. That's why we randomize.

Michael Lamotte/Cole Group/Getty Images

	Age (yr.)	White (%)	Female (%)	# of Children	Income Bracket (1-7)	Wealth Bracket (1-9)	Homeowner? (% Yes)
Sample 1	61.4	85.12	56.2	1.54	3.91	5.29	71.36
Sample 2	61.2	84.44	56.4	1.51	3.88	5.33	72.30

Table 3.1   Means and proportions for seven variables from two samples of size 8000 from the organization's data. The fact that the summaries of the variables from these two samples are so similar gives us confidence that either one would be representative of the entire population.

How well does a sample represent the population from which it was selected? Here's an example using the database of a philanthropic organization with a donor list of about 3.5 million people. We've taken two samples, each of 8000 individuals at random from the population. Table 3.1 shows how the means and proportions match up on seven variables.

Notice that the two samples match closely in every category. This shows how well randomizing has "stirred" the population. We didn't preselect the samples for these variables, but randomizing has matched the results closely. We can reasonably assume that since the two samples don't differ too much from each other, they don't differ much from the rest of the population either.

Even if a survey is given to multiple random samples, the samples will differ from each other, and, therefore, so will the responses. These sample-to-sample differences are referred to as **sampling variability**.

Principle 3: The Sample Size Is What Matters

You probably weren't surprised by the idea that a sample can represent the whole. And the idea of sampling randomly makes sense when you stop to think about it, too. But the third important feature of sampling often surprises people: The *size of the sample* determines what we can conclude from the data *regardless of the size of the population.* Many people think we need a large percentage, or *fraction*, of the population, but in fact all that matters is the **sample size**. The size of the *population* doesn't matter at all.[2] A random sample of 100 students in a university represents the student body just about as well as a random sample of 100 voters represents the entire electorate of Canada. This is perhaps the most surprising key feature behind survey design.

To understand how this works, let's return one last time to our pot of soup. If you're cooking for a banquet-sized group, rather than just for a few people, the amount of soup in your pot will increase, but you won't need a bigger spoon to decide how the soup tastes. The same size spoonful is probably enough to make a decision about the entire pot, no matter how large the pot. What *fraction* of the population you sample doesn't matter. It's the *sample size* itself that's important. This idea is of key importance to the design of any sample survey, because it determines the balance between how well the survey can measure the population and how much the survey costs.

How big a sample do you need? That depends on what you're estimating, but drawing too small a sample won't be representative of the population. To get an idea of what's really in the soup, you need a large enough taste to be a *representative* sample from the pot, including, say, a selection of the vegetables. For a survey that tries to find the proportion of the population falling into a category, you'll usually

---

[2]Well, that's not exactly true. If the sample is more than 10% of the whole population, it *can* matter. It doesn't matter whenever, as usual, our sample is a very small fraction of the population.

need at least several hundred respondents. (Chapter 10 gives the details behind this statement and shows how to decide on a sample size for a survey.) When we survey people, it is important that they actually answer our questions. Professional survey organizations, like Angus Reid and Statistics Canada, recruit a panel of reliable people and pay them to answer questionnaires. That way they are sure to get a good response rate in their surveys.

LO❶ 3.2

A Census—Does It Make Sense?

Why bother determining the right sample size? If you plan to open a store in a new community, why draw a sample of residents to understand their interests and needs? Wouldn't it be better just to include everyone and make the "sample" be the entire population? Such a special sample is called a **census**. Although a census would appear to provide the best possible information about the population, there are a number of reasons why it might not.

First, it can be difficult to complete a census. Some individuals are hard to locate or hard to measure. Do you really need to contact the folks away on vacation when you collect your data? How about those with no telephone or mailing address? The cost of locating the last few cases may far exceed the budget. It can also be just plain impractical to take a census. The quality control manager for Hostess Twinkies doesn't want to census *all* the Twinkies on the production line to determine their quality. Aside from the fact that nobody could eat that many Twinkies, it would defeat the purpose: There would be none left to sell.

Second, the population we're studying may change. For example, in any human population, babies are born, people travel, and folks die during the time it takes to complete the census. News events and advertising campaigns can cause sudden shifts in opinions and preferences. A sample, surveyed in a shorter time frame, may actually generate more accurate information.

Finally, taking a census can be cumbersome. A census usually requires a team of pollsters and/or the cooperation of the population. Some people might have more than one address. For example, students often have one address during the school year and another one during the summer. It takes a lot of effort to figure out which is the "main" or "primary" residence, so as to avoid double-counting.

FOR EXAMPLE   Surveying theatre goers

A nonprofit organization has taken over a historic theatre and hopes to preserve it with a combination of attractive shows and fundraising. The organization has asked a team of students to help it design a survey to better understand the customer base likely to purchase tickets. Fortunately, the theatre's computerized ticket system records contact and some demographic information for ticket purchasers, and that database of 7345 customers is available.

QUESTION What is the population of interest?
What would a census involve in this case? Would it be practical?
What is the sampling frame?

ANSWER The population is all potential ticket purchasers.

A census would have to reach all potential purchasers. We don't know who they are or have any way to contact them.

The sampling frame is the list of previous ticket purchasers.

LO❸ 3.3 Populations and Parameters

> **Statistic**
>
> Any quantity that we calculate from data could be called a "statistic." But in practice, we usually obtain a statistic from a sample and use it to estimate a population parameter.

> **Parameter**
>
> Population model parameters are not just unknown—usually they're *unknowable*. We have to settle for estimates of these from sample statistics.

GfK Roper Reports Worldwide states that 60.5% of people over 50 worry about food safety, but only 43.7% of teens do. What does this claim mean? We can be sure the Roper researchers didn't take a census to obtain the results. So they can't possibly know *exactly* what percentage of teenagers worry about food safety. So what does "43.7%" mean?

It means that 43.7% of the teens in their survey are concerned about food safety, and we call this 43.7% a **sample statistic**. The percentage of *all* teens concerned about food safety should be pretty close to 43.7% (and we will see in Chapter 10 how close) and we call that a **population parameter**.

We use a sample to try to estimate values for the population parameters (see Figure 3.1). Anything calculated from a sample is a statistic. Those statistics that estimate population parameters are particularly interesting.

We draw samples because we can't work with the entire population. We hope that the statistics we compute from the sample will estimate the corresponding population parameters accurately. A sample that does this is said to be a **representative sample**.

JUST CHECKING

1 Various claims are often made for surveys. Why is each of the following claims not correct?

a) It is always better to take a census than to draw a sample.

b) Stopping customers as they are leaving a restaurant is a good way to sample opinions about the quality of the food.

c) We drew a sample of 100 from the 3000 students in a school. To get the same level of precision for a town of 30,000 residents, we'll need a sample of 1000.

d) A poll taken at a popular website (www.statsisfun.org) garnered 12,357 responses. The majority of respondents said they enjoy doing statistics. With a sample size that large, we can be sure that most people feel this way.

e) The true percentage of all people who enjoy statistics is called a "population statistic."

Answers are found in Appendix A.

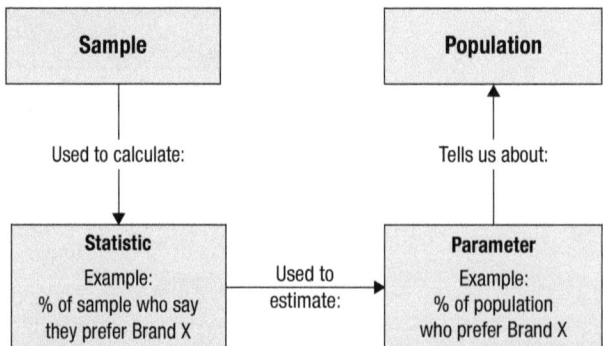

Figure 3.1   A sample is used to calculate a statistic, which in turn is used to estimate a parameter of a population. For example, from surveying a sample of customers, we can calculate the percentage who prefer Brand X. The percentage from the sample can then be used to estimate the percentage of the whole population that prefers Brand X. The end result is that data from a sample is used to tell us something about a population.

LO❶, ❸ 3.4 Simple Random Sampling (SRS)

How would you select a representative sample? It seems fair to say that every individual in the population should have an equal chance to be selected, but that's not sufficient. There are many ways to give everyone an equal chance that still wouldn't generate a representative sample. Consider, for example, a manufacturer that samples customers by drawing at random from product registration forms, half of which arrived by mail and half by online registration. They flip a coin to generate the samples. If it comes up heads, they draw 100 mail returns; tails, they draw 100 electronic returns. Each customer has an equal chance of being selected, but if tech-savvy customers are different, then the samples are hardly representative.

We need to do better. Suppose we insist that every possible *sample* of the size we plan to draw has an equal chance of being selected. This ensures that situations like the all tech-savvy (or not) samples are not likely to occur and still guarantees that each person has an equal chance of being selected. A sample drawn in this way is called a **simple random sample (SRS)**. An SRS is the standard against which we measure other sampling methods, and the sampling method on which the theory of working with sampled data is based.

To select a sample at random, we first need to define a **sampling frame**, a list of individuals from which the sample will be drawn. For example, to draw a random sample of regular customers, a store might sample from its list of all "frequent buyers." In defining the sampling frame, the store must deal with the details of defining the population. Are former frequent buyers who have moved away included? How about those who still live in the area but haven't shopped at the store in over a year? The answers to these questions may depend on the purpose of the survey.

Once we have a sampling frame, the easiest way to choose an SRS is with random numbers. We can assign a sequential number to each individual in the sampling frame. We then draw random numbers to identify those to be sampled. Let's look at an example:

- Suppose we want to select five students from the 80 enrolled in a Business Statistics class. We start by numbering the students from 00 to 79. Now we get a sequence of random digits from a table such as Table 1 in Appendix C. For example, we might get 051662930577482. Taking those random numbers two digits at a time gives us 05, 16, 62, 93, 05, 77, and 48. We ignore 93 because no one had a number that high. And to avoid picking the same person twice, we also skip the repeated number 05. Our simple random sample consists of students with the numbers 05, 16, 62, 77, and 48. Alternatively, statistics packages, spreadsheets, and some internet sites like www.random.org can generate random numbers. You can ask for five random numbers between 00 and 79, and then you don't have to throw out numbers that are too big.

Samples drawn at random generally differ one from another. Each draw of random numbers selects *different* people for our sample. These differences lead to different values for the variables we measure. As was mentioned earlier, we call these sample-to-sample differences *sampling variability*. Surprisingly, sampling variability isn't a problem; it's an opportunity. If different samples from a population vary little from each other, then most likely the underlying population harbours little variation. If the samples show much sampling variability, the underlying population probably varies a lot. In the coming chapters, we'll spend much time and attention working with sampling variability to better understand what we are trying to measure.

> **Sampling Variability vs. Bias**
>
> Sample-to-sample variability is to be expected. It's *bias* we must strive to avoid. Bias means that our sampling method distorts our view of the population. Of course, bias leads to mistakes. Even more insidiously, bias introduces errors that we can't correct with subsequent analysis.

FOR EXAMPLE   Choosing a random sample of theatre goers

Continuing where For Example: "Surveying theatre goers" left off, the student consultants select 200 ticket buyers at random from the database. First, the theatre database is placed in a spreadsheet. Next, to draw random numbers, the students use the Excel command RAND(). (They type = *RAND*() in the top cell of a column next to the data and then use *Fill Down* to populate the column down to the bottom.) They then sort the spreadsheet to put the random column in order and select ticket buyers from the top of the randomized spreadsheet until they complete 200 interviews. This makes it easy to select more respondents when (as always happens) some of the people they select can't be reached or decline to participate.

QUESTION   What is the sampling frame?
If the customer database held 30,000 records instead of 7345, how much larger a sample would we need to get the same information?
If we then draw a different sample of 200 customers and obtain different answers to the questions on the survey, how do we refer to these differences?

ANSWER   The sampling frame is the customer database.

The size of the sample is all that matters, not the size of the population. We would need a sample of 200.

The differences in the responses are called sampling error, or sampling variability.

LO❶, ❸   ## 3.5   Other Random Sample Designs

Simple random sampling is not the only fair way to generate a sample. More complicated designs may save time or money or avert sampling problems. That said, all statistical sampling designs have in common the idea that chance, rather than human choice, is used to select the sample.

Stratified Sampling

Designs that are used to sample from large populations—especially populations residing across large areas—are often more complicated than simple random samples. Sometimes we slice the population into homogeneous groups, called **strata**, and then use simple random sampling within each stratum, combining the results at the end. This is called **stratified random sampling**.

Why would we want to stratify? Suppose we want to survey how shoppers feel about a potential new anchor store at a large suburban mall. The shopper population is 60% women and 40% men, and we suspect that men and women have different views on anchor stores. If we use simple random sampling to select 100 people for the survey, we could end up with 45 men and 55 women or 35 men and 65 women. Our resulting estimates of the attractiveness of a new anchor store could vary widely. To help reduce this sampling variability, we can force a representative balance, selecting 40 men at random and 60 women at random. This would guarantee that the proportions of men and women within our sample match the proportions in the population, and that should make such samples more accurate in representing the opinion of the population.

You can imagine that stratifying by race, income, age, and other characteristics can be helpful, depending on the purpose of the survey. When we use a sampling method based on strata, samples within each stratum are more like one another (see Figure 3.2), so statistics calculated for the sampled values will vary less from one sample to another. This reduced sampling variability is the most important benefit of stratifying. It also means that we can obtain information about the strata themselves in addition to finding out about the whole population. For instance, Statistics Canada uses a sample stratified by age group to estimate the unemployment rate of the Canadian workforce. This gives a more accurate estimate of the national unemployment rate than a simple random sample would. At the same time, it allows us to estimate the unemployment rate of each age group.

Sometimes we may simply not be able to get samples from our strata that are in the same proportions as in the whole population. For instance, suppose we conduct a survey of Canadians to ask whether they support increased use of nuclear power, and find that only 29% of our responses are from Ontario, whereas 38% of the Canadian population are Ontarians. If 54% of Ontarians in our sample support increased use of nuclear power, and 42% of non-Ontarians support it, then in our final results we would weight those figures according to the sizes of the populations, not the sizes of our samples. The percentage of Canadians supporting nuclear power would be estimated as: $54 \times 0.38 + 42 \times 0.62 = 46.56\%$. (It would *not* be correct to weight according to the number of responses to the survey: $54 \times 0.29 + 42 \times 0.71 = 45.48\%$.)

When stratifying a population, we are sometimes tempted to forget about some strata "because they are too small to bother with." This can lead to strange results. When estimating imports and exports from a country, we survey companies, stratifying them by size: large, medium, small. However, it is tempting not to bother with very small companies, since it takes extra time to survey them and they probably don't export or import much anyway. A study by the International Monetary Fund (IMF)[3] investigated the imbalance between world imports and exports. It is no surprise that countries' volumes of exports and imports differ. However, taking the world as a whole, each country's exports become the imports of another country, so globally everything should balance out. Surprisingly, global exports were more than $300 billion higher than global imports were in 2010. Where did all those exports go? Are flying saucers taking exports from planet Earth into space? The IMF's implicit response to that last question was no. Instead, it found that very small companies import more than they export, and the surveys used do not include a stratum for very small companies. The net result is that the surveys underestimate net imports. So the moral of the story is that it's important to take samples from *every* stratum in our population, and not to discard strata because they're inconvenient to survey or because we *think* they'll have only a small impact on the overall results.

Sss78/Fotolia

Cluster Sampling

Suppose our company has offices in 12 different cities in Canada and we want to interview middle managers to get their feedback on a restructuring that is being proposed at the executive level. The interviews need to be conducted in person, but our travel budget will allow us to visit only four of the 12 locations and spend one day in each. Our company has uniform standards for management, so there is no reason to think that the middle managers in Vancouver will have different opinions than the middle managers in Fredericton. We therefore choose four locations at random (e.g., using a simple random sample, or SRS, as we discussed in Section 3.4). We then make another random selection of enough managers at each of these four locations (an SRS will work again here) to keep ourselves busy for the day; see Figure 3.2. Each of the four locations is called a **cluster** and this method is called **cluster sampling**.

---

[3]Based on World Economic Outlook: Sustaining the Recovery.

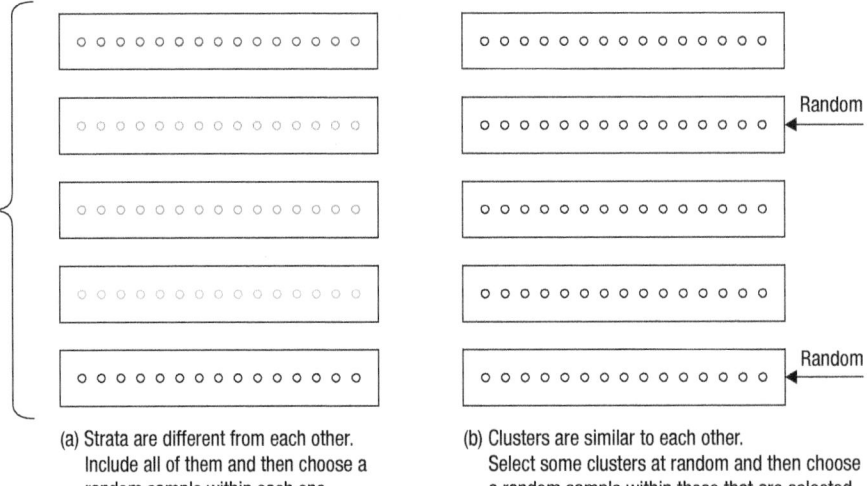

(a) Strata are different from each other. Include all of them and then choose a random sample within each one.

(b) Clusters are similar to each other. Select some clusters at random and then choose a random sample within those that are selected.

Figure 3.2   Strata and clusters.

> **Strata or Clusters?**
> We create strata by dividing the population into groups of similar individuals so that each stratum is different from the others. (For example, we often stratify by age, race, or sex.) By contrast, we create clusters that all look pretty much alike, with each representing the wide variety of individuals seen in the population.

Digital Vision/Getty Images

What's the difference between cluster sampling and stratified sampling? We stratify to ensure that our sample represents different groups in the population, and we sample randomly within each stratum. This reduces the sample-to-sample variability within a stratum. Strata are homogeneous, but differ from one another. By contrast, clusters are more or less alike, each heterogeneous and resembling the overall population. We cluster to save money or even to make the study practical (see Figure 3.2).

Systematic Sampling

Sometimes we draw a sample by selecting individuals systematically. For example, a **systematic sample** might select every 10th person on an alphabetical list of employees. To make sure our sample is random, we still must start the systematic selection with a randomly selected individual—not necessarily the first person on the list. When there is no reason to believe that the order of the list could be associated in any way with the responses measured, systematic sampling can give a representative sample. We compare systematic and simple random sampling in Figure 3.3. One of the virtues of systematic sampling is that it can be much less expensive than simple random sampling.

When using systematic sampling, we must be careful that our sampling frequency is NOT related to something about the process we are sampling. For instance, suppose we're sampling car tires coming off a production line for

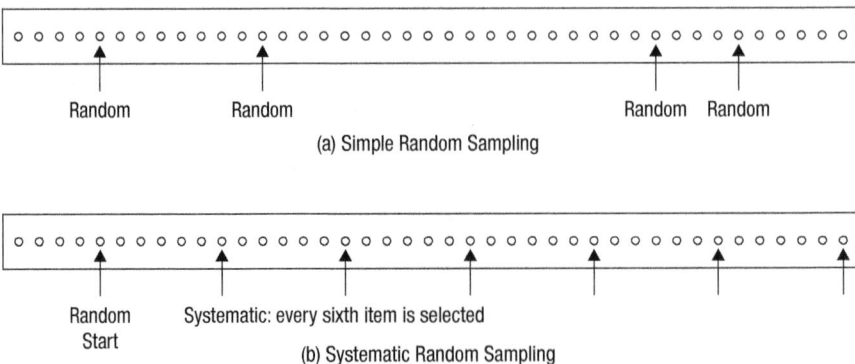

Figure 3.3   Simple and systematic random sampling.

quality-control purposes, and we've decided to sample every 100th tire. If the production-line employees routinely adjust the settings on one of the machines every 100th tire, then our sample will not be random. Instead, we may be sampling tires that are all produced just after the machine is reset, thus biasing our results. Similar problems occur if we sample every 50th tire or every 200th tire. If something about the process being sampled changes regularly (in this case every 100th tire), we should sample at a frequency that is not related to 100. In this case we could, for instance, sample every 87th tire, or every 123rd tire.

JUST CHECKING

2 We need to survey a random sample of the 300 passengers on a flight from Vancouver to Tokyo. Name each sampling method described below.

a) Pick every 10th passenger as people board the plane.
b) From the boarding list, randomly choose five people flying first-class and 25 of the other passengers.
c) Randomly generate 30 seat numbers and survey the passengers who sit there.
d) Randomly select a seat position (right window, right centre, right aisle, etc.) and survey all the passengers sitting in those seats.

Answers are found in Appendix A.

Multistage Sampling

The use of sampling schemes that combine several methods is called **multistage sampling**. Cluster sampling is an example of a multistage sampling method since we first choose a cluster at random and then we choose individuals within that cluster at random. In our example of cluster sampling with managers in 12 different locations, we could introduce another stage if we think that male and female managers might have different opinions on the corporate restructuring. Within each of the four locations where we are conducting our interviews, we could separate the male and female managers into two strata. In this case we would be using stratified sampling within cluster sampling. Most surveys conducted by professional polling organizations and market research firms use some combination of stratified and cluster sampling as well as simple random samples.

FOR EXAMPLE   Sampling theatre goers

The theatre board wants to encourage people to come from out of town to attend theatre events. They know that, in general, about 40% of ticket buyers are from out of town. These customers often purchase dinner at a local restaurant or stay overnight in a local inn, generating business for the town. The board hopes this information will encourage local businesses to advertise in the theatre event program, so they want to be sure out-of-town customers are represented in the samples. The database includes postal codes. The student consultants decide to sample 80 ticket buyers from postal codes outside the town and 120 from the town's own postal code.

QUESTION   What kind of sampling scheme are the student consultants using to replace the simple random sample?
What are the advantages of selecting 80 out-of-town and 120 local customers?

ANSWER   This is a stratified sample, consisting of a sample of 80 out-of-town customers and a sample of 120 local customers.

By stratifying, the consultants can guarantee that 40% of the sample is from out of town, reflecting the overall proportions among ticket buyers. If out-of-town customers differ in important ways from local ticket buyers, a stratified sample will reduce the variation in the estimates for each group so that the combined estimates can be more precise.

GUIDED EXAMPLE   Market Demand Survey

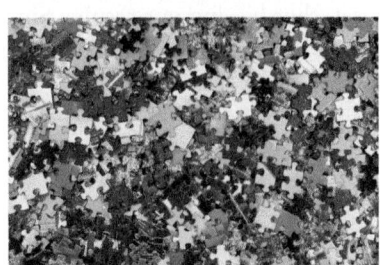

Tatiana Popova/Shutterstock

In a course at a business school, the students form business teams, propose a new product, and use seed money to launch a business to sell the product on campus.

Before committing funds for the business, each team must complete the following assignment: "Conduct a survey to determine the potential market demand on campus for the product you're proposing to sell." Suppose your team's product is a 500-piece jigsaw puzzle of the map of your university campus. Design a marketing survey and discuss the important issues to consider.

PLAN

Setup State the goals and objectives of the survey (the *Why*).

Our team designed a study to find out how likely students at our school are to buy our proposed product—a 500-piece jigsaw puzzle of the map of our university campus.

Population and Parameters Identify the population to be studied and the associated sampling frame. What are the parameters of interest?

The population studied will be students at our school. We've obtained a list of all students currently enrolled to use as the sampling frame. The parameter of interest is the proportion of students likely to buy this product. We'll also collect some demographic information about the respondents.

Sampling Plan Specify the sampling method and the sample size, *n*. Specify how the sample was actually drawn. What is the sampling frame?

We will select a simple random sample of 200 students. The sampling frame is the master list of students we obtained from the registrar. We decided against stratifying by sex or age because we thought that students were all more or less alike in their likely interest in our product.

The description should, if possible, be complete enough to allow someone to replicate the procedure, drawing another sample from the same population in the same manner. The question you ask is important, so state the wording of the question clearly. Make sure the question is useful in helping you with the overall goal of the survey.

We will ask the students we contact:

Do you solve jigsaw puzzles for fun?

Then we'll show them a prototype puzzle and ask:

If this puzzle sold for $10, would you purchase one?

We will also record the respondents' sex and age.

DO

Mechanics Specify *When*, *Where*, and *How* the sampling will be performed. Specify any other details of your survey, such as how respondents were contacted, any incentives that were offered to encourage them to respond, how nonrespondents were treated, and so on.

The survey will be administered in the middle of the fall semester during October. We have a master list of registered students, which we will randomize by matching it with random numbers from www.random.org and sorting on the random numbers, carrying the names. We will contact selected students by phone or email and arrange to meet with them. If students are unwilling to participate, we'll try to persuade them. If they still refuse, the next name from the randomized list will be substituted until a sample of 200 participants is found.

We will meet with students in an office set aside for this purpose so that each will see the puzzle under similar conditions.

Conclusion This report should include a discussion of all the elements needed to design the study. It's good practice to discuss any special circumstances or other issues that may need attention.

MEMO

Re: Survey Plans

Our team's plans for the puzzle market survey call for a simple random sample of students. Because subjects need to be shown the prototype puzzle, we must arrange to meet with selected participants. We have set aside an office for that purpose.

We will also collect demographic information so that we can determine whether there is in fact a difference in interest level across age groups or between men and women.

LO❸   **3.6   Practicalities**

The *Who* of a survey can refer to different groups, and the resulting ambiguity can tell you a lot about the success of a study. First, you should think about the population of interest. Often, this is not a well-defined group. For example, who, exactly, is a mall "shopper"—only the hurrying couples already carrying a purchase, or should we include people eating at the food court? How about teenagers outside the mall's video store, who may be carrying purchases or just hanging out, or both? Even when the population is clear, it may not be a practical group to study.

Second, you must specify the sampling frame. Usually, the sampling frame is not the group you *really* want to know about. For example, election pollsters would like to sample from those who will actually vote in the next election—a group that is particularly tricky to identify before election day. The sampling frame limits what your survey can find out.

Then there's your target sample. These are the individuals for whom you *intend* to measure responses. You're not likely to get responses from all of them. ("I know it's dinner time, but I'm sure you wouldn't mind answering a few questions. It'll only take 20 minutes or so. Oh, you're busy?") Nonresponse is a problem in many surveys.

Finally, there is your sample—the actual respondents. These are the individuals about whom you *do* get data and can draw conclusions. Unfortunately, they might not be representative of either the sampling frame or the population. For instance, the sample likely does not include people who were too busy to answer your questions, a common problem with most samples!

At each step, the group you can study may be constrained further. The *Who* keeps changing, and each constraint can introduce biases. A careful study should address the question of how well each group matches the population of interest. One of the main benefits of simple random sampling is that it never loses its sense of who's *Who*. The *Who* in an SRS is the population of interest from which you've drawn a representative sample. That's not always true for other kinds of samples.

When people (or committees!) decide on a survey, they often fail to think through the important questions about who are the *Who* of the study and whether they're the individuals about whom the answers would be interesting or have meaningful business consequences. This is a key step in performing a survey and should not be overlooked.

> The population is determined by the *Why* of the study. Unfortunately, the sample is just those people we can reach to obtain responses—the *Who* of the study. This difference could undermine even a well-designed study.

LO❷, ❸ ## 3.7   The Valid Survey

It isn't sufficient to draw a sample and start asking questions. You want to feel confident that your survey can yield the information you need about the population you're interested in. In other words, you need a *valid survey*.

To help ensure that you create a valid survey, you need to ask four questions:

- What do I want to know?
- Who are the appropriate respondents?
- What are the best questions?
- What will be done with the results?

These questions may seem obvious, but there are a number of specific pitfalls to avoid:

Know what you want to know. Far too often, decision makers decide to perform a survey without any clear idea of what they hope to learn from it. Before considering a survey, you must be clear about what you hope to learn and from whom you hope to learn it. If you can't identify those two factors, then you can't judge whether you have a valid survey. In other words, the survey *instrument*—the questionnaire itself—can be a source of errors. Perhaps the most common error is to ask unnecessary questions. The longer the survey, the fewer people will complete it, leading to greater nonresponse bias. For each question on your survey, you should ask yourself whether you really want to know the response and what you would do with the responses if you had them. If you don't have a good use for the answer to a question, don't ask it.

Use the right sampling frame. A valid survey obtains responses from *appropriate* respondents. Be sure you have a suitable sampling frame. Have you identified the population of interest and sampled from it appropriately? A company looking to expand its base might survey customers who returned warranty registration cards—after all, that's a readily available sampling frame—but if the company wants to know how to make its product more attractive, it needs to survey customers who rejected its product in favour of a competitor's product. This is the population that can tell the company what it needs to change about its product to capture a larger market share.

It is equally important to be sure that your respondents actually know the information you hope to discover. Your customers may not know much about the competing products, so asking them to compare your product with others may not yield useful information.

Ask specific rather than general questions. It's better to be specific. "Do you usually recall TV commercials?" won't be as useful as "How many TV commercials can you recall from last night?" or, better yet, "Please describe for me all the TV commercials you can recall from your viewing last night."

Watch for biases. Even with the appropriate sampling frame, you must beware of **response bias** in your sample. If customers who purchase more expensive items are less likely to respond to your survey, this can lead to **nonresponse bias**. Although you can't expect all mailed surveys to be returned, if those individuals who don't respond have common characteristics, your sample will no longer represent the population you hope to learn about. Surveys in which respondents volunteer to participate, such as online surveys, suffer from **voluntary response bias**. Individuals with the strongest feelings on either side of an issue are more likely to respond; those who don't care may not bother.

Take care not to confuse accuracy and bias. You're taking a sample in order to estimate something that applies to the whole population; that is, you're trying to get

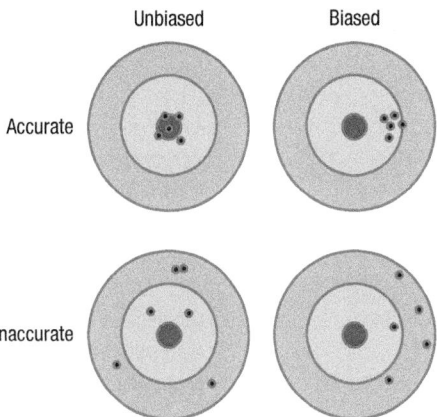

Figure 3.4   The importance of both accuracy and low bias.

the right answer, or hit the target, as shown in Figure 3.4. Bias means that you've designed a survey that will be systematically off, no matter how many people you interview. To reduce bias, you'll need to design a better survey. That's sometimes tough to do, though. Nonresponse bias is particularly difficult to deal with, unless the market research budget is enticing enough to pay respondents fairly for their feedback. Accuracy can be improved by generating a larger sample; however, again the research budget needs to be large enough to pay for all those extra interviews and for the time required to analyze the extra results.

Be careful with question phrasing. Questions must be carefully worded. A respondent may not understand the question—or may not understand the question the way the researcher intended it. For example, "Does anyone in your family own a Ford truck?" leaves the term "family" unclear. Does it include only spouses and children, or parents and siblings, or do in-laws and second cousins count, too? Similarly, a question like "Was your Twinkie fresh?" might be interpreted quite differently by different people.

Be careful with answer phrasing. Respondents and survey-takers may provide inaccurate responses, especially when questions are politically or sociologically sensitive. This also applies when the question doesn't take into account all possible answers, such as a true–false or multiple-choice question to which there may be other answers. Or the respondent may not know the correct answer to the survey question. We refer to an inaccurate response (intentional or unintentional) as a **measurement error**. One way to cut down on measurement errors is to provide a range of possible responses. But be sure to phrase them in neutral terms.

The best way to protect a survey from measurement errors is to perform a pilot test. In a **pilot test**, a small sample is drawn from the sampling frame, and a draft version of the survey instrument is administered. A pilot test can point out flaws in the instrument. For example, during a staff cutback at one of our schools, a researcher surveyed faculty members to ask how they felt about the reduction in staff support. The scale ran from "It's a good idea" to "I'm very unhappy." Fortunately, the pilot study showed that everyone was very unhappy or worse. The scale was retuned to cover responses from "unhappy" to "ready to quit."

Be sure you really want a representative sample. Up to now we've discussed how statisticians choose a sample so as to obtain results that are valid for a population; in other words, a representative sample. But sometimes our objective is different, and we don't want a representative sample. In this case, although we're not doing statistics, we may well be doing something else useful. Table 3.2 contrasts these situations in the case of corporate social responsibility.

Statistical Application of a Representative Sample	Nonstatistical Application of a Nonrepresentative Sample
A topic many companies are interested in is *corporate social responsibility*, or CSR. They want to know how important their CSR efforts are to their customers. We could estimate this by asking Canadians whether they agree with the statement, "I always try to buy from companies that are good corporate citizens." A representative sample of the entire Canadian population would be needed to come to a valid conclusion.	The nonprofit organization Canadian Business for Social Responsibility wanted to encourage small businesses to engage in CSR by showing how other small businesses had done it successfully.[4] To document the tricks of the trade, they interviewed only those small businesses that were interested and engaged in CSR. A *representative* sample of all small businesses, most of which are not involved in CSR, would not have been useful for this particular purpose.

Table 3.2   Applications of representative and nonrepresentative samples. Only the representative sample is used by statisticians.

FOR EXAMPLE   Survey design for theatre goers

A nonprofit organization has enlisted some student consultants to help design a fund-raising survey for the theatre. The student consultants suggest to the board of directors that they may want to rethink their survey plans. The consultants point out that there are differences between the population, the sampling frame, the target sample contacted, and the actual sample.

QUESTION   How do the population sampling frame, target sample, and sample differ?

ANSWER   The population is all potential ticket buyers.
The sampling frame is only those who have previously purchased tickets. Anyone who wasn't attracted to previous productions wouldn't be surveyed. That could keep the board from learning of ways to make the theatre's offerings more attractive to those who hadn't purchased tickets before.

The target sample is those selected from the database who can be contacted by telephone. Those with unlisted numbers or who had declined to give their phone number can't be contacted. It may be more difficult to contact those with caller ID.

The actual sample will be those previous customers selected at random from the database who can be reached by telephone and who agree to complete the survey.

LO❶, ❷, ❸   ## 3.8   How to Sample Badly

Bad sample designs yield worthless data. Many of the most convenient forms of sampling can be seriously biased. And there is no way to correct for the bias from a bad sample. So it's wise to pay attention to sample design—and to beware of reports based on poor samples.

---

[4]Based on Engaging Small Business in Corporate Social Responsibility: A Canadian Small Business Perspective on CSR.

Voluntary Response Sample

One of the most common dangerous sampling methods is the voluntary response sample. In a **voluntary response sample**, a large group of individuals is invited to respond, and all who do respond are counted. This method is used by call-in shows, 900 numbers, internet polls, and questionnaires sent by mail. Voluntary response samples are almost always biased, so conclusions drawn from them are almost always wrong.

It's often hard to define the sampling frame of a voluntary response study. Practically, the frames are groups such as internet users who frequent a particular website or viewers of a particular TV show. But those sampling frames don't correspond to the population you're likely to be interested in.

Even if the sampling frame is of interest, voluntary response samples are often biased toward those with strong opinions or those who are strongly motivated—and especially toward those with strong negative opinions. A request that travellers who have used the local airport visit a survey site to report on their experiences is much more likely to hear from those who had long waits, cancelled flights, and lost luggage than from those whose flights arrived on time and were free of luggage and scheduling-related hassles. The resulting voluntary response bias invalidates the survey.

Convenience Sampling

Another sampling method that doesn't work is convenience sampling. As the name suggests, in **convenience sampling** we simply include the individuals who are convenient. Unfortunately, this group may not be representative of the population. Suppose we read a newspaper article reporting a survey that found 99% of people have an internet connection. Later in the article, we learn that the survey was conducted via the internet. That was a convenient way to collect data and surely easier than drawing a simple random sample, but perhaps it overestimated the percentage of people in the general population with an internet connection.

Many surveys conducted at shopping malls suffer from the same problem. People in shopping malls are not necessarily representative of the population of interest. Mall shoppers tend to be more affluent and include a larger percentage of teenagers and retirees than the population at large. To make matters worse, survey interviewers tend to select individuals who look "safe" or easy to interview.

Convenience sampling is a widespread problem in the business world. When a company wants to find out what people think about its products or services, it may turn to the easiest people to sample: its own customers. But the company will never learn how those who *don't* buy its product feel about it.

Bad Sampling Frame?

An SRS from an incomplete sampling frame introduces bias because the individuals included may differ from the ones not in the frame. It may be easier to sample workers from a single site, but if a company has many sites and they differ in worker satisfaction, training, or job descriptions, the resulting sample can be biased. For example, there is serious concern among professional pollsters that the increasing numbers of people who can be reached only by cell phone may bias telephone-based market research and polling.

Undercoverage

Many survey designs suffer from **undercoverage**, in which some portion of the population isn't sampled at all or has a smaller representation in the sample than it has in the population. Undercoverage can arise for a number of reasons, but it's

---

Do you use the internet?
Click here ○ for yes
Click here ○ for no

Internet convenience surveys are often worthless. As voluntary response surveys, they have no well-defined sampling frame (all those who use the internet and visit their site?) and thus collect little useful information.

always a potential source of bias. Are people who use answering machines to screen callers (and are thus less available to blind calls from market researchers) different from other customers in their purchasing preferences?

FOR EXAMPLE   Common mistakes in survey design

A board member proposes that rather than telephoning past customers, the pollsters should simply post someone at the door to ask theatre goers their opinions. Another suggests that it would be even easier to post a questionnaire on the theatre website and invite responses there. A third member suggests that rather than working with random numbers, the pollsters should simply phone every 200th person on the list of past customers.

QUESTION   Identify the three methods proposed and explain what strengths and weaknesses each has.

ANSWER   Questioning customers at the door would generate a convenience sample. It would be cheap and fast, but is likely to be biased by the quality of the particular performance where the survey takes place.

Inviting responses on the website would generate a voluntary response sample. Only customers who frequented the website and decided to respond would be surveyed. This might, for example, underrepresent older customers or those without home internet access.

Sampling every 200th name from the customer list would lead to a systematic sample. It is slightly easier than randomizing. If the order of names on the list is unrelated to any questions asked, then this might be an acceptable method. But if, for example, the list is kept in the order of first purchases (when a customer's name and information were added to the database), then there might be a relationship between opinions and location on the list.

WHAT CAN GO WRONG?

- **Nonrespondents.** No survey succeeds in getting responses from everyone. The problem is that those who don't respond may differ from those who do. And if they differ on just the variables we care about, the lack of response will bias the results. Rather than sending out a large number of surveys for which the response rate will be low, it's often better to design a smaller, randomized survey for which you have the resources to ensure a high response rate.

- **Long, dull surveys.** Surveys that are too long are more likely to be refused, reducing the response rate and biasing all the results. Keep it short.

- **Response bias.** Response bias includes the tendency of respondents to tailor their responses to please the interviewer and the consequences of slanted question wording.

- **Push polls.** Push polls, which masquerade as surveys, present one side of an issue before asking a question. For example, a question like

    Would the fact that the new store that just opened in the mall sells mostly goods made overseas by workers in sweatshop conditions influence your decision to shop there rather than in the downtown store that features domestically produced products?

    is designed not to gather information, but to spread ill will toward the new store.

How to Think About Biases

- **Look for biases in any survey.** If you design a survey of your own, ask someone else to help look for biases that may not be obvious to you. Do this *before* you collect your data. There's no way to recover from a biased sample or a survey that asks biased questions.

  A bigger sample size for a biased study just gives you a bigger useless study. A really big sample gives you a really big useless study.

- **Spend your time and resources reducing biases.** No other use of resources is as worthwhile as those designed to reduce biases.

- **If you possibly can, pretest or pilot your survey.** Administer the survey in the exact form you intend to use it to a small sample drawn from the population you intend to sample. Look for misunderstandings, misinterpretation, confusion, or other possible biases. Then redesign your survey instrument.

- **Always report your sampling methods in detail.** Others may be able to detect biases where you did not expect to find them.

ETHICS IN ACTION

The Petitcodiac River Group is interested in applying for funds from the New Brunswick provincial government in order to continue its restoration and conservation of the Petitcodiac River. While the group has managed to gain significant support for its cause through education and community involvement, the executive committee is now interested in presenting the province with more compelling evidence. The Petitcodiac Group decided to survey local residents regarding their attitudes toward the proposed expansion of the river restoration and conservation project. With limited time and money (the deadline for the grant application was fast approaching), the executive committee was delighted when one of its members, Harry Greentree, volunteered to undertake the project. Harry owned a local organic food store and agreed to allow a sample of his shoppers to be interviewed during the next one-week period. The committee's only concern was that the shoppers be selected in a systematic fashion—for instance, by interviewing every fifth person who entered the store. Harry had no problem with this request and was eager to help the Petitcodiac River Group.

Ethical Issue *Introducing bias into the results (even if not intentional). One might expect consumers of organic food to be more concerned about the environment than the general* population *(related to Item C, ASA Ethical Guidelines; see Appendix C, the American Statistical Association's Ethical Guidelines for Statistical Practice, also available online at www.amstat.org/about/ethicalguidelines.cfm).*

Ron Garnett/All Canada Photos/Glow images

Ethical Solution *Harry is using a convenience sample from which results cannot be generalized. If the Petitcodiac River Group cannot improve its sampling scheme and survey design (e.g., for lack of expertise or time), the group should openly discuss the weaknesses of its sampling method when it discloses details of the study. When reporting the results, the group should note that findings are from a convenience sample and should include an appropriate disclaimer.*

WHAT HAVE WE LEARNED?

Learning Objectives

❶ We've learned that a representative sample can offer important insights about populations. It's the size of the sample—and not the fraction it represents of the larger population—that determines the precision of the statistics it yields. We've learned several ways to draw samples, all based on the power of randomness to make them representative of the population of interest:

- A simple random sample (SRS) is our standard. Every possible group of individuals has an equal chance of being in our sample. That's what makes it *simple*.
- Stratified samples can reduce sampling variability by identifying homogeneous subgroups and then randomly sampling within each.
- Cluster samples randomly select among heterogeneous subgroups that each resemble the population at large, making our sampling tasks more manageable.
- Systematic samples can work in some situations and are often the least expensive method of sampling. But we still want to start them randomly.
- Multistage samples combine several random sampling methods.

❷ We've learned that bias can also arise from poor sampling methods:

- Voluntary response samples are almost always biased and should be avoided and distrusted.
- Convenience samples are likely to be flawed for similar reasons.

We've learned that bias can destroy our ability to gain insights from our sample:

- Nonresponse bias can arise when sampled individuals will not or cannot respond.
- Response bias arises when respondents' answers might be affected by external influences, such as question wording or interviewer behaviour.

❸ We've learned that a sample is selected from a sampling frame to represent a population.

Terms

Biased	Any systematic failure of a sampling method to represent its population.
Census	An attempt to collect data on the entire population of interest.
Cluster	A representative subset of a population chosen for reasons of convenience, cost, or practicality.
Cluster sampling	A sampling design in which groups, or clusters, representative of the population are chosen at random and a census is then taken of each.
Convenience sampling	A sampling technique that selects individuals who are conveniently available.
Measurement error	Intentional or unintentional inaccurate response to a survey question.
Multistage sampling	Sampling schemes that combine several sampling methods.
Nonresponse bias	Bias introduced to a sample when a large fraction of those sampled fails to respond.
Pilot test	A small trial run of a study to check that the methods of the study are sound.
Population	The entire group of individuals or instances about whom we hope to learn.
Population parameter	A numerically valued attribute of a model for a population. We rarely expect to know the value of a parameter, but we do hope to estimate it from sampled data.
Randomization	A defence against bias in the sample selection process, in which each individual is given a fair, random chance of selection.
Representative sample	A sample from which the statistics computed accurately reflect the corresponding population parameters.
Response bias	Anything in a survey design that influences responses.
Sample	A subset of a population, examined in the hope of learning about the population.
Sample size	The number of individuals in a sample, usually denoted by n.

Sample statistic	A value calculated for sampled data, particularly one that corresponds to, and thus estimates, a population parameter. The term "sample statistic" is sometimes used, usually to parallel the corresponding term "population parameter."
Sample survey	A study that asks questions of a sample drawn from some population in hopes of learning something about the entire population.
Sampling frame	A list of individuals from which the sample is drawn. Individuals in the population of interest who are not in the sampling frame cannot be included in any sample.
Sampling variability	The natural tendency of randomly drawn samples to differ from one another.
Simple random sample (SRS)	A sample in which each set of n individuals in the population has an equal chance of selection.
Strata	Subsets of a population that are internally homogeneous but may differ from one another.
Stratified random sampling	A sampling design in which the population is divided into several homogeneous subpopulations, or strata, and random samples are then drawn from each stratum.
Systematic sample	A sample drawn by selecting individuals systematically from a sampling frame.
Undercoverage	A sampling scheme that biases the sample in a way that gives a part of the population less representation than it has in the population.
Voluntary response bias	Bias introduced to a sample when individuals can choose on their own whether to participate in the sample.
Voluntary response sample	A sample in which a large group of individuals are invited to respond and decide individually whether to participate. Voluntary response samples are generally worthless.

Skills

Plan
- Know the basic concepts and terminology of sampling.
- Be able to recognize population parameters in descriptions of populations and samples.
- Understand the value of randomization as a defence against bias.
- Understand the value of sampling to estimate population parameters from statistics calculated on representative samples drawn from the population.

Do
- Understand that the size of the sample (not the fraction of the population) determines the precision of estimates.
- Know how to draw a simple random sample from a master list of a population, using a computer or a table of random numbers.

Report
- Know what to report about a sample as part of your account of a statistical analysis.
- Be sure to report possible sources of bias in sampling methods. Recognize voluntary response and nonresponse as sources of bias in a sample survey.

MINI case studies

Market Survey Research

You are part of a marketing team that needs to research the potential of a new smartphone. Your team decides to email an interactive survey to a random sample of consumers. Write a short questionnaire that will generate the information you need about the new smartphone. Select a sample of 200 using an SRS from your sampling frame. Discuss how you will collect the data and how the responses will help your market research.

Canadian Labour Force Survey

Most people have heard of the unemployment rate, but not so many know where it comes from. Does the rate simply represent the number of people claiming Employment Insurance (EI)? It turns out that that would be an underestimation of the number of people unemployed, since many people are unemployed but ineligible for EI. Instead, Statistics Canada conducts the Labour Force Survey, interviewing people to find out their employment status and then estimating the unemployment rate for the whole country. During the second half of every month Statistics Canada analysts survey about 50,000 households, analyze the responses, and report the results. The most widely publicized number from this survey is the unemployment rate, but the survey covers much other information; for example, shifts of employees from one industry to another, hours worked, and demographic information about employees including age, sex, marital status, education level, and province or territory of residence. How would you design the Canadian Labour Force Survey?

Photodisc/Getty Images

- What is the population of interest?

- Why might it be difficult to select a simple random sample from this sampling frame?

- What sampling technique would you use to ensure that we have a representative sample of people from each province and territory and from the demographic groups described above?

MyStatLab Students! Save time, improve your grades with MyStatLab. Questions marked in ▇ can be found on MyStatLab. You can practise them as often as you want, and most feature step-by-step guided solutions to help you find the right answer. You'll find a personalized study plan available to you too!

Technology Help: Random Sampling

Computer-generated pseudorandom numbers are usually satisfactory for drawing random samples, but you can also use the truly random values available on the internet. Here's a convenient way to draw an SRS of a specified size using a computer-based sampling frame. The sampling frame can be a list of names or of identification numbers arrayed, for example, as a column in a spreadsheet, statistics program, or database:

1. Generate random numbers of enough digits so that each exceeds the size of the sampling frame list by several digits. This makes duplication unlikely.

2. Assign the random numbers arbitrarily to individuals in the sampling frame list. For example, put them in an adjacent column.

3. Sort the list of random numbers, carrying along the sampling frame list.

4. Now the first *n* values in the sorted sampling frame column are an SRS of *n* values from the entire sampling frame.

EXCEL

To generate random numbers in Excel:

- Choose **Data > Data Analysis > Random Number Generation**. (Note: the Data Analysis add-in must be installed.)

In the Random Number Generation window, fill in

- Number of variables = number of columns of random numbers.

- Number of random numbers = number of rows of random numbers.

Random Number Generation		
Number of Variables:	2	OK
Number of Random Numbers:	10	Cancel
Distribution:	Uniform ▾	Help
Parameters		
Between: 1 and 100		
Random Seed:		
Output options		
○ Output Range:		
● New Worksheet Ply:		
○ New Workbook		

Select a distribution from the drop-down menu. Parameters for your selected distribution will appear below.

- Enter the minimum and maximum bounds for the random numbers. This will be the minimum and maximum of the random numbers generated.
- A list of random numbers will be generated in a new worksheet. The example shown here resulted from parameters of 1 to 100.
- Format cells to obtain values desired.

To sample from a column of data in Excel:

- Choose **Data > Data Analysis > Sampling**.
- Type in or select the cell range containing the data. If this column has a title, place a check in the box marked "Labels."
- Next to Random, indicate the "Number of Samples" desired—this is actually the sample size, *n*.
- Finally, choose a location for the selected sample.

Warning: Excel samples with replacement. This is probably not the sampling method you want for drawing a sample from a population. The method given above using externally generated random numbers may be more appropriate.

MINITAB

To generate a list of random numbers in Minitab:

- Choose **Calc > Random Data > Uniform**.
- Enter the number of rows.
- Select the column where the random numbers will be stored.
- Click **OK**.

To sample from a variable in Minitab:

- Name a column in the data that will contain the sample; this column will be blank.
- Choose **Calc > Random Data > Sample From Columns**.
- Enter the number of rows to sample. This is the sample size, *n*.
- Indicate the column from which to select the data under "From Columns."
- Indicate the column in which the samples data should be placed under "Store Samples In."
- Minitab samples without replacement. To sample with replacement, check the box specifying that alternative.
- Click **OK**.

EXERCISES

SECTIONS 3.1 AND 3.2

1. Indicate whether each statement below is true or false. If false, explain why.

a) We can eliminate sampling error by selecting an unbiased sample.
b) Randomization helps to ensure that our sample is representative.
c) *Sampling error* refers to sample-to-sample differences and is also known as *sampling variability*.
d) It's better to try to match the characteristics of the sample to the population rather than to rely on randomization. **LO ❶**

2. Indicate whether each statement below is true or false. If false, explain why.

a) To get a representative sample, you must sample a large fraction of the population.
b) Using modern methods, it is best to select a representative subset of a population systematically.
c) A census is the only true representative sample.
d) A random sample of 100 students from a school with 2000 students is as representative as a random sample of 100 from a school with 20,000 students. **LO ❶**

SECTION 3.3

3. A consumer advocacy group is interested in gauging perceptions about food safety among professionals in the food industry. Specifically, the analysts in the advocacy group wish to determine the percentage of professional food preparers in Canada who believe food safety has improved. The analysts use an alphabetized list of members of the Chef's Collaborative organization and use Excel to generate a randomly shuffled list of the members. The analysts then select members to contact from this list until they have succeeded in contacting 150 members.

a) What is the population?
b) What is the sampling frame?
c) What is the population parameter of interest?
d) What sampling method is used? **LO ❶, ❸**

4. An airline company is interested in the opinions of its frequent flyer customers about its proposed new routes. Specifically, pollsters want to know what proportion of flyers plan to use one of the airline's new hubs in the next six months. The pollsters take a random sample of 10,000 from the database of all frequent flyers and send them an email message with a request to fill out a survey in exchange for 1500 air miles.

a) What is the population?
b) What is the sampling frame?
c) What is the population parameter of interest?
d) What sampling method is used? **LO❶, ❸**

SECTIONS 3.4 AND 3.5

5. GfK Roper Consulting conducts a global consumer survey to help multinational companies understand different consumer attitudes throughout the world. In India, the researchers interviewed 1000 people aged 13 to 65 (www.gfkamerica.com). Their sample is designed so that they attract 500 males and 500 females.

a) Are they using a simple random sample? How do you know?
b) What kind of design do you think they're using? **LO ❶, ❸**

6. For their class project, a group of Business students decide to survey the student body to assess opinions about a proposed new student coffee shop to judge how successful it might be. Their sample of 200 contained 50 first-year students, 50 second-years, 50 third-years, and 50 fourth-years.

a) Do you think the group was using an SRS? Why?
b) What kind of sampling design do you think they used? **LO❶, ❸**

7. The consumer advocacy group from Exercise 3 that was interested in gauging perceptions about food safety among professionals in the food industry has decided to use a different method to generate a sample. Instead of randomly selecting members from a shuffled list, a representative listed the members in alphabetical order and took every 10th member until they succeeded in contacting 150 members. What kind of sampling method did the group use? **LO❶**

8. The airline company from Exercise 4, which is interested in the opinions of its frequent flyer customers about its proposed new routes, has decided that different types of customers might have different opinions. Of their customers, 50% are silver level, 30% are blue, and 20% are red. The researchers first compile separate lists of silver, blue, and red members and then randomly select 5000 silver members, 3000 blue members, and 2000 red members to email. What kind of sampling method have they used? **LO❶, ❸**

SECTIONS 3.6 AND 3.7

For Exercises 9 and 10, identify the following, if possible. (If not, say why.)

a) The population
b) The population parameter of interest
c) The sampling frame

d) The sample
e) The sampling method, including whether or not randomization was employed
f) Any potential sources of bias you can detect and any problems you see in generalizing to the population of interest.

9. A business magazine mailed a questionnaire to the human resources directors of all Fortune 500 companies and received responses from 23% of them. Those responding reported that they did not find that such surveys intruded significantly into their workday. **LO❷, ❸**

10. A question posted on the Lycos website asked visitors to the site to say whether they thought businesses should be required to pay for their employees' health insurance. **LO❷, ❸**

11. An intern for the consumer advocacy group in Exercise 3 has decided to make the survey process simpler by calling 150 of the members who attended the symposium on "Food Safety in the 21st Century" recently held in Toronto. The intern has the phone numbers of each attendee, so it will be easy to contact them. He'll start calling members from the top of the list, which was generated as the members enrolled for the symposium. He has written the following script to read to them:

"As we learned in Toronto, food safety is of utmost importance in the restaurant business today. Given the enormous effort of the Food Safety Institute in developing proper guidelines and educational tools for food professionals, do you agree that food safety has improved in Canada?"

a) What is the population of interest?
b) What is the sampling frame?
c) Point out any problems you see with the sampling procedure and/or the survey itself. What are the potential impacts of these problems? **LO❷, ❸**

12. The airline company in Exercise 4 has realized that some of its customers either don't have email or don't check it regularly. It decides to restrict the mailing to customers who have recently registered for a "Win a Trip to Miami" contest, figuring that those with internet access are more likely to read and respond to its email. The company sends an email to recent registrants with the following message:

"Did you know that National Airlines has just spent over $3 million refurbishing our brand-new hub in Miami? By answering the following question, you may be eligible to win $1000 worth of coupons that can be spent in any of the fabulous restaurants or shops in the Miami airport. Might you possibly think of travelling to Miami in the next six months on your way to one of your destinations?"

a) What is the population?
b) What is the sampling frame?

c) Point out any problems you see with the sampling procedure and/or the survey itself. What are the potential impacts of these problems? LO ❷, ❸

13. An intern is working for Pacific TV (PTV), a small cable and internet provider, and has proposed some questions that might be used in a survey to assess whether customers are willing to pay $50 for a new service:

Question 1: If PTV offered state-of-the-art high-speed internet service for $50 per month, would you subscribe to that service?

Question 2: Would you find $50 per month—less than the cost of a monthly bus pass in many cities—an appropriate price for high-speed internet service?

a) Do you think these are appropriately worded questions? Why or why not?
b) Which question has more neutral wording? LO ❷, ❸

14. Here are more proposed survey questions for the survey mentioned in Exercise 13:

Question 3: Do you find that the slow speed of dial-up internet access reduces your enjoyment of web services?

Question 4: Given the growing importance of high-speed internet access for your children's education, would you subscribe to such a service if it were offered?

a) Do you think these are appropriately worded questions? Why or why not?
b) Which one has more neutral wording? Explain "what can go wrong." LO ❷, ❸

SECTION 3.8

15. Indicate whether each statement below is true or false. If false, explain why.

a) A local television news program that asks viewers to call in and give their opinion on an issue typically results in a biased voluntary response sample.
b) Convenience samples are generally not representative of the population.
c) Measurement error is the same as sampling error.
d) A pilot test can be useful for identifying poorly worded questions on a survey. LO ❶, ❷, ❸

16. Indicate whether each statement below is true or false. If false, explain why.

a) Asking viewers to call into a 900 number (for which a toll charge will be applicable) is a good way to produce a representative sample.
b) When writing a survey, it's a good idea to include as many questions as possible to ensure efficiency and to lower costs.
c) A recent poll on a website was valid because the sample size was over 1,000,000 respondents.

d) Malls are not necessarily a good place to conduct surveys because people who frequent malls may not be representative of the population at large. LO ❶, ❷, ❸

17. For your Marketing class, you'd like to take a survey from a sample of all the Catholic church members in your city to assess the market for a DVD about the Vatican. A list of churches shows 17 Catholic churches within the city limits. Rather than try to obtain a list of all members of all these churches, you decide to pick three churches at random. For those churches, you'll ask to get a list of all current members and contact 100 members at random.

a) What kind of design have you used?
b) What could go wrong with the design you have proposed? LO ❶, ❷, ❸

18. The Ontario Ministry of Natural Resources plans to study the fishing industry around Port Dover on Lake Erie. To do that, researchers decide to randomly select five fishing boats at the end of a randomly chosen fishing day and to count the numbers and types of all the fish on those boats.

a) What kind of design have they used?
b) What could go wrong with the design they have proposed? LO ❶, ❷, ❸

CHAPTER EXERCISES

19. Software licences. The website www.gamefaqs.com asked, as its question of the day to which visitors to the site were invited to respond, "Do you ever read the end-user licence agreements when installing software or games?" Of the 98,574 respondents, 63.47% said they never read those agreements—a fact that software manufacturers might find important.

a) What kind of sample was this?
b) How much confidence would you place in using 63.47% as an estimate of the fraction of people who don't read software licences? (*Source:* Based on Poll of the Day: Do You Ever Read The End-User Licence Agreements When Installing Software or Games?) LO ❶

20. Drugs in baseball. Major League Baseball, responding to concerns about its "brand," tests players to see whether they're using performance-enhancing drugs. Officials select teams at random, and a drug-testing crew shows up unannounced to test all 40 players on each team selected. Each testing day can be considered a study of drug use in Major League Baseball.

a) What kind of sample is this?
b) Is that choice appropriate? LO ❶

21. Gallup. At its website (www.gallup.com), the Gallup Poll publishes results of a new survey each day. Scroll down to the end, and you'll find a statement that includes an explanation such as this:

Results are based on telephone interviews conducted April 1-30, 2017, with a random sample of 30,401 adults, aged 18 and older, living in all 50 U.S. states and the District of Columbia.

a) For this survey, identify the population of interest.

b) Gallup performs its surveys by phoning numbers generated at random by a computer program. What is the sampling frame?

c) What problems, if any, would you be concerned about in matching the sampling frame with the population? (*Source:* Based on Gallup Poll, www.gallup.com/poll/101905/gallup-poll.aspx.) **LO ❸**

22. Defining the survey. At its website (www.gallup.com), the Gallup World Poll reports results of surveys conducted in various places around the world. At the end of these reports, researchers describe their methods, including explanations such as the following:

Results are based on face-to-face interviews with randomly selected national samples of approximately 1000 adults, aged 15 and older, who live permanently in each of the 21 sub-Saharan African nations surveyed.

a) Gallup is interested in sub-Saharan Africa. What kind of survey design are they using?

b) Some of the countries surveyed have large populations. (Nigeria is estimated to have about 130 million people.) Some are quite small. (Togo's population is estimated at 5.4 million.) Nonetheless, Gallup sampled 1000 adults in each country. How does this affect the precision of its estimates for these countries? (*Source:* Based on Sub-Saharan Africans Rate Their Past, Present, and Future.) **LO ❶**

23–31. Survey details. *For the following reports about statistical studies, identify the following items (if possible). If you can't tell, then say so—this often happens when we read about a survey.*

a) The population

b) The population parameter of interest

c) The sampling frame

d) The sample

e) The sampling method, including whether or not randomization was employed

f) Any potential sources of bias you can detect and any problems you see in generalizing to the population of interest

23. Technology forecasting. To estimate the impact of new technologies on fuel efficiency for motor vehicles, a consulting company requests the opinions of established researchers in the automobile industry, the clean-tech industry, government research labs, and universities. **LO ❸**

24. Alternative medicine. Consumers Union asked all subscribers whether they had used alternative medical treatments and, if so, whether they had benefited from them. For almost all the treatments, approximately 20% of those responding reported cures or substantial improvement in their condition. **LO ❸**

25. Global warming. The Gallup Poll interviewed 1022 randomly selected adults aged 18 and older, March 7–10, 2013. Gallup reports that when asked whether respondents thought that global warming was due primarily to human activities, 57% of respondents said it was. **LO ❸**

26. At the bar. Researchers waited outside a bar they had randomly selected from a list of such establishments. They stopped every 10th person who came out of the bar and asked whether he or she thought drinking and driving was a serious problem. **LO ❸**

27. Election poll. Hoping to learn what issues may resonate with voters in the coming election, the campaign director for a mayoral candidate selects one block from each of the city's election districts. Staff members go there and interview all the residents they can find. **LO ❸**

28. Toxic waste. The Canadian Environmental Assessment Agency took soil samples at 16 locations near a former industrial waste dump and checked each for evidence of toxic chemicals. The researchers found no elevated levels of any harmful substances. **LO ❸**

29. Housing discrimination. Inspectors send trained "renters" of various races and ethnic backgrounds, and of both sexes, to inquire about renting randomly assigned advertised apartments. They look for evidence that landlords deny access illegally based on race, sex, or ethnic background. **LO ❸**

30. Quality control. A company packaging snack foods maintains quality control by randomly selecting 10 cases from each day's production and weighing the bags. Then the quality control staff open one bag from each case and inspect the contents. **LO ❸**

31. Contaminated milk. Dairy inspectors visit farms unannounced and take samples of the milk to test for contamination. If the milk is found to contain dirt, antibiotics, or other foreign matter, the milk will be destroyed and the farm is considered to be contaminated pending further testing. **LO ❸**

32. Pulse poll. A local TV station conducted a "Pulse Poll" to predict the winner in the upcoming mayoral election. Evening news viewers were invited to phone in their votes, with the results to be announced on the late-night news. Based on the phone calls, the station predicted that Amabo would win the election with 52% of the vote. It was wrong: Amabo lost, getting only 46% of the vote. Do you think the station's faulty prediction is more likely to be a result of bias or sampling error? Explain. **LO ❷**

33. Paper poll. Prior to the mayoral election discussed in Exercise 32, the local newspaper conducted a poll. The paper surveyed a random sample of registered voters stratified by political party, age, sex, and area of residence. This poll predicted that Amabo would win the election with 52% of the vote. The newspaper was wrong: Amabo lost, getting only 46% of the vote. Do you think the newspaper's faulty prediction is more likely to be a result of bias or sampling error? Explain. **LO ❷**

34. Cable company market research, part 1. A cable TV company is considering offering optical fibre to residences to improve the speed of its HDTV download service. Before launching the new service, however, the company wants to find out whether customers would pay the $50 per month that the company wants to charge. An intern has prepared several alternative plans for assessing customer demand. For each, indicate what kind of sampling strategy is involved and what (if any) biases might result.

a) Put a big ad in the newspaper asking people to log their opinions on the company's website.
b) Randomly select one of the towns and contact every cable subscriber by phone.
c) Send a survey to each customer and ask each of them to fill it out and return it.
d) Randomly select 20 customers from each town. Send them a survey, and follow up with a phone call if they do not return the survey within a week. **LO ❶, ❷**

35. Cable company market research, part 2. Four new sampling strategies have been proposed to help a cable TV company determine whether enough cable subscribers are likely to purchase the new HDTV download service. For each, indicate what kind of sampling strategy is involved and what (if any) biases might result.

a) Run a poll on the local TV news, asking people to dial one of two phone numbers to indicate whether they would be interested in the new service.
b) Hold a meeting in each of the 15 towns, and tally the opinions expressed by those who attend the meetings.
c) Randomly select one street in each town and contact a random section of the households on that street.
d) Go through the company's customer records, selecting every 40th subscriber. Send employees to those homes to interview the people chosen. **LO ❶, ❷**

36. Canadian research in the Great Lakes. Fisheries and Oceans Canada operates a laboratory in Sault Ste. Marie, Ontario, to study the abundance of species of fish that have invaded the Great Lakes from other ecosystems. Researchers have found 145 such "exotic" species and wish to get more details on each species present. Suppose they take a sample every third day at dawn during June and July from each of the Great Lakes.

a) What kind of design have they used?
b) If they published a report giving estimates for exotic species in the Great Lakes based on this survey, what ethical issues would be involved (see Appendix C)? **LO ❶**

37. Amusement park riders. An amusement park has opened a new roller coaster. It is so popular that people line up and wait for up to three hours for a two-minute ride. Concerned about how patrons (who paid a large amount to enter the park and ride on the rides) feel about this, researchers survey every 10th person who is waiting in line for the roller coaster, starting from a randomly selected individual.

a) What kind of sample is this?
b) Is it likely to be representative?
c) What is the sampling frame? **LO ❶, ❸**

38. Playground. Some people have been complaining that the children's playground at a municipal park is too small and is in need of repair. Managers of the park decide to survey city residents to see if they believe the playground should be rebuilt. Park managers hand out questionnaires to parents who bring children to the park. Describe possible biases in this sample. **LO ❷**

39. Royal Family. An opinion poll needs to assess the popularity of the Royal Family and is choosing among three questions:

Question 1: Do you think the Canadian Head of State should be a member of the Royal Family or elected?

Question 2: Do you think the Canadian Head of State should be a member of the Royal Family or elected as in France and USA?

Question 3: Should laws passed by the Canadian Parliament need approval from the Royal Family as at present?

a) Which question has the least neutral wording? Give your reason.
b) Which is the most appropriately worded question? Give your reason. **LO ❷**

40. More words. Here are more proposed questions for the survey in exercise 13.

Question 3: Many people in Japan have optical fibre connected to their homes. Should it be made available to you?

Question 4: Since HDTV movies can be watched without downloading them, would you pay $50 a month for an HDTV download service?

a) Do you think these are appropriately worded questions? Why or why not?
b) Propose a question with more neutral wording. **LO ❷**

41. Another ride. The survey of patrons waiting in line for the roller coaster mentioned in Exercise 37 asks whether it is worthwhile to wait a long time for the ride and whether the amusement park should install still more roller coasters. What biases might cause a problem for this survey? **LO ❷**

42. Playground bias. The survey described in Exercise 38 asked,

Many people believe this playground is too small and in need of repair. Do you think the playground should be repaired and expanded even if that means raising the entrance fee to the park?

Describe two ways this question may lead to response bias. **LO ❷**

43. (Possibly) biased questions. Examine each of the following questions for possible bias. If you think the question is biased, indicate how and propose a better question.

a) *Should companies that pollute the environment be compelled to pay the costs of cleanup?*

b) *Should a company enforce a strict dress code?* **LO ❷**

44. More possibly biased questions. Examine each of the following questions for possible bias. If you think the question is biased, indicate how and propose a better question.

a) *Do you think price or quality is more important in selecting a tablet computer?*

b) *Given humanity's great tradition of exploration, do you favour continued funding for space flights?* **LO ❷**

45. Phone surveys. Any time we conduct a survey, we must take care to avoid undercoverage. Suppose we plan to select 500 names from the city phone book, call those homes between noon and 4:00 p.m., and interview whoever answers.

a) Why is it difficult to use a simple random sample here?

b) Describe a more convenient, but still random, sampling strategy.

c) What kinds of households are likely to be included in the eventual sample of opinion? Who will be excluded?

d) Suppose instead that we continue calling each number, perhaps in the morning or evening, until an adult is contacted and interviewed. How does this improve the sampling design?

e) Random-digit dialling machines can generate the phone calls for us. How would this improve our design? Is anyone still excluded? **LO ❶, ❷, ❸**

46. Cell phone survey. What about drawing a random sample only from cell phone exchanges? Discuss the advantages and disadvantages of such a sampling method compared with surveying randomly generated telephone numbers from non–cell phone exchanges. Do you think these advantages and disadvantages have changed over time? How do you expect they'll change in the future? **LO ❷**

47. Change. How much cash do you have on you right now? Go ahead, count it.

a) How much cash do you have?

b) Suppose you check on your cash every day for a week as you head for lunch and average the results. What parameter would this average estimate?

c) Suppose you ask 10 friends to average *their* cash every day for a week, and you average those 10 measurements. What is the population now? What parameter would this average estimate?

d) Do you think these 10 average cash amounts are likely to be representative of the population of cash amounts in your class? In your university? In the country? Why or why not? **LO ❶, ❷, ❸**

48. Fuel economy. Occasionally, when I fill my car with gas, I figure out how many litres it consumes per 100 kilometres. I wrote down those results after six gas fill-ups in the past few months. Overall, it appears my car uses 8.1 litres per 100 kilometres.

a) What statistic have I calculated?

b) What is the parameter I'm trying to estimate?

c) How might my results be biased?

d) When *Consumer Reports* checks a car like mine to predict its fuel economy, what parameter is it trying to estimate? **LO ❸**

49. Accounting. Between quarterly audits, a company likes to check on its accounting procedures to address any problems before they become serious. The accounting staff processes payments for at most 120 orders each day. The next day, the supervisor rechecks 10 of the transactions to make sure they were processed properly.

a) Propose a sampling strategy for the supervisor.

b) How would you modify that strategy if the company makes both wholesale and retail sales, requiring different bookkeeping procedures? **LO ❶**

50. Happy workers? A manufacturing company employs 14 project managers, 48 forepersons, and 377 labourers. In an effort to keep informed about any possible sources of employee discontent, management wants to conduct job satisfaction interviews with a simple random sample of employees every month.

a) Do you see any danger of bias in the company's plan? Explain.

b) How might you select a simple random sample?

c) Why do you think a simple random sample might not provide the representative opinion the company seeks?

d) What ethical issue would be involved if the company statistician conducted the survey this way? (See Appendix C.)

e) Propose a better sampling strategy.

f) Listed below are the last names of the project managers. Use random numbers to select two people to be interviewed. Be sure to explain your method carefully. **LO ❶, ❷**

Ahmed	Bowman	Chen
DeLara	DeRoos	Grigorov
Li	Mulvaney	Pagliarulo
Rosica	Smithson	Tadros
Williams	Yamamoto	

51. Quality control. Sammy's Salsa, a small local company, produces 20 cases of salsa a day. Each case contains 12 jars and is imprinted with a code indicating the date on which it was bottled and the batch number. To help maintain consistency, at the end of each day, Sammy selects three bottles of salsa, weighs the contents, and tastes the product.

Help Sammy select the sample jars. Today's cases are coded 07N61 through 07N80.

a) Carefully explain your sampling strategy.

b) Show how to use random numbers to pick the three jars for testing.

c) Did you use a simple random sample? Explain. **LO ❶**

52. Fish quality. Concerned about reports of discoloured scales on fish caught downstream from a newly sited chemical plant, scientists set up a field station in a shoreline public park. For one week they asked people fishing there to bring any fish they caught to the field station for a brief inspection. At the end of the week, the scientists said that 18% of the 234 fish that were submitted for inspection displayed the discolouration. From this information, can the researchers estimate what proportion of fish in the river have discoloured scales? Explain. **LO ❷**

53. Sampling methods. Consider each of these situations. Do you think the proposed sampling method is appropriate? Explain.

a) We want to know if business leaders in the community support the development of an "incubator" site at a vacant lot on the edge of town. We spend a day phoning local businesses listed in the phone book to ask whether they'd sign a petition.

b) We want to know if travellers at the local airport are satisfied with the food available for purchase there. We go to the airport on a busy day and interview every 10th person waiting in line in the food court. **LO ❶**

54. Canadian Census. The Canadian Census collects demographic data for specific groups such as lone-parent families, seniors, and those from specific language groups via what is commonly referred to as the "Short Form." The Short Form questionnaire is issued to each household in Canada, and all Canadian residents are legally required to complete the form. In addition to the "Short Form," a more detailed (long) form, sent for completion to certain households only, used to be mandatory, but became voluntary instead at the time of the 2011 Census. What are the impacts of the change from mandatory to voluntary participation in the longer Census? **LO ❷**

55. Harris Interactive. Harris Interactive conducts surveys online with panels of people who have volunteered to participate. One of these is the "Body Mass Index" panel consisting of people classified into four groups according to their Body Mass Index, BMI:

15,000 underweight adults: BMI < 18.5

38,000 normal weight adults: BMI between 18.5 and 24.9

51,000 overweight adults: BMI between 25 and 29.5

59,000 obese adults: BMI > 29.5

They fill out questionnaires online, which Harris Interactive analyzes to provide information to the food industry on food and drink preferences, how these preferences are affected by attitudes to health, and interest in specialty food products and supplements. Comment on this survey using the concepts discussed in this chapter. (*Source:* Based on Harris Interactive surveys, http://www.theharrispoll.com/.) **LO ❶, ❷, ❸**

Chris Wattie/Reuters

4

Displaying and Describing Categorical Data

Loblaw

As a boy with only a few dollars to his name, Theodore Loblaw arrived in Toronto and got a job in a grocery store, where he fetched items from behind the counter for customers. But Theodore had a new idea, self-service, and opened his own business —Loblaw Groceterias—in Ontario in 1919. Within a decade, he and his partners gained a reputation for efficiency and hence low prices, and opened 70 stores in Ontario, also expanding into New York State, Pennsylvania, and Illinois. In the 1930s, Loblaw was doing so well it built bowling lanes for its employees and supported local hospitals and boys' clubs. Innovation didn't stop at the idea of self-service, and the 1940s and 1950s included "magic carpet" doors that opened automatically to welcome customers, and a loyalty program based on "Lucky Green Stamps" that could be redeemed for gifts. As competition heated up in the 1970s and 1980s, Loblaw introduced No Name and President's Choice products, and in the 1990s and 2000s continued to differentiate itself with PC Financial banking services and Joe Fresh clothing.

Today, the holding company Loblaw Companies Limited is Canada's largest food distributor, and owns Zehrmart, Provigo, Atlantic Wholesalers, National Grocers, Choice Bank, and several other companies. Loblaw saves operating costs and protects the environment by improved lighting, heating, and ventilation systems, reducing energy use by 3% per year in 2012 and 2013. It also has a children's charity that provided $9.9 million for children with disabilities and $4.9 million to child nutrition programs in 2013.

ompanies like Loblaw need data to manage their business. And Loblaw has data on a wide variety of subjects—from sales volume for thousands of products and the employment history of thousands of employees to the purchasing patterns of millions of customers participating in the loyalty programs. Loblaw handles vast amounts of data, and statistical analysis of those data is used to support management decisions.

Let's take the example of the data Loblaw keeps on every store it owns: the manager's name, the street address, the province, the postal code, the phone number, etc. These are all categorical data items, the subject of this chapter. In order to get a concrete example to work with, we'll focus on the provinces in which the stores are located, and, to narrow it down even further, we'll restrict ourselves to eastern Canada. We cannot do numerical calculations on categorical data, but we can count the number of occurrences in each category—that is, the number of stores in each province of eastern Canada.

We show this store information in Table 4.1. To be precise about our data, we need to clarify that we're excluding franchised and associated stores and including only stores owned and operated by companies in the Loblaw holding company.

WHO	Corporate stores
WHAT	Number of corporate stores by province
WHEN	2013
WHERE	Eastern Canada
HOW	Data obtained from Loblaw's "Annual Information Form"
WHY	To investigate whether Loblaw's corporate stores are evenly distributed across eastern Canada

LO❶ 4.1

The Three Rules of Data Analysis

There are three things you should always do with data:

1. **Make a picture.** A display of your data will reveal things you are not likely to see in a table of numbers and will help you to *plan* your approach to the analysis and think clearly about the patterns and relationships that may be hiding in your data.
2. **Make a picture.** A well-designed display will *do* much of the work of analyzing your data. It can show the important features and patterns. A picture will also reveal things you did not expect to see: extraordinary (possibly wrong) data values or unexpected patterns.
3. **Make a picture.** The best way to *report* to others what you find in your data is with a well-chosen picture.

Province	Corporate Stores
Newfoundland and Labrador	12
Prince Edward Island	4
Nova Scotia	32
New Brunswick	22
Quebec	171
Ontario	165

Table 4.1 Frequency table of the number of Loblaw stores in eastern Canada.

Source: Based on Loblaw Companies Limited (2013). Annual information form.

These are the three rules of data analysis. Figure 4.1 is an example of a particularly innovative picture, linking the major that a student took at college with his or her career.

Some displays communicate information better than others. We'll discuss some general principles for displaying data honestly in this chapter.

LO❶ 4.2

Frequency Tables

To make a picture of categorical data, we start by putting the data into piles. That job has already been done in Table 4.1. We've piled together all the stores in each province; that is, we have counted the number of stores in each category. We call this type of table a **frequency table** because it tells us how frequently we find Loblaw stores in Ontario, in New Brunswick, etc. It's tough to read a frequency table if it contains too many piles/categories. In our case there are only six piles, one for each of the provinces in eastern Canada, and that is easy enough to read. If we wanted our table to be smaller, we might combine the data for the three smallest provinces (New Brunswick, Prince Edward Island, and Newfoundland and Labrador) under a single heading "Other," which would have $12 + 4 + 22 = 38$ stores. An "Other" category is particularly useful if we have a very large number of piles in our data, and it might be used if we had data on all 13 provinces and territories throughout Canada, instead of just eastern Canada.

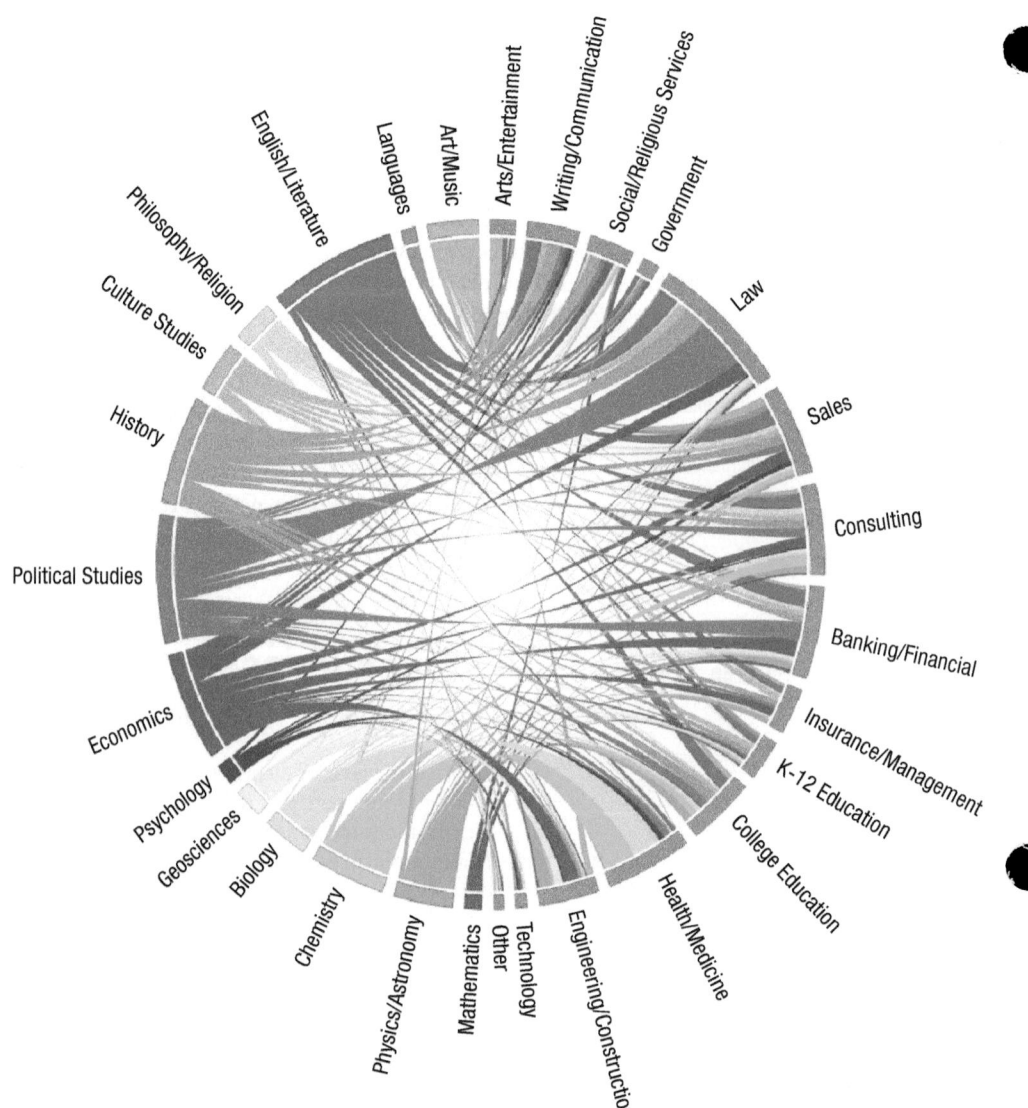

Figure 4.1   Visualization of the link between major in college and career of Williams College alumni. Each individual is graphed as an arc connecting his or her major on the left with a career area on the right. Each major is assigned a colour: Humanities in the blue range, Social Sciences in the reds and oranges, and Sciences in greens. It is easy to see the expected large arc connecting Biology and Health/Medicine and the spread of Math majors to many careers. Possibly less expected is that Economics majors choose a wide range of careers. Banking/Finance draws many from Economics, but also quite a few from History, Political Science, and the Humanities. (This image was created by Satyan Devadoss, Hayley Brooks, and Kaison Tanabe using the CIRCOS software; an interactive version of this graph can be found at http://cereusdata.com.)

Source: From Impact of Major on Career Path for 15600 Williams College Alums by Satyan Devadoss. Copyright © 2012 by Satyan Devadoss. Used by permission of Satyan Devadoss.

Province	Corporate Stores (%)
Quebec	42.12
Ontario	40.64
Nova Scotia	7.88
Other	9.36
Total	100.00

Table 4.2   Relative frequency table showing percentages of Loblaw stores in eastern Canada.

Source: Based on Loblaw Companies Limited (2013). Annual information form.

The number of stores is good factual information, but it is sometimes useful to record proportions or percentages instead of numbers. We have done this in Table 4.2, which is called a **relative frequency table** because the percentages show how many stores there are in each province "relative" to the total for eastern Canada. We have also put the three smallest provinces in an "Other" percentage, to show how this looks. Notice that the "Total" here represents the total for eastern Canada, not the whole of Canada. It is useful to have a "Total" line in a relative frequency table, as it provides a check on our calculations. The total should come to 100%, apart from "rounding errors" (see Table 4.2).

FOR EXAMPLE
Making frequency and relative frequency tables for Super Bowl viewers

The Super Bowl, the championship game of the National Football League, is an important annual social event with tens of millions of viewers. The ads that air during the game are expensive, making them high-profile and much anticipated, so the advertisers feel pressure to be innovative, entertaining, and often humorous. Some people, in fact, watch the Super Bowl mainly for the commercials. Before a recent Super Bowl, the Gallup Poll asked 1008 U.S. adults whether they were more interested in watching the game or the commercials. Here are 40 of those responses (NA/Don't Know = No Answer or Don't Know):

Won't Watch	Game	Commercials	Won't Watch	Game
Game	Won't Watch	Commercials	Game	Game
Commercials	Commercials	Game	Won't Watch	Commercials
Game	NA/Don't Know	Commercials	Game	Game
Won't Watch	Game	Game	Won't Watch	Game
Game	Won't Watch	Won't Watch	Game	Won't Watch
Won't Watch	Commercials	Commercials	Game	Won't Watch
NA/Don't Know	Won't Watch	Game	Game	Game

QUESTION Make a frequency table for this variable. Include the percentages to display both a frequency and a relative frequency table at the same time.

ANSWER There were four different responses to the question about watching the Super Bowl. Counting the number of participants who responded to each of these gives the following table:

RESPONSE	COUNTS	PERCENTAGE
Commercials	8	20.0%
Game	18	45.0%
Won't Watch	12	30.0%
No Answer/Don't Know	2	5.0%
Total	**40**	**100.0%**

LO❷ **4.3   Charts**

The Area Principle

Now that we have a frequency table, we're ready to follow the three rules of data analysis and make a picture of the data. But we can't make just any picture; a bad picture can distort our understanding rather than help it. For example, Figure 4.2 is one way of showing a graph of the frequencies of Table 4.1. What impression do you get of the relative number of stores in each province?

Table 4.2 tells us that there are about five times as many Loblaw stores in Ontario as there are in Nova Scotia, but Figure 4.2 exaggerates this difference. The figure doesn't seem to accurately represent the information in the table. So

Figure 4.2   Although the length of each column corresponds to the correct number of stores, the impression we get is all wrong, because we perceive the entire area of the column as the quantity. In fact, Ontario has only five times as many stores as Nova Scotia.

what's gone wrong? The heights of the images in the figure correspond to the percentages in the table, but our eyes tend to be more impressed by the *area* (or perhaps even the *volume*) than by other aspects of each store image. The area of the image for Ontario is 5 × 5 = 25 times as large as the area of the Nova Scotia image, and this creates a false impression of the number of stores in the two provinces.

The best data displays observe a fundamental principle of graphing data called the **area principle**, which holds that the area occupied by a part of the graph should correspond to the magnitude of the value it represents.

Bar Charts

Figure 4.3 gives us a chart that obeys the area principle. It's not as visually entertaining as the store images, but it does give a more *accurate* visual impression of the **distribution**. The height of each bar shows the percentage of stores in that province. The bars are the same width, so their heights determine their areas, and the areas are proportional to the percentage of stores. Now it's easy to see that there are about five times as many stores in Ontario as there are in Nova Scotia, which was not the impression the store images conveyed in Figure 4.2. Bar charts make these kinds of comparisons easy and natural.

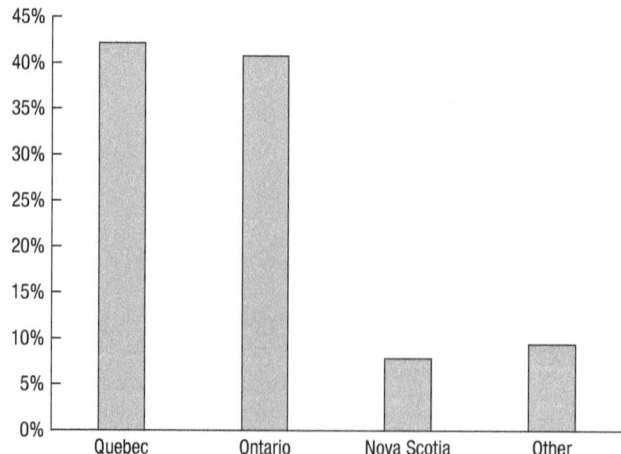

Figure 4.3   Number of Loblaw stores in each province in eastern Canada. With the area principle satisfied, the true distribution is clear.

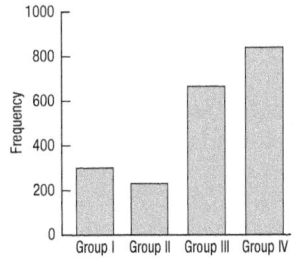

Vertical Bar Chart

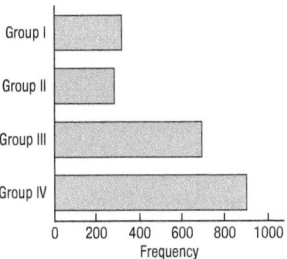

Horizontal Bar Chart

A **bar chart** displays the distribution of a categorical variable, showing the counts for each category next to each other for easy comparison. Bar charts should have small spaces between the bars to indicate that these are freestanding bars that could be rearranged into any order. The bars are lined up along a common base.

Bar charts are usually drawn vertically in columns, but sometimes they are drawn with horizontal bars.[1]

Pie Charts

Another common display that shows how a whole group breaks into several categories is a pie chart. A **pie chart** shows the whole group of cases as a circle. Each "slice" of the "pie" is proportional to the fraction of the whole in each category.

Pie charts give a quick impression of how a whole group is partitioned into smaller groups. Because we're used to cutting up pies into two, four, or eight pieces, pie charts are good for seeing relative frequencies near 1/2, 1/4, or 1/8. For example, in Figure 4.4, you can easily see that the slices representing Ontario and Nova Scotia are almost exactly half the total. Unfortunately, other comparisons are harder to make with pie charts. Are there more stores in Nova Scotia than in "Other"? It's tough to tell, since the two slices look about the same. Comparisons such as these are usually easier to spot in a bar chart. (Compare with Figure 4.3.)

- **Think before you draw.** Our first rule of data analysis is *Make a picture*. But what kind of picture? We don't have a lot of options—yet. There's more to Statistics than pie charts and bar charts, and knowing when to use every type of display we'll discuss is a critical first step in data analysis. That decision depends in part on what type of data you have and on what you hope to communicate.

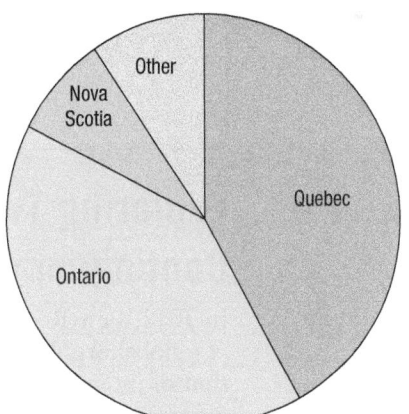

Figure 4.4   Number of Loblaw stores by province in eastern Canada.

We always have to check that the data are appropriate for whatever method of analysis we choose. Before you make a pie chart, always check that the data represent 100% of something, in our case, 100% of Loblaw stores in eastern Canada. Pie charts often have an "Other" category for this reason. You must include everything in the pie so that the slices represent the correct proportion of the whole, which in our case is the proportion of stores in individual provinces.

---

[1] Excel refers to this type of display as a *bar graph*.

If you want to make a pie chart or relative frequency bar chart, you'll need to also make sure that the categories don't overlap, so that no individual is counted in two categories. If the categories do overlap, it's misleading to make a pie chart, since the percentages won't add up to 100%. For the Loblaw stores data, either kind of display is appropriate because the categories don't overlap—each store is located in a single province.

Throughout this course, you'll see that doing statistics effectively means selecting the proper methods. That means you have to think about the situation at hand. An important first step is to check that the type of analysis you plan to conduct is appropriate. Our "100% rule" and "non-overlapping rule" are just the first of many such checks.

FOR EXAMPLE   Making a bar chart of Super Bowl viewers

QUESTION   Make a bar chart for the 40 Super Bowl responses that appear in For Example: "Making frequency and relative frequency tables for Super Bowl viewers."

ANSWER   Use the frequencies in For Example: "Making frequency and relative frequency tables for Super Bowl viewers" to produce the heights of the bars:

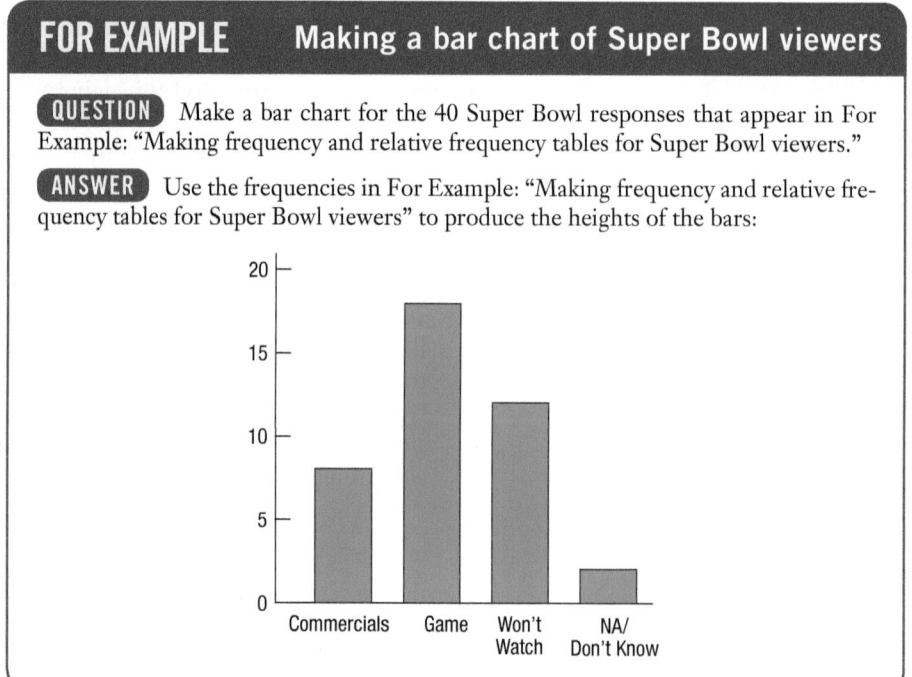

LO❷   **4.4   Exploring Two Categorical Variables: Contingency Tables[2]**

In 2012, Pew Research conducted surveys in countries across the world (www.pewglobal.org/2012/12/12/social-networking-popular-across-globe/). One question of interest to business decision makers is how common it is for people in different countries to use social networking and whether they have it available to them. Table 4.3 gives a table of responses for several of the surveyed countries.

Social Networking	Count	Relative frequency
No	1249	24.787
Yes	2175	43.163
N/A	1615	32.050

Table 4.3   A combined frequency and relative frequency table for the responses from five countries (Britain, Egypt, Germany, Russia, and the United States) to the question "Do you use social networking sites?" N/A means "no internet available."

---

[2]Based on Social Networking Popular Across Globe.

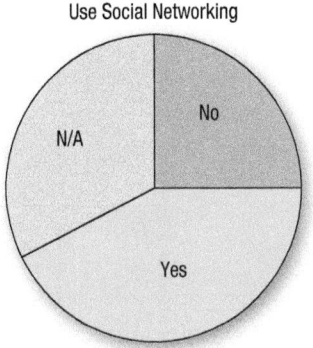
Use Social Networking

Figure 4.5   Responses to the question "Do you use social networking sites?" N/A means "no internet available."

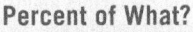

WHO	Respondents in the Pew Research Worldwide Survey
WHAT	Responses to question about social networking
WHEN	2012
WHERE	Worldwide
HOW	Data collected by Pew Research using a multistage design. For details see www.pewglobal.org/2012/12/12/survey-methods-43/
WHY	To understand penetration of social networking worldwide

Percent of What?

The English language can be tricky. If you were asked, "What percent of those answering 'Yes' were in Russia?", it's pretty clear that you should focus only on the *Yes* row. The question itself seems to restrict the *who* in the question to that row, so you should look at the number of those in each country among the 2175 people who replied "Yes." You'd find that in the row percentages.

But if you were asked, "What percent were in Russia and replied 'Yes'?", you'd have a different question. Be careful. That question really means, "What percent of the entire sample were both in Russia and replying 'Yes'?", so the *who* is all respondents. The denominator should be 5039, and the answer is the table percent.

Finally, if you were asked, "What percent of the people in Russia replied 'Yes'?", you'd have a third question. Now the *who* is Russia. So the denominator is the 1010 Russians, and the answer is the column percent.

Note that N/A means "not available" because respondents lacked internet access—a situation that marketers planning for the future might expect to see change.

The pie chart (Figure 4.5) shows clearly that fewer than half of respondents said that they had access to social networking and used it. But if we want to target our online customer relations with social networks differently in different countries, wouldn't it be more interesting to know how social networking use varies from country to country?

To find out, we need to look at the two categorical variables *Social Networking* and *Country* together, which we do by arranging the data in a two-way table such as Table 4.4. Data of this type, which features two variables (in this case, *Social Networking* and *Country*), is sometimes called **bivariate data**, since the prefix "bi" means "two." Because it shows how individuals are distributed along each variable depending on, or *contingent on*, the value of the other variable, a table like this is called a **contingency table**.

The margins of a contingency table give totals. The totals in the right-hand column of Table 4.4 show the frequency distribution of the variable *Social Networking*. We can see, for example, that internet access is certainly not yet universal. The totals in the bottom row of the table show the frequency distribution of the variable *Country*—how many respondents Pew obtained in each country. When presented like this, at the margins of a contingency table, the frequency distribution of either one of the variables is called its **marginal distribution**. The marginal distribution for a variable in a contingency table is the same as its frequency distribution.

Each **cell** of a contingency table (any intersection of a row and column of the table) gives the count for a combination of values of the two variables. For example, in Table 4.4 we can see that 153 respondents did not have internet

	Britain	Egypt	Germany	Russia	United States	Total
No	336	70	460	90	293	1249
Yes	529	300	340	500	506	2175
N/A	153	630	200	420	212	1615
Total	1018	1000	1000	1010	1011	5039

Table 4.4   Contingency table of Social Networking and Country. The right margin "Totals" are the values that were in Table 4.3.

	Britain	Egypt	Germany	Russia	United States	Total
No	336	70	460	90	293	1249
	26.9	5.6	36.8	7.2	23.5	100
	33.0	7.0	46.0	8.9	29.0	24.8
	6.7	1.4	9.1	1.8	5.8	24.8
Yes	529	300	340	500	506	2175
	24.3	13.8	15.6	23.0	23.3	100
	52.0	30.0	34.0	49.5	50.0	43.2
	10.5	6.0	6.8	9.9	10.0	43.2
N/A	153	630	200	420	212	1615
	9.5	39.0	12.4	26.0	13.1	100
	15.0	63.0	20.0	41.6	21.0	32.1
	3.0	12.5	4.0	8.3	4.2	32.1
Total	**1018**	**1000**	**1000**	**1010**	**1011**	**5039**
	20.2	**19.8**	**19.8**	**20.0**	**20.1**	**100**
	100	**100**	**100**	**100**	**100**	**100**
	20.2	**19.8**	**19.8**	**20.0**	**20.1**	**100**

Table contents:
Count
Percent of Row Total
Percent of Column Total
Percent of Table Total

Table 4.5   Another contingency table of *Social Networking* and *Country* showing the counts and the percentages these counts represent. For each count, there are three choices for the percentage: by row, by column, and by table total. There's probably too much information here for this table to be useful.

access in Britain. Looking across the *Yes* row, you can see that the largest number of responses in that row (529) is from Britain. Are Egyptians less likely to use social media than Britons? Questions like this are more naturally addressed using percentages.

We know that 300 Egyptians report that they use social networking. We could display this count as a percentage, but as a percentage of what? The total number of people in the survey? (300 is 5.95% of the total.) The number of Egyptians surveyed? (300 is 30% of the 1000 Egyptians surveyed.) The number of respondents who use social networking? (300 is 13.8% of social networking users.) Most statistics programs offer a choice of **total percent**, **row percent**, or **column percent** for contingency tables. Unfortunately, they often put them all together with several numbers in each cell of the table. The resulting table (Table 4.5) holds lots of information but is hard to understand.

Conditional Distributions

The more interesting questions are contingent on something. We'd like to know, for example, whether these countries are similar in use and availability of social networking. That's the kind of information that could inform a business decision. Table 4.6 shows the distribution of social networking conditional on *Country*.

By comparing the frequencies conditional on *Country*, we can see interesting patterns. For example, Germany stands out as the country in which the largest percentage (46%) have internet access but don't use social networking ("No").

	Britain	Egypt	Germany	Russia	U.S.	Total
No	335	70	460	90	293	1249
	33.0	7.0	46.0	8.9	29.0	**24.8**
Yes	529	300	340	500	506	2175
	52.0	30.0	34.0	49.5	50.0	**43.2**
N/A	153	630	200	420	212	1615
	15.0	63.0	20.0	41.6	21.0	**32.1**
Total	**1018**	**1000**	**1000**	**1010**	**1011**	**5039**
	100	**100**	**100**	**100**	**100**	**100**

Table 4.6 The conditional distribution of *Social Networking* conditioned on two values of *Country.* This table shows the column percentages

Russia and Egypt may have more respondents with no internet access, but those who have access are very likely to use social networking. A distribution like this is called a **conditional distribution** because it shows the distribution of one variable for just those cases that satisfy a condition on another. In a contingency table, when the distribution of one variable is the same for all categories of another variable, we say that the two variables are not associated.

FOR EXAMPLE   Contingency tables and side-by-side bar charts for Super Bowl viewers

Here is a contingency table of the responses to the question Gallup asked about the Super Bowl by gender:

	GENDER		
	FEMALE	MALE	TOTAL
Game	198	277	475
Commercials	154	79	233
NA/Don't Know	4	4	8
Won't Watch	160	132	292
Total	516	492	1008

QUESTION   Does it seem that there is an association between what viewers are interested in watching and their gender?

ANSWER   First, find the conditional distributions of the four responses for each gender:

For Men:

Game = 277/492 = 56.3%

Commercials = 79/492 = 16.1%

NA/Don't Know = 4/516 = 0.8%

Won't Watch = 132/492 = 26.8%

For Women:

Game = 198/516 = 38.4%

Commercials = 154/516 = 29.8%

NA/Don't Know = 4/492 = 0.8%

Won't Watch = 160/516 = 31.0%

Now display the two distributions with side-by-side bar charts:

(*continued*)

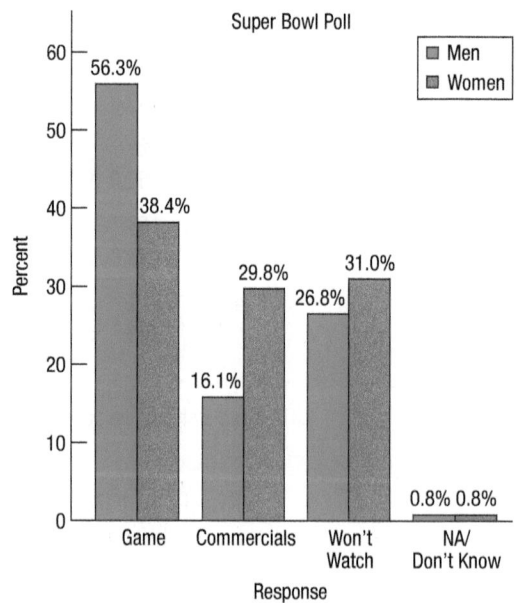

Based on this poll, it appears that women were only slightly less interested than men in watching the Super Bowl telecast: 31% of the women said they didn't plan to watch, compared to just under 27% of men. Among those who planned to watch, however, there appears to be an association between the viewer's gender and what the viewer is most looking forward to. While more women are interested in the game (38%) than the commercials (30%), the margin among men is much wider: 56% of men said they were looking forward to seeing the game, compared to only 16% who cited the commercials.

JUST CHECKING

So that they can balance their inventory, the owners of an optometry store collect the following customer data in the shop:

		Eye Condition			
		Near-sighted	Farsighted	Needs Bifocals	Total
Gender	Males	6	20	6	32
	Females	4	16	12	32
	Total	10	36	18	64

1 What percentage of females are farsighted?

2 What percentage of nearsighted customers are female?

3 What percentage of all customers are farsighted females?

4 What's the distribution of *Eye Condition*?

5 What's the conditional distribution of *Eye Condition* for males?

6 Compare the percentage who are female among near-sighted customers to the percentage of all customers who are female.

7 Does it seem that *Eye Condition* and *Gender* might be associated with each other? Explain.

Answers are found in Appendix A.

Segmented (or Stacked) Bar Charts

We could display the Super Bowl viewer data from For Example: "Contingency tables and side-by-side bar charts for Super Bowl viewers" above as a **segmented bar chart**, or *stacked bar chart*, which treats each bar as the "whole" and divides

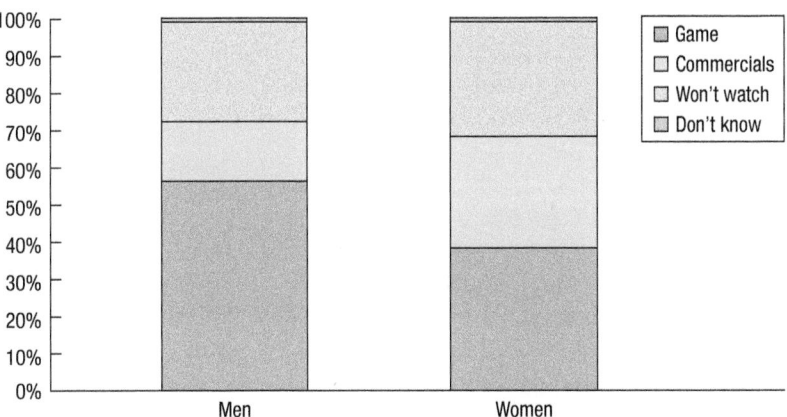

Figure 4.6   Although the totals for men and women are different, the bars are the same height because we have converted the numbers to percentages.

it proportionally into segments corresponding to the percentage in each group. We can see that the distributions of responses to the question are very different between men and women (see Figure 4.6).

GUIDED EXAMPLE   Food Safety

Food storage and food safety are major issues for multinational food companies. A client wants to know if people of all age groups have the same degree of concern, so GfK Roper Consulting asked 1500 people in five countries whether they agree with the following statement: "I worry about how safe store bought food is." We might want to report to a client who was interested in how concerns about food safety are related to age.

 PLAN   **Setup**
- State the objectives and goals of the study.
- Identify and define the variables.
- Provide the time frame of the data collection process.

Determine the appropriate analysis for data type.

The client wants to examine the distribution of responses to the food safety question and see whether they are related to the age of the respondent. GfK Roper Consulting collected data on this question in the fall of 2005 for its 2006 Worldwide report. We will use the data from that study.

The variable is Food Safety. The responses are in nonoverlapping categories of agreement, from Agree Completely to Disagree Completely (and Don't Know). There were originally 12 age groups, which we can combine into 5:

Teen 13–19

Young Adult 20–29

Adult 30–39

Middle-Aged 40–49

Mature 50 and older

Both variables, Food Safety and Age, are categorical variables. To examine any differences in responses across age groups, it is appropriate to create a contingency table and a side-by-side bar chart. Following, you'll see a contingency table of Food Safety by Age.

DO   Mechanics For a large data set like this, we rely on technology to make tables and displays.

		Food Safety						
		Agree Completely	Agree Somewhat	Neither Disagree nor Agree	Disagree Somewhat	Disagree Completely	Don't Know	Total
Age	Teen	16.19	27.50	24.32	19.30	10.58	2.12	100%
	Young Adult	20.55	32.68	23.81	14.94	6.98	1.04	100%
	Adult	22.23	34.89	23.28	12.26	6.75	0.59	100%
	Middle-Aged	24.79	35.31	22.02	12.43	5.06	0.39	100%
	Mature	26.60	33.85	21.21	11.89	5.82	0.63	100%

A side-by-side bar chart is particularly helpful when comparing multiple groups.

A side-by-side bar chart shows the percentage of each response to the question by age group.

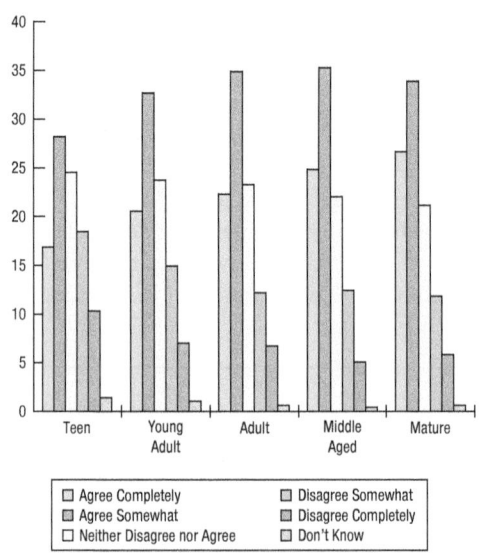

REPORT   Conclusion Summarize the charts and analysis in context. Make recommendations if possible and discuss any further analysis that is needed.

MEMO

Re: Food Safety Concerns by Age

Our analysis of the GfK Roper Reports Worldwide survey data for 2006 shows a pattern of concern about food safety that generally increases from youngest to oldest.

Our analysis thus far has not considered whether this trend is consistent across countries. If it were of interest to your group, we could perform a similar analysis for each of the countries.

The table and chart provide support for these conclusions.

4.5   Simpson's Paradox

One famous example of Simpson's Paradox arose during an investigation of admission rates for men and women at the University of California at Berkeley's graduate schools. As reported in an article in *Science*, about 45% of male applicants were admitted, but only about 30% of female applicants got in. It looked like a clear case of discrimination. However, when the data were broken down by school (Engineering, Law, Medicine, etc.), it turned out that within each school the women were admitted at nearly the same or, in some cases, much *higher* rates than the men. How could this be? Women applied in large numbers to schools with very low admission rates. (Law and Medicine, for example, admitted fewer than 10%.) Men tended to apply to Engineering and Science. Those schools have admission rates above 50%. When the total applicant pool was combined and the percentages were computed, the women had a much lower *overall* rate, but the combined percentage didn't really make sense.

Here's an example showing that combining percentages across very different values or groups can give absurd results. Suppose there are two sales representatives, Peter and Katrina. Peter argues that he's the better salesperson, since he managed to close 83% of his last 120 prospects compared with Katrina's 78%. But let's look at the data a little more closely. Table 4.7 displays the results for each of their last 120 sales calls, broken down by the product they were selling.

| Sales Rep | Product | | |
	Printer Paper	USB Flash Drive	Overall
Peter	90 out of 100	10 out of 20	100 out of 120
	90%	50%	83%
Katrina	19 out of 20	75 out of 100	94 out of 120
	95%	75%	78%

Table 4.7   Look at the percentages within each product category. Who has a better success rate closing sales of paper? Who has the better success rate closing sales of flash drives? Who has the better performance overall?

Look at the sales of the two products separately. For printer paper sales, Katrina had a 95% success rate, and Peter had only a 90% rate. When selling flash drives, Katrina closed her sales 75% of the time, but Peter only 50%. So Peter has better "overall" performance, but Katrina is better at selling each product. How can this be?

This problem is known as **Simpson's Paradox**, named for the statistician who described it in the 1960s. There have been a few well-publicized cases of this statistical phenomenon. As we can see from the example, the problem results from inappropriately combining percentages of different groups. Katrina concentrates on selling flash drives, which is more difficult, so her *overall* percentage is heavily influenced by her flash drive average. Peter sells more printer paper, which appears to be easier to sell. Given the different patterns of selling that emerge between Peter and Katrina, taking an overall percentage is misleading. Their manager should be careful not to conclude rashly that Peter is the better salesperson.

The lesson of Simpson's Paradox is to make sure to combine comparable measurements for comparable individuals. Be especially careful when combining across different levels of a second variable. It's usually better to compare percentages *within* each level, rather than across levels.

WHAT CAN GO WRONG?

- **Don't violate the area principle.** This is probably the most common mistake in a graphical display. Violations of the area principle are often made for the sake of artistic presentation. Here, for example, are two versions of the same pie chart for the *Regional Preference* data:

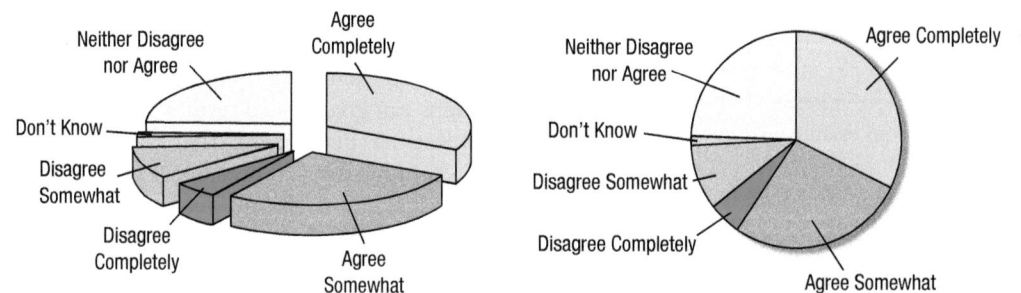

The one on the left looks interesting, doesn't it? But showing the pie three dimensionally on a slant violates the area principle and makes it much more difficult to compare fractions of the whole made up of each category of the response—the principal feature that a pie chart ought to show.

- **Keep it honest.** Here's a pie chart that displays data on the percentage of high school students who engage in specified dangerous behaviours. What's wrong with this chart?

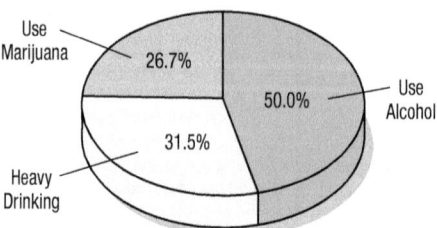

Try adding up the percentages. Or look at the 50% slice. Does it look right? Then think: What are these percentages of? Is there a "whole" that has been sliced up? In a pie chart, the proportions shown by the slices of the pie must add up to 100%, and each individual must fall into only one category. Of course, showing the pie on a slant makes it even harder to detect the error.

Here's another example. This bar chart shows the average number of text messages sent by Canadians in various time periods from 1999 to 2013. Of course, texting didn't suddenly drop in 2009; it's just that the graph displays monthly data from then on but annual data before 2009.

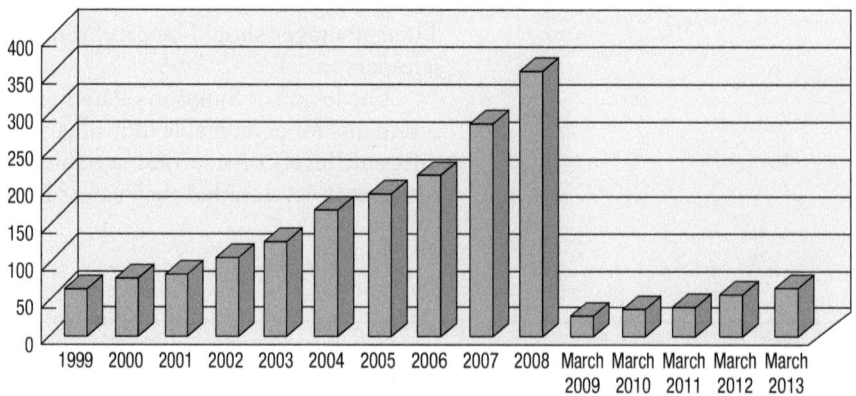

- **Don't confuse percentages.** Many percentages based on conditional and joint distributions sound similar, but are different:

  - *The percentage of French who answered "Agree Completely":* This is 347/1539, or 22.5%.

- *The percentage of those who answered "Agree Completely" who are French:* This is 347/2346, or 14.79%.
- *The percentage of the respondents who were French and answered "Agree Completely":* This is 347/7690, or 4.5%.

		I prefer food from my own country.					
		Agree Completely	**Agree Somewhat**	**Neither Disagree nor Agree**	**Disagree Somewhat**	**Disagree Completely**	**Don't Know**	**Total**
Country	China	518	576	251	117	33	7	1502
	France	347	475	400	208	94	15	1539
	India	960	282	129	65	95	4	1535
	United Kingdom	214	407	504	229	175	28	1557
	United States	307	477	454	192	101	26	1557
	Total	**2346**	**2217**	**1738**	**811**	**498**	**80**	**7690**

- **Don't forget to look at the variables separately, too.** When you make a contingency table or display a conditional distribution, also be sure to examine the marginal distributions. It's important to know how many cases are in each category.

- **Be sure to use enough individuals.** When you consider percentages, make sure that they are based on a large enough number of individuals (or cases). Take care not to make a report such as this one:

    We found that 66.67% of the companies surveyed improved their performance by hiring outside consultants. The other company went bankrupt.

- **Don't overstate your case.** We can't conclude that one variable is totally unassociated with another. Usually, all we know is that little effect was observed in our study. Other studies of other groups under other circumstances could find different results.

- **Don't use unfair or inappropriate percentages.** Sometimes percentages can be misleading. Sometimes they don't make sense at all. Be careful when comparing percentages across different categories not to fall into the trap of Simpson's Paradox described in Section 4.5.

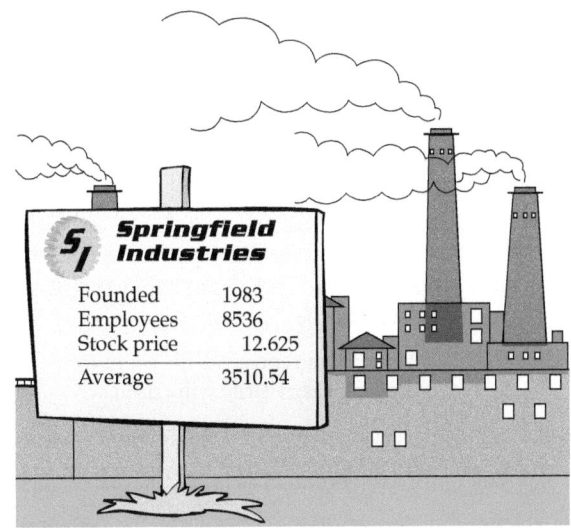

ETHICS IN ACTION

Lyle Erhart has been working in sales for a leading vendor of customer relationship management (CRM) software for the past three years. He was recently made aware of a published research study that examined factors related to the successful implementation of CRM projects among firms in the financial services industry. Lyle read the research report with interest and was excited to see that his company's CRM software product was included. Among the results were tables reporting the number of projects that were successful based on type of CRM implementation (operational vs. analytical) for each of the leading CRM products. Lyle quickly found the results for his company's product and its major competitor. He summarized the results in a table, as follows:

	Lyle's Company	Major Competitor
Operational	16 successes out of 20	68 successes out of 80
Analytical	90 successes out of 100	19 successes out of 20

At first he was a bit disappointed, especially since most of his company's potential clients were interested in operational CRM. He'd hoped to be able to disseminate the findings of this report among the salesforce so that they could refer to it when visiting potential clients. After some thought, however, he realized that he could combine the results. His company's overall success rate was 106 out of 120 (over 88%) and was higher than that of its major competitor. Lyle was now happy that he'd found and read the report.

Ethical Issue *Lyle, intentionally or not, has benefited from Simpson's Paradox. By combining percentages, he can present the findings in a manner favourable to his company (related to Item A, ASA Ethical Guidelines; see Appendix C, the American Statistical Association's Ethical Guidelines for Statistical Practice, also available online at www.amstat.org/about/ethicalguidelines.cfm).*

Ethical Solution *Lyle should not combine the percentages, as the results are misleading. If he decides to disseminate the information to his salesforce, he must do so without combining.*

WHAT HAVE WE LEARNED?

Learning Objectives

❶ We've learned that we can summarize categorical data by counting the number of cases in each category, sometimes expressing the resulting distribution as percentages.

We can display the distribution of data in a bar chart or a pie chart. We use pie charts only to represent the split in something that adds to 100%, and usually when we have just a few options to compare. We use bar charts to compare more options, as displayed in Guided Example: "Food Safety." Bar charts also offer flexible layouts for the data (e.g., stacked bars or side-by-side bars).

❷ When we want to see how two categorical variables are related, we put the counts (and/or percentages) in a two-way table called a contingency table.

- We look at the marginal distribution of each variable (found in the margins of the table).
- We also look at the conditional distribution of a variable within each category of the other variable.
- We can display these conditional and marginal distributions using bar charts or pie charts.
- If the conditional distributions of one variable are the same for every category of the other, the variables are not associated with each other.

Terms

Area principle	A principle that helps to interpret statistical information by insisting that in a statistical display each data value be represented by the same amount of area.
Bar chart	A chart that represents the count (or percentage) of each category in a categorical variable as a bar, allowing easy visual comparison across categories.
Bivariate data	Data about two variables, often represented as a table.
Cell	Each location in a contingency table, representing the values of two categorical variables.
Column percent	The proportion of each column contained in the cell of a contingency table.

Conditional distribution	The distribution of a variable restricting the *Who* to consider only a smaller group of individuals.
Contingency table	A table that displays counts and, sometimes, percentages of individuals falling into named categories on two or more variables. The table categorizes the individuals on all variables at once to reveal possible patterns in one variable that may be contingent on the category of the other.
Distribution	The distribution of a variable is a list of • All the possible values of the variable • The relative frequency of each value
Frequency table	A table that lists the categories in a categorical variable and gives the number of observations for each category.
Marginal distribution	In a contingency table, the distribution of one variable alone. The counts or percentages are the totals found in the margins (usually the rightmost column or bottom row) of the table.
Pie chart	A chart that shows how a "whole" divides into categories by showing a wedge of a circle whose area corresponds to the proportion in each category.
Relative frequency table	A *frequency table* showing proportions or percentages instead of numbers.
Row percent	The proportion of each row contained in the cell of a contingency table.
Segmented bar chart	A bar chart that treats each bar as the "whole" and divides it proportionally into segments corresponding to the percentage in each group.
Simpson's Paradox	A phenomenon that arises when averages, or percentages, are taken across different groups, and these group averages appear to contradict the overall averages.
Total percent	The proportion of the total contained in the cell of a contingency table.

Skills

Plan	• Recognize when a variable is categorical and choose an appropriate display for it. • Understand how to examine the association between categorical variables by comparing conditional and marginal percentages.
Do	• Summarize the distribution of a categorical variable with a frequency table. • Display the distribution of a categorical variable with a bar chart or pie chart. • Construct and examine a contingency table. • Construct and examine displays of the conditional distributions of one variable for two or more groups.
Report	• Describe the distribution of a categorical variable in terms of its possible values and relative frequencies. • Describe any anomalies or extraordinary features revealed by the display of a variable. • Describe and discuss patterns found in a contingency table and associated displays of conditional distributions.

MINI case studies

Loblaw

Loblaw has three types of stores: corporate, franchised, and affiliated. The store banners for the corporate stores include Atlantic Superstore, Cash & Carry, Extra Foods, Loblaws, Loblaw Superstore, Maxi, Maxi & Cie, Provigo, The Real Canadian Superstore, and Zehr. The trade names of the franchised and affiliated stores include Atlantic SaveEasy, Extra Foods, Fortinos, No Frills, Provigo, SuperValu, Valu-mart, and Your Independent Grocer. You may be familiar with one or more of these names depending on what part of Canada you live in. The numbers and types of stores also vary with the province. For instance, some provinces have more franchises; others have more associated or corporate stores. The data file **ch04_MCSP_Loblaws_Store_Numbers** tells

Pat Holmes/Alamy Stock Photo

you how many stores there are of each type in each province and territory in Canada.[3] (a) Use these data to produce a graphical comparison (pie or bar chart) of the *number* of stores of different types in each province and territory. (b) Use these data to produce a graphical comparison (pie or bar chart) of the *percentage* of stores of different types in each province and territory. (c) Give reasons for your choice of graphical format (pie versus bar chart) for (a) and (b). (d) Where are the *highest number* of corporate stores? (e) Where are the *second-highest percentage* of corporate stores? (f) Answer (b) and (c) for a comparison of just two provinces, Ontario and Quebec, using a different type of graph from the one you used before.

KEEN Footwear

Data on the website traffic for KEEN Footwear, obtained from Google Analytics, are in the file **ch04_MCSP_KEEN**. Open the file using a statistics package and find data on *Country of Origin, Top Keywords, Online Retailers, User Statistics,* and *Page Visits*. Create frequency tables, bar charts, and pie charts using your software. What might KEEN want to know about its web traffic? Which of these tables and charts is most useful to address the question of where the company should advertise and how it should position its products? Write a case report summarizing your analysis and results.

---

[3]**Source**: Based on Loblaw Companies Limited (2013). Annual information form.

MyStatLab   Students! Save time, improve your grades with MyStatLab. Questions marked in ▦ can be found on MyStatLab. You can practise them as often as you want, and most feature step-by-step guided solutions to help you find the right answer. You'll find a personalized study plan available to you too!

Technology Help: Displaying Categorical Data on the Computer

Although every statistics package makes a slightly different bar chart, they all have similar features:

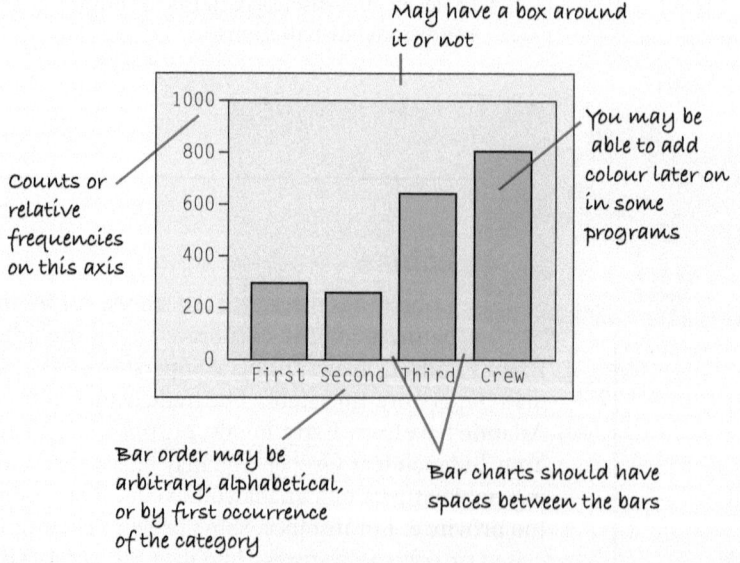

May have a box around it or not

Counts or relative frequencies on this axis

You may be able to add colour later on in some programs

Bar order may be arbitrary, alphabetical, or by first occurrence of the category

Bar charts should have spaces between the bars

(continued)

Sometimes the count or a percentage is printed above or on top of each bar to give some additional information. You may find that your statistics package sorts category names in annoying orders by default. For example, many packages sort categories alphabetically or by the order the categories are seen in the data set. Often, neither of these is the best choice.

EXCEL

To make a pivot table (Excel's term for a contingency table) we first give an overview and then go into more detail:

Sales ($000)	Type	Region
47	Wholesale	East
23	Retail	East
34	Retail	West
4	Retail	East
56	Retail	East
121	Wholesale	East
23	Retail	West
9	Retail	West
345	Wholesale	East
23	Wholesale	East
43	Retail	West

Let's make a pivot table of the sales made by our company's salespeople according to the *Type* of sale, wholesale or retail, and the *Region*, east or west of the country.

In Excel, click a cell within the data area.

Select **Insert** and then **Pivot Table**. The **Pivot Table Field List** pops up, with our three variables: *Sales, Type, Region*.

We need to select which variables to use for the rows, columns, and values in our table. This can be done by checking the box by the variable to use it for the rows of the table, or by dragging it to the area headed **Column Labels** or **Values**. Let's choose *Region* as the rows, *Type* as the columns, and *Sales* as the values. The resulting table is as follows:

Sum of Sales	Column Labels		Grand
Row Labels	Retail	Wholesale	Total
East	83	536	619
West	109		109
Grand Total	192	536	728

Excel has totalled the number of sales in each of the four cells in the table and has added row and column totals to give the marginal distributions.

We can now make graphs by clicking on the pivot table and selecting **Insert** and then **Chart**.

EXCEL

A pivot table can summarize, organize, and present data from an Excel spreadsheet. Pivot tables can be used to create frequency distributions and contingency tables. They provide a starting point for several kinds of displays. Pivot tables are linked to data in your Excel spreadsheet, so they will update when you make changes to your data. They can also be linked directly to a "PivotChart" to display the data graphically.

In a pivot table, all types of data are summarized into a row-by-column table format. Pivot table cells can hold counts, percentages, and descriptive statistics.

To create a pivot table:
- Open a data file in Excel. At least one of the variables in the data set should be categorical.
- **Choose Insert > PivotTable or Data > PivotTable** (Mac). If you are using a PC, choose to put the pivot table in a new worksheet. Macintosh users should choose the option to create a custom pivot table.

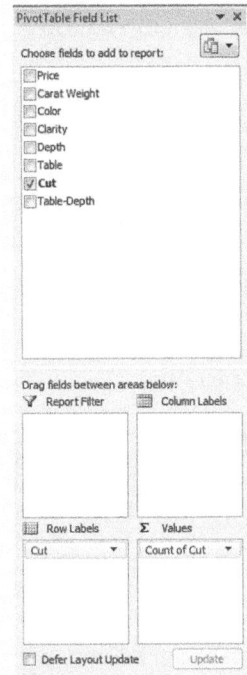

The *PivotTable* builder has five boxes:
- *Field List* (top): variables from the data set linked to the *PivotTable*. (The *PivotTable* tool calls the variables "fields.") Fields can be selected using the checkbox or dragged and dropped into one of the areas below in the *PivotTable* builder.
- *Report Filter* (middle left): Variables placed here filter the data in the pivot table. When selected, the filter variable name appears above the pivot table. Use the drop-down list to the right of the variable name to choose values to display.

- *Row Labels* (bottom left): Values of variables placed here become row labels in the pivot table.

- *Column Labels* (middle right): Values of variables placed here become column labels in the pivot table.

- *Values* (bottom right): Variables placed here are summarized in the cells of the table. Change settings to display count, sum, minimum, maximum, average, and more or to display percentages and ranks.

To create a frequency distribution pivot table:

- Drag a categorical variable from the Field List into **Row Labels**.

- Choose another variable from the data set and drag it into **Values**. Use a unique identifier variable (e.g., subject number) if possible.

- To change what fact or statistic about the **Values** variable is displayed, click the arrow next to the variable in the **Values** box and open the **Value Field Settings**. For a frequency distribution, select **count of [VARIABLE]**. When changing **Value Field Settings**, note the tab **Show Values As**, which provides other display options (e.g., % of row, % of column).

The result will be a frequency table with a column for count.

To create a contingency table using *PivotTable*:

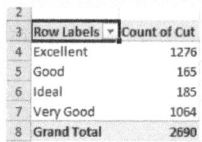

Row Labels	Count of Cut
Excellent	1276
Good	165
Ideal	185
Very Good	1064
Grand Total	**2690**

- Drag a categorical variable from the Field List into **Row Labels**.

- Drag a second categorical variable from the Field List into **Column Labels**.

- Choose another variable from the dataset and drag it into **Values**. The resulting pivot table is a row-by-column contingency table.

Count of Cut	Column Labels							
Row Labels	IF	SI1	SI2	VS1	VS2	VVS1	VVS2	Grand Total
Excellent		92	278	196	184	220	160	146	1276
Good		4	39	47	33	26	4	12	165
Ideal		22	24	24	20	24	41	30	185
Very Good		26	283	263	155	190	64	83	1064
Grand Total		144	624	530	392	460	269	271	2690

NOTE: As with the frequency distribution, you can use the **Value Field Settings** to change the type of summary.

To create a chart from a pivot table frequency distribution or contingency table:

- Place the cursor anywhere on the pivot table.

- Click **PivotTable Tools > PivotChart**.

- Choose the type of chart: options include pie chart, bar chart, and segmented bar graph.

- Move the chart to a new worksheet by right-clicking the chart and selecting **Move chart**.

- In a bar chart created from a contingency table, by default, rows display on the x-axis and the columns are separate bars. To change this, place your cursor in the chart and choose **PivotChart Tools > Design > Switch Row/Column**.

- On Macs, choose the **Charts** tab and select your chart from the ribbon or choose a chart type from the **Chart** menu.

MINITAB

To make a bar chart, choose **Bar Chart** from the **Graph** menu.

Then select either a Simple, Cluster, or Stack chart from the options and click **OK**. To make a **Simple** bar chart, enter the name of the variable to graph in the dialogue box. To make a relative frequency chart, click **Chart Options**, and choose **Show Y as Percent**.

In the **Chart** dialogue, enter the name of the variable that you wish to display in the box labelled **Categorical variables**. Click **OK**.

SPSS

To make a bar chart, open the **Chart Builder** from the **Graphs** menu.
- Click the **Gallery** tab.

- Choose **Bar Chart** from the list of chart types.

- Drag the appropriate bar chart onto the canvas.

- Drag a categorical variable onto the x-axis drop zone.

- Click **OK**.

A similar path makes a pie chart by choosing **Pie Chart** from the list of chart types.

JMP

JMP makes a bar chart and frequency table together.

From the **Analyze** menu, choose **Distribution**.

In the **Distribution** dialogue, drag the name of the variable into the empty variable window beside the label "Y, Columns"; click **OK**.

To make a pie chart, choose **Chart** from the **Graph** menu.

In the **Chart** dialogue, select the variable name from the **Columns** list, click on the button labelled **Statistics**, and select **N** from the drop-down menu.

Click the **Categories, X, Levels** button to assign the same variable name to the x-axis.

Under Options, click on the second button—labelled **Bar Chart**—and select **Pie** from the drop-down menu.

EXERCISES

SECTIONS 4.1 AND 4.2

1. As a member of the human resource group of your company, you are asked to summarize the educational levels of the 512 employees in your division. From company records, you find that 164 have no degree (None), 42 have a community college diploma (AA), 225 have a bachelor's degree (BA), 52 have a master's degree (MA), and 29 have a doctorate (Ph.D.). For the educational level of your division:

a) Make a frequency table.
b) Make a relative frequency table. **LO ❶**

2. As a member of the marketing group at Pixar, you are asked to find out the age distribution of the audience of Pixar's latest film. With the help of 10 of your colleagues, you conduct exit interviews by randomly selecting people to question at 20 different movie theatres. From 470 responses, you find out that 45 are younger than 6 years of age, 83 are 6 to 9 years old, 154 are 10 to 14 years old, l8 are 15 to 21 years old, and 170 are older than 21. For the age distribution:

a) Make a frequency table.
b) Make a relative frequency table. **LO ❶**

SECTION 4.3

3. From the educational level data described in Exercise 1:

a) Make a bar chart using counts on the *y*-axis.
b) Make a relative frequency bar chart using percentages on the *y*-axis.
c) Make a pie chart. **LO ❷**

4. From the age distribution data described in Exercise 2:

a) Make a bar chart using counts on the *y*-axis.
b) Make a relative frequency bar chart using percentages on the *y*-axis.
c) Make a pie chart. **LO ❷**

5. For the educational levels described in Exercise 1:

a) Write two to four sentences summarizing the distribution.
b) What conclusions, if any, could you make about the educational levels of employees at other companies? **LO ❷**

6. For the ages described in Exercise 2:

a) Write two to four sentences summarizing the distribution.
b) What possible problems do you see in concluding that the age distribution from these surveys accurately represents the ages of the national audience for this film? **LO ❷**

SECTIONS 4.4 AND 4.5

7. From Exercise 1, we also have data on how long each person has been with the company (tenure) categorized into three levels: less than one year, between one and five years, and more than five years. A table of the two variables together looks like this:

	None	AA	BA	MA	Ph.D.
<1 year	10	3	50	20	12
1–5 years	42	9	112	27	15
More than 5 years	112	30	63	5	2

a) Find the marginal distribution of the tenure. (*Hint:* Find the row totals.)
b) Verify that the marginal distribution of the education level is the same as that given in Exercise 1. **LO ❷**

8. In addition to their age levels, the movie audiences in Exercise 2 were asked if they had seen the movie before (Never, Once, More than Once). Here's a table showing the responses by age group:

	Under 6	6 to 9	10 to 14	15 to 21	Over 21
Never	39	60	84	16	151
Once	3	20	38	2	15
More than once	3	3	32	0	4

a) Find the marginal distribution of their previous viewing of the movie. (*Hint:* Find the row totals.)
b) Verify that the marginal distribution of the ages is the same as that given in Exercise 2. **LO ❷**

9. For the table in Exercise 7,

a) Find the column percentages.
b) Looking at the column percentages in (a), does the *tenure* distribution (how long the employee has been with the company) for each educational level look the same? Comment briefly.
c) Make a stacked bar chart showing the *tenure* distribution for each educational level.
d) Is it easier to see the differences in the distributions using the column percentages or the stacked bar chart? **LO ❷**

10. For the table in Exercise 8,

a) Find the column percentages.
b) Looking at the column percentages in (a), does the distribution of how many times someone has seen the movie look the same for each age group? Comment briefly.

c) Make a stacked bar chart showing the distribution of viewings for each age level.

d) Is it easier to see the differences in the distributions using the column percentages or the stacked bar chart? **LO ❷**

CHAPTER EXERCISES

11. Graphs in the news, part 1. Find a bar graph of categorical data from a business publication (e.g., *The Economist, The Globe and Mail, The Wall Street Journal*, etc.).

a) Is the graph clearly labelled?

b) Does it violate the area principle?

c) Does the accompanying article identify the Five W's of the variable?

d) Do you think the article correctly interprets the data? Explain. **LO ❶**

12. Graphs in the news, part 2. Find a pie chart of categorical data from a business publication (e.g., *The Economist, The Globe and Mail, The Wall Street Journal*, etc.).

a) Is the graph clearly labelled?

b) Does it violate the area principle?

c) Does the accompanying article identify the Five W's of the variable?

d) Do you think the article correctly interprets the data? Explain. **LO ❶**

13. Tables in the news, part 1. Find a frequency table of categorical data from a business publication (e.g., *The Economist, The Globe and Mail, The Wall Street Journal*, etc.).

a) Is the table clearly labelled?

b) Does it display percentages or counts?

c) Does the accompanying article identify the Five W's of the variable?

d) Do you think the article correctly interprets the data? Explain. **LO ❶**

14. Tables in the news, part 2. Find a contingency table of categorical data from a business publication (e.g., *The Economist, The Globe and Mail, The Wall Street Journal*, etc.).

a) Is the table clearly labelled?

b) Does it display percentages or counts?

c) Does the accompanying article identify the Five W's of the variable?

d) Do you think the article correctly interprets the data? Explain. **LO ❶**

15. U.S. market share. An article in *The Wall Street Journal* (March 18, 2011) reported the 2010 U.S. market share of leading sellers of carbonated drinks, as summarized in the following pie chart:

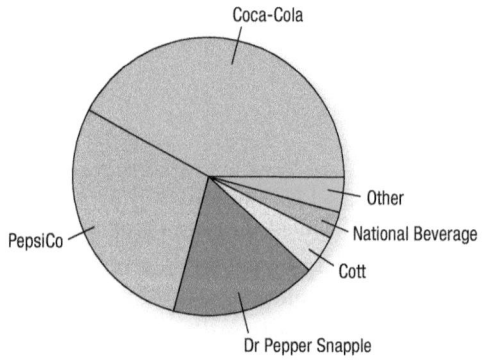

a) Is this an appropriate display for these data? Explain.

b) Which company had the largest share of the market? (*Source:* Based on Pepsi Thirsty for a Comeback by The Wall Street Journal. March 18, 2011.) **LO ❶**

16. World market share, part 1. *The Wall Street Journal* article described in Exercise 15 also indicated the market share for leading brands of carbonated beverages worldwide. The following bar chart displays the values:

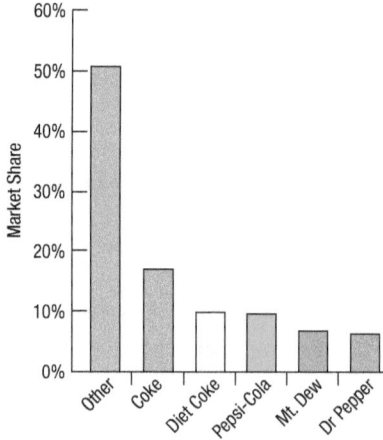

a) Is this an appropriate display for these data? Explain.

b) Which company had the largest share of the carbonated beverage market? (*Source:* Based on Pepsi Thirsty for a Comeback by The Wall Street Journal. March 18, 2011.) **LO ❶**

17. Market share, part 2. Here's a bar chart of the data in Exercise 15:

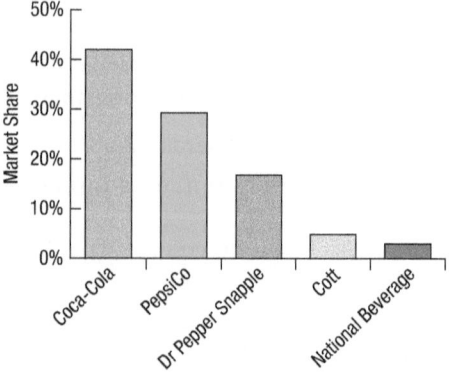

a) Compared to the pie chart in Exercise 15, which is better for displaying the relative portions of market share? Explain.

b) What is missing from this display that might make it misleading? (*Source:* Based on Pepsi Thirsty for a Comeback by The Wall Street Journal. March 18, 2011.) **LO ❶**

18. World market share, part 3. Here's a pie chart of the data in Exercise 16:

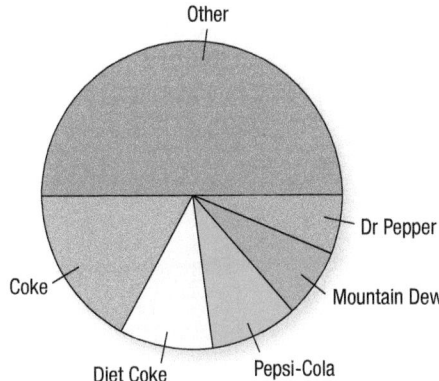

a) Which display of these data is best for comparing the market shares of these companies? Explain.

b) Does Mountain Dew or Dr Pepper have a bigger market share? Is that comparison easier to make with the pie chart or the bar chart of Exercise 16? (*Source:* Based on Pepsi Thirsty for a Comeback by The Wall Street Journal. March 18, 2011.) **LO ❶**

19. Insurance company. An insurance company is updating its payouts and cost structure for its insurance policies. Of particular interest is the risk analysis for customers currently on heart or blood pressure medication. The Centers for Disease Control and Prevention lists causes of death in the United States during one year as follows:

Cause of Death	Percent
Heart disease	30.3
Cancer	23.0
Circulatory diseases and stroke	8.4
Respiratory diseases	7.9
Accidents	4.1

a) Is it reasonable to conclude that heart or respiratory diseases were the cause of approximately 38% of U.S. deaths during this year?

b) What percentage of deaths were from causes not listed here?

c) Create an appropriate display for these data. **LO ❶**

20. Canadian election results, part 1. In the 2008 Canadian federal election, the number of seats was divided among the parties as shown in the table in the next column.

The Conservatives won the election, but formed a "minority" government; that is, they could be defeated on any

particular issue if the other parties banded together and voted against them.

Party	Number of Seats
Conservative	143
Liberal	77
NDP	37
Bloc	49
Green	0
Other	2

a) Draw a graph of this data that shows clearly that the Conservative government was a minority one.

b) Give the reasons for your choice of graph. (*Source:* Based on Electoral Results by Party.) **LO ❶**

21. SaaS. According to a 2013 report by Synergy Research Group (www.informationweek.com/telecom/unified-communications/cisco-rules-saas-uc-conferencing-market/231601562), the market for desktop conferencing apps has been growing rapidly, spurred by a 33% jump in software-as-a-service–delivered conferencing apps revenue. Cisco Systems has a 58% share of this market, followed by Citrix with a 13% share and Microsoft with 11%. Create an appropriate graphical display of this information and write a sentence or two that might appear in a newspaper article about the market share. (*Source:* Based on Cisco Rules SaaS UC Conferencing Market.)

22. Mattel. In its 2013 annual report, Mattel Inc. reported that its domestic market sales were broken down as follows: 49.6% Mattel Girls and Boys brand; 36.1% Fisher-Price brand; and the rest of Mattel's over $3.5 billion revenues were due to its American Girl brand. Create an appropriate graphical display of this information and write a sentence or two that might appear in a newspaper article about the company's revenue breakdown. **LO ❶**

23. Small business productivity. The Wells Fargo/Gallup Small Business Index asked 604 small business owners in October 2011, "How difficult or easy do you think it will be for your company to obtain credit when you need it?" The business owners answered as follows: 22% said "Very difficult"; 21% "Somewhat difficult"; 28% "About average"; 11% "Somewhat easy"; and 11% "Very easy."

a) What do you notice about the percentages listed? How could this be?

b) Make a bar chart to display the results and label it clearly.

c) Would a pie chart be an effective means of communicating this information? Why or why not?

d) Write a couple of sentences on the steps taken by small businesses to increase productivity. **LO ❶**

24. Canadian election results, part 2. In the 2011 Canadian federal election, the number of seats and the percentage of votes were divided among the parties as follows:

	Number of Seats	Percentage of Votes
Conservative	166	39.6%
Liberal	34	18.9%
NDP	103	30.6%
Bloc	4	6.1%
Green	1	3.9%
Other	0	0.9%

Source: Based on Elections Canada Official Voting Results General Election 2011.

a) Draw a graph of this data that allows you to compare the percentage of seats with the percentage of votes for each party.
b) Comment on whether the number of seats reflects the votes of the electorate. **LO ❶**

25. **Environmental hazard.** Data from the International Tanker Owners Pollution Federation Limited (www.itopf.com) give the cause of spillage for small and large oil tanker accidents for 1970–2013. Draw a graph comparing the causes of small spills with the causes of large spills. Give a reason for your choice of graph and write a short report (40–80 words) comparing the causes of the different sizes of spills. (*Source:* Based on ITOPF: Oil Tanker Spill Statistics 2013.) **LO ❶**

Number of Spills From Oil Tankers 1970–2013		
	Number of Small Spills < 7 tonnes	Number of Large Spills > 700 tonnes
Collision	185	136
Grounding	240	150
Hull Failure	576	60
Equipment Failure	1682	18
Fire/Explosion	173	52
Other	1812	29
Unknown	3179	14
Total	7847	459

26. Winter Olympics. Twenty-one countries won gold medals in the 2014 Winter Olympics. The following table lists the countries, along with the total number of medals each won:

Gold Medals Won at 2014 Winter Olympics			
Russia (RUS)	13	China (CHN)	3
Norway (NOR)	11	South Korea (KOR)	3
Canada (CAN)	10	Sweden (SWE)	2
United States (USA)	9	Czech Republic (CZE)	2
Netherlands (NED)	8	Slovenia (SLO)	2
Germany (GER)	8	Japan (JPN)	1
Switzerland (SUI)	6	Finland (FIN)	1
Belarus (BLR)	5	Great Britain (GBR)	1
Austria (AUT)	4	Ukraine (UKR)	1
France (FRA)	4	Slovakia (SVK)	1
Poland (POL)	4		

a) Try to make a display of these data. What problems do you encounter?
b) Can you find a way to organize the data so that the graph is more successful? **LO ❶**

27. Importance of wealth. GfK Roper Reports Worldwide surveyed people in 2004, asking them, "How important is acquiring wealth to you?" The percentage of people who responded that it was of more than average importance were: 71.9% China, 59.6% France, 76.1% India, 45.5% United Kingdom, and 45.3% United States. There were about 1500 respondents per country. A report showed the following bar chart of these percentages:

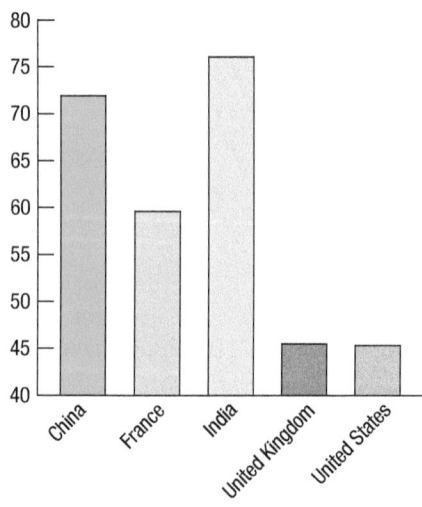

a) How much larger is the proportion of those who said acquiring wealth was important in India than in the United States?
b) Is that the impression given by the display? Explain.
c) How would you improve this display?
d) Make an appropriate display for the percentages.
e) Write a few sentences describing what you have learned about attitudes toward acquiring wealth. (*Source:* Norean Sharpe, Richard D De Veaux, Paul Velleman, David Wright, Business Statistics, Third Canadian Edition, 3e, © 2018, Pearson Education, Inc.) **LO ❶**

28. Importance of power. In the same survey discussed in Exercise 27, GfK Roper Consulting also asked, "How important is having control over people and resources to you?" The percentages of people who responded that it was of more than average importance are given in the following table:

China	49.1%
France	44.1%
India	74.2%
United Kingdom	27.8%
United States	36.0%

Here's a pie chart of the data:

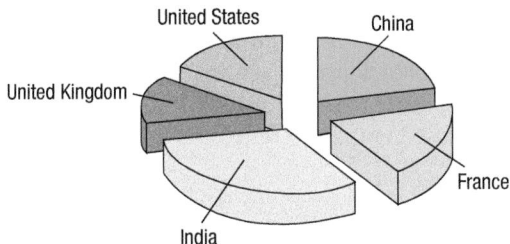

a) List the errors you see in this display.
b) Make an appropriate display for the percentages.
c) Write a few sentences describing what you've learned about attitudes toward acquiring power. (*Source:* Norean Sharpe, Richard D De Veaux, Paul Velleman, David Wright, Business Statistics, Third Canadian Edition, 3e, © 2018, Pearson Education, Inc.) **LO ❶**

29. International debt. The amount of debt for selected countries in 2013 is given in the table below ("trn" means trillions):

Country	Debt
Britain	£1.4 trn
Canada	1.2 $CDN trn
Japan	10.5 $US trn
United States	17.6 $US trn

In what way do you need to transform these data before making a chart that compares debt among the four countries? Do not make the chart, but say what type of chart you would use and provide a reason. **LO ❶**

30. International natural gas reserves and resources. Countries divide natural gas into reserves (the amount economically extractable at current prices) and resources (the amount technically extractable if the price is high enough). Reserves and resources are given in the table below in trillion cubic metres for selected countries as available ("n/a" means not available):

	Reserves	Resources
Australia	3.1	11.6
Canada	1.8	11.0
China	3.0	35.1
Poland	0.2	5.3
Qatar	25.8	n/a
Russia	47.5	n/a
United States	7.7	24.4
World Total	187.1	n/a

a) Compare resources among countries using an appropriate chart.
b) Compare reserves among countries using a different type of chart.

c) Kanika used a bar chart for both comparisons. What ethical issue, if any, does this raise? (See ASA Ethical Guidelines in Appendix C.)
d) Maryam used a pie chart for both comparisons. What ethical issue, if any, does this raise? (See ASA Ethical Guidelines in Appendix C.) **LO ❶**

31. Nuclear reactors around the world. The number of nuclear reactors that were operational in selected countries in 2014 is given in the table below, together with the number of additional nuclear reactors under construction or planned as of the same date.

	Operational	Under Construction or Planned
Canada	19	0
United States	100	5
United Kingdom	16	0
Russia	33	10
China	21	28
India	21	6
Japan	48	2
South Korea	23	4
France	58	1

a) Present these data on a graph that allows you to compare the results among the countries, and give your reason for your choice of graph.
b) Select two countries that are outliers in different ways. In what ways do these countries differ from the other countries with respect to nuclear reactors? **LO ❶**

32. International comparison of government debt. The government net financial liabilities as a percentage of GDP is given in the table below for selected countries in 2015 according to stats.oecd.org. Present these data in a graph that allows you to compare the results among the countries. Give your reason for choosing this type of graph compared with another type of graph. (*Source:* Data from Organisation for Economic Co-operation and Development.http://stats.oecd.org/.) **LO ❶**

	Government Net Financial Liability as a % of GDP
Australia	14.6%
Canada	40.3%
Greece	127.9%
Italy	118.3%
Japan	145.5%
Spain	78.4%
Sweden	−19.9%
United States	84.1%

33. International unemployment rates. The table below gives the 2015 unemployment rate according to stats.oecd.org for selected countries. Create a graphical representation of these data that facilitates comparison among the countries, and state your reason for your choice of graph compared with another type of graph. (*Source:* Data from Organisation for Economic Co-operation and Development.http://stats.oecd.org/.) **LO ❶**

Country	Unemployment Rate
Austria	4.6%
Canada	6.6%
Estonia	8.5%
Germany	4.9%
Iceland	4.2%
Israel	5.8%
Korea	3.0%
Norway	3.5%
Spain	24.4%

34. Gamblers around the world. Which countries are associated with the highest gambling rates? The table below shows gambling losses per person in selected nations in 2013 according to *The Economist*. Make a graphical comparison among these countries to show how they compare. Give the reason for your choice of graph. (*Source:* Based on Gambling: The biggest Losers, May 16th 2011. The Economist.) **LO ❶**

	Loss per Resident Adult
Australia	$1020
Canada	$430
Finland	$610
Ireland	$460
Singapore	$920
Japan	$300

35. Stock performance. The following table displays information for 470 of the S&P 500 stocks on how their one-day change on October 24, 2011 (a day on which the S&P 500 index gained 1.23%) compared with their year to date change as of Oct 21, 2011.

		Year to Date	
		Positive Change	Negative Change
October 24, 2011	Positive Change	164	233
	Negative Change	48	25

a) What percent of the companies reported a positive change in their stock price over the year to date?
b) What percent of the companies reported a positive change in their stock price over both time periods?

c) What percent of the companies reported a negative change in their stock price over both time periods?
d) What percent of the companies reported a positive change in their stock price over one period and a negative change in the other period?
e) Among those companies reporting a positive change in their stock price on October 24 over the prior day, what percentage also reported a positive change over the year to date?
f) Among those companies reporting a negative change in their stock price on October 24 over the prior day, what percentage reported a positive change over the year to date?
g) What relationship, if any, do you see between the performance of a stock on a single day and its year to date performance? **LO ❷**

36. New product. A company started and managed by Business students is selling campus calendars. The students have conducted a market survey with the various campus constituents to determine sales potential and identify which market segments should be targeted. (Should they advertise in the alumni magazine and/or the local newspaper?) The following table shows the results of the market survey.

		Buying Likelihood			
		Unlikely	Moderately Likely	Very Likely	Total
Campus Group	Students	197	388	320	905
	Faculty/Staff	103	137	98	338
	Alumni	20	18	18	56
	Town Residents	13	58	45	116
	Total	333	601	481	1415

a) What percentage of all these respondents are alumni?
b) What percentage of these respondents are very likely to buy the calendar?
c) What percentage of the respondents who are very likely to buy the calendar are alumni?
d) Of the alumni, what percentage are very likely to buy the calendar?
e) What is the marginal distribution of the campus constituents?
f) What is the conditional distribution of the campus constituents among those very likely to buy the calendar?
g) Does this study present any evidence that this company should focus on selling to certain campus constituents? **LO ❷**

37. Transport injuries in Canada. The table below shows the number of injuries in Canada from some forms of transport accidents by gender, in 2011:

	Males	Females
Pedestrian	240	118
Pedal Cyclist	74	13
Motorcyclist	152	18
Car Occupant	380	203
Bus Occupant	5	4

Source: Statistics Canada, Deaths by Cause, Table 1020540, External causes of morbidity and mortality. Copyright © 2011. Reproduced and distributed on an "as is" basis with the permission of Statistics Canada.

a) If possible, calculate the percentage of male injuries from transport accidents that are pedestrians. If this is not possible, state why not.

b) If possible, calculate the percentage of pedal cyclist injuries from transport accidents that are females. If this is not possible, state why not.

c) An analyst concludes, "Women are safer motorcyclists than men." Comment on the ethics of this statement, with reference to the ethical guidelines in Appendix C.

d) An analyst concludes, "Bus is the safest form of transport." Comment on the ethics of this statement, with reference to the ethical guidelines in Appendix C.

e) Draw a chart comparing male and female injuries in transport accidents using the information above, adding a footnote regarding the completeness of the source information. Give your reason for your choice of chart. **LO❶, ❷**

38. Google financials. Google Inc. divides its total costs and expenses into five categories: Costs of Revenues, Research and Development, Sales and Marketing, General and Administrative, and Department of Justice charges (amounts in $Millions).

	2008	2009	2010	2011	2012
Cost of Revenues	$8,612	$8,844	$10,417	$13,188	$20,634
Research and Development	$2,793	$2,843	$3,762	$5,162	$6,793
Sales and Marketing	$1,946	$1,984	$2,799	$4,589	$6,143
General and Administrative	$1,803	$1,667	$1,962	$2,724	$3,845
Department of Justice	$0	$0	$0	$500	$0
Total Costs and Expenses	**$15,154**	**$15,338**	**$18,940**	**$26,163**	**$37,415**

a) What percent of total costs and expenses were sales and marketing in 2008? In 2012?

b) What percent of total costs and expenses were due to research and development in 2008? In 2012?

c) Have general and administrative costs grown as a percentage of total costs and expenses over this time period? **LO❷**

39. Movie ratings. The movie ratings system is a voluntary system operated jointly by the Motion Picture Association of America (MPAA) and the National Association of Theatre Owners (NATO). The ratings themselves are given by a board of parents who are members of the Classification and Ratings Administration (CARA). The board was created in response to outcries from parents in the 1960s for some kind of regulation of film content, and the first ratings were introduced in 1968. Here is information on the ratings of 279 movies that came out in 2011, also classified by their genre:

		Rating				
		G	PG	PG-13	R	Total
Genre	Action/ Adventure	3	19	23	18	63
	Comedy	1	8	13	34	56
	Drama	2	13	36	65	116
	Thriller/ Suspense	0	1	20	23	44
	Total	6	41	91	140	279

a) Find the conditional distribution (in percentages) of movie ratings for action/adventure films.

b) Find the conditional distribution (in percentages) of movie ratings for thriller/suspense films.

c) Create a graph comparing the ratings for the four genres.

d) Are *Genre* and *Rating* independent? Write a brief summary of what these data show about movie ratings and the relationship to the genre of the film. **LO❶, ❷**

40. Canadian reportable accidents. Accidents in Canada involving dangerous goods must be reported to the government and are recorded by Statistics Canada. Set out below is a summary of the number of such accidents in four selected provinces during 2012:

	Road	Rail	Air	Facility
British Columbia	10	0	0	15
Manitoba	0	0	1	5
Saskatchewan	11	1	0	22
Alberta	47	0	0	225

Source: Statistics Canada, CANSIM Table 4090005 Dangerous Goods Reportable Accidents, Copyright © 2012. Reproduced and distributed on an "as is" basis with the permission of Statistics Canada.

a) Complete the table by calculating the marginal distributions for rows and columns.

b) Find the conditional distribution for Saskatchewan.

c) Find the conditional distribution for Alberta.

d) Create a graph that compares Saskatchewan and Alberta using the conditional distributions. **LO❶, ❷**

41. MBAs. A university reported the following data on the gender of its students in its two MBA programs:

		Type		
		Full-Time	Part-Time	Total
Gender	Men	116	66	182
	Women	48	38	86
	Total	164	104	268

a) What percentage of all MBA students were women?
b) What percentage of full-time MBAs were women?
c) What percentage of part-time MBAs were women?
d) Do you see evidence of an association between the *type* of MBA program and the percentage of women students? If so, why do you believe this might be true? **LO❷**

42. Tattoos. A study performed by a medical centre examined 626 people to see whether the presence of a tattoo was associated with an increased risk of contracting hepatitis C. If the subject had a tattoo, researchers asked whether it had been drawn in a commercial tattoo parlour or elsewhere. Write a brief description of the association between tattooing and hepatitis C, including an appropriate graphical display. **LO❶**

	Tattoo Created in Commercial Parlour	Tattoo Created Elsewhere	No Tattoo
Has Hepatitis C	17	8	18
No Hepatitis C	35	53	495

43. Department store. A department store is planning its next advertising campaign. Since different publications are read by different market segments, it would like to know if it should be targeting specific age segments. The results of a marketing survey are summarized in the following table by *Age* and *Shopping Frequency* at the store.

		Age			
		Under 30	30–49	50 and Over	Total
Shopping Frequency	Low	27	37	31	95
	Moderate	48	91	93	232
	High	23	51	73	147
	Total	98	179	197	474

a) Find the marginal distribution of *Shopping Frequency*.
b) Find the conditional distribution of *Shopping Frequency* within each age group.
c) Compare these distributions with a segmented bar graph.
d) Write a brief description of the association between *Age* and *Shopping Frequency* among these respondents.
e) Does this prove that customers aged 50 and over are more likely to shop at this department store? Explain. **LO❶, ❷**

44. Oil and gas drilling in Canada. The name *Encana* combines the words *ENergy*, *CANada*, and *Alberta*. The numbers of oil and gas wells Encana drilled in five major fields during 2012 and 2013 are as follows:

Wells Drilled	2013	2012
Cutbank Ridge	30	41
Bighorn	21	31
Peace River Arch	39	26
Cleanwater	283	260
Greater Sierra	5	6
Other	12	8

Source: Based on Encana annual report 2013, page 106.

a) Draw bar graphs to compare the numbers of wells drilled during 2012 and 2013 with the names of the fields on the horizontal axis.
b) Draw stacked bar graphs to compare the percentages of wells drilled during 2012 and 2013 with the years on the horizontal axis.
c) What proportion of the wells drilled in 2013 were in Bighorn?
d) What percentage of the wells drilled in Peace River Arch (in 2012 and 2013) were drilled in 2013? **LO❶, ❷**

45. Ipsos's Canadian media landscape. This study captures the daily activities of Canadians to show marketers what opportunities they have to present their messages. It finds that, in an average day, adult Canadians divide their time as follows:

Time Spent (hours)	Activity
5.8	Engaging with media (watching, listening, reading, gaming, social networking, browsing)
6.2	Leisure (socializing, attending a live event, playing sport)
10.3	Work, study, child care, commuting
9	Sleep

a) If appropriate, represent this information as a pie chart. If not, give your reason.
b) If appropriate, represent this information as a bar chart. If not, give your reason.
c) In what way are adult Canadians using their time that explains your graph(s) in (a) and (b)? **LO❶**

46. Advertising. A company that distributes a variety of pet foods is planning its next advertising campaign. Since different publications are read by different market segments, the company would like to know how pet ownership is distributed across different income segments. The U.S. Census Bureau (www.allcountries.org/uscensus/424_household_pet_ownership_and_by_selected.html) reports the number of households owning various types of pets. Specifically, it keeps track of dogs, cats, birds, and horses.

		Pet			
		Dog	Cat	Bird	Horse
Income Range	Under $12,500	12.7	13.9	17.3	9.5
	$12,500 to $24,999	19.1	19.7	20.9	20.3
	$25,000 to $39,999	21.6	21.5	22.0	21.8
	$40,000 to $59,999	21.5	21.2	17.5	23.1
	$60,000 and over	25.2	23.7	22.3	25.4

a) Do you think the income distributions of the households who own these different animals would be roughly the same? Why or why not?
b) The table shows the percentages of income levels for each type of animal owned. Are these row percentages, column percentages, or total percentages?
c) Do the data support that the pet food company should not target specific market segments based on household income? Explain. (*Source:* Based on 424. Household Pet Ownership and by Selected Characteristic.)

47. Insurance company. An insurance company that provides medical insurance is concerned with recent data. The company suspects that patients who undergo surgery at large hospitals have their discharges delayed for various reasons—which results in increased medical costs to the insurance company. The recent data for area hospitals and two types of surgery (major and minor) are shown in the following table:

		Discharge Delayed	
		Large Hospital	Small Hospital
Procedure	Major Surgery	120 of 800	10 of 50
	Minor Surgery	10 of 200	20 of 250

a) Overall, for what percent of patients was discharge delayed?
b) Were the percentages different for major and minor surgery?
c) Overall, what were the discharge delay rates at each hospital?
d) What were the delay rates at each hospital for each kind of surgery?
e) The insurance company is considering advising its clients to use large hospitals for surgery to avoid postsurgical complications. Do you think the company should do this?
f) Explain why this confusion occurs. **LO ❶**

48. Delivery service. A company must decide to which of two delivery services it will award contracts. During a recent trial period, the company shipped numerous packages with each service and kept track of how often deliveries did not arrive on time. Here are the data:

Delivery Service	Type of Service	Number of Deliveries	Number of Late Packages
Pack Rats	Regular	400	12
	Overnight	100	16
Boxes R Us	Regular	100	2
	Overnight	400	28

a) Compare the two services' overall percentage of late deliveries.
b) Based on the results in (a), the company has decided to hire Pack Rats. Do you agree that Pack Rats delivers on time more often? Why or why not? Be specific.
c) The results here are an instance of what phenomenon?
d) What ethical issue (Appendix C) is involved in focusing on the answer to (a) for choosing a delivery service? **LO ❷**

49. Graduate admissions. A 1975 article in the magazine *Science* examined the graduate admissions process at the University of California at Berkeley for evidence of gender bias. The following table shows the number of applicants accepted to each of four graduate programs:

Program	Males Accepted (of Applicants)	Females Accepted (of Applicants)
1	511 of 825	89 of 108
2	352 of 560	17 of 25
3	137 of 407	132 of 375
4	22 of 373	24 of 341
Total	1022 of 2165	262 of 849

a) What percentage of total applicants were admitted?
b) Overall, were a higher percentage of males or females admitted?
c) Compare the percentage of males and females admitted in each program.
d) Which of the comparisons you made do you consider most valid? Why? **LO ❷**

50. Simpson's Paradox. Develop your own table of data as a business example of Simpson's Paradox. Explain the conflict between the conclusions made from the conditional and marginal distributions. **LO ❷**

51. Knee surgery. In a certain hospital, knee surgeries are performed by either Dr. Almasri or Dr. Casio. Last year's number of surgeries performed and number that were successful are given in the following tables for three patient age groups.

Number of Knee Surgeries Performed				
	Young	**Middle Aged**	**Elderly**	**Total**
Dr. Almasri	24	35	89	148
Dr. Casio	45	42	21	108
Total	69	77	110	256

Number of Successful Knee Surgeries				
	Young	**Middle Aged**	**Elderly**	**Total**
Dr. Almasri	20	29	52	101
Dr. Casio	35	33	9	77
Total	55	62	61	178

a) Draw a chart showing the number of successful and unsuccessful knee surgeries performed by Dr. Casio, split among the three age groups given. Give your reason for choice of chart.

b) Use a different type of chart to show the number of successful knee surgeries performed by Dr. Almasri, split among the three age groups given.

c) Construct a table showing, for each age group, the proportions of successful knee surgeries performed by the two doctors so that each column adds to 1. What does this table tell us about elderly patients treated by Dr. Almasri?

d) Construct a table showing, for each doctor, the proportions of knee surgeries performed in each age group so that each row adds to 1. What does this table tell us about elderly patients treated by Dr. Almasri?

e) Construct a table with 12 percentages (corresponding to the 12 numbers in the tables at the start of this exercise) showing the success rates in each of the categories given above. Is this a contingency table in the sense that the rows or columns add to the totals? Are the two tables given at the start of this exercise contingency tables? Are the tables in (c) and (d) contingency tables?

f) Dr. Casio claims that she is the more successful doctor since her success rate is $77/108 = 71\%$, whereas Dr. Almasri's success rate is only $101/148 = 68\%$. If you were Dr. Almasri, what response would you give? How do you reconcile Dr. Casio's claim with Dr. Almasri's response?

g) Suppose you are a hospital administrator allocating patients to doctors based on their success rate last year in performing knee surgery. To which doctor would you allocate (i) a young patient, (ii) a middle aged patient, or (iii) an elderly patient? State the reason(s) for your answer. **LO❶, ❷**

52. Pharmaceutical drug development. Small biotechnology companies are research intensive and develop chemical compounds that may prove to be useful drugs, but they typically do not have the funding or global reach to test the compounds for government approval or to market drugs worldwide. Instead, they sell the patents on the chemical compounds to large pharmaceutical companies to test and market. A pharmaceutical company has been buying patents from two biotechnology companies. The numbers of patents that led to successful and unsuccessful drugs during the past five years for three categories of drug are as follows:

Number of Patents	Biotechnology Company A		Biotechnology Company B	
	Successful	**Unsuccessful**	**Successful**	**Unsuccessful**
Genetic Diseases	3	15	11	32
Chemo-therapy	5	26	10	35
Anti-inflammatory	35	51	11	10
Total	**43**	**92**	**32**	**77**

a) Make a contingency table for number of successful patents with three rows for the three categories and two columns for the two companies, and give the row and column totals.

b) Make a table similar to (a), this time giving the proportion of successful patents in each cell of the table. For instance for genetic diseases, Company A had a proportion of $3/(3 + 15) = 0.167$. Do NOT include row or column totals.

c) Draw a graph that compares the success rate from (b) of patents bought from Company A with those bought from Company B for each type of drug.

d) Company A says that it has provided 135 patents, of which 43 were successful, giving a success rate of $43/135 = 31.9\%$. The corresponding figure for Company B is 29.4%. Company A therefore claims to be more successful than Company B. If you were Company B, how would you respond to this claim?

e) If the pharmaceutical company wants to buy a patent, which biotechnology company is better for (i) genetic diseases, (ii) chemotherapy, and (iii) anti-inflammatory? State the reason for your answer. **LO❶, ❷**

53. Advanced robotics in Canada and the world. Boston Consulting Group forecasts the percentage of labour costs that can be saved by 2025 from the adoption of advanced robotics. It projects that 24% of the labour costs in Canada can be saved in this way. Graph the data in the following table to compare Canada with selected other countries, giving your reason for choice of graph. **LO ❶**

	Labour Cost Savings
Korea	33%
Canada	24%
Switzerland	9%
China	18%
Belgium	9%
Brazil	7%

54. Global warming. A study by Angus Reid Strategies shows different attitudes toward global warming (GW) (www.angus-reid.com/wp-content/uploads/archived-pdf/2008.06.25_GreenShift_1.pdf). The table that follows summarizes different attitudes according to different age groups. For instance, 20% of Canadian adults are both above 55 and convinced that global warming is occurring.

		Age		
		18–34	35–54	55+
Attitude	Convinced GW Is Occurring	18%	24%	20%
	Not Fully Convinced GW Is Occurring	6%	12%	13%
	GW Is Not Occurring	2%	2%	1%
	Not Sure	1%	0%	1%

An environmental organization wants to claim that many more people are convinced global warming is occurring than not fully convinced it is occurring. It asks you as its statistician to select one of the age groups in the table above and draw a graph that demonstrates this point most clearly.

a) Which age group would you select? Why?

b) Which ethical issue, if any, does this raise according to the ASA Ethical Guidelines in Appendix C? Why? (*Source:* Norean Sharpe, Richard D De Veaux, Paul Velleman, David Wright, Business Statistics, Third Canadian Edition, 3e, © 2018, Pearson Education, Inc.) **LO ❶, ❷**

Rogan Coles/icpix_can/Alamy

LEARNING OBJECTIVES

In this chapter we show you how to display quantitative data graphically and how to analyze that display. After reading and studying this chapter, you should be able to:

❶ Display data in a histogram and in a stem-and-leaf diagram

❷ Estimate the "centre" of the data distribution

❸ Estimate the spread of the data distribution

❹ Graph the centre of the data distribution and the extent to which it is spread in a "boxplot"

❺ Identify outliers

❻ Standardize data relative to its spread

❼ Graph time series data

5

Displaying and Describing Quantitative Data

Bell Canada

Alexander Graham Bell, who was born in Scotland in 1847, is well known today as the inventor of the telephone. (He wasn't always known by this name, though: His two brothers had been given middle names, and Alexander wanted one too. For his 11th birthday present his parents gave him the middle name Graham, and the rest is history.) He moved to Canada at the age of 23 and worked partly in Brantford, Ontario, and partly in Boston, Massachusetts, where he raced Eliza Gray to the patent office and received patent #174,465 for the telephone.

Alexander licensed the patent to various companies, including the Bell Telephone Company of Canada, which in 1880 was given a monopoly to provide long-distance service in Canada. The telephone equipment, initially manufactured in-house, began to be manufactured in a spinoff company named Northern Electric in 1896. These two companies eventually formed Bell Canada and Nortel Networks, with the former purchasing equipment from the latter.

However, this close relationship ended in the 1990s, when Nortel's price for asynchronous transfer mode (ATM) switches was far above its competitors' price; Bell Canada bought its equipment from General DataComm (GDC). Nortel ultimately went bankrupt in 2009, but Bell Canada continues to thrive, with over 55,000 employees and over $18 billion in revenues in 2013, of which 32% is from wireless services and 26% from internet access.

To learn about the behaviour of Bell Canada's stock, let's start by looking at Table 5.1, which gives the daily changes in stock price (in Canadian dollars) over a 30-day period.

It's hard to tell very much from tables of values like this. We might get a rough idea of how much the stock changed from day to day—usually less than $0.40 in either direction—but that's about it. In what other way might we display this data?

Sept. 12–24	Sept. 25–Oct. 8	Oct. 9–24
	0.57	−0.47
−0.27	−0.1	0.73
−0.23	−0.18	−0.29
0.16	0.32	−0.11
−0.36	−0.01	−0.28
−0.56	−0.09	0.71
−0.15	−0.34	−0.16
−0.06	0.05	0.17
0.62	0.54	0.15
−0.07	−0.63	0.09

Table 5.1   Daily price changes in Bell Canada stock for the period September 12 to October 24, 2014.

WHO	Days
WHAT	Daily changes in Bell Canada's stock price in dollars
WHEN	September 12 to October 24, 2014
WHERE	Toronto Stock Exchange
WHY	To examine Bell Canada stock volatility

LO❶   5.1   Displaying Data Distributions

Let's follow the first rule of data analysis and make a picture. What kind of picture should we make? It can't be a bar chart or a pie chart. Those are only for categorical variables, and Bell's stock price change is a *quantitative* variable, whose units are dollars.

Histograms

Figure 5.1 shows the daily price changes of Bell Canada stock displayed as a frequency distribution and a histogram.

Like a bar chart, a **histogram** plots the bin counts as the heights of bars. A **bin** is one of the groups of values on the horizontal axis of the histogram. In this histogram of daily price changes, each bin has a width of $0.30, so, for example, the height of the tallest bar says that there were 11 daily price changes of between −$0.40 and −$0.10. In this way, the histogram displays the entire distribution of price changes. Unlike a bar chart, which puts gaps between bars to separate the categories, no gaps appear between the bars of a histogram *unless* there are actual gaps in the data. Gaps can be important, so watch out for them.

For categorical variables, each category is represented by its own bar. That was easy; there was no choice, except maybe to combine categories for ease of display. But for quantitative variables, we have to choose how to slice up all the possible values into bins. Once we have equal-width bins, the histogram can count the number of cases that fall into each bin, represent the counts as bars, and plot them against the bin values. In this way, it displays the distribution at a glance.

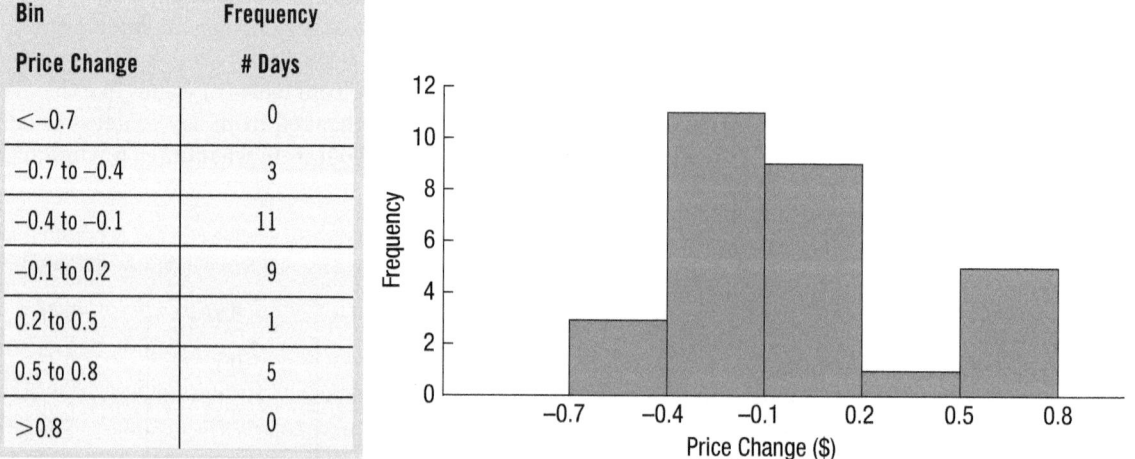

Bin	Frequency
Price Change	# Days
<−0.7	0
−0.7 to −0.4	3
−0.4 to −0.1	11
−0.1 to 0.2	9
0.2 to 0.5	1
0.5 to 0.8	5
>0.8	0

Figure 5.1   Daily price changes of Bell Canada stock. The histogram displays the distribution of price changes by showing, for each "bin" of price changes, the number of days having price changes in that bin.

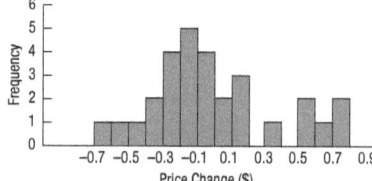

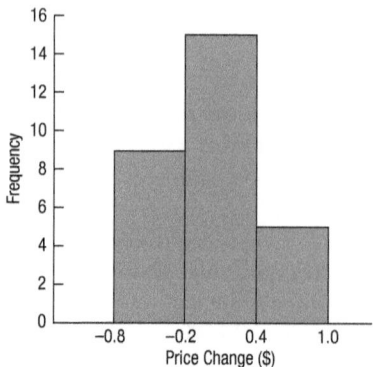

- **How do histograms work?** If you were to make a histogram by hand or in Excel, you'd need to make some decisions about the bins. First, you would need to decide how wide to make the bins. The width of bins is important, because some features of the distribution may appear more obvious at different bin width choices. One rule of thumb is that the number of bins depends on how much data we have. If we have n data points, we use about $\log_2 n$ bins. In our case, with $n = 29$ data points, $\log_2 n = 4.86$, so we have rounded off to five and used five bins. If you don't like logarithms, you can choose a number of bins, b, so that 2^b is approximately equal to n. In our case, $2^5 = 32$, which is pretty close to our $n = 29$. So we choose five bins. This is not an unchangeable rule. More bins will give more detail. Fewer bins will give a smoother histogram. It's your choice.

However, if we use *too many* bins (as in the upper graph on the left with 15 bins), the histogram will look pretty random and the overall shape of Figure 5.1 will be lost. With too few bins (three bins in the lower graph on the left), we lose a lot of information. For example, there are not, in fact, any days with price changes between $0.75 and $1.00, even though we can't tell that from the histogram.

With many statistics packages, you can easily vary the bin width interactively so that you can make sure that a feature you think you see isn't just a consequence of a certain choice of bin width.

Next you'd need to decide where to place the endpoints of the bins. You wouldn't just choose the minimum and maximum values of the stock price changes. Our maximum is $0.73, and we've rounded it up to $0.80 or $1.00 depending on the width of our bins. Choose a round number that is easy to interpret when someone looks at the histogram. Bins are always equal in width. But what do you do with a value of $5 if one bin spans from $0 to $5 and the next bin spans from $5 to $10? It's important to have a consistent rule for a value that falls exactly on a bin boundary; so, for example, you'd put a month with a change of $5 into the $5 to $10 bin rather than the $0 to $5 bin. That said, the purpose of a histogram is to describe the overall "shape" of our data, not to worry too much about individual data values.

From the histogram in Figure 5.1, we can see that the daily price changes were around $0.00. We can also see that, although they vary, most of the daily price changes were between −$0.40 and +$0.20.

If our focus is on the overall pattern of how the values are distributed rather than on the counts themselves, it can be useful to make a relative frequency

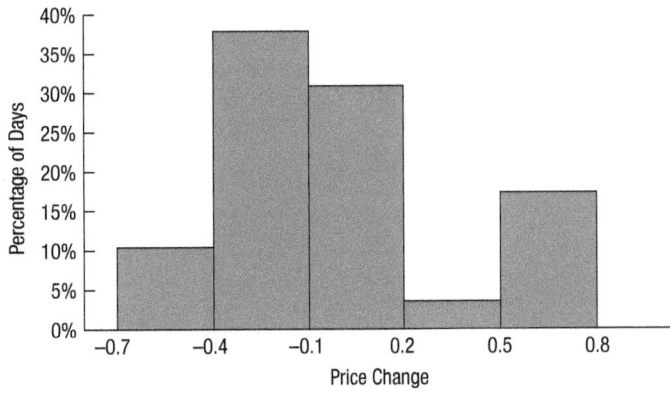

Figure 5.2 A relative frequency histogram looks just like a frequency histogram except that the vertical axis now shows the percentage of days in each bin.

histogram, replacing the counts on the vertical axis with the percentage of the total number of cases falling in each bin (see Figure 5.2). The shape of the histogram is exactly the same (as in Figure 5.1); only the labels are different.

FOR EXAMPLE	Creating a histogram of the number of music downloads

As the chief financial officer of a music download site, you've just secured the rights to offer downloads of a new album. You'd like to see how well it's selling, so you collect the number of downloads per hour for the past 24 hours:

HOUR	DOWNLOADS PER HOUR	HOUR	DOWNLOADS PER HOUR
Midnight	36	Noon	25
1:00 A.M.	28	1:00 P.M.	22
2:00 A.M.	19	2:00 P.M.	17
3:00 A.M.	10	3:00 P.M.	18
4:00 A.M.	5	4:00 P.M.	20
5:00 A.M.	3	5:00 P.M.	23
6:00 A.M.	2	6:00 P.M.	21
7:00 A.M.	6	7:00 P.M.	18
8:00 A.M.	12	8:00 P.M.	24
9:00 A.M.	14	9:00 P.M.	30
10:00 A.M.	20	10:00 P.M.	27
11:00 A.M.	18	11:00 P.M.	30

QUESTION   Make a histogram for this variable.

ANSWER   There are 24 data points, and $\log_2 24 = 4.6$, so we need about four or five bins; $2^4 = 16$ and $2^5 = 32$ and we have 24 data points. The data are in the 0 to 40 range,

(Continued)

so it makes sense to use four bins of width 10. The easiest way to do this is to first put the data in order: 2, 3, 5, 6, 10, 12, 14, 17, 18, 18, 18, 19, 20, 20, 21, 22, 23, 24, 25, 27, 28, 30, 30, 36, and then make a frequency table. We draw the histogram from the frequency table:

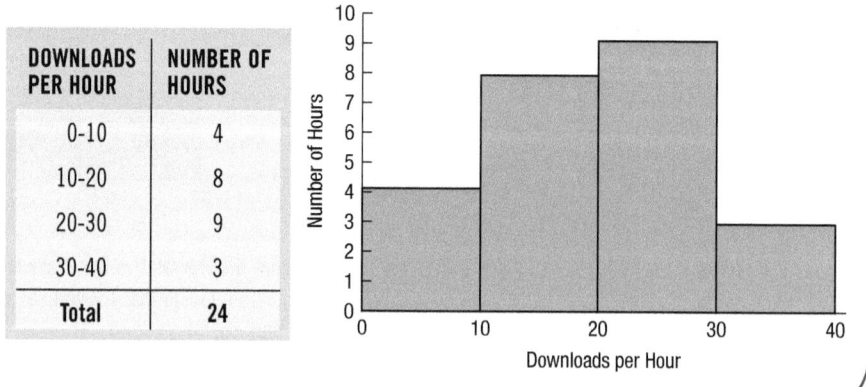

DOWNLOADS PER HOUR	NUMBER OF HOURS
0-10	4
10-20	8
20-30	9
30-40	3
Total	24

Stem-and-Leaf Displays

Histograms provide an easy-to-understand summary of the distribution of a quantitative variable, but they don't show the data values themselves. A **stem-and-leaf display** is like a histogram, but it also gives the individual values. These are easy to make by hand for data sets that aren't too large, so they're a great way to look at a small batch of values quickly. Figure 5.3 compares a stem-and-leaf display with a histogram for some other data on stock price changes. We've used more bins than we normally would in order to provide a detailed example with a small amount of data. As you can see, a stem-and-leaf display is basically a histogram turned on its side.

- **How do stem-and-leaf displays work?** Stem-and-leaf displays use part of each number (called the stem) to name the bins. To make the "leaves," stem-and-leaf diagrams use the next digit of the number. For example, if we had a monthly price change of $2.1, we could write 2 | 1, where 2 serves as the stem and 1 as the leaf. To display the changes 2.06, 2.22, 2.44, 3.28, and 3.34 together, we would first round off to one decimal position and then write

$$2 \mid 124$$
$$3 \mid 33$$

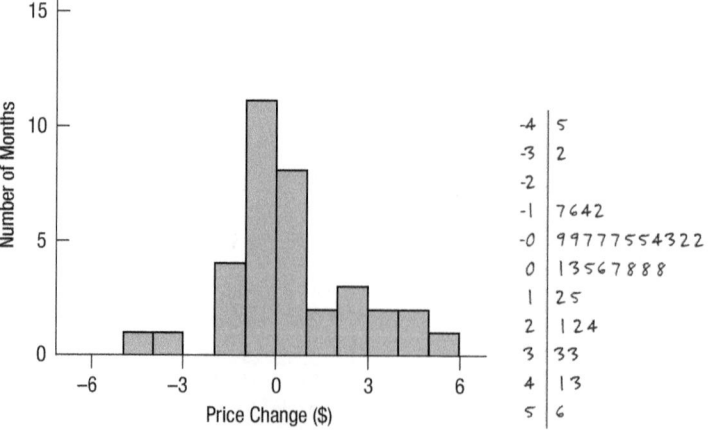

Figure 5.3   Thirty-six months of monthly stock price changes displayed by both a histogram (left) and a stem-and-leaf display (right).

Notice that we've rounded off the data—for example, 2.06 becomes 2.1—so that only one significant figure is used in the "leaf." Often we put the higher numbers on top, but either way is common. Featuring higher numbers on top is often natural, but putting the higher numbers on the bottom keeps the direction of the histogram the same when you tilt your head to look at it—otherwise, the histogram appears reversed.

When you make a stem-and-leaf display by hand, make sure you give each digit about the same width, in order to satisfy the area principle. (That can lead to some fat 1s and thin 8s—but it keeps the display honest.)

There are both positive and negative values in the price changes. Values of $0.3 and $0.5 are displayed as leaves of "3" and "5" on the "0" stem. But values of −$0.3 and −$0.5 must be plotted below zero. So the stem-and-leaf display has a "−0" stem to hold them—again with leaves of "3" and "5." It may seem a little strange to see two zero stems, one labelled "−0." But if you think about it, you'll see that it's a sensible way to deal with negative values.

Stem-and-leaf displays are great pencil-and-paper constructions and are well suited to moderate amounts of data—say, between 10 and a few hundred values. They retain all the quantitative values that are summarized in the graphics of a histogram, but for larger data sets, histograms do a better job. If you're making a stem-and-leaf diagram from more than 100 data points, you may need to "split" the leaves. In the example above,

$$0 \mid 1356788$$

could become:

$$0 \mid 135$$
$$0 \mid 6788$$

In Chapter 4, you learned to check the Categorical Data Condition. Now, by contrast, before making a stem-and-leaf display or a histogram, you need to check the Quantitative Data Condition: that the data represent values of a quantitative variable.

Although a bar chart and a histogram may look similar, they're not the same display, because the horizontal axes are quite different. Always check the condition that confirms what type of data you have before making your display.

LO❷ 5.2 Shape

Once you've displayed the distribution in a histogram or stem-and-leaf display, what can you say about it? When you describe a distribution, you should pay attention to three things: its shape, its centre, and its spread.

We describe the **shape** of a distribution in terms of its mode(s), its symmetry, and whether it has any gaps or outlying values.

Mode

> The *mode* is typically defined as the value that appears most often. But our raw data on Bell Canada stock price changes in Table 5.1 has no value that occurred more than once. We use *mode* to apply to a histogram, not to raw data. In Figure 5.1, we clearly see that the mode is between −$0.40 and −$0.10.

Does the histogram have a single hump (or peak) or several separated humps? These humps are called *modes*.[1] Formally, the **mode** is the most frequent value, but we rarely use the term that way. Sometimes we talk about the mode as being the value of the variable at the centre of this hump. The Bell Canada stock price changes have a single mode at just below $0 (Figure 5.1). We often use modes to describe the shape of the distribution. A distribution whose histogram has one main hump, such as the one for the Bell Canada price changes, is called a **unimodal distribution**;

---

[1]Technically, the mode is the value on the *x*-axis of the histogram below the highest peak, but informally we often refer to the peak or hump itself as a mode.

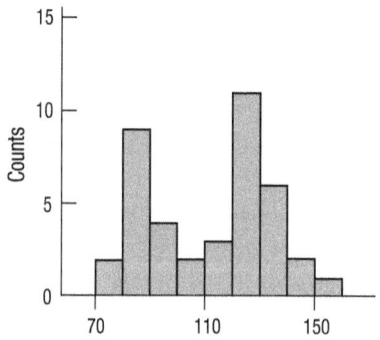

Figure 5.4 A bimodal distribution has two apparent modes.

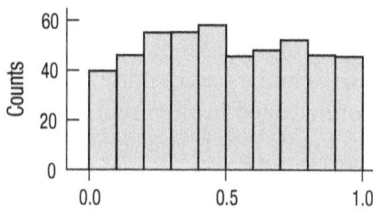

Figure 5.5 In an approximately uniform distribution, bars are all about the same height. The histogram does not have a clearly defined mode.

> Amounts of things (dollars, employees, waiting times) can't be negative and have no natural upper limit. So they often have right-skewed distributions.

distributions whose histograms have two humps are **bimodal distributions**, and those with three or more are called **multimodal distributions**. For example, Figure 5.4 represents a bimodal distribution.

A bimodal histogram is often an indication that there are two groups in the data. It's a good idea to investigate when you see bimodality.

A data distribution whose histogram doesn't appear to have any clear mode and in which all the bars are approximately the same height is approximately **uniform** (see Figure 5.5). (Chapter 9 gives a more formal definition.)

Symmetry

Could you fold the histogram along a vertical line through the middle and have the edges match pretty closely, as in Figure 5.6, or are more of the values on one side, as in the histograms in Figure 5.7? A data distribution is approximately **symmetric** if it can be divided into two parts that look, at least approximately, like mirror images.

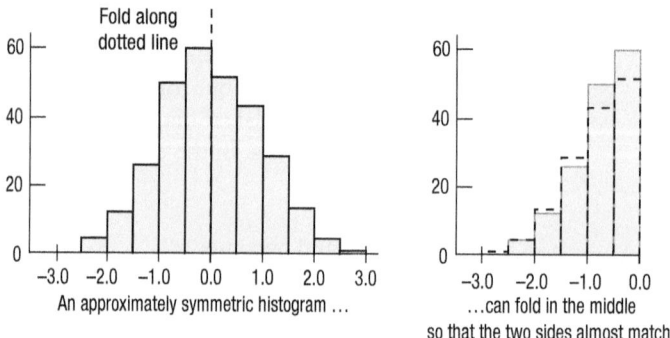

Figure 5.6 An approximately symmetric histogram can be folded in the middle so that the two sides almost match.

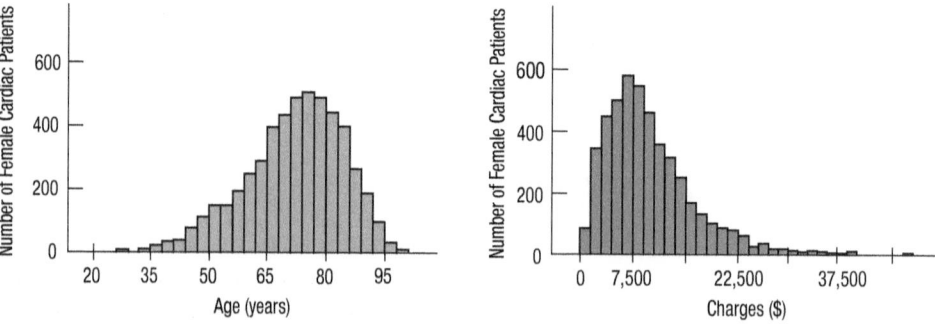

Figure 5.7 Two skewed histograms showing the age (on left) and hospital charges (on right) for all female heart attack patients in New York State in one year. The histogram of *Age* (in blue) is skewed to the left, while the histogram of *Charges* (in purple) is skewed to the right.

Each (usually) thinner end of a distribution is called a **tail**. If one tail stretches out farther than the other, the distribution is said to be **skewed** to the side of the longer tail.

Outliers

Do any features appear to stand out? Often such features tell us something interesting or exciting about the data. You should always point out any stragglers or **outliers** that stand off away from the body of the data distribution. For example, if you're studying personal wealth and Bill Gates is in your sample, he would be an outlier.

Because his wealth would be so obviously atypical, you'd want to point it out as a special feature.

Outliers can affect almost every statistical method we discuss in this book, so we'll always be on the lookout for them. An outlier can be the most informative part of your data, or it might just be an error. Either way, you shouldn't throw it away without comment. Treat it specially and discuss it when you report your conclusions about your data. (Or find the error and fix it if you can.) In Section 5.8, we'll offer you a rule of thumb for how to decide if and when a value might be considered to be an outlier, along with some advice for what to do when you encounter one.

- **Using your judgment.** How you characterize a data distribution is often a judgment call. Does the gap you see in the histogram really reveal that you have two subgroups, or will it go away if you change the bin width slightly? Are those observations at the high end of the histogram truly unusual, or are they just the largest ones at the end of a long tail? These are matters of judgment on which different people can legitimately disagree. There's no automatic calculation or rule of thumb that can make the decision for you. Understanding your data and how they arose can help. What should guide your decisions is an honest desire to understand what is happening in the data.

  Looking at a histogram at several different bin widths can help you see how persistent some of the features are. If the number of observations in each bin is small enough so that moving a couple of values to the next bin changes your assessment of how many modes there are, be careful. Make sure to think about the data, where they came from, and what kinds of questions you hope to answer from them.

FOR EXAMPLE **Describing the shape of the distribution of the number of music downloads**

QUESTION Describe the shape of the distribution of downloads from For Example: "Creating a histogram of the number of music downloads."

ANSWER It is fairly symmetric and unimodal with no outliers.

LO❷ 5.3 ## Centre

NOTATION ALERT

A bar over any symbol indicates the mean of that quantity.

Look again at the Bell Canada price changes in Figure 5.1. If you had to pick one number to describe a *typical* price change, what would you pick? When a histogram is unimodal and symmetric, most people would point to the **centre** of the distribution, where the histogram peaks. The typical price change is between −\$0.20 and +\$0.10.

If we want to be more precise and *calculate* a number, we can *average* the data. In the Bell Canada example, the average price change is \$0.024, about what we might expect from the histogram. You already know how to average values, but this is a good place to introduce notation that we'll use throughout the book. We'll call a generic variable y, and use the Greek capital letter sigma, Σ, to mean "sum" (sigma in Greek is "S" in English), and write[2]

$$\bar{y} = \frac{Total}{n} = \frac{\Sigma y}{n}.$$

---

[2]You may also see the variable called x and the equation written as $\bar{x} = \frac{Total}{n} = \frac{\Sigma x}{n}$. We prefer to call a single variable y instead of x, because x will later be used to name a variable that predicts another (which we'll call y), but when you have only one variable either name is common. Most calculators call a single variable x.

For a histogram,
- The mode is the value that occurs more often than nearby values
- The mean is the average of all the data (the balancing point of a cardboard cut-out of the histogram)
- The median is the value with the same area to the left as to the right (half the data is above it and half below it)"

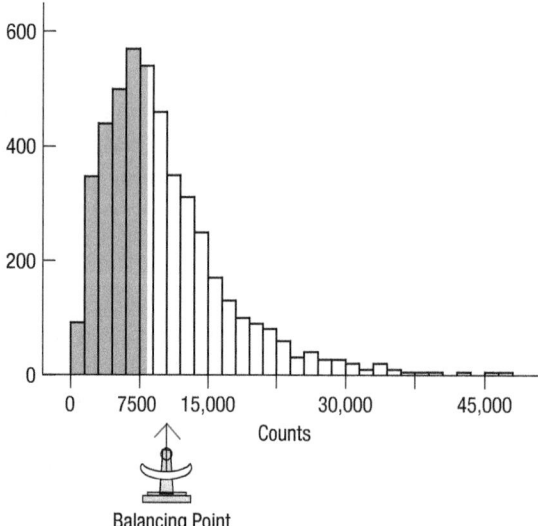

Figure 5.8   The median splits the area of the histogram in half at $8619. Because the distribution is skewed to the right, the mean $10,260 is higher than the median. The points at the right in the tail of the data distribution have pulled the mean toward them, away from the median.

According to this formula, we add up all the values of the variable, y, and divide that sum (*Total*, or Σy) by the number of data values, n. We call this value the **mean** of y.[3]

Although the mean is a natural summary for unimodal, symmetric distributions, it can be misleading for skewed data or for distributions with gaps or outliers. For example, Figure 5.7 showed a histogram of the total charges for hospital stays of female heart attack patients in one year in New York State. The mean value is $10,260.70. Locate that value on the histogram. Does it seem a little high as a summary of a typical cost? In fact, about two-thirds of the charges are lower than that value. It might be better to use the **median**—the value that splits the histogram into two *equal* areas. We find the median by counting in from the ends of the data until we reach the middle value. So the median is resistant; it isn't affected by unusual observations or by the shape of the distribution. Because of its resistance to these effects, the median is commonly used for variables such as cost or income, which are likely to be skewed. For the female heart attack patient charges, the median cost is $8619, which seems like a more appropriate summary (see Figure 5.8).

Finding the Median

Finding the median of a batch of n numbers is easy as long as you remember to order the values first. The median is halfway through the list of numbers, so the first thing to do is to calculate $n/2$. If $n/2$ is an integer, we take the average of the nth and the $(n + 1)^{st}$ numbers. If $n/2$ is not an integer, we round up to the next integer and take that number.

Here are two examples.

Suppose the batch has the values 14.1, 3.2, 25.3, 2.8, −17.5, 13.9, and 45.8. First we order the values: −17.5, 2.8, 3.2, 13.9, 14.1, 25.3, and 45.8. Since there are

---

[3]Once you've averaged the data, you might logically expect the result to be called the *average*. But the word *average* is often used too colloquially, as in the "average" homebuyer, where we don't sum up anything. Even though average *is* sometimes used in the way we intend, as in a batting average, we'll often use the more precise term *mean* throughout the book.

seven values, we find $7/2 = 3.5$, which is not an integer, so we round up to four and take the fourth value counting from the top or bottom: 13.9.

Suppose we had the same batch with another value at 35.7. Then the ordered values are -17.5, 2.8, 3.2, 13.9, 14.1, 25.3, 35.7, and 45.8. Now we have eight values, and $8/2 = 4$, an integer. The median is the average of the fourth and the fifth values. So the median is $(13.9 + 14.1)/2 = 14.0$.

Does it really make a difference whether we choose a mean or a median? The mean price change for the Bell Canada stock is $-\$0.01$. Because the distribution of the price changes is roughly symmetric, we'd expect the mean and median to be close. In fact, we compute the median to be $-\$0.09$. But for variables with skewed distributions the story is quite different. For a right-skewed distribution like the hospital charges in Figure 5.8, the mean is larger than the median: $\$10,260$ compared with $\$8619$. The difference is due to the overall shape of the distributions.

The mean is the point at which the histogram would balance. Just like a child who moves away from the centre of a see-saw, a bar in a histogram that is located far from the centre has more leverage, pulling the mean in its direction. It's hard to argue that the mean, which has been pulled aside by only a few outlying values or by a long tail, is what we mean by the centre of the distribution. That's why the median is usually a better choice for skewed data.

However, when the distribution is unimodal and symmetric, the mean offers better opportunities to calculate useful quantities and to draw more interesting conclusions. It will be the summary value we work with much more throughout the rest of the book.

Geometric Mean

Although the mean is a natural measure of the average of a set of numbers, there are some circumstances in which it would be inappropriate. Suppose you put $\$1000$ into an investment that grows 10% in the first year, 20% in the second year, and 60% in the third year. The average rate of growth of your investment is *not* $(10 + 20 + 60)/3 = 30$. We can see this by calculating the value of your investment at the end of each of those three years:

End of Year	Growth Rate	Value ($)
		1000.00
1	10%	1100.00
2	20%	1320.00
3	60%	2112.00

At 30% growth each year, you would have:

End of Year	Growth Rate	Value ($)
		1000.00
1	30%	1300.00
2	30%	1690.00
3	30%	2197.00

The average rate of growth is the growth rate that generates $2112 after three years. Suppose this rate is r. Then at the end of year 1, you would have $1000 $\times$ (1 + r). At the end of year 3, you would have $1000 \times (1 + r)^3$. Thus:

$$(1 + 0.1) \times (1 + 0.2) \times (1 + 0.6) = (1 + r)^3$$

or

$$(1 + r) = [(1.1) \times (1.2) \times (1.6)]^{1/3}$$
$$r = 28.3\%$$

We also call this the compound annual growth rate (CAGR) of your investment.

End of Year	Growth Rate	Value ($)
		1000.00
1	28.30%	1283.01
2	28.30%	1646.12
3	28.30%	2112.00

1.283 is the geometric mean of 1.1, 1.2, and 1.6.

> ## Optional Math Box
>
> In general, we find the **geometric mean** of a set of n numbers $a_1, a_2, \ldots, a_n$ by multiplying them together and taking the nth root of the product.
>
> Geometric Mean
> $$= (a_1 \times a_2 \times \cdots \times a_n)^{1/n}$$
>
> For comparison, the regular mean (sometimes called the arithmetic mean) $= (a_1 + a_2 + \ldots + a_n)/n$.

> ## FOR EXAMPLE Finding the mean and median of the number of music downloads
>
> **QUESTION**   From the data in For Example: "Creating a histogram of the number of music downloads," what is a typical number of downloads per hour?
>
> **ANSWER**   The mean number is 18.7 downloads per hour. Since there are 24 data values, the median is the average of the 12th and 13th values: $(19 + 20)/2 = 19.5$ downloads per hour. Because the distribution is unimodal and roughly symmetric, we shouldn't be surprised that the two are close. There are a few more hours (in the middle of the night) with small numbers of downloads that pull the mean lower than the median, but either one seems like a reasonable summary to report.

LO❸ 5.4 Spread

Interquartile Range

We know that the typical price change of Bell Canada stock is around $0, but knowing the mean or median alone doesn't tell us about the entire distribution. A stock whose price change doesn't move away from $0 isn't very interesting. The more the data vary, the less a measure of centre can tell us. We need to know how spread out the data are as well.

One simple measure of **spread** is the **range**, defined as the difference between the extremes:

$$\text{Range} = max - min.$$

For the Bell Canada data, the range is $0.73 − (−$0.63) = $1.36. Notice that the range is *a single number* that describes the spread of the data, not an interval of values—as you might think from its use in common speech. If there are any unusual observations in the data, the range is not resistant and will be influenced by them. Concentrating on the middle of the data avoids this problem. The first

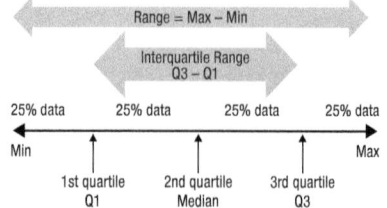

Quartiles

The first quartile, Q1, is one-quarter of the way through our data. So, if we have n data points, the first thing to do is find $n/4$. If $n/4$ is an integer, we take the average of that value and the next one. If $n/4$ is not an integer, we round up to the next integer and take that value. The third quartile, Q3, is three-quarters of the way through our data, so we do the same thing with $3n/4$.

Some software packages use other methods of calculating quartiles, so bear in mind that results may differ slightly.

and third quartiles are values that frame the middle 50% of the data. One-quarter of the data lies below the lower quartile, Q1, and one-quarter of the data lies above the upper quartile, Q3. The **interquartile range (IQR)** summarizes the spread by focusing on the middle half of the data. It's defined as the difference between the two quartiles:

$$IQR = Q3 - Q1.$$

We first sort the Bell Canada data from smallest to largest values and get the following figures:

−0.63; −0.56; −0.47; −0.36; −0.34; −0.29; −0.28; −0.27; −0.23; −0.18; −0.16; −0.15; −0.11; −0.1; −0.09; −0.07; −0.06; −0.01; 0.05; 0.09; 0.15; 0.16; 0.17; 0.32; 0.54; 0.57; 0.62; 0.71; 0.73.

There are 29 values in total. Since $29/2 = 14.5$ is not an integer, we round it up to 15 and take the 15th data value as the median, so that there are 14 data values on either side of it. The median is therefore −$0.09. For the first quartile, Q1, we find that $29/4 = 7.25$ is not an integer, so we round up to eight and take the eighth data value, which equals −$0.27. For Q3, we find that $3 \times 29/4 = 21.75$, which is not an integer, so we round it up to 22 and use the 22nd data value, which gives Q3 = $0.16. So the IQR = Q3 − Q1 = $0.16 − (−$0.27) = $0.43.

The IQR is usually a reasonable summary of spread, but because it uses only two quartiles of the data, it ignores much of the information about how individual values vary.

Standard Deviation

A more powerful measure of spread—and the one we'll use most often—is the standard deviation, which, as we'll see, takes into account how far each value is from the mean. Like the mean, the standard deviation is appropriate only for approximately symmetric data and can be influenced by outlying observations.

As the name implies, the standard deviation uses the *deviations* of all data values from the mean. If we tried to average these deviations, the positive and negative differences would cancel each other out, giving an average deviation of 0—not very useful. Instead, we square each deviation so that we don't get any negative values. The average of the *squared* deviations is called the **variance** and is denoted by s^2:

$$s^2 = \frac{\Sigma(y - \bar{y})^2}{n - 1}.$$

The farther the individual data values, y, are from the mean, $\bar{y}$, the larger the variance. The variance of the Bell Canada stock prices is 0.136. In order to calculate this, we have squared all the deviations of the individual stock prices from the mean (that is, we have squared numbers that are measured in dollars). Our result is therefore measured in square dollars: 0.136 ^{2}. We often end up with strange units for variances. We are used to square metres, but if we are dealing with product volumes measured in litres, then our variance is going to be in square litres.

Finding the Standard Deviation
To find the standard deviation, start with the mean, $\bar{y}$. Then find the deviations by taking $\bar{y}$ from each value: $(y - \bar{y})$. Square each deviation: $(y - \bar{y})^2$.

Now you're nearly home. Just add these up and divide by $n - 1$. That gives you the variance, s^2. To find the standard deviation, s, take the square root.

Suppose the batch of values is 4, 3, 10, 12, 8, 9, and 3.

Data Values, y

X

X

Deviation
$y - \bar{y}$

X

0 — Mean, $\bar{y}$

X

X

X

X

The mean is $\bar{y} = 7$. So, find the deviations by subtracting 7 from each value:

Original Values	Deviations	Squared Deviations
4	$4 - 7 = -3$	$(-3)^2 = 9$
3	$3 - 7 = -4$	$(-4)^2 = 16$
10	$10 - 7 = 3$	9
12	$12 - 7 = 5$	25
8	$8 - 7 = 1$	1
9	$9 - 7 = 2$	4
3	$3 - 7 = -4$	16

Add up the squared deviations: $9 + 16 + 9 + 25 + 1 + 4 + 16 = 80$.
Now, divide by $n - 1$: $80/6 = 13.33$.
Finally, take the square root: $s = \sqrt{13.33} = 3.65$.

You may be surprised that we divide by $n - 1$ in this calculation, whereas when we calculated the mean we divided by n. We calculate the variance by dividing by $n - 1$ whenever our data is just a sample of the complete population of data that could potentially be collected. This is usually the case. Our data on the Bell Canada stock price covers only certain days. There's no point in going back into ancient history and collecting stock prices from the day the company was founded, so a recent sample of stock prices is a realistic sample to work with.

The most common situation in which we have complete data on a population is when we're using census data. In that case, the variance is calculated by dividing by n instead of $n - 1$. We use Greek letters for populations: μ for mean and σ for standard deviation.

$$\sigma^2 = \frac{\sum(y - \mu)^2}{n}$$

The above formulas assume that we've already calculated the mean of our data. An equivalent formula that's easier to use when we don't know the mean is

$$s^2 = \frac{\sum y^2 - (\sum y)^2/n}{n - 1} \text{ for a sample}$$

or

$$\sigma^2 = \frac{\sum y^2 - (\sum y)^2/n}{n} \text{ for a population.}$$

The variance plays an important role in statistics, but as a measure of spread it's problematic. Whatever the units of the original data, the variance is in *squared* units. We often want measures of spread to have the same units as the data, so we usually take the square root of the variance. That gives the **standard deviation**:

$$s = \sqrt{\frac{\sum(y - \bar{y})^2}{n - 1}}.$$

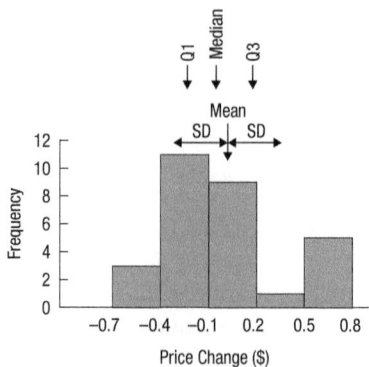

For the Bell Canada stock price changes, $s = \$0.37$. We have added the mean, median, standard deviation, and quartiles to the histogram of the Bell Canada stock price changes in the margin to show what these numbers mean. Notice that

Why do banks favour the formation of a single customer line that feeds several teller windows rather than a separate line for each teller? The waiting time is less variable when a single line is formed, and people prefer consistency.

the standard deviation is a distance measured symmetrically on either side of the mean, whereas the quartiles are points on either side of the median and are not necessarily symmetrically placed. We now have measures of centre and spread that are suited to different types of data, as summarized in the following table:

	Centre	Spread
Approximately Symmetric Data	Mean	Standard deviation
Asymmetric Data	Median	Interquartile range

If only we knew the true population mean, μ, we would find the sample standard deviation using n instead of $n-1$, as $s = \sqrt{\dfrac{\Sigma(y-\mu)^2}{n}}$, and we would call it s. We use $\bar{y}$ instead of μ, though, and that causes a problem. For any sample, $\bar{y}$ will be as close to the data values as possible. Generally, the population mean, μ, will be farther away. Think about it. GMAT scores have a population mean of 525. If you took a random sample of five students who took the test, their sample mean would not be 525. The five data values would be closer to their own $\bar{y}$ than to 525. So if we use $\Sigma(y-\bar{y})^2$ instead of $\Sigma(y-\mu)^2$ in the equation to calculate s, our standard deviation estimate will be too small. The amazing mathematical fact is that we can compensate for the fact that $\Sigma(y-\bar{y})^2$ is too small just by dividing by $n-1$ instead of by n. So that's all the $n-1$ is doing in the denominator of s. We call $n-1$ the degrees of freedom.

FOR EXAMPLE — Describing the spread of the number of music downloads

QUESTION For the data from For Example: "Creating a histogram of the number of music downloads," describe the spread of the number of downloads per hour.

ANSWER The range of downloads is $36 - 2 = 34$ downloads per hour.

The first quartile, Q1, is the median of the first 12 data points (i.e., the average of the sixth and seventh): Q1 = $(12 + 14)/2 = 13$. Likewise, Q3 = $(24 + 25)/2 = 24.5$. So the IQR is $24.5 - 13 = 11.5$ downloads per hour. The standard deviation is $\sqrt{[(2-18.7)^2 + (3-18.7)^2 + \cdots + (36-18.7)^2]/23} = 8.94$ downloads per hour.

Coefficient of Variation

During the period October 2, 2014, to November 13, 2014, the daily closing prices of the Toronto-Dominion Bank (TD) and the Canadian Imperial Bank of Commerce (CIBC) had the means and standard deviations given in the following table:

	Mean ($)	Standard Deviation ($)
TD	54.54	1.37
CIBC	100.92	2.34

The standard deviation for CIBC is higher than for TD, but does that mean the share price was more variable? The mean is also higher for CIBC. If you invested \$54.54 in TD, you got a variability in the value of your investment of \$1.37. A better measure of variability is the variability per dollar invested. For TD, this was \$1.37/\$54.54 = 0.0252. The corresponding figure for CIBC was $2.34/$100.92 = 0.0232. Per dollar invested, TD was more variable, even though the standard deviation for CIBC was higher.

In statistics, we call this the coefficient of variation:

$$CV = \text{Standard deviation/Mean}$$

$$CV = s/\bar{y}$$

It measures how much variability exists compared with the mean. It is obtained by dividing the standard deviation in dollars by the mean in dollars. It therefore has no units, which is why it is called a coefficient.

JUST CHECKING

Thinking About Variation

1 Statistics Canada reports the median family income in its summary of census data. Why do you suppose these statisticians use the median instead of the mean? What might be the disadvantages of reporting the mean?

2 You've just bought a new car that claims to get a highway fuel efficiency of 9 litres per 100 kilometres. Of course, yours will "vary." If you had to guess, would you expect the IQR of the fuel efficiency attained by all cars like yours to be 9, 2, or 0.1 litres per 100 kilometres? Why?

3 A company selling a new cell phone advertises that it has a mean lifetime of three years. If you were in charge of quality control at the factory, would you prefer that the standard deviation in lifespans of the phones you produce be two years or two months? Why?

Answers are found in Appendix A.

LO**❷**, **❸**   5.5   # Reporting the Shape, Centre, and Spread

What should you report about a quantitative variable? Report the shape of its distribution, and include a centre and a spread. But which measure of centre and which measure of spread? The guidelines are straightforward, as described below:

- If the shape is skewed, point that out and report the median and IQR. You may want to include the mean and standard deviation as well, explaining why the mean and median differ. The fact that the mean and median do not agree is a sign that the distribution may be skewed. A histogram will help you make the point.
- If the shape is unimodal and symmetric, report the mean and standard deviation. For unimodal symmetric data, the IQR is usually between one and two standard deviations. If that's not true for your data set, look again to make sure the distribution isn't skewed or mutimodal and that there are no outliers.
- If there are multiple modes, try to understand why. If you can identify a reason for separate modes, it may be a good idea to split the data into separate groups.
- If there are any clearly unusual observations, point them out. If you're reporting the mean and standard deviation, report them computed with and without the unusual observations. The differences may be revealing.
- Always pair the median with the IQR and the mean with the standard deviation. It's not useful to report one without the other. Reporting a centre without a spread can lead you to think you know more about the distribution than you should. Reporting only the spread omits important information.

FOR EXAMPLE   Summarizing data on the number of music downloads

QUESTION   Report on the shape, centre, and spread of the downloads data from For Example: "Creating a histogram of the number of music downloads."

ANSWER   The distribution of downloads per hour over the past 24 hours is unimodal and roughly symmetric. The mean number of downloads per hour is 18.7 and the standard deviation is 8.94. There are several hours in the middle of the night with very few downloads, but none are so unusual as to be considered outliers.

LO❷, ❸ 5.6 Adding Measures of Centre and Spread

We've seen how means and medians are good measures of the centre of a distribution and how IQR, standard deviation, and variance are good measures of spread. This is fine when we have only a single distribution, but often we need more than one. Industrial processes, after all, usually consist of multiple stages. For example, CTS Composites Inc. of Mississauga, Ontario, produces metal matrix composites, which are important materials in the automobile industry for disk brakes and are also used in some high-end bicycle frames. Recently it has been found advantageous to manufacture the metal composites in a two-stage production process instead of a single-stage one.

Let's suppose we have a two-stage industrial process in which we monitor the processing time taken for 100 products in each stage. The results are given in the table. We know the centre and the spread for each stage and would like to calculate the corresponding measures for the total time taken.

Processing Time	Number of Products	Mean (minutes)	Median (minutes)	Mode (minutes)	Interquartile Range, IQR (minutes)	Standard Deviation (minutes)	Variance (minutes ^{2})
Stage 1	100	20	18	17	5	3	9
Stage 2	100	30	26	25	6	4	16
Total	100	50	?	?	?	5 if stages are uncorrelated	25 if stages are uncorrelated

It's no surprise that we can add the means, but note that we can't add the medians. The mean time in each stage is higher than the median, implying that the distribution is skewed. We know that the median is a natural measure to choose for the centre of a skewed distribution, but we'd need to know how skewed the distributions are in order to calculate the median of the total production time. It can't therefore be done using just the information given. The same is true of the modes: The mode of the total production time can't be calculated as the sum of the modes for each stage. To calculate the median or mode of the total production time, we'd need to go back to the raw data on each of the 100 products.

When it comes to calculating measures of spread, we have to be even more careful. The only measure of spread that can be added is the variance, and that can be done only if the times for the two stages are uncorrelated, see chapter 9 section 3. Once we've added the variances, we can take the square root of the answer to get the standard deviation of the total production time. The interquartile range for the total production time is like the median and mode: We can't calculate it from the summary statistics for the two stages—we need to know the whole distribution.

LO❷, ❸ 5.7 Grouped Data

Suppose we ask Canadians how much extra they would be prepared to pay on $100 worth of groceries to get products made in Canada. The results are given in Table 5.2.

We can't tell from the table the exact extra amount people are prepared to pay; instead, we're given a range—for example, $6–10. In order to calculate the average percentage that Canadians as a whole are prepared to pay, we base our calculation on the midpoint of the range. The last range given in the table is $20 or more, so we're going to have to *assume* a midpoint for that range—say, $30. We calculate the mean by multiplying the midpoints by the percentage of people who chose that

Amount Extra a Person Would Be Prepared to Pay($)	Percentage of Sample
0	23%
1–5	14%
6–10	23%
11–19	8%
20 or more	17%
No answer	15%

Table 5.2   How much extra Canadians would be prepared to pay to purchase products made in Canada.

option and adding the results, as shown in Table 5.3. Our result is that, on average, people are prepared to pay about $8.50 extra to buy Canadian products. This result is only approximate, because some people did not answer the survey and because of our assumption about the $30 midpoint. It's always more accurate to use ungrouped data if available.

Range($)	Midpoint($)	% of Sample	MidPt × %
0	0	23%	0.00
1–5	3	14%	0.42
6–10	8	23%	1.84
11–19	15	8%	1.20
>20	30	17%	5.10
		Mean	$8.56

Table 5.3   Calculation of the average extra amount Canadians are prepared to pay in order to buy Canadian products.

The same principle applies to calculating the variance and standard deviation. We use the midpoints of the ranges in our regular formula for variance and also multiply by the percentage, p, of our sample in that group:

$$s^2 = \Sigma(y - \bar{y})^2 p$$

There's no need to divide by n or $n - 1$, since we're working with percentages of the sample, not actual numbers. Once we have the variance, we take its square root to get the standard deviation, as shown in Table 5.4. Note that the standard deviation (SD) is pretty high, due partly to the high percentages of the sample in the lowest and highest categories (23% would pay $0 extra and 17% would pay >$20 extra). The coefficient of variation is also very high: $10.13/8.56 = 1.18$.

Range($)	Midpoint($)	% of Sample	MidPt × %	(MidPt − Mean)^2 × %
0	0	23%	0.00	0.001685
1–5	3	14%	0.42	0.000433
6–10	8	23%	1.84	0.000007
11–19	15	8%	1.20	0.000332
>20	30	17%	5.10	0.007814
		Mean	$8.56	
		Variance =		0.010271
		SD =	$10.13	

Table 5.4   Calculation of variance and standard deviation for grouped data.

LO❹   **5.8**   # Five-Number Summary and Boxplots

The volume of shares traded on the New York Stock Exchange (NYSE) is important to investors, research analysts, and policy-makers. The volume of shares can predict market volatility and has been used in models for predicting price fluctuations. How many shares are typically traded in a day on the NYSE? One good way to summarize a distribution with just a few values is with a five-number summary. The **five-number summary** of a distribution reports its median, quartiles, and extremes (maximum and minimum). The median and quartiles can be calculated by the methods described earlier in this chapter. For example, the five-number summary of NYSE volume during the entire year 2006 looks like the values that appear in Table 5.5 (in billions of shares).

How to build a boxplot:

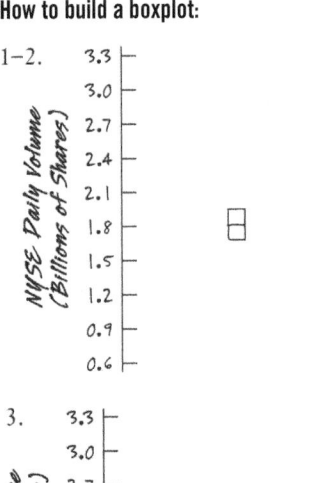

Max	3.287
Upper Quartile, Q3	1.972
Median	1.824
Lower Quartile, Q1	1.675
Min	0.616

Table 5.5   The five-number summary of NYSE daily volume (in billions of shares) for the year 2006.

The five-number summary provides a good overall description of the distribution of data. For example, because the quartiles frame the middle half of the data, we can see that on half of the days the volume was between 1.675 and 1.972 billion shares. This is the interquartile range, IQR = Q3 − Q1 = 0.297. We can also see the extremes of over 3 billion shares on the high end and just over half a billion shares on the low end. Were those days extraordinary for some reason or just the busiest and quietest days? To answer that, we'll need to work with the summaries a bit more.

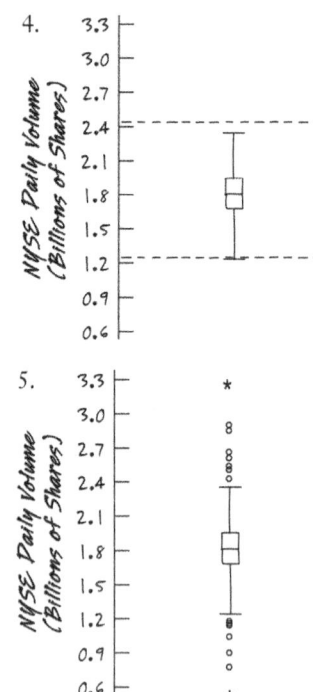

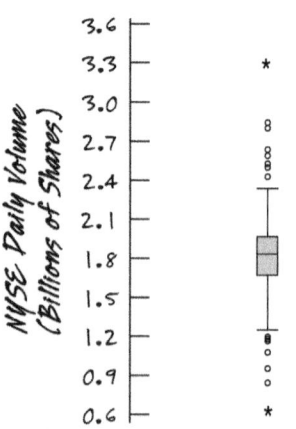

Figure 5.9 Boxplot of daily volume of shares traded on NYSE in 2006 (in billions of shares).

The prominent statistician John W. Tukey, originator of the box-plot, was asked (by one of the authors) why the outlier nomination rule cut at 1.5 IQRs beyond each quartile. His response was that one IQR would be too small and two IQRs would be too large.

Once we have a five-number summary of a (quantitative) variable, we can display that information in a **boxplot**. To make a boxplot of the daily volumes, follow these steps:

1. Draw a single vertical axis spanning the extent of the data.
2. Draw short horizontal lines at the lower and upper quartiles and at the median. Then connect them with vertical lines to form a box. The width isn't important unless you plan to show more than one group.
3. Now erect (but don't show in the final plot) "fences" around the main part of the data, placing the upper fence 1.5 IQRs above the upper quartile and the lower fence 1.5 IQRs below the lower quartile. For the NYSE share volume data, compute:

Upper fence $= Q3 + 1.5\,IQR = 1.972 + 1.5 \times 0.297 = 2.418$ billion shares

and

Lower fence $= Q1 - 1.5\,IQR = 1.675 - 1.5 \times 0.297 = 1.230$ billion shares

4. Grow "whiskers." Draw lines from each end of the box up and down to *the most extreme data values found within the fences.* If a data value falls outside one of the fences, do *not* connect it with a whisker.
5. Finally, add any outliers by displaying data values that lie beyond the fences with special symbols. In the plot that appears in the margin, about 15 such values exist. (We often use one symbol for outliers that lie less than three IQRs from the quartiles and a different symbol for "far outliers"—data values more than three IQRs from the quartiles.)

Now that you've drawn the boxplot, let's summarize what it shows. The centre of a boxplot is (remarkably enough) a box that shows the middle half of the data, between the quartiles. The height of the box is equal to the IQR. If the median is roughly centred between the quartiles, then the middle half of the data is roughly symmetric. If it's not centred, the distribution is skewed. The whiskers show skewness as well, if they are not roughly the same length. Any outliers are displayed individually, both to keep them out of the way for judging skewness and to encourage you to give them special attention. They may signal mistakes, or they may represent the most interesting cases in your data.

The boxplot for NYSE volume (see Figure 5.9) shows the middle half of the days—those with average volume between 1.676 billion and 1.970 billion shares—as the central box. From the shape of the box, it looks like the central part of the distribution of volume is roughly symmetric, and the similar length of the two whiskers shows the outer parts of the distribution to be roughly symmetric as well. We also see several high-volume and low-volume days. Boxplots are particularly good at exhibiting outliers. We see two extreme outliers, one on each side. These extreme days may deserve more attention. (When and why did they occur?)

FOR EXAMPLE   The boxplot rule for identifying outliers

QUESTION   From the histogram in For Example: "Creating a histogram of the number of music downloads," we saw that no points seemed to be so far from the centre as to be considered outliers. Use the 1.5 IQR rule to see if it identifies any points as outliers.

ANSWER   The quartiles are 13 and 24.5 and the IQR is 11.5. $1.5 \times IQR = 17.25$. A point would have to be larger than $24.5 + 17.25 = 41.25$ downloads/hour or smaller than $13 - 17.25 = -4.25$. The largest value was 36 downloads/hour and all values must be nonnegative, so there are no points nominated as outliers.

GUIDED EXAMPLE   Credit Card Company Customers

In order to focus on the needs of particular customers, companies often segment their customers into groups that display similar needs or spending patterns. A major credit card company wanted to see how much money a particular group of cardholders charged per month on their cards in order to understand the potential growth in their card use. The data for each customer was the amount spent using the card during a one-month period last year. Boxplots are especially useful for displaying one variable when combined with a histogram and numerical summaries. Let's summarize the spending of this segment.

PLAN	**Setup** Identify the *variable*, the time frame of the data, and the objective of the analysis.	We want to summarize the average monthly charges (in dollars) made by 500 cardholders from a market segment of interest during a three-month period last year. The data are quantitative, so we'll use histograms and boxplots, as well as numerical summaries.
DO	**Mechanics** Select an appropriate display based on the nature of the data and what you want to know about it. It's always a good idea to think about what you expected to see and to check whether the histogram is close to what you expected. Are the data about what you might expect for customers to charge on their cards in a month? A typical value is a few hundred dollars. That seems to be in the right ballpark. Note that outliers are often easier to see with boxplots than with histograms, but the histogram provides more details about the shape of the distribution. This computer program "jitters" the outliers in the boxplot so they don't lie on top of each other, making them easier to see.	The five-number summary of this data is: | **Max**	6745.01
Q3	738.66
Median	370.65
Q1	114.54
Min	−327.12	 A few people pay off more than they charge so that their balance is negative. 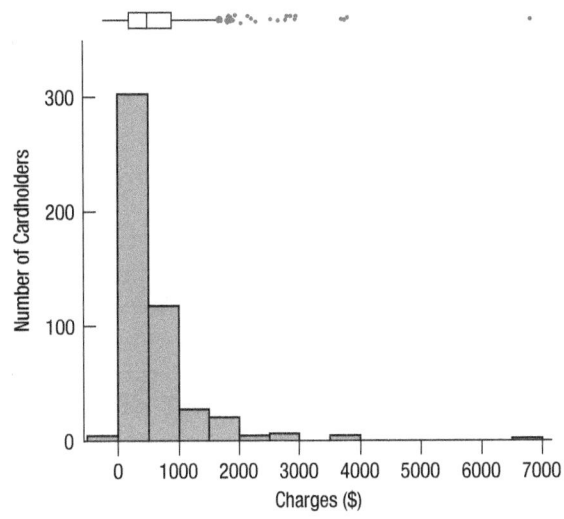

(Continued)

Both the boxplot and the histogram show a distribution that is highly skewed to the right with several outliers, and an extreme outlier near $7000.

Count	500
Mean	544.75
Median	370.65
StdDev	661.24
IQR	624.12

The mean is much larger than the median. The data do not have a symmetric distribution.

REPORT

Interpretation Describe the shape, centre, and spread of the distribution. Be sure to report on the symmetry, number of modes, and any gaps or outliers.

Recommendation State a conclusion and any recommended actions or analysis.

MEMO

Re: Report on Segment Spending

The distribution of charges for this segment during this time period is unimodal and skewed to the right. For that reason, we recommend summarizing the data with the median and interquartile range (IQR).

The median amount charged was $370.65. Half of the cardholders charged between $114.54 and $738.67.

In addition, there are several high outliers, with one extreme value at $6745.

There are also a few negative values. We suspect that these are people who returned more than they charged in a month, but because the values might be data errors, we suggest that they be checked.

Future analyses should look at whether charges during these three months were similar to charges in the rest of the year. We would also like to investigate if there is a seasonal pattern and, if so, whether it can be explained by our advertising campaigns or by other factors.

LO③ 5.9 Percentiles

The box in the middle of the boxplot shows the region between the first quartile, Q1, and the third quartile, Q3, where the centre 50% of the data lies. Twenty-five percent of the data lies below Q1, and another name for Q1 is "25th percentile." Q3 is the 75th percentile. We might also be interested in other percentiles. You can think of a **percentile** as a way of showing where a given percentage of the data lies. For instance, if your mark on this course is at the 82nd percentile, it means that 18% of your classmates got at least as high a mark as you. Notice that 82% is a totally different concept from the 82nd percentile: 82% may be your mark showing what percentage of questions you got right, whereas the 82nd percentile shows how your mark compares with other students' marks.

Calculating Percentiles

Let us take a simple example of just 12 data values to illustrate the calculation of percentiles. Larger data sets give more accurate results, but they are tough to work with for illustrative purposes. Suppose the numbers of passengers on 12 flights from Ottawa to Iqaluit are

24, 18, 31, 27, 15, 16,
26, 15, 24, 26, 25, 30.

Step 1. We first put the data in ascending order, getting

15, 15, 16, 18, 24, 24,
25, 26, 26, 27, 30, 31.

Step 2: Option 1. Suppose we want to calculate the 80th percentile of this data. Since there are 12 data values, we first calculate 80% of 12, which is 9.6. Since 9.6 *is not* an integer, we round it up to 10 and the 80th percentile is the 10th data value, or 27.

Step 2: Option 2. Suppose we want to calculate the 50th percentile of the data. We calculate 50% of 12, giving 6. Since 6 *is* an integer, we don't need to round it up. Instead, we take the average of the sixth and seventh data values: $(24 + 25)/2 = 24.5$. Notice that this follows the same calculation we gave earlier for calculating the median. The median *is* the 50th percentile.

LO❷, ❸   5.10   ## Comparing Groups

As we saw earlier, the volume on the NYSE can vary greatly from day to day, but if we step back a bit, we may be able to find patterns that can help us understand, model, and predict it. We might be interested not only in individual daily values, but also in looking for patterns in the volume when we group the days into time periods such as weeks, months, or seasons. Such comparisons of distributions can reveal patterns, differences, and trends.

Let's start with the big picture. We'll split the year into halves: January through June and July through December. Figure 5.10 shows histograms of the NYSE volume for 2006.

The centres and spreads aren't too different, but the shape appears to be slightly right-skewed in the first half, while the second half of the year appears to be left-skewed with more days on the lower end. There are several noticeable outlying values on the high side in both graphs.

Histograms work well for comparing two groups, but what if we want to compare the volume across four quarters? Or 12 months? Histograms are best at displaying one or two distributions. When we compare several groups, boxplots usually do a better job. Boxplots offer an ideal balance of information and simplicity, hiding the details while displaying the overall summary information. And we can plot boxplots side by side, making it easy to compare multiple groups or categories.

When we place boxplots side by side, we can easily see which group has the higher median, which has the greater IQR, where the central 50% of the data are located, and which has the greater overall range. We can also get a general idea of symmetry from whether the medians are centred within their boxes and whether the whiskers extend roughly the same distance on either side of the boxes. Equally important, we can see past any outliers when making these comparisons because they've been displayed separately. We can also begin to look for trends in the medians and in the IQRs.

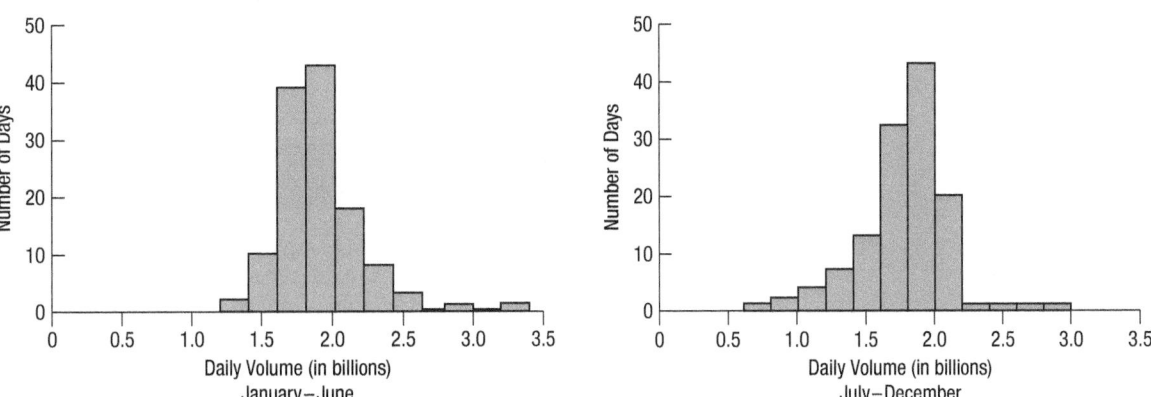

Figure 5.10   Daily volume on the NYSE split into two halves of the year. How do the two distributions differ?

GUIDED EXAMPLE   New York Stock Exchange Trading Volume

Are some months on the NYSE busier than others? Boxplots of the number of shares traded by month are a good way to see such patterns. We're interested not only in the centres, but also in the spreads. Are volumes equally variable from month to month, or are they more spread out in some months?

PLAN	**Setup** Identify the variable, report the time frame of the data, and state the objective.	We want to compare the daily volume of shares traded from month to month on the NYSE during 2006. The daily volume is quantitative and measured in number of shares.
DO	**Mechanics** Choose an appropriate display for the data.	We can partition the values by month and use side-by-side boxplots to compare the volume across months. 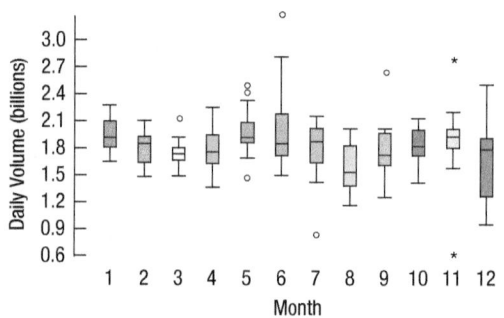
REPORT	**Conclusion** Report what you've learned about the data and any recommended action or analysis.	MEMO **Re: Research on the Trading Volume of the NYSE** We have examined the daily sales volume on the NYSE (number of shares traded) for each month of 2006. As the attached display shows, sales volume has lower median volume in March and August. The highest median trading activity is found in November. The variability of trading volume also shows a pattern. June and December have higher variability than the rest, and March has noticeably less variability. There were several unusually high-volume days that bear investigation and extremely low-volume days in July and November.

FOR EXAMPLE   Comparing boxplots

QUESTION   For the data in For Example: "Creating a histogram of the number of music downloads," compare the A.M. downloads with the P.M. downloads by displaying the two distributions side by side with boxplots.

ANSWER   There are generally more downloads in the afternoon than in the morning. The median number of afternoon downloads is around 22 as compared with 14 for the morning hours. The P.M. downloads are also much more consistent. The entire range of the P.M. hours, 15, is about the size of the IQR for A.M. hours. Both distributions appear to be fairly symmetric, although the A.M. hour distribution has some high points, which seem to give some asymmetry.

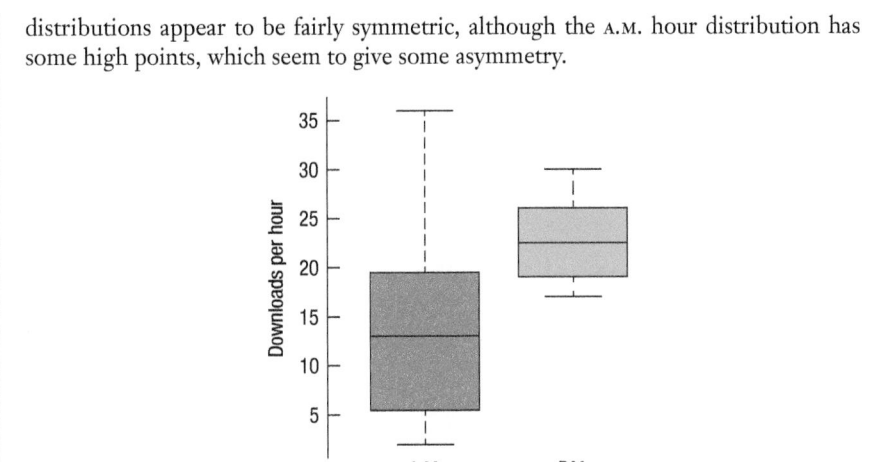

LO⑤ 5.11 Dealing With Outliers

When we looked at a boxplot for NYSE trading volumes of the entire year, there were 15 outliers. Now, when we group the days by *Month*, the boxplots display fewer days as outliers and identify different days as the extraordinary ones. This change occurs because our outlier nomination rule for boxplots depends on the quartiles of the data being displayed. Days that may have seemed ordinary when placed against the entire year's data can look like outliers for the month they're in, and vice versa. That high-volume day in March certainly wouldn't stand out in May or June, but for March it was remarkable, and that very low-volume day in November really stands out now. What should we do with such outliers?

Cases that stand out from the rest of the data deserve our attention. Boxplots have a rule for nominating extreme cases to display as outliers (those more than 1.5 IQRs outside the box), but that's just a rule of thumb—not a definition. Also, the rule doesn't tell you what to do with them.

So, what *should* we do with outliers? The first thing to do is to try to understand them in the context of the data. Look back at the boxplot in Guided Example: "New York Stock Exchange Trading Volume." The boxplot for November (month 11) shows a fairly symmetric body of data, with one low-volume day and one high-volume day set clearly apart from the other days. Such a large gap suggests that the volume really is quite different.

Once you've identified likely outliers, you should always investigate them. Some outliers are unbelievable and may simply be errors. A decimal point may have been misplaced, digits transposed, or digits repeated or omitted. Or the units may be wrong. If you saw the number of shares traded on the NYSE listed as two shares for a particular day, you'd know something was wrong. It could be that it was meant as 2 billion shares, but you'd have to check to be sure. Sometimes a number is transcribed incorrectly, perhaps copying an adjacent value on the original data sheet. If you can identify the error, then you should certainly correct it.

Many outliers are not incorrect; they're just different. These are the cases that often repay your efforts to understand them. You may learn more from the extraordinary cases than from summaries of the overall data set.

What about that low November day? It was November 24, 2006, the Friday after the American Thanksgiving, a day when, most likely, traders would have rather stayed home.

The high-volume day, September 15, was a "triple witching day"—a day when, during the final trading hour, options and futures contracts expire. Such days often experience large trading volume and price fluctuations.

Increase in 14-Year-Old Widowers?

Careful attention to outliers can often reveal problems in data collection and management. Two researchers, Ansley Coale and Fred Stephan, looking at data from the 1950 U.S. census, noticed that the number of widowed 14-year-old boys had increased from 85 in 1940 to a whopping 1600 in 1950. The number of divorced 14-year-old boys had increased, too, from 85 to 1240. Oddly, the number of teen-aged widowers and divorcés *decreased* for every age group after 14, from 15 to 19. When Coale and Stephan also noticed a large increase in the number of young Native Americans in the Northeast United States, they began to look for data problems. As it turns out, data in the 1950 census were recorded on computer cards. Cards are hard to read and mistakes are easy to make. It turned out that data punches had been shifted to the right by one column on hundreds of cards. Because each card column meant something different, the shift turned 43-year-old widowed males into 14-year-olds, 42-year-old divorcés into 14-year-olds, and children of white parents into Native Americans. Not all outliers have such a colourful (or famous) story associated with them, but it's always worthwhile to investigate them. And, as in this case, the explanation is often surprising. (**Source:** Based on Coale, A., & Stephan, F. [1962, June]. The case of the Indians and the teen-age widows. *Journal of the American Statistical Association, 57,* 338–347.)

FOR EXAMPLE — Dealing with outliers and summarizing real estate data

QUESTION   A real estate report lists the following prices for sales of single-family homes in a small town in Alberta (rounded to the nearest thousand). Write a couple of sentences describing house prices in this town.

155,000	329,000	172,000	122,000	260,000
139,000	178,000	339,435,000	136,000	330,000
158,000	194,000	279,000	167,000	159,000
149,000	160,000	231,000	136,000	128,000

ANSWER   A boxplot shows an extreme outlier.

That extreme point is a home whose sale price is listed at $339.4 million.

A check on the Internet shows that the most expensive homes ever sold are less than $300 million.

This is clearly a mistake.

Setting aside this point, we find the following histogram and summary statistics:

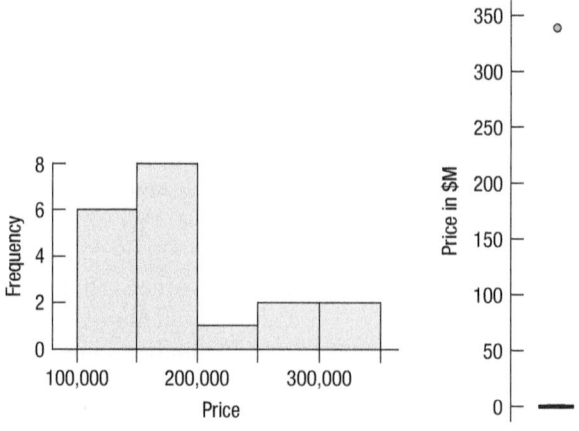

The distribution of prices is strongly skewed to the right. The median price is $160,000. The minimum is $122,000 and the maximum (without the outlier) is $330,000. The middle 50% of house prices lie between $144,000 and $212,500 with an IQR of $68,500.

LO⑥ 5.12   Standardizing

The data we compared by groups in previous sections all represented the same variable. It was easy to compare volume on the NYSE in July with volume on the NYSE in December because the data had the same units. Sometimes, however, we want to compare very different variables—apples to oranges, so to speak. For example, the Great Place to Work Institute in the United States measures more than 50 aspects of companies and publishes, through *Fortune* magazine, a ranking of the top places to work in that country. In 2007, the top honour was won by Google.

What was the key to Google's winning? Was it the free food offered to all employees? Maybe the on-site day care? How about the salaries—do they compare favourably with those of other companies? Did they score better on all 50 variables? Probably not, but it isn't obvious how to combine and balance all these different aspects to come up with a single number. The variables don't even have the same units; for example, average salary is in dollars, perceptions are often measured on a seven-point scale, and diversity measures are in percentages.

The trick to comparing very different-looking values is to standardize them. Rather than working with the original values, we ask, "How far is this value from the mean?" Then—and this is the key—we measure that distance with the standard deviation. The result is the standardized value, which records how many standard deviations each value is above or below the overall mean. The standard deviation provides a ruler, based on the underlying variability of all the values, against which we can compare values that otherwise have little in common.

It turns out that statisticians do this all the time. Over and over during this course (and in any additional Statistics courses you may take), questions such as "How far is this value from the mean?" and "How different are these two values?" will be answered by measuring the distance or difference in standard deviations.

In order to see how standardizing works, we'll focus on just two of the 50 variables that the Great Places to Work Institute reports—the number of *New Jobs* created during the year and the reported *Average Pay* for salaried employees—for two companies. We'll choose two companies that appeared in ranking farther down the list to show how standardization works: Starbucks and the Wrigley Company (the company that makes Wrigley's chewing gum, among other things).[4]

When we compare two variables, it's always a good idea to start with a picture. Here we'll use stem-and-leaf displays (Figure 5.11) so that we can see the individual distances, highlighting Starbucks in red and Wrigley in blue. The mean number of new jobs created for all the companies was 305.9. Starbucks, with over 2000 jobs, is well above average, as we can see from the stem-and-leaf display. Wrigley, with only 16 jobs (rounded to 0 in the stem-and-leaf), is closer to the centre. On

---

[4]The data we analyze here are actually from 2005, the last year for which we have data, and the year Wegman's Supermarkets was the number one company to work for.

	New Jobs		Average Pay
4		2	5
3	67	2	
2	25	2	
1	01234567	1	
0	11111112222223333334445556666677778888	1	
−0	65444332110000	1	45
−1	1	1	222
−2		1	000001
−3	3	0	88889999999999
−4		0	66666666666777777777
−5		0	44444444455555555555
−6		0	3
−7		0	1
−8			
−9	1		2|5 represents 250,000

3\|6 represents 3600

Figure 5.11   Stem-and-leaf displays for both the number of *New Jobs* created and the *Average Pay* of salaried employees at the top 100 companies to work for in 2005 from *Fortune* magazine. Starbucks (in red) created more jobs, but Wrigley (in blue) did better in average pay. Which company did better for both variables combined?

the other hand, Wrigley's average salary was $56,350 (rounded to 6), compared with Starbucks' $44,790 (represented as 4), so even though both are below average, Wrigley is closer to the centre.

Variable	Mean	SD
New Jobs	305.9	1507.97
Avg. Pay	$73,299.42	$34,055.25

When we compare scores from different variables, our eye naturally looks at how far from the centre of each distribution the value lies. We adjust naturally for the fact that these variables have very different scales. Starbucks did better on *New Jobs*, and Wrigley did better on *Average Pay*. To quantify *how much* better each one did and to combine the two scores, we'll ask how many standard deviations they each are from the means.

To find how many standard deviations a value is from the mean, we find

$$z = \frac{y - \bar{y}}{s}.$$

We call the resulting value a **standardized value** and denote it z. Usually, we just call it a **z-score**.

A z-score of 2.0 indicates that a data value is two standard deviations above the mean. Data values below the mean have negative z-scores, so a z-score of −0.84 means that the data value is 0.84 standard deviations *below* the mean. A rule of thumb for identifying outliers is $z > 3$ or $z < −3$.

Starbucks offered more new jobs than Wrigley, but Wrigley had a higher average salary (see Table 5.6). It's not clear which one we should use, but standardizing gives us a way to compare variables even when they're measured in different units.

Standardizing Into z-Scores
- Shifts the mean to 0.
- Changes the standard deviation to 1.
- Does not change the shape.
- Removes the units.

	New Jobs	Average Pay
Mean (all companies)	305.9	$73,299.42
SD	1507.97	$34,055.25
Starbucks	2193	$44,790
z-score	**1.25** = (2193 − 305.9)/1507.97	**− 0.84** = (44,790 − 73,299.42)/34,055.25
Wrigley	16	$56,351
z-score	**− 0.19** = (16 − 305.9)/1507.97	**− 0.50** = (56,351 − 73,299.42)/34,055.25

Table 5.6   For each variable, the z-score for each observation is found by subtracting the mean from the value and then dividing that difference by the standard deviation.

FOR EXAMPLE   Comparing real estate data by standardizing

QUESTION   A real estate analyst finds more data from home sales, as discussed in For Example: "Dealing with outliers and summarizing real estate data." Of 350 recent sales, the average price was $175,000 with a standard deviation of $55,000. The size of the houses (in square feet) averaged 2100 sq. ft. with a standard deviation of 650 sq. ft. Which is more unusual, a house in this town that costs $340,000, or a 5000 sq. ft. house?

ANSWER   Compute the z-scores to compare. For the $340,000 house:

$$z = \frac{y - \bar{y}}{s} = \frac{(340,000 - 175,000)}{55,000} = 3.0$$

The house price is 3 standard deviations above the mean.

For the 5000 sq. ft. house:

$$z = \frac{y - \bar{y}}{s} = \frac{(5,000 - 2,100)}{650} = 4.46$$

This house is 4.46 standard deviations above the mean in size. That's more unusual than the house that costs $340,000.

LO⑦ **5.13   Time Series Plots**

The volume on the NYSE is reported daily. Earlier, we grouped the days into months and half-years, but we could simply look at the volume day by day. Whenever we have time series data, it is a good idea to look for patterns by plotting the data in time (sequential) order. Figure 5.12 shows the *Daily Volumes* plotted over time for 2006.

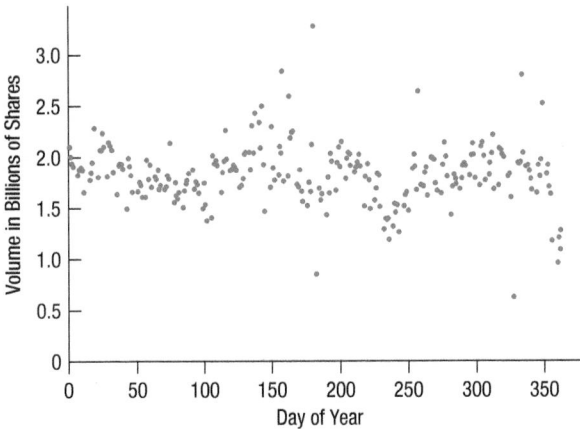

Figure 5.12   A time series plot of *Daily Volume* shows the overall pattern and changes in variation.

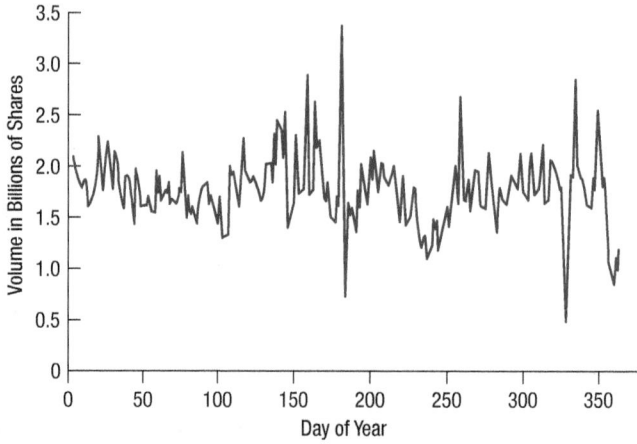

Figure 5.13   The *Daily Volumes* of Figure 5.12, drawn by connecting all the points. Sometimes this can help us see the underlying pattern.

A display of values against time is sometimes called a **time series plot**. This plot reflects the pattern that we saw when we plotted the daily volume by month, but without the arbitrary divisions between months we can see periods of relative calm contrasted with periods of greater activity. We can also see that the volume both became more variable and increased during certain parts of the year.

Time series plots often show a great deal of point-to-point variation, as Figure 5.12 does, and you'll often see time series plots drawn with all the points connected, especially in financial publications (see Figure 5.13).

It's often better to try to smooth out the local point-to-point variability. After all, we usually want to see past this variation to understand any underlying trend and to think about how the values vary around that trend—the time series version of centre and spread. There are many ways for computers to run a smooth trace through a time series plot. Some follow local bumps, others emphasize long-term trends. Some provide an equation that gives a typical value for any given time point, others just offer a smooth trace.

A smooth trace can highlight long-term patterns and help us see them through the more local variation. Figure 5.14 represents the daily volumes of Figures 5.12 and 5.13 with a typical smoothing function, available in many statistics programs. We discuss the main ways to smooth data in Chapter 22. With the smooth trace, it's a bit easier to see a pattern. The trace helps our eye follow the main trend and alerts us to points that don't fit the overall pattern.

It's always tempting to try to extend what we see in a time series plot into the future. Sometimes that makes sense. Most likely, the NYSE volume follows some regular patterns throughout the year. It's probably safe to predict more volume on triple witching days and less activity during the week between Christmas and New Year's Day. But we certainly wouldn't predict a record every June 30.

Other patterns are riskier to extend into the future. If a stock's price has been rising, how long will it continue to go up? No stock has ever increased in value indefinitely, and no stock analyst has consistently been able to forecast when a stock's value will turn around. Stock prices, unemployment rates, and other economic, social, or psychological measures are much harder to predict than physical quantities. The path a ball will follow when thrown from a certain height and at a given speed and direction is well understood. The path interest rates will take is much less clear.

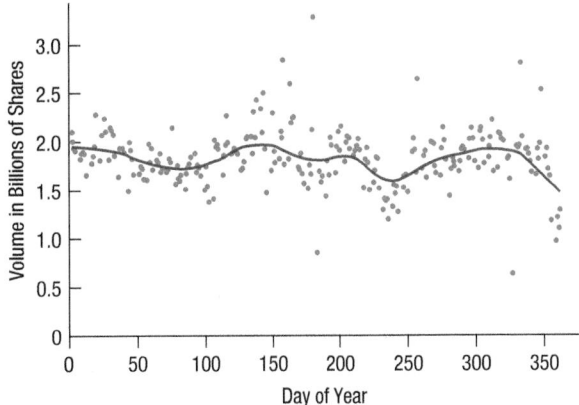

Figure 5.14   The *Daily Volumes* of Figure 5.12 with a smooth trace added to help your eye see the long-term pattern.

Unless we have strong (nonstatistical) reasons for doing otherwise, we should resist the temptation to think that any trend we see will continue indefinitely. Statistical models often tempt those who use them to think beyond the data. We'll pay close attention to this phenomenon later in this book to better understand when, how, and how much we can justify doing that.

Let's return to the Bell Canada data we saw at the beginning of the chapter. The stock price changes are a time series from September 12 to October 24, 2014. The histogram (Figure 5.1) showed a roughly symmetric, unimodal distribution for the most part concentrated between −$0.20 and +$0.10, but it doesn't show whether the pattern changes over time. The time series plot in Figure 5.15 shows a different story.

The time series plot of the Bell Canada stock price changes shows the same variability as was shown by the histogram; it also shows that this pattern is pretty constant throughout the length of the data series. A slight downward trend in the average level of the data is apparent as well. A time series that does *not* change over time is called **stationary**. Our data have a stationary variability and a slightly non-stationary average level. When a data series is very non-stationary, a time series plot is a better graphical representation than a histogram.

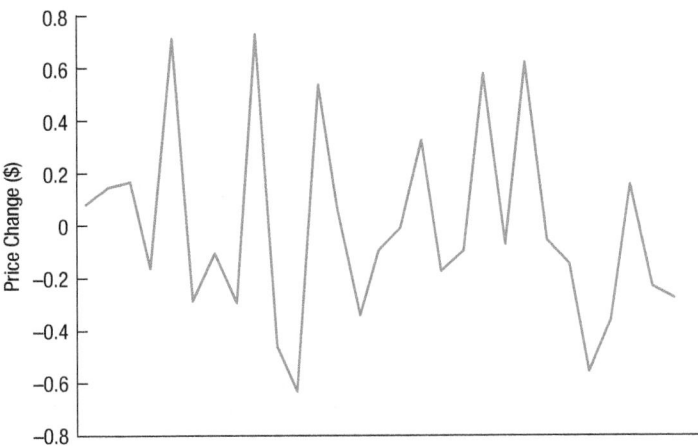

Figure 5.15   A time series plot of daily Bell Canada stock price changes.

FOR EXAMPLE   Plotting the number of music downloads as a time series

QUESTION   The downloads from For Example: "Creating a histogram of the number of music downloads" are a time series. Plot the data by hour of the day and describe any patterns you see.

ANSWER   For this day, downloads were highest at midnight with about 36 downloads/hr, then dropped sharply until about 5:00–6:00 A.M. when they reached their minimum at 2–3 per hour. They gradually increased to about 20/hr by noon, and then stayed in the twenties until midnight, with a slight increase during the evening hours. If we'd represented this data using a histogram, we would have missed this pattern entirely.

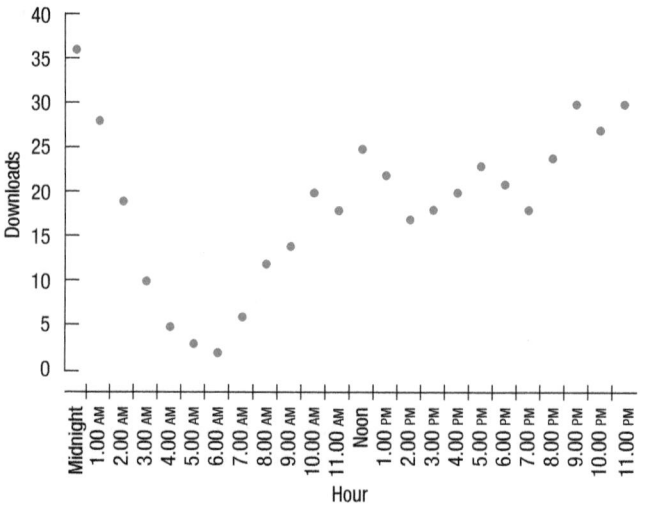

LO❶*5.14   Transforming Skewed Data

When a distribution is skewed, it can be hard to summarize the data simply with a centre and spread, and hard to decide whether the most extreme values are outliers or just part of the stretched-out tail. How can we say anything useful about such data? The secret is to apply a simple function to each data value. One such function that can change the shape of a distribution is the logarithmic function. Let's examine an example in which a set of data is severely skewed.

In 1980, the average CEO made about 42 times the average worker's salary. In the two decades that followed, CEO compensation soared when compared with the average worker's pay; by 2000, that multiple had jumped to 525.[5] What does the distribution of the Fortune 500 companies' CEOs look like? Figure 5.16 shows a histogram of the compensation for a recent year.

These values are reported in *thousands* of dollars. The boxplot indicates that some of the 500 CEOs received extraordinarily high compensation. The first bin of the histogram, containing about half the CEOs, covers the range $0 to $5,000,000. The reason the histogram seems to leave so much of the area blank is that the

---

[5]Based on United for a Fair Economy; *Business Week* annual CEO pay surveys; Bureau of Labor Statistics. Average weekly earnings of production workers, total private sector. Series ID: EEU00500004.

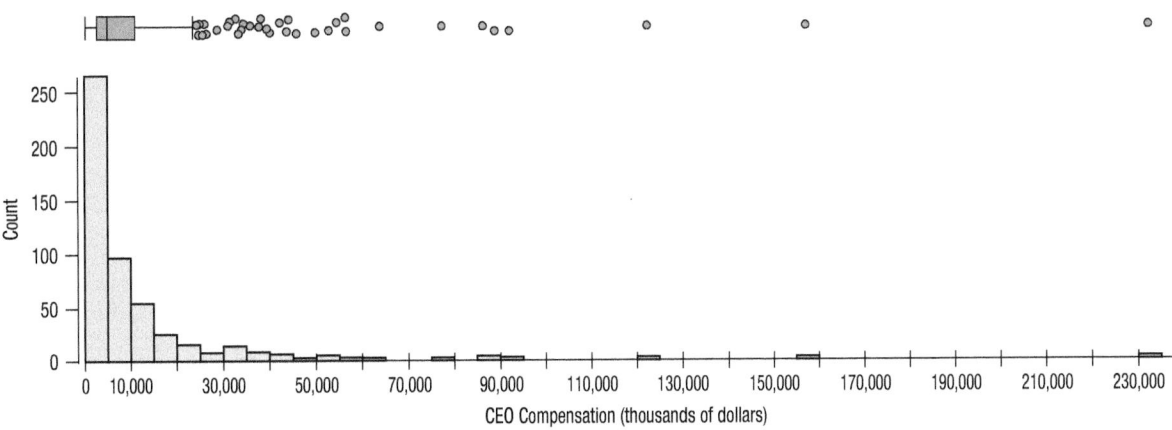

Figure 5.16 The total compensation for CEOs (in $000) of the 500 largest companies is skewed and includes some extraordinarily large values.

largest observations are so far from the bulk of the data, as we can see from the boxplot. Both the histogram and the boxplot make it clear that this distribution is *very* skewed to the right.

Skewed distributions are difficult to summarize. It's hard to know what we mean by the "centre" of a skewed distribution, so it's not obvious what value to use to summarize the distribution. What would you say was a typical CEO total compensation? The mean value is $10,307,000, while the median is "only" $4,700,000. Each tells something different about how the data are distributed.

One way to make a skewed distribution more symmetric is to **re-express or transform** the data by applying a simple function to all the data values. Variables with a distribution that is skewed to the right often benefit from a re-expression by logarithms or square roots. Those skewed to the left may benefit from squaring the data values. It doesn't matter what base you use for a logarithm.

The histogram of the logs of the total CEO compensations in Figure 5.17 is much more symmetric, so we can see that a typical log compensation is between 6.0 and 7.0, which means that it lies between $1 million and $10 million. To be more precise, the mean $\log_{10}$ value is 6.73, while the median is 6.67 (that's $5,370,317 and $4,677,351, respectively). Note that nearly all the values are between 6.0 and 8.0—in other words, between $1,000,000 and $100,000,000 per year. Logarithmic transformations are a helpful tool whenever you have skewed data.

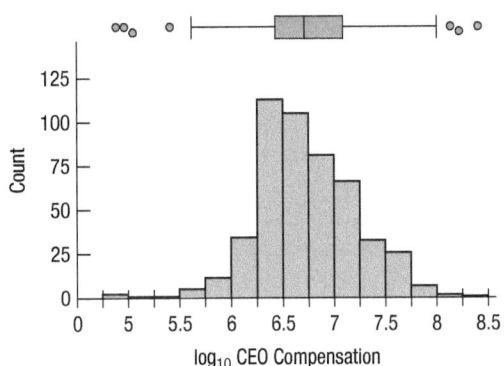

Figure 5.17 Taking logs makes the histogram of CEO total compensation nearly symmetric.

Optional Math Box

Let's calculate the mean of the data after taking logs.

If C_n is the compensation of the nth CEO, then:

$$\log (\text{Mean}) = [\log(C_1) + \log(C_2) + \cdots + \log(C_n)]/n$$
$$= \log [C_1 \times C_2 \times \cdots \times C_n]/n$$
$$= \log [(C_1 \times C_2 \times \cdots \times C_n)^{1/n}]$$
$$\text{Mean} = (C_1 \times C_2 \times \cdots \times C_n)^{1/n}$$

This type of mean is what we called the "geometric mean" in Section 5.3.

When we re-express the compensation of CEOs by taking logs, we end up with a histogram in which the data are more grouped together, which is useful from the standpoint of getting a clear *graphical* representation of the data. Figure 5.17 is easier on the eyes than Figure 5.16. This does *not* imply that the mean of Figure 5.17 is somehow a "better" way of measuring the centre of the data than the mean of Figure 5.16. Each mean is valid so long as we bear in mind what it is the mean of—either the CEO compensation or the log of the CEO compensation. In fact, the Optional Math Box shows that the CEO compensation from calculating the mean of Figure 5.17 is the same as the geometric mean of the original data. It's just another way of calculating the mean. Neither way is right or wrong.

A major advantage of re-expressing or transforming data comes when we make inferences about our data using the statistical tests described in Part 3 of this book. Most of those tests work better when the data have a symmetric, bell-shaped distribution. No data are ever going to be perfectly symmetric or bell-shaped, but the transformed CEO compensation in Figure 5.17 is certainly more amenable to these methods of statistical inference than the raw data in Figure 5.16. Chapter 17, "The Nonparametric Methods," provides methods that can be used on non-symmetric data.

FOR EXAMPLE **Transforming skewed data**

QUESTION Every year *Fortune* magazine publishes a list of the 100 best companies to work for. One statistic often looked at is the average annual pay for the most common job title at the company. Here's a histogram of the average annual pay values and a histogram of the logarithm of the pay values. Which would provide the better basis for summarizing pay?

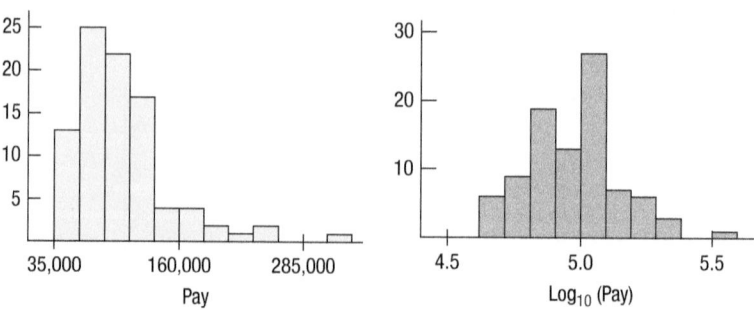

ANSWER The pay values are skewed to the high end. The logarithm transformation makes the distribution more nearly symmetric. A symmetric distribution is more appropriate to summarize with a mean and standard deviation.

WHAT CAN GO WRONG?

A data display should tell a story about the data. To do that, it must speak in a clear language, making plain what variable is displayed, what any axis shows, and what the values of the data are. And it must be consistent in those decisions.

The task of summarizing a quantitative variable requires that we follow a set of rules. We need to watch out for certain features of the data that make summarizing them with a number dangerous. Here's some advice:

- **Don't make a histogram of a categorical variable.** Just because the variable contains numbers doesn't mean it's quantitative. Figure 5.18 is a histogram of the insurance policy numbers of some workers. It's not very informative because the policy numbers are categorical. Generating a histogram or stem-and-leaf display of a categorical variable makes no sense. A bar chart or pie chart may do better.

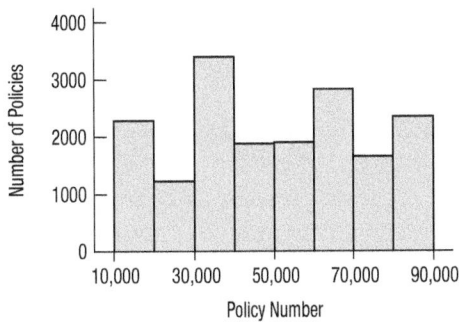

Figure 5.18 It's not appropriate to display categorical data like policy numbers with a histogram.

- **Choose a scale appropriate to the data.** Computer programs usually do a pretty good job of choosing histogram bin widths. Often, there's an easy way to adjust the width, sometimes interactively. If you're not using software with these features, you can always use approximately $\log_2 n$ bins. Bear in mind, though, that using too many bins can result in a random-looking histogram, and using too few bins can result in a loss of detail.

- **Avoid inconsistent scales.** Parts of displays should be mutually consistent. It's not fair to change scales in the middle or plot two variables on different scales within the same display. When comparing two groups, be sure to draw them on the same scale.

- **Label clearly.** Variables should be identified clearly and axes labelled so that readers can understand what the plot displays.

- **Do a reality check.** Don't let the computer (or calculator) do your thinking for you. Make sure the calculated summaries make sense. For example, does the mean look like it's in the centre of the histogram? Think about the spread. An IQR of 20 litres per 100 kilometres would clearly be wrong for a family car. And no measure of spread can be negative. The standard deviation can take the value 0, but only in the very unusual case that all the data values equal the same number. If you see the IQR or standard deviation equal to 0, it's probably a sign that something's wrong with the data.

- **Don't compute numerical summaries of a categorical variable.** The mean employee identification number or the standard deviation of social insurance numbers is not meaningful. If the variable is categorical, you should instead report summaries such as percentages. It's easy to make this mistake when you let technology do the summaries for you. After all, the computer doesn't care what the numbers mean.

- **Watch out for multiple modes.** If the distribution—as seen in a histogram, for example—has multiple modes, consider separating the data into groups. If you can't separate the data in a meaningful way, you shouldn't summarize the centre and spread of the variable.

- **Beware of outliers.** If the data have outliers but are otherwise unimodal, consider holding the outliers out of the further calculations and reporting them individually. If you can find a simple reason for the outlier (for instance, a data transcription error), you should remove or correct it. If you can't do either of these, then choose the median and IQR to summarize the centre and spread.

ETHICS IN ACTION

Beth Ghazi owns Zenna's Café, an independent coffee shop located in a small city in Atlantic Canada. Since opening Zenna's in 2002, she has been steadily growing her business and now distributes her custom coffee blends to a number of regional restaurants and markets. She operates a microroaster that offers specialty-grade Arabica coffees recognized as some of the best in the area. In addition to providing the highest-quality coffees, Beth wants her business to be socially responsible. To that end, she pays fair prices to coffee farmers and donates profits to help charitable causes in Panama, Costa Rica, and Guatemala. She also encourages her employees to get involved in the local community. Recently, one of the well-known multinational coffeehouse chains announced plans to locate shops in her area. This chain is one of the few to offer Certified Free Trade coffee products and work toward social justice in the global community.

Consequently, Beth thought it might be a good idea for her to begin communicating Zenna's message of social responsibility to the public, but with an emphasis on its commitment to the local community. Three months ago, she began collecting data on the number of volunteer hours donated by her employees per week. She has a total of 12 employees, of whom 10 are full-time. Most employees volunteered fewer than two hours per week, but Beth noticed that one part-time employee volunteered more than 20 hours per week. She discovered that her employees collectively volunteered an average of 15 hours per month (with a median of eight hours). She planned to report the average number and believed that most people would be impressed with Zenna's level of commitment to the local community.

Ethical Issue *The outlier in the data affects the average in a direction that benefits Beth Ghazi and Zenna's Café (related to Item C, ASA Ethical Guidelines; see Appendix C, the American Statistical Association's Ethical Guidelines for Statistical Practice, also available online at www.amstat.org/about/ethicalguidelines.cfm).*

Ethical solution *Beth's data are highly skewed. There is an outlier value (for a part-time employee) that pulls the average number of volunteer hours up. Reporting the average is misleading. In addition, there may be justification to eliminate the value, since it belongs to a part-time employee (and 10 of the 12 employees are full-time). It would be more ethical for Beth to (1) report the average but discuss the outlier value; (2) report the average for only full-time employees; or (3) report the median instead of the average.*

WHAT HAVE WE LEARNED?

Learning Objectives   ❶ We've learned how to display and summarize quantitative data to help us see the story the data have to tell.

- We can display the distribution of quantitative data with a histogram or a stem-and-leaf display.
- We've seen the power of transforming our data so that it's not so skewed.

❷ We've learned how to summarize distributions of quantitative variables numerically.

- Measures of centre for a distribution include the median and the mean.

❸ Measures of spread include the range, IQR, and standard deviation.

- We'll report the median and IQR when the distribution is skewed. If it's symmetric, we'll summarize the distribution with the mean and standard deviation. Always pair the median with the IQR and the mean with the standard deviation.
- We've seen how to calculate percentiles and how to use them, particularly with skewed data.

❹ We've learned the value of comparing groups and looking for patterns among groups and over time.

- We've seen that boxplots are very effective for comparing groups graphically.
- When we compare groups, we discuss their shapes, centres, spreads, and any unusual features.

❺ We've experienced the value of identifying and investigating outliers, and we've seen that when we group data in different ways, it can allow different cases to emerge as possible outliers.

❻ We've learned the power of standardizing data.

- Standardizing uses the standard deviation as a ruler to measure distance from the mean, creating z-scores.
- Using these z-scores, we can compare apples and oranges—values from different distributions or values based on different units.
- A z-score can identify unusual or surprising values among data.

❼ We've graphed data that have been measured over time against a time axis and looked for trends both by eye and with a data smoother.

Terms

Bimodal distributions	Distributions with two modes.
Bin	One of the groups of values on the horizontal axis of a histogram.
Boxplot	A boxplot displays the five-number summary as a central box with whiskers that extend to the non-outlying values. Boxplots are particularly effective for comparing groups.
Centre	The middle of the distribution, usually summarized numerically by the mean or the median.

Five-number summary   A five-number summary for a variable consists of

- The minimum and maximum
- The quartiles Q1 and Q3
- The median

Geometric mean	A measure of the centre of a set of data $a_1, a_2, \ldots, a_n$, given by: $(a_1 \times a_2 \times \cdots \times a_n)^{1/n}$
Histogram (relative frequency)	A histogram uses adjacent bars to show the distribution of values in a quantitative variable. Each bar represents the frequency (relative frequency) of values falling in an interval of values.
Interquartile range (IQR)	The difference between the first and third quartiles; IQR $=$ Q3 $-$ Q1.
Mean	A measure of centre found as $\dfrac{\sum y}{n}$.
Median	The middle value with half of the data above it and half below it.
Mode	A peak or local high point in the shape of the data distribution. The apparent location of modes can change as the scale of a histogram is changed.
Multimodal distributions	Distributions with more than two modes.
Outliers	Extreme values that don't appear to belong with the rest of the data. They may be unusual values that deserve further investigation or just mistakes; there's no obvious way to tell just by looking at the numbers. We need to probe further and find out where the numbers came from.

Percentile	A value below which a given percentage of data lies. For instance, 10% of data is below the 10th percentile.
Quartile	The lower quartile (Q1) is the value with a quarter of the data below it. The upper quartile (Q3) has a quarter of the data above it. The median (Q2) and quartiles divide data into four equal parts.
Range	The difference between the lowest and highest values in a data set: Range = $max - min$.
Re-express or transform	We re-express or transform data by taking the logarithm, square root, reciprocal, or some other mathematical operation on all values of the data set.
Shape	The visual appearance of the distribution. To describe the shape, look for • Single vs. multiple modes • Symmetry vs. skewness
Skewed	A distribution is skewed if one tail stretches out farther than the other.
Spread	The description of how tightly clustered the distribution is around its centre. Measures of spread include the IQR and the standard deviation.
Standard deviation	A measure of spread found as $s = \sqrt{\dfrac{\Sigma(y - \bar{y})^2}{n - 1}}$ for sample data, and $\sigma = \sqrt{\dfrac{\Sigma(y - \mu)^2}{n}}$ for population data.
Standardized value	We standardize a value by subtracting the mean and dividing by the standard deviation for the variable. These values, called z-scores, have no units.
Stationary	A time series is said to be stationary if its statistical properties don't change over time.
Stem-and-leaf display	A stem-and-leaf display shows quantitative data values in a way that sketches the distribution of the data. It's best described in detail by example.
Symmetric	A data distribution is approximately symmetric if the two halves on either side of the centre look approximately like mirror images of each other.
Tail	The tails of a distribution are the parts that typically trail off on either side.
Time series plot	Displays data that change over time. Often, successive values are connected with lines to show trends more clearly.
Uniform	A data distribution that's roughly flat is said to be approximately uniform.
Unimodal distribution	A data distribution that has one mode. This is a useful term for describing the shape of a histogram when it's generally mound-shaped.
Variance	The standard deviation squared.
z-score	A standardized value that tells how many standard deviations a value is from the mean; z-scores have a mean of 0 and a standard deviation of 1.

Skills

Plan

• Be able to identify an appropriate display for any quantitative variable.

• Be able to select a suitable measure of centre and a suitable measure of spread for a variable based on information about its distribution.

• Know the basic properties of the median: The median divides the data into the half of the data values that are below the median and the half that are above the median.

• Know the basic properties of the mean: The mean is the point at which the histogram balances.

• Know that the standard deviation summarizes how spread out all the data are around the mean.

• Know that standardizing uses the standard deviation as a ruler.

• Know how to display the distribution of a quantitative variable with a stem-and-leaf display or a histogram.

Do

• Know how to make a time series plot of data that are collected at regular time intervals.

• Know how to compute the mean and median of a set of data and know when each is appropriate.

• Know how to compute the standard deviation and IQR of a set of data and know when each is appropriate.

• Know how to compute a five-number summary of a variable.

- Know how to calculate percentiles.
- Know how to construct a boxplot by hand from a five-number summary.
- Know how to calculate the z-score of an observation.

Report
- Be able to describe and compare the distributions of quantitative variables in terms of their shape, centre, and spread.
- Be able to discuss any outliers in the data, noting how they deviate from the overall pattern of the data.
- Be able to describe summary measures in a sentence. In particular, know that the common measures of centre and spread have the same units as the variable they summarize and that they should be described in those units.
- Be able to compare two or more groups by comparing their boxplots.
- Be able to discuss patterns in a time series plot, in terms of both the general trend and any changes in the spread of the distribution over time.

MINI case studies

Canadian Exports

Statistics on Canadian exports are used for a variety of purposes, from projecting Canada's foreign exchange earnings to planning capacity in Canadian ports. The file **ch05_MCSP_Canadian_Exports** contains monthly export data from Statistics Canada for three geographical areas. Statistics Canada calculates exports on a "Customs" basis and also on a "Balance of Payments" basis, and the file contains footnotes describing the difference.[6]

Radius Images/Alamy

a) Draw time series graphs of this export data and identify any major differences between the "Customs" and "Balance of Payments" series.

b) Explain which basis of calculation, "Customs" or "Balance of Payments," would be appropriate for projecting Canada's foreign exchange earnings.

c) Explain which basis of calculation, "Customs" or "Balance of Payments," would be appropriate for planning capacity in Canadian ports.

d) Are there any exceptional periods during which exports in the three geographical areas have differed from overall trends?

e) In order to forecast future exports, for which geographic region(s) would the mean value of the data be appropriate? Give reasons for your answer.

Solar Power in Ontario

As a result of the *Green Energy Act*, Ontario has led the other Canadian provinces in solar power deployment. Many installers compete to mount solar modules on residential roofs in all the major cities, but an underserved market is small communities.

One installer, based in Kingston, has found people in small communities to be more entrepreneurial than people in large cities and more willing to consider their house as a means of generating electric power and revenue, whereas people in cities

---

[6]Based on Statistics Canada. CANSIM using CHASS, Table 228-0058: Merchandise imports and exports, customs and balance of payments basis for all countries (2014).

regard it primarily as a home to live in. He tests out the market in the small communities of Belleville and Brockville, and during the first year he installs projects producing the amount of power in kilowatts (kW) given in the file **ch05_MCSP_Solar**. Because of the travel time from his base in Kingston to these communities and because of returns to scale, the installer makes more profit on large projects than on small ones.

Write a report (including histograms and measures of centre and spread) comparing the two communities and recommending which one to focus on next year.

Hotel Occupancy Rates

Many properties in the hospitality industry experience strong seasonal fluctuations in demand. To be successful in this industry, it's important to anticipate such fluctuations and to understand demand patterns. The file **ch05_MCSP_Occupancy_Rates** contains data on quarterly *Hotel Occupancy Rates* (in % capacity) for a town in southern Ontario from January 2000 to December 2007.

Examine the data and prepare a report for the manager of a hotel in the town in southern Ontario on patterns in *Hotel Occupancy* during this period. Include both numerical summaries and graphical displays and summarize the patterns that you see. Discuss any unusual features of the data and explain them if you can, including a discussion of whether the manager should take these features into account for future planning.

Aimintang/E+/Getty Images

Lingbeek/E+/Getty Images

Value and Growth Stock Returns

Investors in the stock market have choices in how aggressive they'd like to be with their investments. To help investors, stocks are classified as "growth" or "value" stocks. Growth stocks are generally shares in high-quality companies that have demonstrated consistent performance and are expected to continue to do well. Value stocks, on the other hand, are stocks whose prices seem low compared with their inherent worth (as measured by the book-to-price ratio). Managers invest in these hoping that their low price is simply an overreaction to recent negative events.[7]

In the data set **ch05_MCP_Returns**[8] are the monthly returns of 2500 stocks classified as *Growth* and *Value* for the time period January 1975 to June 1997. Examine the distributions of the two types of stocks and discuss the advantages and disadvantages of each. Is it clear which type of stock offers the best investment? Discuss briefly.

----

[7]The cynical statistician might say that the manager who invests in growth funds puts his faith in extrapolation, while the value manager is putting her faith in the Law of Averages.

[8]Independence International Associates, Inc. maintains a family of international-style indexes covering 22 equity markets. The highest book-to-price stocks are selected one by one from the top of the list. The top half of these stocks become the constituents of the "value index," and the remaining stocks become the "growth index."

Technology Help: Displaying and Summarizing Quantitative Variables

Almost any program that displays data can make a histogram, but some will do a better job of determining where the bars should start and how they should partition the span of the data (see the art).

Many statistics packages offer a prepackaged collection of summary measures. The result might look like this:

Variable: Weight
N = 234
Mean = 143.3 Median = 139
St. Dev = 11.1 IQR = 14

Alternatively, a package might make a table for several variables and summary measures:

Variable	N	Mean	Median	Stdev	IQR
Weight	234	143.3	139	11.1	14
Height	234	68.3	68.1	4.3	5
Score	234	86	88	9	5

It's usually easy to read the results and identify each computed summary. You should be able to read the summary statistics produced by any computer package.

Packages often provide many more summary statistics than you need. Of course, some of these may not be appropriate when the data are skewed or have outliers. It is your responsibility to check a histogram or stem-and-leaf display and decide which summary statistics to use.

It is common for packages to report summary statistics to many decimal places of "accuracy." Of course, it is rare to find data that have such accuracy in the original measurements. The ability to calculate to six or seven digits beyond the decimal point doesn't mean that those digits have any meaning. Generally, it's a good idea to round these values, allowing perhaps one more digit of precision than was given in the original data.

Displays and summaries of quantitative variables are among the simplest things you can do in most statistics packages.

The vertical scale may be counts or proportions. Sometimes it isn't clear which. But the shape of the histogram is the same either way.

The axis should be clearly labelled so that you can tell what "pile" each bar represents. You should be able to tell the lower and upper bounds of each bar.

Most packages choose the number of bars for you automatically. Often you can adjust that choice.

EXCEL

To make a histogram in Excel, use the Data Analysis add-in. If you haven't installed it, you must do that first.

- On the File tab, click **Options**, and then click **Add-Ins**.

- Near the bottom of the Excel Options dialogue box, select **Excel addins** in the Manage box, and then click **Go**.

- In the Add-Ins dialogue box, select the check box for Analysis ToolPak, and then click **OK**.

- If Excel displays a message that states it can't run this add-in and prompts you to install it, click **Yes** to install the add-in.

To make a histogram,

- From the Data ribbon, select the Data Analysis add-in.

- From its menu, select Histograms.

- Indicate the range of the data whose histogram you wish to draw.

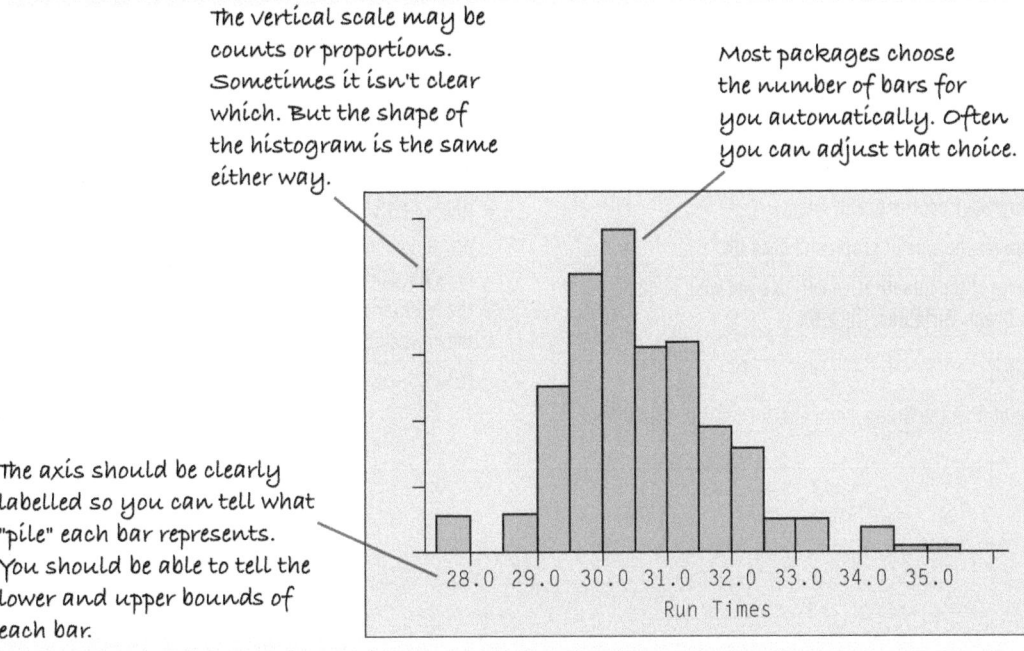

The vertical scale may be counts or proportions. Sometimes it isn't clear which. But the shape of the histogram is the same either way.

Most packages choose the number of bars for you automatically. Often you can adjust that choice.

The axis should be clearly labelled so you can tell what "pile" each bar represents. You should be able to tell the lower and upper bounds of each bar.

(Continued)

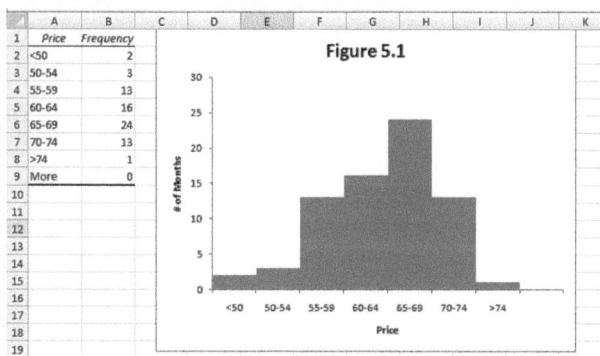

	A	B
1	Price	Frequency
2	<50	2
3	50-54	3
4	55-59	13
5	60-64	16
6	65-69	24
7	70-74	13
8	>74	1
9	More	0

- Indicate the bin ranges that are up to and including the right end points of each bin.
- Check **Labels** if your columns have names in the first cell.
- Check **Chart Output** and click **OK**.
- Right-click on any bar of the resulting graph and, from the menu that drops down, select **Format Data Series...**
- In the dialogue box that opens, select **Series Options** from the sidebar.
- Slide the Gap Width slider to **No Gap,** and click **Close.**
- In the pivot table on the left, use your pointing tool to slide the bottom of the table up to get rid of the "more" bin.
- You can right-click on the legend or axis names to edit or remove them.
- Following these instructions, you can reproduce Figure 5.1 using the data set AIG.

Alternatively, you can set up your own bin boundaries and count the observations tailing within each bin using an Excel function such as FREQUENCY (Data array, Bins array). Consult your Excel manual or help files for details on how to do this.

MINITAB

To make a histogram,

- Choose **Histogram** from the **Graph** menu.
- Select **Simple** for the type of graph and click **OK**.
- Enter the name of the quantitative variable you wish to display in the box labelled **Graph Variables**. Click **OK**.

To make a boxplot:

- Choose **Boxplot** from the **Graph** menu and specify your data format.

To calculate summary statistics:

- Choose **Basic Statistics** from the **Stat** menu. From the **Basic Statistics** submenu, choose **Display Descriptive Statistics**.
- Assign variables from the variable list box to the **Variables** box. MINITAB makes a descriptive statistics table.

SPSS

To make a histogram or boxplot in SPSS, open the Chart Builder from the Graphs menu.

- Click the **Gallery** tab.
- Choose **Histogram** or **Boxplot** from the list of chart types.
- Drag the icon of the plot you want onto the canvas.
- Drag a scale variable to the *y*-axis drop zone.
- Click **OK**.

To make side-by-side boxplots, drag a categorical variable to the *x*-axis drop zone and click **OK**.

To calculate summary statistics:

- Choose **Explore** from the **Descriptive Statistics** submenu of the **Analyze** menu. In the **Explore** dialogue, assign one or more variables from the source list to the Dependent List and click the **OK** button.

JMP

To make a histogram and find summary statistics:

- Choose **Distribution** from the **Analyze** menu.
- In the **Distribution** dialogue box, drag the name of the variable that you wish to analyze into the empty window beside the label **Y, Columns**.
- Click **OK**. JMP computes standard summary statistics along with displays of the variables.

To make boxplots:

- Choose **Fit *y* by *x*.** Assign a continuous response variable to **Y, Response** and a nominal group variable holding the group names to **X, Factor**, and click **OK**. JMP will offer (among other things) dotplots of the data. Click the red triangle and, under **Display Options**, select **Boxplots**. Note: If the variables are of the wrong type, the display options might not offer boxplots.

EXERCISES

SECTION 5.1

1. As part of the marketing team at an internet music site, you want to understand who your customers are. You send out a survey to 25 customers (you use an incentive of $50 worth of downloads to guarantee a high response rate) asking for demographic information. One of the variables is customer age. For the 25 customers, the ages are:

20	32	34	29	30
30	30	14	29	11
38	22	44	48	26
25	22	32	35	32
35	42	44	44	48

a) Make a histogram of the data using a bar width of 10 years.
b) Make a histogram of the data using a bar width of five years.
c) Make a relative frequency histogram of the data using a bar width of five years.
d) Make a stem-and-leaf plot of the data using tens as the stems and putting the youngest customers at the top of the plot. **LO ❶**

2. As the new manager of a small convenience store, you want to understand the shopping patterns of your customers. You randomly sample 20 purchases (in Canadian dollars) from yesterday's records:

39.05	2.73	32.92	47.51
37.91	34.35	64.48	51.96
56.95	81.58	47.80	11.72
21.57	40.83	38.24	32.98
75.16	74.30	47.54	65.62

a) Make a histogram of the data using a bar width of $20.
b) Make a histogram of the data using a bar width of $10.
c) Make a relative frequency histogram of the data using a bar width of $10.
d) Make a stem-and-leaf plot of the data using multiples of $10 as the stems and putting the smallest amounts on top. **LO ❶**

SECTION 5.2

3. For the histogram you made in Exercise 1(a),
a) Is the distribution unimodal or multimodal?
b) Where is (are) the mode(s)?
c) Is the distribution symmetric?
d) Are there any outliers? **LO ❷**

4. For the histogram you made in Exercise 2(a),
a) Is the distribution unimodal or multimodal?
b) Where is (are) the mode(s)?
c) Is the distribution symmetric?
d) Are there any outliers? **LO ❷**

SECTION 5.3

5. For the data in Exercise 1:
a) Would you expect the mean age to be smaller than, bigger than, or about the same size as the median? Explain.
b) Find the mean age.
c) Find the median age. **LO ❷**

6. For the data in Exercise 2:
a) Would you expect the mean purchase to be smaller than, bigger than, or about the same size as the median? Explain.
b) Find the mean purchase.
c) Find the median purchase. **LO ❷**

SECTION 5.4

7. For the data in Exercise 1:
a) Find the quartiles using the method in the "Quartiles" section of this chapter.
b) Find the IQR using the quartiles from (b).
c) Find the standard deviation. **LO ❸**

8. For the data in Exercise 2:
a) Find the quartiles using the method in the "Quartiles" section of this chapter.
b) Find the IQR using the quartiles from (b).
c) Find the standard deviation. **LO ❸**

SECTION 5.5

9. The histogram shows the December charges (in $) for 5000 customers in one marketing segment of a credit card company. (Negative values indicate customers who received more credits than charges during the month.)

a) Write a short description of this distribution (shape, centre, spread, unusual features).
b) Would you expect the mean or the median to be larger? Explain.
c) Which would be a more appropriate summary of the centre: the mean or the median? Explain. **LO ❷, ❸**

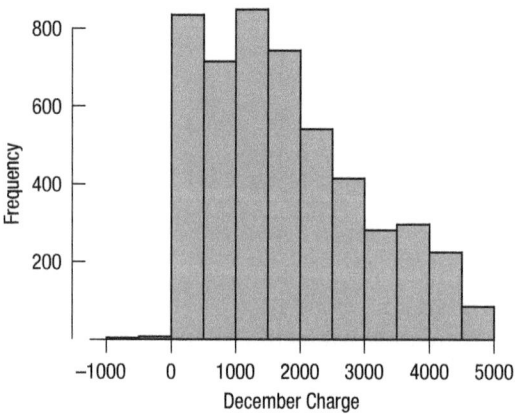

10. Adair Vineyard is a 10-acre vineyard in New Paltz, New York. The winery itself is housed in a 200-year-old historic Dutch barn, with the wine cellar on the first floor and the tasting room and gift shop on the second. Since the managers are considering an expansion of their relatively small establishment, they're curious about how their size compares to other vineyards. The histogram shows the sizes (in acres) of 36 wineries in upstate New York.

a) Write a short description of this distribution (shape, centre, spread, unusual features).
b) Would you expect the mean or the median to be larger? Explain.
c) Which would be a more appropriate summary of the centre: the mean or the median? Explain. **LO ❷, ❸**

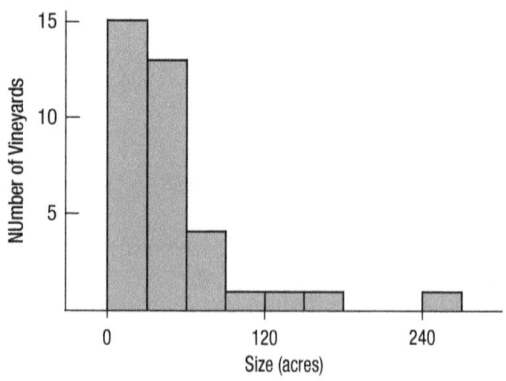

SECTION 5.6

11. The spending in dollars of 26,790 customers in one marketing segment of a credit card company, during June and July last year, is summarized in the table below:

	Mean	First Quartile	Median	Third Quartile	Standard Deviation
June	876	328	731	1658	986
July	793	387	798	1980	1298

If possible, calculate the mean, median, interquartile range, and standard deviation for the total spending of these customers for June plus July. State any assumptions you make. **LO ❷, ❸**

12. In order to get to campus, a student has to walk to the bus stop and then take a bus to the university. She monitors how much time this journey takes for 55 days. The time taken in minutes for each stage of her journey varies according to the information in the following table:

	Mean	Median	Interquartile Range	Standard Deviation
Walk	11	10	3	2
Bus	14	12	4	3

If possible, calculate the mean, median, interquartile range, and standard deviation of the total travel time. State any assumptions you make. **LO ❷, ❸**

SECTION 5.7

The table below gives the age distribution of the Canadian population in 2014:

	Male	Female
0 to 4 years	986,314	938,636
5 to 9 years	982,928	935,316
10 to 14 years	958,809	906,664
15 to 19 years	1,099,561	1,039,139
20 to 24 years	1,263,092	1,209,017
25 to 29 years	1,225,436	1,212,340
30 to 34 years	1,237,253	1,242,611
35 to 39 years	1,179,781	1,187,352
40 to 44 years	1,179,503	1,179,190
45 to 49 years	1,250,319	1,241,828
50 to 54 years	1,393,217	1,381,410
55 to 59 years	1,276,205	1,281,111
60 to 64 years	1,071,261	1,096,869
65 to 69 years	893,066	937,811
70 to 74 years	623,234	691,447
75 to 79 years	443,596	528,586
80 to 84 years	314,275	422,342
85 to 89 years	172,779	292,540
90 to 94 years	64,773	149,176
95 to 99 years	8,644	35,381
100 years and over	944	6,663

Source: From Annual Demographic Estimates: Canada, Provinces and Territories. Published by Statistics Canada, © 2014.

13. Calculate the average age of males in the Canadian population in 2014, assuming that the average (midpoint) age of people over 100 is 103. **LO ❷, ❸**

14. Calculate the average age of females in the Canadian population in 2014, assuming that the average (midpoint) age of people over 100 is 103. **LO ❷, ❸**

SECTION 5.8

15. For the data in Exercise 1:

a) Draw a boxplot using the quartiles from Exercise 7(b).
b) Does the boxplot nominate *any* outliers?
c) What age would be considered a high outlier? **LO ❹**

16. For the data in Exercise 2:

a) Draw a boxplot using the quartiles from Exercise 8(b).
b) Does the boxplot nominate any outliers?
c) What purchase amount would be considered a high outlier? **LO ❹**

17. Here are summary statistics for the sizes (in acres) of upstate New York vineyards from Exercise 10:

Variable	N	Mean	StDev	Minimum	Q1	Median	Q3	Maximum
Acres	36	46.50	47.76	6	18.50	33.50	55	250

a) From the summary statistics, would you describe this distribution as symmetric or skewed? Explain.
b) From the summary statistics, are there any outliers? Explain.
c) Using these summary statistics, sketch a boxplot. What additional information would you need to complete the boxplot? **LO ❹**

18. A survey of major universities asked what percentage of incoming students usually graduate "on time" in four years. Use the summary statistics given to answer these questions.

	% on Time
Count	48
Mean	68.35
Median	69.90
StdDev	10.20
Min	43.20
Max	87.40
Range	44.20
25th %tile	59.15
75th %tile	74.75

a) Would you describe this distribution as symmetric or skewed?
b) Are there any outliers? Explain.
c) Create a boxplot of these data. **LO ❹**

SECTION 5.9

19. Calculate the 10th and 80th percentiles of the ages of the customers in Exercise 1. Interpret the meaning of the 80th percentile. **LO ❸**

20. Calculate the 12th and 60th percentiles of the purchases of the customers in Exercise 2. Interpret the meaning of the 12th percentile. **LO ❸**

SECTION 5.10

21. The survey from Exercise 1 also asked the customers to say whether they were male or female. Here are the data:

Age	Sex	Age	Sex	Age	Sex	Age	Sex	Age	Sex
20	M	32	F	34	F	29	M	30	M
30	F	30	M	14	M	29	M	11	M
38	F	22	M	44	F	48	F	26	F
25	M	22	M	32	F	35	F	32	F
35	F	42	F	44	F	44	F	48	F

Construct boxplots to compare the ages of men and women and write a sentence summarizing what you find. **LO ❷, ❸**

22. The store manager from Exercise 2 collected data on purchases from weekdays and weekends. Here are some summary statistics (rounded to the nearest dollar):

Weekdays $n = 230$

Min = 4, Q1 = 28, Median = 40, Q3 = 68, Max = 95

Weekend $n = 150$

Min = 10, Q1 = 35, Median = 55, Q3 = 70, Max = 100

From these statistics, construct side-by-side boxplots and write a sentence comparing the two distributions. **LO ❷, ❸**

SECTION 5.11

23. The five-number summary for the total revenue (in $millions) of the top 100 movies of 2012 looks like this:

Min	Q1	Med	Q3	Max
28.8	44.9	64.1	123.0	623.4

Are there any outliers in these data? How can you tell? What might your next steps in the analysis be?

24. The five-number summary for the ages of 100 respondents to a survey on cell phone use looks like this:

Min	Q1	Med	Q3	Max
13	24	38	49	256

Are there any outliers in these data? How can you tell? What might your next steps in the analysis be?

25. Here are boxplots of the weekly sales over a two-year period for a regional food store for two locations. Location #1 is a metropolitan area that is known to be residential and where shoppers walk to the store. Location #2 is a suburban area where shoppers drive to the store. Assume that the two regions have similar populations and that the two stores are similar in square footage. Write a brief report discussing what these data show. **LO ❺**

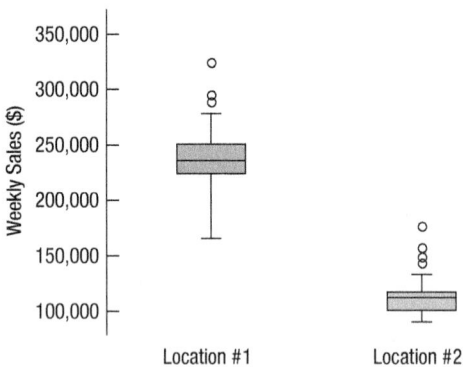

26. Recall the distributions of the weekly sales for the regional stores in Exercise 25. Following are boxplots of weekly sales for this same food store chain for stores of similar size and location in two different provinces: Alberta (AB) and Saskatchewan (SK). Compare the distribution of sales for the two provinces and describe it in a report. **LO ❺**

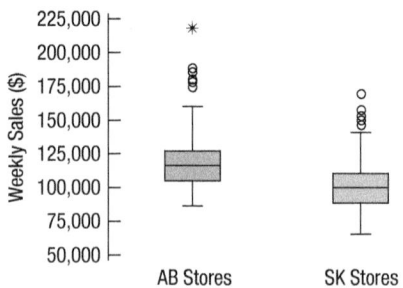

SECTION 5.12

27. Using the ages from Exercise 1:

a) Standardize the minimum and maximum ages using the mean from Exercise 5(b) and the standard deviation from Exercise 7(c).
b) Which has the more extreme z-score: the min or the max?
c) How old would someone with a z-score of 3 be? **LO ❻**

28. Using the purchases from Exercise 2:

a) Standardize the minimum and maximum purchase using the mean from Exercise 6(b) and the standard deviation from Exercise 8(d).
b) Which has the more extreme z-score: the min or the max?
c) How large would a purchase with a z-score of 3.5 be? **LO ❻**

SECTION 5.13

The table below gives the percentage of the Ontario and British Columbia population aged 65 years and older according to the Canadian Census from 1956 to 2006:

	ON	BC
1956	8.4	10.8
1961	8.1	10.2
1966	8.2	9.5
1971	8.4	9.4
1976	8.9	9.8
1981	10.1	10.9
1986	10.9	12.1
1991	11.7	12.9
1996	12.4	12.8
2001	12.9	13.6
2006	13.6	14.6

29. Draw a time series plot of the percentage of the Ontario population aged 65 years and older from 1956 to 2006. Describe the trends that emerge. **LO ❼**

30. Draw a time series plot of the percentage of the British Columbia population aged 65 years and older from 1956 to 2006. Describe the trends that emerge. **LO ❼**

SECTION 5.14

31. When analyzing data on the number of employees in small companies in one town, a researcher took square roots of the counts. Some of the resulting values, which are reasonably symmetric, were:

4, 4, 6, 7, 7, 8, 10

What were the original values, and how are they distributed? **LO ❶**

32. You wish to explain to your boss what effect taking the base-10 logarithm of the salary values in the company's database will have on the data. As a simple example, you compare a salary of $10,000 earned by a part-time shipping clerk, a salary of $100,000 earned by a manager, and the CEO's $1,000,000 compensation package. Why might the average of these values be a misleading summary? What would the logarithms of these three values be? **LO ❶**

CHAPTER EXERCISES

33. Statistics in business, part 1. Find a histogram that shows the distribution of a variable as it appeared in a business publication (e.g., *The Wall Street Journal, National Post, The Economist,* etc.).

a) Does the article identify the Five W's?
b) Discuss whether the display is appropriate for the data.
c) Discuss what the display reveals about the variable and its distribution.

d) Does the article accurately describe and interpret the data? Explain. **LO ❶**

34. Statistics in business, part 2. Find a box plot or stem & leaf diagram that shows the distribution of a quantitative variable as it appeared in a business publication (e.g., *The Wall Street Journal, The Globe and Mail, The Economist,* etc.).

a) Does the article identify the Five W's?

b) Discuss whether the display is appropriate for the data.

c) Discuss what the display reveals about the variable and its distribution.

d) Does the article accurately describe and interpret the data? Explain. **LO ❶, ❹**

35. Gas prices, part 1. The histogram below shows the price of regular gas at 17 gas stations on a specific day in 2016. Describe the shape of the distribution and its centre and spread. **LO ❶, ❷, ❸**

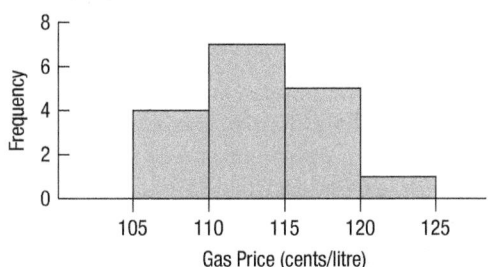

Gas Price (cents/litre)

❶ 36. Mutual funds, part 1. The histogram that follows displays the 12-month returns (in percent) for a collection of mutual funds in 2017. Give a short summary of this distribution (shape, centre, spread, unusual features). **LO ❶, ❷, ❸**

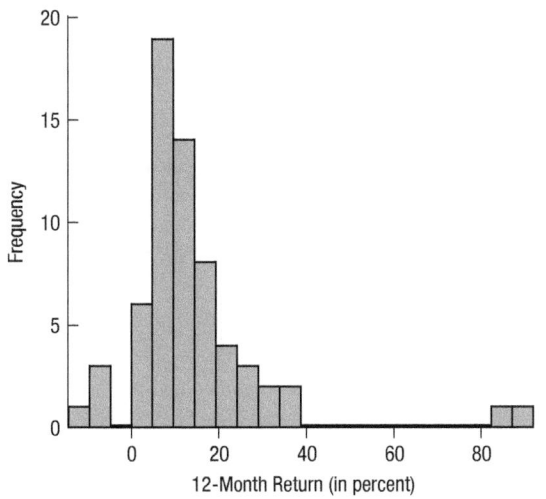

12-Month Return (in percent)

❶ 37. Car discounts, part 1. A researcher, interested in studying gender differences in negotiations, collects data on the prices that men and women pay for new cars. Here is a histogram of the discounts (the amount in $ below the list price) that men and women received at one car dealership for the last 100 transactions (54 men and 46 women). Give a short summary of this distribution (shape, centre, spread, unusual features). What do you think might account for this particular shape? **LO ❶, ❷, ❸**

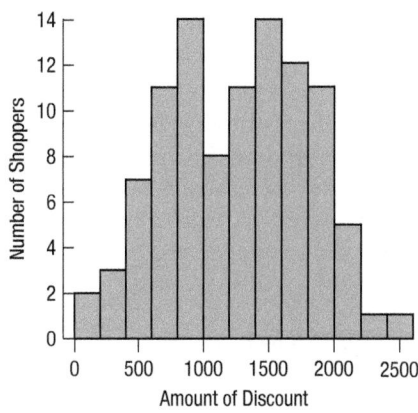

Amount of Discount

38. Mutual funds, part 2. Use the data set in Exercise 36 to answer the following questions:

a) Find the five-number summary for these data.

b) Find appropriate measures of centre and spread for these data.

c) Create a boxplot for these data.

d) What can you see, if anything, in the histogram that isn't clear in the boxplot? **LO ❶, ❷, ❸, ❹**

39. Car discounts, part 2. Use the data set in Exercise 37 to answer the following questions:

a) Find the five-number summary for these data.

b) Create a boxplot for these data.

c) What can you see, if anything, in the histogram of Exercise 37 that isn't clear in the boxplot? **LO ❶, ❷, ❸, ❹**

40. Hockey, part 1. During his 20 seasons in the National Hockey League, from 1979 to 1998, Wayne Gretzky scored 50% more points than anyone else who ever played professional hockey. He accomplished this amazing feat while playing in 280 fewer games than Gordie Howe, the previous record holder. Here are the numbers of games Gretzky played during each season:

79, 80, 80, 80, 74, 80, 80, 79, 64, 78, 73, 78, 74, 45, 81, 48, 80, 82, 82, 70

a) Create a stem-and-leaf display.

b) Sketch a boxplot.

c) Briefly describe this distribution.

d) What unusual features do you see in this distribution? What might explain this? **LO ❶, ❷, ❸, ❹**

41. Baseball, part 1. In his 16-year career as a player in Major League Baseball, Mark McGwire hit 583 home runs, placing him eighth on the all-time home-run list (as of 2008). Here are the numbers of home runs that McGwire hit for each year from 1986 through 2001:

3, 49, 32, 33, 39, 22, 42, 9, 9, 39, 52, 58, 70, 65, 32, 29

a) Create a stem-and-leaf display.

b) Sketch a boxplot.

c) Briefly describe this distribution.

d) What unusual features do you see in this distribution? What might explain this? **LO ❶, ❷, ❸, ❹**

42. **Hockey, part 2.** Look once more at data of hockey games played each season by Wayne Gretzky, seen in Exercise 40.

a) Would you use the mean or the median to summarize the centre of this distribution? Why?

b) Without actually finding the mean, would you expect it to be lower or higher than the median? Explain.

c) A student was asked to make a histogram of the data in Exercise 40 and produced the following. Comment. **LO ❶, ❷**

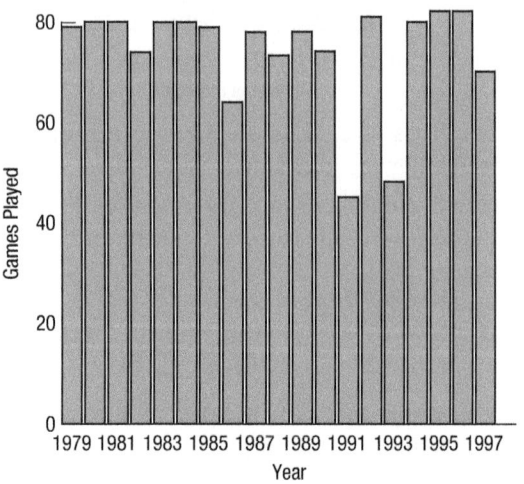

43. **Baseball, part 2.** Look once more at data of home runs hit by Mark McGwire during his 16-year career, as seen in Exercise 41.

a) Would you use the mean or the median to summarize the centre of this distribution? Why?

b) Find the median.

c) Without actually finding the mean, would you expect it to be lower or higher than the median? Explain.

d) A student was asked to make a histogram of the data in Exercise 41 and produced the following. Comment. **LO ❶, ❷, ❹**

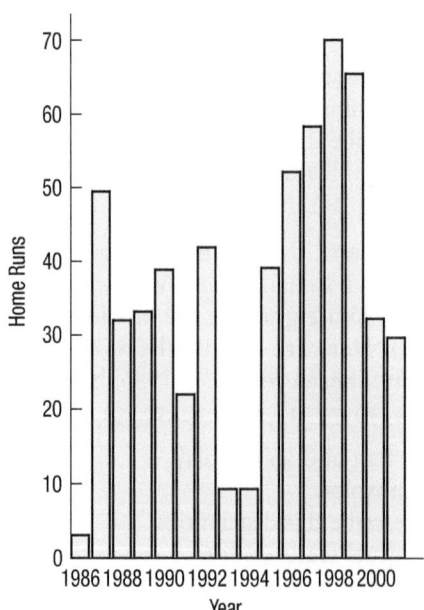

44. **Pizza prices, part 1.** The weekly prices of one brand of frozen pizza over a three-year period in Vancouver are provided in the data file. Use the price data to answer the following questions:

a) Find the five-number summary for these data.

b) Find the range and IQR for these data.

c) Create a boxplot for these data.

d) Describe this distribution.

e) Describe any unusual observations. **LO ❷, ❸, ❹, ❺**

45. **Pizza prices, part 2.** The weekly prices of one brand of frozen pizza over a three-year period in Montreal are provided in the data file. Use the price data to answer the following questions:

a) Find the five-number summary for these data.

b) Find the range and IQR for these data.

c) Create a boxplot for these data.

d) Describe the shape (centre and spread) of this distribution.

e) Describe any unusual observations. **LO ❷, ❸, ❹, ❺**

46. **Earnings of Canadians.** Statistics Canada's National Housing Survey shows that, in 2013, median individual income was $27,600, 10% of individuals made more than $80,400, and the top 1% got more than $191,100. Why does Statistics Canada report the median earnings instead of the mean or mode of the earnings? What would be the appropriate measure for the spread of this earnings distribution? **LO ❷, ❸**

47. **Canadian Consumer Price Index.** Calculate the median, quartiles, mean, standard deviation, and coefficient of variation of the Consumer Price Indexes of Canadian provinces in 2013, from the data in the following table. Comment on whether the mean or median is higher. Is any province an outlier? **LO ❷, ❸, ❺**

Province	All-Items CPI
Newfoundland and Labrador	126
Prince Edward Island	128
Nova Scotia	126.6
New Brunswick	123
Quebec	121.7
Ontario	123
Manitoba	123
Saskatchewan	125.7
Alberta	128.9
British Columbia	117.7

Source: Statistics Canada, CANISM Table 326-0021: Consumer Price Index, Annual (2002=100), Copyright © 2013. Reproduced and distributed on an "as is" basis with the permission of Statistics Canada.

48. **Canadian weekly earnings.** Canadian average weekly earnings (in $) classified by province and territory are given in the table on the next page for 2013.

a) Calculate the median earnings.

b) Calculate the interquartile range.

c) Are any of the provinces or territories outliers with respect to average weekly earnings in 2013? **LO ❷, ❸, ❺, ❻**

Province/Territory	Weekly Earnings ($)
Newfoundland and Labrador	949.33
Prince Edward Island	753.58
Nova Scotia	798.13
New Brunswick	807.9
Quebec	830.44
Ontario	920.12
Manitoba	833.14
Saskatchewan	945.5
Alberta	1,108.01
British Columbia	873.14
Yukon	989.03
Northwest Territories	1,303.26
Nunavut	1,033.75

Source: Based on Statistics Canada. (2014). CANSIM Table 281-0044. Earnings, average weekly, including overtime

49. Startup. A company is planning to build a new golf course. For marketing purposes, the company would like to be able to advertise the new course as one of the more difficult courses in Ontario. One measure of the difficulty of a golf course is its length: the total distance (in metres) from tee to hole for all 18 holes. Here are the histogram and summary statistics for the lengths of all the golf courses in Ontario:

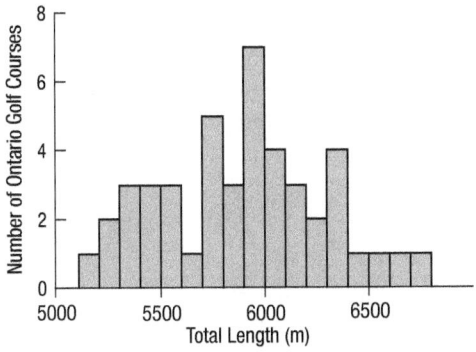

Count	45
Mean	5892.91 m
StdDev	386.59 m
Min	5185 m
Q1	5585.75 in
Median	5928 m
Q3	6131m
Max	6796 m

a) What is the range of these lengths?

b) Between what lengths do the central 50% of these courses lie?

c) What summary statistics would you use to describe these data?

d) Write a brief description of these data (shape, centre, and spread).

e) How long would the new golf course need to be in order to advertise it as being in the 10% longest for Ontario? **LO ❷, ❸**

50. Real estate, part 1. A real estate agent has surveyed houses in 20 nearby postal codes in an attempt to put together a comparison for a new property she'd like to put on the market. She knows that the size of the living area of a house is a strong factor in the price, and she'd like to market this house as being one of the biggest in the area. Here are a histogram and summary statistics for the sizes of all the houses in the area:

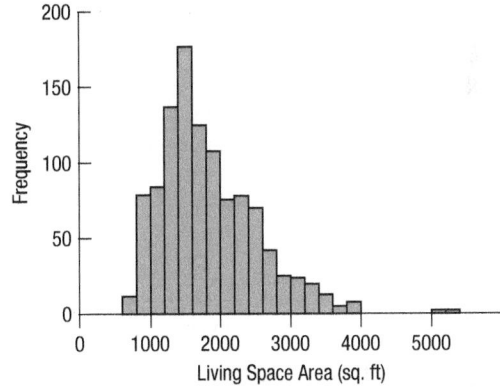

Count	1057
Mean	1819.498 sq. ft
StdDev	662.9414
Min	672
Q1	1342
Median	1675
Q3	2223
Max	5228

a) What is the range of these sizes?

b) Between what sizes do the central 50% of these houses lie?

c) What summary statistics would you use to describe these data?

d) Write a brief description of these data (shape, centre, and spread).

e) How large would the living area of the new house need to be in order to advertise it as being among the 10% largest in the area? **LO ❷, ❸**

⊤ 51. Food sales. Sales (in $) for one week were collected for 18 stores in a food store chain in Atlantic Canada and are provided in the data file. The stores and the towns in which the chain is located vary in size.

a) Make a suitable display of the sales from the data provided.

b) Summarize the central value for sales for this week with a median and mean. Why do they differ?

c) Given what you know about the distribution, which of these measures does the better job of summarizing the stores' sales? Why?

d) Summarize the spread of the sales distribution with a standard deviation and with an IQR.

e) Given what you know about the distribution, which of these measures does the better job of summarizing the spread of the stores' sales? Why?

f) If we were to remove the outliers from the data, how would you expect the mean, median, standard deviation, and IQR to change? LO ❶, ❷, ❸, ❹, ❺

⊕ 52. Insurance profits. Life insurance companies don't know whether a policy is profitable until the policy matures (expires). To see how one company has performed recently, an analyst looked at mature policies and investigated the net profit to the company (in $), which are included in the data file.

a) Make a suitable display of the profits from the data provided.

b) Summarize the central value for the profits with a median and mean. Why do they differ?

c) Given what you know about the distribution, which of these measures might do a better job of summarizing the company's profits? Why?

d) Summarize the spread of the profit distribution with a standard deviation and with an IQR.

e) Given what you know about the distribution, which of these measures might do a better job of summarizing the spread in the company's profits? Why?

f) If we were to remove the outliers from the data, how would you expect the mean, median, standard deviation, and IQR to change? LO ❶, ❷, ❸, ❹, ❺

⊕ 53. International unemployment. The data set provided contains 2012 (second quarter) unemployment rates for 34 developed countries (www.oecd.org). Produce an appropriate graphical display and briefly describe the distribution of unemployment rates. Report and comment on any outliers you may see. LO ❶, ❷, ❸, ❹, ❺

54. Gas prices, part 2. Here are boxplots of weekly gas prices at a service station in Alberta (in $/L):

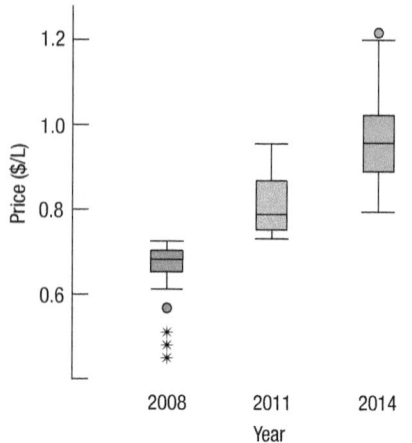

a) Compare the distribution of prices over the three years.

b) In which year were the prices least stable (most volatile)? Explain. LO ❷, ❸, ❹, ❺

55. Fuel economy. A new hybrid car uses 3.8 litres of gasoline per 100 kilometres for city driving, according to websites advertising the car. Of course, not all of these cars are going to get the same fuel economy in all cities with all drivers. Would you expect the interquartile range (IQR) to be approximately 0.01, 1.0, or 5.0 L/100 km? Give a reason for your answer. Given your estimate of the IQR, what is your estimate of a range of reasonable values for the variance? Be sure to state the units of measurement, and give a reason for your answer. LO ❷, ❸, ❹, ❺

56. Wine prices. The boxplots display case prices (in dollars) of wines produced by vineyards along three of the Finger Lakes in upstate New York:

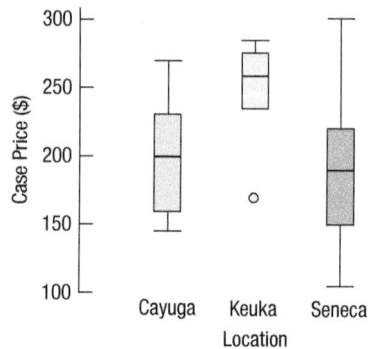

a) Which lake region produces the most expensive wine?

b) Which lake region produces the cheapest wine?

c) In which region are the wines generally more expensive?

d) Write a few sentences describing these prices. LO ❷, ❸, ❹, ❺

57. Ozone. Ozone levels (in parts per billion, ppb) were recorded monthly at three different sites. Here are boxplots of the data for each month (over 46 years), lined up in order (January = 1):

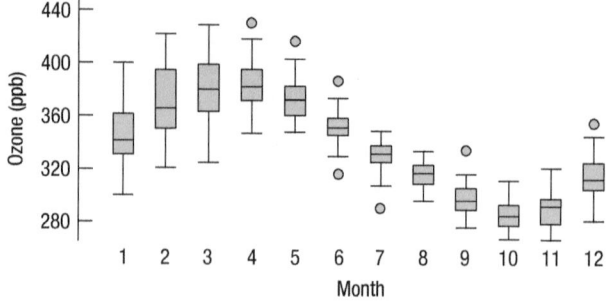

a) In what month was the highest ozone level ever recorded?

b) Which month has the largest IQR?

c) Which month has the smallest range?

d) Write a brief comparison of the ozone levels in January and June.

e) Write a report on the annual patterns you see in the ozone levels. **LO ❷, ❸**

58. Test scores, part 1. Three Statistics classes all took the same test. Here are histograms of the scores for each class:

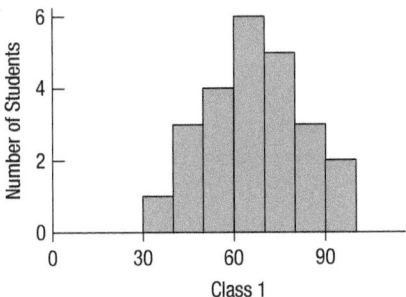

Class 1

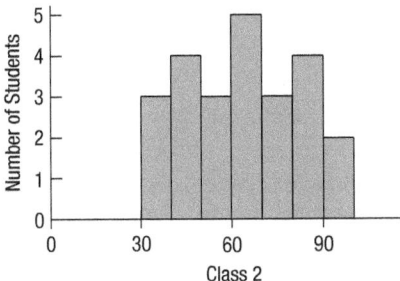

Class 2

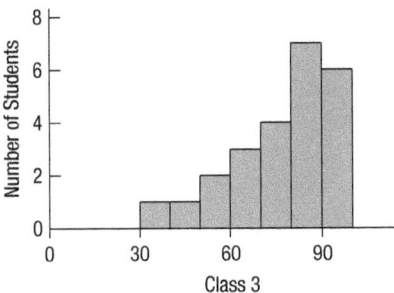

Class 3

a) Which class had the highest mean score?
b) Which class had the highest median score?
c) For which class are the mean and median most different? Which is higher? Why?
d) Which class had the smallest standard deviation?
e) Which class had the smallest IQR? **LO ❷, ❸**

59. Test scores, part 2. Look again at the histograms of test scores for the three Statistics classes in Exercise 58.

a) Overall, which class do you think performed better on the test? Why?
b) How would you describe the shape of each distribution? **LO ❷, ❸**

Ⓣ 60. Quality control. Engineers at a computer production plant tested two methods for accuracy in drilling holes into a PC board. They tested how fast they could set the drilling machine by running 10 boards at each of two different speeds. To assess the results, they measured the distance (in centimetres) from the centre of a target on the board to the centre of the hole. The data and summary statistics are shown in the table:

	Fast	Slow
	0.000102	0.000098
	0.000102	0.000096
	0.000100	0.000097
	0.000102	0.000095
	0.000101	0.000094
	0.000103	0.000098
	0.000104	0.000096
	0.000102	0.975600
	0.000102	0.000097
	0.000100	0.000096
Mean	0.000102	0.097647
StdDev	0.000001	0.308481

Write a report summarizing the findings of the experiment. Include appropriate visual and written displays of the distributions, and make a recommendation to the engineers about the accuracy of the methods. **LO ❷, ❸, ❹, ❺**

Ⓣ 61. Fire sale. A real estate agent notices that houses with fireplaces often fetch a premium in the market and wants to assess the difference in sales price of 60 recently sold homes. The data and summary are shown in the table:

No Fireplace ($)	Fireplace ($)
142,212	134,865
206,512	118,007
50,709	138,297
108,794	129,470
68,353	309,808
123,266	157,946
80,248	173,723
135,708	140,510
122,221	151,917
128,440	235,105,000
221,925	259,999
65,325	211,517
87,588	102,068
88,207	115,659
148,246	145,583
205,073	116,289
185,323	238,792
71,904	310,696
199,684	139,079
81,762	109,578
45,004	89,893

(continued)

(continued)

	No Fireplace ($)	Fireplace ($)
	62,105	132,311
	79,893	131,411
	88,770	158,863
	115,312	130,490
	118,952	178,767
		82,556
		122,221
		84,291
		206,512
		105,363
		103,508
		157,513
		103,861
Mean	116,597.54	7,061,657.74
Median	112,053	136,581

Write a report summarizing the findings of the investigation. Include appropriate visual and verbal displays of the distributions, and make a recommendation to the agent about the average premium that a fireplace is worth in this market. **LO ❶, ❷, ❸, ❹, ❺**

62. Houses for sale. Each house listed on the multiple listing service (MLS) is assigned a sequential ID number. A recently hired real estate agent decided to examine the MLS numbers in a recent random sample of homes for sale by one real estate agency in nearby towns. To begin the analysis, the agent produced the following histogram of ID numbers:

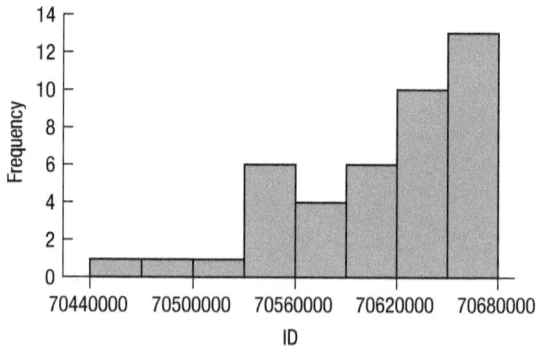

a) What might account for the distribution seen in the histogram?
b) What advice might you give the analyst about the appropriateness of this display? **LO ❶**

63. Car discounts, part 3. The discounts negotiated by the car buyers in Exercise 37 are classified by whether the buyer was male (code = 0) or female (code = 1). Compare the discounts of men and of women using an appropriate display and write a brief summary of the differences. **LO ❶, ❷, ❸, ❹**

Ⓣ 64. Hurricanes, part 1. Buying insurance for property loss from hurricanes has become increasingly difficult since Hurricane Katrina caused record property damage and loss. Many companies have refused to renew policies or write new ones. The data set provided contains the total number of hurricanes by every full decade from 1851 to 2000 (from the U.S. National Hurricane Center). Some scientists claim that the number of hurricanes has increased in recent years.

a) Create a histogram of these data.
b) Describe the distribution.
c) Create a time series plot of these data.
d) Discuss the time series plot. Does this graph support the claim of these scientists, at least up to the year 2000? **LO ❶, ❼**

Ⓣ 65. Hurricanes, part 2. Using the hurricanes data set, examine the number of major hurricanes (Category 3, 4, or 5) by every full decade from 1851 to 2000.

a) Create a histogram of these data.
b) Describe the distribution.
c) Create a time series plot of these data.
d) Discuss the time series plot. Does this graph support the scientists' claim that the number of major hurricanes has been increasing (at least up to the year 2000)? **LO ❶, ❼**

66. Productivity study, part 1. A national productivity research centre releases information on the efficiency of workers. In a recent report, it included the following graph showing a rapid rise in productivity. What questions do you have about this? **LO ❼**

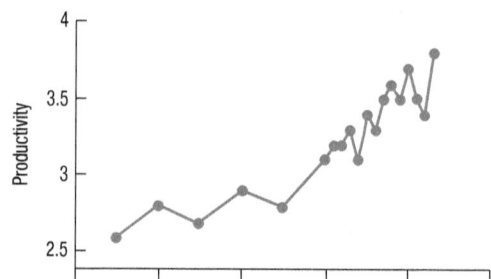

67. Productivity study, part 2. A second report by the research centre analyzed the relationship between productivity and wages. Comment on the graph it used. **LO ❼**

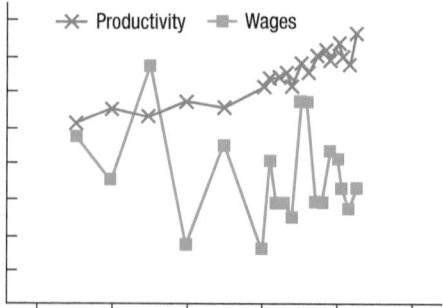

68. Assets, part 1. Here is a histogram of the assets (in millions of dollars) of 79 companies chosen from the *Forbes* list of the top U.S. corporations:

a) What aspect of this distribution makes it difficult to summarize, or to discuss, centre and spread?
b) What would you suggest doing with these data if we want to understand them better? **LO ❶**

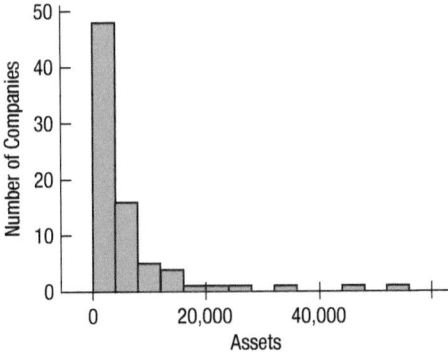

69. Assets, part 2. Here are the same data you saw in Exercise 68 after re-expressions as the square root of assets and the logarithm of assets:

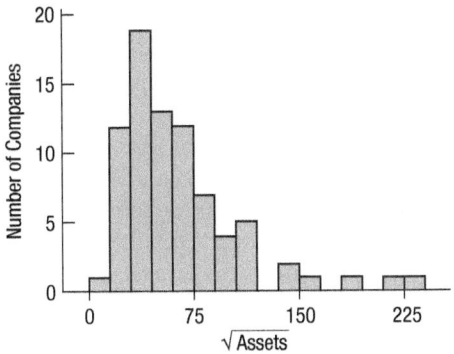

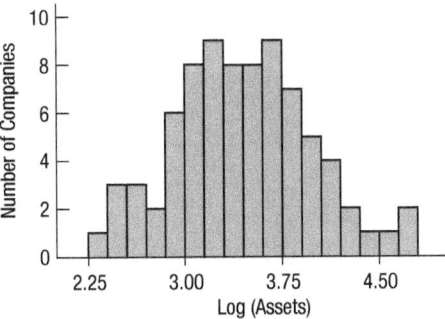

a) Which re-expression do you prefer? Why?
b) In the square root re-expression, what does the value 50 actually indicate about the companies' assets? **LO ❶**

70. Real estate, part 2. The 1057 houses described in Exercise 50 have a mean price of $167,900, with a standard deviation of $77,158. The mean living area is 1819 square feet, with a standard deviation of 663 square feet. Which is more unusual: a house in that market that sells for $400,000, or a house that has 4000 square feet of living area? Explain.

71. World Bank. The World Bank, through its Doing Business project (www.doingbusiness.org), ranks nearly 200 economies on the ease of doing business. One of its rankings measures the ease of starting a business and is made up (in part) of the following variables: number of required startup procedures, average startup time (in days), and average startup cost (in % of per capita income). The following table gives the mean and standard deviations of these variables for 95 economies:

	Procedures (no.)	Time (days)	Cost (%)
Mean	7.9	27.9	14.2
SD	2.9	19.6	12.9

Here are the data for three countries:

	Procedures (no.)	Time	Cost
Spain	10	47	15.1
Guatemala	11	26	47.3
Fiji	8	46	25.3

a) Use z-scores to compare the three measures.
b) Interpret the meaning of the lowest and highest z-scores. **LO ❻**

72. GDP per capita. The GDP per capita for 2007 in selected eurozone countries is given in the table. Calculate the mean, median, and standard deviation of this data. **LO ❶, ❷**

Austria	29,188
Cyprus	16,133
France	26,326
Germany	27,215
Greece	16,433
Ireland	41,662
Luxembourg	61,609
Malta	10,842
Portugal	12,413
Slovenia	12,983

73. Unemployment rate, 2013. The histogram shows the monthly U.S. unemployment rate from January 2003 to January 2013 (data.bls.gov/timeseries/LNS14000000):

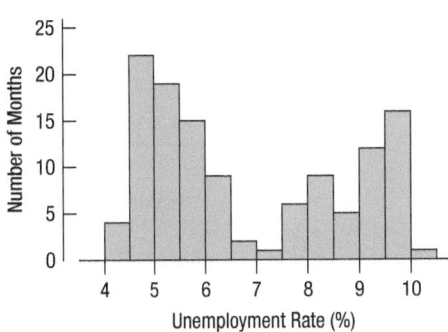

Here is the time series plot for the same data:

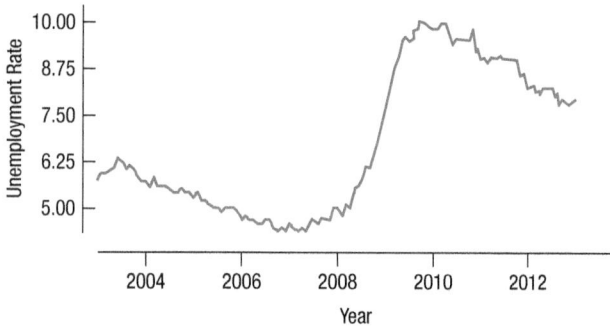

a) What features of the data can you see in the histogram that aren't clear in the time series plot?
b) What features of the data can you see in the time series plot that aren't clear in the histogram?
c) Which graphical display seems the more appropriate for these data? Explain.
d) Write a brief description of unemployment rates over this time period in the United States. (*Source:* From Time Series Plot from Labor Force Statistics from the Current Population Survey, U S Bureau of Labor Statistics.)

74. Mutual fund performance. The following histogram displays the monthly returns for a group of mutual funds considered aggressive (or high-growth) over a period of 22 years, from 1975 to 1997:

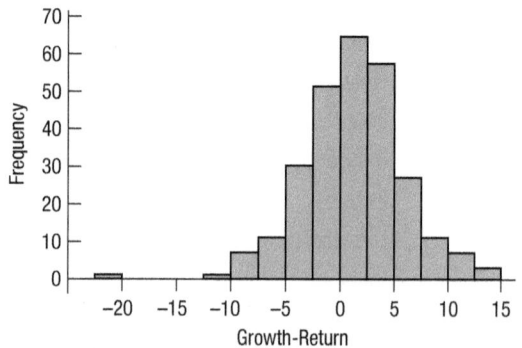

Here is the time series plot for the same data:

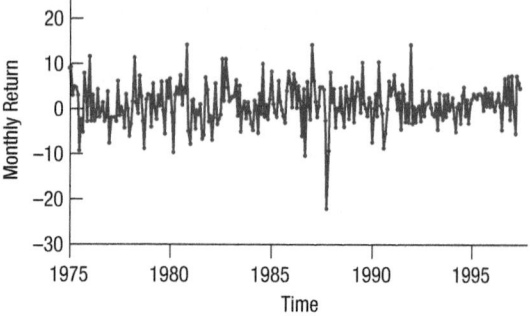

a) What features of the data can you see in the histogram that aren't clear from the time series plot?
b) What features of the data can you see in the time series plot that aren't clear in the histogram?

c) Which graphical display seems more appropriate for these data? Explain.
d) Write a brief description of monthly mutual fund returns over this time period. **LO ❶, ❼**

75. Gas prices, part 3. The actual prices at the 17 gas stations referred to in Exercise 35 were as follows:

Gas Prices (cents/litre)			
108.9	110.1	118.9	114.9
109.4	110.1	118.9	114.7
109.8	110.1	118.9	
109.8	113.7	118.6	
110.1	124.9	118.4	

Construct a stem-and-leaf diagram of this data and point out any unusual features that are not evident from the histogram in Exercise 35. **LO ❶**

ⓣ 76. Food consumption. FAOSTAT, the Food and Agriculture Organization of the United Nations, collects information on the production and consumption of more than 200 food and agricultural products for 200 countries around the world. The following table lists meat consumption (per capita in kilograms per year) and alcohol consumption (per capita in gallons per year) for selected countries. The United States leads in meat consumption with 267.30 kilograms, while Ireland is the largest alcohol consumer at 55.80 gallons.

Calculate the z-scores for meat and alcohol consumption in Ireland and the United States, and interpret the meaning of the scores. **LO ❷, ❸, ❻**

Country	Alcohol	Meat	Country	Alcohol	Meat
Australia	29.56	242.22	Luxembourg	34.32	197.34
Austria	40.46	242.22	Mexico	13.52	126.50
Belgium	34.32	197.34	Netherlands	23.87	201.08
Canada	26.62	219.56	New Zealand	25.22	228.58
Czech Republic	43.81	166.98	Norway	17.58	129.80
Denmark	40.59	256.96	Poland	20.70	155.10
Finland	25.01	146.08	Portugal	33.02	194.92
France	24.88	225.28	Slovakia	26.49	121.88
Germany	37.44	182.82	South Korea	17.60	93.06
Greece	17.68	201.30	Spain	28.05	259.82
Hungary	29.25	179.52	Sweden	20.07	155.32
Iceland	15.94	178.20	Switzerland	25.32	159.72
Ireland	55.80	194.26	Turkey	3.28	42.68
Italy	21.68	200.64	United Kingdom	30.32	171.16
Japan	14.59	93.28	United States	26.36	267.30

77. Investments. Four people each invest $1000, with each person garnering a different rate of return.

a) The first three people invest $1000 each for one year in three different investments. The first person gets a return of 16% and the other two get 1% and 27%, respectively. What is the average return on the three investments?

b) The fourth investor invests $1000 for three years. At the end of each year he reinvests his return plus capital for the next year. He makes 16%, 1%, and 27% in the three years, respectively. What is his average rate of return over the three years? **LO ❷**

78. Canadian bond yields and ethics. Alfredo Wagar, an analyst, produced the graph below showing how Canadian government bond yields depend on the amount of time left until the maturity of the bond. He recommends "buying bonds with three-month, six-month, and 20-year maturities, since their yields are above the general trend."

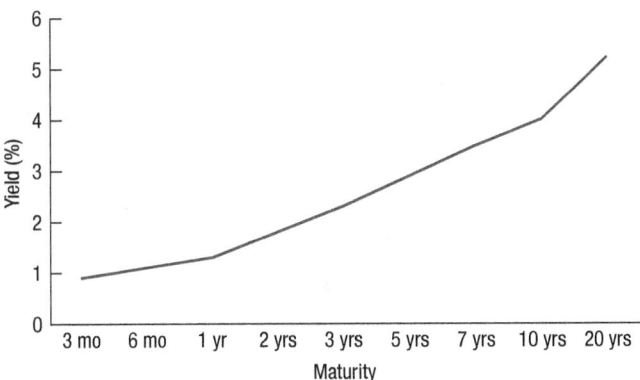

a) Comment on the ethics of Alfredo's recommendation as it relates to the ASA Ethical Guidelines in Appendix C.

b) Draw a better graph of the data and state the improvement(s) you have made.

c) Using your graph, do you agree with Alfredo's recommendation? **LO ❼**

79. Copper production, part 1. Production of copper from a mine in Quebec increased by 4%, 7%, and 21% in the last three years, respectively. What is the average rate of increase over those three years? **LO ❷**

80. Copper production, part 2. Production of copper from a mine in Quebec increased by 4% per year during the five years 2002-2006, by 7% per year during the three years 2007-2010, and by 21% per year during the 8 years 2010-2017. What is the average rate of increase per year during the 16 years 2002-2017? **LO ❷**

81. GIC rates. A bank offers a guaranteed investment certificate (GIC) in which the interest rate is 0.5% in the first year, 1.2% in the second year, and 2.3% in the third year. Investors can withdraw their money at any time, but the increasing interest rate provides an incentive to keep the money invested. What is the average rate of interest over the three years? **LO ❷**

82. Water use in Canadian office buildings, part 1. The Real Property Association of Canada surveyed 82 office buildings as to their water usage and obtained the following results in terms of the number of litres of water used per square foot of office space per year (L/ft^2/yr) normalized for type of building:

Water Usage (L/ft^2/yr)	Number of Buildings	Water Usage (L/ft^2/yr)	Number of Buildings
0-19	1	100-119	1
20-39	11	120-139	8
40-59	11	140-159	2
60-79	22	160-179	2
80-99	14	180-199	0
		>200	10

Source: Based on Water Benchmarking Pilot Report: Performance of the Canadian Office Sector.

a) Taking into account the number of buildings surveyed, draw a histogram of this data. Identify the mode of the histogram.

b) Using the midpoint of each range, and assuming that the average water use of buildings over 200 L/ft^2/yr is 300 L/ft^2/yr, estimate the mean and the standard deviation of the water usage of the office buildings surveyed.

c) Again, using the midpoint of each range, calculate the quartiles and median of this data. Identify how many buildings are outliers. **LO ❶, ❷, ❸, ❺**

83. Water use in Canadian office buildings, part 2. The Real Property Association of Canada surveyed 82 office buildings as to their water usage and graphed the number of litres of water used per square foot of office space per year (L/ft^2/yr) for each building (actual data, not normalized for type of building).

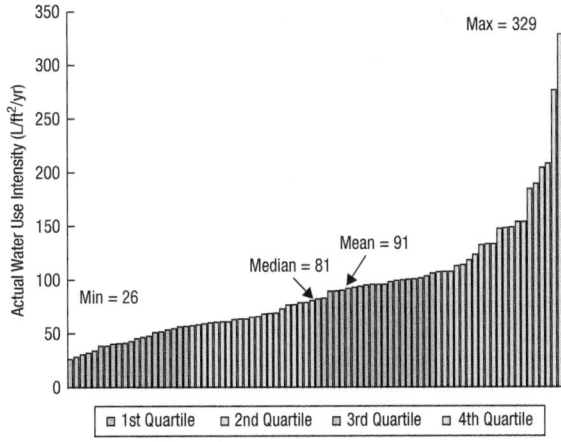

Source: From "Analysis and Results" in Water Benchmarking Pilot Report: Performance of the Canadian Office Sector. Copyright © 2012 by Real Property Association of Canada. Used by permission of Real Property Association of Canada.

a) Construct a histogram of this data and identify the mode of the histogram.

b) What is implied by the fact that the median given on the diagram is lower than the mean? How does this correspond to features in your histogram?

c) By reading the numbers off the vertical axis, estimate the quartiles and identify how many buildings are outliers. **LO ❶, ❷, ❸, ❺**

84. Gender gap. Each year, the World Economic Forum produces a Global Gender Gap Index which measures the differences between men and women with regard to four factors: (i) health and survival, (ii) educational attainment, (iii) economic participation and opportunity, and (iv) political empowerment. A higher score implies more gender equality. The results for the top 20 ranked countries for 2014 are as follows:

Iceland	0.8594	Switzerland	0.7798
Finland	0.8453	Germany	0.778
Norway	0.8374	New Zealand	0.7772
Sweden	0.8165	Netherlands	0.773
Denmark	0.8025	Latvia	0.7691
Nicaragua	0.7894	France	0.7588
Rwanda	0.7854	Burundi	0.7565
Ireland	0.785	South Africa	0.7527
Philippines	0.7814	Canada	0.7464
Belgium	0.7809	United States	0.7463

a) Draw a histogram of these results, using endpoints of 0.74 and 0.86, and identify the mode.
b) Calculate the mean and median of the distribution.
c) Calculate the z-scores for Canada and Finland.
d) What do your answers to (a), (b), and (c) say about the symmetry of the distribution? **LO ❶, ❷, ❻**

85. Retail resource usage. A major Canadian retailer with stores only in large cities includes food items in some stores but not in others. Selling food requires refrigeration equipment, which considerably increases the electricity bill. It also increases water usage for washing fresh food. The retailer is investigating ways of reducing water and electricity usage, to reduce both operating costs and its environmental footprint. It wants to identify stores that have particularly low water and electricity usage as examples of what other stores might achieve and obtains two histograms:

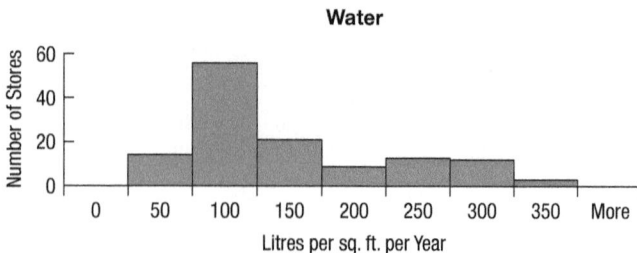

Water

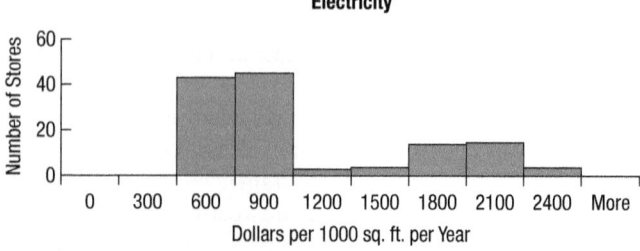

Electricity

The mean and standard deviations are:

	Mean	Standard Deviation
Water (litres per sq. ft. per year)	124.37	79.38
Electricity (dollars per 1000 sq. ft. per year)	956.78	565.66

a) Using z-scores, compare the following stores:

	Water (litres per sq. ft. per year)	Electricity (dollars per 1000 sq. ft. per year)
Mississauga, ON	253.78	1265.56
Burnaby, BC	156.65	2157.54

b) Describe the shapes of the histograms and the format in which they are drawn. What might the shapes imply? What should be the next step in analyzing this data? (You are not asked to perform this next step, just to say what it is.)
c) In order to select stores that have low water and electricity usage as an example to other stores, the company instructs its statisticians to select stores toward the left end of the two histograms. Comment on the ethics of this instruction using the ethical guidelines in Appendix C. **LO ❶, ❷, ❸, ❻**

86. Canadian Call Centre Wait Times. We are experiencing longer than "usual" wait times. I got this message on 75% (i.e., 24) of 32 calls for customer service. For simplicity assume the maximum wait time is 11 minutes and use 11 bins in your histograms.

a) Suppose "usual" means the mode of the wait time distribution. If possible draw a histogram where 75% of the wait times are above the mode.
b) Suppose "usual" means the median of the wait time distribution. If possible draw a histogram where 75% of the wait times are above the median.
c) Suppose "usual" means the mean of the wait time distribution. If possible draw a histogram where 75% of the wait times are above the mean. **LO ❶, ❷**

87. Is Your Driving Ability Better than that of an Average Canadian Driver? When asked this question in a survey, 70% (i.e., 21) of 30 people responded "yes". Using a horizontal axis on which "driving ability" is rated on a scale from 1 (low) to 10 (high).

a) Draw a histogram with 10 bins of a distribution of drivers in which 70% are above average.
b) Identify the mean, median and mode of your distribution. **LO ❶, ❷**

David Parker/Alamy Stock Photo

LEARNING OBJECTIVES

In this chapter we show you how to investigate the relationship between two variables. After reading and studying this chapter, you should be able to:

❶ Draw a scatterplot and use it to analyze the relationship between two variables

❷ Calculate the correlation as a measure of a linear relationship between two variables

❸ Distinguish between correlation and causation

6

Scatterplots, Association, and Correlation

Tangerine Bank

Tangerine is a bank without branches. It has a few cafés in the major cities, and you can use Scotiabank ATMs, but it is primarily an online bank.

Tangerine started as ING Direct in 1997, part of the Netherlands-based ING Group. In 2012, it was bought by Scotiabank for $3.1 billion and maintained a separate identity from Scotiabank. It could not continue to use the ING name and surveyed thousands of people before choosing a new name. It decided to call itself Tangerine, a cool name for a bank that wanted to have a different image from the other banks.

Tangerine frequently offers promotions on new money transferred to savings accounts. A high rate of interest is offered for the first few months. How much new money will be attracted if the promotional interest rate is 1% higher than the base rate? What if it is 2% higher? Tangerine has vast amounts of data from previous promotions to answer these important questions.

We can represent the relationship between two variables (e.g., amount invested and interest rate) using a **scatterplot** with one variable on the horizontal axis and the other on the vertical axis. If there is a lot of scatter, the relationship is weak and may not be useful for management decision making. If customers are offered a 1% promotional interest rate, then the amount of money they invest depends on the state of the economy and on the age group and income level of the customers who move their money. We can reduce the scatter and find a relationship that is more useful by narrowing down the customers we are including, for example, customers aged 18–25 during last year's promotions.

Whenever you want to understand the relationship between two quantitative variables, you should make a scatterplot. Just by looking at a scatterplot you can see patterns, trends, relationships, and even the occasional unusual values standing apart from the others. Scatterplots are the best way to start observing the relationship between two *quantitative* variables.

Relationships between variables are often at the heart of what we'd like to learn from data.

- Is consumer confidence related to oil prices?
- What happens to customer satisfaction as sales increase?
- What happens to reaction time as alcohol consumption increases?
- Is an increase in money spent on advertising related to sales?
- What is the relationship between a stock's sales volume and its price?

Questions such as these relate two quantitative variables and ask whether there is an **association** between them. Scatterplots are the ideal way to *picture* such associations.

LO❶ 6.1 Looking at Scatterplots

WHO	Months (However, *Who* does not mean much for scatterplots like this one.)
WHAT	Canadian/U.S. exchange rate and oil prices
WHEN	January–November 2014
WHERE	International
WHY	To examine whether there is a relationship between oil price and exchange rate

> Look for *direction:* What's the sign—positive, negative, or neither?

> Look for *form:* Is it straight, curved, something exotic, or no pattern?

Canada's economy is resource-based, with large mining and agricultural sectors. We might therefore expect it to do well when resource prices are high, and this would be reflected in the exchange rate. Resources make up a smaller proportion of the U.S. economy than of the Canadian economy, so we might expect the Canadian dollar to improve relative to the U.S. dollar when resource prices are high. In Figure 6.1, we look at just one resource—an important one, oil—to see whether its price is related to the Canadian/U.S. exchange rate over the 11-month period from January to November of 2014.

Anyone can look at a scatterplot. But many people would find it hard to say what to look for in a scatterplot. What do *you* see? Try to describe the scatterplot of *Oil Price* and *Exchange Rate.*

You might say that the **direction** of the association is important. As oil price goes up, so does exchange rate. A pattern that runs from the upper left to the lower right is said to be *negative.* A pattern running the other way is called *positive.*

The second thing to look for in a scatterplot is its **form.** If there's a straight-line relationship, it will appear as a cloud or swarm of points stretched out in a generally consistent straight form. For example, the scatterplot of *Exchange*

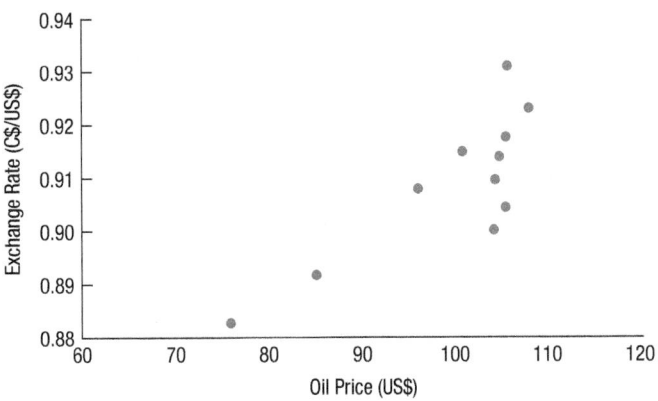

Figure 6.1 Monthly Canadian/U.S. exchange rate and oil prices.
Sources: Based on OPEC basket price of oil; Bank of Canada exchange rates (January–November 2014).

Rate and *Oil Price* has an underlying *linear* form, although some points stray from it.

Scatterplots can reveal many different kinds of patterns. Often they will not be straight, but straight-line patterns are both the most common and the most useful for statistics.

If the relationship isn't straight, but curves gently while still increasing or decreasing steadily, we can often find ways to straighten it out. But if it curves sharply—up and then down, for example, —then you'll need more advanced methods.

The third feature to look for in a scatterplot is the **strength** of the relationship.

At one extreme, do the points appear tightly clustered in a single stream (whether straight, curved, or bending all over the place)? Or, at the other extreme, do the points seem to be so variable and spread out that we can barely discern any trend or pattern? The *Exchange Rate* and *Oil Price* plot shows moderate scatter around a generally straight form. This indicates a moderately strong linear relationship between exchange rate and oil price.

Finally, always look for the unexpected. Often the most interesting discovery in a scatterplot is something you never thought to look for. One example of such a surprise is an unusual observation, or **outlier**, standing away from the overall pattern. Such a point is almost always interesting and deserves special attention.

Outliers can lead us to probe further to understand our data more clearly. In the case of the oil price and exchange rate data in Figure 6.1, the two points on the lower right could be regarded as outliers. You may see entire clusters or subgroups that stand apart or show a trend in a different direction than the rest of the plot. That should raise questions about why they are different. They may be a clue that you should split the data into subgroups instead of looking at them all together.

Look for *strength:* How much scatter?

Look for *unusual features:* Are there unusual observations or subgroups?

FOR EXAMPLE   Creating a scatterplot of cycling accidents

Cycle/car accidents are a serious concern for insurance companies. About 53,000 cyclists have died in traffic crashes in the United States since 1932. Demographic information such as this is often available from government agencies. It can be useful to insurers, who use it to set appropriate rates, and to retailers, who must plan what safety equipment to stock and how to present it to their customers. This becomes a more pressing concern when the demographic profiles change over time.

Here are data on the mean age of cyclists killed each year during the decade from 1998 to 2010. (**Source:** National Highway Transportation Safety Agency, www-nrd.nhtsa. dot.gov/Pubs/811156.PDF)

Year	1998	1999	2000	2001	2002	2003	2004	2005	2006	2007	2008	2009	2010
Mean Age	32	33	35	36	37	36	39	39	41	40	41	41	42

QUESTION Make a scatterplot and summarize what it says.

ANSWER

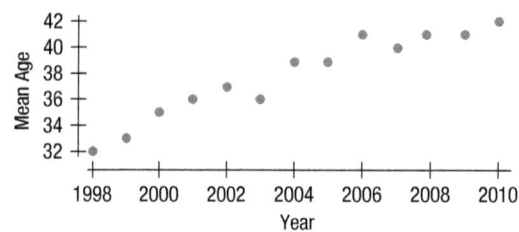

The mean age of cyclist traffic deaths increased almost linearly during this period. The trend is a strong one.

Note: We discussed time series plots in Section 5.13. They are a special case of a scatterplot.

LO❶ 6.2   Assigning Roles to Variables in Scatterplots

Scatterplots were among the first modern mathematical displays. The idea of using two axes at right angles to define a field on which to display values can be traced back to René Descartes (1596–1650), and the playing field he defined in this way is formally called a *Cartesian plane* in his honour.

The two axes Descartes specified characterize the scatterplot. The axis that runs up and down is, by convention, called the *y*-axis, and the one that runs from side to side is called the *x*-axis. Since we are now investigating two variables, we call this branch of statistics **bivariate analysis**.

To make a scatterplot of two quantitative variables, assign one to the *y*-axis and the other to the *x*-axis. As with any graph, be sure to label the axes clearly, and indicate the scales of the axes with numbers. Scatterplots display *quantitative* variables. Each variable has units, and these should appear with the display—usually near each axis.

Scatterplots made by computer programs (such as those we've seen in this chapter) often do not—and usually should not—show the *origin*, the point at $x = 0$, $y = 0$ where the axes meet. If both variables have values near or on both sides of zero, then the origin will be part of the display. If the values are far from zero, though, there's no reason to include the origin. In fact, it's far better to focus on the part of the Cartesian plane that contains the data.

Which variable should go on the *x*-axis and which on the *y*-axis? What we want to know about the relationship can tell us how to make the plot. Tangerine Bank may have questions such as these:

- How are Guaranteed Investment Certificate (GIC) purchases related to income level?
- Are increased mortgage rates discouraging mortgage applications?
- How are service fees at Scotiabank related to transfers of funds from Scotiabank to Tangerine?

In all of these examples, one variable plays the role of the **explanatory, independent, or predictor variable (*x*-variable)** while the other takes on the role of the **response or dependent variable (*y*-variable)**. We place the explanatory variable on the *x*-axis and the response variable on the *y*-axis. When you make a scatterplot, you can assume that those who view it will think this way, so choose which variables to assign to which axes carefully.

The roles that we choose for variables have more to do with how we *think* about them than with the variables themselves. Just placing a variable on the *x*-axis doesn't necessarily mean that it explains or predicts *anything*, and the variable on the *y*-axis may not respond to it in any way. We plotted oil price horizontally and exchange rate vertically, but we could equally have done it the other way round. We are investigating any relation between these two variables, not whether one causes the other.

The *x*- and *y*-variables are sometimes referred to as the *independent variable* and *dependent variable* respectively. The idea is that the *y*-variable *depends* on the *x*-variable and the *x*-variable acts *independently* to make *y* respond. These names, however, conflict with other uses of the same terms in Statistics. Instead, we'll sometimes use the terms "explanatory" or "predictor variable" and "response variable" when we're discussing roles, but we'll often just say *x*-variable and *y*-variable.

NOTATION ALERT

So *x* and *y* are reserved letters, but not just for labelling the axes of a scatterplot. In Statistics, the assignment of variables to the *x*- and *y*-axes (and choice of notation for them in formulas) often conveys information about their roles as predictor or response.

| **FOR EXAMPLE** | **Assigning roles to variables: Designing the scatterplot for cycling accidents** |

QUESTION   When examining the ages of victims in cycle/car accidents, why does it make the most sense to plot *Year* on the *x*-axis and *Mean Age* on the *y*-axis? (See For Example: "Creating a scatterplot of cycling accidents.")

ANSWER   We're interested in how the age of accident victims might change over time, so we think of the year as the basis for prediction and the mean age of victims as the variable that is predicted.

LO❷   **6.3   Understanding Correlation**

If you had to put a number (say, between 0 and 1) on the strength of the linear association between exchange rate and oil price in Figure 6.1, what would it be? Your measure shouldn't depend on the choice of units for the variables. Regardless of the units, the scatterplot would look the same. When we change units, the direction, form, and strength won't change, so neither should our measure of the association's (linear) strength.

We saw a way to remove the units in Chapter 5. We can standardize each of the variables, finding $z_x = \left(\dfrac{x - \bar{x}}{s_x}\right)$ and $z_y = \left(\dfrac{y - \bar{y}}{s_y}\right)$. With these, we can compute a measure of strength that you've probably heard of—the **correlation coefficient**:

$$r = \frac{\sum z_x z_y}{n - 1}.$$

Covariance

An alternative to the correlation coefficient is the **covariance**, $Cov(X, Y)$:

$$Cov(X, Y) = r\, s_x s_y$$

Keep in mind that the x-values and y-values are paired. For each book, we have a price and a weight. To find the correlation we multiply each standardized value by the standardized value it is paired with and add up those *cross products*. We divide the total by the number of pairs (n) minus one: $n - 1$.[1]

There are alternative formulas for the correlation in terms of the variables x and y. Here are two of the more common:

$$r = \frac{\sum (x - \bar{x})(y - \bar{y})}{\sqrt{\sum (x - \bar{x})^2 \sum (y - \bar{y})^2}} = \frac{\sum (x - \bar{x})(y - \bar{y})}{(n - 1)s_x s_y}.$$

These formulas can be more convenient for calculating correlation by hand, but the form using z-scores is best for understanding what correlation means.

FOR EXAMPLE   **Finding the correlation coefficient for the cycling accident data**

QUESTION What is the correlation of *mean age* and *year* for the cyclist accident data in For Example: "Creating a scatterplot of cycling accidents"?

ANSWER Working by hand:

$$\bar{x} = 2004, s_x = 3.89$$

$$\bar{y} = 37.85, s_y = 3.26$$

The sum of the cross product of the deviations is found as follows:

$$\sum (x - \bar{x})(y - \bar{y}) = 147$$

Putting the sum of the cross products in the numerator and $(n - 1) \times s_x \times s_y$ in the denominator, we get

$$\frac{147}{(13 - 1) \times 3.89 \times 3.26} = 0.966$$

For *mean age* and *year*, the correlation coefficient is 0.96. That indicates a strong linear association. Because this is a time series, we refer to it as a strong "trend."

---

[1]This is the same $n - 1$ used for calculating the standard deviation.

Examples of the correlation coefficients for different amounts of scatter of are shown in the left margin.

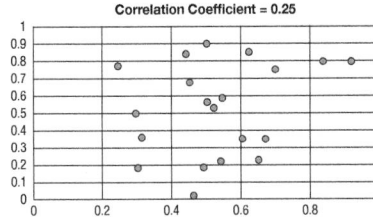

Correlation Coefficient = 0.25

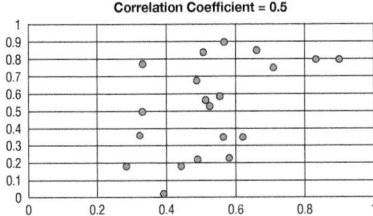

Correlation Coefficient = 0.5

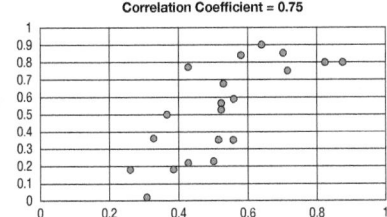

Correlation Coefficient = 0.75

Optional Math Box

Standardizing the variables first gives us an easy-to-understand expression for the correlation.

$$r = \frac{\sum z_x z_y}{n - 1}$$

But sometimes you'll see other formulas. Remembering how standardizing works gets us from one formula to the other.

Since

$$z_x = \frac{x - \bar{x}}{s_x}$$

and

$$z_y = \frac{y - \bar{y}}{s_y},$$

we can substitute these and get

$$r = \left(\frac{1}{n - 1}\right)\sum z_x z_y = \left(\frac{1}{n - 1}\right)\sum \frac{(x - \bar{x})}{s_x} \frac{(y - \bar{y})}{s_y} = \sum \frac{(x - \bar{x})(y - \bar{y})}{(n - 1)s_x s_y}.$$

That's one version. And since we know the formula for standard deviation,

$$s_y = \sqrt{\frac{\sum(y - \bar{y})^2}{n - 1}},$$

we could use substitution to write

$$r = \left(\frac{1}{n - 1}\right)\sum \frac{(x - \bar{x})}{s_x} \frac{(y - \bar{y})}{s_y}$$

$$= \left(\frac{1}{n - 1}\right)\frac{\sum(x - \bar{x})(y - \bar{y})}{\sqrt{\frac{\sum(x - \bar{x})^2}{n - 1}}\sqrt{\frac{\sum(y - \bar{y})^2}{n - 1}}}$$

$$= \left(\frac{1}{n - 1}\right)\frac{\sum(x - \bar{x})(y - \bar{y})}{\left(\frac{1}{n - 1}\right)\sqrt{\sum(x - \bar{x})^2}\sqrt{\sum(y - \bar{y})^2}}$$

$$= \frac{\sum(x - \bar{x})(y - \bar{y})}{\sqrt{\sum(x - \bar{x})^2 \sum(y - \bar{y})^2}}.$$

Finding the Correlation Coefficient

To find the correlation coefficient by hand, we'll use a formula in original units, rather than z-scores. This will save us the work of having to standardize each individual data value first. Start with the summary statistics for both variables: $\bar{x}$, $\bar{y}$, s_x, and s_y. Then find the deviations as we did for the standard deviation, but now in both x and y: $(x - \bar{x})$ and $(y - \bar{y})$. For each data pair, multiply these deviations together: $(x - \bar{x}) \times (y - \bar{y})$. Add the products up for all data pairs. Finally, divide the sum by the product of $(n - 1) \times s_x \times s_y$ to get the correlation coefficient.

Here we go.

Suppose the data pairs are:

x	6	10	14	19	21
y	5	3	7	8	12

Then $\bar{x} = 14$, $\bar{y} = 7$, $s_x = 6.20$, and $s_y = 3.39$.

Deviations in x	Deviations in y	Product
6–14 = –8	5–7 = –2	–8 × –2 = 16
10–14 = –4	3–7 = –4	16
14–14 = 0	7–7 = 0	0
19–14 = 5	8–7 = 1	5
21–14 = 7	12–7 = 5	35

Add up the products: $16 + 16 + 0 + 5 + 35 = 72$
Finally, we divide by $(n - 1) \times s_x \times s_y = (5 - 1) \times 6.20 \times 3.39 = 84.07$. The ratio is the correlation coefficient:

$$r = 72/84.07 = 0.856.$$

Correlation Conditions

Correlation measures the strength of the *linear* association between two *quantitative* variables. Before you use correlation, you must check three *conditions:*

- **Quantitative Variables Condition:** Correlation applies only to quantitative variables. Don't apply correlation to categorical data masquerading as quantitative. Check that you know the variables' units and what they measure.
- **Linearity Condition:** Sure, you can *calculate* a correlation coefficient for any pair of variables. But correlation measures the strength only of the *linear* association and will be misleading if the relationship is not straight enough. What is "straight enough"? This question may sound too informal for a statistical condition, but that's really the point. We can't verify whether a relationship is linear or not. Very few relationships between variables are perfectly linear, even in theory, and scatterplots of real data are never perfectly straight. How nonlinear looking would the scatterplot have to be to fail the condition? This is a judgment call that you just have to think about. Do you think that the underlying relationship is curved? If so, then summarizing its strength with a correlation would be misleading.
- **Outlier Condition:** Unusual observations can distort the correlation and can make an otherwise small correlation look big or, on the other hand, hide a large correlation. It can even give an otherwise positive association a negative correlation coefficient (and vice versa). When you see one or more outliers, it's often a good idea to report the correlation both with and without those points.

Each of these conditions is easy to check with a scatterplot. Many correlations are reported without supporting data or plots. You should still think about the conditions. You should be cautious in interpreting (or accepting others' interpretations of) the correlation when you can't check the conditions for yourself.

Throughout this course, you'll see that doing Statistics right means selecting the proper methods. That means you have to think about the situation at hand. An important first step is to check that the type of analysis you plan is appropriate. These conditions are just the first of many such checks.

JUST CHECKING

For the years 1992 to 2014, the quarterly stock prices of the semiconductor companies Cypress and Intel have a correlation of 0.79.

1 Before drawing any conclusions from the correlation, what would you like to see? Why?

2 If your co-worker tracks the same prices in euros, how will this change the correlation? Will you need to know the exchange rate between euros and U.S. dollars to draw conclusions?

3 If you standardize both prices, how will this affect the correlation?

4 In general, if on a given day the price of Intel is relatively low, is the price of Cypress likely to be relatively low as well?

5 If on a given day the price of Intel stock is high, is the price of Cypress stock definitely high as well?

Answers are found in Appendix A.

GUIDED EXAMPLE   Customer Spending

Epsicons/Shutterstock

A major credit card company sends an incentive to its best customers in the hope that the customers will use the card more. The company wonders how often it can offer the incentive. Will repeated offerings of the incentive result in repeated increased credit card use? To examine this question, an analyst took a random sample of 184 customers from the company's highest-use segment and investigated the charges in the two months in which the customers had received the incentive.

PLAN	**Setup** State the objective. Identify the quantitative variables to examine. Report the time frame over which the data have been collected and define each variable. (State the Five W's.)	Our objective is to investigate the association between the amount customers charge during the two months in which they received an incentive. The customers have been randomly selected from among the highest-use segment of customers. The variables measured are the total credit card charges (in $) in the two months of interest.
		✓ **Quantitative Variable Condition.** Both variables are quantitative. Both charges are measured in dollars.
	Make the scatterplot and clearly label the axes to identify the scale and units.	Because we have two quantitative variables measured on the same cases, we can make a scatterplot.

(continued)

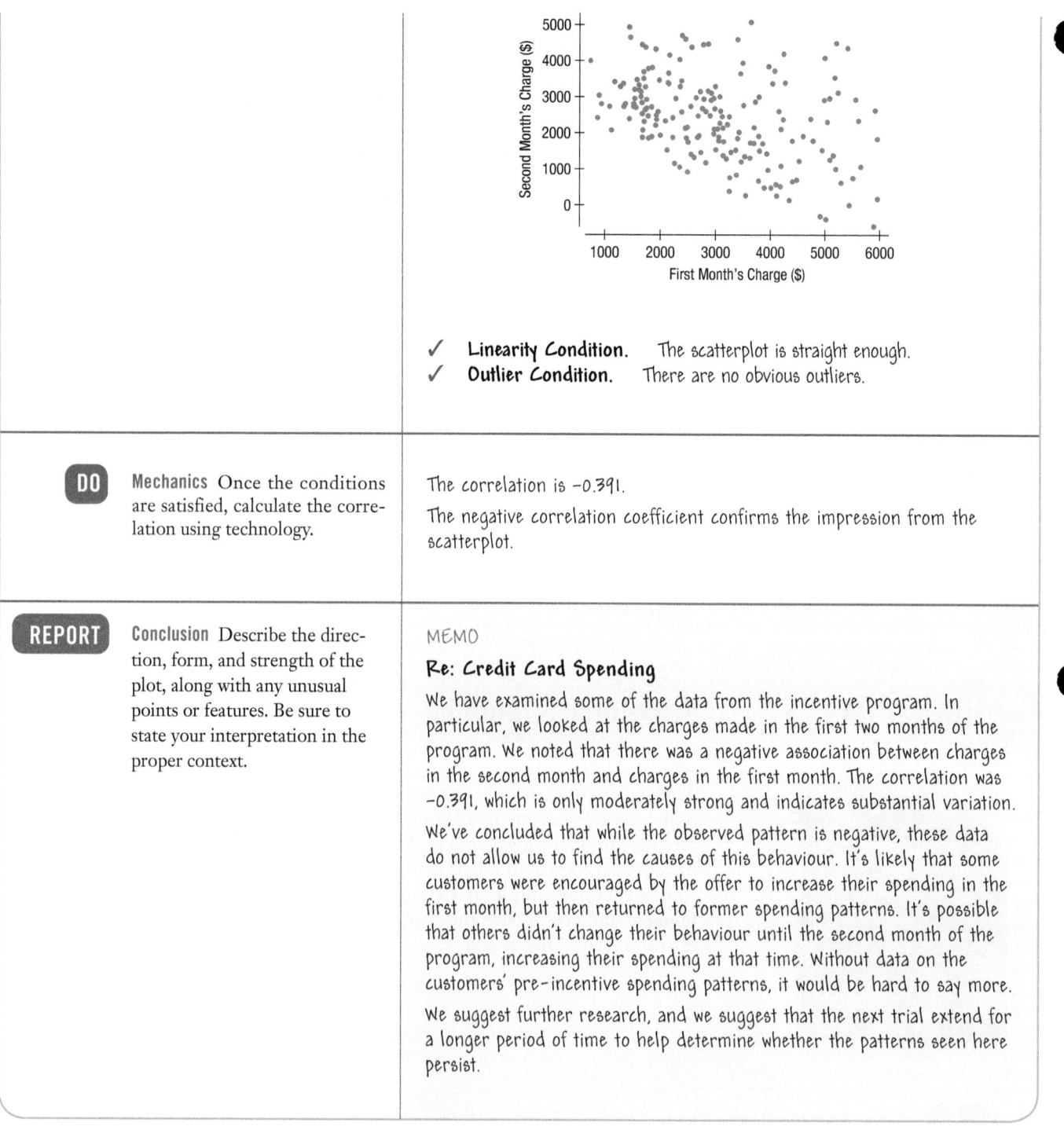

✓ **Linearity Condition.**   The scatterplot is straight enough.
✓ **Outlier Condition.**   There are no obvious outliers.

| **DO** | **Mechanics** Once the conditions are satisfied, calculate the correlation using technology. | The correlation is −0.391.

The negative correlation coefficient confirms the impression from the scatterplot. |

| **REPORT** | **Conclusion** Describe the direction, form, and strength of the plot, along with any unusual points or features. Be sure to state your interpretation in the proper context. | MEMO

Re: Credit Card Spending
We have examined some of the data from the incentive program. In particular, we looked at the charges made in the first two months of the program. We noted that there was a negative association between charges in the second month and charges in the first month. The correlation was −0.391, which is only moderately strong and indicates substantial variation.

We've concluded that while the observed pattern is negative, these data do not allow us to find the causes of this behaviour. It's likely that some customers were encouraged by the offer to increase their spending in the first month, but then returned to former spending patterns. It's possible that others didn't change their behaviour until the second month of the program, increasing their spending at that time. Without data on the customers' pre-incentive spending patterns, it would be hard to say more.

We suggest further research, and we suggest that the next trial extend for a longer period of time to help determine whether the patterns seen here persist. |

Correlation Properties

Because correlation is so widely used as a measure of association it's a good idea to remember some of its basic properties. Here's a useful list of facts about the correlation coefficient:

- **The sign of a correlation coefficient gives the direction of the association.**
- **Correlation is always between −1 and +1.** Correlation *can* be exactly equal to −1.0 or +1.0, but watch out. These values are unusual in real data because they mean that all the data points fall *exactly* on a single straight line.

- **Correlation treats x and y symmetrically.** The correlation of x with y is the same as the correlation of y with x.
- **Correlation has no units.** This fact can be especially important when the data's units are somewhat vague to begin with (customer satisfaction, worker efficiency, productivity, etc.).
- **Correlation is not affected by changes in the centre or scale of either variable.** Changing the units or baseline of either variable has no effect on the correlation coefficient because the correlation depends only on the z-scores.
- **Correlation measures the strength of the *linear* association between the two variables.** Variables can be strongly associated but still have a small correlation if the association is not linear.
- **Correlation is sensitive to unusual observations.** A single outlier can make a small correlation large or make a large one small.

Correlation Tables

Sometimes you'll see the correlations between pairs of variables in a data set arranged in a table, like Table 6.1. The rows and columns of the table name the variables, and the cells hold the correlations.

Correlation tables are compact and give a lot of summary information at a glance. The diagonal cells of a correlation table always show correlations of exactly 1.000, and the upper half of the table is symmetrically the same as the lower half (Can you see why?), so by convention, only the lower half is shown. A table like this can be an efficient way to start looking at a large dataset, but be sure to check for linearity and unusual observations or the correlations in the table may be misleading or meaningless. Can you be sure, looking at Table 6.1, that the variables are linearly associated? Correlation tables are often produced by statistical software packages. Fortunately, these same packages often offer simple ways to make all the scatterplots you need to look at.[2]

	#Pages	Width	Thick	Thick
#Pages	1.000			
Width	0.003	1.000		
Thick	0.813	0.074	1.000	
Pub year	0.253	0.012	0.309	1.000

Table 6.1   A correlation table for some variables collected on a sample of Amazon books.

LO❶, ❷   6.4   Straightening Scatterplots

The cost of generating electric power from solar has been steadily declining, and Figure 6.2 shows the price of systems installed in Germany, during 2009–2013, measured in euros per watt of generating capacity. The correlation between price and month is very high and negative because price declines over

---

[2]A table of scatterplots arranged just like a correlation table is sometimes called a *scatterplot matrix*, or SPLOM, and is easily created using a statistics package.

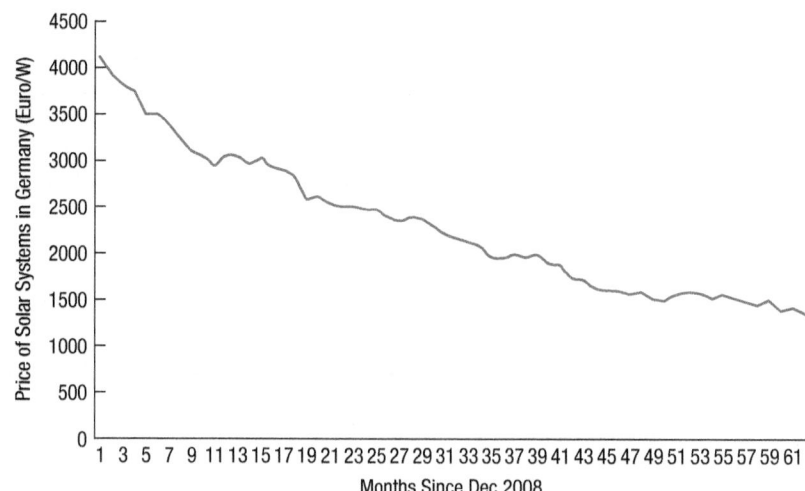

Figure 6.2   Price of solar installations in Germany, 2009–2013, in euros/watt.
Source: "Analysis of 13 years of successful PV development in Germany under the EEG with a focus on 2013," Renewable International, March 2014, Bernard Chabot.

the months, $r = -0.97$. However, this correlation coefficient is not meaning-ful, since the scatterplot in Figure 6.2 is not linear. We need to transform the data in order to straighten the scatterplot and then calculate the correlation coefficient. In Figure 6.3 we show the result of taking the logarithm of price and plotting that on the vertical axis. The scatterplot is straighter than Figure 6.2, but the first year of prices are declining faster than the rest. It is only to be expected that prices will come down fast initially for a new technology until the technology matures. We therefore ignore the first year of data and calcu-late the correlation from the rest of the data in Figure 6.3 as $r = -0.99$, even higher than for Figure 6.2.

Simple transformations such as the logarithm, square root, and reciprocal can sometimes straighten a scatterplot's form.

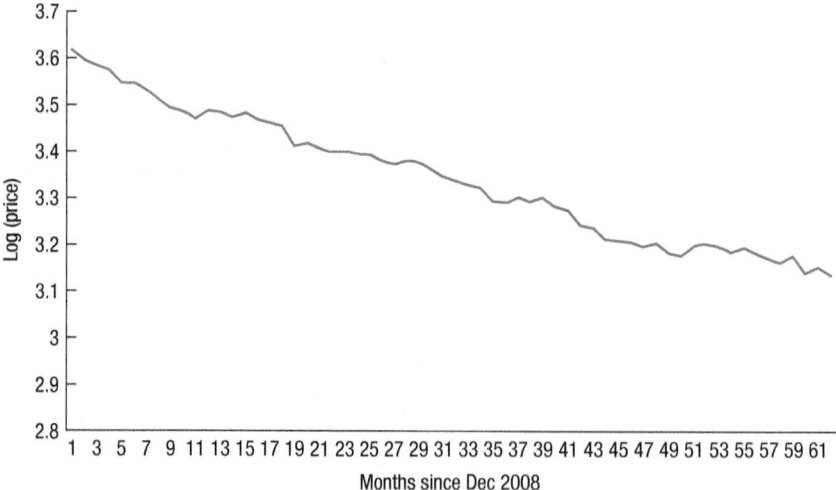

Figure 6.3   Logarithm (to the base 10) of the price of solar installations in Germany shown in Figure 6.2.

Gelpi/Shutterstock

LO③ **6.5** # Lurking Variables and Causation

An educational researcher finds a strong association between height and reading ability among elementary school students in a nationwide survey. Taller children tend to have higher reading scores. Does that mean students' heights *cause* their reading scores to go up? No matter how strong the correlation is between two variables, there's no simple way to show from observational data that one variable causes the other. A high correlation just increases the temptation to think and to say that the *x*-variable *causes* the *y*-variable. Just to make sure, let's repeat the point again.

No matter how strong the association, no matter how large the *r* value, no matter how straight the form, there is no way to conclude from a high correlation *alone* that one variable causes the other. It might be causation but there's always the possibility that some third variable—a **lurking variable**—is affecting both of the variables you have observed. In the reading score example, you may have already guessed that the lurking variable is the age of the child. Older children tend to be taller and have stronger reading skills. But even when the lurking variable isn't as obvious, resist the temptation to think that a high correlation implies causation. Figure 6.4 illustrates another example.

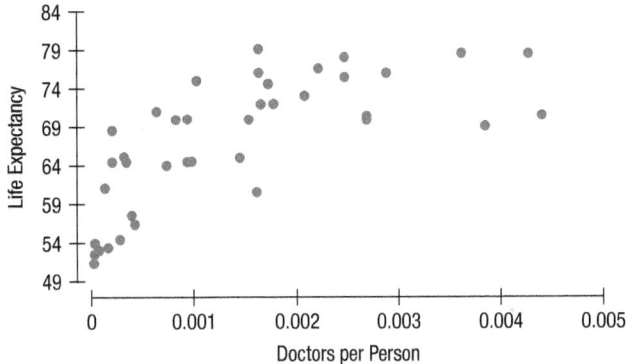

Figure 6.4 *Life Expectancy* and numbers of *Doctors per Person* in 40 countries shows a fairly strong, positive linear relationship with a correlation of 0.705.

The scatterplot shows the *Life Expectancy* (average of men and women, in years) for each of 40 countries of the world, plotted against the number of *Doctors per Person* in each country. The strong positive association ($r = 0.705$) seems to confirm our expectation that more *Doctors per Person* improves health care, leading to longer lifetimes and a higher *Life Expectancy*. Perhaps we should send more doctors to developing countries to increase life expectancy.

If we increase the number of doctors, will the life expectancy indeed increase? That is, would adding more doctors *cause* greater life expectancy? Could there be another explanation of the association? Here's another scatterplot (see Figure 6.5). *Life Expectancy* is still the response, but this time the predictor variable is not the number of doctors, but the number of *Televisions per Person* in each country. The positive association in this scatterplot looks even *stronger* than the association in the previous plot. If we wanted to calculate a correlation, we should straighten the plot first, but even from this plot it's clear that higher life expectancies are associated with more televisions per person. Should we conclude that increasing the number of televisions extends lifetimes? If so, we should send televisions instead of doctors to developing countries. Not only is the association with life expectancy stronger, but televisions are cheaper than doctors.

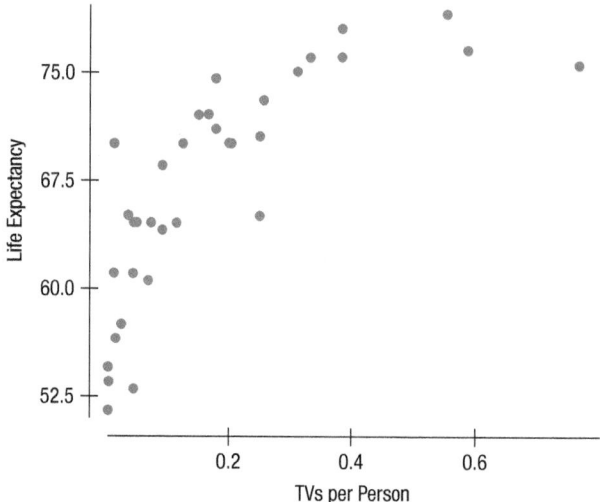

Figure 6.5 *Life Expectancy* and *Televisions per Person* shows a strong, positive (although clearly not linear) relationship.

What's wrong with this reasoning? Maybe we were a bit hasty earlier when we concluded that doctors *cause* greater life expectancy. Maybe there's a lurking variable here. Countries with higher standards of living have both longer life expectancies *and* more doctors. Could higher living standards cause changes in the other variables? If so, then improving living standards might be expected to prolong lives, increase the number of doctors, and increase the number of televisions. From this example, you can see how easy it is to fall into the trap of mistakenly inferring causality from a correlation. For all we know, doctors (or televisions) *do* increase life expectancy. But we can't tell that from data like these no matter how much we'd like to. Resist the temptation to conclude that *x* causes *y* from a correlation, regardless of how obvious that conclusion seems to you.

FOR EXAMPLE   Understanding causation for cyclist deaths

QUESTION An insurance company analyst suggests that the data on ages of cyclist accident deaths are actually due to the entire population of cyclists getting older and not to a change in the safe riding habits of older cyclists (see For Example: "Creating a scatterplot of cycling accidents"). What type of variable is *mean cyclist age*?

ANSWER It would be a lurking variable. If the entire population of cyclists is aging, then that would lead to the average age of cyclists in accidents increasing.

WHAT CAN GO WRONG?

* **Don't say "correlation" when you mean "association."** How often have you heard the word "correlation"? Chances are pretty good that when you've heard the term, it's been misused. In fact, it's one of the most widely misused statistics terms, and given how often statistics are misused that's saying a lot. One of the problems is that many people use the specific term *correlation* when they really mean the more general term *association*. Association is a deliberately vague term used to describe the relationship between two

variables. Correlation is a precise term used to describe the strength and direction of a *linear* relationship between quantitative variables.

- **Don't correlate categorical variables.** Be sure to check the Quantitative Variables Condition. It makes no sense to compute a correlation of categorical variables.

- **Make sure the association is linear.** Not all associations between quantitative variables are linear. Correlation can miss even a strong nonlinear association. For example, a company, concerned that customers might use ovens with imperfect temperature controls, performed a series of experiments[3] to assess the effect of baking temperature on the quality of brownies made from their freeze-dried reconstituted brownies. The company wanted to understand the sensitivity of brownie quality to variation in oven temperatures around the recommended baking temperature of 325°F. The lab reported a correlation of −0.05 between the scores awarded by a panel of trained taste-testers and baking temperature and told management that there was no relationship. Before printing directions on the box telling customers not to worry about the temperature, a savvy intern asked to see the scatterplot (Figure 6.6).

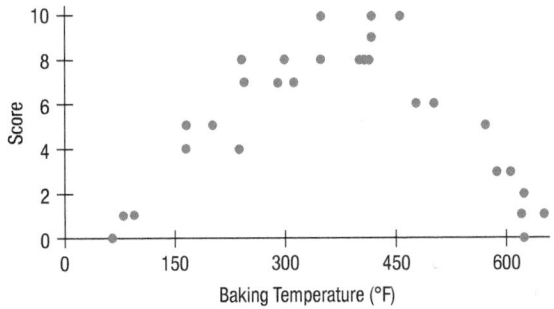

Figure 6.6 The relationship between brownie taste score and baking temperature is strong, but not linear.

The plot actually shows a strong association—but not a linear one. Don't forget to check the Linearity Condition.

- **Beware of outliers.** You can't interpret a correlation coefficient safely without a background check for unusual observations. Here's an example. The relationship between IQ and shoe size among comedians shows a surprisingly strong positive correlation of 0.50. To check assumptions, we look at the scatterplot (Figure 6.7).

From this "study," what can we say about the relationship between the two? The correlation is 0.50. But who *does* that point in the upper right-hand corner belong to? The outlier is Bozo the Clown, known for his large shoes and widely acknowledged to be a comic "genius." Without Bozo, the correlation is near zero.

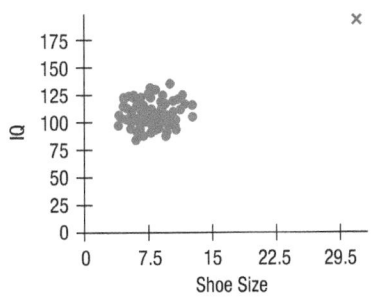

Figure 6.7 *IQ* vs. *Shoe Size.*

(continued)

---

[3]Experiments designed to assess the impact of environmental variables outside the control of the company on the quality of the company's products were advocated by Japanese quality expert Dr. Genichi Taguchi starting in the 1980s in the United States.

Even a single unusual observation can dominate the correlation value. That's why you need to check the Unusual Observations Condition.

- **Beware of multiple clusters.** If the scatterplot shows several clusters of data points separated from each other, don't calculate the correlation for the whole data set. Instead, look to see whether there is some management significance in the individual clusters. If so, calculate separate correlation coefficients for each cluster. Figure 6.8 shows marketing cost and sales revenue for a product in 45 cities across Canada. Closer examination of the clusters shows that they correspond to sales in Western, Central, and Eastern Canada, respectively. We can calculate three correlation coefficients, one for each geographic region.

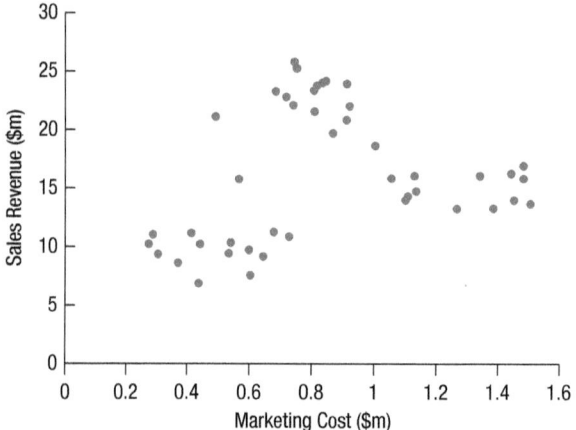

Figure 6.8   Relationship between sales revenue and marketing cost for 45 cities across Canada. The clusters represent Western, Central, and Eastern Canada, and correlations should be calculated for each region individually.

- **The correlation between just two data points is meaningless.** If you only have two data points, for instance in an outlying cluster, the correlation coefficient will always come to 1, since it is always possible to fit a straight line perfectly between two points. You need three or more data points (the more the better) to get meaningful correlations.

- **Don't confuse correlation with causation.** Once we have a strong correlation, it's tempting to try to explain it by imagining that the predictor variable has *caused* the response to change. Humans are like that; we tend to see causes and effects in everything. Just because two variables are related does not mean that one *causes* the other.

    Scatterplots and correlation coefficients *never* prove causation. This is, for example, partly why it took so long for governments to require warning labels on cigarettes. Although there was plenty of evidence that increased smoking was *associated* with increased levels of lung cancer, it took years to provide evidence that smoking actually *causes* lung cancer. (The tobacco companies used this to great advantage.)

- **Watch out for lurking variables.** A scatterplot of the damage (in dollars) caused to a house by fire would show a strong correlation with the number of firefighters at the scene. Surely the damage doesn't cause firefighters. And firefighters actually do cause damage, spraying water all around and chopping holes, but does that mean we shouldn't call the fire department? Of course not. There is an underlying variable that leads to both more damage and more firefighters—the size of the blaze. A hidden variable that stands behind a relationship and determines it by simultaneously affecting the other two variables is called a *lurking variable*. You can often debunk claims made about data by finding a lurking variable behind the scenes.

ETHICS IN ACTION

An ad agency hired by a well-known manufacturer of dental hygiene products (electric toothbrushes, oral irrigators, etc.) put together a creative team to brainstorm ideas for a new ad campaign. Trisha Simes was chosen to lead the team, as she's had the most experience with this client to date. At their first meeting, Trisha communicated to her team the client's desire to differentiate itself from its competitors by not focusing its message on the cosmetic benefits of good dental care. As they brainstormed, one member of the team, Brad Jonns, recalled a recent CNN broadcast that reported a "correlation" between flossing teeth and reducing the risk of heart disease. Seeing potential in promoting the health benefits of proper dental care, the team agreed to pursue this idea further. At their next meeting several team members commented on how surprised they were to find so many articles—medical, scientific, and popular—that seemed to claim good dental hygiene resulted in good health. One member noted that he found articles that linked gum disease not only to heart attacks and strokes but to diabetes and even cancer. While Trisha puzzled over why their client's competitors hadn't yet capitalized on these research findings, her team was on a roll and had already begun to focus on designing the campaign around this core message.

Ethical Issue *Correlation does not imply causation. The possibility of lurking variables is not explored. For example, it's likely that those who take better care of themselves would floss regularly and also have less risk of heart disease (related to Item C, ASA Ethical Guidelines; see Appendix C, the American Statistical Association's Ethical Guidelines for Statistical Practice, also available online at www.amstat.org/about/ethicalguidelines.cfm).*

Ethical Solution *Refrain from implying cause and effect from correlation results.*

WHAT HAVE WE LEARNED?

Learning Objectives

❶ We've learned to begin our investigation of two quantitative variables by looking at a scatterplot. We're interested in the *direction* of the association, the *form* it takes, and its *strength*.

❷ We've learned that, although not every relationship is linear, when the scatterplot is straight enough, the *correlation coefficient* is a useful numerical summary.

- The sign of the correlation tells us the direction of the association.
- The magnitude of the correlation tells us the *strength* of a linear association. Strong associations have correlations near +1 or −1, and very weak associations have correlations near 0.
- Correlation has no units, so shifting or scaling the data, standardizing, or even swapping the variables has no effect on the numerical value.

We've learned that to use correlation we have to check certain conditions for the analysis to be valid.

- Before finding or talking about a correlation, we'll always check the Linearity Condition.
- And, as always, we'll watch out for unusual observations!

❸ Finally, we've learned not to make the mistake of assuming that a high correlation or strong association is evidence of a cause-and-effect relationship. Beware of lurking variables!

Terms	
Association	• **Direction**. A positive direction or association means that, in general, as one variable increases, so does the other. When increases in one variable generally correspond to decreases in the other, the association is negative. • **Form.** The form we care about most is straight, but you should certainly describe other patterns you see in scatterplots. • **Strength.** A scatterplot is said to show a strong association if there is little scatter around the underlying relationship.
Bivariate analysis	Statistical analysis of two variables at the same time, as in our calculation of the correlation coefficient and plotting of scatter diagrams.
Correlation coefficient	A numerical measure of the direction and strength of a linear association: $$r = \frac{\sum z_x z_y}{n - 1}$$
Covariance	An alternative to correlation coefficient: $\mathrm{Cov}(X,Y) = r\, s_x\, s_y$
Explanatory, independent, or predictor variable (*x*-variable)	The variable that accounts for, explains, predicts, or is otherwise responsible for the *y*-variable.
Lurking variable	A variable other than *x* and *y* that simultaneously affects both variables, accounting for the correlation between the two.
Outlier	A point that does not fit the overall pattern seen in the scatterplot.
Response or dependent variable (*y*-variable)	The variable that the scatterplot is meant to explain or predict.
Scatterplot	A graph that shows the relationship between two quantitative variables measured on the same cases.
Skills	
Plan	• Recognize when interest in the pattern of a possible relationship between two quantitative variables suggests making a scatterplot. • Be able to identify the roles of the variables and to place the response variable on the *y*-axis and the explanatory variable on the *x*-axis. • Know the conditions for correlation and how to check them. • Know that correlations are between −1 and +1 and that each extreme indicates a perfect linear association. • Understand how the magnitude of the correlation reflects the strength of a linear association as viewed in a scatterplot. • Know that the correlation has no units. • Know that the correlation coefficient is not changed by changing the centre or scale of either variable. • Understand that causation cannot be demonstrated by a scatterplot or correlation.
Do	• Be able to make a scatterplot by hand (for a small set of data) or with technology. • Know how to compute the correlation of two variables. • Know how to read a correlation table produced by a statistics program.
Report	• Be able to describe the direction, form, and strength of a scatterplot. • Be prepared to identify and describe points that deviate from the overall pattern. • Be able to use correlation as part of the description of a scatterplot. • Be alert to misinterpretations of correlation. • Understand that finding a correlation between two variables does not indicate a causal relationship between them. Beware the dangers of suggesting causal relationships when describing correlations.

MINI case studies

Fuel Efficiency

With the ever-increasing price of gasoline, both drivers and auto companies are motivated to raise the fuel efficiency of cars. There are many simple ways to increase fuel efficiency: Avoid rapid acceleration, avoid driving over 90 km/h, reduce idling, and reduce the vehicle's weight. An extra 100 kilograms can reduce fuel efficiency by up to 2%. A marketing executive is studying the relationship between the fuel efficiency of cars (as measured in litres per 100 kilometres [L/100km]) and their weight to design a new compact car campaign. In the data set **ch06_MCSP_Fuel_Efficiency_Canadian_Edition** you'll find data on the variables below:

- *Model of Car*
- *Engine Size* (L)
- *MSRP* (Manufacturer's Suggested Retail Price in $)
- *City* (L/100 km)
- *Highway* (L/100 km)
- *Weight* (pounds)
- *Type* and *Country of Manufacturer*

Barney Boogles/Fotolia

Describe the relationship of weight, MSRP, and engine size with fuel efficiency (both city and highway) in a written report. Be sure to transform the variables if necessary.

Jonathan Hayward/
The Canadian Press

Crime in Canada

Is crime worse in larger cities? Many people think it is, but what do the data say? Of course there are many types of crime, with some worse than others. A large city might have more traffic offences and fewer assault cases. We need a way of combining all types of crime, weighted according to how severe the crime is. That's what Statistics Canada's "Crime Severity Index" does. Each type of offence is assigned a weight derived from actual sentences handed down by courts. More serious crimes are assigned higher weights, less serious offences lower weights. As a result, the index reflects the overall severity of crime in a given city. For a full explanation of the index and how it's calculated, refer to the 2008 report "Measuring Crime in Canada: Introducing the Crime Severity Index and Improvements to the Uniform Crime Reporting Survey" (Statistics Canada, Catalogue No. 85-004-X).

The data file **ch06_MCSP_Crime_in_Canada** contains the crime severity index and the population of certain Canadian cities. Draw scatterplots and calculate the correlation coefficients for the whole of Canada and then separately for each region of Canada. (Ottawa-Gatineau should be included in both the Ontario and the Quebec regions.) Comment on whether you think your correlation coefficients are

(continued)

representative of those regions, giving reasons for any doubts you may have. Finally, tackle the question: Is crime worse in larger cities?

The Cost of Solar Power

Not only is the cost of conventional solar modules declining, as shown in Figure 6.5, but a new solar technology, known as concentrating photovoltaics, or CPV, is emerging as a potentially lower cost competitor. The data file **ch06_MCSP_Solar** gives data on the cost of CPV in dollars per watt of installed capacity for the 19 major installations that took place during 2007–2013, from a study by the SunLab at the University of Ottawa. It is clear that the cost came down rapidly during this early period in the commercialization of CPV. But why do costs come down over time? Is it just the passing of time itself, or is it due to the industry gaining experience with the new technology and figuring out ways to implement it more efficiently? If it is the latter, how can we measure "experience"? We need to understand what it is that leads to a decline in costs so that we can project future costs and plan when to install a CPV project. The data file also gives information on the volume of CPV that has been installed to date (in megawatts, MW) as a measure of how much experience the industry has accumulated as each major installation is completed.

Plot (i) cost against time and (ii) cost against cumulative volume, and describe the scatterplots you obtain. Can a correlation coefficient be calculated for these data? Take the logarithm of cost and answer the same questions. Finally, plot the logarithm of cost against the logarithm of cumulative volume and answer the same questions. This final log/log plot is known as the "experience curve" and has been used to track how cost depends on experience for a wide range of technologies, including microwave ovens, light bulbs, and military equipment. Which of your graphs would you choose as the best means of showing the correlation in the data about CPV? Give your reasons.

(*Source:* Haysom, J., Jafarieh, O., Anis, H., Hinzer, K., and Wright, D.J. (2015). "Learning Curve Analysis of Concentrated Photovoltaic Systems." Progress in Photovoltaics: Research and Applications.)

MyStatLab   Students! Save time, improve your grades with MyStatLab. Questions marked in ▦ can be found on MyStatLab. You can practise them as often as you want, and most feature step-by-step guided solutions to help you find the right answer. You'll find a personalized study plan available to you too!

Technology Help: Scatterplots and Correlation

Statistics packages generally make it easy to look at a scatterplot to check whether the correlation is appropriate. Some packages make this easier than others.

Many packages allow you to modify or enhance a scatterplot, altering the axis labels, the axis numbering, the plot symbols, and the colours used. Some options, such as colour and symbol choice, can be used to display additional information on the scatterplot.

EXCEL

To make a scatterplot:

- Highlight the two columns or rows of data that you wish to plot.
- Click the **Insert** tab.
- In the **Charts** group, select **Scatter**.
- The **Design** tab then allows you to fine-tune the design to what you want.

(*continued*)

To calculate a correlation coefficient:

- Select the cell where you want the correlation coefficient to be displayed and start typing **=CORREL(**
- You are then prompted to select the two "arrays" (i.e., rows or columns) of data that you wish to use.

MINITAB

To make a scatterplot:

- Choose **Scatterplot** from the **Graph** menu.
- Choose **Simple** for the type of graph. Click **OK.**
- Enter variable names for the *y*-variable and *x*-variable into the table. Click **OK.**

To compute a correlation coefficient:

- Choose **Basic Statistics** from the **Stat** menu.
- From the Basic Statistics submenu, choose **Correlation**. Specify the names of at least two quantitative variables in the **Variables** box.
- Click **OK** to compute the correlation table.

SPSS

To make a scatterplot in SPSS, open the **Chart Builder** from the **Graphs** menu. Then

- Click the **Gallery** tab.
- Choose **Scatterplot** from the list of chart types.

- Drag the scatterplot onto the canvas.
- Drag the scale variable you want as the response variable to the *y*-axis drop zone.
- Click **OK**.

To compute a correlation coefficient:

- Choose **Correlate** from the **Analyze** menu.
- From the Correlate submenu, choose **Bivariate**.
- In the **Bivariate Correlations** dialogue box, use the arrow button to move variables between the source and target lists. Make sure the **Pearson** option is selected in the Correlation Coefficients field.

JMP

To make a scatterplot and compute correlation, choose **Fit Y by X** from the **Analyze** menu.

In the Fit Y by X dialogue box, drag the *y*-variable into the **Y, Response** box, and drag the *x*-variable into the **X, Factor** box. Click the **OK** button.

Once JMP has made the scatterplot, click on the red triangle next to the plot title to reveal a menu of options. Select **Density Ellipse** and select **.95**. JMP draws an ellipse around the data and reveals the **Correlation** tab. Click the blue triangle next to Correlation to reveal a table containing the correlation coefficient.

EXERCISES

Note: The calculations for correlation and regression models can be very sensitive to how intermediate results are rounded. If you find your answers using a calculator and writing down intermediate results, you may obtain slightly different answers than you would have had you used statistics software. Different programs can also yield different results. So your answers may differ in the trailing digits from those in Appendix A. That should not concern you. The meaningful digits are the first few; the trailing digits may be essentially random results of the rounding of intermediate results.

SECTION 6.1

1. Consider the following data from a small bookstore:

Number of Salespeople Working	Sales (in $1000)
2	10
3	11
7	13
9	14
10	18
10	20
12	20
15	22
16	22
20	26
$\bar{x} = 10.4$	$\bar{y} = 17.6$
$SD(x) = 5.64$	$SD(y) = 5.34$

a) Prepare a scatterplot of *Sales* against *Number of Salespeople Working*.
b) What can you say about the direction of the association?
c) What can you say about the form of the relationship?
d) What can you say about the strength of the relationship?
e) Does the scatterplot show any outliers? **LO ❶**

2. The capacity of computer storage devices is often given in *terabytes* (TB), where 1 TB = 1000 gigabytes, or about a trillion bytes. A survey of prices for storage devices found the following data:

Capacity (in TB)	Price (in $)
0.080	29.95
0.120	35.00
0.200	299.00
0.250	49.95
0.320	69.95
1.0	99.00
2.0	205.00
4.0	449.00

a) Prepare a scatterplot of *Price* against *Capacity*.
b) What can you say about the direction of the association?
c) What can you say about the form of the relationship?
d) What can you say about the strength of the relationship?
e) Does the scatterplot show any outliers? **LO ❶**

SECTION 6.2

3. The human resources department at a large multinational corporation wants to be able to predict average salary for a given number of years of experience. Data on salary (in $1000s) and years of experience were collected for a sample of employees.

a) Which variable is the explanatory or predictor variable?
b) Which variable is the response variable?
c) Which variable would you plot on the *y*-axis? **LO ❶**

4. A company that relies on internet-based advertising linked to key search terms wants to understand the relationship between the amount it spends on this advertising and revenue (in $).

a) Which variable is the explanatory or predictor variable?
b) Which variable is the response variable?
c) Which variable would you plot on the *x*-axis? **LO ❶**

SECTION 6.3

5. If we assume that the conditions for correlation are met, which of the following are true? If false, explain briefly.

a) A correlation of –0.98 indicates a strong, negative association.
b) Multiplying every value of *x* by two will double the correlation.
c) The units of the correlation are the same as the units of *y*. **LO ❷**

6. If we assume that the conditions for correlation are met, which of the following are true? If false, explain briefly.

a) A correlation of 0.02 indicates a strong positive association.
b) Standardizing the variables will make the correlation 0.
c) Adding an outlier can dramatically change the correlation. **LO ❷**

SECTION 6.4

7. A biotechnology company wants to be sure that education level is rewarded by higher salary, and obtains the following table of average salary for number of years of formal education ranging from 12 to 20 years:

Years of Education	Average Salary ($)
12	29,785
13	33,167
14	39,702
15	42,322
16	50,987
17	56,238
18	70,125
19	85,005
20	105,720

a) Draw a scatterplot of the data.
b) Use logarithms to re-express one of the variables in order to make the relationship more linear.
c) Draw a scatterplot of the re-expressed data. **LO ❶, ❷**

8. A chain of beauty salons has recently hired staff who appear to be overqualified for the job. The human resources department checks the average salary of staff with different levels of formal education ranging from 12 to 20 years (see the table on the next page).

a) Draw a scatterplot of the data.
b) Use logarithms to re-express one of the variables in order to make the relationship more linear.
c) Draw a scatterplot of the re-expressed data. **LO ❶, ❷**

Years of Education After Grade 10	Average Salary ($)
2	29,105
3	41,239
4	49,870
5	57,200
6	63,280
7	67,985
8	71,345
9	73,455
10	76,255

SECTION 6.5

9. A larger firm is considering acquiring the bookstore from Exercise 1. An analyst for the firm, noting the relationship seen in Exercise 1, suggests that when it acquires the store it should hire more people because that will drive sales higher. Is his conclusion justified? What alternative explanations can you offer? Use appropriate statistics terminology. **LO ❸**

10. A study finds that during blizzards online sales are highly associated with the number of snow plows on the road; the more plows, the more online purchases. The director of an association of online merchants suggests that the organization should encourage municipalities to send out more plows whenever it snows because, he says, that will increase business. Comment.

CHAPTER EXERCISES

11. Association, part 1. Suppose you were to collect data for each pair of variables below. You want to make a scatterplot. Which variable would you use as the explanatory variable and which as the response variable? Why? What would you expect to see in the scatterplot? Discuss the likely direction and form.

a) Cell phone bills: Number of text messages, cost
b) Automobiles: Fuel efficiency (L/100 km), sales volume (number of autos)
c) For each week: Ice cream cone sales, air conditioner sales
d) Product: Price ($), demand (number sold per day) **LO ❶**

12. Association, part 2. Suppose you were to collect data for each pair of variables below. You want to make a scatterplot. Which variable would you use as the explanatory variable and which as the response variable? Why? What would you expect to see in the scatterplot? Discuss the likely direction and form.

a) T-shirts at a store: Price of each, number sold
b) Real estate: House price, house size (square footage)

c) Economics: Interest rates, number of mortgage applications
d) Employees: Salary, years of experience **LO ❶**

13. Scatterplots, part 1. Which of the scatterplots that follow show:

a) Little or no association?
b) A negative association?
c) A linear association?
d) A moderately strong association?
e) A very strong association? **LO ❶**

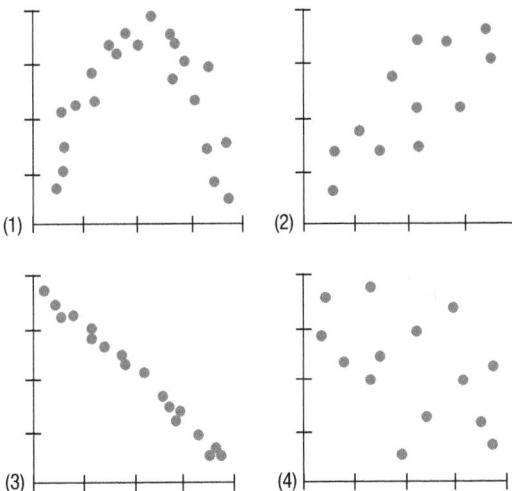

14. Scatterplots, part 2. Which of the scatterplots below show:

a) Little or no association?
b) A negative association?
c) A linear association?
d) A moderately strong association?
e) A very strong association? **LO ❶**

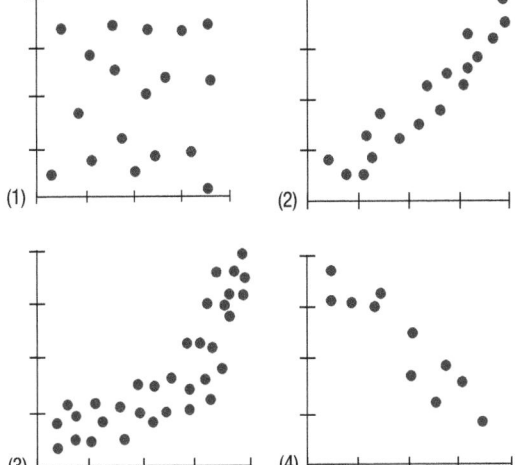

15. Manufacturing. A ceramics factory can fire eight large batches of pottery a day. Sometimes a few of the pieces break in the process. In order to understand the problem better, the factory records the number of broken pieces in each batch for three days and then creates the scatterplot shown:

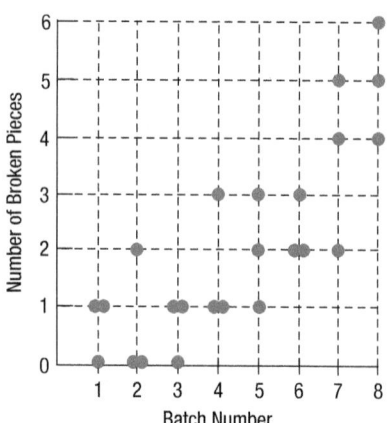

a) Make a histogram showing the distribution of the number of broken pieces in the 24 batches of pottery examined.
b) Describe the distribution as shown in the histogram. What feature of the problem is more apparent in the histogram than in the scatterplot?
c) What aspect of the company's problem is more apparent in the scatterplot? **LO ❶**

16. Coffee sales. Owners of a new coffee shop tracked sales for the first 20 days and displayed the data in a scatterplot (by day):

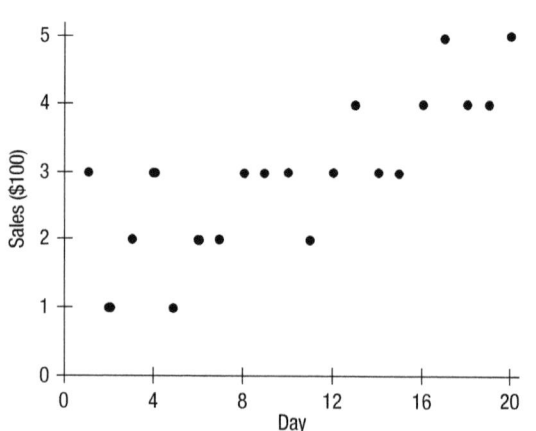

a) Make a histogram of the daily sales since the shop opened for business.
b) State one fact that is obvious from the scatterplot, but not from the histogram.
c) State one fact that is obvious from the histogram, but not from the scatterplot. **LO ❶**

17. Matching, part 1. Here are several scatterplots. The calculated correlations are −0.923, −0.487, 0.006, and 0.777. Which is which? **LO ❷**

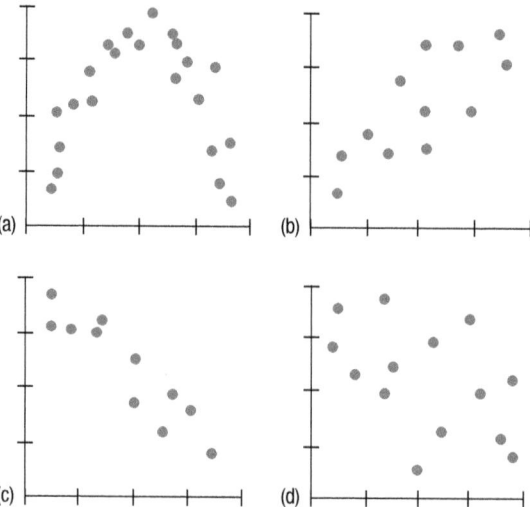

18. Matching, part 2. Here are several scatterplots. The calculated correlations are −0.977, −0.021, 0.736, and 0.951. Which is which? **LO ❷**

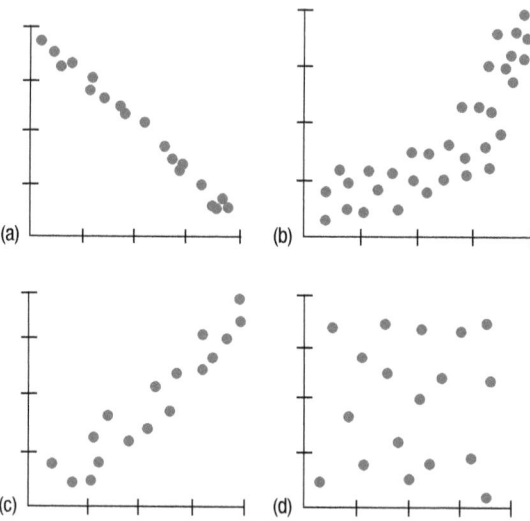

19. Packaging. A CEO announces at the annual shareholders' meeting that the new see-through packaging for the company's flagship product has been a success. In fact, he says, "There is a strong correlation between packaging and sales." Criticize this statement on statistical grounds. **LO ❷**

20. Insurance. Insurance companies carefully track claims histories so that they can assess risk and set rates appropriately. The National Insurance Crime Bureau reports that Honda Accords, Honda Civics, and Toyota Camrys are the cars most frequently reported stolen, while Ford Tauruses, Pontiac Vibes, and Buick LeSabres are stolen least often. Is it reasonable to say that there's a correlation between the type of car you own and the risk that it will be stolen? **LO ❷**

21. Canadian household income. Canadians derive income from investment, employment, and government. Regions with high employment income would be expected to have less income from government sources.

a) Draw a scatterplot and use it to verify whether this is true.
b) Is the correlation coefficient an appropriate measure of the extent of the relationship between income from employment and from government sources? **LO❶, ❷**

Province/Territory	Employment (%)	Government (%)
Alberta	73.7	10.7
British Columbia	70.4	16.8
Manitoba	63.2	19.2
New Brunswick	68.8	20.4
Newfoundland and Labrador	69.7	26.3
Northwest Territories	88.6	9.6
Nova Scotia	72.6	17.4
Ontario	62.1	20.4
Prince Edward Island	66.7	26.7
Quebec	80.6	12.2
Saskatchewan	65.2	15.6
Yukon	86.9	7.8

❶ 22. Canadian crime rate. Many people believe that the crime rate declines with age.

a) Take data from the data file to verify whether this is true using a scatterplot.
b) Is the relationship between crime rate and age strong, medium, or weak?
c) A statistician calculates the correlation coefficient for crime rate and age. Comment on the ethics of this calculation as it relates to the ASA Ethical Guidelines in Appendix C. **LO❶, ❷**

❶ 23. Landing at Pearson. The altitude and speed of a Boeing 737 landing at Pearson Airport in Toronto are recorded at one minute intervals in the data file. Describe the strength, form, and direction of the relationship among three pairs of variables:

a) Speed and time
b) Altitude and time
c) Speed and altitude
d) A statistician calculates the correlation coefficient for speed and altitude to be 0.916. Comment on the ethics of this calculation as it relates to the ASA Ethical Guidelines in Appendix C. **LO❶, ❷**

24. Aluminum and Alzheimer's disease. The relatives of a man recently diagnosed with Alzheimer's disease are suing a company that sells drinks in aluminum cans, claiming damages. They say that the man consumed one to two of these drinks per day and that the cans contained no warning that the aluminum from the can could be absorbed into the drink and cause Alzheimer's. They call an expert witness, who states, "There are numerous studies in the medical literature showing an increased level of aluminum in the brains of patients with Alzheimer's. These aluminum deposits are in the precise area of the brain affected by the disease. There is a clear link between the concentration of these aluminum deposits and the 'Alzheimer's Severity Index,' which measures the seriousness of this terrible disease." You are called as an expert witness for the drinks manufacturer.

a) What would you say to the court in response to the statement of the other expert witness?
b) In what way is your testimony consistent with the ASA guidelines on ethics in Appendix C?
c) How do these ASA guidelines apply to the testimony of the expert witness for the other side? **LO❸**

❶ 25. Diamond prices. The price of a diamond depends on its colour, cut, clarity, and carat weight. Here are data from a quality diamond merchant (so we can assume good cut) for diamonds of the best colour (D) and high clarity (VS1).

Carat	Price	Carat	Price
0.33	1079	0.62	3116
0.33	1079	0.63	3165
0.39	1030	0.64	2600
0.40	1150	0.70	3080
0.41	1110	0.70	3390
0.42	1210	0.71	3440
0.42	1210	0.71	3530
0.46	1570	0.71	4481
0.47	2113	0.72	4562
0.48	2147	0.75	5069
0.51	1770	0.80	5847
0.56	1720	0.83	4930
0.61	2500		

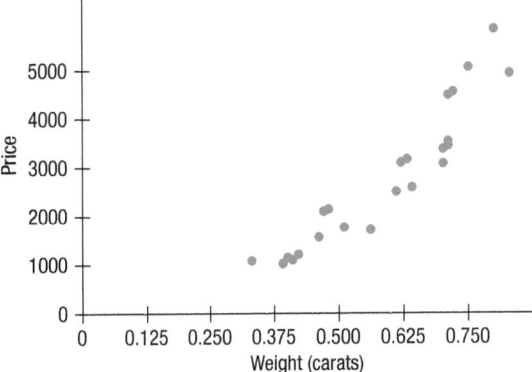

a) Are the assumptions and conditions met for finding a correlation?
b) The correlation is 0.937. Using that information, describe the relationship. **LO❷**

T 26. Interest rates and mortgages. Since 1980, average mortgage interest rates have fluctuated from a low of under 6% to a high of over 14%. Is there a relationship between the amount of money people borrow and the interest rate that's offered? Here is a scatterplot of *Total Mortgages* in the country (in millions of 2005 dollars) vs. *Interest Rate* at various times from 1980 to 2006. The correlation is –0.84.

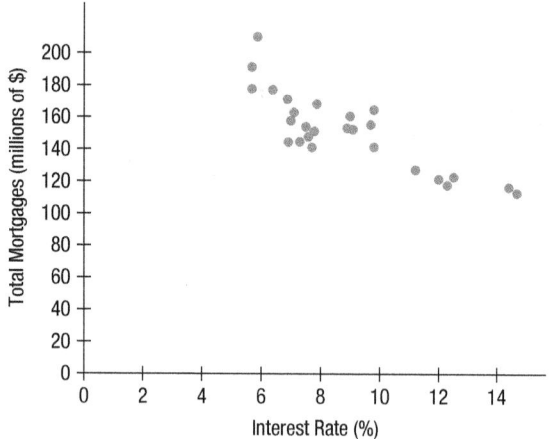

a) Describe the relationship between *Total Mortgages* and *Interest Rate*.
b) If we standardized both variables, what would the correlation coefficient between the standardized variables be?
c) If we were to measure *Total Mortgages* in thousands of dollars instead of millions of dollars, how would the correlation coefficient change?
d) Suppose that in another year, interest rates were 11%, and mortgages totalled $250 million. How would including that year with these data affect the correlation coefficient?
e) Do these data provide proof that if mortgage rates are lowered, people will take out more mortgages? Explain. **LO❶, ❷, ❸**

T 27. Vineyards, part 1. Here is the scatterplot and correlation for *Case Price* of wines from 36 vineyards in the Finger Lakes region of New York State and the *Age* of those vineyards. Correlation = 0.16.

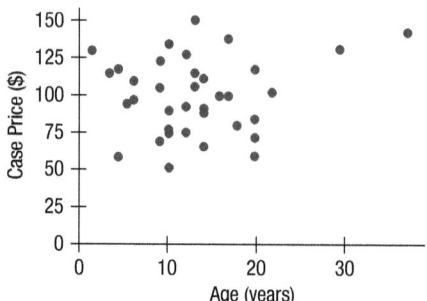

a) Check the assumptions and conditions for correlation.
b) Does it appear that older vineyards get higher prices for their wines? Explain.
c) What does this analysis tell us about vineyards in the rest of the world? **LO❷**

28. Vineyards, part 2. Instead of the age of a vineyard, considered in Exercise 27, perhaps the *Size* of the vineyard (in hectares) is associated with the price of the wines. Look at the scatterplot:

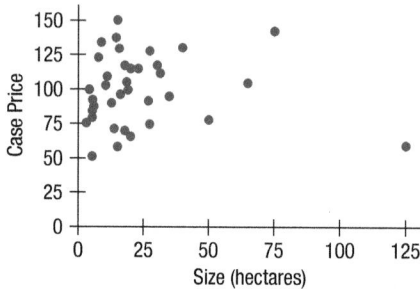

a) The correlation is −0.022. Does price get lower with increasing vineyard size? Explain.
b) If the point corresponding to the largest vineyard were removed, what effect would that have on the correlation? **LO❷**

T 29. Real estate, part 1. Using a random sample of homes for sale, a prospective buyer is interested in examining the relationship between price and number of bedrooms. The graph shows the scatterplot for *Price* vs. number of *Bedrooms*. The correlation is 0.723.

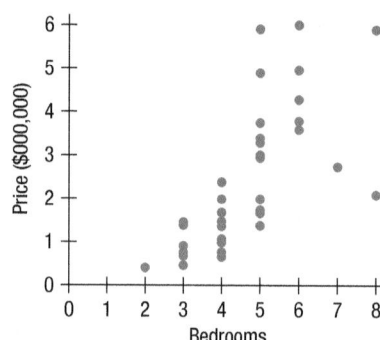

a) Check the assumptions and conditions for correlation.
b) Describe the relationship. **LO❶, ❷**

30. Real estate, part 2. Maybe the number of total *Rooms* in the house is associated with the price of a house. Here is the scatterplot for the same homes we examined in Exercise 29:

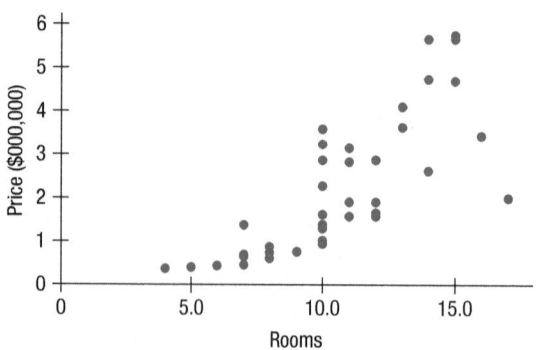

a) Is there an association?

b) Check the assumptions and conditions for correlation. **LO ❶, ❷**

31. Canadian regional sales. The head of the salesforce for a Canadian retail clothing chain is analyzing whether the company does better in some parts of the country than others. She examines a scatterplot of last year's total *Sales* by *Province*, in which the provinces are numbered in alphabetical order, Alberta = 1, British Columbia = 2, etc. The correlation is only 0.045, from which she concludes that there are no differences in sales across the provinces. Comment. **LO ❷**

32. Human resources. At a small company, the chief financial officer (CFO) is concerned about absenteeism among the employees and asks the head of human resources to investigate. The jobs are coded from 01 to 99, with 01 = Stockroom Clerk and 99 = President. The human resources manager plots number of days absent last year by job type and finds a correlation of −0.034 and no obvious trend. He then reports to the CFO that there seems to be no relationship between absenteeism and job type. Comment. **LO ❷**

33. Investments. An investment analyst looking at the association between sales and assets of companies was surprised when she calculated the correlation. She had expected to find a fairly strong association, yet the correlation was near 0. Explain how a scatterplot could still reveal the strong associations she anticipated. **LO ❶, ❷**

34. Used cars. A customer shopping for a used car believes there should be a negative association between the kilometrage a used car has on it and the price of the car. Yet when she runs a correlation, it's near 0, and she's surprised. Explain how a scatterplot could help her understand the relationship. **LO ❶, ❷**

35. Oil consumption. There is a strong association between the logarithm of oil consumption and life expectancy across many countries of the world.

a) Does this mean that consuming oil is good for health?

b) What might explain the strong correlation? **LO ❷, ❸**

36. Age and income. The correlations between *Age* and *Income* as measured on 100 people is $r = 0.75$. Explain whether each of these possible conclusions is justified:

a) When *Age* increases, *Income* increases as well.

b) The form of the relationship between *Age* and *Income* is straight.

c) There are no outliers in the scatterplot of *Income* vs. *Age*.

d) Whether we measure *Age* in years or months, the correlation will still be 0.75. **LO ❷, ❸**

37. Reducing truck shipping costs. Regulators must keep an eye on the weights of trucks on major highways, but making trucks stop to be weighed is costly for both the regulators and the truckers. A transport department hoped to keep costs down by measuring the weights of big trucks without actually stopping the vehicles and instead using a newly developed "weight in motion" scale. To see if the new device was accurate, workers conducted a calibration test. They weighed several trucks when stopped (static weight), assuming that this weight was correct. Then they weighed the trucks again while they were moving to see how well the new scale could estimate the actual weight. Their data are given in the table:

Weight of a Truck (thousands of pounds)	
Weight in Motion	**Static Weight**
26.0	27.9
29.9	29.1
39.5	38.0
25.1	27.0
31.6	30.3
36.2	34.5
25.1	27.8
31.0	29.6
35.6	33.1
40.2	35.5

a) Make a scatterplot for these data.

b) Describe the direction, form, and strength of the plot.

c) Write a few sentences telling what the plot says about the data. (*Note:* The sentences should be about weighing trucks, not about scatterplots.)

d) Find the correlation.

e) If the trucks were weighed in kilograms (1 kilogram = 2.2 pounds), how would this change the correlation?

f) Do any points deviate from the overall pattern? What does the plot say about a possible recalibration of the weight-in-motion scale? **LO ❶, ❷**

38. Pizza sales. Here is a scatterplot for the weekly sales of a brand of frozen pizza (in kilograms) for every fourth week vs. the unit price of the pizza for a sample of stores:

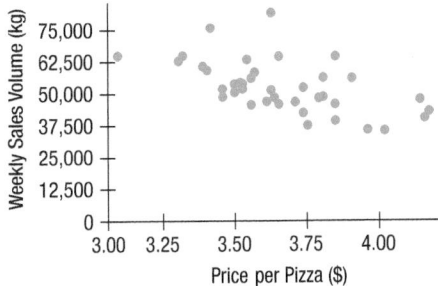

a) Check the assumptions and conditions for correlation.

b) Compute the correlation between sales and price.

c) Does this graph support the theory that as prices drop, demand for the product will increase?

d) If we assume that the number of kilograms of pizza per box is consistent and we measure sales in the number of pizza boxes sold instead of kilograms, will the correlation change? Explain. **LO ❷, ❸**

39. Fundraising. Analysts at a philanthropic organization want to predict who is most likely to give to their next fundraising campaign. They considered the potential donors' *Marital Status* (single = 1, married = 2, divorced = 3, widowed = 4) and *Giving* (no = 0, yes = 1). They found a correlation of 0.089 between the two variables. Comment on their conclusion that this shows that marital status has no association with whether the person will respond to the campaign. What should the organization have done with these data? **LO ❷, ❸**

40. High school performance. The Organisation for Economic Co-operation and Development (OECD) monitors math, reading, and science performance of high school students in 64 countries using standardized scores. The scores for 10 selected countries at the top of the rankings in 2012 are given in the following table:

	Math	**Reading**	**Science**
Shanghai-China	613	570	580
Singapore	573	542	551
Hong Kong-China	561	545	555
Chinese Taipei	560	523	523
Korea	554	536	538
Macao-China	538	509	521
Japan	536	538	547
Liechtenstein	535	516	525
Switzerland	531	509	515
Netherlands	523	511	522
Estonia	521	516	541
Finland	519	524	545
Canada	518	523	525
Poland	518	518	526
Belgium	515	509	505
Germany	514	508	524

Source: Organisation for Economic Co-operation and Development (OECD), PISA Programme of International Student Assessment. (2014) "PISA 2012 Results in Focus."

Investigate the relationship among math, reading, and science performance as follows:

a) Draw scatterplots between pairs of variables (three graphs). Comment on whether these graphs indicate that it's appropriate to calculate correlation coefficients.
b) Calculate a 3 × 3 correlation matrix giving the correlation between pairs of variables.
c) Interpret the meaning of the diagonal terms in the matrix from (b).

d) Comment on whether there is any relationship among math, reading, and science performance in the 10 selected countries.
e) Does this data indicate any relationship among math, reading, and science performance in all 64 countries? **LO ❶, ❷**

41. International economics correlation errors. The instructor in your International Economics course asks your class to investigate factors associated with the gross domestic product (GDP) of nations. Each student examines a different factor (such as *Life Expectancy*, *Literacy Rate*, etc.) for a few countries and reports to the class. Apparently, some of your classmates don't understand statistics very well, because several of their conclusions are incorrect. Explain the mistakes they made.

a) "There was a very strong correlation of 1.22 between *Life Expectancy* and *GDP*."
b) "The correlation between *Literacy Rate* and *GDP* was 0.83. This shows that countries wanting to increase their standard of living should invest heavily in education." **LO ❷**

42. What's the cause? A researcher gathering data for a pharmaceutical firm measures blood pressure and the percentage of body fat for several adult males and finds a strong positive association. Describe three different possible cause-and-effect relationships that might be present. **LO ❸**

43. What's the effect? Published reports about violence in computer games have become a concern to developers and distributors of these games. One firm commissioned a study of violent behaviour in elementary school children. The researcher asked the children's parents how much time each child spent playing computer games and had their teachers rate each child's level of aggressiveness when playing with other children. The researcher found a moderately strong positive correlation between computer game time and aggressiveness score. But does this mean that playing computer games increases aggression in children? Describe three different possible cause-and-effect explanations for this relationship. **LO ❸**

44. Colour-blindness. Although some women are colour-blind, this condition is found primarily in men. An advertisement for socks—which were marked so that they were easy for someone who was colour-blind to match—started out, "There's a strong correlation between sex and colour-blindness." Explain in statistics terms why this isn't a correct statement (whether or not it might be a good ad). **LO ❷**

45. Alzheimer's disease. Consider the following two statements. (i) "The level of aluminum in the brain is higher in patients with Alzheimer's disease than in other people." (ii) "The 'Alzheimer Severity Index,' which measures the seriousness of Alzheimer's disease, is related to the level of aluminum in the brain."

a) Is the correlation coefficient a useful measure of the extent of the relationship in statement (i)? State your reasons clearly.

b) Is the correlation coefficient a useful measure of the extent of the relationship in statement (ii)? State your reasons clearly.

c) What assumption would you need to make before using the correlation coefficient in this way? **LO ❷**

46. Video recommendations. The online video streaming service of a Canadian cable company offers recommendations to viewers based on their past viewing choices. They monitor 1.7 million customers' viewing habits by keeping track of four variables about each video viewed: (i) viewer's age; (ii) hour when a video was viewed according to the 24-hour clock; (iii) genre of video (action, sports, drama, romance, other); and (iv) viewing device (phone, computer, TV). The vice president of Marketing instructs the Statistics Department to calculate correlation coefficients between pairs of these four variables. "We need to understand how these things are related," she says.

a) What ethical issue does this raise according to the ethical guidelines in Appendix C?

b) What correlation coefficient(s) could the Statistics Department calculate?

c) How could this be done in a way that takes the other variables into account? **LO ❷**

47. Water and electricity use in retail stores. A big box retailer with 87 stores across Canada wants to reduce its water and electricity usage to reduce both dollar costs and its environmental footprint, and it needs to know whether these two costs are correlated. For a preliminary analysis, it collects data on five stores that sell household items and five stores that sell both household items and groceries. It expects the stores selling groceries to use more electricity for refrigeration and more water for preparing fresh food. The data are measured per square foot of retail space (for each entire store) per year and are given in the table:

Grocery	Water Usage (Litres per sq. ft. per year)	Electricity Usage ($ per 1000 sq. ft. per year)
No	109.6	695.3
No	115.2	677.5
No	77.6	817.0
No	98.0	683.8
No	93.2	797.3
Yes	339.2	2208.5
Yes	344.1	1760.2
Yes	308.6	2002.7
Yes	329.5	2078.2
Yes	358.5	2011.2

a) Calculate the correlation between water and electricity usage over all 10 stores. Comment on whether this calculation is statistically sound.

b) Calculate the correlation between water and electricity usage over the five stores not selling groceries. Comment on whether this calculation is statistically sound.

c) Calculate the correlation between water and electricity usage over the five stores selling groceries. Comment on whether this calculation is statistically sound.

d) Give reasons for the differences in the correlations you just calculated. Which of these correlations would you recommend the retail chain calculate when it does a complete analysis of all its 87 retail stores in Canada? **LO ❶, ❸**

48. Breakfast at IKEA. IKEA sells a broad range of household products and offers a low-cost breakfast in its store restaurants to attract customers into the stores early in the day. Suppose you are the manager of a store like IKEA and are making a loss on the breakfasts. You need to know whether the breakfast attracts customers to shop for the more profitable household items, and you decide to calculate the correlation between the number of customers taking breakfast and the number buying household items. (You could get more accurate information by tracking all customers as they leave the breakfast using the store's video surveillance system, but your head of security advises that this is unethical.) Analyze the following sample data that are collected during the course of one week:

Day	Number of Customers at Breakfast	Number of Customers Buying Household Items
Monday	73	54
Tuesday	52	45
Wednesday	56	26
Thursday	81	57
Friday	83	34
Saturday	297	285
Sunday	253	231

a) What is the correlation coefficient over the whole week?

b) What is the correlation coefficient over the weekdays only?

c) What is the correlation coefficient on the weekend?

d) How realistic are the above correlation coefficients for analyzing whether the number of customers buying household items is related to the number taking breakfast?

e) If you want to extend this analysis with data covering several weeks, which correlations would you calculate? **LO ❶, ❷**

Felix Choo/Alamy Stock Photo

7

Introduction to Linear Regression

LEARNING OBJECTIVES

In this chapter we show you how to model a linear relationship between two variables. After reading and studying this chapter, you should be able to:

❶ Choose a linear model of the relationship between two variables

❷ Use the correlation coefficient to analyze the usefulness of the model

❸ Deal with nonlinear relationships

Sport Chek

Sport Chek, the largest Canadian sporting goods retailer, is owned by The Forzani Group Ltd. of Calgary, which in turn is owned by Canadian Tire Corporation, a name more familiar to many for its hardware stores. The Forzani Group has revenues of around $1 billion annually from its 500 stores across Canada and also owns Sports Experts, one of the major competitors of Sport Chek. Many parents buy their children's first pair of skates and first bike at Canadian Tire, but as they get older those children prefer the fancier gear they can get at Sport Chek and Sports Experts. Owning those stores means that Canadian Tire keeps revenues streaming in from sporting goods sold to a broad range of age groups.

WHO	Months
WHAT	Monthly advertising expenses and sales
UNITS	Dollars
WHEN	Last four years
WHY	To predict future sales

Retailers like Sport Chek spend a lot on advertising, as do its competitors like Sports Experts and its owner Canadian Tire. It is important to track the effect of advertising on sales, although many other factors (such as general economic conditions and consumer confidence) also play major roles.

Imagine you are vice president of Marketing at a major retailer with stores across Canada and you track monthly advertising expenditures against sales. The result is given in Figure 7.1 for the past four years.

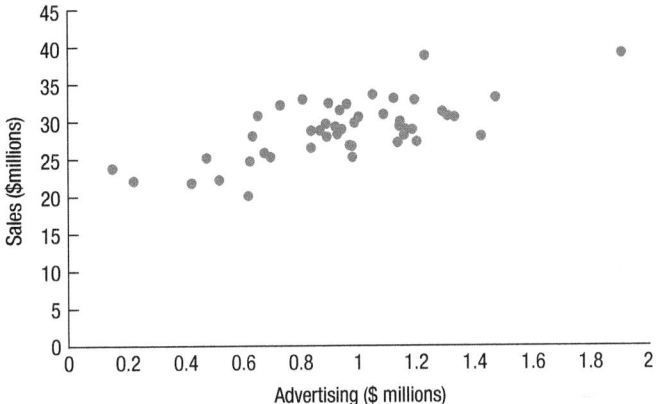

Figure 7.1   Monthly advertising expenses and sales over the past four years.

From the scatterplot, you can see that the relationship between sales and advertising is positive and linear and the correlation turns out to be 0.693, which indicates medium strength. But the strength of the relationship is only part of the picture. You might want to estimate the sales associated with $1.42 million in advertising expenditures next month. That's a reasonable business question, but we can't read the answer directly from the scatterplot. We need a model for the trend. The correlation says, "There seems to be a linear association between these two variables," but it doesn't tell us *what the line is*.

Extrapolation

A prediction just one year ahead doesn't seem like an unusual request. But whenever we reach beyond the range of the data, such an *extrapolation* can be dangerous. The model can provide a prediction for any value, but management should be cautious when using any model to make predictions for values that lie far beyond the data on which the model was built.

LO❶   7.1   The Linear Model

Since the data in Figure 7.1 is fairly linear, we can use a linear model to describe the relationship between advertising costs and sales. A **linear model (line of best fit)** is just an equation of a straight line through the data. The points in the scatterplot don't all line up, but a straight line can summarize the general pattern and help us understand how the variables are associated. Figure 7.2 shows a linear model, $\hat{y} = 21.1 + 8.31x$, that would forecast sales of $32.9 million given $1.42 million in advertising expenditures ($21.1 + 8.31 \times 1.42 = 32.9$).

The above short paragraph illustrates the three basic steps of regression analysis:

1. Start with some *data*.
2. Fit a *model* to the data.
3. Use the model to *predict* an estimate of something you would like to know.

In our case, it is natural to think that advertising affects sales rather than the other way around. We therefore call advertising the **explanatory variable** and usually put it on the horizontal x-axis. Sales is the variable we would like to predict and we therefore call it the **predicted variable** and usually put it on the vertical y-axis.

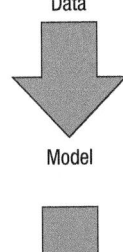

Data
↓
Model
↓
Prediction

The three steps of regression analysis

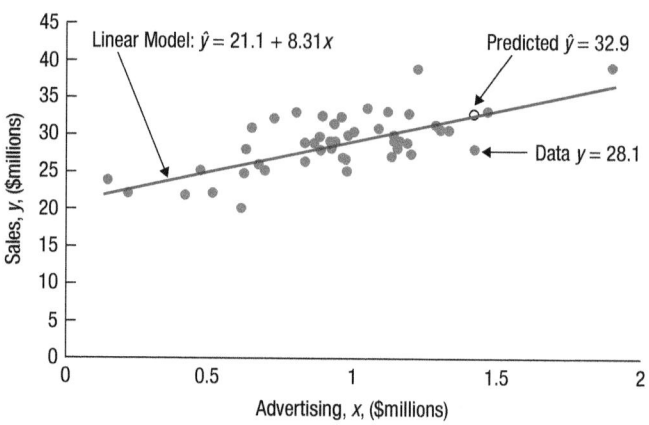

Figure 7.2   A linear model for monthly advertising expenses and sales over the past four years.

Another way of looking at sales is that it will respond to a change in advertising, so an alternative name for it is **response variable**. Yet a third name for it is **dependent variable** since it depends on the explanatory or independent variable. By contrast the explanatory variable is also known as the **independent variable**. We prefer the terms **explanatory variable** and **response variable** since the terms dependent and independent are also used in conjunction with the probabilities of events, see Chapter 8.

Residuals

We know the model won't be perfect. No matter what line we draw, it won't go through many of the points. The best line might not even hit *any* of the points. Then how can it be the "best" line? We want to find the line that somehow comes *closer* to all the points than any other line. Some of the points will be above the line and some below. A linear model can be written as $\hat{y} = b_0 + b_1x$, where b_0 and b_1 are numbers estimated from the data and $\hat{y}$ (pronounced "y hat") is the **predicted value**. We use the *hat* to distinguish the predicted value from the observed value y. The difference between these two is called the **residual**:

$$e = y - \hat{y}$$

The residual value tells us how far the model's prediction is from the observed value at that point. For example, in Figure 7.2, for advertising expenses of $1.42 million, the actual sales are $28.1 million and the predicted sales are $32.9 million. The residual is $28.1 million – $32.9 million = –$4.8 million of sales. To calculate the residuals, we always subtract the predicted values from the observed ones. The negative residual of –$4.8 million tells us that the actual sales were *less* than the model predicts with advertising costs of $1.42 million.

Our question now is how to find the right line.

The Line of "Best Fit"

When we draw a line through a scatterplot, some residuals are positive and some are negative. We can't assess how well the line fits by adding up all the residuals—the positive and negative ones would just cancel each other out. We need to find the line that's closest to all the points, and to do that, we need to make all the distances positive. We faced the same issue when we calculated a standard deviation to measure spread. And we deal with it the same way here: by squaring the residuals to make them positive. The sum of all the squared residuals tells us how well the line we drew fits the data—the smaller the sum, the better the fit. A different line will produce a different sum, maybe bigger, maybe

NOTATION ALERT!

"Putting a hat on it" is standard statistics notation to indicate that something has been predicted by a model. Whenever you see a hat over a variable name or symbol (e.g., $\hat{y}$), you can assume it is the predicted version of that variable name or symbol (e.g., y).

Here is an example with simplified data for illustrative purposes.

The line shown minimizes the sum of the squared residuals. The minimum value is $0.3^2 + 0.9^2 + 0.9^2 + 0.3^2 = 1.8$.

smaller. The **line of best fit (least squares line)** is the line for which the sum of the squared residuals is smallest.

This line has the special property that the variation of the data around the model, as seen in the residuals, is the smallest it can be for any straight line model for these data. No other line has this property. Speaking mathematically, we say that this line minimizes the sum of the squared residuals. You might think that finding this "least squares line" would be difficult. Surprisingly, it's not, although it was an exciting mathematical discovery when Legendre published it in 1805.

LO❶ 7.2   Correlation and the Line

Any straight line can be written as

$$\hat{y} = b_0 + b_1 x.$$

We'll use this form for our linear model. Of course, the actual data points (x, y) won't all fall on the line. So we write our model as $\hat{y} = b_0 + b_1 x$, using $\hat{y}$ for the predicted values, because it's the predicted values (not the data values) that fall on the line. If the model is a good one, the data values will scatter closely around it.

The **intercept**, b_0, is the value of the line when the x-variable is zero. In our case, this would be the predicted sales without any advertising at all. Intercepts have the same units as the y-variable, in our case, millions of dollars ($m). The **slope**, b_1, is the increase in sales that we expect when advertising is increased by one unit. In our case, the units for advertising expenditure are also millions of dollars. Slopes are always expressed in y-units per x-units, in our case millions of dollars per millions of dollars.

JUST CHECKING

A scatterplot of sales per month (in thousands of dollars) versus number of employees for all the outlets of a large computer chain shows a relationship that is straight, with only moderate scatter and no outliers. The correlation between *Sales* and *Employees* is 0.85, and the equation of the least squares model is:

$$\widehat{Sales} = 9.564 + 122.74\,Employees$$

1 What does the slope of 122.74 mean?

2 What are the units of the slope?

3 The outlet in Mississauga, Ontario, has 10 more employees than the outlet in Markham. How much more *Sales* do you expect it to have?

Answers are found in Appendix A.

How do we find the slope and intercept of the least squares line? The formulas are simple. The model is built from the summary statistics we've used before. We'll need the correlation (to tell us the strength of the linear association), the standard deviations (to give us the units), and the means (to tell us where to locate the line).

The slope of the line is computed as

$$b_1 = r\frac{s_y}{s_x}$$

where r is the correlation coefficient and s_x and s_y are the standard deviations of x and y, respectively.

We've already seen that the correlation tells us the sign and the strength of the relationship, so it should be no surprise to see that the slope inherits this sign as well. If the correlation is positive, the scatterplot runs from lower left to upper right, and the slope of the line is positive and said to be upward sloping.

Correlations don't have units, but slopes do. How x and y are measured—what units they have—doesn't affect their correlation, but it does change the slope. The slope gets its units from the ratio of the two standard deviations. Each standard deviation has the units of its respective variable. So the units of the slope are a ratio, too, and are always expressed in units of y per unit of x.

How do we find the intercept? If you had to predict the y-value for a data point whose x-value was average, what would you say? The best-fit line predicts $\bar{y}$ (the average value of y) when x takes its average value $\bar{x}$. Putting that into our equation and using the slope we just found gives

$$\bar{y} = b_0 + b_1 \bar{x}$$

and we can rearrange the terms to find

$$b_0 = \bar{y} - b_1 \bar{x}.$$

For our example of sales and advertising expenses, we need the means and standard deviations of our data, which are:

$$\textit{Sales: } \bar{y} = 29.0; \, s_y = 3.838$$

$$\textit{Advertising expenses: } \bar{x} = 0.948; \, s_x = 0.3201$$

Also, the correlation we saw earlier is $r = 0.693$.
So we calculate:

$$b_1 = r \, s_y / s_x = 0.693 \times 3.838 / 0.3201 = 8.31 \, \$m/\$m$$

$$b_0 = \bar{y} - b_1 \bar{x} = 29.0 - 8.31 \times 0.948 = 21.1 \, \$m$$

Our regression model is therefore:

$$\hat{y} = 21.1 + 8.31x$$

as shown in Figure 7.2. If we spend zero on advertising, it predicts $21.1 million in sales, and for each additional million dollars spent on advertising, the predicted increase in sales is $8.31 million. Of course, models cannot be expected to apply everywhere, and they should be used with caution outside the range of the original data upon which they are based. We did not have data for zero advertising, and the model may not be a good representation of our market outside the range of advertising from $0.15 million to $1.9 million for which Figure 7.2 shows our data. Chapter 18 will tell us just how good a regression model is.

A least squares line is commonly called a **regression line**. Although this name is an accident of history (as we'll soon see), "regression" almost always means "the linear model fit by least squares." Clearly, regression and correlation are closely related. We'll need to check the same conditions for regression as we did for correlation:

1. **Quantitative Variables Condition**
2. **Linearity Condition**
3. **Outlier Condition**

A little later in the chapter, in Section 7.5, we'll add a fourth condition.

FOR EXAMPLE — Interpreting the equation of a linear model of cycling accidents

Refer to For Example: "Finding the correlation coefficient for cycling accidents" in Chapter 6, page 148. Cycle/car accidents are a serious concern for insurance companies. Here are data on the mean age of cyclists killed each year in the United States during the decade from 1998 to 2010:

Year	1998	1999	2000	2001	2002	2003	2004	2005	2006	2007	2008	2009	2010
Mean Age	32	33	35	36	37	36	39	39	41	40	41	41	42

Here is a scatterplot of the data:

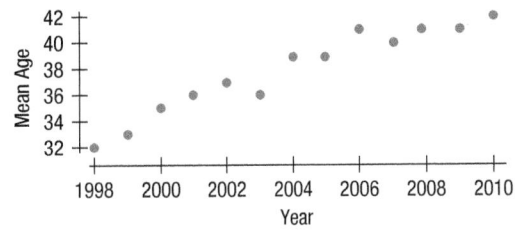

QUESTION   The data on cyclist accident deaths show a linear pattern. Find and interpret the equation of a linear model for that pattern.

ANSWER
$$b_1 = 0.966 \times \frac{3.26}{3.89} = 0.810$$
$$b_a = 37.85 - 0.810 \times 2004 = -1585$$
$$\widehat{MeanAge} = -1585 + 0.810\,Year$$

The mean age of cyclists killed in vehicular accidents has increased by about 0.80 years of age (about 10 months) per year during the years observed by these data.

> The data on *MeanAge* are given to only 2 significant figures of accuracy. We have retained 3 significant figures through this calculation, so that any estimates of *MeanAge* based on this regression equation would be accurate to 2 significant figures, that is, as accurate as the data. Software that retains full accuracy throughout may result in different numerical values.

Working in Standard Deviations

In Section 6.3, we saw how to standardize variables in terms of z-scores and how to calculate the correlation from the z-scores. These z-scores are also useful in interpreting regression models because they have the simple properties that their means are zero and their standard deviations are 1. Suppose we standardize our sales and advertising data and then calculate the regression coefficients as above. Since the standard deviations are 1, the equation for b_1 becomes:

$$b_1 = r$$

Since the means are zero, the equation for b_0 becomes:

$$b_0 = 0$$

Our regression model is now as simple as we could possibly hope for:

$$\hat{z}_y = r z_x$$

This simple equation tells us a lot, not only about these standardized variables, but also about how regression works in general. For example, it says that if you have an observation one standard deviation (SD) above the mean in x (with a z_x score of 1), you'd expect y to have a z-score of r. Now we can see that the correlation is more than just a vague measure of strength of association: It's a great way to think about what the model tells us.

For our data on advertising costs and sales, the correlation is 0.693. So we know immediately that:

$$z_y = 0.693\ z_x.$$

But we don't have to standardize the two variables to get the benefit of this equation. It tells us about the original variables as well, saying that for every standard deviation above (or below) the mean we are in advertising expenses, we'll predict that the sales are 0.693 standard deviations above (or below) their mean.

FOR EXAMPLE   **A linear model for retail expansion across Canada**

As a retailer expands across Canada, its sales increase. Here are some data on sales and number of stores over the last 10 years, including the means, standard deviations, and correlation coefficient:

	Number of Stores	Sales ($millions)
	119	270.1
	125	273.8
	145	362.9
	147	328.6
	151	299.3
	165	394.0
	178	409.6
	192	436.7
	201	433.0
	202	492.0
Mean	162.5	370.0
SD	28.52	71.7
Correlation	0.9491	

QUESTION   Obtain and interpret a linear model to estimate sales from the number of stores.

ANSWER   First we check our three conditions. Certainly, the variables are quantitative. Then we draw a scatterplot of the data:

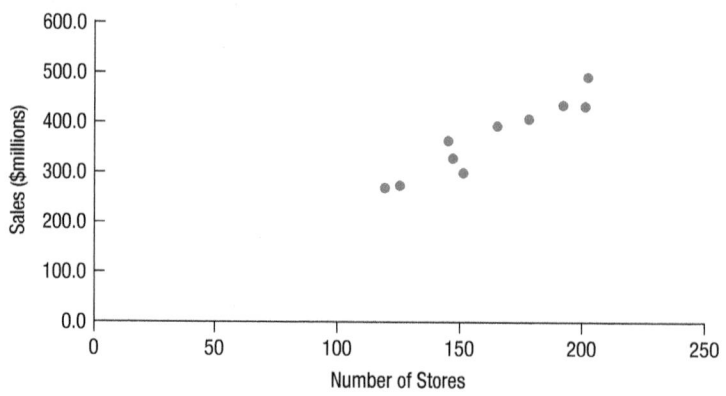

It is linear and there are no outliers, so our three conditions are satisfied. We now calculate the coefficients of the linear model:

$$b_1 = 0.9491 \times \frac{71.7}{28.52} = 2.3861$$

$$b_0 = 370.0 - 2.3861 \times 162.5 = -17.741$$

Estimated Sales $= -17.741 + 2.3861 \times$ *Stores*

The estimated sales are increased by $2.3861 million for each new store opened. The base value of –$17.741 million for zero stores is not meaningful since our data covers the range from 119 to 202 stores and cannot therefore be used to estimate sales far outside that range.

> The data are given to 4 significant figures of accuracy, so we have retained 5 significant figures in this calculation. *Estimated Sales* can therefore be expected to be as accurate as the data. Software that retains full accuracy throughout the calculation may result in different numerical values.

JUST CHECKING

To continue our Just Checking example: Suppose a chain of retail outlets does a regression of sales (in thousands of dollars) vs. employees. The correlation between *Sales* and *Employees* is 0.85, and the equation of the regression model is

$$\widehat{Sales} = 9.564 + 122.74 \ Employees.$$

4 How much do sales increase for each additional employee?

5 If an outlet were one SD above the mean in number of *Employees*, how many SDs above the mean would you predict its *Sales* to be?

6 What would you predict about the sales of an outlet that's two SDs below average in number of employees?

Answers are found in Appendix A.

LO❷ **7.3** ## Regression to the Mean

Pavel L Photo and Video/Shutterstock

Statistics Trumps Intuition

Instructors training aircraft pilots severely reprimanded trainees who did a very bumpy landing. They found that the trainees' next landing wasn't so bumpy, and concluded that verbal punishments are beneficial in training. In fact, the trainees were just "regressing toward the mean." Someone who does a really bad landing on one flight will "on average" do a better one next time.

Source Tversky, A., and Kahneman, D. "Judgement under Uncertainty: Heuristics and Biases," *Science*, Vol. 185, 1974.

Suppose you were told that a new male student was about to join the class, and you were asked to guess his height in inches. What would be your guess? A good guess would be the mean height of male students. Now suppose you are also told that this student had a grade point average (GPA) of 3.9—about two SDs above the mean GPA. Would that change your guess? Probably not. The correlation between GPA and height is near 0, so knowing the GPA value doesn't tell you anything and doesn't move your guess. (And the standardized regression equation, $\hat{z}_y = rz_x$, tells us that as well, since it says that we should move 0×2 SDs from the mean.)

On the other hand, if you were told that, measured in centimetres, the student's height was two SDs above the mean, you'd know that his height in inches is also two SDs above the mean. There's a perfect correlation between *Height* in inches and *Height* in centimetres ($r = 1$). (The standardized regression equation would tell us to move 1.0×2 SDs from the mean.)

What if you were told that the student was two SDs above the mean in shoe size? Would you still guess that he's of average height? You might guess that he's taller than average, since there's a positive correlation between height and shoe size. But would you guess that he's two SDs above the mean? When there was no correlation, we didn't move away from the mean at all. With a perfect correlation, we moved our guess the full two SDs. Any correlation between these extremes should lead us to move somewhere between zero and two SDs above the mean. (To be exact, the standardized regression equation tells us to move $r \times 2$ standard deviations away from the mean.)

Notice that if x is two SDs above its mean, we won't ever move more than two SDs away from y, since r can't be bigger than 1.0. So, each predicted y tends to be closer to its mean (in standard deviations) than its corresponding x was. This property of the linear model is called **regression to the mean**. This is why the line is called the regression line.

The First Regression

Sir Francis Galton related the heights of sons to heights of their fathers with a regression line. The slope of his line was less than 1. That is, sons of tall fathers were tall, but not as much above the average height as their fathers had been above their mean. Sons of short fathers were short, but generally not as far from their mean as their fathers. Galton interpreted the slope correctly as indicating a "regression" toward the mean height—and "regression" stuck as a description of the method he had used to find the line.

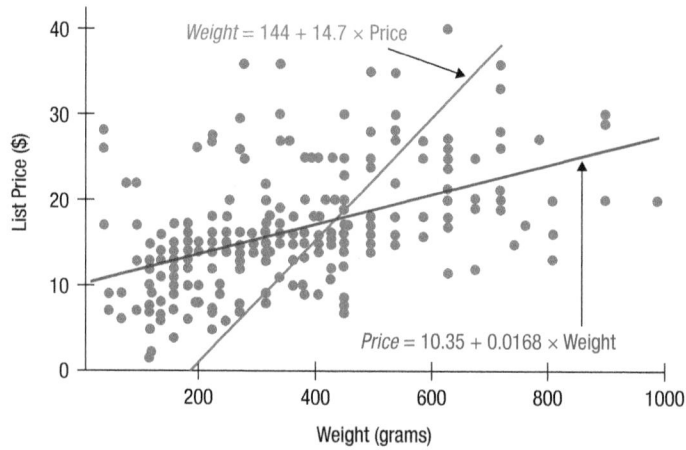

Figure 7.3   Price and weight for 307 books on Amazon, showing two regression lines. The red line estimates price when we know weight. The blue line estimates weight when we know price.

One Correlation but Two Regressions

For two variables, x and y, there is only one correlation coefficient, r, but there are two regression lines: one in which x is the explanatory variable and one in which y is the explanatory variable. In the case of advertising costs and sales, it makes sense to predict sales when we know advertising costs, but not the other way around. A scatterplot of price against weight for 307 books on Amazon has a correlation of 0.498. In this case, we can predict price knowing weight, or we may want to predict weight knowing price. We need a different regression depending on what we want to predict, and the two linear models are shown in Figure 7.3.

The moral of this story is that we have to be sure which variable we want to estimate from the other one before we do a regression analysis. The lower the correlation coefficient, the more difference there will be between the two regression lines. When the correlation coefficient is 1, the two lines are identical and all the data points lie exactly on that one line.

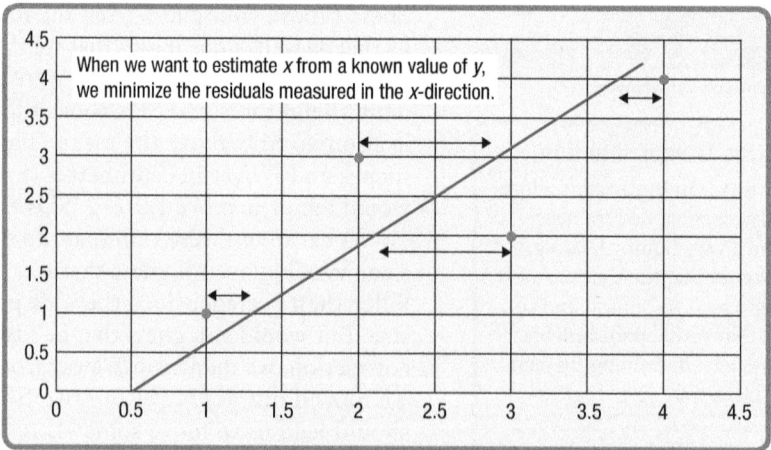

LO❶   7.4   **Checking the Model**

The linear regression model is perhaps the most widely used model in all of Statistics. It has everything we could want in a model: two easily estimated parameters, a meaningful measure of how well the model fits the data, and the ability to predict new values. Most models are useful only when specific *assumptions* are true. Of course, assumptions are hard—often impossible—to check. That's why we *assume* them. But we should check to see whether the assumptions are *reasonable*. Fortunately, we can often check *conditions* that provide information about the assumptions. For the linear model, we start by checking the same ones we check for using correlation.

Linear models make sense only for quantitative data. The **Quantitative Variables Condition** is pretty easy to check, but don't be fooled by categorical data recorded as numbers. You don't want to try to predict postal codes from credit card account numbers.

The regression model *assumes* that the relationship between the variables is, in fact, linear. If you try to model a curved relationship with a straight line, you'll usually get what you deserve: nonsense. We can't ever verify that the underlying relationship between two variables is truly linear, but an examination of the scatterplot will let you decide whether the **Linearity Assumption** is reasonable. The **Linearity Condition** we use for correlations is designed to do precisely that and is satisfied if the scatterplot looks reasonably straight. If the scatterplot isn't straight enough, stop. You can't use a linear model for just *any* two variables, even if they are related. The two variables must have a *linear* association, or the model won't mean a thing. Some nonlinear relationships can be handled by re-expressing the data to make the scatterplot more linear.

Watch for outliers. The linearity assumption also requires that no points lie far enough away to distort the line of best fit. Check the **Outlier Condition** to make sure no point needs special attention. Outlying values may have large residuals, and squaring makes their influence that much greater. Outlying points can dramatically change a regression model. Unusual observations can even change the sign of the slope, misleading us about the direction of the underlying relationship between the variables.

> **Make a Picture**
>
> Check the scatterplot. The shape must be linear, or you can't use linear regression for the variables in their current form. And watch out for outliers.

LO❶   7.5

Learning More From the Residuals

We always check conditions with a scatterplot of the data, but we can learn even more after we've fit the regression model. There's extra information in the residuals that we can use to help us decide how reasonable our model is and how well the model fits. So we plot the residuals and check the conditions again.

The residuals are the part of the data that *hasn't* been modelled. We can write

$$Data = Predicted + Residual$$

or, equivalently,

$$Residual = Data - Predicted.$$

Or, as we showed earlier, in symbols,

$$e = y - \hat{y}.$$

> **Why *e* for Residual?**
>
> The easy answer is that *r* is already taken for correlation, but the truth is that *e* stands for "error." It's not that the data point is a mistake, but rather that statisticians often refer to variability not explained by a model as error.

Residuals help us to see whether the model makes sense. When a regression model is appropriate, it should model the underlying relationship. Nothing interesting should be left behind. So after we fit a regression model, we usually plot the residuals in hopes of finding . . . nothing. (See Figure 7.4.)

We check the Linearity Condition and Outlier Condition in this plot. It shouldn't have any interesting features—no direction, no shape. It should stretch horizontally, showing no bends, and it should have no outliers. If you see nonlinearities, outliers, or clusters in the residuals, find out what the regression model missed.

Not only can the residuals help check the conditions, but they can also tell us how well the model performs. The better the model fits the data, the less the residuals will vary around the line. The **standard deviation of the residuals**, s_e,

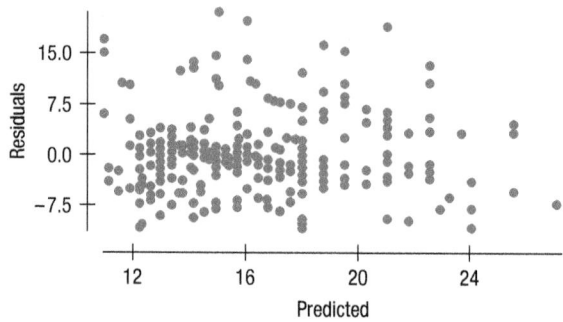

Figure 7.4   Residuals of a regression model predicting Amazon book prices from weights.

gives us a measure of how much the points spread around the regression line. Of course, for this summary to make sense, the residuals should all share the same underlying spread. So we must *assume* that the standard deviation around the line is the same wherever we want the model to apply.

This new assumption about the standard deviation around the line gives us a new fourth condition in addition to the three that we introduced in Section 7.2:

Equal Spread Condition

The associated question to ask is: Does the plot thicken—or fan out? We check to make sure that the spread is about the same throughout. We can check that either in the original scatterplot of *y* against *x* or in the scatterplot of residuals (or, preferably, in both plots). We estimate the standard deviation of the residuals in almost the way you'd expect:

$$s_e = \sqrt{\frac{\sum e^2}{n - 2}}$$

We don't need to subtract the mean of the residuals because $\bar{e} = 0$. Why divide by $n - 2$ rather than $n - 1$? We used $n - 1$ for s when we estimated the mean. Now we're estimating both a slope and an intercept. This looks like a pattern— and it is. We subtract one more for each parameter we estimate.

> **Equal Spread Condition**
> This condition requires that the scatter is about equal for all values. It's often checked using a plot of residuals against predicted values. The underlying assumption of equal variance is also called *homoscedasticity*. If we don't have many data points, it's tough to check this condition, so we skip it.

FOR EXAMPLE   **Examining the residuals for retail expansion across Canada**

Here is a scatterplot of the residuals for the linear model found in For Example: "A linear model for retail expansion across Canada" plotted against the predicted values:

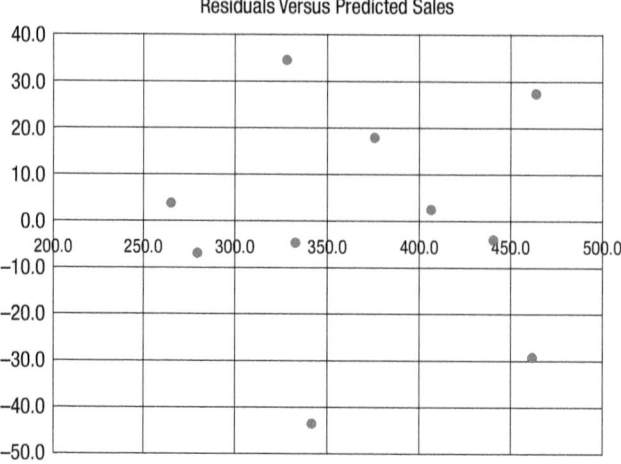

> **QUESTION**   Show how the plotted values were calculated. What pattern(s) do you see in the plot? What conclusions do you draw?
>
> **ANSWER**   The residuals are the values of *Actual Sales – Predicted Sales*. The residuals look random without any pattern, indicating that the linear model is a good representation of the data.

LO❷   7.6   Variation in the Model and R^2

The variation in the residuals is the key to assessing how well the model fits. We saw in Section 7.2 that sales have a standard deviation of $3.84 million to 3 significant figures. If we had to guess the sales without knowing the advertising expenses, we might guess the mean of $29.0 million. The SD would be $3.84 million. We might expect to be wrong by roughly twice the SD—plus or minus $7.68 million—probably not accurate enough for planning. But, after fitting the line, the residuals have a standard deviation of only $2.77 million, so knowing the advertising expenses allows us to make much better predictions. If the correlation were 1.0 and the model predicted the sales perfectly, the residuals would all be zero and have no variation. We couldn't possibly do any better than that.

If the correlation had been zero, the model would simply predict the mean (as we might do, if we didn't know the number of stores). The residuals from that prediction would just be the observed values minus their mean. These residuals would have the same spread as the original data because, as we know, just subtracting the mean doesn't change the spread.

How well does our model do? The variation in the residuals is certainly smaller than in the data, but still bigger than zero. How much of the variation is left in the residuals? If you had to put a number between 0% and 100% on the fraction of the variation left in the residuals, what would you say?

All regression models fall somewhere between the two extremes of zero correlation and perfect correlation ($r = \pm 1$). We'd like to gauge where our model falls. Can we use the correlation to do that? Well, a regression model with correlation –0.5 is doing as well as one with correlation +0.5. They just have different directions. But if we *square* the correlation coefficient, we'll get a value between 0 and 1, and the direction won't matter. It turns out that this works perfectly. The squared correlation, r^2, gives the fraction of the data's variation accounted for by the model, and $1 - r^2$ is the fraction of the original variation left in the residuals. For our model, $r^2 = 0.693^2 = 0.481$, so $1 - r^2 = 0.519 = 51.9\%$, and 51.9% of the variability in monthly sales has been left in the residuals.

All regression analyses include this statistic, although by tradition it's written with a capital letter, R^2, pronounced "R squared." An R^2 of zero means that none of the variance in the data is in the model; all of it is still in the residuals. It would be hard to imagine using that model for anything. Because R^2 is a fraction of a whole, it's often given as a percentage.[1]

When interpreting a regression model, you need to report what R^2 means. According to our linear model, 48.1% of the variation in sales is accounted for by the variation in advertising expenses.

- **How can we see that R^2 is really the fraction of variance accounted for by the model?** It's a simple calculation. The variance of sales is $3.84^2 = 14.7$; the variance of the residuals is 7.65. As a fraction of the variance of sales, that's 0.519 or 51.9%. That's the fraction of the variance that is not accounted for by

Sum of Squares

The sum of the squared residuals $\sum(y - \hat{y})^2$ is sometimes written as SSE (sum of squared errors). If we let $\sum(y - \bar{y})^2 = SST$ (for total sum of squares), then

$$R^2 = 1 - \frac{SSE}{SST}.$$

Is a correlation of 0.80 twice as strong as a correlation of 0.40? Not if you think in terms of R^2. A correlation of 0.80 means an R^2 of $0.80^2 = 64\%$. A correlation of 0.40 means an R^2 of $0.40^2 = 16\%$—only a quarter as much of the variability is accounted for. A correlation of 0.80 gives an R^2 *four* times as strong as a correlation of 0.40 and accounts for four times as much of the variability.

---

[1]By contrast, we give correlation coefficients as decimal values between –1.0 and 1.0.

the model. The fraction that *is* accounted for is $100\% - 51.9\% = 48.1\%$, just the value we got for R^2.

JUST CHECKING

Let's go back to our regression of sales ($000) on number of employees again.

$$\widehat{Sales} = 9.564 + 122.74\ Employees$$

The R^2 value is reported as 72.2%.

7 What does the R^2 value mean about the relationship of *Sales* and *Employees*?

8 Is the correlation of *Sales* and *Employees* positive or negative? How do you know?

9 If we measured the *Sales* in thousands of euros instead of thousands of dollars, would the R^2 value change? How about the slope?

Answers are found in Appendix A.

How Big Should R^2 Be?

The value of R^2 is always between 0% and 100%. But what is a "good" R^2 value? The answer depends on the kind of data you're analyzing and on what you want to do with it. Just as with correlation, there is no value for R^2 that automatically determines that the regression is "good." Data from scientific experiments often have R^2 in the 80% to 90% range and even higher. Data from observational studies and surveys, though, often show relatively weak associations because it's so difficult to measure reliable responses. An R^2 of 30% to 50% or even lower might be taken as evidence of a useful regression. The standard deviation of the residuals can give us more information about the usefulness of the regression by telling us how much scatter there is around the line.

As we've seen, an R^2 of 100% is a perfect fit, with no scatter around the line. The s_e would be zero. All the variance would be accounted for by the model, with none left in the residuals. This sounds great, but it's too good to be true for real data.[2]

FOR EXAMPLE   Understanding R^2 for retail expansion across Canada

QUESTION   Find and interpret the R^2 for the regression found in For Example: "A linear model for retail expansion across Canada". (*Hint:* The calculation is a simple one.)

ANSWER   We are given the correlation, $r = 0.9491$. R^2 is the square of this, or 0.9008. It tells us that 90.08% of the variation in the retail sales can be accounted for by the number of stores in Canada.

LO❶ 7.7   Reality Check: Is the Regression Reasonable?

Statistics don't come out of nowhere; they're based on data. So the results of a statistical analysis should reinforce common sense. If the results are surprising, then either you've learned something new about the world or your analysis is wrong.

---

[2]If you see an R^2 of 100%, it's a good idea to investigate what happened. You may have accidentally regressed two variables that measure the same thing.

Whenever you perform a regression, think about the coefficients and ask whether they make sense. Is the slope reasonable? Does the direction of the slope seem right? The small effort of asking whether the regression equation is plausible will be repaid whenever you catch errors or avoid saying something silly or absurd about the data. It's too easy to take something that comes out of a computer at face value and assume that it makes sense.

Always be skeptical and ask yourself if the answer is reasonable.

GUIDED EXAMPLE   Home Size and Price

Real estate agents know that the three most important factors in determining the price of a house are *location, location,* and *location.* But what other factors help determine the price at which a house should be listed? Number of bathrooms? Size of the yard? A student amassed publicly available data on thousands of homes and drew a random sample of 1057 homes to examine house pricing. Among the variables she collected were the total living area (in square feet), number of bathrooms, number of bedrooms, size of lot (in acres), and age of house (in years). We will investigate how well the size of the house, as measured by living area, can predict the selling price.

| **PLAN** | **Setup** State the objective of the study. | We want to find out how well the living area of a house can predict its selling price. |

Identify the variables and their context.

We have two quantitative variables: the living area (in square feet) and the selling price ($). These data come from public records.

✓ **Quantitative Variables Condition**

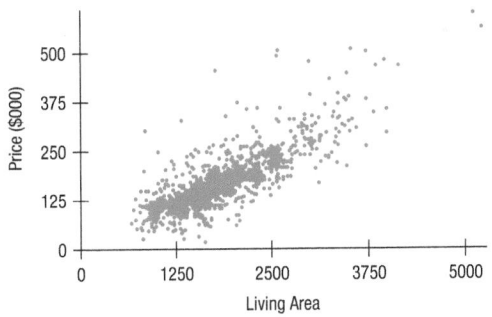

Model We need to check the same conditions for regression as we did for correlation. To do that, make a picture. Never fit a regression without looking at the scatterplot first.

Check the Linearity, Equal Spread, and Outlier Conditions.

✓ **Linearity Condition** The scatterplot shows two variables that appear to have a fairly strong positive association. The plot appears to be fairly linear.

✓ **Outlier Condition** There appear to be a few possible outliers, especially among large, relatively expensive houses. A few smaller houses are expensive for their size. We'll check their influence on the model later.

✓ **Equal Spread Condition** The scatterplot shows a consistent spread across all the x-values we're modelling.

We have two quantitative variables that appear to satisfy the conditions, so we'll model this relationship with a regression line.

(continued)

DO **Mechanics** Find the equation of the regression line using a statistics package. Remember to write the equation of the model using meaningful variable names.

Once you have the model, plot the residuals and check the Equal Spread Condition again.

Our software produces the following output:

Dependent variable is Price

1057 total cases

R squared = 62.43%

s = 57,930 with 1000 − 2 = 998 df

Variable Coefficient

Intercept 6378.08

Living Area 115.13

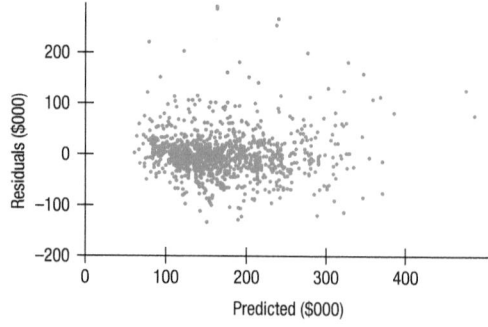

The residual plot appears generally patternless, thus satisfying our 'Equal Spread Condition'. The few relatively expensive small houses are evident, but setting them aside and refitting the model did not change either the slope or the intercept very much, so we left them in. There's a slight tendency for cheaper houses to have less variation, but the spread is roughly the same throughout.

REPORT **Conclusion** Interpret what you have found in the proper context.

MEMO:

Re: Report on Housing Prices

We examined how well the size of a house could predict its selling price. Data were obtained from sales of 1057 homes. The model is:

$$\widehat{Price} = \$6376.08 + 115.13 \times Living\ Area$$

In other words, from a base of $6376.08, houses cost about $115.13 per square foot.

This model appears reasonable from both a statistical and a real estate perspective. While we know that size isn't the only factor in pricing a house, the model accounts for 62.4% of the variation in selling price.

As a reality check, we consulted two real estate pricing sites (www.realestateabc.com, www.zillow.com) and found that houses in this region were averaging $100 to $150 per square foot, so our model is plausible.

Of course, not all house prices are predicted well by the model. We computed the model without several of these houses, but their impact on the regression model was small. We believe that this is a reasonable place to start to assess whether a house is priced correctly for this market. Future analysis might benefit by considering other factors, e.g., the number of bathrooms, the number of fireplaces, etc.

LO❸ **7.8   Nonlinear Relationships**

Everything we've discussed in this chapter requires that the underlying relationship between two variables be linear. But what should we do when the relationship is nonlinear and we can't use the correlation coefficient or a linear model?

Let's consider an example. The Human Development Index (HDI) was introduced by the United Nations as a general measure of quality of life in countries around the world. It combines economic information (GDP), life expectancy, and education. The growth of cell phone usage has been phenomenal worldwide. Is cell phone usage related to the developmental state of a country? Figure 7.5 shows a scatterplot of number of *Cell Phones* vs. *HDI* for 152 countries of the world.

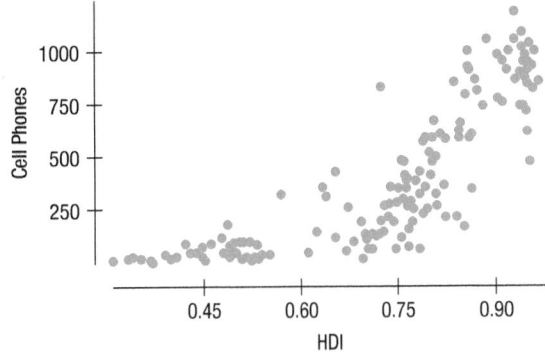

Figure 7.5   The scatterplot of number of *Cell Phones* (000s) vs. *HDI* for countries shows a bent relationship not suitable for correlation or regression.

We can look at the scatterplot and see that cell phone usage increases with increasing HDI. But the relationship isn't straight. In Figure 7.5, we can easily see the bend in the form. But that doesn't help us summarize or model the relationship.

The main way to deal with a nonlinear relationship is to transform or re-express one or both of the variables by a function such as the square root, logarithm, or reciprocal. We saw in Chapter 5 that a transformation can improve the symmetry of the distribution of a single variable. In the same way—and often with the same transforming function—transformations can make a relationship more nearly linear.

Figure 7.6, for example, shows the relationship between the log of the number of cell phones and the HDI for the same countries.

The advantage of re-expressing variables is that we *can* use regression models, along with all the supporting statistics still to come. The disadvantage is that we must interpret our results in terms of the re-expressed data, and it can be difficult to explain what we mean by the logarithm of the number of cell phones in a country. We can, of course, reverse the transformation to transform a predicted value

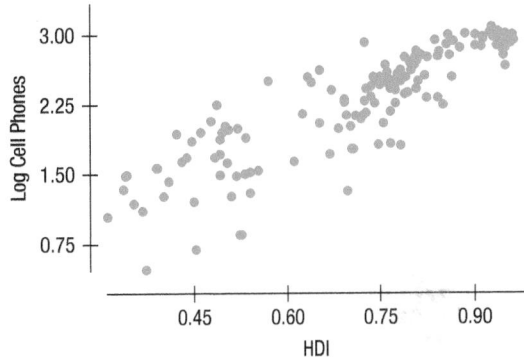

Figure 7.6   Taking the logarithm of cell phones results in a more nearly linear relationship.

or residual back to the original units. (In the case of a logarithmic transformation, calculate 10^y to get back to the original units.) For more on re-expression, see Chapter 19, Sections 19.6, 19.7, and 19.8.

FOR EXAMPLE   Re-expressing for linearity

Consider the relationship between a company's *Assets* and its *Sales* as reported in annual financial statements. Here's a scatterplot of those variables for 79 of the largest companies together with a scatterplot of the logarithm of each variable:

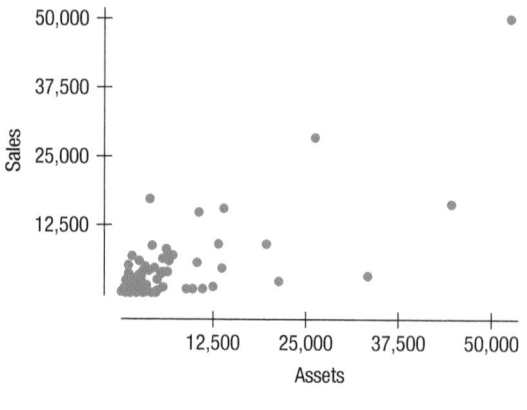

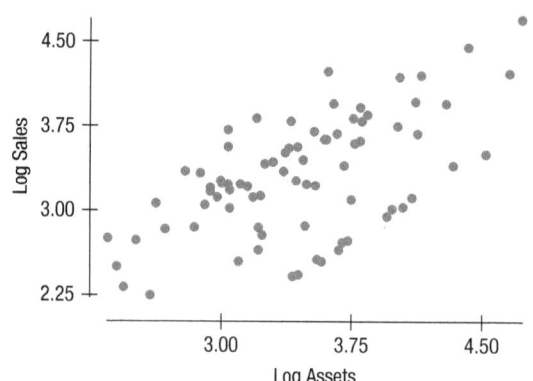

QUESTION   What should we say about the relationship between *Assets* and *Sales*?

ANSWER   The scatterplot of the log transformed variables is linear and shows a medium strength pattern. We could find a linear model for this relationship, but we'd have to interpret it in terms of log *Sales* and log *Assets*.

WHAT CAN GO WRONG?

Regression analyses can be more subtle than they seem at first. Here are some guidelines to help you use this powerful method effectively.

- **Don't fit a straight line to a nonlinear relationship.** Linear regression is suited only to relationships that are, in fact, linear.

- **Beware of extraordinary points.** Data values can be extraordinary or unusual in a regression in two ways. They can have *y*-values that stand out from the linear pattern suggested by the bulk of the data. These are what we've been calling outliers; although with regression, a point can be an outlier by being far from the linear pattern even if it's not the largest or smallest y-value. Points can also be extraordinary in their x-values. Such points can exert a strong influence on the line. Both kinds of extraordinary points require attention.

- **Don't extrapolate far beyond the data. A linear model will often do a reasonable job of summarizing a relationship in the range of observed x-values.** Once we have a working model for the relationship, it's tempting to use it. But beware of predicting y-values for x-values that lie too far outside the range of the original data. The model may no longer hold there, so such extrapolations too far from the data are dangerous.

- **Don't infer that x causes y just because there's a good linear model for their relationship.** When two variables are strongly correlated, it's often tempting to assume a causal relationship between them. Putting a regression line on a scatterplot tempts us even further, but it doesn't make the assumption of causation any more valid.

- **Don't choose a model based on R^2 alone.** Although R^2 measures the *strength* of the linear association, a high R^2 does not demonstrate the *appropriateness* of the regression. A single unusual observation, or data that separate into two groups, can make the R^2 seem quite large when in fact the linear regression model is simply inappropriate. Conversely, a low R^2 value may be due to a single outlier. It may be that most of the data fall roughly along a straight line, with the exception of a single point. Always look at the scatterplot.

- **Be sure to get the regression the right way around.** If you want to estimate y from x, then you need to regress y against x, with x as the explanatory variable. Conversely, to estimate x from a known value of y, you need to regress x against y, with y as the explanatory variable. Always be sure how you're going to use the regression line (which variable you want to estimate from the other one) before deciding which way to do the regression.

ETHICS IN ACTION

Jill Hathway is looking for a career change and is interested in starting a franchise. After spending the past 20 years working as a mid-level manager for a major corporation, Jill wants to indulge her entrepreneurial spirit and strike out on her own. She is considering a franchise in the health and fitness industry. She's looking at several possibilities, including GoodLife Fitness, for which she requested a franchise packet. Included in the packet information were data showing how various regional demographics (age, gender, income) related to franchise success (revenue, profit, return on investment). GoodLife Fitness reported various graphs and data analysis results based on a random sample of their existing locations to help prospective franchisers in their decision-making process. Jill was particularly interested in the graph and the regression analysis that related the proportion of women over the age of 40 within a 30-kilometre radius of a GoodLife Fitness location to return on investment for the franchise. She noticed that there was a positive relationship. With a little research, she discovered that the proportion of women over the age of 40 in her city was higher than for any other GoodLife Fitness location (attributable, in part, to the large number of retirees relocating to her city). She then used the regression equation to project return on investment for a GoodLife Fitness located in her city and was very pleased with the result. With such objective data, she felt confident that GoodLife Fitness was the franchise for her.

Ethical Issue *GoodLife Fitness is reporting analysis based on a random sample of their existing locations and Jill is extrapolating beyond the range of x-values (related to Item C, ASA Ethical Guidelines; see Appendix C, the American Statistical Association's Ethical Guidelines for Statistical Practice, also available online at www.amstat.org/about/ethicalguidelines.cfm).*

Ethical Solution *GoodLife Fitness should include a disclaimer that the analysis was based on very few observations and that the equation should not be used to predict success at other locations or beyond the range of x-values used in the analysis.*

WHAT HAVE WE LEARNED?

Learning Objectives	**1** We've learned that when the relationship between quantitative variables is linear, a linear model can help summarize that relationship and give us insights about it.
	• The regression (best-fit) line doesn't pass through all the points, but it is the best compromise in the sense that the sum of squares of the residuals is the smallest possible.
	2 We've learned several things that the correlation, r, tells us about the regression:
	• The slope of the line is based on the correlation, adjusted for the standard deviations of x and y. We've learned to interpret that slope in context.
	• For each SD that a case is away from the mean of x, we expect it to be r SDs in y away from the y mean.
	• Because r is always between −1 and +1, each predicted y is fewer SDs away from its mean than the corresponding x was, a phenomenon called *regression to the mean*.
	• The square of the correlation coefficient, R^2, gives us the fraction of the variation of the response accounted for by the regression model. The remaining $1 - R^2$ of the variation is left in the residuals.
	3 We've learned how to transform variables to convert a nonlinear relationship to a linear one, on which we can use linear regression.

Terms	
Dependent variable	The variable whose value depends on the value of the explanatory variable, usually denoted by y and plotted on the vertical axis of a graph. Also known as *predicted variable* or *response variable*.
Explanatory variable	The variable used to explain the value of another variable, usually denoted by x and plotted on the horizontal axis of a graph. Also known as the *independent variable*.
Independent variable	See *explanatory variable*
Intercept	The intercept, b_0, gives a starting value in y-units. It's the $\hat{y}$ value when x is 0. $$b_0 = \bar{y} - b_1\bar{x}$$
Line of best fit (least squares line)	The unique line that minimizes the variance of the residuals or, equivalently, the sum of the squared residuals.
Linear model (line of best fit)	The linear model of the form $\hat{y} = b_0 + b_1 x$ fit by least squares. Also called the *regression line*. To interpret a linear model, we need to know the variables and their units.
Predicted value	The prediction for y found for each x-value in the data. A predicted value, $\hat{y}$, is found by substituting the x-value in the regression equation. The predicted values are the values on the fitted line; the points $(x, \hat{y})$ lie exactly on the fitted line.
Predicted variable	See *dependent variable*.
Regression line	The particular linear equation that satisfies the least squares criterion, often called the *line of best fit*.
Regression to the mean	Because the correlation is always less than 1.0 in magnitude, each predicted y tends to be fewer standard deviations from its mean than its corresponding x is from its mean.
Residual	The difference between the actual data value and the corresponding value predicted by the regression model—or, more generally, predicted by any model.
Response variable	See *dependent variable*.
R^2	• The square of the correlation between y and x. • The fraction of the variability of y accounted for by the least squares linear regression on x. • An overall measure of how successful the regression is in linearly relating y to x.
Slope	The slope, b_1, is given in y-units per x-unit. Differences of one unit in x are associated with differences of b_1 units in predicted values of y: $$b_1 = r\frac{s_y}{s_x}$$

Standard deviation of the residuals	s_e is found by

$$s_e = \sqrt{\frac{\sum e^2}{n-2}}.$$

Skills

Plan
- Know how to identify response (y) and explanatory (x) variables in context.
- Understand how a linear equation summarizes the relationship between two variables.
- Recognize when a regression should be used to summarize a linear relationship between two quantitative variables.
- Know how to judge whether the slope of a regression makes sense.
- Examine a scatterplot of your data for violations of the Linearity, Equal Spread, and Outlier Conditions that would make it inappropriate to compute a regression.
- Understand that the least squares slope is easily affected by extreme values.
- Define residuals as the differences between the data values and the corresponding values predicted by the line, and recognize that the least squares criterion finds the line that minimizes the sum of the squared residuals.

Do
- Know how to find the slope and intercept values of a regression.
- Be able to use regression to predict a value of y for a given x.
- Know how to compute the residual for each data value and how to compute the standard deviation of the residuals.
- Be able to evaluate the Equal Spread Condition with a scatterplot of the residuals after computing the regression.

Report
- Write a sentence explaining what a linear equation says about the relationship between y and x, basing it on the fact that the slope is given in y-units per x-unit.
- Understand how the correlation coefficient and the regression slope are related. Know that R^2 describes how much of the variation in y is accounted for by its linear relationship with x.
- Be able to describe a prediction made from a regression equation, relating the predicted value to the specified x-value.

MINI case studies

Canadian Retail Sales

Companies marketing to consumers are very interested in statistics on retail sales. Statistics Canada puts out a monthly publication called "Retail Trade," which is based on information from a sample of Canadian retailers who contribute to the Monthly Retail Trade Survey. Other commercial organizations assemble their own data and make their own projections about trends in retail sales. For instance, the *Financial Post* publishes "FP Markets—Canadian Demographics," which contains estimates of retail sales for the current year together with "buying power indices" such as income per capita. A major question is which buying power indices are related to which retail sales data.

A selection from "FP Markets—Canadian Demographics," is available in the data file **ch07_MCSP_Retail_Sales_Canada** for Canadian cities with over 500,000 population. It includes data based on households (people living under the same roof) and also data based on individuals (per capita data).[3] In order to estimate total retail sales, we need to find some strong relationships—for example, regression lines with

Gaertner/Alamy Stock Photo

[3]Based on *Financial Post*, Canwest Digital Media. (2010). FP Markets—Canadian Demographics, 2009, pp. 18-20, 36-41.

(continued)

high R^2. (a) Examine a regression of "sales per household" based on the explanatory variable "income per household," and then examine a regression of "sales per capita" based on the explanatory variable "income per capita." What happens if we remove the two cities at the top right of the scatterplot?

(b) Next focus on clothing sales per capita and examine the strength of its relationship to income per capita. What happens if we remove the two cities that we removed in (a)?

Cost of Living

The Mercer Human Resource Consulting website (www.mercer.com) lists prices of certain items in selected cities around the world. It also reports an overall cost of living index for each city compared with the costs of hundreds of items in New York City. For example, London at 110.6 is 10.6% more expensive than New York. You'll find the 2006 data for 16 cities in the data set **ch07_MCSP_Cost_of_Living.** Included are the 2006 cost of living index, the cost of a luxury apartment (per month), the price of a bus or subway ride, the price of a CD, the price of an international newspaper, the price of a cup of coffee (including service), and the price of a fast-food hamburger meal. All prices are in U.S. dollars.

Examine the relationship between the overall cost of living and the cost of each of these individual items. Verify the necessary conditions and describe the relationship in as much detail as possible. (Remember to look at direction, form, and strength.) Identify any unusual observations.

Based on the correlations and linear regressions, which item would be the best predictor of overall cost in these cities? Which would be the worst? Are there any surprising relationships? Write a short report detailing your conclusions.

Motivating Students: Carrots or Sticks or ...

Professor A. Voidim looked through the midterm exam marks of his 100 students and wondered whether there was a way to motivate them to do better on the final exam. He decided to try out two ideas. First, he sent a harsh email to the 10 students whose midterm marks were the lowest. He criticized their performance and said they should quit the video games and parties and hit the books. Second, he wrote to the top 10 students, praised their achievement, and wished them even more success on the final exam. When he had marked the final exam, he checked out the marks of the students who were in the top 10 on the midterm and was dismayed to find that their final exam marks were on average 5.5% *lower* than on the midterm. "So much for encouraging them!" he thought. But the lowest 10 students on the midterm had *increased* their marks on the final by an average of 4.1%. "Harsh, critical emails work better than congratulatory ones," thought Professor A. Voidim. "I'll send out more harsh emails in future."

Using the data in the file **ch07_MCSP_Motivating_Students**, assess whether the emails affected student performance. Would we expect similar emails to be effective in other classes where the correlation between midterm and final exam marks is lower?

Let us call the students with the 10 lowest marks on the midterm Group A, and the students with the 10 highest marks on the midterm Group B. (a) Perform a linear regression of the final exam marks using the midterm marks as the explanatory variable (checking the four conditions). (b) If the emails affected student performance, the residuals for the students who received emails would be expected to be higher/lower than the residuals for the rest of the class. Check to see whether this is true (i) for Group A, and (ii) for Group B. (c) Based on the regression equation, compare the expected marks on the final exam with the marks students actually got on the midterm exam averaged for Groups A and B. Compare your results for (b), (c), and Professor A. Voidim's results. (d) Calculate the means and standard deviations of the midterm marks and of the expected final exam marks from the regression. How many standard deviations below/above the mean is the average of the midterm exam marks of the students in Groups A and B? How many standard deviations below/above the mean is the average of the expected final exam marks (from the regression) of the students in Groups A and B? (e) Calculate the correlation coefficient between the midterm and the final exam marks for all students. What is the connection between this correlation coefficient and your answers to (d)? (f) Suppose we had a different set of data, with the same means and standard deviations, but with a different correlation coefficient. If the correlation coefficient is lower in the new data, would the effect that Professor A Voidim observed (the students in Group A improving and the students in Group B getting lower marks) be greater or less? Include the extreme case with correlation coefficient equal to zero. (g) Did Professor A. Voidim's emails affect student performance? If not, why are the final exam marks higher for the students in Group A and lower for those in Group B?

MyStatLab Students! Save time, improve your grades with MyStatLab. Questions marked in ▪ can be found on MyStatLab. You can practise them as often as you want, and most feature step-by-step guided solutions to help you find the right answer. You'll find a personalized study plan available to you too!

Technology Help: Regression

All statistics packages make a table of results for a regression. These tables may differ slightly from one package to another, but all are essentially the same—and all include much more than we need to know for now. Every computer regression table includes a section that looks something like this:

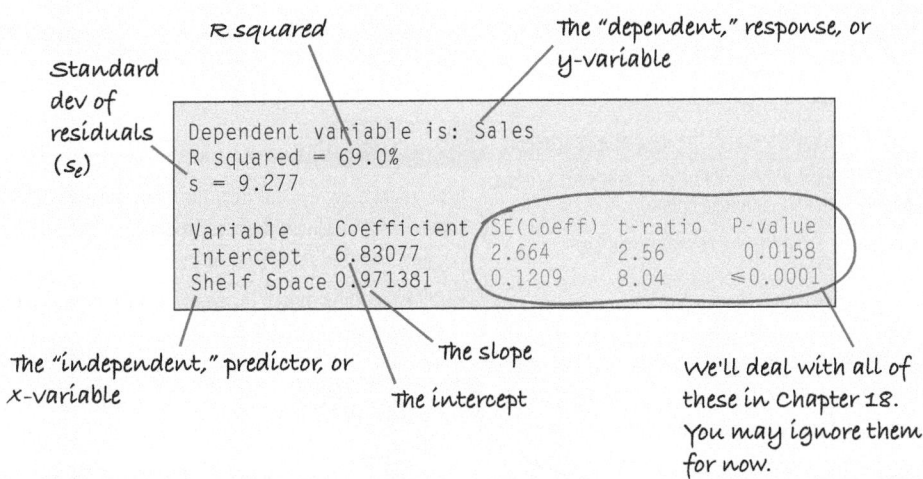

The slope and intercept coefficient are given in a table such as this one. Usually the slope is labelled with the name of the *x*-variable, and the intercept is labelled "Intercept" or "Constant." So the regression equation shown here is

$$\widehat{Sales} = 6.83077 + 0.97138 \text{ Shelf Space.}$$

It's not unusual for statistics packages to give many more digits of the estimated slope and intercept than could possibly be estimated from the data. (The original data were reported to the nearest gram.) Ordinarily, you should round most of the reported numbers to one digit more than the precision of the data, and the slope to two. We'll learn about the other numbers in the regression table in Chapter 18. For now, all you need to be able to do is find the coefficients, the s_e, and the R^2 value.

EXCEL

To calculate the correlation coefficient:

• Click on a blank cell in the spreadsheet.

(*continued*)

- Go to the **Formulas** tab in the ribbon and click **More Functions: Statistical**.

- Choose the **CORREL** function from the drop-down menu of functions.

- In the dialogue box that pops up, enter the range of one of the variables in the space provided.

- Enter the range of the other variable in the space provided.

- Click **OK**.

To make a regression, first install the Data Analysis add-in using **File > Options > Add-ins:**

- From the Data ribbon, select the Data Analysis add-in.

- From its menu, select **Regression**.

- Indicate the range of the data whose scatterplot you wish to draw.

- Check the Labels box to see if your data columns have names in the first cell.

- Check the **Line Fit Plots** box, and click **OK**.

- Excel will place regression output and the scatterplot on a new sheet.

- The correlation is in cell B4.

- The slope and *y*-intercept are in cells B18 and B17, respectively.

- You can edit or remove any part of the scatterplot by right-clicking on the part you want to edit.

- For example, to remove the Predicted Values, right-click on one of the points and **Delete**.

- To add the Least Squares Regression Line, right-click on the data and **Add Trendline…**

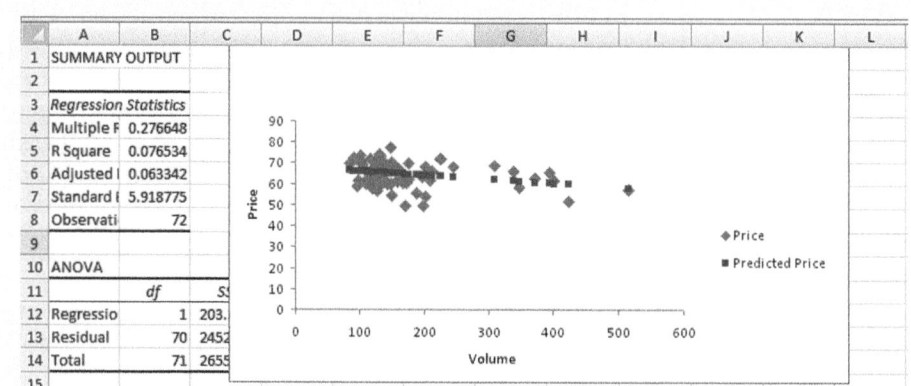

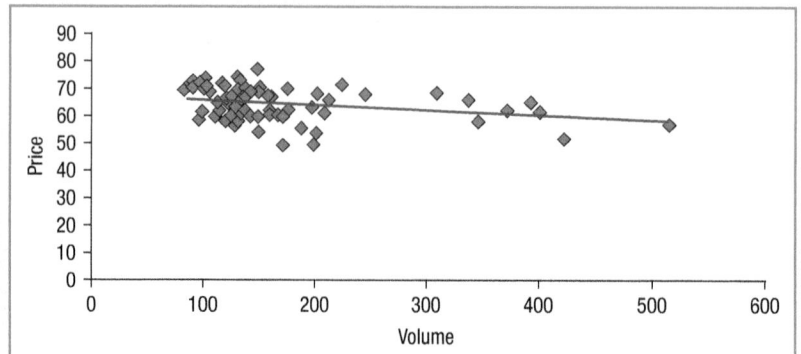

But we aren't quite done yet. Excel always scales the axes of a scatterplot to show the origin (00). But most data are not near the origin, so you may get a plot that, like this one, is bunched up in one corner.

- Right-click on the *y*-axis labels. From the menu that drops down, choose **Format Axis…**

- Choose **Scale**.

- Set the *y*-axis minimum value.

One useful trick is to use the dialogue box itself as a straightedge to read over to the *y*-axis so that you can estimate a good minimum value. Here 40 seems appropriate.

- Repeat the process with the *x*-axis.

MINITAB

Choose **Regression** from the **Stat** menu. From the Regression submenu, choose **Fitted Line Plot**. In the Fitted Line Plot dialogue, click in the **Response Y** box, and assign the *y*-variable from the Variable list. Click in the **Predictor X** box, and assign the *x*-variable from the Variable list. Make sure that the Type of Regression Model is set to Linear. Click the **OK** button.

SPSS

To compute a regression, from the Analyze menu, choose **Regression > Linear…** In the Linear Regression dialogue box, specify the Dependent (*y*), and Independent (*x*) variables.

- Click the **Plots** button to specify plots and Normal Probability Plots of the residuals. Click **OK**.

JMP

To compute a regression:

- Choose **Fit Y by X** from the Analyze menu. Specify the *y*-variable in the Select Columns box and click the **Y, Response** button.

- Specify the *x*-variable and click the **X, Factor** button.

- Click **OK** to make a scatterplot.

- In the scatterplot window, click on the red triangle beside the heading labelled **Bivariate Fit…** and choose **Fit Line**. JMP draws the least squares regression line on the scatterplot and displays the results of the regression in tables below the plot.

EXERCISES

SECTION 7.1

1. True or false? If false, explain briefly.

a) We choose the linear model that passes through the most data points on the scatterplot.

b) The residuals are the observed y-values minus the y-values predicted by the linear model.

c) Least squares means that the square of the largest residual is as small as it could possibly be. **LO ❶**

2. True or false? If false, explain briefly.

a) Some of the residuals from a least squares linear model will be positive and some will be negative.

b) Least squares means that some of the squares of the residuals are minimized.

c) We write $\hat{y}$ to denote the predicted values and y to denote the observed values. **LO ❶**

SECTION 7.2

3. For the following bookstore sales data, the correlation is 0.965.

Number of Salespeople Working	Sales (in $1000)
2	10
3	11
7	13
9	14
10	18
10	20
12	20
15	22
16	22
20	26
$\bar{x} = 10.4$	$\hat{y} = 17.6$
$SD(x) = 5.64$	$SD(y) = 5.34$

a) If the number of people working is two standard deviations above the mean, how many standard deviations above or below the mean do you expect sales to be?

b) What value of sales does that correspond to?

c) If the number of people working is one standard deviation below the mean, how many standard deviations above or below the mean do you expect sales to be?

d) What value of sales does that correspond to? **LO ❶**

4. For the bookstore in Exercise 3, the manager wants to predict *Sales* from *Number of Salespeople Working*.

a) Find the slope estimate, b_1.

b) What does it mean, in this context?

c) Find the intercept, b_0.

d) What does it mean, in this context? Is it meaningful?

e) Write down the equation that predicts *Sales* from *Number of Salespeople Working*.

f) If 18 people are working, what *Sales* do you predict?

g) If sales are actually $25,000, when 18 people are working, what is the value of the residual?

h) Have we overestimated or underestimated the sales? **LO ❶**

SECTION 7.3

5. A CEO complains that the winners of his "rookie junior executive of the year" award often turn out to have less impressive performance the following year. He wonders whether the award actually encourages them to slack off. Can you offer a better explanation? **LO ❷**

6. An online investment blogger advises investing in mutual funds that have performed badly in the past year because "regression to the mean tells us that they'll do well next year." Is he correct? **LO ❷**

SECTIONS 7.4 AND 7.5

7. Here are the residuals for a regression of *Sales* on *Number of Salespeople Working* for the bookstore in Exercise 3:

Salespeople Working	Residual
2	0.07
3	0.16
7	−1.49
9	−2.32
10	0.77
10	2.77
12	0.94
15	0.20
16	−0.72
20	−0.37

a) What are the units of the residuals?

b) Which residual contributes the most to the sum that was minimized according to the least squares criterion to find this regression?

c) Which residual contributes least to that sum? **LO ❶**

8. Here are residual plots (residuals plotted against predicted values) for three linear regression models. Indicate which condition appears to be violated (Linearity, Outlier, or Equal Spread) in each case. **LO ❶**

a)

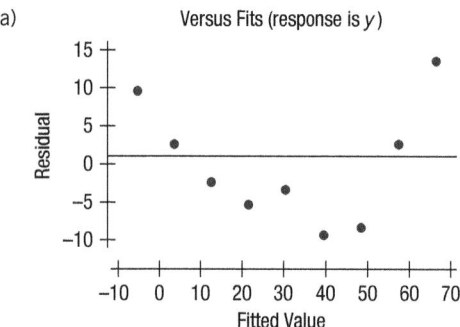

b)

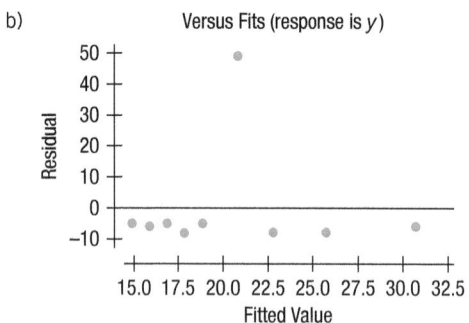

c)

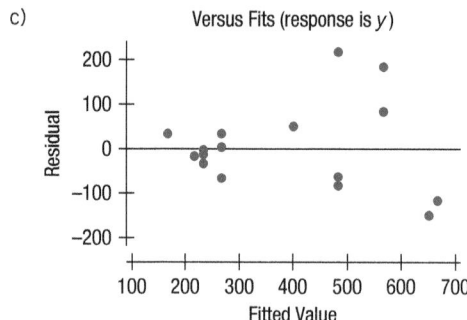

SECTIONS 7.6 AND 7.7

9. For the regression model of the bookstore in Exercise 3, what is the value of R^2 and what does it mean? **LO ❷**

10. A linear regression of the price of external hard drives against their capacity in terabytes had a correlation coefficient of 0.994. What is the value of R^2 for this regression and how do you interpret its meaning? **LO ❷**

SECTION 7.8

11. When analyzing data on the number of employees in small companies in one town, a researcher took the square root of the counts. Some of the resulting values, which are reasonably symmetric, were

4, 4, 6, 7, 7, 8, 10

What were the original values, and how are they distributed? **LO ❸**

12. You wish to explain to your boss what effect taking the base-10 logarithm of the salary in the company's database

will have on the data. As simple example values, you compare a salary of $10,000 earned by a part-time shipping clerk, a salary of $100,000 earned by a manager, and the CEO's $1,000,000 compensation package. Why might the average of these values be a misleading summary? What would the logarithms of these three values be? **LO ❸**

CHAPTER EXERCISES

13. Pizza sales and price, part 1. A linear model fit to predict weekly *Sales* of frozen pizza (in kilograms) from the average *Price* ($/unit) charged by a sample of stores in 39 recent weeks is

$$\widehat{Sales} = 141{,}865.53 - 24{,}369.49\ Price.$$

a) What is the explanatory variable?
b) What is the response variable?
c) What does the slope mean in this context?
d) What does the *y*-intercept mean in this context? Is it meaningful?
e) What do you predict the sales to be if the average price charged was $3.50 for a pizza?
f) If the sales for a price of $3.50 turned out to be 60,000 kilograms, what would the residual be? **LO ❶**

⊤ 14. 2012 Honda prices, part 1. A linear model to predict the *Price* of a 2012 Honda Civic EX (in dollars) from its *Mileage* (in miles) was fit to 18 cars that were available during the week of March 1, 2013 (Kelly's Blue Book, www.kbb.com) within 200 miles of San Francisco, CA. The model was

$$\widehat{Price} = 21{,}253.58 - 0.11097\ Mileage$$

a) What is the explanatory variable?
b) What is the response variable?
c) What does the slope mean in this context?
d) What does the *y*-intercept mean in this context? Is it meaningful?
e) What do you predict the price to be for a car with 50,000 miles on it?
f) If the price for a car with 50,000 miles on it was $14,000, what would the residual be?
g) Would that car for $14,000 and 50,000 miles seem like a good deal or a bad deal? Explain. (*Source:* From Kelly's Blue Book, www.kbb.com.) **LO ❶**

15. Pizza sales and price, part 2. For the data in Exercise 13, the average *Sales* was 52,697 kilograms (SD = 10,261 kilograms), and the correlation between *Price* and *Sales* was −0.547.

If the *Price* in a particular week was one SD higher than the mean *Price*, how much pizza would you predict was sold that week? **LO ❷**

⊤ 16. 2012 Honda prices, part 2. The 18 cars in Exercise 14 had an average price of +19,843.50 (SD = 1853.592), and the correlation between *Price* and *Mileage* was

−0.889. If the *Mileage* of a 2012 Honda Civic EX was one SD below the average number of miles, what *Price* would you predict for it? **LO ❷**

17. Sales by region. A sales manager for a major pharmaceutical company analyzes last year's sales data for 96 sales representatives, grouping them by region (1 = East Coast U.S.; 2 = Midwest U.S.; 3 = West U.S.; 4 = South U.S.; 5 = Canada; 6 = Rest of World). She plots *Sales* (in $1000) against *Region* (1–6) and sees a strong negative correlation:

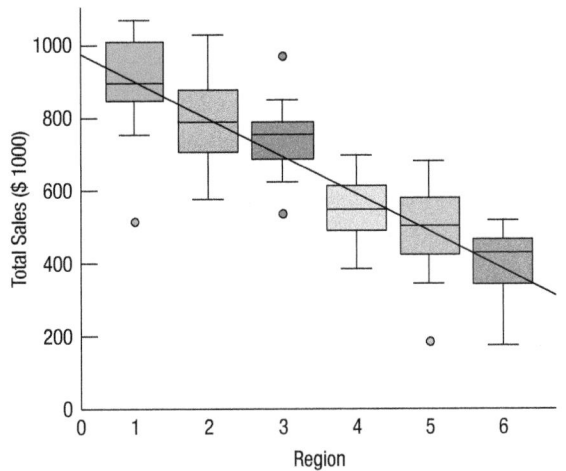

She fits a regression to the data and finds

$$\widehat{Sales} = 1002.5 - 102.7\ Region.$$

The R^2 is 70.5%.

Write a few sentences interpreting this model and describing what she can conclude from this analysis. **LO ❶**

18. Salary by job type. A human resources manager wants to examine salary in order to prepare annual reviews. He selects 28 employees at random with job types ranging from 01 = Stocking clerk to 99 = President. He plots *Salary* ($) against *Job Type* and finds a strong linear relationship with a correlation of 0.96.

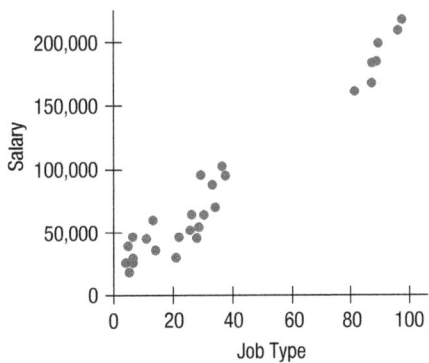

The regression output gives

$$\widehat{Salary} = 15827.9 + 1939.1\ Job\ Type.$$

Write a few sentences interpreting this model and describing what he can conclude from this analysis. **LO ❶**

Ⓣ 19. GDP growth 2012, part 1. Is economic growth in the developing world related to growth in the industrialized countries? Here's a scatterplot of the growth (in percent of gross domestic product) of 180 developing countries versus the growth of 33 developed countries as grouped by the World Bank (www.ers.usda.gov/data/macroeconomics). Each point represents one of the years from 1970 to 2011. The output of a regression analysis follows.

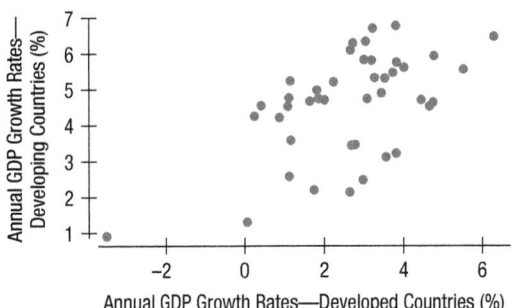

Dependent variable: GDP Growth Developing Countries
$R^2 = 31.64\%$
  $s = 1.201$

Variable	Coefficient
Intercept	3.38
GDP Growth Developed Countries	0.468

a) Check the assumptions and conditions for the linear model.
b) Explain the meaning of R^2 in this context. (*Source:* United States Department of Agriculture.) **LO ❶, ❷**

Ⓣ 20. European GDP growth 2012, part 1. Is economic growth in Europe related to growth in the United States? Here's a scatterplot of the average growth in 25 European countries (in percent of gross domestic product) versus the growth in the United States. Each point represents one of the years from 1970 to 2011.

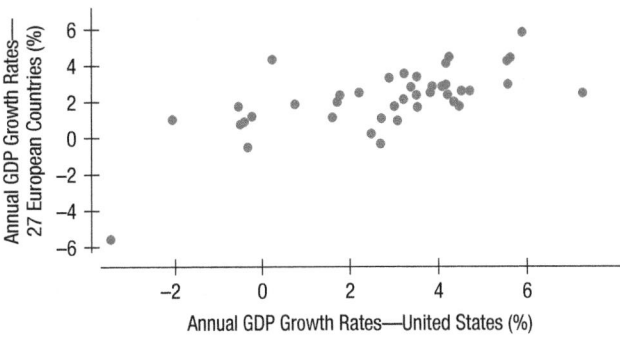

Dependent variable: European Countries GDP Growth
$R^2 = 44.92\%$
  $s = 1.352$

Variable	Coefficient
Intercept	0.693
U.S. GDP Growth	534

a) Check the assumptions and conditions for the linear model.

b) Explain the meaning of R^2 in this context. **LO ❶, ❷**

❶ 21. GDP growth 2012, part 2. From the linear model fit to the data on GDP growth in Exercise 19:

a) Write the equation of the regression line.

b) What is the meaning of the intercept? Does it make sense in this context?

c) Interpret the meaning of the slope.

d) In a year in which the developed countries grow at 4%, what do you predict for the developing world?

e) During a year in which the developed countries experienced 2.65% growth, the developing countries grew at a rate of 6.09%. Is this more or less than you would have predicted?

f) What is the residual for this year? **LO ❶, ❷**

❶ 22. European GDP growth 2012, part 2. From the linear model fit to the data on GDP growth in Exercise 20:

a) Write the equation of the regression line.

b) What is the meaning of the intercept? Does it make sense in this context?

c) Interpret the meaning of the slope.

d) In a year in which the United States grows at 0%, what do you predict for European growth?

e) During a year in which the United States experienced 3.00% growth, Europe grew at a rate of 1.78%. Is this more or less than you would have predicted?

f) What is the residual for this year? **LO ❶, ❷**

23. Mutual funds. As the nature of investing shifted in the 1990s (more day traders and faster flow of information using technology), the relationship between mutual fund monthly performance (*Return*) in percent and money flowing (*Flow*) into mutual funds ($ million) shifted. Using only the values for the 1990s (we'll examine later years in later chapters), answer the following questions. (You may assume that the assumptions and conditions for regression are met.)

The least squares linear regression is

$$\widehat{Flow} = 9747 + 771 \; Return.$$

a) Interpret the intercept in the linear model.

b) Interpret the slope in the linear model.

c) What is the predicted fund *Flow* for a month that had a market *Return* of 0%?

d) If, during this month, the recorded fund *Flow* was $5 billion, what is the residual using this linear model? Did the model provide an underestimate or overestimate for this month? **LO ❶**

24. Online clothing purchases. An online clothing retailer examined its transactional database to see if total yearly *Purchases* ($) were related to customers' *Incomes* ($). (You may assume that the assumptions and conditions for regression are met.)

The least squares linear regression is

$$\widehat{Purchases} = -31.6 + 0.012 \; Income.$$

a) Interpret the intercept in the linear model.

b) Interpret the slope in the linear model.

c) If a customer has an *Income* of $20,000, what are his or her predicted total yearly *Purchases*?

d) This customer's yearly *Purchases* were actually $100. What is the residual using this linear model? Did the model provide an underestimate or overestimate for this customer? **LO ❶**

❶ 25. The Home Depot, part 1. Analysts at The Home Depot want to predict quarterly sales from housing and find the correlation is 0.70. They then examine the scatterplot and decide it is appropriate to fit a regression model to predict *Sales* ($ billion) from *Housing Starts* (in thousands).

a) What units does the slope have?

b) What is the R^2 value for the model?

c) What would you predict about the *Sales* for a quarter that has housing starts one standard deviation below average in *Housing Starts*? **LO ❶, ❷**

❶ 26. House prices. House prices are subject to a variety of economic factors but are, to some extent, based on the living area of the house. Analysts examined the recent sales of 1000 homes and found the correlation to be 0.79. After examining a scatterplot, they decide a linear model is appropriate and fit a regression model to predict *House Price* ($) from *Living Area* (sq. ft.).

a) What units does the slope have?

b) What is the R^2 value for the model?

c) What would you predict about the *Price* of a house that is two standard deviations larger in *Living Area* than the mean? **LO ❶, ❷**

27. Retail sales, part 1. Sales are often related to economic indicators. One possible indicator is the unemployment rate. Data for a large retail store were used to obtain a linear regression model to predict quarterly *Sales* ($ billion) based on unemployment *Rate* (in %) over a period of four years. This regression model produced an $R^2 = 88.3\%$ and a slope of −2.99.

a) Interpret the meaning of R^2.

b) What is the correlation of *Sales* and unemployment *Rate*?

c) If a quarter has an unemployment *Rate* 1% larger than another, what is the predicted impact on *Sales*? **LO ❷**

28. Pizza sales and price, part 3. The linear model in Exercise 13 predicting *Sales* of frozen pizza (in kilograms) from *Price* ($/unit) has an R^2 of 32.9% and a slope of −24,369.5.

a) Interpret the meaning of R^2.

b) What is the correlation of *Sales* and *Price*?

c) If in one week the *Price* is $0.50 higher than in another, what is the predicted difference in *Sales*? **LO ❶, ❷**

29. Residual plots, part 1. Tell what each of the following residual plots indicates about the appropriateness of the linear model that was fit to the data. **LO ❶**

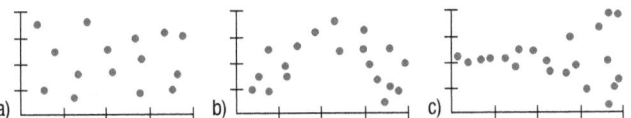

30. Residual plots, part 2. Tell what each of the following residual plots indicates about the appropriateness of the linear model that was fit to the data. **LO ❶**

31. The Home Depot, part 2. Consider the quarterly Home Depot *Sales* in Exercise 25 again. The regression analysis gives the model

$$\widehat{Sales} = -11.5 + 0.0535 \text{ } Housing \text{ } Starts.$$

a) Explain what the slope of the line says.
b) What would you predict for quarterly sales when housing starts are 500,000 units?
c) If quarterly sales are $3 billion higher than predicted given the reported housing starts during a quarter, what is this difference called? **LO ❶**

32. Retail sales, part 2. Consider the regression described in Exercise 27 again. The regression analysis gives the model

$$\widehat{Sales} = 20.91 - 2.994 \text{ } Rate.$$

a) Explain what the slope of the line says.
b) If the unemployment *Rate* is 6.0%, how much do you predict *Sales* will be?
c) If the unemployment *Rate* next quarter is 4.0% and *Sales* are reported as $8.5 billion, is this less than or more than you would predict? By how much? What is that called? **LO ❶**

Ⓣ 33. Consumer spending. An analyst at a large credit card company is looking at the relationship between customers' charges to the bank's card in two successive months. He selects 150 customers at random, regresses charges in *March* ($) on charges in *February* ($), and finds an R^2 of 79%. The intercept is $730.20, and the slope is 0.79. After verifying all the data, he concludes that the model is a useful one for predicting one month's charges from the other. Examine the data in the data file and comment on his conclusions. **LO ❶**

Ⓣ 34. Insurance policies. An actuary at a mid-sized insurance company is examining the sales performance of the company's salesforce. She has data on the average size of the policies ($) written in two consecutive years by 200 salespeople. She fits a linear model and finds the slope to be 3.00 and the R^2 to be 99.92%. She concludes that the predictions for next year's policy sizes will be very accurate. Examine the data on the data file and comment on her conclusions. **LO ❶**

Ⓣ 35. Supermarket sales, part 1. A regional high-end specialty supermarket is considering opening a new store and is curious about the relationship between demographic data and store sales for its existing stores. For example, are store sales related to the population in the town where the store is located? Data for 10 stores produced this scatterplot and regression:

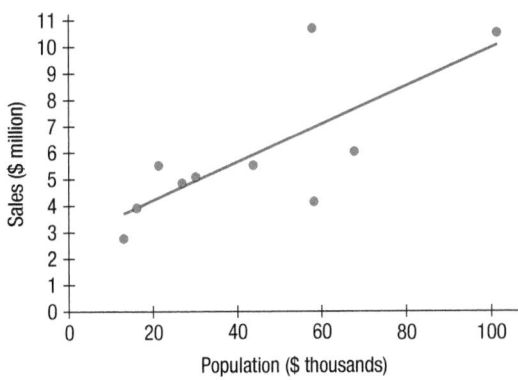

Predictor	Coef
Intercept	2.924
Population	0.0703
$s = 1.842$	
$RSq = 56.9\%$	

a) Do you think a linear model is appropriate here? Explain.
b) What is the correlation between store *Sales* and town *Population*?
c) Explain the meaning of R^2 in this context. **LO ❷**

36. Supermarket sales, part 2. Take another look at the regression analysis of *Sales* and *Population* in Exercise 35.

a) Estimate the *Sales* of a store located in a town with a population of 80,000.
b) Interpret the meaning of the slope of the regression line in this context.
c) What does the intercept mean? Does this make sense? **LO ❶**

37. Misinterpretations, part 1. An advertising agent who created a regression model using amount spent on *Advertising* to predict annual *Sales* for a company made these two statements. Assuming the calculations were done correctly, explain what is wrong with each interpretation.

a) "My R^2 of 93% shows that this linear model is appropriate."
b) "If this company spends $1.5 million on advertising, then annual sales will be $10 million." **LO ❶, ❷**

38. Misinterpretations, part 2. An economist investigated the association between a country's *Literacy Rate* and *Gross Domestic Product (GDP)* and used the association to draw the following conclusions. Explain why each statement is incorrect. (Assume that all the calculations were done properly.)

a) The *Literacy Rate* determines 64% of the *GDP* for a country.

b) The slope of the line shows that an increase of 5% in *Literacy Rate* will produce a $1 billion improvement in *GDP.* **LO❶, ❷**

Ⓣ 39. Used BMW prices 2013, part 1. A business student needs cash, so he decides to sell his car. The car is a valuable BMW 850CSi that was only made over the course of a few years in the 1990s. He would like to sell it on his own, rather than through a dealer, so he'd like to predict the price he'll get for his car's model year.

a) Make a scatterplot for the data on used BMW 850SCi models provided.
b) Describe the association between year and price.
c) Do you think a linear model is appropriate?
d) Computer software says that $R^2 = 57.3\%$. What is the correlation between year and price?
e) Explain the meaning of R^2 in this context.
f) Why doesn't this model explain 100% of the variability in the price of a used BMW 850CSi? **LO❶, ❷**

Ⓣ 40. Used BMW prices 2013, part 2. Use the advertised prices for BMW 850CSi vehicles given in Exercise 39 to create a linear model for the relationship between a car's *Model Year* and its *Price.*

a) Find the equation of the regression line.
b) Explain the meaning of the slope of the line.
c) Explain the meaning of the intercept of the line.
d) If you wanted to sell a 1997 BMW 850CSi, what price seems appropriate?
e) You have a chance to buy one of two cars. They are about the same age and appear to be in equally good condition. Would you rather buy the one with a positive residual or the one with a negative residual? Explain. **LO❶, ❷**

41. Supermarket sales, part 3. The following table shows the total sales for 10 high-end supermarket stores. These are the same stores that you examined in Exercises 35 and 36. In addition to the population of the towns in which the stores are located, supermarket executives believe their store products appeal to a younger generation. Here are the data for total annual *Sales* and *Median Age* of residents of the town:

Sales($M)	5.540	10.700	10.532	5.995	5.090
Median Age	39.5	34.5	30.4	36.2	40.8
Sales ($M)	3.955	2.774	4.828	5.511	4.195
Median Age	41.5	34.7	41.4	38.0	40.0

a) Examine a scatterplot and describe the general relationship between *Sales* and *Median Age* of the town residents.
b) Do you think a linear model is appropriate?
c) The marketing manager fit the regression line. What is the equation of that line?
d) Using this model, predict the annual sales of a supermarket of this type in a town whose median age is 32 years.
e) Do you have any reservations about the prediction you found in (d)? Explain. **LO❶**

42. Supermarket sales, part 4. Executives at the same high-end specialty supermarket in Exercise 35 are trying to determine the best location for a new store. They believe that sales are also related to the total number of housing units in the towns. Based on census data, they would like to develop a model to describe this relationship.

a) Examine a scatterplot and describe the general relationship between *Sales* and *Housing Units* in the town.
b) Do you think a linear model is appropriate?
c) The marketing manager fit the regression line. What is the equation of that line?
d) Using this model, predict the annual sales of a supermarket of this type in a town that has 100,000 housing units.
e) Do you have any reservations about the prediction you found in (d)? Explain. **LO❶**

Ⓣ 43. Expensive cities. The *Worldwide Cost of Living Survey City Rankings* determine the cost of living in the most expensive cities in the world as an index. This index scales New York City as 100 and expresses the cost of living in other cities as a percentage of the New York cost. For example, in 2007, the cost of living index in Tokyo was 122.1, which means that it was 22% higher than New York. The scatterplot shows the index for 2013 plotted against the 2007 index for the 15 most expensive cities of 2007:

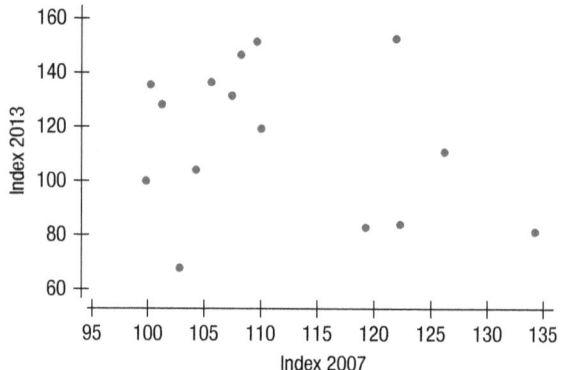

a) Describe the association between cost of living indices in 2007 and 2013.
b) The R^2 for the regression equation is 0.070. Interpret the value of R^2.
c) Find the correlation.
d) Using the data provided, find the least squares fit of the 2013 index to the 2007 index.
e) Predict the 2013 cost of living index of Moscow and find its residual. (The 2007 and 2013 indices for Moscow are 134.4 and 81.58, respectively.) **LO❶, ❷**

44. El Niño. Concern over the weather associated with El Niño has increased interest in the possibility that the climate on Earth is getting warmer. The most common theory relates an increase in atmospheric levels of carbon dioxide (CO_2), a greenhouse gas, to increases in temperature. Here is a scatterplot showing the mean annual CO_2

concentration in the atmosphere, measured in parts per million (ppm) at the top of Mauna Loa in Hawaii, and the mean annual air temperature over both land and sea across the globe, in degrees Celsius (C):

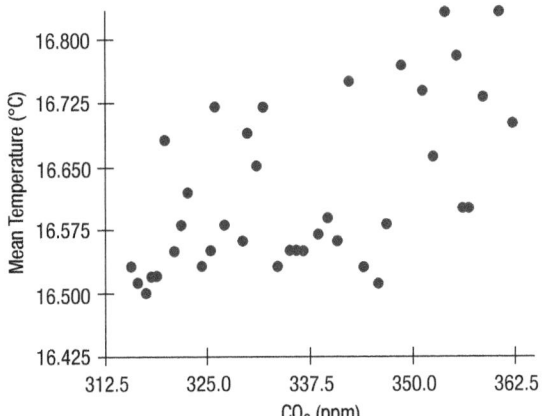

A regression predicting *Mean Temperature* from CO_2 produces the following output table (in part):

Dependent variable: Temperature
R squared $= 33.4\%$

Variable	Coefficient
Intercept	15.3066
CO_2	0.004

a) What is the correlation between CO_2 and *Mean Temperature?*
b) Explain the meaning of R^2 in this context.
c) Give the regression equation.
d) What is the meaning of the slope in this equation?
e) What is the meaning of the intercept of this equation?
f) Below is a scatterplot of the residuals versus CO_2. Does this plot show evidence of the violations of any of the assumptions of the regression model? If so, which ones?

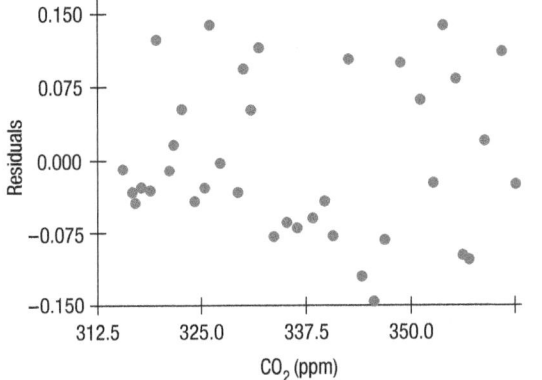

g) CO_2 levels may reach 364 ppm in the near future. What mean temperature does the model predict for that value? **LO ❶, ❷**

45. Global fertility rate. The global fertility rate (number of live births per woman) is given in the table as five-year averages from 1955 to 2015:

1955	5
1960	4.9
1965	4.9
1970	4.8
1975	4.4
1980	3.8
1985	3.5
1990	3.3
1995	3
2000	2.7
2005	2.6
2010	2.5
2015	2.4

a) Draw a time series graph of this data.
b) Comment on whether linear regression can be used on this entire data set to forecast the global fertility rate for 2020, either directly or by transforming the data using logarithms, squares, or square roots.
c) Transform the data using log(fertility rate - 2), and choose the part of the data set from 1970 onward. Use a linear regression (checking the conditions) to forecast the global fertility rate in 2020. Give a reason for subtracting 2 from the fertility rate and for choosing only the data from 1970 onward. **LO ❶, ❸**

46. Solar power. An emerging technology known as concentrating photovoltaics (CPV) has recently been introduced into the market. Morgan Solar of Toronto specializes in CPV. The cost of new technology is related to cumulative volume deployed since the industry gains more experience of the technology as it is deployed, resulting in cost reductions. The corresponding data for CPV are:

Cost ($/W)	Cumulative Volume to Date (MW)	Cost ($/W)	Cumulative Volume to Date (MW)
8.5	1.5	5.15	28
8.5	3.3	4.66	29.2
8.5	10.2	4.72	46
9.4	13	3.9	86.75
8.5	13	3.08	91.2
5.75	15.6	3.54	108
3.8	15.6	2.3	160
5.76	17.7	3.02	160
4.85	18	2.62	275
9.63	20		

Note: The cost is measured in dollars per watt of power-generating capacity; cumulative volume is measured in megawatts of power-generating capacity.

a) Check the conditions for fitting a linear regression model to this data.

b) An experience curve is often used for new technology to represent the relationship between cost and cumulative volume deployed. It relates the logarithm of cost to the logarithm of cumulative volume and is used to estimate costs after a certain cumulative volume has been deployed. Fit an experience curve to the CPV data above, using a linear model with log(cumulative volume) as the explanatory variable and log(cost) as the dependent variable. Comment on the conditions.

c) Forecast the cost of CPV when cumulative volume is 400 MW using your answer to (b).

d) The CEO of a CPV manufacturer disagrees with the idea that cumulative volume determines cost. "It's the cost that determines the volume deployed," he says, "and the lower the cost, the more will be deployed." Fit a different linear model to represent this CEO's view, again using log(cost) and log(cumulative volume) as your variables. Comment on the conditions.

e) Using your answer to (d), estimate how much cumulative volume will be deployed by the time the cost reaches $1.50/W.

f) What fraction of the variability in the data is explained by these two models? Why is the answer the same for each model? **LO❶, ❷, ❸**

47. Commercial bakery. A commercial bakery produces gluten-free pizza dough and sells it to chains of retail stores across Canada. The product is profitable, although some has to be discarded as spoilage since it is too close to its expiry date to be accepted by any of the retailers. Quarterly data over the past three years are as follows:

Volume Shipped (tonnes)	Spoilage (%)	Volume Shipped (tonnes)	Spoilage (%)
1.98	10.40%	2.73	8.61%
2.16	9.26%	2.82	8.20%
2.94	8.71%	3.26	7.99%
2.92	8.19%	3.49	6.59%
2.64	9.06%	2.9	7.50%
2.39	9.53%	3.06	7.67%

a) The logistics manager explains to the product manager that when sales volumes are small, it is difficult to deliver the product to the retailer on time. "The more product you can sell, the lower I can get the spoilage rate," she says. Use a linear model to predict the spoilage rate from the volume shipped. Comment on the conditions.

b) If the volume shipped can be increased to 4 tonnes next quarter, what do you estimate the spoilage rate will be?

c) "Nonsense," retorts the product manager. "It is because the spoilage rate is so high that I have dissatisfied customers

who don't want to order from us." Use a linear model to estimate the volume shipped from the spoilage rate. Comment on the conditions.

d) If the spoilage rate can be reduced to 5% next quarter, what volume do you estimate will be shipped?

e) What fraction of the variability in the data is explained by these two models? Comment on whether the answer is the same for each model.

f) Interpret the meaning of the slope coefficient in the models you derived in (a) and (c). **LO❶, ❷, ❸**

48. LEED certified condominiums in Toronto. Leadership in Energy and Environmental Design (LEED) is a program that certifies that buildings meet a range of energy and environmental efficiency standards, including extra insulation to reduce energy consumption for heating and cooling the building and efficient water use. Meeting these standards adds to the capital cost of the building but reduces the operating costs (e.g., utility bills for energy and water). LEED certified condominiums sell at a higher price than comparable regular condos, but cost less in monthly utility bills. A property developer is building 10 condo buildings in Toronto and estimates the additional cost per unit of making them LEED certified, together with the reduction in monthly energy and water bills that can be expected as a result:

Additional Cost per Unit of LEED Certification ($K)	Reduction in Monthly Utility Bills per Unit ($)	Additional Cost per Unit of LEED Certification ($K)	Reduction in Monthly Utility Bills per Unit ($)
9.6	45.3	12.9	52.1
3.4	26	2.2	15.4
9	50.5	12	47.8
10.3	51.1	1.4	7.8
6.1	41.5	6.3	41

a) Check the conditions for using a linear model to represent this data.

b) Which variable should be the explanatory variable from which the other is estimated? Give your reasons.

c) Transform the additional cost by taking its logarithm to the base 10, and then fit a linear model, commenting on the conditions.

d) If the unit cost increases by $5.2K as a result of obtaining LEED certification, what do you predict would be the reduction in utility bills per unit?

e) What fraction of the variability in the transformed data is accounted for by this model?

f) Interpret the meaning of the slope coefficient in this model. **LO❶, ❷, ❸**

49. High quality paper. A company makes high quality paper for use in the printing of glossy corporate reports. Its monthly sales in three Canadian provinces over the past year are:

Month	British Columbia ($m)	Ontario ($m)	Quebec ($m)
1	2.65	5.35	3.36
2	2.46	5.56	3.14
3	2.37	5.64	3.22
4	2.23	5.64	4.11
5	2.07	5.77	3.12
6	2.07	5.73	3.39
7	2.11	5.81	2.55
8	2.22	5.91	3.28
9	2.30	6.10	3.37
10	2.42	6.23	3.38
11	2.62	6.28	3.26
12	2.88	6.52	3.18

Next year, the company will give an additional marketing budget to the province that has shown a consistent increase in sales over the past year. The amount in $m will be calculated as the increase of sales per month multiplied by 0.5.

a) Check the conditions for using a linear model for each of the three provinces.
b) Specify a linear model wherever appropriate.
c) In what way does your model determine a "consistent increase in sales"? How much of the variability in the data does your model explain?
d) To which province should the additional marketing budget be awarded and how much should it be? LO ❶, ❷

50. Racing cars. After a successful business career, you decide to retire early and go into car racing, not as a driver yourself, but as an entrepreneur. You buy a car and a workshop and hire a celebrity driver who tells you that the key to winning is the car's transmission. "The faster I can shift those gears," he says, "the more power goes to the wheels." You therefore decide to hire some engineering developers to take transmissions apart, adjust and modify them, and reassemble them as a custom transmission that only your car has. At the end of each season, you negotiate next season's contract with your driver, depending on the winnings he brought in during the season that has just finished. You also pay bonuses in the current season to your other employees dependent on the winnings during the same season.

You love the sport, as does everyone in your team, and have enough savings that you don't need to make a profit, but decide to hire an accountant to take a look at your financial performance to date (currently the end of your fifth season):

Season	1	2	3	4	5	6
Revenue						
Sponsorships	3.1	3.1	2.1	3.2	2.3	
Winnings	1.41	0.82	1.23	0.65	1.17	
Expenditures						
Driver	2.1	2.45	2.1	2.2	1.52	2.15
Mechanics	0.8	0.6	0.75	0.55	0.7	
Developers	0.6	0.4	0.55	0.35	0.5	
Car and parts	0.9	0.2	0.22	0.19	0.24	
Profits	0.11	0.27	−0.29	0.56	0.51	

Here are the comments of the accountant. For each comment, say whether you agree and fit a linear model if possible. If you can help the accountant by estimating something using your linear model, then do so.

a) "Winnings are an unpredictable fraction of total income. It's tough to estimate what fraction it's going to be next season."
b) "Your profits don't seem to be related to your winnings."
c) "The contract you have with your driver seems to be closely related to the winnings. It would be good to have a measure of how close."
d) "The amounts you pay your mechanics and developers also seem to be closely related to your winnings, but some of them told me they are concerned with how much they would get if winnings dropped to $0.5m one year." LO ❶, ❷

51. Bricks. A building supply company provides bricks to retail chains and construction companies across Canada. The marketing department decides on the price at which bricks will be sold according to the design of the brick, sales of similar designs in previous years, and whether the company has other bricks selling at similar prices. They aim to offer bricks at a broad range of prices. The table gives sales of bricks at different prices last year, and the company is planning to sell the same bricks this year:

Selling Price per Brick ($)	Sales Revenue ($m)
0.42	8.1
0.49	9.4
0.56	10.8
0.76	12.8
0.98	16.1
1.12	17.3
1.28	14.8
1.39	16.8
1.54	14.3
1.72	15.3
1.89	12.4
1.99	10.9

The purchasing department has a good deal from a manufacturer to supply a brick that could sell in the range $0.50–$1.00. The marketing department would like to sell the brick at either $0.67 or $0.87 so as to fill the gaps in the prices of the current offerings. Use a linear model to estimate the number of bricks the company could expect to sell at these two prices. **LO ❶, ❸**

52. Gas pipeline costs. The materials cost per kilometre of constructing a gas pipeline depends on the diameter of the pipe, and the table below summarizes such costs in thousands of dollars per kilometre for two recent years from the *Oil and Gas Journal*:

Diameter (inches)	Year 1 Materials Cost ($K/km)	Year 2 Materials Cost ($K/km)
8	380	117.5
12	450.625	199.375
16	302.5	179.375
20	395	211.25
24	326.875	389.375
30	431.25	637.5
36	691.25	875.625

a) Taking the two years together, obtain a linear regression of materials cost per kilometre as a function of pipe diameter.
b) Larger pipes are also made of thicker metal, so the cost may be dependent on the square of the diameter. Obtain a linear regression of materials cost per kilometre as a function of the square of pipe diameter.
c) Compare the results of (a) and (b). Which do you prefer? **LO ❶, ❸**

53. Piston ring entrepreneur. For his Master's degree thesis in Metallurgy at McGill University, Larry developed an alloy that was flexible but also very hard, making it ideal for piston rings in internal combustion engines. Upon graduation, Larry set up his own production facility, and his piston rings were so popular that during some quarters he ran out of production capacity and had to install new equipment. He has now been in business for 11 quarters and wants to forecast demand for the next year so that he can plan upgrades to his production facilities ahead of time. His sales to date are:

Quarter	Sales (million units)
1	0.14
2	0.31
3	1.1
4	1.22
5	1.67
6	1.89
7	1.91
8	2.25
9	2.41
10	2.42
11	2.67

a) Fit a linear regression of demand against quarter.
b) Sales grew quickly at first but are now slackening off like a log function. Fit a linear regression of demand against $\log_{10}$(quarter).
c) Compare the results of (a) and (b). Which do you prefer? *Hint:* The data are for "sales." Larry wants to forecast "demand." In some quarters, sales were less than demand because Larry had insufficient production equipment. **LO ❶, ❸**

Congratulations! You have now completed all seven chapters of Part I, "Exploring and Collecting Data." A comprehensive case study available online in MyStatLab draws together many of the topics you have learned in Part I. Here is a brief synopsis:

AIDS in Canada

How do we tell the difference between a few isolated cases of a new disease and the start of an epidemic? This case study puts you in the position of a manager at Health Canada, the Canadian Institute for Health Information, and/or the Public Health Agency of Canada when confronted by a new disease. It is based on real data that was available to such a person when AIDS was new and illustrates how to analyze unusual patterns and formats of data using the information from Part I of this book.

Learning Objectives

Chapter	1	2	3	4	5	6	7
Learning Objective	1	1, 2	1	1	5, 7	1, 2	1, 2, 3

Mario Beauregard/Fotolia

LEARNING OBJECTIVES

In this chapter we show you how to estimate the probability of events occurring and how to make calculations based on probabilities of different events. After reading and studying this chapter, you should be able to:

❶ Estimate probability using empirical, theoretical, and subjective methods

❷ Combine probabilities of one event and/or another

❸ Determine whether events are independent or disjoint

❹ Represent probabilities of multiple events using a probability tree

❺ Update estimates of probability using additional information

8

Randomness and Probability

Equifax, Consumer Services Canada

Even if you've never heard of Equifax, Consumer Services Canada, it probably knows you. It's a credit reporting agency, and whenever you apply for a loan, a credit card, an apartment, or even a job, your "credit report" may be used to determine whether you're a good risk.

Financial institutions that lend you money send Equifax such information as when you obtain a credit card, whether you make payments on time, and whether you've exceeded your credit limit. Equifax then compiles this information in your "credit report," which can be lengthy. Fair, Isaac & Company (FICO) has developed proprietary software to convert the report into a "credit score," a number between 300 and 850 that summarizes your "credit worthiness." It's a snapshot of your credit risk today based on your credit history and past behaviour.

Lenders of all kinds use credit scores to predict behaviour, such as how likely you are to make your loan payments on time or to default on a loan. They use them to determine not only whether to give credit, but also the cost of the credit they'll offer. About 57% of Canadians have FICO scores over 760, which are considered excellent, and applicants with those scores get the best rates. The chance of someone with a credit rating over 760 failing to make necessary payments within 90 days is only about 1%. This is known as the delinquency rate. About 4% of Canadians have FICO scores below 560, which is generally considered a very poor risk since the delinquency rate is around 40%. It's important that you be able to verify the information your score is based on, so all Canadians have access to their credit reports. Consumers can request changes to erroneous information, and can also see which organizations have accessed their credit reports recently.[1]

---

[1]Based on data from Equifax Canada, www.econsumer.equifax.ca

---

Companies have to manage risk to survive, but by its nature, risk carries uncertainty. A bank, for instance, can't know for certain that you'll pay your mortgage on time—or at all. So what can companies do with events they can't predict? They start with the fact that, although individual outcomes cannot be anticipated with certainty, random phenomena do, in the long run, settle into patterns that are consistent and predictable. And it's this property of random events that makes Statistics very useful in the financial services industry.

LO❶ 8.1   Random Phenomena and Empirical Probability

When a customer calls the 800 number of a credit card company, he or she is asked for a card number before being connected with an operator. As the connection is made, the purchase records of that card and the demographic information of the customer are retrieved and displayed on the operator's screen. If the customer's FICO score is high enough, the operator may be prompted to "cross-sell" another service—perhaps a new "platinum" card for customers with a credit score of at least 750.

Of course, the company doesn't know which customers are going to call. Call arrivals are an example of a **random phenomenon**. With random phenomena, we can't predict the individual outcomes, but we can hope to understand characteristics of their long-run behaviours. We don't know whether the *next* caller will qualify for the platinum card, but as calls come into the call centre, the company will find that the percentage of platinum-qualified callers will settle into a pattern, like that shown in the graph in Figure 8.1.

As calls come into the call centre, the company might record whether each caller qualifies. The first caller today qualified. Then the next five callers' qualifications were no, yes, yes, no, and no. If we plot the percentage who qualify against the call number, the graph would start at 100% because the first caller qualified (one out of one, for 100%). The next caller didn't qualify, so the accumulated percentage dropped to 50% (one out of two). The third caller qualified (two out of three, or 67%), and so on (Table 8.1). With each new call, the new datum is a smaller fraction of the accumulated experience, so, in the long run, the graph settles down. As it settles down, it appears that, in fact, the fraction of customers who qualify is about 35%.

When talking about long-run behaviour, it helps to define our terms. For any random phenomenon, each attempt, or **trial**, generates an **outcome**. For the call centre, each call is a trial. Something happens on each trial, and we call whatever happens the outcome. Here the outcome is whether the caller qualifies or not. We use the more general term **event** to refer to outcomes or combinations of outcomes. For example, suppose we categorize callers into six risk categories and number these outcomes from 1 to 6 (of increasing credit worthiness). The three outcomes 4, 5, or 6 could make up the event "caller is at least a category 4."

We sometimes talk about the collection of *all possible outcomes*, a special event that we'll refer to as the **sample space**. We denote the sample space **S**. But

A random phenomenon consists of *trials*.

Each trial has an *outcome*.

Outcomes combine to make *events*.

Call	FICO Score	Qualify?	% Qualifying
1	750	Yes	100
2	640	No	50
3	765	Yes	66.7
4	780	Yes	75
5	680	No	60
6	630	No	50
⋮	⋮	⋮	⋮

Table 8.1   Data on the first six callers showing their FICO score, whether they qualified for the platinum card offer, and a running percentage of number of callers who qualified.

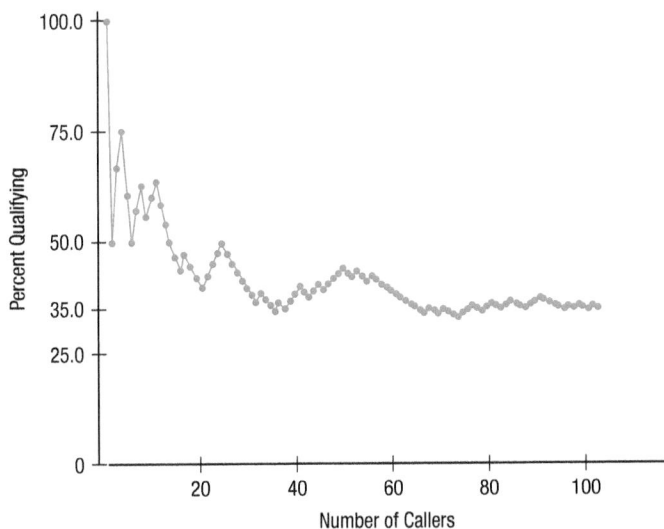

Figure 8.1   The percentage of credit card customers who qualify for the platinum card.

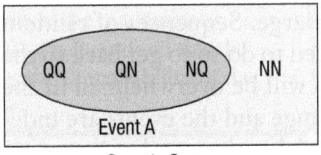

Figure 8.2   The sample space for two calls together and the event, A, for which at least one of the two callers is qualified.

The *empirical probability* of an event is its long-run relative frequency. A relative frequency is a fraction, so we can write it as $\frac{35}{100}$; as a decimal, 0.35; or as a percentage, 35%.

Law of Large Numbers

The *long-run relative frequency* of repeated, independent events eventually homes in on the *empirical probability* as the number of trials increases.

whatever symbol we use, the sample space is the set that contains all the possible outcomes. For the calls, if we let Q = qualified and N = not qualified, the sample space is simple: **S** = {Q, N}. If we look at two calls together, the sample space has four outcomes: **S** = {QQ, QN, NQ, NN}. If we were interested in at least one qualified caller from the two calls, we'd be interested in the event (call it **A**) consisting of the three outcomes QQ, QN, and NQ, and we'd write **A** = {QQ, QN, NQ} (Figure 8.2).

Empirical Probability

Although we may not be able to predict a *particular* individual outcome, such as which incoming call represents a potential upgrade sale, we can say a lot about the long-run behaviour. Look back at Figure 8.1. If you were asked for the probability that a random caller will qualify, you might say that it was 35% because, in the *long run*, the percentage of the callers who qualify is about 35%. And that's exactly what we mean by **probability**. Because it's based on repeatedly observing the event's outcome, this definition of probability is often called **empirical probability**.

It really simplifies things if the individual trials are independent. Roughly speaking, **independence** means that the outcome of one trial doesn't influence or change the outcome of another. Recall that in Chapter 4 we called two variables *independent* if the value of one categorical variable did not influence the value of another categorical variable. (We checked for independence by comparing relative frequency distributions across variables.) There's no reason to think that whether one caller qualifies influences whether another caller qualifies, so these are independent trials. We'll see a more formal definition of independence later in the chapter.

Fortunately, for independent events, we can depend on a principle called the **Law of Large Numbers (LLN)**, which states that if the events are independent, then as the number of calls increases, over days or months or years, the long-run relative frequency of qualified calls gets closer and closer to a single value. This gives us the guarantee we need and makes probability a useful concept.

Because the LLN guarantees that relative frequencies settle down in the long run, we can give a name to the value that they approach. We call it the probability

In Canada, there is only one civil standard of proof . . . and that is proof on a balance of probabilities.

—Judge Marshall Rothstein, *Canadian Supreme Court*

Subjective or Personal Probability

What's the probability that gold will sell for more than $2000 an ounce at the end of next year? You may be able to come up with a number that seems reasonable. How did you come up with this probability? In our discussion of probability, we've defined probability in two ways: (1) in terms of the relative frequency—or the fraction of times—that an event occurs in the long run; or (2) as the number of outcomes in the event divided by the total number of outcomes. Neither situation applies to your assessment of gold's chances of selling for more than $2000 per ounce.

We use the *language* of probability in everyday speech to express a degree of uncertainty without basing it on long-run relative frequencies. Your personal assessment of an event expresses your uncertainty about the outcome. We call this kind of probability a **subjective probability** or **personal probability**.

Bias

In May 1996, two teams of mountaineers started their final ascent of Everest, the world's highest peak. Both were led by experienced climbers who had reached the summit on several previous expeditions. When they selected the day to start the ascent, they took into account the weather forecast and the state of readiness of their team members. They subjectively assessed their probability of success. But did their success on previous climbs make them overconfident of success this time? If a partner in a consulting company puts in a bid on a major government contract, will she overestimate the chance of getting the contract, simply because of being overconfident in her team's ability? These may be examples of *overconfidence bias.*

On that final push to the summit of Everest, climbers set out before dawn on an 18-hour day, to climb the lower part of the route in darkness, saving the daylight for the more treacherous upper crags. In particular, you don't want to be climbing down the mountain in darkness, so it is essential to reach the summit by about 1:00 p.m., to leave time for the descent. But on that day in 1996, the climbers were still several hundred metres from the summit at 1:00 p.m. The team leaders subjectively assessed that they had a high probability that the weather would stay good and that they would be able to climb back down in darkness. So, instead of turning back, they pushed on, reaching the summit very late at between 3:00 and 4:00 p.m. They may have suffered from a *sunk cost bias.* They had spent months of training and tens of thousands of dollars getting so near the top, so they overestimated the probability of being able to make the descent in darkness. If an energy company executive has invested billions in exploratory drilling of a gas field, does he overestimate the probability that the field will be economic just because he has invested so much to date?

The leaders of the mountaineering teams had climbed Everest several times during the 1990s, and on each occasion the weather had been fine for their final ascent. But in the 1980s there had been several years when no one climbed Everest because of ferocious winds. Had they forgotten those earlier years and based their judgment on their more recent experience? Will a marketing manager be susceptible to *recency bias* and overestimate the probability that a new product will be successful, just because the last few product launches were successful, even though earlier ones had been less successful? Gamblers who think they are in a winning streak suffer from recency bias.

Subjective probability assessment suffers from three types of bias, as illustrated in the above examples:

- Overconfidence bias
- Sunk cost bias
- Recency bias

Maybe you can think of other sources of bias. For instance, do you think some managers might surround themselves by people who share their views, resulting in *self-confirmation bias*?

In May 1996, both Everest expedition leaders and three team members died when a storm struck during the evening as they attempted their descent in failing light conditions. Bias can have serious implications in business, too. Subjective probability assessment is less reliable than empirical or theoretical probability assessment, even when it is done by experts. But often we don't have a choice, and subjective probability assessment is the only applicable method for our situation. In this case we have to use it, being aware, as we do so, of how bias might make things go disastrously wrong.

LO❷ 8.4 Probability Rules

For some people, the phrase "50/50" means something vague like "I don't know" or "whatever." But when we discuss probabilities, 50/50 has the precise meaning that two outcomes are *equally likely*. Speaking vaguely about probabilities can get you into trouble, so it's wise to develop some formal rules about how probability works. These rules apply to probability whether we're dealing with empirical, theoretical, or personal probability.

Rule 1. If the probability of an event occurring is 0, the event can't occur; likewise, if the probability is 1, the event *always* occurs. Even if you think an event is very unlikely, its probability can't be negative, and even if you're sure it will happen, its probability can't be greater than 1. So we require that:

A probability is a number between 0 and 1.

For any event A, $0 \leq P(A) \leq 1$.

Rule 2. If a random phenomenon has only one possible outcome, it's not very interesting (or very random). So we need to distribute the probabilities among all the outcomes a trial can have. How can we do that so that it makes sense? For example, consider the behaviour of a certain stock. The possible daily outcomes might be:

A: The stock price goes up.

B: The stock price goes down.

C: The stock price remains the same.

When we assign probabilities to these outcomes, we should make sure to distribute all of the available probability. Something always occurs, so the probability of *something* happening is 1. This is called the **Probability Assignment Rule**:

The probability of the set of all possible outcomes must be 1.

$$P(S) = 1$$

where **S** represents the *sample space*, the set of all possible outcomes.

Rule 3. Suppose the probability that you get to class on time is 0.8. What's the probability that you don't get to class on time? Yes, it's 0.2. The set of outcomes that are *not* in the event **A** is called the "complement" of **A**, and is denoted $\mathbf{A}^C$ (Figure 8.3). This leads to the **Complement Rule**:

The probability of an event occurring is 1 minus the probability that it doesn't occur.

$$P(\mathbf{A}) = 1 - P(\mathbf{A}^c)$$

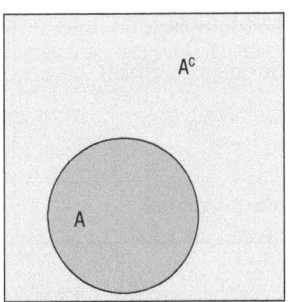

Figure 8.3 The event **A** and its complement $\mathbf{A}^C$. Together, they make up the entire sample space **S**.

> ### FOR EXAMPLE   Applying the Complement Rule to retail purchases
>
> Lee's Lights sells lighting fixtures. Some customers are there only to browse, so Lee records the behaviour of all customers for a week to assess how likely it is that a customer will make a purchase. Lee finds that of 1000 customers entering the store during the week, 300 make purchases. Lee concludes that the probability of a customer making a purchase is 0.30.
>
> **QUESTION** If $P(\text{purchase}) = 0.30$, what is the probability that a customer *doesn't* make a purchase?
>
> **ANSWER** Because "no purchase" is the complement of "purchase,"
>
> $$P(\text{no purchase}) = 1 - P(\text{purchase})$$
> $$= 1 - 0.30 = 0.70.$$
>
> There is a 70% chance that a customer won't make a purchase.

Rule 4. Whether or not the next caller has a high enough credit score to qualify for a platinum card is a random outcome. Suppose the probability of qualifying is 0.35. What's the chance that the next two callers qualify? The **Multiplication Rule** says that to find the probability that two independent events occur, we multiply the probabilities:

For two independent events A and B, the probability that both A *and* B occur is the product of the probabilities of the two events.

$$P(\mathbf{A} \text{ and } \mathbf{B}) = P(\mathbf{A}) \times P(\mathbf{B}), \text{ if } \mathbf{A} \text{ and } \mathbf{B} \text{ are independent.}$$

Thus, if $\mathbf{A} = \{\text{customer 1 qualifies}\}$ and $\mathbf{B} = \{\text{customer 2 qualifies}\}$, the chance that both qualify is $0.35 \times 0.35 = 0.1225$

Of course, to calculate this probability, we've used the assumption that the two events are independent. We'll expand the Multiplication Rule to be more general later in this chapter.

> ### FOR EXAMPLE   Using the Multiplication Rule for retail purchases
>
> Lee knows that the probability that a customer will make a purchase is 30%.
>
> **QUESTION** If we can assume that customers behave independently, what is the probability that the next two customers entering Lee's Lights make purchases?
>
> **ANSWER** Because the events are independent, we can use the Multiplication Rule.
>
> $P(\text{first customer makes a purchase } and \text{ second customer makes a purchase})$
>
> $$= P(\text{purchase}) \times P(\text{purchase})$$
> $$= 0.30 \times 0.30 = 0.09$$
>
> There's a 9% chance that the next two customers will both make purchases.

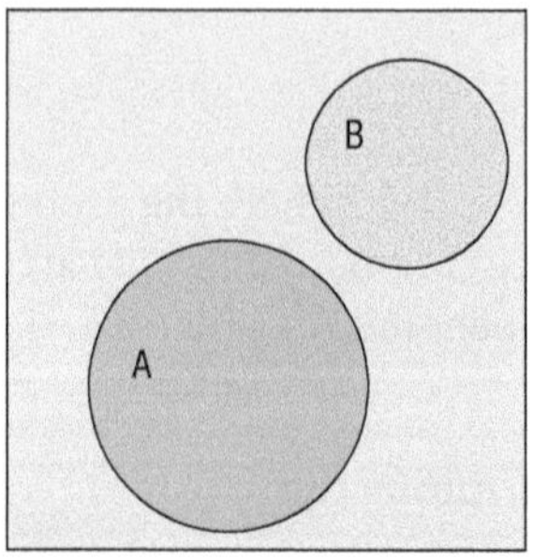

Figure 8.4 Two disjoint events, **A** and **B**. $P(\mathbf{A} \text{ or } \mathbf{B}) = P(\mathbf{A}) + P(\mathbf{B})$

Rule 5. Suppose the call centre operator has more options. She or he can **A**: offer a special travel deal, or **B**: offer a platinum card. If she or he can do one, but only one, of these, then these outcomes are **disjoint (or mutually exclusive) events** (Figure 8.4). To see whether two events are disjoint, we separate them into their component outcomes and check whether they have any outcomes in common. For example, if the operator can choose to both offer the travel deal and the platinum card, those would not be disjoint. The **Addition Rule** allows us to add the probabilities of disjoint events to get the probability that *either* event occurs:

$$P(\mathbf{A} \text{ or } \mathbf{B}) = P(\mathbf{A}) + P(\mathbf{B}) \text{ if } \mathbf{A} \text{ and } \mathbf{B} \text{ are disjoint.}$$

Thus, the probability that the caller is *either* offered the travel deal or the platinum card is the sum of the two probabilities, since the events are disjoint.

FOR EXAMPLE **Using the Addition Rule for retail purchases**

Some customers prefer to see the merchandise in the store but then make their purchase later using Lee's Lights's new internet site. Tracking customer behaviour, Lee determines that there's a 9% chance of a customer making a purchase in this way. We know that about 30% of customers make purchases when they enter the store.

QUESTION What is the probability that a customer who enters the store makes a purchase either online or in the store?

ANSWER We can use the Addition Rule because the alternatives "no purchase," "purchase in the store," and "purchase online" are disjoint events.

$$P(\text{purchase in the store } or \text{ online}) = P(\text{purchase in store}) + P(\text{purchase online})$$
$$= 0.30 + 0.09 = 0.39$$

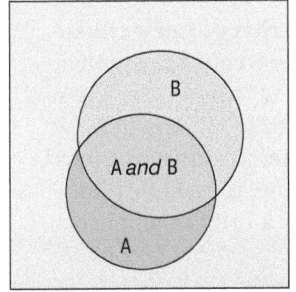

Figure 8.5   Two events **A** and **B** that are not disjoint. The event (**A** and **B**) is their intersection: $P(\mathbf{A} \text{ or } \mathbf{B}) = P(\mathbf{A}) + P(\mathbf{B}) - P(\mathbf{A} \text{ and } \mathbf{B})$

Rule 6. Suppose we'd like to know the probability that either of the next two callers is qualified for a platinum card. We know $P(\mathbf{A}) = P(\mathbf{B}) = 0.35$, but $P(\mathbf{A} \text{ or } \mathbf{B})$ isn't simply the sum $P(\mathbf{A}) + P(\mathbf{B})$ because the events **A** and **B** are not disjoint in this case (Figure 8.5). Both customers could qualify. So we need a new probability rule.

We can't simply add the probabilities of **A** and **B** because that would count the outcome of *both* customers qualifying twice. So, if we started by adding the probabilities that each customer qualifies, we could compensate by subtracting the probability that both customers qualify. In this way, we don't double-count the overlap region in the diagram. In other words,

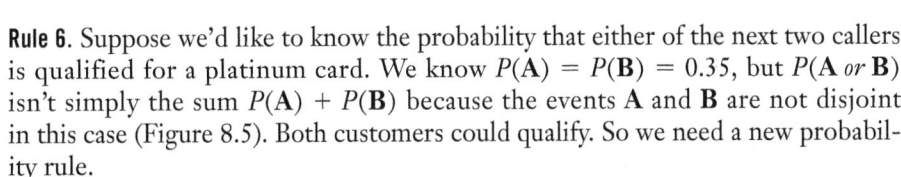

$$
\begin{aligned}
P(\text{customer } \mathbf{A} \text{ } or \text{ customer } \mathbf{B} \text{ qualifies}) &= P(\text{customer } \mathbf{A} \text{ qualifies}) + P(\text{customer } \mathbf{B} \text{ qualifies}) - P(\text{both customers qualify}) \\
&= (0.35) + (0.35) - (0.35 \times 0.35) \text{ (since events are independent)} \\
&= (0.35) + (0.35) - (0.1225) \\
&= 0.5775
\end{aligned}
$$

It turns out that this method works, in general. We add the probabilities of two events and then subtract out the probability of their intersection. This gives us the **General Addition Rule**, which does not require disjoint events:

$$P(\mathbf{A} \text{ } or \text{ } \mathbf{B}) = P(\mathbf{A}) + P(\mathbf{B}) - P(\mathbf{A} \text{ } and \text{ } \mathbf{B})$$

FOR EXAMPLE   **Using the General Addition Rule for retail purchases**

Lee notices that when two customers enter the store together, their behaviour isn't independent. In fact, there's a 20% chance they'll *both* make a purchase.

QUESTION When two customers enter the store together, what is the probability that *at least one* of them will make a purchase?

ANSWER Now we know that the events are not independent, so we must use the General Addition Rule:

$$
\begin{aligned}
P(\text{At least one of them purchases}) &= P(\textbf{A} \text{ purchases } or\ \textbf{B} \text{ purchases}) \\
&= P(\textbf{A} \text{ purchases}) + P(\textbf{B} \text{ purchases}) \\
&\quad - P(\textbf{A} \text{ and } \textbf{B} \text{ both purchase}) \\
&= 0.30 + 0.30 - 0.20 = 0.40
\end{aligned}
$$

GUIDED EXAMPLE   M&M'S Modern Market Research

In 1941, when M&M'S milk chocolate candies were introduced, there were six colours: brown, yellow, orange, red, green, and violet. Mars, the company that manufactures M&M'S, has used the introduction of a new colour as a marketing and advertising event several times in the years since then. In 1980 the candy went international, adding 16 countries to Mars's markets; in 1995 the company conducted a "worldwide survey" to vote on a new colour. Over 10 million people voted to add blue. (Mars even got the lights of the Empire State Building in New York City to glow blue to help announce the addition.) In 2002, the company used the internet to help pick a new colour. Children from over 200 countries were invited to respond via the internet, telephone, or mail. Millions of voters chose from among purple, pink, and teal. The global winner was purple, and for a brief time, purple M&M'S could be found in packages worldwide (although in 2013, the colours were brown, yellow, red, blue, orange, and green). But in Japan, the percentages were 38% pink, 36% teal, and only 16% purple. Let's use Japan's percentages to ask some questions.

1. What's the probability that a Japanese M&M'S survey respondent selected at random preferred either pink or teal?

2. If we pick two Japanese respondents at random, what's the probability that they *both* selected purple?

3. If we pick three Japanese respondents at random, what's the probability that *at least one* preferred purple?

PLAN **Setup** The empirical probability of an event is its long-term relative frequency. This can be determined in several ways: by looking at many replications of an event, by deducing it from equally likely events, or by using some other information. Here, we are told the relative frequencies of the three responses.

The M&M'S website reports the proportions of Japanese votes by colour. These give the probability of selecting a voter who preferred each of the colours:

$$P(\text{pink}) = 0.38$$
$$P(\text{teal}) = 0.36$$
$$P(\text{purple}) = 0.16$$

Make sure the probabilities are legitimate. Here, they're not. Either there was a mistake or the other voters must have chosen a colour other than the three given. A check of other countries shows a similar deficit, so we're probably seeing those who had no preference or who wrote in another colour.	Each is between 0 and 1, but these don't add up to 1. The remaining 10% of the voters must not have expressed a preference or written in another colour. We'll put them together into "other" and add $P(\text{other}) = 0.10$. With this addition, we have a legitimate assignment of probabilities.

Question 1: What's the probability that a Japanese M&M'S survey respondent selected at random preferred either pink or teal?

PLAN	Setup Decide which rules to use and check the conditions they require.	The events "pink" and "teal" are individual outcomes (a respondent can't choose both colours), so they are disjoint. We can apply the Addition Rule, Rule 5.
DO	Mechanics Show your work.	$P(\text{pink or teal}) = P(\text{pink}) + P(\text{teal})$ $= 0.38 + 0.36 = 0.74$
REPORT	Conclusion Interpret your results in the proper context.	The probability that the respondent said pink or teal is 0.74.

Question 2: If we pick two Japanese respondents at random, what's the probability that they both selected purple?

PLAN	Setup The word "both" suggests we want $P(\textbf{A} \text{ and } \textbf{B})$, which calls for the Multiplication Rule. Check the required condition.	**Independence.** It's unlikely that the choice made by one respondent affected the choice of the other, so the events seem to be independent. We can use the Multiplication Rule.
DO	Mechanics Show your work. For both respondents to pick purple, each one has to pick purple.	$P(\text{both purple})$ $= P(\text{first respondent picks purple and second respondent picks purple})$ $= P(\text{first respondent picks purple}) \times P(\text{second respondent picks purple})$ $= 0.16 \times 0.16 = 0.0256$
REPORT	Conclusion Interpret your results in the proper context.	The probability that both respondents picked purple is 0.0256.

Question 3: If we pick three Japanese respondents at random, what's the probability that at least one preferred purple?

(continued)

PLAN	Setup The phrase "at least one" often flags a question best answered by looking at the complement, and that's the best approach here. The complement of "at least one preferred purple" is "none of them preferred purple." Check the conditions.	$P(\text{at least one picked purple})$ $= P(\{\text{ none picked purple }\}^c)$ $= 1 - P(\text{none picked purple}).$ **Independence.** These are independent events because they are choices by three random respondents. We can use the Multiplication Rule.
DO	Mechanics We calculate $P(\text{none purple})$ by using the Multiplication Rule. Then we can use the Complement Rule to get the probability we want.	$P(\text{none picked purple}) = P(\text{first not purple})$ $\times\ P(\text{second not purple})$ $\times\ P(\text{third not purple})$ $= [\,P(\text{not purple})\,]^3.$ $P(\text{not purple}) = 1 - P(\text{purple})$ $= 1 - 0.16 = 0.84.$ So $P(\text{none picked purple}) = (0.84)^3 = 0.5927.$ $P(\text{at least 1 picked purple})$ $= 1 - P(\text{none picked purple})$ $= 1 - 0.5927 = 0.4073$
REPORT	Conclusion Interpret your results in the proper context.	There's about a 40.7% chance that at least one of the respondents picked purple.

JUST CHECKING

2 MP3 players have relatively high failure rates for a consumer product. The worst failure rate for all iPod models was the 40GB click wheel (as reported by MacIntouch.com) at 30%. If a store sells this model and failures are independent,

a What is the probability that the next one it sells will have a failure?

b What is the probability that there will be failures on *both* of the next two?

c What is the probability that the store's first failure problem will be with the third one it sells?

d What is the probability that the store will have a failure problem with at least one of the next five that it sells?

Answers are found in Appendix A.

LO❷ 8.5 Joint Probability and Contingency Tables

As part of a Pick Your Prize Promotion, a chain store invited customers to choose which of three prizes they'd like to win (while providing name, gender, address, phone number, and email address). At one store, the responses were placed in the contingency table in Table 8.2.

Gender	Prize Preference Skis	Prize Preference Camera	Prize Preference Bike	Total
Man	117	50	60	227
Woman	130	91	30	251
Total	247	141	90	478

Table 8.2   Prize preference for 478 customers.

A *marginal probability* uses a marginal frequency (from either the Total row or the Total column) to compute the probability.

If the winner is chosen at random from these customers, the probability that we select a woman is just the corresponding relative frequency (since we're equally likely to select any of the 478 customers). There are 251 women in the data out of a total of 478, giving a probability of

$$P(\text{woman}) = 251/478 = 0.525.$$

This is called a **marginal probability**, because it depends only on totals found in the margins of the table. The same method works for more complicated events. For example, what's the probability of selecting a woman whose preferred prize is the camera? Well, 91 women named the camera as their preference, so the probability is

$$P(\text{woman } and \text{ camera}) = 91/478 = 0.190.$$

Probabilities such as these are called **joint probabilities** because they give the probability of two events occurring together.

The probability of selecting a customer whose preferred prize is a bike is

$$P(\text{bike}) = 90/478 = 0.188.$$

FOR EXAMPLE   Marginal probabilities for retail purchases

Lee suspects that men and women make different kinds of purchases at Lee's Lights (see For Example: "Using the General Addition Rule for retail purchases"). The table shows the purchases made by the last 100 customers who actually made a purchase:

	Utility Lighting	Fashion Lighting	Total
Men	40	20	60
Women	10	30	40
Total	50	50	100

QUESTION   What's the probability that one of Lee's customers is a woman? What's the probability that a random customer is a man who purchases fashion lighting?

ANSWER   From the marginal totals we can see that 40% of Lee's customers are women, so the probability that a customer is a woman is 0.40. The cell of the table for men who purchase fashion lighting has 20 of the 100 customers, so the probability of that event is 0.20.

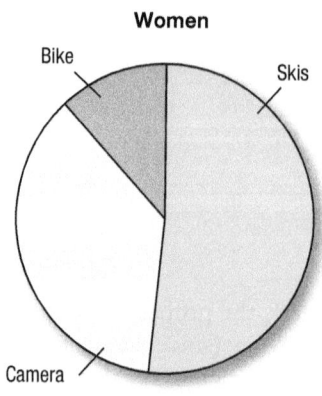

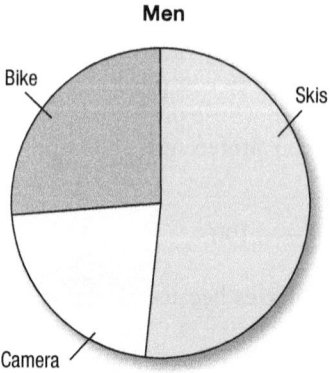

Figure 8.6 Conditional distributions of *Prize Preference* by *Gender*.

NOTATION ALERT

$P(\mathbf{B}|\mathbf{A})$ is the conditional probability of **B** *given* **A**.

Conditional Probability and Independence

Since our sample space is these 478 customers, we can recognize the relative frequencies as probabilities. What if we're given the information that the selected customer is a woman? Would that change the probability that the selected customer's preferred prize is a bike? You bet it would! The pie charts in Figure 8.6 show that women are much less likely to say their preferred prize is a bike than are men. When we restrict our focus to women, we look only at the women's row of the table, which gives the conditional distribution of preferred prizes given "Woman." Of the 251 women, only 30 of them said their preferred prize was a bike. We write the probability that a selected customer wants a bike *given* that we have selected a woman as

$$P(\text{bike}|\text{woman}) = 30/251 = 0.120.$$

For men, we look at the conditional distribution of preferred prizes given "Man" shown in the top row of the table. There, of the 227 men, 60 said their preferred prize was a bike. So, $P(\text{bike}|\text{man}) = 60/227 = 0.264$, more than twice the women's probability (see Figure 8.6).

In general, when we want the probability of an event from a *conditional* distribution, we write $P(\mathbf{B}|\mathbf{A})$ and pronounce it "the probability of **B** *given* **A**." A probability that takes into account a given *condition* such as this is called a **conditional probability**.

Let's look at what we did. We worked with the counts, but we could work with the probabilities just as well. There were 30 women who selected a bike as a prize, and there were 251 women customers. So we found the probability to be 30/251. To find the probability of the event **B** *given* the event **A**, we restrict our attention to the outcomes in **A**. We then find in what fraction of *those* outcomes **B** also occurred. Formally, we write:

$$P(\mathbf{B}|\mathbf{A}) = \frac{P(\mathbf{A}\text{ and }\mathbf{B})}{P(\mathbf{A})}$$

We can use the formula directly with the probabilities derived from the contingency table (Table 8.2) to find:

$$P(\text{bike}|\text{woman}) = \frac{P(\text{bike }\textit{and}\text{ woman})}{P(\text{woman})} = \frac{30/478}{251/478} = \frac{0.063}{0.525} = 0.120 \text{ as before}$$

The formula for conditional probability requires one restriction. The formula works only when the event that's given has a probability of greater than 0. The formula doesn't work if $P(\mathbf{A})$ is 0 because that would mean we'd been "given" the fact that **A** was true even though the probability of **A** is 0, which would be a contradiction.

Remember the Multiplication Rule for the probability of **A** *and* **B**? It said:

$$P(\mathbf{A} \textit{ and } \mathbf{B}) = P(\mathbf{A}) \times P(\mathbf{B}) \text{ when } \mathbf{A} \text{ and } \mathbf{B} \text{ are independent.}$$

Now we can write a more general rule that doesn't require independence. In fact, we've already written it. We just need to rearrange the equation a bit.

Rule 7. The equation in the definition for conditional probability contains the probability of **A** *and* **B**. Rearranging the equation gives the **General Multiplication Rule** for compound events that does not require the events to be independent:

$$P(\mathbf{A} \textit{ and } \mathbf{B}) = P(\mathbf{A}) \times P(\mathbf{B}|\mathbf{A})$$

The probability that two events, **A** and **B**, both occur is the probability that event **A** occurs multiplied by the probability that event **B** *also* occurs—that is, by the probability that event **B** occurs given that event **A** occurs.

Of course, there's nothing special about which event we call **A** and which one we call **B**. We should be able to state this the other way around. Indeed, we can. It is equally true that:

$$P(\textbf{A } and \textbf{ B}) = P(\textbf{B}) \times P(\textbf{A} | \textbf{B}).$$

Let's return to the question of just what it means for events to be independent. We said informally in Chapter 4 that what we mean by independence is that the outcome of one event does not influence the probability of the other. With our new notation for conditional probabilities, we can write a formal definition of **independence**. Events **A** and **B** are independent whenever:

$$P(\textbf{B} | \textbf{A}) = P(\textbf{B}).$$

Now we can see that the Multiplication Rule for independent events is just a special case of the General Multiplication Rule. The general rule says:

$$P(\textbf{A } and \textbf{ B}) = P(\textbf{A}) \times P(\textbf{B} | \textbf{A})$$

whether the events are independent or not. But when events **A** and **B** are independent, we can write $P(\textbf{B})$ for $P(\textbf{B} | \textbf{A})$ and we get back our simple rule:

$$P(\textbf{A } and \textbf{ B}) = P(\textbf{A}) \times P(\textbf{B}).$$

> If we had to pick one key idea in this section that you should understand and remember, it's the definition and meaning of independence.

Sometimes people use this statement as the definition of independent events, but we find the other definition more intuitive. Either way, the idea is that the probabilities of independent events don't change when you find out that one of them has occurred.

Using our earlier example, is the probability of the event *choosing a bike* independent of the sex of the customer? We need to check whether

$$P(\text{bike} | \text{man}) = \frac{P(\text{bike } and \text{ man})}{P(\text{man})} = \frac{0.126}{0.475} = 0.265$$

is the same as $P(\text{bike}) = 0.188$.

Because these probabilities aren't equal, we can say that prize preference is *not* independent of the sex of the customer. Whenever at least one of the joint probabilities in the table is *not* equal to the product of the marginal probabilities, we say that the variables are not independent.

Rules 4, 5, 6, and 7 are the main rules we will be using to calculate probabilities, and we therefore summarize them in a table:

OR	In general	$P(A \text{ or } B) = P(A) + P(B) - P(A \text{ and } B)$	Rule 6
	If events are disjoint	$P(A \text{ or } B) = P(A) + P(B)$	Rule 5
AND	In general	$P(A \text{ and } B) = P(A) \times P(B \mid A) = P(A \mid B) \times P(B)$	Rule 7
	If events are independent	$P(A \text{ and } B) = P(A) \times P(B)$	Rule 4

Independent vs. Disjoint

Are disjoint events independent? Both concepts seem to have similar ideas of separation and distinctness about them, but in fact disjoint events *cannot* be independent.[3] Let's see why. Consider the two disjoint events {you get an A in this course}

---

[3]Technically, two disjoint events *can* be independent, but only if the probability of one of the events is 0. For practical purposes we can ignore this case, since we don't anticipate collecting data about things that can't possibly happen.

and {you get a B in this course}. They're disjoint because they have no outcomes in common. Suppose you learn that you *did* get an A in the course. Now what is the probability that you got a B? You can't get both grades, so it must be 0.

Think about what that means. Knowing that the first event (getting an A) occurred changed your probability for the second event (down to 0). So these events aren't independent.

Mutually exclusive events can't be independent. They have no outcomes in common, so knowing that one occurred means the other didn't. A common error is to treat disjoint events as if they were independent and apply the Multiplication Rule for independent events. Don't make that mistake.

The way to check whether events are independent and disjoint is summarized in the following table:

Independent	Check whether $P(\mathbf{B}|\mathbf{A}) = P(\mathbf{B})$
	or
	Check whether $P(\mathbf{A}|\mathbf{B}) = P(\mathbf{A})$
	or
	Check whether $P(\mathbf{A}\text{ } and \text{ }\mathbf{B}) = P(\mathbf{A}) \times (\mathbf{B})$
Disjoint (mutually exclusive)	Check whether $P(\mathbf{A}\text{ } and \text{ }\mathbf{B}) = 0$
	or
	Check whether events **A** and **B** overlap in the sample space diagram
	or
	Check whether the two events can occur together

Note that we can check whether events are disjoint just by looking at the sample space diagram, or asking ourselves whether the two events could occur together. However, we need to calculate probabilities in order to check for independence.

FOR EXAMPLE   **Conditional probability for retail purchases**

QUESTION Using the table from For Example: "Marginal probabilities for retail purchases," if a customer purchases a fashion light, what is the probability that the customer is a woman?

ANSWER $P(\text{woman}|\text{fashion}) = P(\text{woman } and \text{ fashion})/P(\text{fashion})$

$$= 0.30/0.50 = 0.60$$

LO❷ **8.7** **Constructing Contingency Tables**

Sometimes we're given probabilities without a contingency table. You can often construct a simple table to correspond to the probabilities.

A survey of real estate in rural Manitoba classified homes into two price categories (low—less than $275,000, and high—over $275,000). It also noted whether the houses had at least two bathrooms or not (true or false). We are told that 56% of the houses had at least two bathrooms, 62% of the houses were low-priced, and 22% of the houses were both. That's enough information to fill out the table. Translating the percentages to probabilities, we have:

LM Productions/Photodisc/Getty Images

		At Least Two Bathrooms		
		True	False	Total
Price	Low	0.22		0.62
	High			
	Total	0.56		1.00

The 0.56 and 0.62 are marginal probabilities, so they go in the margins. What about the 22% of houses that were both low-priced and had at least two bathrooms? That's a *joint* probability, so it belongs in the interior of the table.

Because the cells of the table show disjoint events, the probabilities always add to the marginal totals going across rows or down columns:

		At Least Two Bathrooms		
		True	False	Total
Price	Low	0.22	0.40	0.62
	High	0.34	0.04	0.38
	Total	0.56	0.44	1.00

Now, finding any other probability is straightforward. For example, what's the probability that a high-priced house has at least two bathrooms?

P(at least two bathrooms | high-priced)

   $= P$(at least two bathrooms and high-priced)$/P$(high-priced)

   $= 0.34/0.38 = 0.895$ or 89.5.

JUST CHECKING

3 Suppose a supermarket is conducting a survey to find out the busiest time and day for shoppers. Survey respondents are asked (1) whether they shopped at the store on a weekday or on the weekend and (2) whether they shopped at the store before or after 5 P.M. The survey revealed that

- 48% of shoppers visited the store before 5 P.M.
- 27% of shoppers visited the store on a weekday (Monday to Friday)
- 7% of shoppers visited the store before 5 P.M. on a weekday.

a) Make a contingency table for the variables *Time of Day* and *Day of Week*.
b) What is the probability that a randomly selected shopper who shops before 5 P.M. also shops on a weekday?
c) Are "before 5 P.M." and "weekday" disjoint events?
d) Are "before 5 P.M." and "weekday" independent events?

Answers are found in Appendix A.

LO❹ ## 8.8   Probability Trees

Some business decisions involve more subtle evaluation of probabilities. Given the probabilities of various circumstances that can affect the business, we can use a picture called a "probability tree*" or "tree diagram" to help think through the decision-making process. A tree shows sequences of events as paths that look like branches of a tree. This can enable us to compare several possible scenarios. Here's a manufacturing example.

---

*Don't confuse probability trees with decision trees, which are dealt with in Section 23.2.

Kim Steele/Photodisc/Getty Images

Personal electronic devices, such as smart phones and tablets, are getting more capable all the time. Manufacturing components for these devices is a challenge, and at the same time, consumers are demanding more and more functionality and increasing sturdiness. Microscopic and even submicroscopic flaws can develop during their fabrication that can blank out pixels on the screens or cause intermittent performance failures. Defects will always occur, so the quality engineer in charge of the production process must monitor the number of defects and take action if the process seems out of control.

Let's suppose that the engineer is called down to the production line because the number of defects has crossed a threshold. She must decide between two possible actions. She knows that a small adjustment to the robots that assemble the components can fix a variety of problems, but for more complex problems, the entire production line needs to be shut down in order to pinpoint the source. The adjustment requires that production be stopped for about an hour. But shutting down the line takes at least an entire shift (eight hours). Naturally, her boss would prefer that she make the simple adjustment. But without knowing the source or severity of the problem, she can't be sure whether that will be successful.

If the engineer wants to predict whether the smaller adjustment will work, she can use a probability tree to help make the decision. Based on her experience, the engineer thinks there are three possible problems: (1) The motherboards could have faulty connections, (2) the memory could be the source of the faulty connections, or (3) some of the cases may simply be seating incorrectly in the assembly line. She knows from past empirical data how often these types of problems crop up and how likely it is that just making an adjustment will fix each type of problem. *Motherboard* problems are rare (10%), *memory* problems have been showing up about 30% of the time, and *case* alignment issues occur most often (60%). We can put those probabilities on the first set of branches, as shown in Figure 8.7.

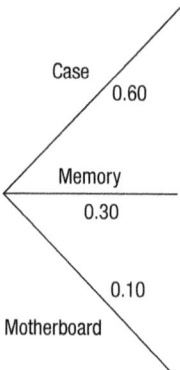

Figure 8.7 Possible problems and their probabilities.

Notice that we've covered all the possibilities, and so the probabilities sum to one. To this diagram we can now add the *conditional* probabilities that a minor adjustment will fix each type of problem. Past data indicate that $P(\text{fix} \mid \text{case motherboard}) = 0.10$, $P(\text{fix} \mid \text{memory}) = 0.50$, and $P(\text{fix} \mid \text{case alignment}) = 0.80$. At the end of each branch representing the problem type, we draw two possibilities (*Fixed* or *Not Fixed*) and write the conditional probabilities on the branches, as shown in Figure 8.8.

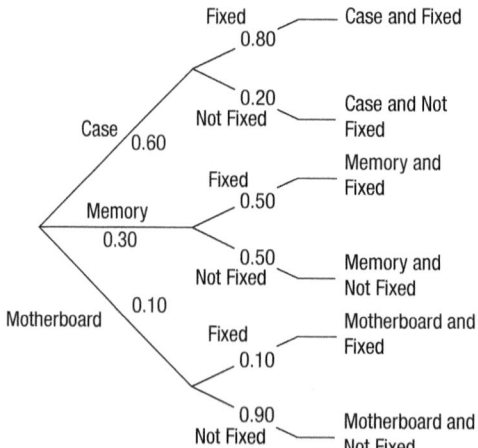

Figure 8.8 Extending the tree diagram, we can show both the problem class and the outcome probabilities of a minor adjustment. The outcome (*Fixed* or *Not Fixed*) probabilities are conditional on the problem type, and they change depending on which branch we follow.

At the end of each second branch, we write the *joint event* corresponding to the combination of the two branches. For example, the top branch is the combination of the problem being case alignment, and the outcome of the small adjustment is that the problem is now fixed. For each of the joint events, we can use the General Multiplication Rule to calculate its joint probability. For example,

$$P(\text{case } and \text{ fixed}) \; = \; P(\text{case}) \; \times \; P(\text{fixed} | \text{case})$$
$$= \; 0.60 \times 0.80 = 0.48$$

We write this probability next to the corresponding event. Doing this for all branch combinations gives Figure 8.9.

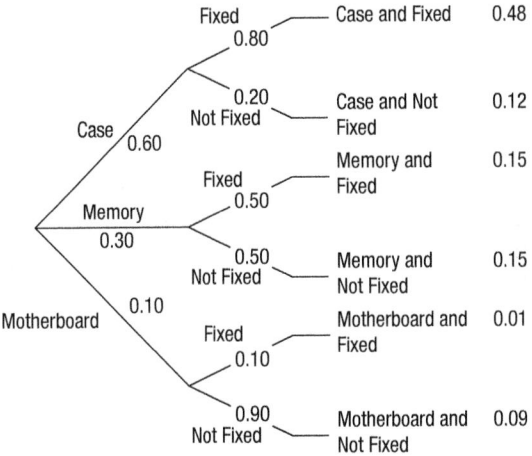

Figure 8.9   We can find the probabilities of compound events by multiplying the probabilities along the branch of the tree that leads to the event, just the way the General Multiplication Rule specifies.

All the outcomes at the far right are disjoint—i.e., they don't overlap with each other because at every node, all the choices are disjoint alternatives. And those alternatives are *all* the possibilities, so the probabilities on the far right must add up to one.

Because the final outcomes are disjoint, we can add up any combination of probabilities to find probabilities for compound events. In particular, the engineer can answer her question: What's the probability that the problem will be fixed by a simple adjustment? She finds all the outcomes on the far right in which the problem was fixed. There are three (one corresponding to each type of problem), and she adds their probabilities: 0.48 + 0.15 + 0.01 = 0.64. So 64% of all problems are fixed by the simple adjustment. The other 36% require a major investigation.

In this section we've drawn our probability trees from left to right. We can also draw them vertically, from top to bottom.

FOR EXAMPLE   Probability trees

A recent Ontario highway safety study found that in 77% of all accidents the driver was wearing a seat belt. Accident reports indicated that 92% of those drivers escaped serious injury (defined as hospitalization or death), but only 63% of the non-belted drivers were so fortunate.

(continued)

> **QUESTION** Draw the probability tree.
>
> **ANSWER** Let B = the driver was wearing a seat belt, and NB = no belt.
>
> Let I = serious injury or death, and OK = not seriously injured.
>
> We know that $P(B) = 0.77$, so $P(NB) = 1 - 0.77 = 023$.
>
> Also, $P(OK|B) = 0.92$, so $P(I|B) = 0.08$
>
> and $P(OK|NB) = 0.63$, so $P(I|NB) = 0.37$

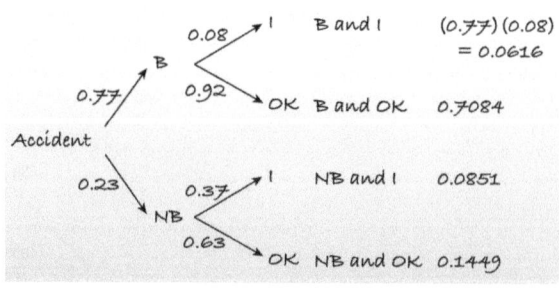

LO❺ 8.9   Reversing the Conditioning: Bayes's Rule

The engineer in our story decided to try the simple adjustment and, fortunately, it worked. Now she needs to report to the quality engineer on the next shift what she thinks the problem was. Was it more likely to be a case alignment problem or a motherboard problem? We know the probabilities of those problems beforehand, but they change now that we have more information. What are the likelihoods that each of the possible problems was, in fact, the one that occurred?

Unfortunately, we can't read those probabilities from the tree in Figure 8.9. For example, the tree gives us $P(\text{fixed and case}) = 0.48$, but we want $P(\text{case}|\text{fixed})$. We know that $P(\text{fixed}|\text{case}) = 0.80$, but that's not the same thing. It isn't valid to reverse the order of conditioning in a conditional probability statement. To "turn" the probability around, we need to go back to the definition of conditional probability:

$$P(\text{case}|\text{fixed}) = \frac{P(\text{case and fixed})}{P(\text{fixed})}$$

We can read the probability in the numerator from the tree, and we've already calculated the probability in the denominator by adding all the probabilities on the final branches that correspond to the event *Fixed*. Putting those values in the formula, the engineer finds

$$P(\text{case}|\text{fixed}) = \frac{0.48}{0.48 + 0.15 + 0.01} = 0.75.$$

She knew that 60% of all problems were due to case alignment, but now that she knows the problem has been fixed, she knows more. Given the additional information that a simple adjustment was able to fix the problem, she now can increase the probability that the problem was case alignment to 0.75.

Optional Math Box

Bayes's Rule

This Optional Math Box provides a justification for calculating probabilities with reversed conditioning from reading probabilities off the probability tree. If you don't like probability trees, you can use the formula in this box directly.

Let $\mathbf{A}_1 = \{\text{Case}\}$, $\mathbf{A}_2 = \{\text{Memory}\}$, and $\mathbf{A}_3 = \{\text{Motherboard}\}$ represent the three types of problems. Let $\mathbf{B} = \{\text{Fixed}\}$, meaning that the simple adjustment fixed the problem. We know $P(\mathbf{B}|\mathbf{A}_1) = 0.80$, $P(\mathbf{B}|\mathbf{A}_2) = 0.50$, and $P(\mathbf{B}|\mathbf{A}_3) = 0.10$. We want to find the reverse probabilities, $P(\mathbf{A}_i|\mathbf{B})$, for the three possible problem types. From the definition of conditional probability, we know (for any of the three types of problems)

$$P(\mathbf{A}_i|\mathbf{B}) = \frac{P(\mathbf{A}_i \text{ and } \mathbf{B})}{P(\mathbf{B})}$$

We still don't know either of these quantities, but we use the definition of conditional probability again to find $P(\mathbf{A}_i \text{ and } \mathbf{B}) = P(\mathbf{B}|\mathbf{A}_i) P(\mathbf{A}_i)$, both of which we know. Finally, we find $P(\mathbf{B})$ by adding up the probabilities of the three events:

$$P(\mathbf{B}) = P(\mathbf{A}_1 \text{ and } \mathbf{B}) + P(\mathbf{A}_2 \text{ and } \mathbf{B}) + P(\mathbf{A}_3 \text{ and } \mathbf{B})$$
$$= P(\mathbf{B}|\mathbf{A}_1)P(\mathbf{A}_1) + P(\mathbf{B}|\mathbf{A}_2)P(\mathbf{A}_2) + P(\mathbf{B}|\mathbf{A}_3)P(\mathbf{A}_3)$$

In general, we can write this for n events $\mathbf{A}_i$ that are mutually exclusive (each pair is disjoint) and exhaustive (their union is the whole space). Then:

$$P(\mathbf{A}_i|\mathbf{B}) = \frac{P(\mathbf{B}|\mathbf{A}_i)P(\mathbf{A}_i)}{\sum_j P(\mathbf{B}|\mathbf{A}_j)P(\mathbf{A}_j)}$$

The general formula at the end of the Optional Math Box is known as **Bayes's Rule**, after the Reverend Thomas Bayes (1702–1761), even though historians doubt that it was actually Bayes who first came up with the reverse conditional probability. When you need to find reverse conditional probabilities, we recommend drawing a tree and finding the appropriate probabilities as we did at the beginning of the section, but the formula gives the general rule.

Bayes's Rule does two things for us. First, it reverses the conditioning. We knew $P(\text{fixed} \mid \text{case})$ and we wanted to know $P(\text{case} \mid \text{fixed})$. Second, it allows us to update our estimate of a probability given additional information. Our initial information as to whether the problem was caused by the case alignment, $P(\text{case}) = 0.60$, was updated to $P(\text{case} \mid \text{fixed}) = 0.75$ as a result of the additional information that the problem was fixed by a minor adjustment. We need to look for these two points in order to decide whether to use Bayes's Rule.

When an auditor checks a small company's accounts, he has an initial idea of the probability of an error in the accounts based on the average error rate in small-company accounts he's audited in the past. Let's call this $P(\text{error}) = 0.05$. Auditors are not infallible, though. They may audit perfectly good accounts and think there's an error, $P(\text{report an error} \mid \text{no error}) = 0.04$. We call this a false positive. Or they may find an error that is in fact there, $P(\text{report an error} \mid \text{error}) = 0.94$. But sometimes they may fail to find it, $P(\text{report no error} \mid \text{error}) = 0.06$—i.e., a false negative. Suppose the auditor reports an error, and we'd like to know the probability, $P(\text{error} \mid \text{report an error})$, that there is in fact an error in the accounts. This situation is one in which we should use Bayes's Rule because it fits our two criteria.

First, it reverses the conditioning. We know $P(\text{report an error} \mid \text{error}) = 0.94$ and would like to know $P(\text{error} \mid \text{report an error})$.

Second, we start with an initial estimate of our probability, $P(error)$, and would like to update it as a result of the auditor's report, $P(error \mid report\ an\ error)$.

In order to use Bayes's Rule we draw a probability tree, and it's important to get the starting point of the tree right. We could start with a branch between "error" and "no error," or we could start with a branch between "report an error" and "report no error." We should start with the thing we're asking about, the probability of an error. Once we've got the starting point right, the rest of the tree and the numerical calculations are relatively simple; see Figure 8.10. Once we've drawn the probability tree, we can answer the original question about calculating $P(error \mid report\ an\ error)$ by picking off the appropriate probabilities from the right-hand side.

$$P(error \mid report\ an\ error) = P(error\ AND\ report\ an\ error)/P(report\ an\ error)$$

$$= 0.047/(0.047 + 0.038)$$

$$= 0.55.$$

Although auditors don't do a perfect job, when they report an error, it increases the probability of there actually being an error from 0.05 to 0.55.

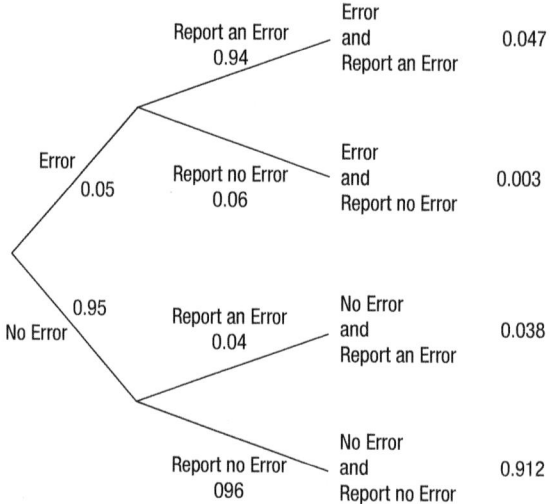

Figure 8.10   Probability tree for auditing small-company accounts.

Suppose auditors want to improve their performance, so that if they report an error the chance of there actually being an error is higher than 0.55. What should they reduce: their false positives or their false negatives? Repeating the above calculation shows that reducing the false negatives from 0.06 to 0.01 only increases the 0.55 probability to 0.57. However, reducing the false positives from 0.04 to 0.01 increases the probability from 0.55 to 0.83. If auditors want to increase the probability of there actually being an error when they report an error, clearly they should spend time and effort in reducing their false positives. Reducing their false negatives would do something different. It would increase the probability that there is *no* error when they report *no* error.

JUST CHECKING

Refer to the box "Statistics Trumps Intuition."

4 My friend is 45 years old, married with one son and one daughter, generally liked by co-workers, capable at work, and expecting a promotion soon. My friend is either an engineer or a librarian. What is the probability that this person is an engineer?

5 My female friend is either an engineer or a librarian. What is the probability that she is an engineer? *Hint:* 20% of engineers are women; 75% of librarians are women

Answers are found in Appendix A.

FOR EXAMPLE   Reversing the conditioning: Bayes's Rule for promoting employees

Bob is 70% sure that Helen should be promoted to a management position. In order to increase the probability of making the right decision, he sends her for a psychological test. The test isn't perfect, but the company has records of the test results from people who've gone on to become either successful or unsuccessful managers in the past. $P(\text{pass} \mid \text{successful manager}) = 0.95$; $P(\text{pass} \mid \text{unsuccessful manager}) = 0.1$. Helen passes the test.

QUESTION   What is the probability of Helen becoming a successful manager?

ANSWER   We want to know $P(\text{successful manager} \mid \text{pass})$. We know the probability with the conditioning the other way around, $P(\text{pass} \mid \text{successful manager}) = 0.95$. We also have an initial estimate, $P(\text{successful}) = 0.70$, and want to update it as a result of information from the test. These are the two criteria for using Bayes's Rule.

First we draw a probability tree, starting with a node that represents what we're asked about, that is, successful or not.

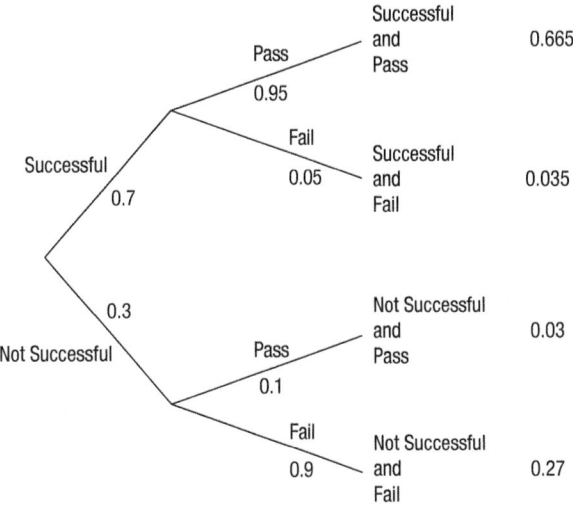

$$P(\text{successful} \mid \text{pass}) = P(\text{successful AND pass})/P(\text{pass})$$
$$= 0.665/(0.665 + 0.03)$$
$$= 0.96$$

WHAT CAN GO WRONG?

- **Beware of probabilities that don't add up to 1.** To be a legitimate assignment of probability, the sum of the probabilities for all possible outcomes must total 1. If the sum is less than 1, you may need to add another category ("other") and assign the remaining probability to that outcome. If the sum is more than 1, check that the outcomes are disjoint. If they're not, then you can't assign probabilities by counting relative frequencies.

- **Don't add probabilities of events if they're not disjoint.** Events must be disjoint to use the Addition Rule. The probability of being under 80 *or* a female is not the probability of being under 80 *plus* the probability of being female. That sum may be more than 1.

- **Don't multiply probabilities of events if they're not independent.** The probability of selecting a customer at random who's over 70 years old *and* retired is not the probability that the customer is over 70 years old *times* the probability the customer is retired. Knowing that the customer is over 70 changes the probability of his or her being retired. You can't multiply these probabilities. The multiplication of probabilities of events that are not independent is one of the most common errors people make in dealing with probabilities.

- **Don't confuse disjoint and independent.** Disjoint events *can't* be independent. If **A** = {you get a promotion} and **B** = {you don't get a promotion}, **A** and **B** are disjoint. Are they independent? If you find out that **A** is true, does that change the probability of **B**? You bet it does! So they can't be independent.

ETHICS IN ACTION

A national chain of hair salons is considering the inclusion of some spa services. A management team was organized to investigate the possibility of entering the spa market via two offerings: facials or massages. One member of the team, Sherrie Trapper, had found some results published by a spa industry trade journal regarding the probability of salon customers purchasing these types of services. She wasn't quite sure how to interpret the probabilities, but reported them this way. "There is an 80% chance that a customer visiting a hair salon that offers spa services will be there for hair styling services. Of those, 50% will purchase facials. On the other hand, 90% of customers visiting salons that offer spa services will be there for hair styling services or massages." Consequently, she argued in favour of offering massages rather than facials on the chain's initial spa menu.

Ethical Issue Sherrie doesn't understand what she's reporting, and consequently should not use this information to persuade others on the team (related to Item A, ASA Ethical Guidelines; see Appendix C, the American Statistical Association's Ethical Guidelines for Statistical Practice, also available online at www.amstat.org/about/ethicalguidelines.cfm).

Ethical Solution Sherrie should share all details of the published results with the management team. The probabilities she's reporting are not comparable (one is conditional and the other is the probability of a union).

WHAT HAVE WE LEARNED?

Learning Objectives

❶ We've learned that empirical probability is based on long-run relative frequencies and that the Law of Large Numbers speaks only of long-run behaviour. Because the long run is a very long time, we need to be careful not to misinterpret the Law of Large Numbers as a law of averages. Even when we've observed a string of heads, we shouldn't expect extra tails in subsequent coin flips.

Probability can also be estimated theoretically when we know in advance the number of ways an event can occur. As well, it can be estimated subjectively, for example, from the informed opinion of an expert.

❷ We've learned some basic rules for combining probabilities of outcomes to find probabilities of more complex events. These include:

1. Probability for any event is between 0 and 1.

2. Probability of the sample space, $\mathbf{S}$; the set of possible outcomes $= 1$.

3. Complement Rule: $P(\mathbf{A}) = 1 - P(\mathbf{A}^C)$.

4. Multiplication Rule for independent events: $P(\mathbf{A} \text{ and } \mathbf{B}) = P(\mathbf{A}) \times P(\mathbf{B})$.

5. Addition Rule for disjoint events: $P(\mathbf{A} \text{ or } \mathbf{B}) = P(\mathbf{A}) + P(\mathbf{B})$.

6. General Addition Rule: $P(\mathbf{A} \text{ or } \mathbf{B}) = P(\mathbf{A}) + P(\mathbf{B}) - P(\mathbf{A} \text{ and } \mathbf{B})$.

7. General Multiplication Rule. $P(\mathbf{A} \text{ and } \mathbf{B}) = P(\mathbf{A}) \times P(\mathbf{B} \mid \mathbf{A}) = P(\mathbf{A} \mid \mathbf{B}) \times P(\mathbf{B})$.

❸ If one event does not affect the probability of another event, they are independent. If two events cannot both occur, they are disjoint or mutually exclusive.

❹ Probability trees can be used to represent the probabilities of multiple events, some of which depend on the others.

❺ Given more information, a probability estimate can be updated using a probability tree and Bayes's Rule.

Terms

Addition Rule

If $\mathbf{A}$ and $\mathbf{B}$ are disjoint events, then the probability of $\mathbf{A}$ or $\mathbf{B}$ is:

$$P(\mathbf{A} \text{ or } \mathbf{B}) = P(\mathbf{A}) + P(\mathbf{B}).$$

Bayes's Rule

A rule for calculating one conditional probability from another:

$$P(\mathbf{A}_i \mid \mathbf{B}) = \frac{P(\mathbf{B} \mid \mathbf{A}_i)P(\mathbf{A}_i)}{\sum_{\mathcal{J}} P(\mathbf{B} \mid \mathbf{A}_j) P(\mathbf{A}_j)}$$

Complement Rule

The probability of an event occurring is 1 minus the probability that it doesn't occur:

$$P(\mathbf{A}) = 1 - P(\mathbf{A}^C).$$

Conditional probability

$$P(\mathbf{B} \mid \mathbf{A}) = \frac{P(\mathbf{A} \text{ and } \mathbf{B})}{P(\mathbf{A})}.$$

$P(\mathbf{B} \mid \mathbf{A})$ is read as "the probability of $\mathbf{B}$ *given* $\mathbf{A}$."

Disjoint (or mutually exclusive) events

Two events are disjoint if they share no outcomes in common. If $\mathbf{A}$ and $\mathbf{B}$ are disjoint, then knowing that $\mathbf{A}$ occurs tells us that $\mathbf{B}$ cannot occur. Disjoint events are also called "mutually exclusive."

Empirical probability

When the probability comes from the long-run relative frequency of the event's occurrence, it is an empirical probability.

Event

A collection of outcomes. Usually, we identify events so that we can attach probabilities to them. We denote events with bold capital letters such as $\mathbf{A}$, $\mathbf{B}$, or $\mathbf{C}$.

General Addition Rule

For any two events, $\mathbf{A}$ and $\mathbf{B}$, the probability of $\mathbf{A}$ *or* $\mathbf{B}$ is

$$P(\mathbf{A} \text{ or } \mathbf{B}) = P(\mathbf{A}) + P(\mathbf{B}) - P(\mathbf{A} \text{ and } \mathbf{B}).$$

General Multiplication Rule

For any two events, $\mathbf{A}$ and $\mathbf{B}$, the probability of $\mathbf{A}$ *and* $\mathbf{B}$ is

$$P(\mathbf{A} \text{ and } \mathbf{B}) = P(\mathbf{A}) \times P(\mathbf{B} \mid \mathbf{A}) \text{ or } P(\mathbf{A} \text{ and } \mathbf{B}) = P(\mathbf{B}) \times P(\mathbf{A} \mid \mathbf{B}).$$

Independence (used informally)

Two events are *independent* if the fact that one event occurs does not change the probability of the other.

Independence (used formally)	Events **A** and **B** are independent when $P(\mathbf{B}\,|\,\mathbf{A}) = P(\mathbf{B})$, or when $P(\mathbf{A}\,|\,\mathbf{B}) = P(\mathbf{A})$.
Joint probabilities	The probability that two events both occur.
Law of Large Numbers (LLN)	The Law of Large Numbers states that the *long-run relative frequency* of repeated, independent events settles down to the *true relative frequency* as the number of trials increases.
Marginal probability	In a joint probability table, a marginal probability is the probability distribution of either variable separately, usually found in the rightmost column or bottom row of the table.
Multiplication Rule	If **A** and **B** are independent events, then the probability of **A** *and* **B** is $$P(\mathbf{A}\ and\ \mathbf{B}) = P(\mathbf{A}) \times P(\mathbf{B}).$$
Outcome	The outcome of a trial is the value measured, observed, or reported for an individual instance of that trial.
Personal probability	A probability that is subjective and represents your personal degree of belief.
Probability	A number between 0 and 1 that reports the likelihood of an event's occurrence. We write $P(\mathbf{A})$ for the probability of the event **A**.
Probability Assignment Rule	The probability of the entire sample space must be 1: $P(\mathbf{S}) = 1$.
Random phenomenon	A phenomenon is random if we know what outcomes could happen, but not which particular values will happen.
Sample space	The collection of all possible outcome values. The sample space has a probability of 1.
Subjective probability	Same as *personal probability*.
Theoretical probability	A probability that comes from a mathematical model of the number of possible outcomes.
Trial	A single attempt or realization of a random phenomenon.

Skills

Plan

- Be able to understand that random phenomena are unpredictable in the short term but show long-run regularity.
- Know how to recognize random outcomes in a real-world situation.
- Know that the relative frequency of an outcome of a random phenomenon settles down as we gather more random outcomes. Be able to state the Law of Large Numbers.
- Know the basic definitions and rules of probability.
- Be able to recognize when events are disjoint and when events are independent. Understand the difference and that disjoint events cannot be independent.

Do

- Be able to use the facts about probability to determine whether an assignment of probabilities is legitimate. Each probability must be a number between 0 and 1, and the sum of the probabilities assigned to all possible outcomes must be 1.
- Know how and when to apply the General Addition Rule. Know when events are disjoint.
- Know how and when to apply the General Multiplication Rule. Be able to use it to find probabilities for combinations of both independent and nonindependent events.
- Know how to use the Complement Rule to make calculating probabilities simpler. Recognize that probabilities of "at least" are likely to be simplified in this way.

Report

- Be able to use statements about probability in describing a random phenomenon. You will need this skill soon for making statements about statistical inference.
- Know and be able to use correctly the terms "sample space," "disjoint events," and "independent events."
- Be able to make a statement about a conditional probability that makes clear how the condition affects the probability.
- Avoid making statements that assume independence of events when there is no clear evidence that they are in fact independent.

Market Segmentation

The marketing manager for a department store wants to know how important quality is to her customers. A consultant reports that based on past research, 30% of all consumers nationwide are more interested in quantity than quality. The marketing manager suspects that customers from her store are different, and that customers of different ages might have different views as well. Using conditional probabilities, marginal probabilities, and joint probabilities constructed from the data in the file **ch08_MCSP_Market_Segmentation**,[4] write a report to the manager on what you find.

As you do your analysis and write up your report, keep in mind that the manager may be more interested in the opinions of "frequent" customers than those who never or hardly ever shop at her store. These "frequent" customers contribute a disproportionate amount of profit to the store.

Variable and Question	Categories
Age *Which age group are you in?*	18–24 years old 25–34 35–44 45–54 55–64 65 or over
Frequency *How often do you shop for women's clothing at [this department store]?*	Never–hardly ever 1–2 times per year 3–4 times per year 5 times or more
Quality *For the same amount of money, I will generally buy one good item in preference to several of lower price and quality.*	1. Definitely disagree 2. Generally disagree 3. Moderately disagree 4. Moderately agree 5. Generally agree 6. Definitely agree

Air Canada

Air Canada and United Continental sell seats on each other's cross-border flights, coordinating fare structures and discounts while competing for passengers. In 2011 they proposed a closer collaboration involving sharing revenue and coordinating schedules on 19 Canada–U.S. routes.

In Canada, deals of this type are evaluated by the Competition Bureau, and if there are objections to its rulings, a final decision is made by the Competition Tribunal. In mid-2011 the Canadian Competition Bureau ruled against the deal on the grounds that it would monopolize 10 key Canada–U.S. routes and significantly reduce competition on nine others, possibly resulting in increased prices. In August 2011, Air

(continued)

---

[4]For a version with the categories coded as integers, see **ch08_MCSP_Market_Segmentation_Coded**.

Canada objected to the Competition Bureau ruling, saying that its judgment was "fundamentally misconceived" and that the proposed joint venture would result in "substantial gains in efficiency."

A few days later, WestJet intervened in the case on the side of the Competition Bureau, arguing that the deal between United Continental and Air Canada would prevent it from competing on equal terms on trans-border routes. WestJet has a deal with American Airlines, but that deal is more restrictive than the one proposed between Air Canada and United Continental.

The case then went to the Competition Tribunal for a decision as to whether to allow the collaboration agreement between Air Canada and United Continental.

Put yourself in the position of an investment banker early in 2011, prior to the above events taking place. You know that Air Canada might propose a closer collaboration agreement with United Continental, and you believe this will be profitable for Air Canada. You need to calculate the chance that such a deal will eventually go through. You assess that Air Canada will propose the collaboration agreement with a probability of 0.6. You also know that, if it does, the Competition Bureau might oppose the deal with a probability of 0.8. If that happens, Air Canada might object with a probability of 0.9. And if it does, WestJet could intervene.

You assess the probability of WestJet intervening in the case at 0.75, which you believe will affect the decision of the Competition Tribunal. If WestJet intervenes, you believe that the chance of the Competition Tribunal blocking the deal is 0.85, and that without WestJet it's 0.7.

What is the probability of a closer collaboration agreement between Air Canada and United Continental? In your answer, (a) draw a probability tree, (b) clearly indicate which probabilities are joint and which are conditional, and (c) show your calculations clearly.

MyStatLab   Students! Save time, improve your grades with MyStatLab. Questions marked in ▪ can be found on MyStatLab. You can practise them as often as you want, and most feature step-by-step guided solutions to help you find the right answer. You'll find a personalized study plan available to you too!

EXERCISES

SECTION 8.1

1. Indicate which of the following represent independent events. Explain briefly.

a) The gender of successive customers using an ATM machine.
b) The last digit of the social insurance numbers of students in a class.
c) The scores you receive on the first midterm, second midterm, and final exam of a course. **LO ❶**

2. Indicate which of the following represent independent events. Explain briefly.

a) Prices of houses on the same block.
b) Successive measurements of your heart rate as you exercise on a treadmill.
c) Measurements of the heart rates of all students in the gym. **LO ❶**

SECTION 8.2

3. In many lotteries you can choose which numbers to play. Consider a common form in which you choose five numbers. Which of the following strategies can improve your chance of winning? If the method works, explain why. If not, explain why, using appropriate Statistics terms.

a) Always play 1, 2, 3, 4, 5.
b) Generate random numbers using a computer or calculator and play those. **LO ❶**

4. For the same kind of lottery as in Exercise 3, which of the following strategies can improve your chance of winning? If the method works, explain why. If not, explain why, using appropriate Statistics terms.

a) Choose randomly from among the numbers that have *not* come up in the last three lottery drawings.
b) Choose the numbers that did come up in the most recent lottery drawing. **LO ❶**

SECTIONS 8.1 AND 8.3

5. Which probability assessment method was used in each of the following examples: empirical, theoretical, or subjective?

a) A construction company bids on a contract to build a new bridge over a river and assesses the probability of getting the contract to be 0.6.
b) A bank analyzes the balances in customers' chequing accounts and assesses that when the balance exceeds $5000, the probability of that customer transferring some money to a savings account is 0.87.
c) A gambler tosses two dice and assesses the probability of getting two sixes to be 1/36. **LO ❶**

6. Which probability assessment method was used in each of the following examples: empirical, theoretical, or subjective?

a) An insurance company analyzes past automobile claims and assesses the probability of a male driver aged 18–25 making a claim to be 0.43 in any given year.
b) An economist assesses the probability of the Bank of Canada increasing the interest rate next month to be 0.4.
c) One door prize is given to a randomly selected person attending an event. There are 50 people attending the event. An attendee assesses the probability that he or she will get the prize as 0.02. **LO ❶**

SECTION 8.4

7. You and your friend decide to get your cars inspected. You are informed that 75% of cars pass inspection. If the event of your car's passing is independent of your friend's car,

a) What is the probability that your car passes inspection?
b) What is the probability that your car doesn't pass inspection?
c) What is the probability that both of the cars pass?
d) What is the probability that at least one of the two cars passes? **LO ❷**

8. At your school, 10% of the class are Marketing majors. If you are randomly assigned to two partners in your Statistics class,

a) What is the probability that the first partner will be a Marketing major?
b) What is the probability that the first partner won't be a Marketing major?
c) What is the probability that both will be Marketing majors?
d) What is the probability that one or the other will be a Marketing major? **LO ❷**

SECTION 8.5

9. The following contingency table shows opinions about global warming (nonissue vs. serious concern) among registered voters, broken down by political party affiliation (Liberal, Conservative, and Independent).

		Opinion on Global Warming		
		Nonissue	Serious Concern	Total
Political Party	Liberal	60	440	500
	Conservative	290	210	500
	Independent	90	110	200
	Total	440	760	1200

a) What is the probability that a registered voter selected at random believes that global warming is a serious issue?
b) What type of probability did you find in (a)?
c) What is the probability that a registered voter selected at random is a Conservative and believes that global warming is a serious issue?
d) What type of probability did you find in (c)? **LO ❷**

10. Multigenerational families can be categorized as having two adult generations, such as parents living with adult children; "skip" generation families, such as grandparents living with grandchildren; and three or more generations living in the household. Pew Research in the United States surveyed multigenerational households. This table is based on its reported results:

	2 Adult Gens	2 Skip Gens	3 or More Gens	Total
White	509	55	222	786
Hispanic	139	11	142	292
Black	119	32	99	250
Asian	61	1	48	110
Total	828	99	511	1438

a) What is the probability that a multigenerational family is Hispanic?
b) What is the probability that a multigenerational family selected at random is a black, two-adult-generation family?

c) What type of probability did you find in (a) and (b)? **LO ❷**

SECTION 8.6

11. Using the table from Exercise 9,

a) What is the probability that a randomly selected registered voter who is a Conservative believes that global warming is a serious issue?
b) What is the probability that a randomly selected registered voter is a Conservative given that he or she believes global warming is a serious issue?
c) What is P(serious concern | Liberal)? **LO ❸**

12. Using the table from Exercise 10,

a) What is the probability that a randomly selected black multigenerational family is a two-generation family?
b) What is the probability that a randomly selected multigenerational family is white given that it's a "skip" generation family?
c) What is P(3 or more generations | Asian)? **LO ❸**

SECTION 8.7

13. A national survey indicated that 30% of adults conduct their banking online. It also found that 40% are under the age of 50, and that 25% are under the age of 50 and conduct their banking online.

a) What percentage of adults do not conduct their banking online?
b) What type of probability is the 25% mentioned above?
c) Construct a contingency table showing all joint and marginal probabilities.
d) What is the probability that an individual conducts banking online given that the individual is under the age of 50?
e) Are *Banking Online* and *Age* independent? Explain. **LO ❷**

14. Facebook reports that 70% of its users are from outside the United States and that 50% of its users log on to Facebook every day. Suppose that 20% of its users are U.S. users who log on every day.

a) What percentage of Facebook's users are from the United States?
b) What type of probability is the 20% mentioned above?
c) Construct a contingency table showing all the joint and marginal probabilities.
d) What is the probability that a user is from the United States given that he or she logs on every day?
e) Are *From United States* and *Log on Every Day* independent? Explain. **LO ❷**

SECTION 8.8

15. According to U.S. Census data, 68% of the civilian U.S. labour force self-identifies as white, 11% as black, 13% as Hispanic or Latino, and the remaining 8% as other

ethnic origin. Among whites in the labour force, 54% are male and 46% are female. Among blacks, 52% are male and 48% are female, and among Hispanic/Latinos, 58% are male and 42% are female. Breakdowns by gender are not available for other categories.

a) Here is a probability tree for these relationships. Fill in the probabilities as given:

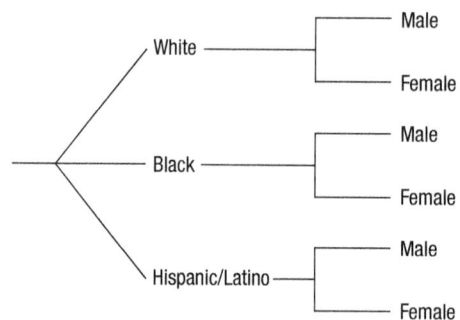

b) What is the probability that a randomly selected worker is a female Hispanic/Latino?
c) For a randomly selected worker, what is

P(female | white)? **LO ❹**

16. Lie detectors are controversial instruments, barred from use as evidence in many courts. Nonetheless, many employers use lie detector screening as part of their hiring process. There has been some research, but no agreement, about the reliability of polygraph tests. Based on this research, suppose that a polygraph can detect 65% of lies, but incorrectly identifies 15% of true statements as lies.

The company gives everyone a polygraph test, asking "Have you ever stolen anything from your place of work?" Naturally, all the applicants answer "No," but the company has evidence to suggest that 5% of the applicants are lying. When the polygraph indicates that the applicant is lying, that person is ineligible for a job.

a) Here is the outline of a probability tree for this situation. Fill in the probabilities.

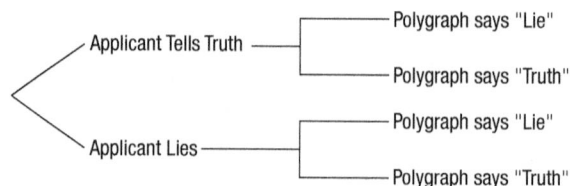

b) What is the probability that a random job applicant tells the truth and is cleared by the polygraph? **LO ❹**

SECTION 8.9

17. Using the probability tree in Exercise 15, if a randomly selected worker is female, what is the probability that she is white? **LO ❺**

18. Using the probability tree in Exercise 16, what is the probability that a job applicant who is rejected by the polygraph was actually telling the truth? **LO ❺**

CHAPTER EXERCISES

19. What does it mean?, part 1. Respond to the following questions:

a) A casino claims that its roulette wheel is truly random. What should that claim mean?
b) A reporter says that there's a 50% chance that the Bank of Canada will cut interest rates by a quarter point at its next meeting. What is the meaning of such a phrase? **LO ❶**

20. What does it mean?, part 2. Respond to the following questions:

a) After an unusually dry autumn, a radio announcer is heard to say, "Watch out! We'll pay for these sunny days later on this winter." Explain what he's trying to say, and comment on the validity of his reasoning.
b) A batter who had failed to get a hit in seven consecutive times at bat then hits a game-winning home run. When talking to reporters afterward, he says he was very confident that last time at bat because he knew he was "due for a hit." Comment on his reasoning. **LO ❶**

21. Airline safety. Even though commercial airlines have excellent safety records, in the weeks following a crash airlines often report a drop in the number of passengers, probably because people are afraid to risk flying.

a) A travel agent suggests that since the law of averages makes it highly unlikely to have two plane crashes within a few weeks of each other, flying soon after a crash is the safest time. What do you think?
b) If the airline industry proudly announces that it has set a new record for the longest period of safe flights, would you be reluctant to fly? Are the airlines due to have a crash? **LO ❶**

22. Economic predictions. An investment company's newsletter makes general predictions about the economy to help its clients make sound investment decisions.

a) Recently the company said that because the stock market had been up for the past three months in a row, it was "due for a correction" and advised clients to reduce their holdings. What "law" is the company applying? Comment.
b) The company advised buying a stock that had gone down in the past four sessions, saying that it was clearly "due to bounce back." What "law" is it applying? Comment. **LO ❶**

23. Toy company. A toy company manufactures a spinning game and needs to decide what probabilities are involved in the game. The plastic arrow on the spinner stops rotating to point at a colour that will determine what happens next. Knowing these probabilities will help determine how easy or difficult it is for a person to win the game and how long the average game will last. Are each of the following probability assignments possible? Why or why not? **LO ❷**

| | **Probabilities of:** | | | |
	Red	Yellow	Green	Blue
a)	0.25	0.25	0.25	0.25
b)	0.10	0.20	0.30	0.40
c)	0.20	0.30	0.40	0.50
d)	0	0	1.00	0
e)	0.10	0.20	1.20	−1.50

24. Store discounts. Many stores run "secret sales": Shoppers receive cards that determine how large a discount they get, but the percentage is revealed by scratching off that black stuff (What *is* that?) only after the purchase has been totalled at the cash register. The store is required to reveal (in the fine print) the distribution of discounts available. A store has four possible discounts: 10%, 20%, 30%, and 50%. Are each of these probability assignments plausible? Why or why not? **LO ❷**

| | **Probabilities of:** | | | |
	10% Off	20% Off	30% Off	50% Off
a)	0.20	0.20	0.20	0.20
b)	0.50	0.30	0.20	0.10
c)	0.80	0.10	0.05	0.05
d)	0.75	0.25	0.25	−0.25
e)	1.00	0	0	0

25. Quality control. A tire manufacturer recently announced a recall because 2% of its tires are defective. If you just bought a new set of four tires from this manufacturer, what is the probability that at least one of your new tires is defective? **LO ❷**

26. Pepsi promotion. For a sales promotion, the manufacturer places winning symbols under the caps of 10% of all Pepsi bottles selected at random. If you buy a six-pack of Pepsi, what is the probability that you'll win something? **LO ❷**

27. Auto warranty, part 1. In developing its warranty policy, an automobile manufacturer estimates that over a four-year period, 17% of its new cars will need to be repaired once, 7% will need repairs twice, and 4% will require three or more repairs. If you buy a new car from this company, what is the probability that your car will need

a) No repairs?
b) No more than one repair?
c) Some repairs? **LO ❷**

28. Consulting team, part 1. You work for a large global management consulting company. Of the entire workforce of analysts, 55% have had no experience in the telecommunications industry, 32% have had limited experience (less than five years), and the rest have had extensive experience (five years or more). On a recent project, you and two other analysts were chosen at random to constitute a team. It turns out that part of the project involves telecommunications. What is the probability that the first teammate you meet has

a) Extensive telecommunications experience?
b) Some telecommunications experience?
c) No more than limited telecommunications experience?
LO ❷

29. Auto warranty, part 2. Consider again the auto repair rates described in Exercise 27. If you bought two new cars from the company, what is the probability that over a four-year period

a) Neither will need repair?
b) Both will need repair?
c) At least one car will need repair? **LO ❷**

30. Consulting team, part 2. You are assigned to be part of a team of three analysts in a global management consulting company, as described in Exercise 28. What is the probability that of your other two teammates

a) Neither has any telecommunications experience?
b) Both have some telecommunications experience?
c) At least one has had extensive telecommunications experience? **LO ❷**

31. Auto warranty, part 3. You used the Multiplication Rule to calculate repair probabilities for your cars in Exercise 29.

a) What must be true about your car in order to make that approach valid?
b) Do you think this assumption is reasonable? Explain.
LO ❷, ❸

32. Consulting team, part 3. You used the Multiplication Rule to calculate probabilities about the telecommunications experience of your consulting teammates in Exercise 30.

a) What must be true about the groups in order to make that approach valid?
b) Do you think this assumption is reasonable? Explain.
LO ❷, ❸

33. Real estate, part 1. Real estate ads suggest that 64% of homes for sale have garages, 21% have swimming pools, and 17% have both features. What is the probability that a home for sale has

a) A pool or a garage?
b) Neither a pool nor a garage?
c) A pool but no garage? **LO ❷**

34. Human resource data. Employment data at a large company reveal that 72% of the workers are married, 44% are university graduates, and half of the university grads are married. What is the probability that a randomly chosen worker is

a) Neither married nor a university graduate?
b) Married but not a university graduate?
c) Married or a university graduate? **LO ❷**

35. Market research on energy, part 1. A Gallup Poll in March 2007 asked 1005 adults whether increasing domestic energy production or protecting the environment should be given higher priority. Here are the results:

Response	Number
Increase Production	342
Protect the Environment	583
Equally Important	50
No Opinion	30
Total	**1005**

If we select a person at random from this sample of 1005 adults,

a) What is the probability that the person responded "Increase Production"?
b) What is the probability that the person responded "Equally Important" or had "No Opinion"? **LO ❷**

36. Market research on energy, part 2. Exercise 35 shows the results of a Gallup Poll about energy. Suppose we select three people at random from this sample.

a) What is the probability that all three responded "Protect the Environment"?
b) What is the probability that none responded "Equally Important"?
c) What assumption did you make in computing these probabilities?
d) Explain why you think that assumption is reasonable.
LO ❷, ❸

37. Telemarketing contact rates, part 1. Marketing research firms often contact their respondents by sampling random telephone numbers. Although interviewers currently reach about 76% of selected households, the percentage of those contacted who agree to cooperate with the survey has fallen and is now only 38%. Each household is assumed to be independent of the others.

a) What is the probability that the next household on the list will be contacted but will refuse to cooperate?
b) What is the probability of failing to contact a household or of contacting the household but not getting them to agree to the interview?

c) Show another way to calculate the probability in (b). **LO❶, ❷**

38. Telemarketing contact rates, part 2. Following from Exercise 37, according to Pew Research, the contact rate (probability of contacting a selected household) in 1997 was 69%, and in 2003 it was 76%. However, the cooperation rate (probability of someone at the contacted household agreeing to be interviewed) was 58% in 1997 and dropped to 38% in 2003.

a) What is the probability (in 2003) of obtaining an interview with the next household on the sample list? (To obtain an interview, an interviewer must both contact the household and get agreement for the interview.)

b) Was an interviewer more likely to obtain an interview from a randomly selected household in 1997 or in 2003? **LO❷**

39. Canadian Blood Services, part 1. Canadian Blood Services has to track the supply of and demand for various blood types. It estimates that 46% of the Canadian population has Type O blood, 42% Type A, 9% Type B, and the rest Type AB. (**Source:** Based on data from Canadian Blood Services, www.bloodservices.ca)

a) If a Canadian volunteers to give blood, what is the probability that this donor
  i) Has Type AB blood?
  ii) Has Type A or Type B blood?
  iii) Is not Type O?

b) Among four potential donors, what is the probability that
  i) All are Type O?
  ii) None have Type AB blood?
  iii) Not all are Type A?
  iv) At least one person is Type B? **LO❷**

40. Canadian Blood Services, part 2. In Exercise 39, you calculated probabilities involving various blood types.

a) If you examine one donor, are the events of the donor being Type A and the donor being Type B disjoint or independent or neither? Explain your answer.

b) If you examine two donors, are the events that the first donor is Type A and the second donor is Type B disjoint or independent or neither?

c) Can disjoint events ever be independent? Explain. **LO❸**

41. Canadian mining company. A Canadian mining company explores a site in Zambia for copper and zinc using exploratory drilling to obtain samples. The probability that a sample contains copper is 0.6 and the probability that a sample contains zinc is 0.5. The probability that a sample contains both zinc and copper is 0.4.

a) What is the probability that a sample containing zinc also contains copper?

b) Is the presence of copper and zinc in samples (i) mutually exclusive or (ii) independent? State your reasons clearly.

c) What is the probability that five consecutive samples contain either copper or zinc? **LO❷, ❸**

42. Barrick Gold. The Canadian mining company Barrick Gold operates the Donlin Creek mining project in the Yukon–Kuskokwin region, today providing stable employment with 90% First Nations people as employees and supervisors. When another mining company started the project in 1996, employment conditions were much worse. There was a 50% probability of employees failing drug screening tests and hence being fired. Of those who passed the test, there was a 70% chance that they would resign from their jobs. What was the probability that an employee would leave employment either as a result of failing the drug test or as a result of resignation? State your reasoning and assumptions clearly. (**Source:** Based on data from Barrick Gold Corporation. Corporate responsibility—Case studies & success stories. Retrieved from www.barrick.com/CorporateResponsibility/CaseStudies/default.aspx) **LO❷, ❹**

43. International food survey, part 1. A GfK Roper Worldwide survey asked consumers in five countries whether they agreed with the statement "I am worried about the safety of the food I eat." Here are the responses, classified by the age of the respondent:

Age	Agree	Neither Agree nor Disagree	Disagree	Don't Know/No Response	Total
13–19	661	368	452	32	1513
20–29	816	365	336	16	1533
30–39	871	355	290	9	1525
40–49	914	335	266	6	1521
50+	966	339	283	10	1598
Total	4228	1762	1627	73	7690

If we select a person at random from this sample,

a) What is the probability that the person agreed with the statement?

b) What is the probability that the person is younger than 50 years old?

c) What is the probability that the person is younger than 50 *and* agrees with the statement?

d) What is the probability that the person is younger than 50 *or* agrees with the statement? (*Source:* Norean Sharpe, Richard D De Veaux, Paul Velleman, David Wright, Business Statistics, Third Canadian Edition, 3e, © 2018, Pearson Education, Inc.) **LO❷**

44. Cosmetics marketing, part 1. A GfK Roper Worldwide survey asked consumers in five countries whether they agreed with the statement "I follow a skin care routine every day." Here are the responses classified by the country of the respondent:

		Agree	Disagree	Don't Know	Total
		Response			
Country	China	361	988	153	1502
	France	695	763	81	1539
	India	828	689	18	1535
	U.K.	597	898	62	1557
	U.S.	668	841	48	1557
	Total	3149	4179	362	7690

If we select a person at random from this sample,

a) What is the probability that the person agrees with the statement?
b) What is the probability that the person is from China?
c) What is the probability that the person is from China *and* agrees with the statement?
d) What is the probability that the person is from China *or* agrees with the statement? (*Source:* Norean Sharpe, Richard D De Veaux, Paul Velleman, David Wright, Business Statistics, Third Canadian Edition, 3e, © 2018, Pearson Education, Inc.) **LO ❷**

45. E-Commerce. Suppose an online business organizes an email survey to find out if online shoppers are concerned about the security of business transactions on the web. Of the 42 individuals who respond, 24 are concerned and 18 are not concerned. Eight of those concerned about security are male and six of those not concerned are male. If a respondent is selected at random, find each of the following conditional probabilities:

a) The respondent is male, given that the respondent is not concerned about security.
b) The respondent is not concerned about security, given that the respondent is female.
c) The respondent is female, given that the respondent is concerned about security. **LO ❷**

46. Automobile inspection. Twenty percent of cars that are inspected have faulty pollution control systems. The cost of repairing a pollution control system exceeds $250 about 40% of the time. When a driver takes a car in for inspection, what's the probability of paying more than $250 to repair the pollution control system? **LO ❷**

47. Pharmaceutical company, part 1. A pharmaceutical company is considering manufacturing and marketing a drug that will help to lower both an individual's blood pressure and cholesterol. The company is interested in understanding the demand for such a product. The joint probabilities that an adult male has high blood pressure and/or high cholesterol are shown in the table.

		Blood Pressure	
		High	OK
Cholesterol	High	0.11	0.21
	OK	0.16	0.52

a) What's the probability that an adult male has both conditions?
b) What's the probability that an adult male has high blood pressure?
c) What's the probability that an adult male with high blood pressure also has high cholesterol?
d) What's the probability that an adult male has high blood pressure if it's known that he has high cholesterol? **LO ❷**

48. International relocation, part 1. A European department store chain is developing an advertising campaign for its new Canadian location, and its marketing managers need to better understand their target market. Based on survey responses, a joint probability table that an adult shops at the new Canadian store classified by age is shown below:

		Shop		
		Yes	No	Total
Age	<20	0.26	0.04	0.30
	20–40	0.24	0.10	0.34
	>40	0.12	0.24	0.36
	Total	0.62	0.38	1.00

a) What's the probability that a survey respondent will shop at the Canadian store?
b) What's the probability that a survey respondent will shop at the store given that he or she is younger than 20 years old? **LO ❷**

49. Pharmaceutical company, part 2. Given the table of probabilities in Exercise 47, are high blood pressure and high cholesterol independent? Explain. **LO ❸**

50. International relocation, part 2. Given the table of probabilities compiled for a department store chain in Exercise 48, are age <20 and shopping at the department store independent? Explain. **LO ❸**

51. International food survey, part 2. Look again at the data from the GfK Roper Worldwide survey on food attitudes in Exercise 43.

a) If we select a respondent at random, what's the probability that we choose a person between 13 and 19 years old who agreed with the statement?

b) Among the 13- to 19-year-olds, what is the probability that a person responded "Agree"?

c) What's the probability that a person who agreed was between 13 and 19?

d) If the person responded "Disagree," what is the probability that he or she is at least 50 years old?

e) What's the probability that a person 50 years or older disagreed?

f) Are response to the question and age independent? **LO❷, ❸**

52. Cosmetics marketing, part 2. Look again at the data from the GfK Roper Worldwide survey on skin care in Exercise 44.

a) If we select a respondent at random, what's the probability that we choose a person from France who agrees with the statement?

b) Among those from India, what is the probability that a person responded "Agree"?

c) What's the probability that a person who agrees was from the United Kingdom?

d) If the person responded "Disagree," what is the probability that he or she is from China?

e) What's the probability that a person from the United States disagrees?

f) Are agreeing with the question and being from India independent? **LO❷, ❸**

53. Real estate, part 2. In the real estate research described in Exercise 33, 64% of homes for sale have garages, 21% have swimming pools, and 17% have both features.

a) What is the probability that a home for sale has a garage but not a pool?

b) If a home for sale has a garage, what's the probability that it has a pool, too?

c) Are having a garage and a pool independent events? Explain.

d) Are having a garage and a pool mutually exclusive? Explain. **LO❷, ❸**

54. Employee benefits. Fifty-six percent of all American workers have a workplace retirement plan, 68% have health insurance, and 49% have both benefits. If we select a worker at random,

a) What's the probability that the worker has neither employer-sponsored health insurance nor a retirement plan?

b) What's the probability that the worker has health insurance if he or she has a retirement plan?

c) Are having health insurance and a retirement plan independent? Explain.

d) Are having these two benefits mutually exclusive? Explain. **LO❷, ❸**

55. Selling cars. A recent ad campaign for a major automobile manufacturer is clearly geared toward an older demographic. You're surprised, so you decide to conduct a quick survey of your own. Your random survey of autos parked in the student and staff lots at your university classified the brands by country of origin, as seen in the table. Is having an American car independent of being a student? **LO❸**

		Driver	
		Student	Staff
Origin	American	107	105
	European	33	12
	Asian	55	47

56. Fire sale. A survey of 1056 houses found the following relationship between price (in $) and whether the house had a fireplace in 2006. Is the price of the house independent of whether it has a fireplace? **LO❸**

		Fireplace	
		No	Yes
House Price	Low—less than $112,000	198	66
	Med. Low ($112k to $152K)	133	131
	Med. High ($152k to $207K)	65	199
	High—over $207,000	31	233

57. Website experiment, part 1. Summit Projects provides marketing services and website management for many companies that specialize in outdoor products and services (www.summitprojects.com). To understand customer web behaviour, the company experiments with different offers and website design. The results of such experiments can help maximize the probability that customers will purchase products during a visit to a website. Possible actions by the website include offering the customer an instant discount, offering the customer free shipping, or doing nothing. A recent experiment found that customers made purchases 6% of the time when offered the instant discount, 5% when offered free shipping, and 2% when no special offer was given. Suppose 20% of the customers were offered the discount and an additional 30% were offered free shipping.

a) Construct a probability tree for this experiment.

b) What percentage of customers who visited the site made a purchase?

c) Given that a customer made a purchase, what is the probability that the customer was offered free shipping? (*Source:* Norean Sharpe, Richard D De Veaux, Paul Velleman, David Wright, Business Statistics, Third Canadian Edition, 3e, © 2018, Pearson Education, Inc.) **LO❷, ❹, ❺**

58. Website experiment, part 2. The company in Exercise 57 performed another experiment in which they tested three website designs to see which one would lead to the highest probability of purchase. The first (design A) used enhanced product information, the second (design B) used extensive iconography, and the third (design C) allowed customers to submit their own product ratings. After six weeks of testing, the designs delivered probabilities of purchase of 4.5%, 5.2%, and 3.8%, respectively. Equal numbers of customers were sent randomly to each website design.

a) Construct a probability tree for this experiment.
b) What percentage of customers who visited the site made a purchase?
c) What is the probability that a randomly selected customer was sent to design C?
d) Given that a customer made a purchase, what is the probability that the customer had been sent to design C? **LO❷, ❹, ❺**

59. Contract bidding. As the manager of a construction firm, you're in charge of bidding on two large contracts. You believe that the probability of getting contract 1 is 0.8. If you get contract 1, the probability of also getting contract 2 will be 0.2, and if you don't get 1, the probability of getting 2 will be 0.4.

a) Sketch the probability tree.
b) What is the probability that you'll get both contracts?
c) Your competitor hears that you got the second contract but hears nothing about the first contract. Given that you got the second contract, what is the probability that you also got the first contract? **LO❷, ❹, ❺**

60. Extended warranties. A company that manufactures and sells consumer video cameras sells two versions of its popular hard-disk camera as well as a basic camera for $750 and a deluxe version for $1250. About 75% of customers select the basic camera. Of those, 60% purchase the extended warranty for an additional $200. Of the people who buy the deluxe version, 90% purchase the extended warranty.

a) Sketch the probability tree for total purchases.
b) What is the percentage of customers who buy an extended warranty?
c) What is the expected revenue of the company from a camera purchase (including warranty, if applicable)?
d) Given that a customer purchases an extended warranty, what is the probability that he or she will buy the deluxe version? **LO❷, ❹, ❺**

61. Computer reliability. Laptop computers have been growing in popularity and now represent more than half of computer sales. A campus bookstore sells both types, and in the last semester sold 56% laptops and 44% tablets. Reliability rates for the two types of machines are quite different, however. In the first year, 5% of tablets require

service, while 15% of laptops have problems requiring service.

a) Sketch a probability tree for this situation.
b) What percentage of computers sold by the bookstore last semester required service?
c) Given that a computer required service, what is the probability that it was a laptop? **LO❷, ❹, ❺**

62. *Titanic* survival. Of the 2201 passengers on the RMS *Titanic*, only 711 survived. The practice of "women and children first" was first used to describe the chivalrous actions of the sailors during the sinking of the HMS *Birkenhead* in 1852, but it became popular after the sinking of the *Titanic*, during which 53% of the children and 73% of the women, but only 21% of the men, survived. Part of the protocol stated that passengers enter lifeboats by ticket class as well. Here is a table showing survival by ticket class:

		First	Second	Third	Crew	Total
Survival	**Alive**	203	118	178	212	711
		28.6%	16.6%	25.0%	29.8%	100%
	Dead	122	167	528	673	1490
		8.2%	11.2%	35.4%	45.2%	100%

a) Find the conditional probability of survival for each type of ticket.
b) Draw a probability tree for this situation.
c) Given that a passenger survived, what is the probability that he or she had a first-class ticket? **LO❷, ❹, ❺**

63. Casinos. Because gambling is big business, calculating the odds of a gambler winning or losing in every game is crucial to a casino's financial forecasting. A standard slot machine has three wheels that spin independently. Each has 10 equally likely symbols: four bars, three lemons, two cherries, and a bell. If you play once, what is the probability that you will get

a) Three lemons?
b) No fruit symbols?
c) Three bells (the jackpot)?
d) No bells?
e) At least one bar (an automatic loser)? **LO❷**

64. Marijuana in Canada. In the 2006 federal election, the Liberal government that decriminalized the possession of small quantities of marijuana was replaced by a Conservative government. The new government considered modifying the Liberal legislation. In 2007, Angus Reid conducted a survey of 1028 adult Canadians, finding that 55% supported legalization of marijuana. The percentage of support was different among supporters of the three major political parties, as indicated in the table. For instance, 39% of Conservative voters supported the legalization of marijuana. Out of the 1028 people surveyed, the percentages of Conservative, Liberal, and NDP voters were 44%, 31%, and 25%, respectively.

	Conservative	Liberal	NDP	Total
Support	39%	68%	71%	55%
Oppose	59%	29%	27%	41%
Not Sure	2%	3%	1%	3%

Source: Based on Angus Reid Strategies. (2007). "Illegal drugs: Drugs a national problem—Canadians would mix Grit and Tory policies."

a) Convert the table into a contingency table in which the response percentages add to 100%.
b) What is the probability that a Liberal voter opposed the legalization of marijuana?
c) What is the probability that someone who supported the legalization of marijuana was an NDP voter?
d) Draw a probability tree in which the first branch gives the voting split and the second gives the opinion on legalizing marijuana. You don't need to include the people who were "not sure."
e) Often people are unwilling to disclose their voting preference. Let's investigate whether we can use someone's opinion on marijuana to predict his or her voting preference. From this survey, we know that the probability of someone being a Conservative voter was 44% in 2007. Suppose we interviewed someone at random and found that he or she opposed the legalization of marijuana. What's the probability that this person is a Conservative voter? LO ❷, ❹, ❺

65. Planet B. Environmentalists concerned that global warming may make planet Earth uninhabitable sometimes emphasize their point of view by saying "There is no Planet B." But space agencies around the world have been cataloguing planets orbiting other stars to try to find potential candidates for Planet B. Not many planets are suitable for human life. The chance of having an acceptable surface gravity is 0.09. The chance of having an acceptable surface temperature is 0.02.

Assuming that surface gravity and surface temperature are independent, construct a table of probabilities to represent this information using the following format: LO ❷, ❸

		Surface Temperature		
		Acceptable	Unacceptable	Total
Surface Gravity	Acceptable			
	Unacceptable			
	Total			1.00

66. Canadian entrepreneurs. Researchers studying government records of small businesses found that the probability of a newly established small business still being operational in five years was 0.35. However, entrepreneurs starting new businesses estimate that the chance of their own business still being in operation in five years is 0.75, on average.

a) Which methods of probability assessment were used by the researchers?
b) Which methods were used by the entrepreneurs?
c) What reason can you suggest for the difference in the resulting probabilities? LO ❶, ❷, ❸

67. Canadian mining company. You're considering buying shares in a small Canadian mining company that has just issued an initial public offering (IPO) of shares on the Vancouver Stock Exchange at $8 per share. A limited number of "early" investors were able to purchase these shares at $8 on the IPO date, but you weren't able to get any shares at that price. Instead, you plan to buy on the open market the day after the IPO. After an IPO, two things may happen: (i) The underwriters may purchase shares if they think the price is dropping too low, and (ii) the "early" investors who bought shares the day before at the IPO price may sell. You ask the advice of a stockbroker about the likelihood of each of these. "Looking at data from similar recent IPOs, the probabilities of those things happening are 0.27 and 0.34, respectively," he replies.

a) Which method of probability assessment did the stockbroker use?
b) Do you think the underwriters purchasing and the "early" investors selling are independent events?
c) What's the minimum probability that the underwriters will purchase and the "early" investors will sell? LO ❶, ❷, ❸

68. Baffin Bay oil exploration. Baffin Bay, located between Canada and Greenland, is being explored for oil and natural gas. First, an energy company conducts a geological survey, and if the data look promising it starts drilling. After one area's recent survey, which cost $65 million, the geologists and engineers came to a consensus that drilling a first well would be successful with a probability of 0.2. Company data from previous drilling indicate that if the first well is successful, the probability of the second well being successful in this area is increased from 0.2 to 0.6.

a) Which method of probability assessment did the engineers and geologists use to estimate the probability of the first well's success?
b) Which method of probability assessment did the engineers and geologists use to estimate the probability of the second well's success?
c) Which of these probabilities is a conditional probability? LO ❶, ❷

69. Niagara tunnel. According to a treaty with the United States, Canada may withdraw one-third of the water from the Niagara River before it reaches Niagara Falls. Canada uses a canal and two tunnels to take water to the Sir Adam Beck hydroelectric generating stations downstream. The geology of the area is complex, including a buried gorge and flaky shale that crumbles and requires the roof of the tunnel to be reinforced as it is dug. Before work on the second tunnel started, the geologists conducted many surveys and discussed the results with the engineers. Suppose that, when they finally came up with an estimate of the cost of the tunnel, there was a 20% probability that the cost would be 30% higher. What type of probability assessment did they use? LO ❶

70. Oil extraction. In Canada, provincial governments allocate to oil companies geographical regions in which to explore for oil. If they discover oil, they do not necessarily extract the oil since the cost of extraction may be higher than the market price for oil. However, the market price for oil continuously changes, so the oil may be commercially exploited at some date in the future. Oil companies own the rights to extract oil that they have discovered, but the value of that oil to the company depends on when in the future the oil price will be sufficiently high to make it worth extracting. An oil company estimates that, for a certain oil field, the probability that the oil price will be high enough to extract the oil is given in the following table. Assume that these events are independent of each other.

Number of Years in the Future	Probability of Oil Price Being Sufficiently High to Extract Oil
1	0.1
2	0.25
3	0.32
4	0.45
5	0.5

Calculate the probability that the oil company will *start* to extract oil (a) in year 1; (b) in year 2; (c) in year 3; (d) in year 4; or (e) in year 5. LO ❷, ❸

71. MBA admissions. When a university sends out an offer of a place on an MBA program, it requires the applicant to respond to the offer within four weeks. The applicant may accept the offer within four weeks (in which case she or he is automatically admitted into the program), or reject the offer, or accept the offer after more than four weeks. If the applicant accepts the offer after more than four weeks, there is a 0.5 probability that he or she is admitted into the program. If the applicant accepts

the offer, she or he may or may not actually arrive at the start of the academic year to take the MBA program. From experience over the past five years, a business school has found that the associated probabilities are as in the table. The business school has decided to improve its MBA program and the table also contains estimates of the corresponding probabilities for the new program, which will be offered for the first time next year.

	Probabilities	
	Existing MBA Program	New MBA Program
Accept offer within four weeks	0.61	0.8
Accept offer after more than four weeks	0.12	0.1
Reject offer	0.27	0.1
Arrive at the start of the academic year	0.92	0.95

a) What method of probability assessment was used to estimate the probabilities for the existing MBA program?
b) What method of probability assessment was used to estimate the probabilities for the new MBA program?
c) Suppose the university has sent out an offer to an applicant. Which of the probabilities in the question are conditional upon other events (i.e., other than the university sending the offer)? Identify which events they are dependent upon.
d) The university sends out an offer of a place in its existing MBA program. What is the probability that the applicant will arrive at the start of the academic year to take the program?
e) The university sends out an offer of a place in its new MBA program. What is the probability that the applicant will arrive at the start of the academic year to take the program? LO ❶, ❷, ❸

72. Customer satisfaction. A call centre receives calls from customers that are dealt with by agents. Records indicate that 4.2% of customers are not satisfied with the agent and ask to speak with a supervisor. The supervisor is able to resolve the issue 43% of the time so that the customer ends up satisfied. When the customers who have not requested to speak with a supervisor finish speaking with the agent, they are transferred to an automated system that asks whether they are satisfied with the service; 79% of them say yes.

a) Draw a probability tree for the above situation.
b) What is the probability that a customer will end up satisfied?
c) Which method of probability assessment has been used?
d) Which of the probabilities are conditional?

e) What is the probability that a customer who ended up satisfied spoke with a supervisor? **LO ❶, ❸, ❹, ❺**

73. Corporate merger. A mining company listed on the Toronto Stock Exchange is considering a merger with another company. The CEO thinks that the probability of the deal being acceptable to his shareholders is 0.9. He has lunch with the CEO of the other company and afterward assesses the probability of the merger being acceptable to the other company's shareholders as 0.8. A stockbroker hears of this possible deal and finds that 78% of similar deals have been acceptable to both groups of shareholders in the past.

a) What methods of probability assessment have been used by (i) the CEO and (ii) the stockbroker?

b) Using the CEO's estimates and making an assumption about the two groups of shareholders, estimate the probability that the deal will be acceptable to both groups of shareholders. Comment on whether your assumption is likely to be valid. **LO ❶, ❷, ❸**

74. Minerals in the Canadian Arctic. An oil company executive and an executive of a mining company meet during the coffee break of a conference about opportunities in the Canadian Arctic. "They say 30% of the world's undiscovered oil is in the Arctic," started the oil man. "We've drilled 43 exploratory wells and all but 17 of them were dry. Only two of those 17 are economical with the oil prices being projected for the next 10 years. The good news is that 90% of these projects get environmental approvals."

"It's just as bad in mining," replied the mining executive. "We know where there's uranium in Nunavut, but with the current unpopularity of nuclear power, we estimate the chance of it being profitable is less than 10%."

a) What method of probability assessment is being used by the mining executive?

b) What method of probability assessment is being used by the oil executive?

c) Draw a probability tree for drilling an exploratory oil well in the Arctic based on the information above.

d) Which probability(ies) in your tree is/are conditional?

e) If the oil company were to drill an exploratory oil well in the Arctic, what is the probability that the company would actually extract oil from it? **LO ❶, ❷, ❸, ❹**

75. Testing pharmaceutical drugs. Clinical testing of chemical compounds for approval as drugs goes through three successive stages. A compound that fails in one phase does not proceed to subsequent phases.

i) Phase 1: testing on about 50 healthy individuals to investigate possible side effects; 70% of compounds pass Phase 1 testing and proceed to Phase 2.

ii) Phase 2: testing on about 200 patients to investigate effectiveness in curing illness; 43% of compounds pass Phase 2 testing and proceed to Phase 3.

iii) Phase 3: testing on about 3000 patients to investigate effectiveness in curing illness; 67% of compounds pass Phase 3 testing and are approved for clinical use.

a) Draw a probability tree to represent this situation.

b) What method of probability assessment is used to estimate the probabilities in your tree?

c) Which probabilities are conditional?

d) What is the probability of a chemical compound passing all three phases of testing and becoming approved for clinical use? **LO ❶, ❷, ❸, ❹**

76. Serial entrepreneur. Alice started a company upon graduating from the University of Guelph, and a few years later she sold it to a larger firm in the same industry. She used the money from that sale to start a second company that she also sold, and repeated the process for five companies in total, each time selling the company for more than she had put into it. Now she is about to start her sixth company, the largest to date, and estimates that she will be able to sell it for over $100 million with a probability of 0.8. Describe ways in which her estimate may suffer from:

a) Overconfidence bias

b) Sunk cost bias

c) Recency bias **LO ❶**

77. Mining equipment. A German company has just submitted a 220-page bid on a contract to supply state-of-the-art mining equipment to the Canadian mining company Barrick Gold. The supplier has supplied most of the major mining companies in the world and has equipment that it believes is not matched by its competitors. Profits have increased over each of the last eight quarters. The CEO estimates the probability of getting the contract is 0.75. Describe ways in which this estimate may suffer from:

a) Overconfidence bias

b) Sunk cost bias

c) Recency bias **LO ❶**

78. Photographing Canada geese. Last year, Maria sold a photo of a Canada goose to a nature magazine for $7,500, and she is keen to get some good shots again this year. She booked a spot in a hide at the edge of a lake in northeastern Manitoba for late September, the middle of the autumn migration. She believes the best shots of geese are as they land on the water with the geese coming directly toward the camera and with the sun shining out of a clear sky across the shot. The hide is on the south side of the lake, so she will need the wind coming from the south (since geese land into the wind) and either morning or evening sun. Weather records indicate that, at that time of year, the chance of the wind coming from the south is 0.56 and the chance of a clear sky is 0.64 on any particular day.

a) What is the probability that Maria will have the conditions she wants on her first day in the hide? State your assumptions clearly and comment on whether you think the assumptions are true.

b) Maria booked four days in the hide. What is the probability that she will get the conditions she wants on all four days? State your assumptions clearly and comment on whether you think the assumptions are valid. **LO ❷, ❸**

79. Solar panel manufacture. When solar panels rated at 250 watts of power are manufactured, the power of a given panel is not exactly 250 watts, but there is a 0.5 probability that it is less than 250 watts and a 0.5 probability that it is more than 250 watts. When solar panels are connected together in series on a roof, the power generated is limited by the panel with the least power. For example, if three panels of 240 watts, 250 watts, and 260 watts are connected in series, the total power is NOT 240 + 250 + 260 = 750 watts. Instead, it is 3 × 240 = 720 watts (limited by the 240 watt panel). We need to connect eight panels together in series on a roof. What is the probability that the total power generated will be more than 2000 watts? **LO ❷**

Peter Dejong/AP Images

Francis Vachon/The Canadian Press

9

Random Variables and Probability Distributions

Intact Financial Corporation

Intact, the leading property and casualty insurer in Canada, traces its origins back to the very first property insurance company, the Halifax Fire Insurance Association, founded in 1809. You'll probably notice the word "fire" in the name, something we don't see with today's insurance companies. It was there with good reason, because fire was the major risk to property in the 19th century. Two thousand buildings were destroyed by fires in Quebec City in 1815 and 1845. By 1905 there were 40 fire insurance companies in Canada, taking in $14 million in premiums and paying out $6 million in claims. After the Second World War many Dutch immigrants came to Canada, and Nationale Nederlander bought the Halifax Fire Insurance Association to serve its needs. Following many other acquisitions and mergers, the company joined other insurers in 1993 under the umbrella of ING Canada, which was owned at that time by ING Group. It had an initial public offering on the Toronto Stock Exchange in 2004, with ING Group maintaining 70% ownership.

By this time things had changed, and the risk of fire damage was much less, due to the efforts of property owners and provincial and municipal governments imposing strict safety standards on buildings, and changes in construction materials. In the 1800s, most homes would be made of wood. But with a decrease in one type of risk comes an increase in another: floods. The year 2004 saw $143 million of claims from basement flooding due to two rainstorms in Edmonton. A severe rainfall in the Greater Toronto Area in 2005 resulted in 13,000 claims for flooded basements, costing insurers

$247 million. Insurers need to assess the risk of weather events such as these, and to assess the "risk" of homeowners doing a quality job when finishing their basements, hence increasing the amount of a claim. Another risk the industry needs to take into account that wasn't around in the 19th century is that of car accidents. Recently, courts have been awarding multimillion-dollar payments for injuries sustained in this type of risk.

In 2009 a group of Canadian institutional investors bought ING Group's 70% holding and changed the name of the company from ING Canada to Intact Financial Corporation. Today Intact is a widely held company that collects $4 billion in premiums every year and provides insurance to 4 million individuals and businesses.[1]

---

[1]Based on McGillivray, G. (2009, June). Fires to floods. *Canadian Underwriter,* 76(6), 34–36; Gambrill, G. (2009, May). Ontario's ailing auto insurance. *Canadian Underwriter,* 76(5); ABI/INFORM Global, 24–29; Intact Financial Corporation. ING Canada becomes Intact Financial Corporation. [Press release.] Retrieved from http://www.intactfc.com/English/Press-Centre/Press-Releases/Press-Release-etails/2009/INGCanadabecomesIntactFinancialCorporation/default.aspx

---

There are worse things in life than death. Have you ever spent an evening with an insurance salesman?

—Woody Allen

Insurance companies make bets all the time. For example, they bet that you're going to live a long life. Ironically, you bet that you're going to die sooner. Both you and the insurance company want the company to stay in business, so it's important to find a "fair price" for your bet. Of course, the right price for *you* depends on many factors, and nobody can predict exactly how long you'll live. But when the company averages its bets over enough customers, it can make reasonably accurate estimates of the amount it can expect to collect on a policy before it has to pay out the benefit. In order to do that effectively, it must model the situation with a probability model. Using the resulting probabilities, the company can find the fair price of almost any situation involving risk and uncertainty.

Here's a simple example. An insurance company offers a "death and disability" policy that pays $100,000 when a client dies or $50,000 if the client is permanently disabled. It charges a premium of only $500 per year for this benefit. Is the company likely to make a profit selling such a plan? To answer this question, the company needs to know the *probability* that a client will die or become disabled in any year. From actuarial information such as this and the appropriate model, the company can calculate the expected value of this policy.

LO❶ 9.1 Expected Value of a Random Variable

To model the insurance company's risk, we need to define a few terms. The amount the company pays out on an individual policy is an example of a **random variable**, called that because its value is based on the outcome of a random event. We use a capital letter, in this case X, to denote a random variable. We'll denote a particular *value* that it can have by the corresponding lowercase letter, in this case x. For the insurance company, x can be $100,000 (if you die that year), $50,000 (if you're disabled), or $0 (if neither occurs). Because we can list all the outcomes, we call this random variable a **discrete random variable**. A random variable that can take on any value between two values is called a **continuous random variable**. Continuous random variables are common in business applications for modelling physical quantities like heights and weights and monetary quantities such as profits, revenues, and spending.

Sometimes it's obvious whether to treat a random variable as discrete or continuous, but at other times the choice is more subtle. Age, for example, might be viewed as discrete if it's measured only to the nearest decade with possible values 10, 20, 30, …. In a scientific context, however, it might be measured more precisely and treated as continuous.

For both discrete and continuous variables, the collection of all the possible values and the probabilities associated with them is called the **probability distribution** for the random variable. It shows how the probability is "distributed" over all those possible values, showing which values have a higher probability than others. Alternatively, we sometimes use the term **probability model** to mean the same thing as probability distribution. For a discrete random variable, we can list the probability of all possible values in a table, or describe it by a formula. For example, to model the possible outcomes of a fair die, we can let X be the number showing on the face. The probability model for X is simply

$$P(X = x) = \begin{cases} 1/6 & \text{if } x = 1, \ 2, \ 3, \ 4, \ 5, \text{ or } 6 \\ 0 & \text{otherwise.} \end{cases}$$

Suppose in our insurance risk example that the death rate in any year is 1 out of every 1000 people and that another 2 out of 1000 suffer some kind of disability. The payout, which we'll denote as X, is a discrete random variable because it takes on only three possible values. We can display the probability model for X in a table, as in Table 9.1.

Of course, we can't predict exactly what *will* happen during any given year, but we can say what we *expect* to happen—in this case, what we expect the profit of a policy will be. The expected payout of a policy is a parameter of the probability model. In fact, it's the mean. We'll signify this with the notation $E(X)$, for expected value (or sometimes EV, or sometimes μ). We use the term "mean" for this quantity just as we did for data, but be careful: This isn't an average of data values, so we won't estimate it. Instead, we calculate it directly from the probability model for the random variable. Because it comes from a model and not data, we use the parameter μ to denote it (and *not* $\bar{y}$ or $\bar{x}$). The Greek letter μ (mu) corresponds to m (for mean) in English.

To see what the insurance company can expect, think about some (convenient) number of outcomes. For example, imagine that the company has exactly 1000 clients and that the outcomes in one year followed the probability model exactly: 1 died, 2 were disabled, and 997 survived unscathed. Then its total payout per policy would be

$$E(X) = \frac{100{,}000(1) + 50{,}000(2) + 0(997)}{1000} = 200.$$

Policyholder Outcome	Payout x (cost)	Probability $P(X = x)$
Death	100,000	$\frac{1}{1000}$
Disability	50,000	$\frac{2}{1000}$
Neither	0	$\frac{997}{1000}$

Table 9.1 Probability model for an insurance policy.

So its total payout comes to $200 per policy.

Instead of writing the expected value as one big fraction, we can rewrite it as separate terms, each divided by 1000:

$$E(X) = \$100{,}000 \left(\frac{1}{1000}\right) + \$50{,}000 \left(\frac{2}{1000}\right) + \$0 \left(\frac{997}{1000}\right)$$
$$= \$200$$

Writing it this way, we can see that for each policy there's a 1/1000 chance that the company will have to pay $100,000 for a death and a 2/1000 chance that it'll have to pay $50,000 for a disability. Of course, there's a 997/1000 chance that it won't have to pay anything.

So the **expected value** of a (discrete) random variable is found by multiplying each possible value of the random variable by the probability that it occurs and then summing all those products. This gives the general formula for the expected value of a discrete random variable:[2]

$$E(X) = \sum x \cdot P(x).$$

Here we've used $P(x)$ as an abbreviation for $P(X = x)$. Make sure that *every* possible outcome is included in the sum. Verify that you have a valid probability model to start with—the probabilities should each be between 0 and 1 and should sum to one. Recall the rules of probability in Chapter 8.

FOR EXAMPLE   Calculating the expected value of a lottery ticket

QUESTION   A fundraising lottery offers 500 tickets for $3 each. If the grand prize is $250 and four second prizes are $50 each, what is the expected value of a single ticket? (Don't count the price of the ticket in this yet.) Now, including the price, what is the expected value of the ticket? (Knowing this value, does it make any "sense" to buy a lottery ticket?) The fundraising group has a target of $1000 to be raised by the lottery. Can it expect to make this much?

ANSWER   Each ticket has a 1/500 chance of winning the grand prize of $250, a 4/500 chance of winning $50, and a 495/500 chance of winning nothing. So $E(X) = (1/500) \times \$250 + (4/500) \times \$50 + (495/500) \times \$0 = \$0.50 + \$0.40 + \$0.00 = \$0.90$. Including the price, the expected value is $\$0.90 - \$3 = -\$2.10$. The expected value of a ticket is $-\$2.10$. Although no single person will lose $2.10 (he or she either loses $3 or wins $50 or $250), $2.10 is the amount, on average, that the lottery gains per ticket. Therefore, it can expect to make $500 \times \$2.10 = \$1050$.

LO❶   9.2   Standard Deviation and Variance of a Random Variable

Of course, this expected value (or mean) isn't what actually happens to any *particular* policyholder. No individual policy actually costs the company $200. We're dealing with random events, so some policyholders receive big payouts and others

---

[2]The concept of expected values for continuous random variables is similar, but the calculation requires calculus and is beyond the scope of this text.

Policyholder Outcome	Payout x (cost)	Probability $P(X = x)$	Deviation $(x - E(x))$
Death	100,000	$\dfrac{1}{1000}$	$(100,000 - 200) = 99,800$
Disability	50,000	$\dfrac{2}{1000}$	$(50,000 - 200) = 49,800$
Neither	0	$\dfrac{997}{1000}$	$(0 - 200) = -200$

Table 9.2   Deviations between the expected value and each payout (cost).

nothing. Because the insurance company must anticipate this variability, it needs to know the standard deviation of the random variable.

For data, we calculate the standard deviation by first computing the deviation of each data value from the mean and squaring it. We perform a similar calculation when we compute the **standard deviation of a (discrete) random variable** as well. First, we find the deviation of each payout from the mean (expected value). (See Table 9.2.)

Next, we square each deviation. The **variance** is the expected value of those squared deviations. To find it, we multiply each by the appropriate probability and sum those products:

$$Var(X) = 99,800^2 \left(\frac{1}{1000}\right) + 49,800^2 \left(\frac{2}{1000}\right) + (-200)^2 \left(\frac{997}{1000}\right)$$
$$= 14,960,000$$

Finally, we take the square root to get the standard deviation (SD):

$$SD(X) = \sqrt{14,960,000} \approx \$3867.82$$

The insurance company can expect an average payout of $200 per policy, with a standard deviation of $3867.82.

Think about that. The company charges $500 for each policy and expects to pay out $200 per policy. Sounds like an easy way to make $300. (In fact, most of the time—probability 997/1000—the company pockets the entire $500.) But would you be willing to take on this risk yourself and sell all your friends policies like this? The problem is that occasionally the company loses big. With a probability of 1/1000, it will pay out $100,000, and with a probability of 2/1000, it will pay out $50,000. That may be more risk than you're willing to take on. The standard deviation of $3867.82 gives an indication of the uncertainty of the profit, and that seems like a pretty big spread (and risk) for an average profit of $300.

Here are the formulas for these arguments. Because these are parameters of our probability model, the variance and standard deviation can also be written as σ^2 and σ, respectively (sometimes with the name of the random variable as a subscript). The Greek letter σ (sigma) corresponds to s (for standard deviation) in English. You should recognize both kinds of notation:

$$\sigma^2 = Var(X) = \sum (x - E(x))^2 P(x) = \sum (x - \mu)^2 P(x), \text{ and}$$

$$\sigma = SD(X) = \sqrt{Var(X)}$$

FOR EXAMPLE   Calculating the standard deviation of the gain on a lottery ticket

QUESTION   In For Example: "Calculating the expected value of a lottery ticket," we found the expected gain per ticket to be −$2.10. What is the standard deviation? What does it say about your chances in the lottery? Comment.

ANSWER

$$\sigma^2 = Var\ (X) = \sum (x - E(X))^2 P(X) = \sum (x + 2.10)^2 P(x)$$
$$= (250 + 2.10)^2 \frac{1}{500} + (50 + 2.10)^2 \frac{4}{500} + (0 + 2.10)^4 \frac{495}{500}$$
$$= 61{,}454.41 \times \frac{1}{500} + 2{,}294.41 \times \frac{4}{500} + 4.41 \times \frac{495}{500}$$
$$= 153.19$$

so $\sigma = \sqrt{153.19} = \$12.38$

That's a lot of variation for a mean of −$2.10, which reflects the fact that there's a small chance you'll win a lot but a large chance you'll win nothing.

GUIDED EXAMPLE   Computer Inventory

As the head of inventory for a computer company, you've had a challenging couple of weeks. One of your warehouses recently had a fire, and you had to flag all the computers stored there to be recycled. On the positive side, you were thrilled that you'd managed to ship two computers to your biggest client last week. But then you discovered that your assistant hadn't heard about the fire and had mistakenly transported a whole truckload of computers from the damaged warehouse to the shipping centre. It turns out that 30% of all the computers shipped last week were damaged. You don't know whether your biggest client received two damaged computers, two undamaged ones, or one of each. Computers were selected at random from the shipping centre for delivery.

    If your client received two undamaged computers, everything is fine. If the client got one damaged computer, it will be returned at your expense—$100—and you can replace it. However, if both computers are damaged, the client will cancel all other orders this month, and you'll lose $10,000. What are the expected value and the standard deviation of your loss under this scenario?

PLAN	**Setup** State the problem.	We want to analyze the potential consequences of shipping damaged computers to a large client. We'll look at the expected value and standard deviation of the amount we'll lose.
		Let X = amount of loss. We'll denote the receipt of an undamaged computer by U and the receipt of a damaged computer by D. The three possibilities are: two undamaged computers (U and U), two damaged computers (D and D), and one of each (UD or DU). Because the computers were selected randomly and the number in the warehouse is large, we can assume independence.

DO

Model List the possible values of the random variable, and compute all the values you'll need to determine the probability model.

Mechanics Find the expected value.

Find the variance.

Find the standard deviation.

Because the events are independent, we can use the Multiplication Rule (see Chapter 8) and find

$$P(UU) = P(U) \times P(U)$$
$$= 0.7 \times 0.7 = 0.49$$
$$P(DD) = P(D) \times P(D)$$
$$= 0.3 \times 0.3 = 0.09.$$

So, $P(UD \text{ or } DU) = 1 - (0.49 + 0.09) = 0.42$

We have the following model for all possible values of X:

Outcome	x	$P(X = x)$
Two damaged	10,000	$P(DD) = 0.09$
One damaged	100	$P(UD \text{ or } DU) = 0.42$
Neither damaged	0	$P(UU) = 0.49$

$$E(X) = 0(0.49) + 100(0.42) + 10,000(0.09)$$
$$= \$942$$
$$Var(X) = (0 - 942)^2 \times (0.49)$$
$$+ (100 - 942)^2 \times (0.42)$$
$$+ (10,000 - 942)^2 \times (0.09)$$
$$= 8,116,836$$
$$SD(X) = \sqrt{8,116,836} = \$2849.01$$

REPORT

Conclusion Interpret your results in context.

MEMO
Re: Damaged Computers
The recent shipment of two computers to our large client may have some serious negative impact. Even though there's about a 50% chance that the client will receive two perfectly good computers, there is a 9% chance that it will receive two damaged computers and will cancel the rest of its monthly order. We've analyzed the expected loss to the firm as $942 with a standard deviation of $2849.01. The large standard deviation reflects the fact that there's a real possibility of losing $10,000 from the mistake.

Both numbers seem reasonable. The expected value of $942 is between the extremes of $0 and $10,000, and there's great variability in the outcome values.

LO❷ **9.3** **Adding and Subtracting Random Variables**

Our example insurance company expected to pay out an average of $200 per policy, with a standard deviation of about $3868. The expected profit then was $500 − $200 = $300 per policy. Suppose that the company decides to lower the price of the premium by $50 to $450. It's pretty clear that the expected profit would drop an average of $50 per policy, to $450 − $200 = $250. This is an example of **changing a random variable by a constant**.

What about the standard deviation? We know that adding or subtracting a constant from data shifts the mean but doesn't change the variance or standard deviation. The same is true of random variables:[3]

$$E(X \pm c) = E(X) \pm c,$$
$$Var(X \pm c) = Var(X), \text{ and}$$
$$SD(X \pm c) = SD(X)$$

What if the company decides to *double* all the payouts—that is, pay $200,000 for death and $100,000 for disability? This would double the average payout per policy and also increase the variability in payouts. In general, multiplying each value of a random variable by a constant multiplies the mean by that constant and multiplies the variance by the *square* of the constant:

$$E(aX) = aE(X), \text{ and}$$
$$Var(aX) = a^2 Var(X)$$

Taking square roots of the last equation shows that the standard deviation is multiplied by the absolute value of the constant:

$$SD(aX) = |a| SD(X)$$

Adding Random Variables

This insurance company sells policies to more than just one person. We've just seen how to compute means and variances for one person at a time. What happens to the mean and variance when we have a collection of customers? The profit on a group of customers is the *sum* of the individual profits, so we'll need to know how to find expected values and variances for sums. To start, consider a simple case with just two customers, whom we'll call Mr. Ecks and Ms. Wye. With an expected payout of $200 on each policy, we might expect a total of $200 + $200 = $400 to be paid out on the two policies—nothing surprising there. In other words, we have the **Addition Rule for Expected Values of Random Variables**: *The expected value of the sum (or difference) of random variables is the sum (or difference) of their expected values:*

$$E(X \pm Y) = E(X) \pm E(Y)$$

The variability is another matter. Is the risk of insuring two people the same as the risk of insuring one person for twice as much? We wouldn't expect both clients to die or become disabled in the same year. In fact, because we've spread the risk, the standard deviation should be smaller. Indeed, this is the fundamental principle behind insurance. By spreading the risk among many policies, a company can keep the standard deviation quite small and predict costs more accurately. It's much less risky to insure thousands of customers than one customer when the total expected payout is the same, assuming that the events are independent. Catastrophic events such as hurricanes or earthquakes that affect large numbers of customers at the same time destroy the independence assumption, and often the insurance company along with it.

But how much smaller is the standard deviation of the sum? It turns out that if the random variables are independent, we have the **Addition Rule for Variances of Random Variables**: *The variance of the sum or difference of two independent random variables is the sum of their individual variances:*

---

[3]The rules in this section are true for both discrete *and* continuous random variables.

$$Var(X \pm Y) = Var(X) + Var(Y) \text{ if } X \text{ and } Y \text{ are independent.}$$

For Mr. Ecks and Ms. Wye, the insurance company can expect their outcomes to be independent, so (using X for Mr. Ecks's payout and Y for Ms. Wye's):

$$\begin{aligned} Var(X + Y) &= Var(X) + Var(Y) \\ &= 14{,}960{,}000 + 14{,}960{,}000 \\ &= 29{,}920{,}000. \end{aligned}$$

Let's compare the variance of writing two independent policies with the variance of writing only one for twice the size. If the company had insured only Mr. Ecks for twice as much, the variance would have been

$$Var(2X) = 2^2 Var(X) = 4 \times 14{,}960{,}000 = 59{,}840{,}000, \text{ or}$$

twice as big as with two independent policies, even though the expected payout is the same.

Of course, variances are in squared units. The company would prefer to know standard deviations, which are in dollars. The standard deviation of the payout for two independent policies is $SD(X + Y) = \sqrt{Var(X + Y)} = \sqrt{29{,}920{,}000} = \$5469.92$. But the standard deviation of the payout for a single policy of twice the size is twice the standard deviation of a single policy: $SD(2X) = 2SD(X) = 2(3867.82) = 7735.64$, or about 40% more than the standard deviation of the sum of the two independent policies, \$5469.92.

Optional Math Box

Pythagorean Theorem of Statistics

We often use the standard deviation to measure variability, but when we add independent random variables, we use their variances. Think of the Pythagorean Theorem. In a right triangle (only), the *square* of the length of the hypotenuse is the sum of the *squares* of the lengths of the other two sides:

$$c^2 = a^2 + b^2$$

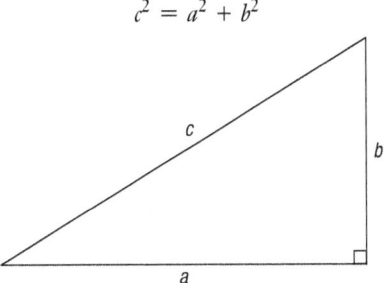

For independent random variables (only), the *square* of the standard deviation of their sum is the sum of the *squares* of their standard deviations:

$$SD^2(X + Y) = SD^2(X) + SD^2(Y)$$

It's simpler to write this with *variances*:

$$Var(X + Y) = Var(X) + Var(Y)$$

But we'll often use the standard deviation formula as well:

$$SD(X + Y) = \sqrt{Var(X) + Var(Y)}$$

If the company has two customers, then it will have an expected annual total payout (cost) of $400 with a standard deviation of about $5470. If it writes one policy with an expected annual payout of $400, it increases the standard deviation by about 40% to $7736. Spreading risk by insuring many independent customers is one of the fundamental principles in insurance and finance.

Subtracting Random Variables

Even when we take the *difference* between two random variables, we *add* the variances. The federal government frequently needs to calculate the balance of trade between exports and imports. Canadian exports and imports of natural gas to and from the United States are given in Figure 9.1 and summarized in Table 9.3.

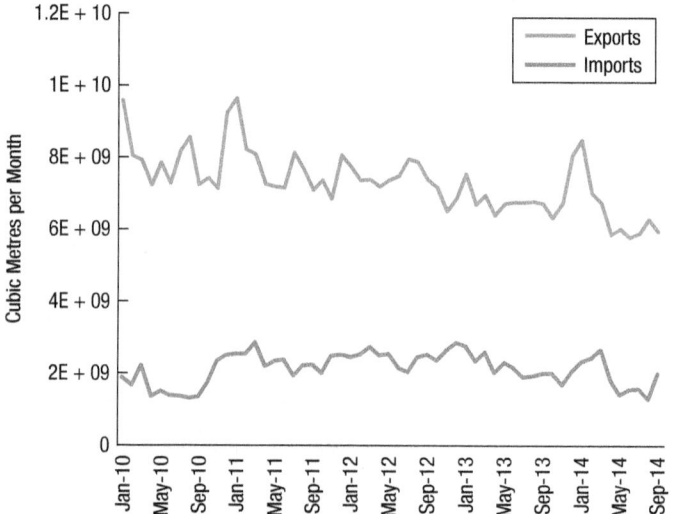

Figure 9.1   Canadian trade in natural gas with the United States, monthly, January 2010 to September 2014.

	Exports	Imports
Expected value (billion m³/mo)	7.317	2.125
Variance (billion m³/mo)²	0.709	0.187

Table 9.3   Canadian trade in natural gas with the United States, January 2010 to September 2014, monthly data.

Source: Based on Statistics Canada. (2014). Series v47815 and v47839.

We can use the information in this table to calculate the mean and variance of the balance of trade (exports, E, minus imports, I), assuming imports and exports are uncorrelated:

> Here we're using E to mean *expected value* and also to mean *exports*. For instance, $E(E)$ means the expected value of exports.

$$E(E - I) = E(E) - E(I)$$
$$= 7.317 - 2.125 = 5.192 \text{ billion m}^3$$
$$Var(E - I) = Var(E) + Var(I)$$
$$= 0.709 + 0.187 = 0.896 \text{ (billion m}^3)^2$$
$$SD(E - I) = \sqrt{Var(E - I)}$$
$$= 0.947 \text{ billion m}^3$$

We should note two important points about this calculation:

- When we *subtract* the variables, $E - I$, we *add* the variances, $Var(E) + Var(I)$.
- Standard deviations don't add or subtract. The standard deviation is obtained by taking the square root of the variance.

Let's review the rules of expected values and variances for sums and differences:

- The expected value of the sum of two random variables is the sum of the expected values.
- The expected value of the difference of two random variables is the difference of the expected values:

$$E(X \pm Y) = E(X) \pm E(Y)$$

- If the random variables are independent, the variance of their sum or difference is always the sum of the variances:

$$Var(X \pm Y) = Var(X) + Var(Y)$$

Dealing With Correlation

Everything we've said up to now about adding and subtracting random variables has assumed that the variables are uncorrelated. But in fact, pretty much any two variables have some degree of correlation with each other, and Canadian exports and imports of natural gas are no exception. During the period January 2010 to September 2014, the correlation coefficient was $r = 0.176$. A positive correlation implies that there are several months with both high imports and high exports and/or several months with both low imports and low exports. When exports and imports are moving in the same direction, there is less variability in the balance of trade than if exports and imports had been behaving independently of each other. We therefore have to reduce our estimate of the variance of the balance of trade, and we do that by using a modified formula for the variance:

$$
\begin{aligned}
Var(E - I) &= Var(E) + Var(I) - 2 \times SD(E) \times SD(I) \times r \\
&= 0.709 + 0.187 - 2 \times 0.842 \times 0.433 \times 0.176 \\
&= 0.768 \\
SD(E - I) &= \sqrt{0.768} \\
&= 0.876
\end{aligned}
$$

John T Fowler/Alamy Stock Photo

Notice that the correlation affects the variance and hence the standard deviation of the balance of trade, but it does not affect the expected value.

Correlation not only affects the *difference* between two random variables; it also affects their *sum*, which is important in financial investments. Suppose you invest in a single share in BlackBerry. The price may go up or down, and a good measure of your risk is the variance of the price. The variance of the price of Black-Berry shares during the last 30 trading days toward the end of 2014 on the Toronto Stock Exchange was $0.2724\ \$^2$. Now suppose you want to buy another share. The variance (riskiness) of two shares in BlackBerry is

$$Var(2R) = 2^2\, Var(R) = 4 \times 0.2724 = 1.090\ \$^2,$$

where R is the price of one BlackBerry share.

In order to reduce your risk, you may alternatively decide not to put all your eggs in one basket, but to buy your second share in a company in a totally different industry—say, Barrick Gold in the mining industry. Figure 9.2 shows the share prices of BlackBerry and Barrick Gold on the Toronto Stock Exchange from

HP Canada/Alamy Stock Photo

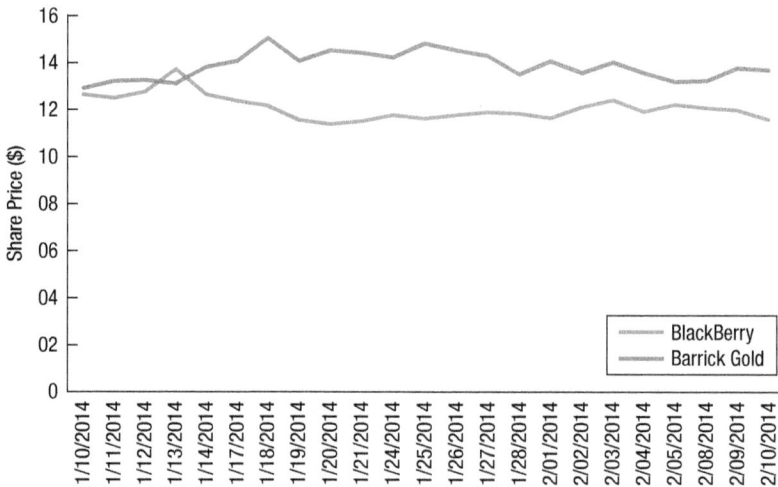

Figure 9.2   Share prices for BlackBerry and Barrick Gold on the Toronto Stock Exchange from November 10 to December 10, 2014.
Source: Based on Toronto Stock Exchange. (2008).

November 10 to December 10, 2014. They're negatively correlated with a correlation coefficient of $r = -0.5904$, which means that when one price goes up there's a good chance the other will go down (more so than if there was no correlation). This movement of the two share prices in opposite directions decreases your risk compared with investing in companies that are totally uncorrelated or companies that are positively correlated. The riskiness of your investment is now

$$Var(R + B) = Var(R) + Var(B) + 2 \times SD(R) \times SD(B) \times r,$$

where B is the share price of Barrick Gold, and $Var(B)$ is 0.3214.

Notice that the last term in the equation is added when we are adding our two variables R and B, whereas it was subtracted when we were subtracting $E - I$ to get the balance of trade. As it happens, r is negative, so that the riskiness (variance) of your investment is reduced:

$$Var(R + B) = 0.2724 + 0.3214 + 2 \times \sqrt{0.2724} \times \sqrt{0.3214} \times (-0.5904)$$

$$= 0.2444 \text{ } \$^2$$

The negative correlation between BlackBerry and Barrick Gold has significantly reduced the riskiness of this investment compared with buying two shares in BlackBerry.

It's not much fun buying just one share in a company. Let's suppose we buy n shares in BlackBerry and m shares in Barrick Gold. The expected value of that portfolio is

$$E(nR + mB) = n \times E(R) + m \times E(B).$$

The riskiness of that portfolio is

$$Var(nR + mB) = n^2 \times Var(R) + m^2 \times Var(B) + 2 \times n \times m \times SD(R) \times SD(B) \times r.$$

The Optional Math Box gives a derivation of this formula for anyone interested. This is the most general-purpose formula for calculating the variance of combinations of random variables, and other formulas can be derived from it. For instance, if $n = 1$ and $m = -1$, we get the formula we used for the balance of trade. If $n = 1$ and $m = 1$, we get the formula we used for investment in BlackBerry and Barrick Gold.

Using Covariance

In Chapter 6 we saw that covariance can be used as an alternative to correlation.

$$Cov(R, B) = SD(R) \times SD(B) \times r$$

This gives us another way of writing the result for the variance of our portfolio:

$$Var(nR + mB) = n^2 \times Var(R) + m^2 \times Var(B) + 2 \times n \times m \text{ } Cov(R,B)$$

Optional Math Box

Let's take a portfolio of n shares of a company whose share price is X, and m shares of a company whose share price is Y. We're interested in the riskiness of our portfolio—that is, the variance of its total value $T = nX + mY$.

The variance of X is $V[X] = \dfrac{1}{n-1}\sum_{i=1}^{n}(x_i - \bar{x})^2 = \dfrac{1}{n-1}\sum_{i=1}^{n}w^2$,

where $w = x_i - \bar{x}$.

The variance of Y is $V[Y] = \dfrac{1}{n-1}\sum_{i=1}^{n}(y_i - \bar{y})^2 = \dfrac{1}{n-1}\sum_{i=1}^{n}z^2$,

where $z = y_i - \bar{y}$.

The variance of

$$T = nX + mY \text{ is } V[T] = \frac{1}{n-1}\sum_{i=1}^{n}\left[nx_i + my_i - (n\bar{x} + m\bar{y})\right]^2$$

$$= \frac{1}{n-1}\sum_{i=1}^{n}\left[nw + mz\right]^2$$

$$= \frac{1}{n-1}\sum_{i=1}^{n}\left[n^2w^2 + m^2z^2 + 2nmwz\right]$$

$$= n^2V[X] + m^2V[T] + \frac{1}{n-1}\sum_{i=1}^{n}2(x_i - \bar{x})(y_i - \bar{y})$$

$$= n^2V[X] + m^2V[T] + 2nm\,rs_xs_y,$$

where r is the correlation coefficient.

Let's review the rules for combining correlated random variables together:

- The expected value behaves as expected:

$$E(aX + bY) = a \times E(X) + b \times E(Y)$$

- The variance is the one we need to watch out for:

$$Var(aX + bY) = a^2 \times Var(X) + b^2 \times Var(Y) + 2 \\ \times a \times b \times SD(X) \times SD(Y) \times r$$

FOR EXAMPLE   Sums of random variables

You are considering investing $1000 into one or possibly two different investment funds. Historically, each has delivered 5% a year in profit with a standard deviation of 3%. So, a $1000 investment would produce $50 with a standard deviation of $30.

QUESTION   Assuming the two funds are independent, what are the relative advantages and disadvantages of putting $1000 into one, or splitting the $1000 and putting $500 into each? Compare the means and SDs of the profit from the two strategies.

ANSWER   Let $X =$ amount gained by putting $1000 into one:

$$E(X) = 0.05 \times 1000 = \$50 \text{ and } SD(X) = 0.03 \times 1000 = \$30$$

Let $W =$ amount gained by putting $500 into each. W_1 and W_2 are the amounts from each fund, respectively. $E(W_1) = E(W_2) = 0.05 \times 500 = \$25$. So $E(W) = E(W_1) + E(W_2) = \$25 + \$25 = \$50$. The expected values of the two strategies are the same. You expect on average to earn $50 on $1000 invested.

(Continued)

$$SD(W) = \sqrt{SD^2(W_1) + SD^2(W_2)}$$
$$= \sqrt{(0.03 \times 500)^2 + (0.03 \times 500)^2}$$
$$= \sqrt{15^2 + 15^2}$$
$$= \$21.213$$

The standard deviation of the amount earned is \$21.213 by splitting the investment amount compared with \$30 for investing in one. The expected values are the same. Spreading the investment into more than one vehicle *reduces* the variation. On the other hand, keeping it all in one vehicle increases the chances of both extremely good and extremely bad returns. Which one is better depends on an individual's appetite for risk.[4]

JUST CHECKING

1 Suppose that the time it takes you to get and pay for seats at the ticket window of a baseball park is a random variable with a mean of 100 seconds and a standard deviation of 50 seconds. When you get there, you find only two people in line in front of you.

a) How long do you expect to wait for your turn to get tickets?

b) What's the standard deviation of your wait time?

c) What assumption did you make about the two customers in front of you in finding the standard deviation?

Answers are found in Appendix A.

LO❸   ## 9.4   Introduction to Discrete Probability Distributions

Sam Savage, a professor at Stanford University, says in his book, *The Flaw of Averages*, that plans based only on averages are, on average, wrong.[5] Unfortunately, many business owners make decisions based solely on averages—the average amount sold last year, the average number of customers seen last month, etc. Instead of relying on averages, the business decision maker can incorporate much more by modelling the situation with a probability model. Probability models, also known as probability distributions, can play an important and pivotal role in helping decision makers better predict both the outcome and the consequences of their decisions. In this section we'll see that some fairly simple models provide a framework for thinking about how to model a wide variety of business phenomena.

The Uniform Distribution

When we first studied probability in Chapter 8, we saw that equally likely events were the simplest case. For example, a single die can turn up 1, 2, . . . , 6 on one toss. A probability model for the toss is uniform because each of the outcomes has the same probability (1/6) of occurring. Similarly, if X is a random variable with possible outcomes 1, 2, . . . , n and $P(X = i) = 1/n$ for each value of i, then we say X has a discrete **Uniform distribution**.

---

[4]The assumption of independence is crucial, but not always (or ever) reasonable. As a March 3, 2010, article on *CNN Money* stated: "It's only when economic conditions start to return to normal . . . that investors, and investments, move independently again. That's when diversification reasserts its case. . . ." (http://money.cnn.com/2010/03/03/pf/funds/diversification.moneymag/index.htm)

[5]The Flaw of Averages: Why We Underestimate Risk in the Face of Uncertainty by Sam L Savage and Harry M Markowitz. Published by John Wiley & Sons, © 2009.

Bernoulli Trials

When Google Inc. designed its Chrome web browser, programmers worked hard to minimize the probability that their browser would have trouble displaying a website. Before releasing the product, they had to test many websites to discover those that might fail. Although web browsers are relatively new, *quality control inspection* such as this is common throughout manufacturing worldwide and has been in use in industry for nearly 100 years.

The developers of Chrome sampled websites, recording whether the browser displayed the website correctly or had a problem. We call the act of inspecting a website a trial. There are two possible outcomes—either the website renders correctly or it doesn't. Early on in this work, the probability of a success didn't change from trial to trial. Situations like this occur often and are called **Bernoulli trials,** after the 17th century Swiss mathematician, Jacob Bernoulli. To summarize, trials are Bernoulli if the following conditions are met:

- There are only two possible outcomes (called *success* and *failure*) for each trial.
- The probability of success, denoted p, is the same for every trial. (The probability of failure, $1 - p$, is often denoted q.)
- The trials are independent.

Common examples of Bernoulli trials include tossing a coin, collecting responses on yes/no questions from surveys, and even shooting free throws in a basketball game. Bernoulli trials are remarkably versatile and can be used to model a wide variety of real-life situations. The specific question you might ask in different situations will give rise to different random variables that, in turn, have different probability models.

Of course, the Chrome developers wanted to find websites that wouldn't display so they could fix any problems in the browser. So for them a "success" was finding a failed website. The labels "success" and "failure" are often applied arbitrarily, so be sure you know what they mean in any particular situation.

Independence Assumption

One of the important requirements for Bernoulli trials is that the trials be independent. Sometimes that's a reasonable assumption. Is it true for our example? It's easy to imagine that related sites might have similar problems, but if the sites are selected at random, whether one has a problem should be independent of others.

The 10% Condition

In theory, we need to sample from a population that's infinitely big. However, if the population is finite, it's still okay to proceed as long as the sample is smaller than 10% of the population. In Google's case, it just happened to have a directory of millions of websites, so most samples would easily satisfy the 10% Condition.

When the Independence Condition and the 10% Condition are both satisfied, we can use two probability distributions to model different aspects of Bernoulli trials: the Geometric distribution described in Section 9.5 and the Binomial distribution described in Section 9.6.

LO❸ 9.5 The Geometric Distribution

What's the probability that the first website that fails to display is the second one that we test? Let X denote the number of trials (websites) until the first such "success." For X to be 2, the first website must have displayed correctly (which has probability $1 - p$), and then the second one must have failed to display correctly—a success, with probability p. Since the trials are independent, these probabilities can be multiplied, and so $P(X = 2) = (1 - p)(p)$, or qp. Maybe you won't find a success until the fifth trial. What are the chances of that? You'd have to fail four times in a row and then succeed, so $P(X = 5) = (1 - p)^4(p) = q^4p$. See the Optional Math Box for an extension and more explanation.

Optional Math Box

We want to find the mean (expected value) of random variable X using a Geometric distribution with probability of success p.

First write the probabilities:

x	1	2	3	4	...
$P(X = x)$	p	qp	q^2p	q^3p	...

The expected value is: $E(X) = 1p + 2qp + 3q^2p + 4q^3p + \dots$

Since $p = 1 - q$: $\qquad = (1 - q) + 2q(1 - q) + 3q^2(1 - q) + \dots$

Simplify: $\qquad = 1 - q + 2q - 2q^2 + 3q^2 - 3q^3 + \dots$

$\qquad = 1 + q + q^2 + \dots$

That's an infinite geometric series, with first term 1 and common ratio q:

$$= \frac{1}{1 - q}$$

So, finally $\qquad E(X) = \dfrac{1}{p}.$

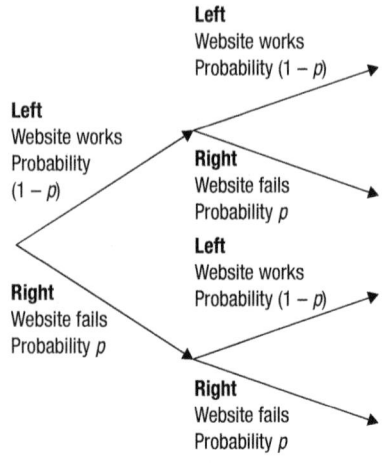

Left
Website works
Probability $(1 - p)$

Left
Website works
Probability $(1 - p)$

Right
Website fails
Probability p

Left
Website works
Probability $(1 - p)$

Right
Website fails
Probability p

Right
Website fails
Probability p

Website 1   **Website 2**

Figure 9.3 Testing websites is like following a path that keeps branching.

Testing a sequence of websites is like finding your way through the jungle on a path that keeps branching. At each branch you choose "right" with probability p and "left" with probability $(1 - p) = q$, as shown in Figure 9.3. What is the probability that the first time you turn right is on the second branch? We can read the answer off the diagram, turning left the first time and right the second: $P(X = 2) = (1 - p)p$. The probability that we don't turn right until the fifth branch would involve a longer diagram, but we can easily imagine turning left four times and then making a right, for a probability of $P(X = 5) = (1 - p)^4p$.

Whenever we want to know how long (how many trials) it will take us to achieve the first success, the model that tells us this probability is called the **Geometric probability distribution**. Geometric models are completely specified by one parameter, p, the probability of success.

The Geometric model can tell Google something important about its software. No large, complex program is free of bugs. So before releasing a program or upgrade, developers typically ask not whether it's bug-free, but how long it's likely to be until the next bug is discovered. If the expected number of pages displayed until the next failure is high enough, then the program is ready to ship.

> **Geometric Probability Model for Bernoulli Trials**
>
> p = Probability of success (and $q = 1 - p$ = probability of failure)
> X = Number of trials until the first success occurs
>
> $$P(X = x) = q^{x-1}p$$
>
> Expected value: $\mu = \dfrac{1}{p}$
>
> Standard deviation: $\sigma = \sqrt{\dfrac{q}{p^2}}$

FOR EXAMPLE   Attracting investors

A venture capital firm has a list of potential investors who have previously invested in new technologies. On average, these investors invest in about 5% of the opportunities presented to them. A new client of the firm is interested in finding investors for a 3-D printing technology for printing semiconductors. An analyst at the firm starts calling potential investors.

QUESTIONS

1. How many investors will she have to call, on average, to find someone interested?
2. What is the probability that the number of calls she needs to make before finding someone interested is 7?

ANSWERS   The probability of finding an interested investor is $p = 0.05$.

1. Let X = number of people she calls until she finds someone interested. $E(X) = 1/p = 1/(0.05) = 20$ people.
2. $P(X = 7) = (1 - p)^6\, p = 0.95^6 \times 0.05 = 0.037$

LO❸ 9.6 The Binomial Distribution

Suppose Google tests five websites. What's the probability that *exactly* two of them have problems (two "successes")? When we studied the Geometric model, we asked how long it would take until our first success. Now we want to find the probability of getting exactly two successes among the five trials. We're still talking about Bernoulli trials, but we're asking a different question.

Referring back to our analogy of branching paths through the jungle in Figure 9.3, we are asking the probability that we turn right exactly twice in five branches. We don't care which of the five are right and which are left, as long as there's a total of exactly two rights (and therefore three lefts).

This time we're interested in the *number of successes* in the five trials, which we'll denote by X. We want to find $P(X = 2)$. Whenever the random variable of interest is the number of successes in a series of Bernoulli trials, it's called a *binomial random variable*. The "bi" in *binomial* means "two," for the two options left/right or failure/success. It takes two parameters to define this **Binomial probability distribution**: the number of trials, n, and the probability of success, p.

Suppose that, in this phase of development, 10% of the sites exhibited some sort of problem, so that $p = 0.10$. Exactly two successes in five trials means two successes and three failures. It seems logical that the probability should be

$(p)^2(1 - p)^3$. Unfortunately, it's not *quite* that easy. That calculation would give you the probability of finding two successes and then three failures—*in that order*. But you could find the two successes in a lot of other ways—for example, in the second and fourth websites you test. The probability of that sequence is $(1 - p)p(1 - p)(p)(1 - p)$, which is also $p^2(1 - p)^3$. In fact, as long as there are two successes and three failures, the probability will always be the same, regardless of the order of the sequence of successes and failures. The probability will be $(p)^2(1 - p)^3$. To find the probability of getting two successes in five trials in any order, we just need to know how many ways that outcome can occur.

Fortunately, all the possible sequences that lead to the same number of successes are *disjoint*. (For example, if your successes came in the first two trials, they couldn't come in the last two.) So once we find all the different sequences, we can add up their probabilities. And since the probabilities are all the same, we just need to find how many sequences there are and multiply $(p)^2(1 - p)^3$ by that number.

Each different order in which we can have x successes in n trials is called a "combination." The total number of ways this can happen is written $\binom{n}{x}$ or $_nC_x$, and pronounced "n choose x":

> The 10 ways of getting two successes, S, and hence three failures, F, out of five websites are as follows:
>
> SSFFF
> SFSFF
> SFFSF
> SFFFS
> FSSFF
> FSFSF
> FSFFS
> FFSSF
> FFSFS
> FFFSS

$$\binom{n}{x} = {_nC_x} = \frac{n!}{x!(n - x)!} \text{ where } n! = n \times (n - 1) \times \cdots \times 1$$

For two successes in five trials,

$$\binom{5}{2} = \frac{5!}{2!(5 - 2)!} = \frac{(5 \times 4 \times 3 \times 2 \times 1)}{(2 \times 1 \times 3 \times 2 \times 1)} = \frac{(5 \times 4)}{(2 \times 1)} = 10.$$

So there are 10 ways to get two successes in five websites, and the probability of each is $(p)^2(1 - p)^3$. To find the probability of exactly two successes in five trials, we multiply the probability of any particular order by this number:

$$P(\textit{exactly two successes in five trials}) = 10p^2(1 - p)^3 = 10(0.10)^2(0.90)^3 = 0.0729$$

In general, we can write the probability of exactly x successes in n trials as

$$P(X = x) = \binom{n}{x}p^x q^{n-x}.$$

If the probability that any single website has a display problem is 0.10, what's the expected number of websites with problems if we test 100 sites? You probably said 10 and you would be correct. We suspect you didn't use the formula for expected value that involves multiplying each value times its probability and adding them up. In fact, there's an easier way to find the expected value for a binomial random variable. You just multiply the probability of success by n. In other words, $E(X) = np$. We prove this in the next Optional Math Box.

The standard deviation is less obvious, so you can't just rely on your intuition. Fortunately, the formula for the standard deviation also comes down to something simple: $SD(X) = \sqrt{npq}$. If you're curious to know where that comes from, it's in the next Optional Math Box, too.

In our website example, with $n = 100$, $E(X) = np = 100(0.10) = 10$, so we expect to find 10 successes out of the 100 trials. The standard deviation is

$$\sqrt{100 \times 0.10 \times 0.90} = \text{three websites.}$$

To summarize, a Binomial probability model describes the distribution of the number of successes in a specified number of trials.

> **Binomial Model for Bernoulli Trials**
>
> n = Number of trials
> p = Probability of success (and $q = 1 - p$ = probability of failure)
> X = Number of successes in n trials
>
> $$P(X = x) = \binom{n}{x} p^x q^{n-x}, \text{ where } \binom{n}{x} = \frac{n!}{x!(n-x)!}$$
>
> Mean: $\mu = np$
> Standard deviation: $\sigma = \sqrt{npq}$

When $p = 0.5$, the Binomial distribution is symmetric (as we can see from Figure 9.4) for $n = 10$, but when $p < 0.5$ it is skewed to the right, and when $p > 0.5$ it is skewed to the left, as we can see from Figures 9.5 and 9.6. In all these graphs, we note that there's a limit to the value of X on the horizontal axis. It can't go above 10, since X is the number of successes in 10 trials. If there are only 10 trials, the number of successes can't be more than 10. This makes the Binomial distribution different from the Geometric distribution, where there is no upper limit on X.

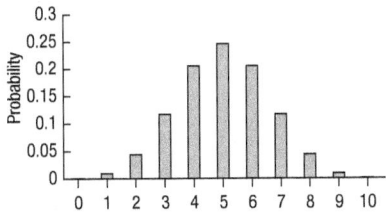

Figure 9.4   Binomial distribution with $n = 10$ and $p = 0.5$.

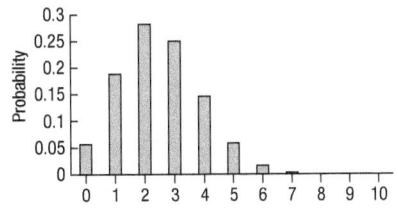

Figure 9.5   Binomial distribution with $n = 10$ and $p = 0.25$.

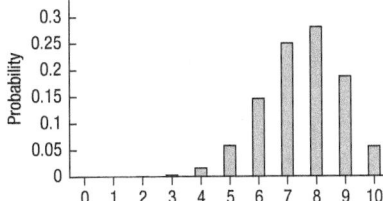

Figure 9.6   Binomial distribution with $n = 10$ and $p = 0.75$.

Richard Lam/The Canadian Press

A major application of the Binomial distribution in business is quality control. A Canadian company that outsources manufacturing abroad needs to monitor products not just when they roll off the overseas production line but also when they're imported into Canada. Its customers will also probably check them when they're received. Some companies, like SGS Canada of Mississauga, Ontario, specialize in monitoring, testing, and inspecting for quality-control purposes. lululemon, which creates yoga-inspired athletic clothing, is one of SGS's clients, and SGS provides independent tests of lululemon's fabrics at the start of each season, checking a range of properties, including content, shrinkage, and colourfastness.

No production process is perfect, so let's suppose that we operate a manufacturing facility where, on average, 1% of our products do not measure up to our standards, and that this is acceptable to our distributors. However, we want to watch out for the rate going above 1%, and therefore we hire SGS Canada to take samples of 10 products every hour in our production facility and test them. The number that fail the test is therefore given by a Binomial distribution with $n = 10$ and $p = 0.01$. Suppose 1 product out of the sample of 10 fails the test. This means that 10% of our sample failed the test. But is this an indication that the overall failure rate has gone above the acceptable level of 1%? To answer this, we need to know how unlikely it is to have 1 out of 10 failing when $p = 1\%$. If it's very unlikely, perhaps p has increased above 1%. The probability of 1 out of 10 failing when $p = 1\%$ is

$$P(X = 1) = (10!/(1! \times 9!)) \times 0.01^1 \times 0.99^9 = 0.091.$$

In other words, it happens 9.1% of the time, not that unlikely. Often, as a rule of thumb, we use 5% as our criterion for raising a red flag and alerting management that the failure rate seems to have gone too high. If we'd found 2 products out of 10 failing our test, it would raise a red flag, since the probability of that occurring is way below 5%:

$$P(X = 2) = (10!/(2! \times 8!)) \times 0.01^2 \times 0.99^8 = 0.0042$$

We could therefore use an operating rule whereby if there is at most 1 product out of a sample of 10 failing our test, everything is fine. "At most one" means either zero or one, so the probability of this happening is

$$
\begin{aligned}
P(X = 0) + P(X = 1) &= 0.99^{10} + 0.091 \\
&= 0.904 + 0.091 \\
&= 0.995.
\end{aligned}
$$

Whenever we need to calculate the probability of "at most three" or "at least four," we add up the corresponding probabilities. However, we can also sometimes use a shortcut. Suppose we need to know the probability that SGS Canada will find more than 1 product in a sample of 10 failing its test. We could calculate this as

$$
\begin{aligned}
P(X > 1) = P(X = 2) + P(X = 3) + P(X = 4) + P(X = 5) + P(X = 6) \\
+ P(X = 7) + P(X = 8) + P(X = 9) + P(X = 10),
\end{aligned}
$$

which involves a lot of calculation. It saves time to calculate:

$$
\begin{aligned}
P(X > 1) &= 1 - P(X \leq 1) \\
&= 1 - P(X = 0) - P(X = 1) \\
&= 1 - 0.904 - 0.091 \\
&= 0.005
\end{aligned}
$$

FOR EXAMPLE   Attracting investors continued

The venture capital firm described in For Example: "Attracting investors" at the end of Section 9.5 has a 5% success rate in attracting investors to new technology opportunities. An analyst calls potential investors.

QUESTIONS

1. If she calls 10 investors, what is the probability that exactly 2 of them will be interested?
2. If she calls 10 investors, what is the probability that at least 2 of them will be interested?

ANSWERS

1. $n = 10, x = 2, p = 0.05$

   $P(X = 2) = (10 \times 9 / 2) \times (0.05)^2 \times (0.95)^8 = 0.0746$

2. $P(\text{at least 2}) = 1 - P(X = 0) - P(X = 1) = 1 - (0.95)^{10} - 10 \times (0.05)^1 \times (0.95)^9 = 0.086$

Optional Math Box

To derive the formulas for the mean and standard deviation of the Binomial model, we start with the most basic situation.

   Consider a single Bernoulli trial with probability of success p. Let's find the mean and variance of the number of successes.

Here's the probability model for the number of successes:

X	0	1
$P(X = x)$	q	p

Find the expected value: $E(X) = 0q + 1p$

$$E(X) = p$$

   Now the variance: $Var(X) = (0 - p)^2q + (1 - p)^2p$

$$= p^2q + q^2p$$
$$= pq(p + q)$$
$$= pq(1)$$
$$Var(X) = pq$$

What happens when there's more than one trial? A Binomial model simply counts the number of successes in a series of n independent Bernoulli trials. That makes it easy to find the mean and standard deviation of a binomial random variable, Y.

$$Let\ Y = X_1 + X_2 + X_3 + \cdots + X_n$$
$$E(Y) = E(X_1 + X_2 + X_3 + \cdots + X_n)$$
$$= E(X_1) + E(X_2) + E(X_3) + \cdots + E(X_n)$$
$$= p + p + p + \cdots + p\ (\text{There are } n \text{ terms.})$$

So, as we thought, the mean is $E(Y) = np$.

   And since the trials are independent, the variances add:

$$Var(Y) = Var(X_1 + X_2 + X_3 + \cdots + X_n)$$
$$= Var(X_1) + Var(X_2) + Var(X_3) + \cdots + Var(X_n)$$
$$= pq + pq + pq + \cdots + pq\ (\text{Again, } n \text{ terms.})$$
$$Var(Y) = npq$$

Voilà! The standard deviation is $SD(Y) = \sqrt{npq}$.

GUIDED EXAMPLE   Canadian Blood Services

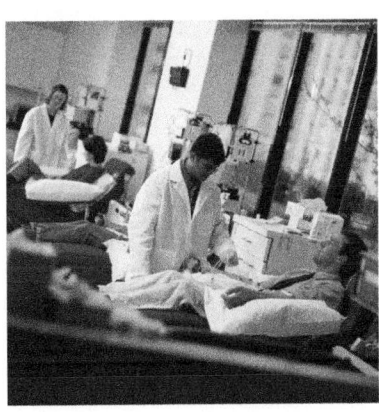

Keith Brofsky/Photodisc/Getty Images

Every minute, on average, someone in Canada needs blood. In over half of Canadian families, someone has received a blood transfusion. Many people donate blood, and it takes just an hour to donate enough blood to save up to three lives.

   Canadian Blood Services is a not-for-profit organization that runs as a large business and receives funding to the tune of $400 million from provincial and territorial ministries of health. Over 4000 staff and 17,000 volunteers collect over 800,000 units of blood per year.

   The balancing of supply and demand is complicated not only by the logistics of finding donors who meet health criteria, but by the fact that the blood type of donor and patient must be matched. People with O-negative blood are called "universal donors" because O-negative blood can be given to patients

(Continued)

with any blood type. Only about 6% of people have O-negative blood, which presents a challenge in managing and planning. This is especially true because, unlike a manufacturer that can balance supply by planning to produce or to purchase more or less of a key item, Canadian Blood Services gets its supply from volunteer donors who show up more or less at random (at least in terms of blood type). Modelling the arrival of samples with various blood types helps Canadian Blood Services managers plan their blood allocations.

Here's a small example of the kind of planning required. In the next 20 donors to arrive at a blood donation centre, how many universal donors can be expected? Specifically, what are the mean and standard deviation of the number of universal donors? What is the probability that there are two or three universal donors?

Question 1: What are the mean and standard deviation of the number of universal donors?

Question 2: What is the probability that there are exactly two or three universal donors out of the 20?

PLAN	**Setup** State the question.	We want to know the mean and standard deviation of the number of universal donors among 20 people and the probability that there are two or three of them.
	Check to see that these are Bernoulli trials.	✓ There are two outcomes: Success = O-negative Failure = other blood types
	Variable Define the random variable.	✓ $p = 0.06$
	Model Specify the model.	✓ 10% Condition: Fewer than 10% of all possible donors have shown up. Let X = Number of O-negative donors among $n = 20$ people. We therefore use a Binomial distribution with $n = 20$ and $p = 0.06$.
DO	**Mechanics** Find the expected value and standard deviation.	$E(X) = np = 20(0.06) = 1.2$ $SD(X) = \sqrt{npq} = \sqrt{20(0.06)(0.94)} \approx 1.06$
	Calculate the probability of two or three successes.	$P(X = 2 \text{ or } 3) = P(X = 2) + P(X = 3)$ $= \binom{20}{2}(0.06)(0.94) + \binom{20}{3}(0.06)^3(0.94)^{17}$ $\approx 0.2246 + 0.0860$ $= 0.3106$
REPORT	**Conclusion** Interpret your results in context.	MEMO **Re: Blood Drive** In groups of 20 randomly selected blood donors, we'd expect to find an average of 1.2 universal donors, with a standard deviation of 1.06. About 31% of the time, we'd expect to find exactly two or three universal donors among the 20 people.

LO❸ 9.7 The Poisson Distribution

Not all discrete events can be modelled as Bernoulli trials. Sometimes we're interested simply in the number of events that occur over a given interval of time or space. For example, we might want to model the number of customers arriving in our store in the next 10 minutes, the number of visitors to our website in the next minute, or the number of defects that occur in a computer monitor of a certain size. In cases like these, the number of occurrences can be modelled by a Poisson random variable. The Poisson's parameter, the mean of the distribution, is usually denoted by λ.

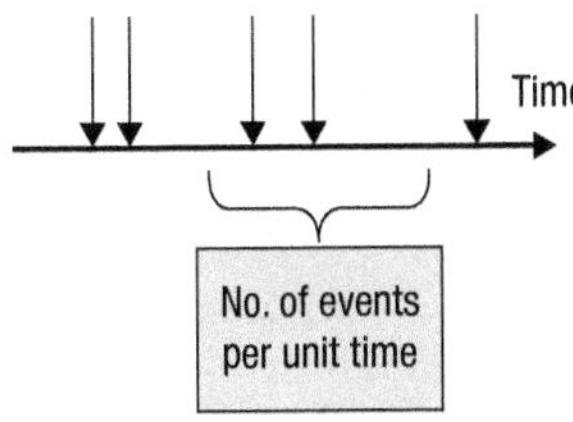

Figure 9.7 The Poisson distribution models the number of random events per unit time.

You can think of a Poisson situation as a timeline with events occurring at random times, as in Figure 9.7. We know the *average* number of events per unit of time; for example, four website hits per minute. The Poisson distribution describes the number we actually get. It gives us the *probability that in fact we will get, say*, zero hits or two hits during the next minute.

There is one major assumption that needs to be satisfied when we use the **Poisson distribution**.

- **Independence Assumption** The events must be independent of each other. Another way of looking at this is that the events must occur at random, with no discernible pattern.

  For example, customers making purchases on a website clearly make their decisions independently of each other. They don't even know each other. Another example is customers arriving to check in at a hotel (unless, of course, a whole busload of customers arrives at the hotel, in which case the independence assumption is broken, since they've all arrived in a group).

  Conversely, an airport is a good example of a place where events occur that are *not* independent of each other.

- Flights landing at an airport are not independent of each other since they're under the central management of the air traffic controllers. You wouldn't want to be on a flight in which the captain decides to land without knowing whether another aircraft is already using the runway!
- The arrivals of passengers at the baggage check-in aren't independent of each other, since passengers time their arrivals according to when their flights depart. This makes their arrivals at the baggage check-in coordinated with each other to some degree, and therefore not independent of each other. This can easily be seen for airlines with only a few flights per day, but is less clear for airlines that have a continual stream of flights and therefore a continual stream of passengers. Nonetheless, the independence assumption is broken in both cases.

The Poisson distribution was the model used in the famous 1982 Woburn toxic waste trial, when eight families from Woburn, Massachusetts, sued W. R. Grace & Company, alleging that the company contaminated the public water supply by dumping toxic materials near city wells. The families argued that eight recent cases of leukemia were the result of the company's actions. The resulting trial was the basis for the book and movie *A Civil Action*. For the Woburn case, the probability (based on national averages) for eight leukemia cases in a town of that size in the given time period was determined to be about 0.04.

Poisson Probability Model for Occurrences

λ = Mean number of occurrences per unit of time

X = Number of occurrences per unit of time

$$P(X = x) = \frac{e^{-\lambda}\lambda^{x}}{x!}$$

Expected value: $E(X) = \lambda$

Standard deviation: $SD(X) = \sqrt{\lambda}$

Returning to the website-hits-per-minute example, data show an average of four hits per minute to a small business website during the afternoon hours from 1:00 P.M. to 5:00 P.M. We can use the Poisson model to find the probability that any number of hits will arrive. For example, if we let X be the number of hits arriving in the next minute, then $P(X = x) = \dfrac{e^{-\lambda}\lambda^x}{x!} = \dfrac{e^{-4}4^x}{x!}$, using the given average rate of four per minute. So the probability of no hits during the next minute would be

$$P(X = 0) = \frac{e^{-4}4^0}{0!} = e^{-4} = 0.0183 \text{ (Recall that } e \approx 2.7182818 \text{ and that } 0! = 1).$$

One interesting and useful feature of the Poisson distribution is that it scales according to the interval size. For example, suppose we want to know the probability of no hits to our website in the next 30 seconds. Since the mean rate is four hits per minute, it's two hits per 30 seconds, so we can use the model with $\lambda = 2$ instead. If we let Y be the number of hits arriving in the next 30 seconds, then

$$P(Y = 0) = \frac{e^{-2}2^0}{0!} = e^{-2} = 0.1353.$$

The Poisson model has been used to model phenomena such as customer arrivals, hot streaks in sports, and disease clusters.

GUIDED EXAMPLE   New Listings on the Toronto Stock Exchange

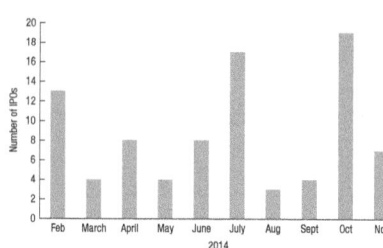

Source: Based on Toronto Stock Exchange. (2014).

The Toronto Stock Exchange (TSX) has been around for over 150 years and has a reputation for being a good place for Canadian companies to raise capital.

The number of initial public offerings on the Toronto Stock Exchange from February to November of 2014 is shown in the bar chart. The average number is 8.7 per month, and we assume that the number per month follows a Poisson distribution. Suppose that next month only three companies listed: Should the TSX regard this month as exceptional and start to investigate how to attract more listings? Suppose that next month 15 companies listed. Should the TSX regard this as exceptionally high and start to expand its IPO department? Give reasons for and against using a Poisson distribution for this data.

PLAN Setup State the objectives.	We want to know whether 3 or 15 listings are exceptionally low or high.
DO Mechanics Is three listings exceptionally low? If so, two listings is also. What this question is really asking is whether the probability of *three or fewer* listings is very low. Is 15 listings exceptionally high? If it is, 16 listings is also. What this question is really asking is whether the probability of *15 or more* listings is very high. Give reasons for and against using a Poisson distribution for this data.	$\lambda = 8.7$ $P(X \leq 3) = P(X = 0) + P(X = 1) + P(X = 2) + P(X = 3)$ $\quad = e^{-8.7}[8.7^0/0! +$ $\quad\quad 8.7^1/1! + 8.7^2/2! + 8.7^3/3!]$ $\quad = 0.026$ $P(X \geq 15) = 1 - P(X < 15)$ $\quad = 1 - P(X = 0) - P(X = 1) - \cdots - P(X = 14)$ $\quad = 1 - e^{-8.7}[8.7^0/0! + 8.7^1/1! + \cdots +$ $\quad\quad 8.7^{14}/14!]$ $\quad = 0.016$

At first sight it may appear that companies apply for listing on the TSX in much the same way as customers arrive at a website—at random. There's an overall average number, but each company behaves independently of the others and makes its own decision to apply for a listing at a time of its own choosing. In that case, the Poisson distribution would be applicable to this situation.

On the other hand, we can read the number of listings per month off the graph and calculate the variance to be 32.9. For a Poisson distribution, this should equal the mean, which is only 8.7. Although we have only a few months of data available, the new listings during those months are more variable than a Poisson distribution.

| **REPORT** | Conclusion Interpret your results in context. | MEMO

Re: Listings

The probability of three or fewer IPOs per month is 2.6%. The TSX needs to establish its own criteria for whether it regards this as exceptionally low. For many business applications, 5% is used as a rule of thumb.

The probability of 15 or more IPOs per month is 1.6%. However, we note from the graph above that in July and October it did in fact occur. Also, there were only three IPOs in August. The fact that the probabilities derived from the Poisson distribution are very low for events that did in fact occur within a timespan of just 10 months casts doubt on the validity of the Poisson assumptions for IPOs at the TSX. The number of IPOs per month is more variable than the Poisson distribution predicts. |

Whenever or wherever rare events happen closely together, people want to know whether the occurrence happened by chance or whether an underlying change caused the unusual occurrence. The Poisson model can be used to find the probability of the occurrence and can be the basis for making the judgment.

FOR EXAMPLE   Earthquakes in Charlevoix, Quebec

The Charlevoix Seismic Zone (CSZ) is the most seismically active region of eastern Canada. Earthquakes of magnitude 6.0 and over occur once every 52.4 years on average. The last one occurred in 1925. Let us assume that earthquakes occur independently of each other and so follow a Poisson distribution.

QUESTIONS

1. What was the probability of one large quake (magnitude 6.0 and over) in CSZ during the next 10 years for someone living in 1926?

2. What is the probability for someone living today?

3. Explain how your answers to Questions 1 and 2 compare to each other.

ANSWERS

1. The average number of large quakes during 10 years is $10/52.4 = 0.1908$.
   X = number of quakes during next 10 years: 1926–1936
   $P(X = 1) = \exp(-0.1908) \times 0.1908 = 0.158$

2. The answer is the same for the 10-year period starting today: 0.158.

3. The answers are the same because quakes occur independently of each other. The fact that today it's been a long time since the last large quake makes no difference to the probability of a quake occurring.

JUST CHECKING

Roper Worldwide reports that it is able to contact 76% of the randomly selected households drawn for a telephone survey.

2 Explain why these phone calls can be considered Bernoulli trials.

3 Which of the models of this chapter (Geometric, Binomial, or Poisson) would you use to model the number of successful contacts from a list of 1000 sampled households?

4 Roper also reports that even after it contacted a household, only 38% of the contacts agreed to be interviewed. So the probability of getting a completed interview from a randomly selected household is only 0.29 (38% of 76%). Which of the models of this chapter would you use to model the number of households Roper has to call before it gets the first completed interview?

Answers are found in Appendix A.

LO❹   9.8   **Continuous Random Variables**

Discrete random variables are great for modelling occurrences or small counts. But in industry we often measure quantities that a discrete variable just can't handle. For example, the time until a computer battery needs to be charged might take on any value between two and four hours.

When a random variable can take on any value in an interval, we can no longer model it using a discrete probability distribution and must use a continuous probability distribution instead. For any continuous random variable, the distribution of its probability can be shown with a curve. That curve is called the **probability density function (pdf)**, usually denoted as $f(x)$, and an example is known as the Normal probability density function (see Figure 9.8).

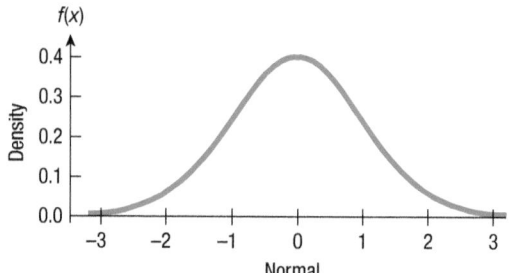

Figure 9.8   The standard Normal density function (a normal with mean 0 and standard deviation 1). The probability of finding a z-score in any interval is simply the area over that interval under the curve. For example, the probability that the z-score falls between −1 and 1 is about 68%, which can be seen from the density function or found more precisely from a table or technology.

Density functions must satisfy two requirements. They must stay non-negative for every possible value, and the total area under the curve must be exactly 1.0. This last requirement corresponds to saying that the total probability (equal to 1.0) must be assigned somewhere.

Any density function can give the probability that the random variable lies in an interval. But remember, the probability that X lies in the interval from a to b is the *area* under the density function, $f(x)$, between the values a and b and not the value $f(a)$ or $f(b)$. You can contrast Figure 9.8 for the Normal distribution (which is continuous) with Figures 9.4 to 9.6 that we had earlier for the Binomial distribution (which is discrete). For discrete distributions, probability is measured on the vertical axis, whereas for continuous distributions it is the area under the curve.

In general, finding that area requires calculus or numerical analysis and is beyond the scope of this text. But for the models we'll discuss, the probabilities are found either from tables (Normal distribution) or simple computations (Uniform and Exponential distributions). They can also be calculated using computer software.

There are many possible continuous distributions, but we'll explore only three of the most commonly used to model business phenomena: the *Uniform distribution*, the *Normal distribution*, and the *Exponential distribution*.

LO❹ 9.9 The Uniform Distribution

We've already seen the discrete version of the Uniform distribution in Section 9.4. A continuous Uniform model shares the principle that all events should be equally likely, but with a continuous model, we can't talk about the probability of a particular value because each value has probability zero (we will expand on this later in the chapter). Instead, for a continuous random variable X, we say that the probability that X lies in any interval depends only on the length of that interval. Not surprisingly, the density function of a continuous uniform random variable looks flat (see Figure 9.9).

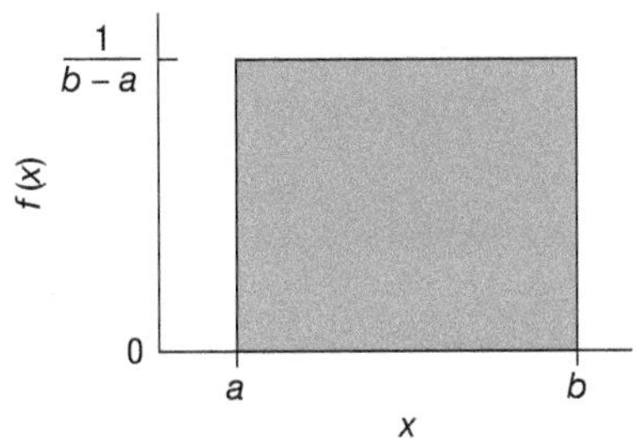

The density function of a continuous uniform random variable on the interval $[a, b]$, where $a < b$, can be defined by the formula

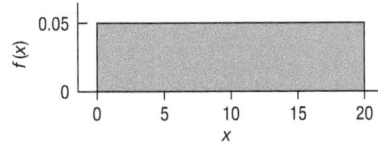

Figure 9.9   The density function of a continuous uniform random variable on the interval from *a* to *b*.

$$f(x) = \begin{cases} \dfrac{1}{b - a} & \text{if} \quad a \leq x \leq b \\ 0 & \text{otherwise.} \end{cases}$$

From Figure 9.9, it's easy to see that the probability that X lies in any interval between a and b is the same as any other interval of the same length. In fact, the probability is just the ratio of the length of the interval to the total length: $b - a$. In other words,

For values c and d ($c \leq d$) both within the interval $[a, b]$,

$$P(c \leq X \leq d) = \frac{(d - c)}{(b - a)}.$$

As an example, suppose you are monitoring energy wastage by a robot on the production line of a manufacturing facility. The robot starts its function every 20 minutes. You go to the robot with a heat imaging camera. The amount of time you should wait until the robot starts can be modelled using the uniform density function:

$$f(x) = \begin{cases} \dfrac{1}{20} & \text{if} \quad 0 \leq x \leq 20 \\ 0 & \text{otherwise,} \end{cases}$$

and would look as shown in Figure 9.10.

Just as the mean of a data distribution is the balancing point of a histogram, the mean of any continuous random variable is the balancing point of the density function. Looking at Figure 9.10, we can see that the balancing point is halfway between the end points at 10 minutes. In general, the expected value is

Figure 9.10   The density function of a continuous uniform random variable on the interval [0, 20]. Notice that the mean (the balancing point) of the distribution is at 10 minutes.

$$E(X) = \frac{a + b}{2}$$

for a Uniform distribution on the interval (a, b). With $a = 0$ and $b = 20$, the expected value would be 10 minutes.

The variance and standard deviation are less intuitive:

$$Var(X) = \frac{(b - a)^2}{12}; \; SD(X) = \sqrt{\frac{(b - a)^2}{12}}$$

Using these formulas, our waiting time for the robot will have an expected value of 10 minutes with a standard deviation of $\sqrt{\frac{(20 - 0)^2}{12}} = 5.77$ minutes.

The Uniform distribution is the simplest possible continuous distribution. We present it here not because it is widely used in business, but because it provides an introduction to the other continuous distributions we are going to discuss next. The concepts to understand from the Uniform distribution are (i) the fact that the vertical axis represents probability density, (ii) the fact that the area under the curve represents the probability of the random variable, x, being between two values, and (iii) the fact that the mean (expected value) of the distribution is the balancing point of the curve.

LO④   9.10   # The Normal Distribution

NOTATION ALERT

The symbol μ, pronounced "mew," is the Greek letter for "m" and represents the mean. The symbol σ, sigma, is the lowercase Greek letter for "s" and represents the standard deviation.

You've probably seen the **Normal distribution** before, and if you've seen a "bell-shaped curve" chances are it was a Normal model. Normal models are defined by two parameters: a mean and a standard deviation. By convention, we denote parameters with Greek letters. For example, we denote the mean of such a model with the Greek letter μ, which is the Greek equivalent of "m," for *m*ean, and the standard deviation with the Greek letter σ, the Greek equivalent of "s," for *s*tandard deviation.

There's a different Normal model for every combination of μ and σ, but if we standardize our data first, creating z-scores by subtracting the mean to make the mean 0 and dividing by the standard deviation to make the standard deviation 1, then we'll need only the model with mean 0 and standard deviation 1. We call this the **standard Normal model or standard Normal distribution**.

Of course, we shouldn't use a Normal model for every data set. If the histogram isn't bell-shaped to begin with, the z-scores won't be well modelled by the Normal model. And standardizing won't help, because standardizing doesn't change the shape of the distribution. So always check the histogram of the data before using the Normal model.

JUST CHECKING

5 Your Accounting teacher has announced that the lower of your two tests will be dropped. You got a 90 on Test 1 and an 80 on Test 2. You're all set to drop the 80 until she announces that she grades "on a curve." She standardized the scores in order to decide which is the lower one. If the mean on the first test was 88 with a standard deviation of 4 and the mean on the second was 75 with a standard deviation of 5,

a) Which one will be dropped?
b) Does this seem "fair"?

Answers are found in Appendix A.

z-Scores

$$z = \frac{y - \bar{y}}{s}$$

for data.

$$z = \frac{y - \mu}{\sigma}$$

for models.

The 68-95-99.7 Rule

Normal models are useful because they can give us an idea of how extreme a value is by telling us how likely we are to find one that far from the mean. We'll soon see how to find these values for any z-score, but for now, there's a simple rule, called the **68-95-99.7 Rule**, that tells us roughly how the values are distributed.

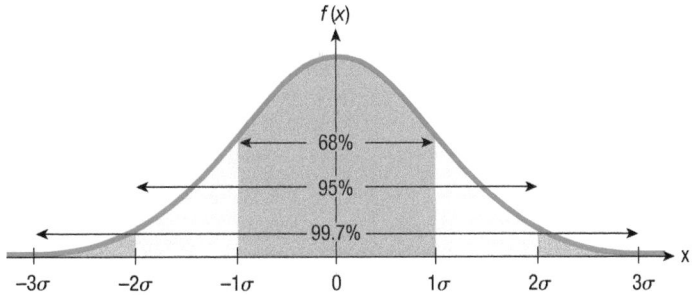

Figure 9.11 Reaching out one, two, and three standard deviations in a bell-shaped distribution gives the 68-95-99.7 Rule.

In bell-shaped distributions, about 68% of the values fall within one standard deviation of the mean, about 95% of the values fall within two standard deviations of the mean, and about 99.7%—almost all—of the values fall within three standard deviations of the mean (Figure 9.11).[6]

Finding Other Percentiles

Finding the probability that a value is at least one SD above the mean is easy. We know that 68% of the values lie within one SD of the mean, so 32% lie farther away. Since the Normal model is symmetric, half of those 32% (or 16%) are more than one SD above the mean. But what if we want to know the percentage of observations that fall more than 1.8 SDs above the mean?

When the value doesn't fall exactly zero, one, two, or three standard deviations from the mean, we can look it up in a table of **Normal percentiles**.[7] Tables use the standard Normal model, so we'll have to convert our data to z-scores before using the table. If our data value was 1.8 standard deviations above the mean, we would standardize it to a z-score of 1.80, and then find the value associated with a z-score of 1.80. If we use a table, as shown in Figure 9.12, we find the z-score by looking down the left column for the first two digits (1.8) and across the top row for the third digit, 0. The table gives the percentile as 0.9641. That means that 96.4% of the z-scores are less than 1.80. Since the total area is always 1, and $1 - 0.9641 = 0.0359$, we know that only 3.6% of all observations from a Normal model have z-scores higher than 1.80. We can also find the probabilities associated with z-scores using technology such as calculators, statistical software, and various websites.

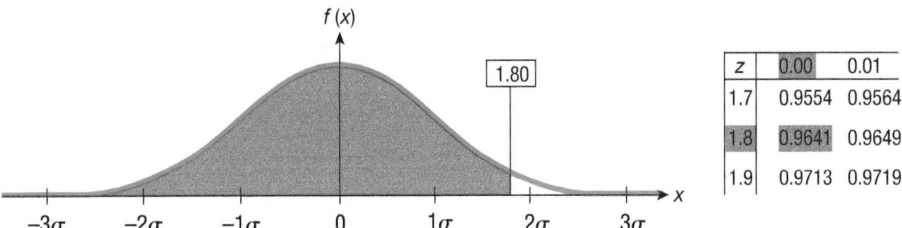

Figure 9.12 A table of Normal percentiles (Table Z in Appendix B) lets us find the percentage of individuals in a standard Normal distribution falling below any specified z-score value.

---

[6]This rule was first recognized by the mathematician Abraham De Moivre in 1733, based on empirical observations of data, so it's sometimes called the *Empirical Rule*. But it's a better mnemonic to call it the 68-95-99.7 Rule, for the three numbers that define it.

[7]See Table Z in Appendix B. Many calculators and statistics computer packages do this as well.

How Can *Every* Value Have Probability 0?

At first it may seem illogical that every value of a continuous random variable has probability 0. Let's look at the standard Normal random variable, Z. We could find (from a table, website, or computer program) that the probability that Z lies between 0 and 1 is 0.3413, which is the area under the Normal pdf (in red) between the values 0 and 1.

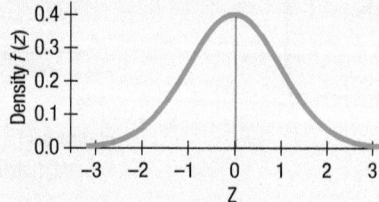

So what's the probability that Z is between 0 and 1/10?

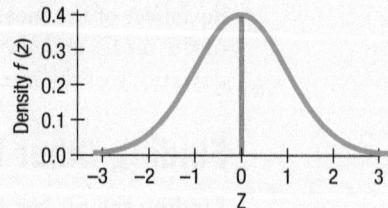

That area is only 0.0398. What is the chance then that Z will fall between 0 and 1/100? There's not much area—the probability is only 0.0040. If we kept going, the probability would keep getting smaller. The probability that Z is between 0 and 1/100,000 is less than 0.0001.

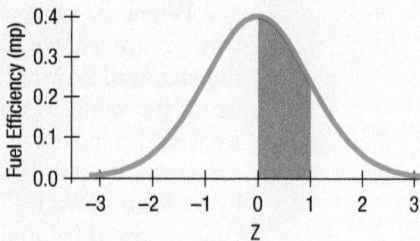

So what's the probability that Z is *exactly* 0? Well, there's *no* area under the curve right at $x = 0$, so the probability is 0. It's only intervals that have positive probability, but that's okay. In real life we never mean exactly 0.0000000000 or any other value. If you say "exactly 164 pounds," you might really mean between 163.5 and 164.5 pounds or even between 163.99 and 164.01 pounds, but realistically not 164.000000000 . . . pounds.

Practice With Normal Distribution Calculations

The basic equation from which all Normal distribution calculations are done is

$$z = (y - \mu)/\sigma.$$

The probability, P, is related to z, using a table, a calculator, or software.

FOR EXAMPLE   **GMAT scores and the Normal model**

The Graduate Management Admission Test (GMAT) has scores from 200 to 800. Scores are supposed to follow a distribution that is roughly unimodal and symmetric and is designed to have an overall mean of 500 and a standard deviation of 100. In any one year, the mean and standard deviation may differ from these target values by a small amount, but we can use these values as good overall approximations.

QUESTION Suppose you earned a 600 on your GMAT. From that information and the 68-95-99.7 Rule, where do you stand among all students who took the GMAT?

ANSWER Because we're told that the distribution is unimodal and symmetric, we can approximate the distribution with a Normal model. We're also told that the scores have a mean of 500 and an SD of 100. It's good practice at this point to draw the distribution. Find the score whose percentile you want to know and locate it on the picture. When you finish the calculation, you should check to make sure that it's a reasonable percentile from the picture.

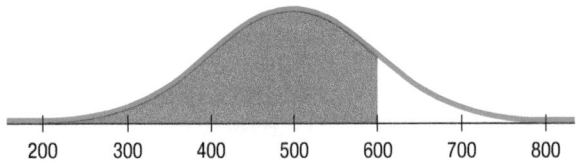

A score of 600 is 1 SD above the mean. That corresponds to one of the points in the 68-95-99.7% Rule. About 32% (100% − 68%) of those who took the test were more than one standard deviation from the mean, but only half of those were on the high side. So about 16% (half of 32%) of the test scores were better than 600.

FOR EXAMPLE   More GMAT scores

QUESTION Assuming the GMAT scores are nearly Normal with a mean of 500 and a standard deviation of 100, what proportion of GMAT scores falls between 450 and 600?

ANSWER *The first step is to find the z-scores associated with each value.* Standardizing the scores we're given, we find that for 600, $z = (600 − 500)/100 = 1.0$ and for 450, $z = (450 − 500)/100 = −0.50$. We can label the axis below the picture either in the original values or in the z-scores, or even use both scales, as the following picture shows:

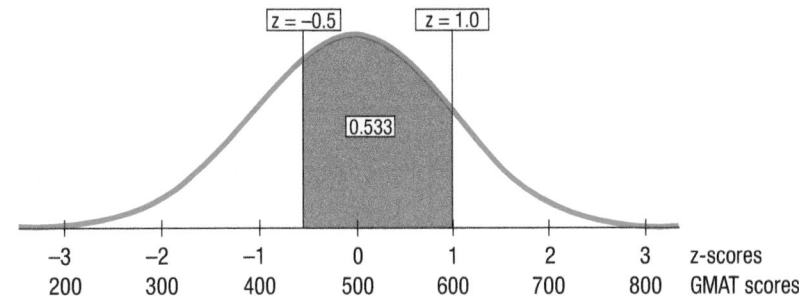

From Table Z, we find the area $z \leq 1.0 = 0.8413$, which means that 84.13% of scores fall below 1.0, and the area $z \leq −0.50 = 0.3085$, which means that 30.85% of the values fall below 0.5, so the proportion of z-scores *between* them is 84.13% − 30.85% = 53.28%. So, the Normal model estimates that about 53.3% of GMAT scores fall between 450 and 600.

Finding areas from z-scores is the simplest way to work with the Normal distribution. But sometimes we start with areas and are asked to work backward to find the corresponding z-score or even the original data value. For instance, what z-score represents the first quartile, Q1, in a Normal distribution? In our first set of examples, we knew the z-score and used the table or technology to find the percentile. Now we want to find the cut point for the 25th percentile. Make a picture, shading the leftmost 25% of the area. Look in Table Z for an area of 0.2500. The exact area isn't there, but 0.2514 is the closest number. That shows up in the table with −0.6 in the left margin and 0.07 in the top margin. The z-score for Q1, then, is approximately $z = -0.67$. This means that there is a probability of 0.25 of being less than 0.67 standard deviations below the mean. Computers and calculators can determine the cut point more precisely (and more easily).[8]

FOR EXAMPLE   An exclusive MBA program

QUESTION   Suppose an MBA program says it admits only people with GMAT scores among the top 10%. How high a GMAT score does it take to be eligible?

ANSWER   The program takes the top 10%, so its cutoff score is the 90th percentile. Draw an approximate picture like the one below:

	0.07	0.08	0.09
1.0	0.8577	0.8599	0.8621
1.1	0.8790	0.8810	0.8830
1.2	0.8980	0.8997	0.9015
1.3	0.9147	0.9162	0.9177
1.4	0.9292	0.9306	0.9319

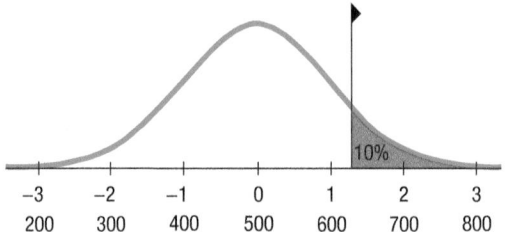

	−3	−2	−1	0	1	2	3
	200	300	400	500	600	700	800

From our picture we can see that the z-value is between 1 and 1.5 (if we've judged 10% of the area correctly), and so the cutoff score is between 600 and 650 or so. Using technology, you may be able to select the 10% area and find the z-value directly. Using a table, such as Table Z, locate 0.90 (or as close to it as you can; here 0.8997 is closer than 0.9015) in the *interior* of the table and find the corresponding z-score (see table above). Here the 1.2 is in the left margin, and the 0.08 is in the margin above the entry. Putting them together gives 1.28. Now, convert the z-score back to the original units. From Table Z, the cut point is $z = 1.28$. A z-score of 1.28 is 1.28 standard deviations above the mean. Since the standard deviation is 100, that's 128 GMAT points. The cutoff is 128 points above the mean of 500, or 628. Because the program wants GMAT scores in the top 10%, the cutoff is 628. (Actually, since GMAT scores are reported only in multiples of 10, you'd have to score at least a 630.)

---

[8]We'll often use those more precise values in our examples. If you're finding the values from the table, you may not get *exactly* the same number to all decimal places as your classmate who's using a computer package.

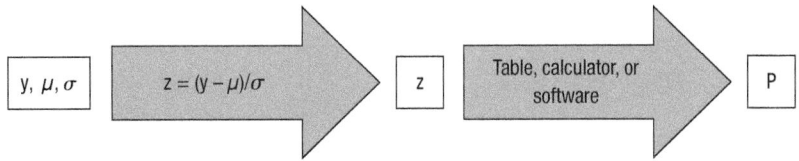

Figure 9.13   Calculating the probability, P, from y, μ, and σ.

If we know y, μ, and σ, we can calculate P, as shown in Figure 9.13. We illustrate this in Question 1 in Guided Example: "Cereal Company," which follows.

We can also work the other way. If we know P, y, and σ, then we can calculate μ, as in Figure 9.14. This corresponds to Question 2 in the Guided Example.

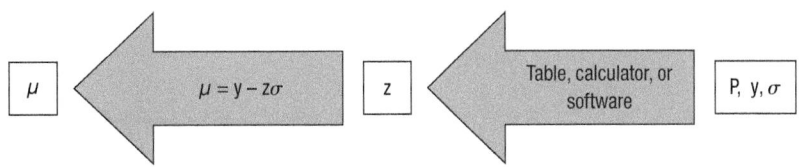

Figure 9.14   Calculating the mean, μ, from P, y, and σ.

Another option, illustrated in Question 3 in the Guided Example, is to calculate σ from P, y, and μ, as shown in Figure 9.15.

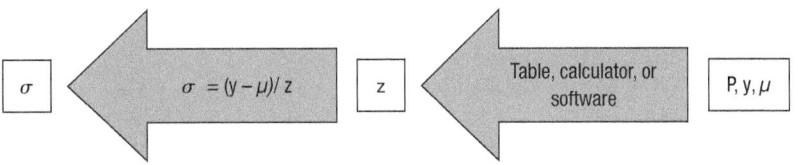

Figure 9.15   Calculating the standard deviation, σ, from P, y, and μ.

GUIDED EXAMPLE   Cereal Company

David Buffington/Blend Images/Getty Images

A cereal manufacturer has a machine that fills the boxes. Boxes are labelled "16 oz.," so the company wants to have that much cereal in each box. But since no packaging process is perfect, there will be minor variations. If the machine is set at exactly 16 oz. and the Normal model applies (or at least the distribution is roughly symmetric), then about half of the boxes will be underweight, making consumers unhappy and exposing the company to bad publicity and possible lawsuits. To prevent underweight boxes, the manufacturer has to set the mean a little higher than 16.0 oz. Based on its experience with the packaging machine, the company believes that the amount of cereal in the boxes fits a Normal model with a standard deviation of 0.2 oz. The manufacturer decides to set the machine to put an average of 16.3 oz. in each box. Let's use that model to answer a series of questions about these cereal boxes.

Question 1:   What fraction of the boxes will be underweight?

(Continued)

PLAN	**Setup** State the variable and the objective.	The variable is weight of cereal in a box. We want to determine what fraction of the boxes risk being underweight.
	Model Check to see if a Normal model is appropriate. Specify which Normal model to use.	We have no data, so we can't make a histogram. But we are told that the company believes the distribution of weights from the machine is Normal. We use a model with mean = 16.3 and SD = 0.2.
DO	**Mechanics** Make a graph of this Normal model. Locate the value you're interested in on the picture, label it, and shade the appropriate region.	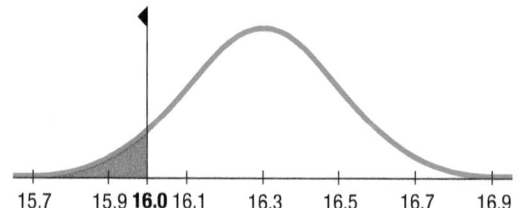
		15.7 15.9 **16.0** 16.1 16.3 16.5 16.7 16.9
	Estimate from the picture the percentage of boxes that are underweight. (This will be useful later to check that your answer makes sense.) Convert your cutoff value into a z-score. Look up the area in the Normal table, or use your calculator or software.	(It looks like a low percentage—maybe less than 10%.) We want to know what fraction of the boxes will weigh less than 16 oz. $$z = \frac{y - \mu}{\sigma} = \frac{16 - 16.3}{0.2} = -1.50$$ Area $(y < 16) =$ Area $(z < -1.50) = 0.0668.$
REPORT	**Conclusion** State your conclusion in the context of the problem.	We estimate that approximately 6.7% of the boxes will contain less than 16 oz. of cereal.

Question 2: The company's lawyers say that 6.7% is too high. They insist that no more than 4% of the boxes can be underweight. So the company needs to set the machine to put a little more cereal in each box. What mean setting does it need?

PLAN	**Setup** State the variable and the objective.	The variable is weight of cereal in a box. We want to determine a setting for the machine.
	Model Check to see if a Normal model is appropriate. Specify which Normal model to use. This time you are not given a value for the mean. We found out earlier that setting the machine to $\mu = 16.3$ oz. made 6.7% of the boxes too light. We'll need to raise the mean a bit to reduce this fraction.	We have no data, so we can't make a histogram. But we are told that a Normal model applies. We don't know μ, the mean amount of cereal. The standard deviation for this machine is 0.2 oz. We're told that no more than 4% of the boxes can be below 16 oz.

DO	**Mechanics** Make a graph of this Normal model. Centre it at μ (since you don't know the mean) and shade the region below 16 oz. Using the Normal table, a calculator, or software, find the z-score that cuts off the lowest 4%. Use this information to find μ. It's located 1.75 standard deviations to the right of 16.	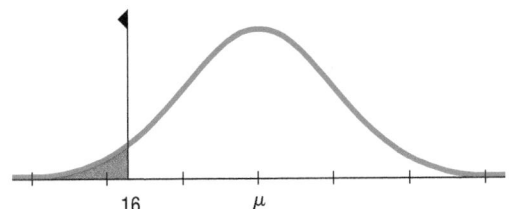 The z-score that has 0.04 area to the left of it is $z = -1.75$. Since 16 must be 1.75 standard deviations below the mean, we need to set the mean at $16 + 1.75 \times 0.2 = 16.35$.
REPORT	**Conclusion** State your conclusion in the context of the problem.	The company must set the machine to average 16.35 oz. of cereal per box.

Question 3: The company president vetoes that plan, saying the company should give away less free cereal, not more. His goal is to set the machine no higher than 16.2 oz. and still have only 4% underweight boxes. The only way to accomplish this is to reduce the standard deviation. What standard deviation must the company achieve, and what does that mean about the machine?

PLAN	**Setup** State the variable and the objective. **Model** Check that a Normal model is appropriate. Specify which Normal model to use. This time you don't know σ. We know the new standard deviation must be less than 0.2 oz.	The variable is weight of cereal in a box. We want to determine the necessary standard deviation to have only 4% of boxes underweight. The company believes that the weights are described by a Normal model. Now we know that the mean is 16.2, but we don't know the standard deviation.
DO	**Mechanics** Make a graph of this Normal model. Centre it at 16.2, and shade the area you're interested in. We want 4% of the area to be to the left of 16 oz. Find the z-score that cuts off the lowest 4%. Solve for σ. (Note that we need 16 to be 1.75 σ s below 16.2, so 1.75σ must be 0.2 oz. You could just start with that equation.)	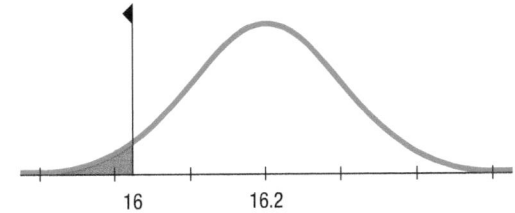 We already know that the z-score with 4% below it is $$z = -1.75.$$ $$z = \frac{y - \mu}{\sigma}$$ $$-1.75 = \frac{16 - 16.2}{\sigma}$$ $$1.75\sigma = 0.2$$ $$\sigma = 0.114$$

REPORT	Conclusion State your conclusion in the context of the problem.	The company must set the machine to box cereal with a standard deviation of only 0.114 oz. This means the machine must be more consistent (by nearly a factor of two) in filling the boxes.
	As we expected, the standard deviation is lower than before—actually, quite a bit lower.	

JUST CHECKING

6 As a group, the Dutch are among the tallest people in the world. The average Dutch man is 184 centimetres tall—just over 6 feet (and the average Dutch woman is 170.8 centimetres tall—just over 5 feet 7 inches). If a Normal model is appropriate and the standard deviation for men is about 8 centimetres, what percentage of all Dutch men will be over 2 metres tall?

7 Suppose it takes you 20 minutes, on average, to drive to work, with a standard deviation of 2 minutes. Suppose a Normal model is appropriate for the distributions of driving times.

a) How often will you arrive at work in less than 22 minutes?

b) How often will it take you more than 24 minutes?

c) Do you think the distribution of your driving times is unimodal and symmetric?

d) What does this say about the accuracy of your prediction? Explain.

Answers are found in Appendix A.

Normal Probability Plots

A specialized graphical display can help you decide whether the Normal model is appropriate: the *Normal probability plot*. If the distribution of the data is roughly Normal, the plot is roughly a diagonal straight line. Deviations from a straight line indicate that the distribution is not Normal. This plot is usually able to show deviations from Normality more clearly than the corresponding histogram, but it's usually easier to understand *how* a distribution fails to be Normal by looking at its histogram. It is therefore important to use both Normal probability plots and histograms in assessing whether your data are Normally distributed. Normal probability plots are difficult to make by hand, but are provided by most statistics software.

Some data on a car's fuel efficiency provide an example of data that are nearly Normal (Figure 9.16). The overall pattern of the Normal probability

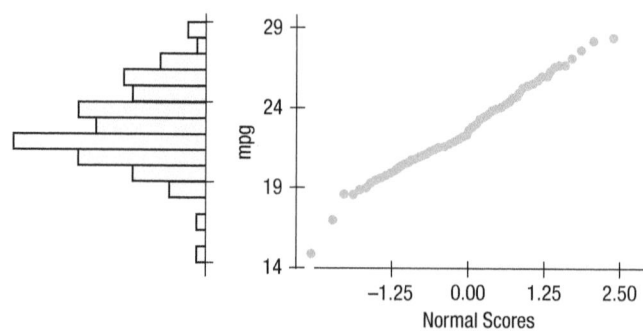

Figure 9.16 Histogram and Normal probability plot for gas mileage (mpg) recorded for a Nissan Maxima. The vertical axes are the same, so each dot on the probability plot would fall into the bar on the histogram immediately to its left.

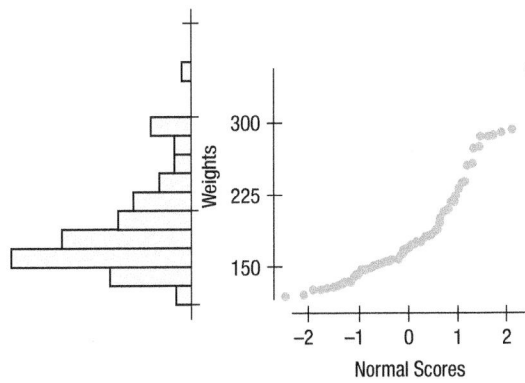

Figure 9.17 Histogram and Normal probability plot for men's weights. Note how a skewed distribution corresponds to a bent probability plot.

plot is straight. The two trailing low values correspond to the values in the histogram that trail off the low end. They're not quite in line with the rest of the data set. The Normal probability plot shows us that they're a bit lower than we'd expect of the lowest two values in a Normal distribution. In this way the Normal probability plot can be used to identify which points are outliers (e.g., hybrid cars), as well as showing us that the remaining points follow a Normal distribution.

By contrast, the Normal probability plot of a sample of men's weights in Figure 9.17 from a study of lifestyle and health is far from straight. The weights are skewed to the high end, and the plot is curved. We'd conclude from these pictures that approximations using the Normal model for these data would not be very accurate.

FOR EXAMPLE   Using a normal probability plot

The Cyclically Adjusted Price/Earnings ratio (CAPE10) smooths out short-term fluctuations in the price/earnings ratio of companies traded on the stock market and is used by some investors as an indicator of when to buy and sell. A normal probability plot of the CAPE10 for the New York Stock Exchange from 1881 to 2010 looks like this:

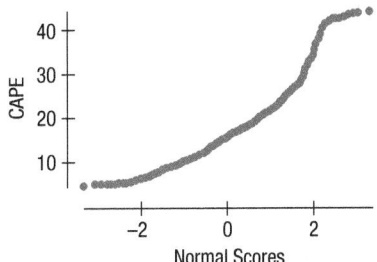

QUESTION   What does this plot say about the distribution of the CAPE10 scores?

ANSWER   The bent shape of the probability plot indicates a deviation from Normality. The upward bend is because the distribution is skewed to the high end. The "kink" in that bend suggests a collection of values that are clumped close to each other and don't continue that skewness consistently. We should not use a Normal model for these data.

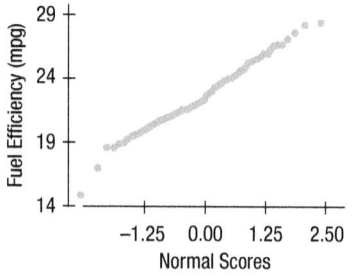

Adding and Subtracting Normally Distributed Variables

Normal models show up so often because they have some special properties. An important one is that the sum or difference of independent Normal random variables is also Normal. Their expected values add and their variances also add. Note that we're making two assumptions here:

- **Normal Model Assumption:** Each random variable must follow a Normal distribution.
- **Independence Assumption:** Each random variable must be independent of the other(s).

A company manufactures small stereo systems. At the end of the production line, the stereos are packaged and prepared for shipping. Stage 1 of this process is called "packing." Workers must collect all the system components (a main unit, two speakers, a power cord, an antenna, and some wires), put each in plastic bags, and then place everything inside a protective form. The packed form then moves on to Stage 2, called "boxing," in which workers place the form and a packet of instructions in a cardboard box and then close, seal, and label the box for shipping.

Because the times required for packing and boxing can take on any value, they must be modelled by a continuous random variable. In particular, the company says that times required for the packing stage are unimodal and symmetric and can be described by a Normal model with a mean of 9 minutes and standard deviation of 1.5 minutes. (See Figure 9.18.) The times for the boxing stage can also be modelled as Normal, with a mean of 6 minutes and standard deviation of 1 minute.

The company is interested in the total time that it takes to get a system through both packing and boxing, so it wants to model the sum of the two random variables. Fortunately, the special property that adding independent Normals yields another Normal model allows us to apply our knowledge of Normal probabilities to questions about the sum or difference of independent random variables. To use this property of Normals, we'll need to check the Independence Assumption as well as the Normal Model Assumption for each variable.

[9]Sometimes the Normal probability plot switches the two axes, putting the data on the x-axis and the z-scores on the y-axis.

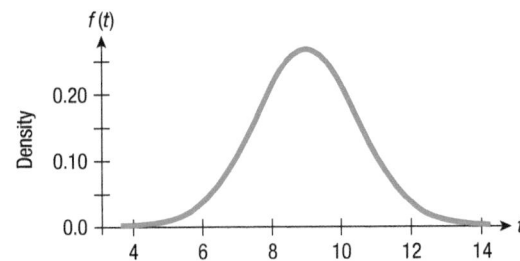

Figure 9.18 The Normal model for the packing stage with a mean of 9 minutes and a standard deviation of 1.5 minutes.

GUIDED EXAMPLE   Packaging Stereos

Consider the company we just discussed that manufactures and ships small stereo systems.

If the time required to pack the stereos can be described by a Normal model, with a mean of 9 minutes and standard deviation of 1.5 minutes, and the times for the boxing stage can also be modelled as Normal, with a mean of 6 minutes and standard deviation of 1 minute, what is the probability that packing an order of two systems takes over 20 minutes? What percentage of the stereo systems takes longer to pack than to box?

Question 1: What is the probability that packing an order of two systems takes over 20 minutes?

PLAN	Setup State the problem.	We want to estimate the probability that packing an order of two systems takes more than 20 minutes.
	Variables Define your random variables.	Let P_1 = Time for packing the first system $\quad P_2$ = Time for packing the second system $\quad T$ = Total time to pack two systems
	Write an appropriate equation for the variables you need.	$T = P_1 + P_2$
	Think about the model assumptions.	✓ **Normal Model Assumption.** We're told that packing times are well modelled by a Normal model, and we know that the sum of two Normal random variables is also Normal.
		✓ **Independence Assumption.** There is no reason to think that the packing time for one system would affect the packing time for the next, so we can reasonably assume that the two are independent.
DO	Mechanics Find the expected value. (Expected values always add.)	$$\begin{aligned} E(T) &= E(P_1 + P_2) \\ &= E(P_1) + E(P_2) \\ &= 9 + 9 = 18 \; minutes \end{aligned}$$
	Find the variance. For sums of independent random variables, variances add. (In general, we don't need the variables to be Normal for this to be true—just independent.)	Since the times are independent, $$\begin{aligned} Var(T) &= Var(P_1 + P_2) \\ &= Var(P_1) + Var(P_2) \\ &= 1.5^2 + 1.5^2 \end{aligned}$$

(Continued)

Find the standard deviation.

Now we use the fact that both random variables follow Normal models to say that their sum is also Normal.

Sketch a picture of the Normal model for the total time, shading the region representing over 20 minutes.

Find the z-score for 20 minutes.

Use technology or a table to find the probability.

$$Var(T) = 4.50$$
$$SD(T) = \sqrt{4.50} \approx 2.12 \text{ minutes.}$$

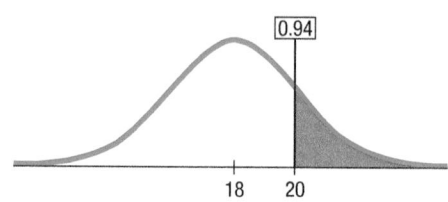

$$z = \frac{20 - 18}{2.12} = 0.94$$

$$P(T > 20) = P(z > 0.94) = 0.1736$$

REPORT   **Conclusion**   Interpret your result in context.

MEMO

Re: Stereo Systems Packing

Using past history to build a model, we find slightly more than a 17% chance that it will take more than 20 minutes to pack an order of two stereo systems.

Question 2:   What percentage of stereo systems takes longer to pack than to box?

PLAN   **Setup**   State the question.

Variables   Define your random variables.

Write an appropriate equation.

What are we trying to find? Notice that we can tell which of two quantities is greater by subtracting and asking whether the difference is positive or negative.

Don't forget to think about the assumptions.

We want to estimate the percentage of the stereo systems that takes longer to pack than to box.

Let P = Time for packing a system

B = Time for boxing a system

D = Difference in times to pack and box a system

$D = P - B$

A system that takes longer to pack than to box will have $P > B$, so D will be positive. We want to find $P(D > 0)$.

✓ **Normal Model Assumption.** We are told that both random variables are well modelled by Normal models, and we know that the difference of two Normal random variables is also Normal.

✓ **Independence Assumption.** There is no reason to think that the packing time for a system will affect its boxing time, so we can reasonably assume that the two are independent.

DO   **Mechanics**   Find the expected value.

For the difference of independent random variables, the variance is the sum of the individual variances.

$$E(D) = E(P - B)$$
$$= E(P) - E(B)$$
$$= 9 - 6 = 3 \text{ minutes}$$

Since the times are independent,

Find the standard deviation.	$Var(D) = Var(P - B)$
	$= Var(P) + Var(B)$
	$= 1.5^2 + 1^2$
State what model you will use.	$Var(D) = 3.25$
	$SD(D) = \sqrt{3.25} \approx 1.80 \ minutes.$

Sketch a picture of the Normal model for the difference in times and shade the region representing a difference greater than zero.

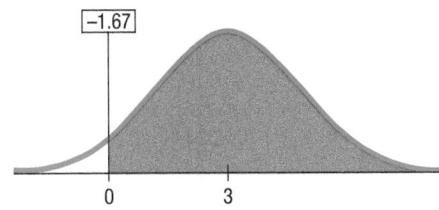

Find the z-score. Then use a table or technology to find the probability.

$$z = \frac{0 - 3}{1.80} = -1.67$$

$$P(D > 0) = P(z > -1.67) = 0.9525$$

REPORT   **Conclusion** Interpret your result in context.

MEMO

Re: Stereo Systems Packing

In our second analysis, we found that just over 95% of all the stereo systems will require more time for packing than for boxing.

LO❸, ❹ **9.11**   # The Normal Approximation to the Binomial

Even though the Normal is a continuous model, it's often used as an approximation for discrete events when the number of possible events is large. In particular, it's a good approximation to Binomially distributed variables, as you can see from the similarity in the bell-shapes of the two distributions in Figures 9.4 and 9.8.

Suppose that Canadian Blood Services anticipates the need for at least 1850 units of O-negative blood this year. It estimates that it will collect blood from 32,000 donors. How likely is Canadian Blood Services to meet its need? We've just learned how to calculate such probabilities. We could use the Binomial model with $n = 32,000$ and $p = 0.06$. The probability of getting *exactly* 1850 units of O-negative blood from 32,000 donors is $\binom{32,000}{1850} \times 0.06^{1850} \times 0.94^{30,150}$. No calculator on Earth can calculate that first term (it has more than 100,000 digits). And that's just the beginning. The problem said *at least* 1850, so we'd have to do it again for 1851, for 1852, and all the way up to 32,000. (No thanks.)

When we're dealing with a large number of trials like this, making direct calculations of the probabilities becomes tedious (or outright impossible). But the Normal model can come to the rescue.

The Binomial model has mean $np = 1920$ and standard deviation $\sqrt{npq} \approx 42.48$. We could try approximating its distribution with a Normal model, using the same mean and standard deviation. Remarkably enough, that turns out to be a very good approximation. Using that mean and standard deviation, we can find the probability:

$$P(X \geq 1850) = P\left(z \geq \frac{1850 - 0.5 - 1920}{42.48}\right) \approx P(z \geq -1.6596) \approx 0.952$$

Notice that, whenever we're calculating the probability that X is greater than or equal to a certain value, we subtract 0.5 in the calculation of z. When we're dealing with X less than or equal to a given value, we add 0.5. (See "The Continuity Correction" box.)

The Continuity Correction

When we use a continuous model to model a set of discrete events, we may need to make an adjustment called the *continuity correction*. We approximated the Binomial distribution (50, 0.2) with a Normal model. But what does the Normal model say about the probability that $X = 10$? Every specific value in the Normal probability model has probability 0. That's not the answer we want.

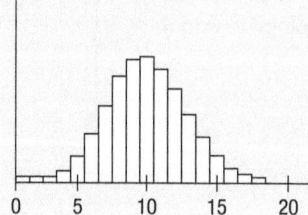

Because X is really discrete, it takes on the exact values 0, 1, 2, . . . , 50, each with positive probability. The histogram holds the secret to the correction. Look at the bin corresponding to $X = 10$ in the histogram. It goes from 9.5 to 10.5. What we really want is to find the area under the normal curve *between* 9.5 and 10.5. So when we use the Normal model to approximate discrete events, we go halfway to the next value on the left and/or the right. We approximate $P(X = 10)$ by finding $P(9.5 \leq X \leq 10.5)$. For a binomial with $n = 50$ and $p = 0.2$, $\mu = 10$ and $\sigma = 2.83$.

So $P(X = 10) \approx P\left(\dfrac{9.5 - 10}{2.83} \leq z \leq \dfrac{10.5 - 10}{2.83}\right)$

$= P(-0.177 \leq z \leq 0.177)$

$= 0.1405.$

By comparison, the exact Binomial probability is 0.1398.

We also need the continuity correction to use the Normal distribution as an approximation when dealing with ranges of values of X. For instance,

$$P(X \leq 9) \approx P\left(z \leq \dfrac{9.5 - 10}{2.83}\right)$$

$$= P(z \leq -0.177)$$

$$= 0.430.$$

$$P(X \geq 9) \approx \left(z \geq \dfrac{8.5 - 10}{2.83}\right)$$

$$= P(z \geq -0.530) = 0.702.$$

There's about a 95% chance that this Canadian Blood Services chapter will have enough O-negative blood.

Can we *always* use a Normal model to make estimates of binomial probabilities? No. It depends on the sample size. Suppose we're searching for a prize in cereal boxes, where the probability of finding a prize is 20%. If we buy five boxes, the actual binomial probabilities that we get zero, one, two, three, four, or five prizes are 33%, 41%, 20%, 5%, 1%, and 0.03%, respectively, using the formula in section 9.6. The histogram on the upper left shows that this probability model is skewed. That makes it clear that we shouldn't try to estimate these probabilities by using a Normal model.

If we open 50 boxes of this cereal and count the number of prizes we find, we get the second histogram on the lower left. It's centred at $np = 50(0.2) = 10$ prizes, as expected, and it appears to be fairly symmetric around that centre.

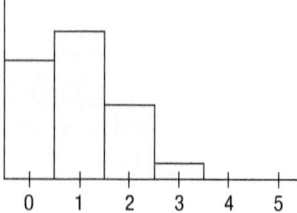

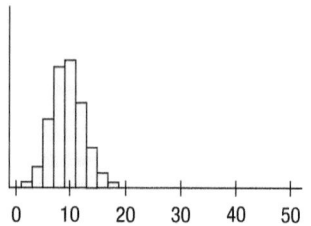

Let's have a closer look. The third histogram (in the box, "The Continuity Correction) shows the same distribution, but this time magnified somewhat and centred at the expected value of 10 prizes. It looks close to Normal for sure. With this larger sample size, it appears that a Normal model might be a useful approximation.

A Normal model is a close enough approximation to the Binomial only for a large enough number of trials. And what we mean by "large enough" depends on the probability of success. We'd need a larger sample if the probability of success were very low (or very high). It turns out that a Normal model works pretty well if we expect to see at least 10 successes and 10 failures. That is, we check the Success/Failure Condition.

Success/Failure Condition: A Binomial model is approximately Normal if we expect at least 10 successes and 10 failures:

$$np \geq 10 \text{ and } nq \geq 10$$

Why 10? Well, actually it's 9, as revealed in the Optional Math Box.

Optional Math Box

It's easy to see where the magic number 10 comes from. You just need to remember how Normal models work. The problem is that a Normal model extends infinitely in both directions. But a Binomial model must have between 0 and n successes, so if we use a Normal to approximate a Binomial, we have to cut off its tails. That's not very important if the centre of the Normal model is so far from 0 and n that the lost tails have only a negligible area. More than three standard deviations should do it because a Normal model has little probability past that.

So the mean needs to be at least three standard deviations from 0 and at least three standard deviations from n. Let's look at the zero end.

We require:	$\mu - 3\sigma > 0$
Or, in other words:	$\mu > 3\sigma$
For a Binomial that's:	$np > 3\sqrt{npq}$
Squaring yields:	$n^2p^2 > 9npq$
Now simplify:	$np > 9q$
Since:	$q \leq 1$
We require:	$np > 9$

For simplicity, we usually demand that np (and nq for the other tail) be at least 10 to use the Normal approximation that gives the Success/Failure Condition.[10]

FOR EXAMPLE   Normal approximation to the Binomial for quality control

Some LCD screens have stuck or "dead" pixels that have defective transistors and are permanently unlit. If a screen has too many dead pixels, it must be rejected. A manufacturer knows that when the production line is working correctly, the probability of rejecting a screen is 0.07.

(Continued)

---

[10]Looking at the final step, we see that we need $np > 9$ in the worst case, when q (or p) is near 1, making the Binomial model quite skewed. When q and p are near 0.5—for example, between 0.4 and 0.6—the Binomial model is nearly symmetric, and $np > 5$ ought to be safe enough. Although we'll always check for 10 expected successes and failures, keep in mind that for values of p near 0.5, we can be somewhat more forgiving.

QUESTIONS

1. How many screens does the manufacturer expect to reject in a day's production run of 500 screens? What is the standard deviation?

2. If it rejects 40 screens today, is that a large enough number to raise concern that something may have gone wrong with the production line?

3. In the past week of five days of production, the manufacturer has rejected 200. Should that raise concern?

ANSWERS

1. $\mu = 0.07 \times 500 = 35$ is the expected number of rejects

   $\sigma = \sqrt{npq} = \sqrt{500 \times 0.07 \times 0.93} = 5.7$

2. $np = 35; nq = 465$ Since these are both ≥ 10, we can use the Normal approximation to the Binomial $P(X \geq 40) = P\left(z \geq \dfrac{40 - 0.5 - 35}{5.7}\right)$

   $= P(z \geq 0.789) \approx 0.215$, not an extraordinarily large number of rejects.

3. $np = 175; nq = 2325$. Since these are both ≥ 10, we can use the Normal approximation:

   $\mu = 0.07 \times 2500 = 175$

   $\sigma = \sqrt{2500 \times 0.07 \times 0.93} = 12.757$

   $P(X \leq 200) = P\left(z \leq \dfrac{200 - 0.5 - 175}{12.757}\right) = P(z \leq 1.92) \approx 0.0274.$

Since this is a very small probability, it raises concern that something is wrong with the production line.

LO ➍ 9.12   The Exponential Distribution

We saw earlier that the Poisson model is a good model for the arrival, or occurrence, of events. We found, for example, the probability that x visits to our website will occur within the next minute. The **Exponential distribution** with parameter λ can be used to model the time *between* those events and is shown in Figure 9.19. Its density function has the form

$$f(x) = \lambda e^{-\lambda x} \quad \text{for } x \geq 0 \text{ and } \lambda > 0.$$

The use of the parameter λ again is not coincidental. It highlights the relationship between the Exponential and the Poisson.

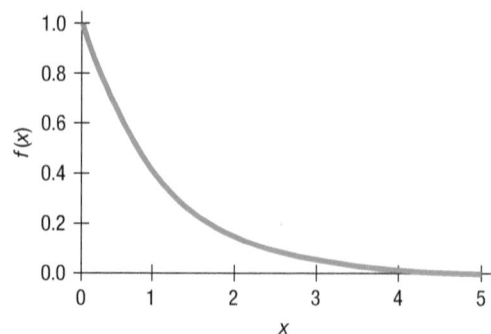

Figure 9.19   The Exponential density function (with $\lambda = 1$).

You can think of an Exponential situation as a timeline with events occurring at random times—for example, customers arriving at a website—as we did for the Poisson situation in Figure 9.7. We know the *average* number of events per unit of time—for example, four website hits per minute. The Exponential distribution describes the *time interval between events*. It gives us *the probability that we'll have to wait a certain time before the next event*—say, half a minute until the next hit on the website. Figure 9.20 shows the relationship between Poisson and Exponential.

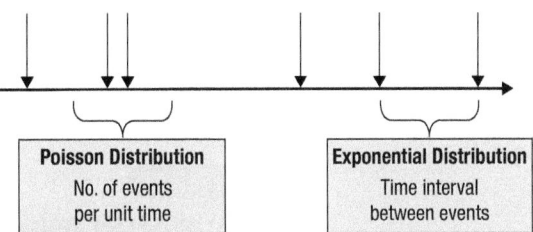

Figure 9.20   The relationship between Poisson and Exponential.

If a discrete random variable can be modelled by a Poisson model with rate λ, then the times between events can be modelled by an Exponential model with the same parameter λ. The mean of the exponential is $1/\lambda$. The inverse relationship between the two means makes intuitive sense. If λ increases and we expect *more* hits per minute, then the expected time between hits should go down. The standard deviation of an exponential random variable is $1/\lambda$.

Like any continuous random variable, probabilities of an exponential random variable can be found only through the density function. Fortunately, the area under the exponential density between any two values, s and t $(s \leq t)$, has a particularly easy form:

$$P(s \leq X \leq t) = e^{-\lambda s} - e^{-\lambda t}$$

In particular, by setting s to be 0, we can find the probability that the waiting time will be less than t from

$$P(X \leq t) = P(0 \leq X \leq t) = e^{-\lambda 0} - e^{-\lambda t} = 1 - e^{-\lambda t}.$$

The function $P(X \leq t) = F(t)$ is called the **cumulative distribution function (cdf)** of the random variable X. If arrivals of hits to our website can be well modelled by a Poisson with $\lambda = 4/\text{minute}$, then the probability that we'll have to wait less than 20 seconds (1/3 of a minute) is $F(1/3) = P(0 \leq X \leq 1/3) = 1 - e^{-4/3} = 0.736$. That seems about right. Arrivals are coming about every 15 seconds on average, so we shouldn't be surprised that nearly 75% of the time we won't have to wait more than 20 seconds for the next hit.

The following example takes the same situation of earthquakes in the Charlevoix region of Quebec that we used for our example of the Poisson distribution in Section 9.7. You should compare these examples carefully. In Section 9.7 we asked the question: "What is the probability of *one* large quake occurring during the next 10 years?" Now we ask the question: "What is the probability that *the next* large quake will occur during the next 10 years?" At first sight these two questions look alike. However, there is a difference between "one" and "the next." "One" means one, not two, not three, but one. But if "the next" quake occurs during the next 10 years, it could be followed by a second one also within those 10 years, or even three or more. "The next" therefore means one or more, whereas "one" means one. If we are asked about an exact number of quakes—e.g., one—we must use the Poisson distribution. If we are asked about "one or more" or "the next," then we can use the Exponential distribution or the Poisson distribution. To use the Poisson distribution, we calculate $1 - P(X = 0)$. The next example shows how to use the Exponential distribution.

FOR EXAMPLE   Earthquakes in Charlevoix, Quebec, continued

The Charlevoix Seismic Zone (CSZ) is the most seismically active region of eastern Canada. Earthquakes of magnitude 6.0 and over occur once every 52.4 years on average. The last one occurred in 1925. Let us assume that earthquakes occur independently of each other and so the time interval between them follows an Exponential distribution.

QUESTIONS

1. What was the probability that the next large quake (magnitude 6.0 and over) in CSZ would occur during the next 10 years for someone living in 1926?

2. What is the probability for someone living today?

3. Explain how your answers to Questions 1 and 2 compare with each other.

ANSWERS

1. The average time between large quakes is 52.4 years.
   The parameter of the Exponential distribution is therefore $1/52.4 = 0.01908$
   X = time to wait until next large quake
   $P(X < 10) = 1 - \exp(-0.01908 \times 10) = 0.174$

2. The answer is the same for the 10-year period starting today: 0.174.

3. The answers are the same because quakes occur independently of each other. The fact that today it's been a long time since the last large quake makes no difference to the probability of a quake occurring.

JUST CHECKING

Toronto's Union train station is busy with trains arriving and departing all day. Passengers arrive by subway, by bus, by foot, and by taxi.

8 Discuss whether the arrivals of passengers by these methods follows a Poisson distribution.

9 For passengers that do arrive according to the Poisson distribution, what is it about their arrival pattern that is (i) Poisson; (ii) Exponential?

10 For passengers that do arrive according to the Poisson distribution, suppose we want to calculate the probability of more than 10 arriving per minute. Which probability distribution should we use? Could we have used another distribution to answer the same question?

11 For passengers that do arrive according to the Poisson distribution, suppose we want to calculate the probability that the time between arrivals is less than 6 seconds. Which probability distribution should we use? Could we have used another distribution to answer the same question?

Answers are found in Appendix A.

WHAT CAN GO WRONG?

- **Variances of independent random variables add.** Standard deviations do not. This is true whether we're adding or subtracting the random variables, but the variables must be independent of each other. This is different from the situation for expected values. Expected values of random variables add or subtract, depending on whether we're adding or subtracting the random variables. The variables can be dependent or independent of each other.

- **Probability models are still just models.** Models can be useful, but they are not reality. Think about the assumptions behind your models.

- **Don't assume that everything's Normal.** Just because a random variable is continuous or you happen to know a mean and standard deviation doesn't mean that a Normal model will be useful. You need to check the Normal probability plot to see whether the Normal model assumption is justified.

- **Make sure you have Bernoulli trials.** If you're using the Binomial or Geometric distributions, be sure to check the requirements first: two possible outcomes per trial ("success" and "failure"), a constant probability of success, and independence. Remember that the 10% Condition provides a reasonable substitute for independence.

- **Don't confuse Geometric and Binomial models.** Both involve Bernoulli trials, but the issues are different. If you're repeating trials until your first success, that's a Geometric probability. You don't know in advance how many trials you'll need—theoretically, it could take forever. If you're counting the number of successes in a specified number of trials, that's a Binomial probability.

- **Don't use the Normal approximation with small *n*.** To use a Normal approximation in place of a Binomial model, there must be at least 10 expected successes and 10 expected failures.

- **Don't confuse Poisson and Exponential distributions.** Both apply to events that occur at random over time, like the arrival of customers for service. The Poisson helps us calculate the probability of a *specific number* of arrivals within a specified time interval. The Exponential helps us calculate the probability of *at least one* arrival within a specified time interval.

ETHICS IN ACTION

While government services are available online, many Canadians, especially those who are older, prefer to deal with government agencies in person. For this reason, Service Canada has local offices distributed across the country. Akbar Kabir is the office manager for the Service Canada office in Kelowna, B.C. Since the government expects most people to use the Service Canada website, the office staff is small.

Yet, because of the number of retirees in the area, Akbar's office is one of the busiest. Although there have been no formal complaints, Akbar expects that customer wait times have increased. He decides to keep track of customer wait times for a one-month period in the hopes of making a case for hiring additional staff. He finds that the average wait time is 5 minutes with a standard deviation of 6 minutes. He reasons that 50% of customers who visit his office wait longer than 5 minutes for service. The target wait time is 10 minutes or less. Applying the Normal probability model, Akbar finds that more than 20% of customers will have to wait longer than 10 minutes! He has uncovered what he suspected. His next step is to request additional staff based on his findings.

Ethical Issue *Waiting times are generally skewed and therefore not usually modelled using the Normal distribution. Akbar should have checked the data to see if a Normal model was appropriate. Using the Normal for data that are highly skewed to the right will inflate the probability that a customer will have to wait longer than 10 minutes (related to Item A, ASA Ethical Guidelines; see Appendix C, the American Statistical Association's Ethical Guidelines for Statistical Practice, also available online at www.amstat.org/about/ethicalguidelines.cfm).*

Ethical Solution *Check the reasonableness of applying the Normal probability model.*

WHAT HAVE WE LEARNED?

Learning Objectives

❶ We've learned to work with random variables. We can use the probability model for a discrete random variable to find its expected value and its standard deviation.

❷ We've learned that the mean of the sum or difference of two random variables, discrete or continuous, is just the sum or difference of their means. And we've learned the Pythagorean Theorem of Statistics: *For independent random variables*, the variance of their sum or difference is always the *sum* of their variances. When we're adding dependent random variables, their means add fine, but for the variances we use a formula that takes into account the correlation between the variables.

❸ Depending on the random variable of interest, we can use one of four models to estimate probabilities for discrete random variables:

- A Geometric model, when we're interested in the number of Bernoulli trials until the next success
- A Binomial model, when we're interested in the number of successes in a certain number of Bernoulli trials
- A Normal model, which can approximate a Binomial model when we expect at least 10 successes and at least 10 failures
- The Poisson distribution, which is used for random independent arrivals, such as the number of customers arriving for service

❹ We've also learned that Normal models are once again special: Sums or differences of Normally distributed random variables also follow Normal models.

We've seen how the Exponential distribution can be used to address some of the situations for which the Poisson distribution is also appropriate.

Terms

68-95-99.7 Rule

In a Normal distribution, 68% of values fall within one standard deviation of the mean, 95% fall within two standard deviations of the mean, and 99.7% fall within three standard deviations of the mean. It is also called the *Empirical Rule*.

Addition Rule for Expected Values of Random Variables

$E(X \pm Y) = E(X) \pm E(Y)$

Addition Rule for Variances of Random Variables

If X and Y are *independent* (Pythagorean Theorem of Statistics),
$Var(X \pm Y) = Var(X) + Var(Y).$

If X and Y are dependent,

$$Var(X + Y) = Var(X) + Var(Y) + 2 \times SD(X) \times SD(Y) \times r$$

$$Var(X - Y) = Var(X) + Var(Y) - 2 \times SD(X) \times SD(Y) \times r,$$

where r is the correlation coefficient.

In general,

$$Var(aX + bY) = a^2 \times Var(X) + b^2 \times Var(Y) + 2 \times a \times b \times SD(X) \times SD(Y) \times r.$$

$$SD(X \pm Y) = \sqrt{Var(X \pm Y)}.$$

Bernoulli trials

A sequence of trials is called Bernoulli if:

1. There are exactly two possible outcomes (usually denoted *success* and *failure*).
2. The probability of success is constant.
3. The trials are independent.

Binomial probability distribution

A Binomial model is appropriate for a random variable that counts the number of successes in a fixed number of Bernoulli trials.

Changing a random variable by a constant	$E(X \pm c) = E(X) \pm c$ $Var(X \pm c) = Var(X)$ $SD(X \pm c) = SD(X)$ $E(aX) = aE(X)$ $Var(aX) = a^2Var(X)$ $SD(aX) = |a|SD(X)$
Continuous random variable	A random variable that can take any numeric value within a range of values. The range may be infinite or bounded at either or both ends.
Cumulative distribution function (cdf)	For any random variable X, and any value x, the cumulative distribution function is $$F(x) = P(X \leq x).$$
Discrete random variable	A random variable that can take one of a finite number[11] of distinct outcomes.
Expected value	The expected value of a random variable is its theoretical long-run average value, the centre of its model. Denoted μ or $E(X)$, it's found (if the random variable is discrete) by summing the products of variable values and probabilities: $$\mu = EV = E(X) = \sum x \cdot P(x)$$
Exponential distribution	A model often used for waiting times between events, when the number of arrivals of those events are well modelled by a Poisson model.
Geometric probability distribution	A model appropriate for a random variable that counts the number of Bernoulli trials until the first success.
Normal distribution	The most famous continuous probability model, the Normal is used to model a wide variety of phenomena whose distributions are unimodal and symmetric. The Normal model is also used as an approximation to the Binomial model for large n, when np and $nq \geq 10$, and used as the model for sampling distributions of sums and means under a wide variety of conditions.
Normal percentile	A percentile corresponding to a z-score that gives the percentage of values in a standard Normal distribution found at that z-score or below.
Poisson distribution	A discrete model often used to model the number of arrivals of events, such as customers arriving in a queue or calls arriving at a call centre.
Probability density function (pdf)	A function $f(x)$ that represents the probability distribution of a random variable X. The probability that X is in an interval A is the area under the curve $f(x)$ over A.
Probability distribution	A function that associates a probability P with each value of a discrete random variable X, denoted $P(X = x)$, or with any interval of values of a continuous random variable.
Probability model	Alternative term for probability distribution.
Random variable	Assumes any of several different values as a result of some random event. Random variables are denoted by a capital letter, such as X.
Standard deviation of a (discrete) random variable	Describes the spread in the model and is the square root of the variance.
Standard Normal model or standard Normal distribution	A Normal distribution, with mean $\mu = 0$ and standard deviation $\sigma = 1$.

---

[11]Technically, there could be an infinite number of outcomes as long as they're *countable*. Essentially, that means we can imagine listing them all in order, like the counting numbers 1, 2, 3, 4, 5, ...

Uniform distribution	For a discrete Uniform model over a set of n values, each value has probability $1/n$. For a continuous uniform random variable over an interval $[a, b]$, the probability that X lies in any subinterval within $[a, b]$ is the same and is just equal to the length of the interval divided by the length of $[a, b]$, which is $b - a$.
Variance	The variance of a random variable is the expected value of the squared deviations from the mean. For discrete random variables, it can be calculated as $$\sigma^2 = Var(X) = \sum (x - \mu)^2 P(x).$$

Skills

Plan
- Be able to recognize random variables.
- Understand that random variables must be independent in order to determine the variability of their sum or difference by adding variances.

Do
- Be able to find the probability model for a discrete random variable.
- Know how to find the mean (expected value) and the variance of a random variable.
- Always use the proper notation for these population parameters: μ or $E(X)$ for the mean and σ, $SD(X)$, σ^2, or $Var(X)$ when discussing variability.
- Know how to determine the new mean and standard deviation after adding a constant, multiplying by a constant, or adding or subtracting two independent random variables.

Report
- Be able to interpret the meaning of the expected value and the standard deviation of a random variable in the proper context.

Air Canada and the Competition Bureau

Air Canada and United have for many years been members of the Star Alliance, selling seats on each other's flights while competing for passengers. In 2011 they proposed a closer collaboration involving exchanging information about sales and fares and coordinating schedules on 19 Canada–U.S. routes. The Canadian Competition Bureau blocked the deal on the grounds that it was uncompetitive. Air Canada objected to the Competition Bureau's decision, and the case went before the Competition Tribunal for a decision.

Since this was an unusual case, it was tough to predict the outcome; some lawyers put it at 50/50. Suppose that the following table represents the increase in Air Canada's profits under "good" or "bad" economic conditions, which have probabilities of 0.3 and 0.7, respectively:

		ECONOMIC CONDITIONS	
		Good	**Bad**
Tribunal Outcome	Win	+$840m	+$210m
	Lose	+$150m	−$500m

Air Canada needs to assess the expected benefit and riskiness of objecting to the Competition Tribunal decision compared to accepting that decision.

a. What is the expected increase in Air Canada profits?

b. What is the standard deviation of the increase in Air Canada profits?

c. How do your answers to (a) and (b) compare with simply accepting the Competition Tribunal's decision (i.e., the "lose" scenario in the table)?

d. Is it worth it for Air Canada to spend $32 million on lawyers' fees to fight the case?

Royal Bank of Canada

Don Denton/The Canadian Press

The Royal Bank of Canada (RBC) is the largest bank in Canada and employs about 79,000 full-time and part-time employees who serve 15 million customers in Canada, the United States, and 44 other countries. The performance of the five major segments of the bank in 2013 is summarized in the following table, derived from the RBC's 2013 annual report:

	Revenue	Expenses
Personal & Commercial Banking	13,223	7,237
Wealth Management	5,487	4,252
Insurance	3,928	3,333
Investor and Treasury Services	1,804	1,343
Capital Markets	6,580	4,032

Source: Derived from the RBC 2013 annual report, Note 29, page 174.

Suppose that, on reading RBC's annual report for 2013, you wish to project future revenues and expenses for the five segments listed in the table. You project that they'll remain constant, but, in view of uncertain economic conditions, you give upper and lower limits on your projection of plus or minus 12% for Personal & Commercial Banking, Wealth Management, and Insurance, and plus or minus 18% for Investor and Treasury Services and Capital Markets. The upper and lower limits on your projections represent the range within which you are 95% confident your projection will lie.

Assuming that your projections are Normally distributed, and that all the revenues and expenses for each segment are uncorrelated, calculate dollar values for your projections for total revenue and total expenses over all five segments. Express your projections of the total revenue and expenses in terms of a 95% confidence range, as above—that is, Projected total revenue = x plus or minus y%. Now do the same thing for net income = revenue − expenses for the total of the five segments. Explain why your percentages y% vary with what it is you're projecting. Which of your percentages y% is larger than the others? Why? What difference does it make if you assume that revenues for Canadian banking and insurance have a correlation of 0.38, and why?

Tim Hortons

Tim Hortons was founded in 1964 in Hamilton, Ontario, where it served coffee and doughnuts. As the chain has expanded throughout Canada, so have its product offerings, including the very popular Timbits, soups, cappuccinos, and breakfast sandwiches. In 2014, Tim Hortons was acquired by Burger King. Although good taste and friendly service are important at Tim Hortons, fast service is valued, too, and several servers are often employed to serve customers at the same time.

Mario Beauregard/The Canadian Press

(*Continued*)

Suppose you were the manager of a coffee shop with three servers, who each take an average of 1.8 minutes to serve a customer. You have, on average, a customer arriving every 0.8 minutes, and you're considering two options for ensuring fast service: (a) hiring a fourth server at an annual cost of $36,000 or (b) renting faster dispensing machines at an annual cost of $23,000, which would reduce the service time to 1.45 minutes, on average. You decide to base your decision on the number of customers who arrive during the time you can serve them. You don't want to have more than a 10% chance of more customers arriving than you can serve. For instance, with your current operation, you can serve three customers in 1.8 minutes, so you don't want the chance of more than three customers arriving in 1.8 minutes to be greater than 10%. What should you do—continue the current operation, hire a fourth server, or rent faster dispensing machines?

CAPE10

The CAPE10 index is based on the price/earnings (P/E) ratios of stocks. We can examine the P/E ratios without applying the smoothing techniques used to find the CAPE10. The file **CAPE10** holds the data, giving dates, CAPE10 values, and P/E values.

Examine the P/E value. Would you judge that a Normal model would be appropriate for those values from the 1880s through the 1980s? Explain (and show the plots you made).

Now consider the more recent P/E value in this context. Do you think the values have been extreme? Explain.

MyStatLab   Students! Save time, improve your grades with MyStatLab. Questions marked in ▦ can be found on MyStatLab. You can practise them as often as you want, and most feature step-by-step guided solutions to help you find the right answer. You'll find a personalized study plan available to you too!

Technology Help: Probability Distributions

EXCEL XLSTAT

To calculate a probability from a distribution,

- Select the cell where you want the probability to be calculated.
- Click the **Insert Function** symbol f_x to the left of the formula bar.
- Type a description of the probability distribution you want calculated. Sometimes Excel offers multiple options for a single probability distribution. Here are some of the most popular Excel functions for probability distributions:

Binomial:	BINOM.DIST
Poisson:	POISSON.DIST
Standard Normal:	NORM.S.DIST
Exponential:	EXPON.DIST

Each of these offers a **Cumulative** option. If you set this to **True**, the function will give the total probability to the left of the value you specify. For continuous distributions, that is usually what we want to calculate. For discrete distributions, we sometimes need the probability of the exact value we specify, in which case **Cumulative** should be set to **False**.

JMP

To make a "Normal Quantile Plot" in JMP,

- Make a histogram using **Distributions** from the **Analyze** menu.
- Click on the drop-down menu next to the variable name.
- Choose **Normal Quantile Plot** from the drop-down menu.
- JMP opens the plot next to the histogram.

Comments

JMP places the ordered data on the vertical axis and the Normal scores on the horizontal axis. The vertical axis aligns with the histogram's axis, a useful feature.

MINITAB

To calculate a probability distribution, e.g., Binomial or Poisson,

- Choose **Probability Distributions** from the **Calc** menu.
- Choose **Binomial** from the **Probability Distributions** submenu.
- To calculate the probability of getting *x* successes in *n* trials, choose **Probability**.
- To calculate the probability of getting *x* or fewer successes among *n* trials, choose **Cumulative Probability**.

- For Poisson, choose **Poisson** from the **Probability Distributions** submenu.

SPSS

To make a Normal "P-P plot" in SPSS,

- Choose **P-P** from the **Graphs** menu.
- Select the variable to be displayed in the source list.
- Click the arrow button to move the variable into the target list.
- Click the **OK** button.

Comments

SPSS places the ordered data on the horizontal axis and the Normal scores on the vertical axis. You may safely ignore the options in the P-P dialogue.

EXERCISES

SECTION 9.1

1. A company's employee database includes data on whether the employee has a dependent child in his or her health insurance.

a) Is this variable discrete or continuous?
b) What are the possible values it can take on? **LO ❶**

2. The database also, of course, includes each employee's compensation.

a) Is this variable discrete or continuous?
b) What are the possible values it can take on? **LO ❶**

3. Suppose that the probabilities of a customer purchasing zero, one, or two books at a bookstore are 0.2, 0.4, and 0.4, respectively. What is the expected number of books a customer will purchase? **LO ❶**

4. A day trader buys an option on a stock that will return $100 profit if the stock goes up today and lose $400 if it goes down. If the trader thinks there's a 75% chance that the stock will go up

a) What is her expected value of the option's profit?
b) What do you think of this option? **LO ❶**

SECTION 9.2

5. Find the standard deviation of the book purchases in Exercise 3. **LO ❶**

6. Find the standard deviation of the day trader's option value in Exercise 4. **LO ❶**

7. An orthodontist has three financing packages, and each has a different service charge. She estimates that 30% of patients use the first plan, which has a $10 finance charge; 50% use the second plan, which has a $20 finance charge; and 20% use the third plan, which has a $30 finance charge.

a) Find the expected value of the service charge.
b) Find the standard deviation of the service charge. **LO ❶**

8. A marketing agency has developed its vacation packages to promote a timeshare plan at a new resort. It estimates that 20% of potential customers will choose the Day Plan, which does not include overnight accommodations; 40% will choose the Overnight Plan, which includes one night at the resort; and 40% will choose the Weekend Plan, which includes two nights.

a) Find the expected value of the number of nights potential customers will need.
b) Find the standard deviation of the number of nights potential customers will need. **LO ❶**

SECTION 9.3

9. Given independent random variables, X and Y, with means and standard deviations as shown, find the mean and standard deviation of each of the variables in (a) to (d).

a) $3X$
b) $Y + 6$
c) $X + Y$
d) $X - Y$ **LO ❷**

	Mean	SD
X	10	2
Y	20	5

10. Given independent random variables, X and Y, with means and standard deviations as shown, find the mean and standard deviation of each of the variables in (a) to (d).

a) $X - 20$
b) $0.5Y$
c) $X + Y$
d) $X - Y$ **LO ❷**

	Mean	SD
X	80	12
Y	12	3

11. A broker has calculated the expected values of two different financial instruments X and Y. Suppose that $E(X) = \$100$, $E(Y) = \$90$, $SD(X) = \$12$, and $SD(Y) = \$8$. Find each of the following:

a) $E(X + 10)$ and $SD(X + 10)$
b) $E(5Y)$ and $SD(5Y)$
c) $E(X + Y)$ and $SD(X + Y)$
d) What assumption must you make in (c)? **LO ❷**

12. Canada's annual exports to India are $2.8 billion on average with a standard deviation of $0.35 billion. Canada's annual imports from India are $3.1 billion on average with a standard deviation of $0.25 billion. Calculate the mean and standard deviation of Canada's balance of trade with India (i.e., exports – imports). State your assumptions clearly. **LO ❷**

SECTION 9.4

13. At many airports, travellers entering a country are sent randomly to one of several stations where passports and visas are checked. If each of the six stations is equally likely, can the probabilities of which station a traveller will be sent to be modelled with a Uniform model? **LO ❸**

14. At the airport entry sites in Exercise 13, a computer is used to randomly decide whether a traveller's baggage should be opened for inspection. If the chance of being selected is 12%, can you model your chance of having your baggage opened with a Bernoulli model? Check each of the conditions specifically. **LO ❸**

SECTIONS 9.5 AND 9.6

15. The 2000 Census showed that 26% of all firms in the United States are owned by women. You're phoning local businesses, assuming that the national percentage is true in your area. You wonder how many calls you'll have to make before you find one owned by a woman. What probability model should you use? (Specify the parameters as well.) **LO ❸**

16. As in Exercise 15, you're phoning local businesses. You call three firms. What is the probability that all three are owned by women? **LO ❸**

SECTION 9.7

17. A manufacturer of clothing knows that the probability of a button flaw (broken, sewed on incorrectly, or missing) is 0.002. An inspector examines 50 shirts in an hour, each with six buttons. Using a Poisson probability model:

a) What is the probability that she finds no button flaws?
b) What is the probability that she finds at least one?
LO ❸

18. Replacing the buttons with snaps increases the probability of a flaw to 0.003, but the inspector can check 70 shirts an hour (still with six snaps each). Now what is the probability she finds no snap flaws? **LO ❸**

SECTIONS 9.8 AND 9.9

19. Is a continuous Uniform distribution appropriate for the following situations? If so, state which variable is uniformly distributed.

a) A manufacturer of cells for solar modules ordered some germanium, an essential element in one of the layers on the solar cell. The supplier said, "It will be delivered sometime in the next three weeks. I can't be more precise than that."

b) We have installed 500 solar panels at a solar farm. Any one of them is as likely to fail as any other. **LO ❹**

20. Is a continuous Uniform distribution appropriate for the following situations? If so, state which variable is uniformly distributed.

a) Subway trains depart every five minutes. You have just arrived on the platform to catch a train.

b) The last four digits of your new phone number will be assigned at random by the phone company. **LO ❹**

SECTION 9.10

21. An incoming MBA student took placement exams in Economics and Mathematics. In Economics she scored 82 and in Math 86. The overall results on the Economics exam had a mean of 72 and a standard deviation of 8, while the mean Math score was 68 with a standard deviation of 12. On which exam did she do better compared with the other students? **LO ❹**

22. The first Statistics exam had a mean of 65 and a standard deviation of 10 points; the second had a mean of 80 and a standard deviation of 5 points. Derrick scored an 80 on both tests. Julie scored a 70 on the first test and a 90 on the second. They both totalled 160 points on the two exams, but Julie claims that her total is better. Explain. **LO ❹**

23. Your company's Human Resources department administers a test of "executive aptitude." It reports test grades as z-scores, and you got a score of 2.20. What does this mean? **LO ❹**

24. After examining a child at his two-year checkup, the boy's pediatrician said that the z-score for his height relative to Canadian two-year-olds is −1.88. Write a sentence to explain to the parents what that means. **LO ❹**

25. Your company will admit to the executive training program only people who score in the top 3% on the executive aptitude test discussed in Exercise 23. Use the 68-95-99.7 Rule.

a) With your z-score of 2.20, did you make the cut?

b) What do you need to assume about test scores to find your answer in (a)? **LO ❹**

26. The pediatrician in Exercise 24 explains to the parents that the most extreme 5% of cases (2.5% above and 2.5% below the mean) often require special treatment or attention. Use the 68-95-99.7 Rule.

a) Does this child fall into that group?

b) What do you need to assume about the heights of two-year-olds to find your answer to (a)? **LO ❹**

27. The Environmental Protection Agency's (EPA) fuel economy estimates for automobiles suggest a mean of 24.8 mpg and a standard deviation of 6.2 mpg for highway driving. Assume that a Normal model can be applied.

a) Draw the model for auto fuel economy. Clearly label it, showing what the 68-95-99.7 Rule predicts about miles per gallon.

b) In what interval would you expect the central 68% of autos to be found?

c) About what percentage of autos should get more than 31 mpg?

d) About what percentage of cars should get between 31 and 37.2 mpg?

e) Describe the gas mileage of the worst 2.5% of all cars. **LO ❹**

28. Some IQ tests are standardized to a Normal model with a mean of 100 and a standard deviation of 16.

a) Draw the model for these IQ scores. Clearly label it, showing what the 68-95-99.7 Rule predicts about the scores.

b) In what interval would you expect the central 95% of IQ scores to be found?

c) About what percentage of people should have IQ scores above 116?

d) About what percentage of people should have IQ scores between 68 and 84?

e) About what percentage of people should have IQ scores above 132? **LO ❹**

29. Speeds of cars were measured as they passed one point on a road to study whether traffic speed controls were needed. Here's a histogram and normal probability plot of the measured speeds. Is a Normal model appropriate for these data? Explain. **LO ❹**

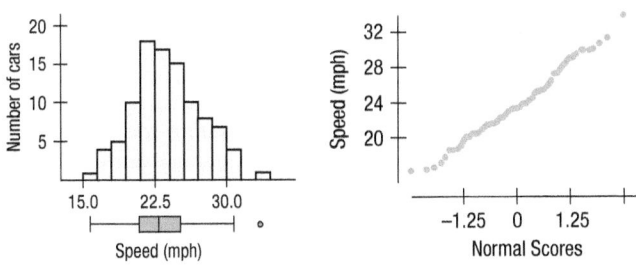

30. Has the Consumer Price Index (CPI) fluctuated around its mean according to a Normal model? Here are some displays. Is a Normal model appropriate for these data? Explain. **LO ❹**

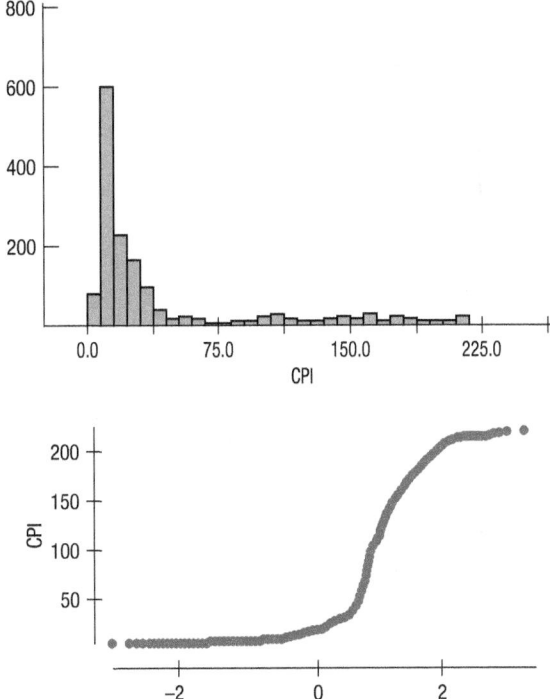

SECTION 9.11

31. Because many passengers who make reservations do not show up, airlines often overbook flights (sell more tickets than there are seats). A Boeing 767-400ER holds 245 passengers. If the airline believes the rate of passenger no-shows is 5% and sells 255 tickets, is it likely that it won't have enough seats and someone will get bumped?

a) Use the Normal model to approximate the Binomial to determine the probability of at least 246 passengers showing up.

b) Should the airline change the number of tickets it sells for the flight? Explain. **LO ❸, ❹**

32. Shortly after the introduction of the Belgian euro coin, newspapers around the word published articles claiming the coin is biased. The stories were based on reports that someone had spun the coin 250 times and gotten 140 heads—that's 56% heads.

a) Use the Normal model to approximate the Binomial to determine the probability of spinning a fair coin 250 times and getting at least 140 heads.

b) Do you think this is evidence that spinning a Belgian euro is unfair? Would you be willing to use it at the beginning of a sports event? Explain. **LO ❸, ❹**

SECTION 9.12

33. A manufacturer of a robot used on production lines for car manufacturing tests the accuracy of the robot operation and finds that, on average, the accuracy becomes unacceptable after 5850 hours of operation. The manufacturer specifies that the robot must be serviced to maintain its accuracy after 1000 hours of operation. What is the probability that the robot will become unacceptable before it's serviced? Assume an Exponential distribution for this "time to failure." **LO ❹**

34. A warehouse is lit by 1000 fluorescent tubes, each of which fails, on average, after 4250 hours of operation. It's costly to send a technician to replace an individual tube when it fails, so the warehouse manager decides to replace all the tubes after 3000 hours of operation, whether they have failed or not. On average, how many failed tubes will be replaced? Assume an Exponential distribution for this "time to failure." **LO ❹**

CHAPTER EXERCISES

35. New website, part 1. You've just launched the website for your company that sells nutritional products online. Suppose X = the number of different pages that a customer hits during a visit to the website.

a) Assuming that there are n different pages in total on your website, what are the possible values that this random variable may take on?

b) Is the random variable discrete or continuous? **LO ❶**

36. New website, part 2. For the website described in Exercise 35, let Y = the total time (in minutes) that a customer spends during a visit to the website.

a) What are the possible values of this random variable?

b) Is the random variable discrete or continuous? **LO ❶**

37. Job interviews. Through the career services office, you have arranged preliminary interviews at four companies for summer jobs. Each company will either ask you to come to its site for a follow-up interview or not. Let X be the random variable equal to the total number of follow-up interviews you might have.

a) List all the possible values of X.

b) Is the random variable discrete or continuous?

c) Do you think a Uniform distribution might be appropriate as a model for this random variable? Explain briefly. **LO ❶**

38. Help desk. The computer help desk is staffed by students during the 7 P.M. to 11 P.M. shift. Let Y denote the random variable that represents the number of students seeking help during the 15-minute time slot 10 P.M. to 10:15 P.M.

a) What are the possible values of Y?

b) Is the random variable discrete or continuous? **LO ❶**

39. 4 × 100 medley relay. In the 4 × 100 medley relay event, four swimmers swim 100 metres, each using a different stroke. A university team coach preparing for the conference championship looks at the times her swimmers have posted and creates a model based on the following assumptions:

• The swimmers' performances are independent.
• Each swimmer's times follow a Normal model.
• The means and standard deviations of the times (in seconds) are as shown here:

Swimmer	Mean	SD
1 (backstroke)	50.72	0.24
2 (breaststroke)	55.51	0.22
3 (butterfly)	49.43	0.25
4 (freestyle)	44.91	0.21

a) What are the mean and standard deviation for the relay team's total time in this event?

b) The team's best time so far this season was 3:19.48. (That's 199.48 seconds.) What is the probability that they'll beat that time in the next event? **LO ❹**

40. Software company. A small software company will bid on a major contract. It anticipates a profit of $50,000 if it gets it, but thinks there's only a 30% chance of that happening.

a) What's the expected profit?

b) Find the standard deviation for the profit. **LO ❶**

41. Commuting, part 1. A commuter must pass through five traffic lights on her way to work and of course has to stop at each one that's red. After keeping a record for several months, she developed the following probability model for the number of red lights she hits:

X = No. of red	0	1	2	3	4	5
P (X = x)	0.05	0.25	0.35	0.15	0.15	0.05

a) How many red lights should she expect to hit each day?

b) What's the standard deviation? **LO ❶**

42. Defects. A consumer organization inspecting new cars found that many had appearance defects (dents, scratches, paint chips, etc.). While none had more than three of these defects, 7% had three, 11% had two, and 21% had one.

a) Find the expected number of appearance defects in a new car.
b) What is the standard deviation? **LO ❶**

43. Commuting, part 2. A commuter finds that she waits an average of 14.8 seconds at each of five stoplights, with a standard deviation of 9.2 seconds. Find the mean and the standard deviation of the total amount of time she waits at all five lights. What, if anything, did you assume? **LO ❷**

44. Repair calls. A small engine shop receives an average of 1.7 repair calls per hour, with a standard deviation of 0.6. What is the mean and standard deviation of the number of calls it receives for an eight-hour day? What, if anything, did you assume? **LO ❷**

45. Insurance company. An insurance company estimates that it should make an annual profit of $150 on each home-owner's policy written, with a standard deviation of $6000.

a) Why is the standard deviation so large?
b) If the company writes only two of these policies, what are the mean and standard deviation of the annual profit?
c) If the company writes 1000 of these policies, what are the mean and standard deviation of the annual profit?
d) What circumstances could violate the assumption of independence of the policies? **LO ❷**

46. Contracts. Your company bids for two contracts. You believe that the probability of getting contract 1 is 0.8. If you get contract 1, the probability that you also get contract 2 will be 0.2, and if you don't get contract 1, the probability that you get contract 2 will be 0.3.

a) Are the outcomes of the two contract bids independent? Explain.
b) Find the probability that you get both contracts.
c) Find the probability that you get neither contract.
d) Let X be the number of contracts you get. Find the probability model for X.
e) Find the expected value and standard deviation of X.
LO ❶

47. Bike sale. A bicycle shop plans to offer two specially priced children's models at a sidewalk sale. The basic model will return a profit of $120 and the deluxe model $150. Past experience indicates that sales of the basic model will have a mean of 5.4 bikes with a standard deviation of 1.2, and sales of the deluxe model will have a mean of 3.2 bikes with a standard deviation of 0.8 bikes. The cost of setting up for the sidewalk sale is $200.

a) Define random variables and use them to express the bicycle shop's net profit.
b) What's the mean of the net profit?

c) What's the standard deviation of the net profit?
d) Do you need to make any assumptions in calculating the mean? How about the standard deviation? **LO ❷**

48. Farmers' market. A farmer has 100 kilograms of apples and 50 kilograms of potatoes for sale. The market price for apples (per kilogram) each day is a random variable with a mean of 0.5 dollars and a standard deviation of 0.2 dollars. Similarly, for a kilogram of potatoes, the mean price is 0.3 dollars and the standard deviation is 0.1 dollars. It also costs the farmer 2 dollars to bring all the apples and potatoes to the market. The market is busy with eager shoppers, so we can assume that he'll be able to sell all of each type of produce at that day's price.

a) Define your random variables, and use them to express the farmer's net income.
b) Find the mean of the net income.
c) Find the standard deviation of the net income.
d) Do you need to make any assumptions in calculating the mean? How about the standard deviation? **LO ❷**

49. eBay. A collector purchased a quantity of action figures and is going to sell them on eBay. He has 19 Hulk figures. In recent auctions, the mean selling price of similar figures has been $12.11, with a standard deviation of $1.38. He also has 13 Iron Man figures, which have had a mean selling price of $10.19, with a standard deviation of $0.77. His listing fee will be $0.55 on each item, and the closing fee will be 8.75% of the selling price. He assumes that all will sell without having to be relisted.

a) Define your random variables, and use them to create a random variable for the collector's net income.
b) Find the mean (expected value) of the net income.
c) Find the standard deviation of the net income.
d) Do you have to assume independence for the sales on eBay? Explain. **LO ❷**

50. Real estate. A real estate broker purchased three two-bedroom houses in a depressed market for a combined cost of $71,000. He expects the cleaning and repair costs on each house to average $3700, with a standard deviation of $1450. When he sells them, after subtracting taxes and other closing costs, he expects to realize an average of $39,000 per house, with a standard deviation of $1100.

a) Define your random variables and use them to create a random variable for the broker's net profit.
b) Find the mean (expected value) of the net profit.
c) Find the standard deviation of the net profit.
d) Do you have to assume independence for the repairs and sale prices of the houses? Explain. **LO ❷**

51. Bernoulli, part 1. Can we use probability models based on Bernoulli trials to investigate the following situations? Explain.

a) Each week a doctor rolls a single die to determine which of his six office staff members gets the preferred parking space.

b) A medical research lab has samples of blood collected from 120 different individuals. How likely is it that the majority of them are Type A blood, given that Type A is found in 43% of the population?

c) From a workforce of 13 men and 23 women, all five promotions go to men. How likely is that, if promotions are based on qualifications rather than gender?

d) We poll 500 of the 3000 stockholders to see how likely it is that the proposed budget will pass.

e) A company realizes that about 10% of its packages are not being sealed properly. In a case of 24 packages, how likely is it that more than three are unsealed? **LO ❸**

52. Bernoulli, part 2. Can we use probability models based on Bernoulli trials to investigate the following situations? Explain.

a) You are rolling five dice. How likely are you to get at least two sixes to win the game?

b) You survey 500 potential customers to determine their colour preference.

c) A manufacturer recalls a doll because about 3% have buttons that are not properly attached. Customers return 37 of these dolls to the local toy store. How likely is the manufacturer to find any buttons not properly attached?

d) A city council of 11 Conservatives and eight Liberals picks a committee of four at random. How likely are they to choose all Liberals?

e) An executive reads that 74% of employees in his industry are dissatisfied with their jobs. How many dissatisfied employees can he expect to find among the 481 employees in his company? **LO ❸**

53. Closing sales. A sales associate normally makes a sale (closes) on 80% of his presentations. Assuming the presentations are independent, find the probability of each of the following:

a) He fails to close for the first time on his fifth attempt.

b) He closes his first presentation on his fourth attempt.

c) The first presentation he closes will be on his second attempt.

d) The first presentation he closes will be on one of his first three attempts. **LO ❸**

54. Computer chip manufacturer. Suppose a computer chip manufacturer rejects 2% of the chips produced because they fail presale testing. Assuming the bad chips are independent, find the probability of each of the following:

a) The fifth chip the manufacturer tests is the first bad one it finds.

b) It finds a bad one within the first 10 it examines.

c) The first bad chip it finds will be the fourth one it tests.

d) The first bad chip it finds will be one of the first three it tests. **LO ❸**

55. Side effects. Researchers testing a new medication find that 7% of users have side effects. To how many patients would a doctor expect to prescribe the medication before finding the first one who has side effects? **LO ❸**

56. Credit cards. University students are a major target for advertisements for credit cards. At a university, 65% of students surveyed said they had opened a new credit card account within the past year. If that percentage is accurate, how many students would you expect to survey before finding one who had not opened a new account in the past year? **LO ❸**

57. Missing pixels. A company that manufactures large LCD screens knows that not all pixels on its screens light, even if it takes great care when making them. In a sheet 6 metres by 10 metres that will be cut into smaller screens, it finds an average of 4.7 blank pixels. It believes that the occurrences of blank pixels are independent. Its warranty policy states that it will replace any screen sold that shows more than two blank pixels.

a) What is the mean number of blank pixels per square metre?

b) What is the standard deviation of blank pixels per square metre?

c) What is the probability that a 0.6 metre by 1 metre screen will have at least one defect?

d) What is the probability that a 0.6 metre by 1 metre screen will be replaced because it has too many defects? **LO ❸**

58. Bean bags. Cellophane that's going to be formed into bags for items such as dried beans or bird seed is passed over a light sensor to test if the alignment is correct before it passes through the heating units that seal the edges. Small adjustments can be made by the machine automatically. But if the alignment is too bad, the process is stopped and an operator has to manually adjust it. These misalignment stops occur randomly and independently. On one line, the average number of stops is 52 per eight-hour shift.

a) What is the mean number of stops per hour?

b) What is the standard deviation of stops per hour?

c) When the machine is restarted after a stop, what is the probability that it will run at least 15 minutes before the next stop? **LO ❸**

59. Hurricane insurance, part 1. An insurance company needs to assess the risks associated with providing hurricane insurance. During the 22 years from 1990 through 2011, Florida was hit by 27 major hurricanes (Level 3 and above). If hurricanes are independent and the mean has not changed, what is the probability of having a year in Florida with each of the following?

a) No hits

b) Exactly one hit

c) More than one hit **LO ❸**

60. Hurricane insurance, part 2. During the 18 years from 1995 through 2012, there were 144 hurricanes in the Atlantic basin. Assume that hurricanes are independent and the mean has not changed.

a) What is the mean number of major hurricanes per year?
b) What is the standard deviation of the annual frequency of major hurricanes?
c) What is the probability of having a year with no major hurricanes?
d) What is the probability of going three years in a row without a major hurricane? **LO ❸**

61. **Professional tennis, part 1.** Serena Williams made a successful first serve 67% of the time in a Wimbledon finals match against her sister, Venus. If she continues to serve at the same rate the next time they play and serves six times in the first game, determine the following probabilities. (Assume that each serve is independent of the others.)

a) All six first serves will be in.
b) Exactly four first serves will be in.
c) At least four first serves will be in. **LO ❸**

62. **Crime in Canada.** Statistics Canada provides data on the number of cases in adult criminal court by type of sentence: "fine," "restitution," and "other." In a recent year, the probability that property crime cases in Canada resulted in a sentence of "restitution" (as opposed to other sentences) was 0.154.

a) Suppose there were 14 property crime cases in Manitoba last week. What is the probability that exactly two will result in a sentence of restitution?
b) State your assumptions about Manitoba clearly.
c) Suppose that two cases did in fact result in a sentence of restitution last week. What conclusion do you draw about Manitoba last week? **LO ❸**

63. **Canadian traffic accidents, part 1.** Statistics Canada provides data on the number of reportable transport accidents involving dangerous goods. The probability that reportable transport accidents involving dangerous goods in Canada occur on the roads (as opposed to other forms of transport) is 0.295.

a) Out of 10 reportable transport accidents involving dangerous goods in Nova Scotia last week, what is the probability that exactly two occurred on the roads?
b) State your assumptions about Nova Scotia clearly.
c) Suppose that in fact two of the 10 accidents in Nova Scotia did occur on roads. What conclusion do you draw about Nova Scotia last week? **LO ❸**

64. **Canadian Blood Services, part 1.** Only 4% of people have Type AB blood. A bloodmobile has 12 vials of blood on a rack. If the distribution of blood types at this location is consistent with the general population, what's the probability that Canadian Blood Services finds AB blood in

a) None of the 12 samples?
b) At least two samples?
c) Three or four samples? **LO ❸**

65. **Professional tennis, part 2.** Suppose Serena continues to make 67% of her first serves, as in Exercise 61, and serves 80 times in a match.

a) What are the mean and standard deviation of the number of good first serves expected?
b) Justify why you can use a Normal model to approximate the distribution of the number of good first serves.
c) What's the probability that she makes at least 65 first serves in the 80 attempts? **LO ❸**

66. **Canadian Blood Services, part 2.** The bloodmobile in Exercise 64 received 300 donations in one day.

a) Assuming that the frequency of AB blood is 4%, determine the mean and standard deviation of the number of donors who are AB.
b) Justify why you can use a Normal model to approximate the distribution of Type AB blood.
c) How likely would it be to find 10 or more samples with Type AB blood in 300 samples? **LO ❸**

For Exercises 67 to 74, use the 68-95-99.7 Rule to approximate the probabilities rather than using technology to find the values more precisely.

67. **Mutual fund returns 2013, part 1.** In the first quarter of 2013, a group of domestic equity mutual funds had a mean return of 6.2% with a standard deviation of 1.8%. If a Normal model can be used to model them, what percent of the funds would you expect to be in each region? Be sure to draw a picture first.

a) Returns of 8.0% or more
b) Returns of 6.2% or less
c) Returns between 2.6% and 9.8%
d) Returns of more than 11.6% **LO ❹**

68. **Human resource testing, part 1.** Although controversial, some Human Resources departments administer standard IQ tests to potential employees. The Stanford-Binet test scores are well modelled by a Normal model with mean 100 and standard deviation 16. If the applicant pool is well modelled by this distribution, a randomly selected applicant would have what probability of scoring in the following regions?

a) 100 or below
b) Above 148
c) Between 84 and 116
d) Above 132 **LO ❹**

69. **Mutual fund returns 2013, part 2.** For a group of mutual funds with quarterly returns that are well modelled by a Normal model with a mean of 2.4% and a standard deviation of 5.6%, find the cutoff return value(s) that would separate the

a) Highest 50%.   b) Highest 16%.
c) Lowest 2.5%.   a) Middle 68%. **LO ❹**

70. Human resource testing, part 2. For the IQ test administered by Human Resources and discussed in Exercise 68, what cutoff value would separate the

a) Lowest 0.15% of all applicants?
b) Lowest 16%?
c) Middle 95%?
d) Highest 2.5%? **LO ❹**

71. Currency exchange rates, part 1. The daily exchange rates for the five-year period 2008 to 2013 between the euro (EUR) and the British pound (GBP) can be modelled by a Normal distribution with mean 1.19 euros (to pounds) and standard deviation 0.043 euros. Given this model, what is the probability that on a randomly selected day during this period the pound was worth

a) Less than 1.19 euros?
b) More than 1.233 euros?
c) Less than 1.104 euros?
d) Which would be more unusual: a day on which the pound was worth less than 1.126 euros or a day when it was worth more than 1.298 euros? **LO ❹**

72. Stock prices, part 1. For the 300 trading days from January 11, 2012, to March 22, 2013, the daily closing price of IBM stock (in $) is well modelled by a Normal model with mean $197.92 and standard deviation $7.16. According to this model, what is the probability that on a randomly selected day in this period the stock price closed

a) Above $205.08?
b) Below $212.24?
c) Between $183.60 and $205.08?
d) Which would be more unusual: a day on which the stock price closed above $206 or a day when it was below $180? **LO ❹**

73. Currency exchange rates, part 2. For the model of the EUR/GBP exchange rate discussed in Exercise 71, what would the cutoff rates be that would separate the

a) Highest 16% of EUR/GBP rates?
b) Lowest 50%?
c) Middle 95%?
d) Lowest 2.5%? **LO ❹**

74. Stock prices, part 2. According to the model in Exercise 72, what cutoff value of price would separate the

a) Lowest 16% of the days?
b) Highest 0.15%?
c) Middle 68%?
d) Highest 50%? **LO ❹**

Answers given for probabilities or percentages from Exercise 75 onward assume that a calculator or software has been used. Answers found from using Z-tables may vary slightly.

75. Mutual fund returns 2013, part 3. For mutual funds with Normally distributed returns with a mean of 6.2% and a standard deviation of 1.8%, what are the cutoff values for the

a) Highest 10% of these funds?
b) Lowest 20%?
c) Middle 40%?
d) Highest 80%? **LO ❹**

76. Human resource testing, part 3. In the Normal model for IQ scores from Exercise 68, what cutoff value bounds the

a) Highest 5% of all IQs?
b) Lowest 30% of the IQs?
c) Middle 80% of the IQs?
d) Lowest 90% of all IQs? **LO ❹**

77. Management survey. A survey of 200 middle managers showed a distribution of the number of hours of exercise they participated in per week with a mean of 3.66 hours and a standard deviation of 4.93 hours.

a) According to the Normal model, what percentage of managers will exercise fewer than one standard deviation below the mean number of hours?
b) For these data, what does that mean? Explain.
c) Explain the problem in using the Normal model for these data. **LO ❹**

78. Selling tomatoes. Agricultural scientists are working on developing an improved variety of Roma tomatoes. Marketing research indicates that customers are likely to bypass Romas that weigh less than 70 grams. The current variety of Roma plants produces fruit that average 74 grams, but 11% of the tomatoes are too small. It is reasonable to assume that a Normal model applies.

a) What is the standard deviation of the weights of Romas now being grown?
b) Scientists hope to reduce the frequency of undersized tomatoes to no more than 4%. One way to accomplish this is to raise the average size of the fruit. If the standard deviation remains the same, what target mean should they have as a goal?
c) The researchers produce a new variety with a mean weight of 75 grams, which meets the 4% goal. What is the standard deviation of the weights of these new Romas?
d) Based on their standard deviations, compare the tomatoes produced by the two varieties. **LO ❹**

79. Drug company. Manufacturing and selling drugs that claim to reduce an individual's cholesterol level is big business. A company would like to market its drug to women if their cholesterol is in the top 15%. Assume the cholesterol levels of adult women can be described by a Normal model with a mean of 188 mg/dL and a standard deviation of 24.

a) Draw and label the Normal model.
b) What percentage of adult women do you expect to have cholesterol levels over 200 mg/dL?
c) What percentage of adult women do you expect to have cholesterol levels between 150 and 170 mg/dL?
d) Estimate the interquartile range of the cholesterol levels.

e) Above what value are the highest 15% of women's cholesterol levels? **LO ❹**

80. Tire company. A tire manufacturer believes that the tread-life of its snow tires can be described by a Normal model with a mean of 32,000 kilometres and a standard deviation of 2500 kilometres.

a) If you buy one of these tires, would it be reasonable for you to hope that it will last 40,000 kilometres? Explain.
b) Approximately what fraction of these tires can be expected to last less than 30,000 kilometres?
c) Approximately what fraction of these tires can be expected to last between 30,000 and 35,000 kilometres?
d) Estimate the interquartile range for these data.
e) In planning a marketing strategy, a local tire dealer wants to offer a refund to any customer whose tires fail to last a certain number of kilometres. However, the dealer doesn't want to take too big a risk. If the dealer is willing to give refunds to no more than 1 of every 25 customers, for what mileage can he guarantee these tires to last? **LO ❹**

81. Good eggs. A farmer is concerned about the number of eggs he's been collecting that are "below weight," because this impacts his bottom line. Hens usually begin laying eggs when they're about six months old. Young hens tend to lay smaller eggs, often weighing less than the desired minimum weight of 54 grams.

a) The average weight of the eggs produced by the young hens is 50.9 grams, and only 28% of their eggs exceed the desired minimum weight. If a Normal model is appropriate, what would the standard deviation of the egg weights be?
b) By the time these hens have reached the age of one year, the eggs they produce average 67.1 grams, and 98% of them are above the minimum weight. What is the standard deviation for the appropriate Normal model for these older hens?
c) Are egg sizes more consistent for the younger hens or the older ones? Explain.
d) A certain poultry farmer finds that 8% of his eggs are underweight and that 12% weigh over 70 grams. Estimate the mean and standard deviation of his eggs. **LO ❹**

82. Web visitors, part 1. A website manager has noticed that during the evening hours, about three people per minute check out from their shopping cart and make an online purchase. She believes that each purchase is independent of the others and wants to model the number of purchases per minute.

a) What model might you suggest to model the number of purchases per minute?
b) What is the probability that in any one minute at least one purchase is made?
c) What is the probability that no one makes a purchase in the next two minutes? **LO ❸**

83. Quality control, part 1. A cell phone manufacturer has noticed that the number of faulty cell phones in a production run of cell phones is usually small and that the quality of one day's run seems to have no bearing on the next day.

a) What model might you use to model the number of faulty cell phones produced in one day?
b) If the mean number of faulty cell phones is two per day, what is the probability that no faulty cell phones will be produced tomorrow?
c) If the mean number of faulty cell phones is two per day, what is the probability that three or more faulty cell phones were produced in today's run? **LO ❸**

84. Homicide in Canada. Statistics Canada provides data on the number of cases in adult criminal court by type of crime. In a recent year the average number of homicide cases was 6.83 per month.

a) What probability distribution is appropriate for modelling the number of cases per month? State your assumptions clearly.
b) During that year, what was the probability of getting fewer than three homicide cases in a given month?
c) Suppose that last month there were two homicide cases. What conclusion do you draw about last month? **LO ❸**

85. Canadian traffic accidents, part 2. Statistics Canada provides data on the number of reportable transport accidents involving dangerous goods. In a recent year the average rate of occurrence of such accidents was 8.15 per week.

a) What probability distribution is appropriate for modelling the number of these accidents per week? State your assumptions clearly.
b) During that year, what was the probability of getting more than two such accidents in a given week?
c) Suppose that in the last week of the current year, there were two such accidents. What conclusion do you draw about last week? **LO ❸**

86. Web visitors, part 2. The website manager in Exercise 82 wants to model the time between purchases. Recall that the mean number of purchases in the evening is three per minute.

a) What model would you use to model the time between events?
b) What is the mean time between purchases?
c) What is the probability that the time to the next purchase will be between one and two minutes? **LO ❸**

87. Quality control, part 2. The cell phone manufacturer in Exercise 83 wants to model the time between faulty phones. The mean number of defective cell phones is two per day.

a) What model would you use to model the time between faulty phones?
b) What would the probability be that the time to the next failure is one day or less?
c) What is the mean time between failures? **LO ❸**

88. Economics. Anna, a business major, took final exams in both Microeconomics and Macroeconomics and scored 83 on both. Her roommate, Li, also taking both courses, scored 77 on the Micro exam and 95 on the Macro exam. Overall, student scores on the Micro exam were Normally distributed with a mean of 81 and a standard deviation of 5, and the Macro scores were Normally distributed with a mean of 74 and a standard deviation of 15. Which student's overall performance was better? Which student's scores were better compared with her classmates' scores? Explain. **LO ④**

89. Moose in Newfoundland. During May, young moose, unfamiliar with roads and traffic, are wandering around at night in Newfoundland, causing risk of road accidents. Suppose that in 2016 the average number of road accidents involving moose was 4.1 per day during May. The government increased the number of hunting licences and cleared brush from the roadsides to improve drivers' visibility. On one day in May 2017 there were two road accidents involving moose.

a) What would be the chance of two such accidents or fewer, assuming the government's measures were ineffective?

b) Do you think the government's measures were effective? State your reasons clearly. **LO ❸**

90. Bombardier of Montreal. Bombardier designs and manufactures trains and planes and relies on large deals from its customers for these high-cost products. This series of large contracts makes for a very variable revenue stream compared with the more even income it derives from long-term service contracts. Nina Gupta, an analyst, predicts that Bombardier's service share will drop to 13% with a standard deviation of 1% next year and that Rolls-Royce's service share will increase to 54% with a standard deviation of 2%. Assuming you believe Nina's forecast, what is the probability that

a) Bombardier's service share will be lower than 14% next year?

b) Rolls-Royce's service share will be higher than 51% next year?

c) State your assumptions clearly and indicate whether you think the assumptions are true. **LO ④**

91. Ottawa weather. In July, on average, Ottawa has 4.2 thunderstorms. What is the probability that next July

a) Ottawa will have six thunderstorms?

b) Ottawa will have fewer than four thunderstorms?

c) State your assumptions clearly. **LO ❸**

92. Canadian Aboriginals, part 1. Aboriginals make up 3.9% of the Canadian population, and in 2014, 7 out of the 308 federal Members of Parliament were Aboriginal. Using the methods given in this chapter, compare these pieces of information to answer the question, "Are Aboriginals under-represented in Parliament?" State your

assumptions clearly and indicate whether you think the assumptions are true. **LO ❸**

93. Canadian Aboriginals, part 2. During the entire history of Canada, 0.74% of the 4201 federal Members of Parliament have been Aboriginals. In 2014, 7 out of the 308 federal Members of Parliament were Aboriginal. Using the methods given in this chapter, compare these pieces of information to answer the question, "Were Aboriginals better represented in Parliament in 2014 than previously?" State your assumptions clearly and indicate whether you think the assumptions are true. **LO ❸**

94. Canadian Arctic. Since 1961, NRCan researchers have been visiting the Devon Island icecap in Nunavut to monitor the effects of global warming. They've found that the thickness of the ice has decreased by about five metres. Now they don't have to travel to the icecap as frequently, since they also have available data from the European Space Agency (ESA) satellite CryoSat-2. The ESA website claims to measure ice thickness to an accuracy of plus or minus one centimetre. Give a precise statistical interpretation of what you think it means by "plus or minus one centimetre." **LO ④**

95. Baffin Bay oil exploration, part 1. Baffin Bay, located between Canada and Greenland, is being explored for oil and natural gas. First an energy company conducts a geological survey, and if the data look promising it starts drilling. A recent survey of one area cost $65 million and indicates that drilling will be successful with a probability of 0.2. Drilling costs $0.3 billion with a probability of 0.7 and $0.6 billion with a probability of 0.3, due to the fact that the survey does not identify the geological structures precisely. If drilling is successful, revenue from the sale of oil and gas will be $2.7 billion with a probability of 0.75 and $3.2 billion with a probability of 0.25 due to uncertainty about future prices at which the company can sell the oil and gas.

a) What is the expected cost of drilling?

b) What is the expected profit? **LO ❶**

96. Baffin Bay oil exploration, part 2. A survey of another area of Baffin Bay indicates that drilling will be successful with a probability of 0.4. Drilling a single well costs $0.65 billion and brings in a revenue of $2.2 billion. If the first well is successful, the chance of a second well being successful is increased from 0.4 to 0.9. If the first well is not successful, the chance of a second well being successful is decreased from 0.4 to 0.2.

a) What is the expected profit from drilling the first well?

b) What is the expected profit from drilling two wells? **LO ❶**

97. Niagara tunnel. Canada extracts water from the Niagara River upstream of Niagara Falls and uses it to generate hydroelectric power at two generating stations downstream.

Until 2013, water was taken to the generating stations in a tunnel and a canal, which were used to capacity 65% of the time. In 2006 work got underway on a second tunnel, and in 2013 it started delivering an Olympic-sized swimming pool of water to the generating stations every five minutes. Suppose that at the planning stage for the second tunnel, the geologists and engineers reach a consensus that it will cost $1.5 billion with a probability of 0.6 and $2.5 billion with a probability of 0.4. What is the expected cost of the tunnel? **LO ❶**

98. Nuclear tests in North Korea. North Korea conducted nuclear tests in 2009 and 2013, and South Korea's defence ministry estimated their power at between 2 and 6 kilotonnes of TNT in 2009 and between 6 and 7 kilotonnes of TNT in 2013. "The power of North Korea's nuclear tests increased between 2009 and 2013," stated a commentator. Assume that the ranges given by the South Korean defence ministry represent the ranges within which the actual power of the tests lies with a probability of 0.9. Also assume that the defence ministry's estimates are Normally distributed.

a) What is the probability that the actual power of the 2009 test was greater than 7 kilotonnes of TNT?

b) What is the probability that the actual power of the test was higher in 2009 than in 2013? **LO ❹**

99. An elevating business. The elevator market is dominated by four suppliers: Otis of the United States, Kone of Finland, Thyssen-Krupp of Germany, and Schindler of Switzerland. Elevators are installed in buildings of a range of heights and incorporate a range of features, resulting in a range of prices from $50,000 to $300,000. After an elevator is installed, the building owner also needs it to be maintained and therefore negotiates a service contract with a price ranging from $2,000 to $5,000 per year. Elevator suppliers make 10% profit on sales and 30% profit on service contracts. Assume that the price ranges for sales and service represent 90% confidence intervals on Normal distributions.

Next year, an elevator supplier projects selling 15,000 elevators and 12,000 new service contracts.

a) What is the expected total revenue from sales and service contracts?

b) What is the expected total profit from sales and service contracts?

c) What is the range of total profits from sales and service contracts? Give a profit range that represents a 90% confidence interval. What assumptions are you making? **LO ❶, ❷**

100. Effect of volcanoes on solar power. When a volcano erupts, it sends ash into the upper atmosphere, partially blocking out the sun, and thus reducing the amount of electric power generated by solar panels. During the 35-year period 1980–2015, there were four volcanic eruptions

sufficiently powerful to reduce the amount of power generated by solar panels by at least 20% for a period of a year. We will call these "Class D20" volcanoes. Solar panels typically have a 25-year warranty, and therefore the return on investment from installing solar panels is often calculated over a 25-year period. What is the probability that, during a 25-year period, there will be two or more "Class D20" volcanic eruptions? **LO ❸**

101. Purchasing mining equipment. Mining companies purchase large and specialized equipment. The company specifies the features required for the product in a request for quotations (RFQ) and suppliers submit bids. Because of the complex nature of the equipment, an RFQ and each individual bid can run into hundreds of pages of detail. A Canadian mining company has purchasing offices in three regions of the world that issue RFQs for their region and analyze the resulting bids. The chief purchasing officer for the company wants to reduce the workload of the individual purchasing offices by using past data to estimate in advance the likely range of prices in each of the three parts of the world. The purchasing office of a region where the price is estimated to be high will not be asked to issue an RFQ or to analyze any bids. The table gives his estimates for 10 large bulldozers the company needs to purchase, together with the standard deviations of those estimates. Assume the estimates follow a Normal distribution.

Region	Purchasing Office City	Estimated Price	Standard Deviation
Asia	Osaka	$7.8m	$2.3m
N. America	Toronto	$6.1m	$1.2m
EU	Frankfurt	$7.1m	$0.6m

He decides to get the Toronto office to issue an RFQ because the estimated price there is lowest. He will ask the other offices to issue RFQs if there is at least a 0.25 probability that their price will be less than that in Toronto.

a) Should the company issue RFQs in Osaka?

b) Should the company issue RFQs in Frankfurt?

c) Give an intuitive explanation of your result. **LO ❹**

102. Car manufacturing plant. In a car manufacturing plant, parts are delivered by truck, workers arrive and work, equipment fails, equipment has to be serviced even if it hasn't failed, options and features have to be added to some vehicles and not to others, demand for the colour of bodywork changes, incoming parts and finished vehicles have to be tested, etc. Give examples from the operation of a car manufacturing plant of each of the topics discussed in the 12 sections of this chapter (except for Section 9.8). You can use the examples in the description above, plus your own ideas. Give your reasons for choosing each example and describe how the statistical topic applies to the operation of the plant. You are not asked to do any quantitative analysis. **LO ❶, ❷, ❸, ❹**

103. Vancouver International Airport. At Vancouver International Airport, passengers arrive and depart, aircraft arrive and depart, service vehicles refuel planes, planes are serviced for scheduled maintenance and if they have a fault, passengers eat at restaurants, buses and taxis come and go, employees come and go, flight crews come and go, etc. Give examples from the operation of an airport of each of the topics discussed in the 12 sections of this chapter (except for Section 9.8). You can use the examples in the description above, plus your own ideas. Give your reasons for choosing each example plus the way in which the statistical topic applies to the operation of the airport. You are not asked to do any quantitative analysis. **LO ❶, ❷, ❸, ❹**

104. Photographing Canada geese. Maria is starting a career as a professional wildlife photographer and plans to photograph Canada geese at one of their staging grounds during their migration in northeastern Manitoba. She booked a place in a hide at the edge of a lake and plans to photograph the geese as they land on the water. For the price of a room in the Hilton ($200 per day), she gets a spot on a wooden bench shared by other photographers, a muddy floor, a bracket to mount her telephoto lens, a tent to sleep in, and delicious meals of freshly caught fish. Meteorological records indicate ideal conditions with a probability of 0.42 on any individual day. In those conditions last year, she got two shots worth $5000 each in three days. Non-ideal conditions do not result in commercially acceptable photographs. To establish her reputation, Maria only sells $5000 photographs. This year, she has booked four days in the hide.

a) What is Maria's expected revenue from one day in the hide?
b) What is Maria's expected revenue from her four days?
c) What is the standard deviation of her revenue from one day?
d) What is the standard deviation of her revenue from the four days?
e) State your assumptions clearly.
f) Compare the risk of four days with the risk of one day.
g) What is the chance of getting two or more saleable photos on Maria's first day?

h) The return charter flight from Winnipeg where Maria lives costs $1200. How much net income can she expect from the trip?
i) What is the advantage to Maria of staying more than four days? **LO ❶, ❷, ❸**

105. Supernovas. When a very large star reaches the end of its life it explodes, causing a supernova, a very intense burst of radiation that is sufficient to destroy almost all life on planets of nearby stars. Some simple organisms may remain, but all animals and plants are destroyed and evolution has to start again from the simple organisms. On Earth it took 100 million years to get from such a simple organism to humans.

a) In our part of the galaxy (toward the edge), supernovas sufficiently powerful to have such an impact on life on Earth occur at random on average every 500 million years. Suppose such a supernova occurred tomorrow. What is the probability of another one occurring in the next 100 million years and thus delaying the evolution of human-like life?
b) At the centre of our galaxy, stars are closer together. There, supernovas of this destructive power occur on average once every 50 million years. Suppose such a supernova occurred tomorrow, wiping out all but simple organisms on a planet. What is the probability of no supernova occurring in the next 100 million years and thus allowing human-like life to evolve? **LO ❸**

106. Solar panel manufacture. When solar panels rated at 250 watts of power are manufactured, the power of the panels is not exactly 250 watts, but is Normally distributed with a mean of 250 watts and a standard deviation of 7.5 watts. When solar panels are connected together in series on a roof, the power generated is limited by the panel with the least power. For example, if three panels of 240 watts, 250 watts, and 260 watts are connected in series, the total power is NOT $240 + 250 + 260 = 750$ watts. Instead, it is $3 \times 240 = 720$ watts (limited by the 240-watt panel). We need to connect eight panels together in series on a roof. What is the probability that the total power generated will be less than 1920 watts? **LO ❸, ❹**

107. *Maclean's* magazine. A corner store stocks *Maclean's* magazine and on average 4.5 customers purchase the magazine each month. The store owner orders six copies of the magazine each month. What is the probability of running out of stock? **LO ❸**

Pat Crowe II/AP Imagesk

10

Sampling Distributions

MBNA in Canada

MBNA Canada, headquartered in Ottawa, first opened its doors for business in 1997, issuing MasterCard branded credit cards, and was acquired by Toronto-Dominion Bank in 2011. That made TD Bank the largest MasterCard issuer in Canada. One reason for MBNA's success is its affiliate program, in which it issues credit cards endorsed by financial institutions, sports associations, educational institutions, and professional associations. These groups receive a percentage of the profits MBNA generates from their members.

MBNA was founded in 1982 as the Maryland Bank National Association and rapidly grew to become the third-largest U.S. credit card bank in 2006, with 50 million cardholders and $82.1 billion in credit card loans. It expanded into Canada and Europe, with operations in Ireland, Spain, and the United Kingdom, and was bought by Bank of America in 2005. MBNA retains its name for its operations in Canada and Europe, but in the United States, Bank of America started issuing all cards in its own name in 2007.

MBNA Canada actively practises corporate social responsibility, funding many community projects. The affiliates program contributes to MBNA's environmental policy, and MBNA also has a longstanding relationship with the Canadian Wildlife Federation in helping expand its conservation programs.

U nlike the early days of the credit card industry when MBNA established itself, the environment today is intensely competitive, with companies constantly looking for ways to attract new customers and to maximize the profitability of the customers they already have. Many of the large companies have millions of customers, so instead of trying out a new idea with all of them, they almost always launch a pilot study or trial first, conducting a survey or an experiment on a sample of their customers.

Credit card companies make money on their cards in three ways: They earn a percentage of every transaction, they charge interest on balances that are not paid in full, and they collect fees (yearly fees, late fees, etc.). To generate all three types of revenue, the marketing departments of credit card banks constantly seek ways to encourage customers to increase the use of their cards.

A marketing specialist at one company had an idea of offering double air miles to its customers with an airline-affiliated card if they increased their spending by at least $800 in the month following the offer. This is a clear Yes/No situation. Either spending increased by $800 or it did not. In order to forecast the cost and revenue of the offer, the finance department needed to know what percentage of customers would actually qualify for the double miles. The marketer decided to send the offer to a random sample of 1000 customers to find out. In that sample, she found that 211 (21.1%) of the cardholders increased their spending by more than the required $800. But another analyst drew a different sample of 1000 customers, of whom 202 (20.2%) of the cardholders exceeded $800.

The two samples don't agree. We know that observations vary, but how much variability among samples should we expect to see?

Why do sample proportions vary at all? How can two samples of the same population measuring the same quantity get different results? The answer is fundamental to statistical inference. Each proportion is based on a *different* sample of cardholders. The proportions vary from sample to sample because the samples comprise different people.

A credit card company is interested in not only the proportion of its customers increasing their spending by a certain amount, but also how many dollars those customers spend. These are two fundamentally different things. In the first case it's a simple Yes/No situation. Either the customer increased his or her spending by $800 or not. We record the proportion of customers who did. That proportion is one single number to represent all the customers in our sample. By contrast, the actual amount they spend is a numerical measure that we record for each customer individually. We can then calculate the mean amount spent averaged over all customers. Clearly the first situation (proportions) is simpler than the second (means), and it turns out that the math is simpler, too. We therefore cover proportions first in this chapter (Sections 10.1 and 10.2). Then we cover means in Sections 10.3 and 10.4.

WHO	Cardholders of a bank's credit card
WHAT	Whether cardholders increased their spending by at least $800 in the subsequent month
WHEN	Today
WHERE	North America
WHY	To predict costs and benefits of a program offer

Type of Sampling Distribution	Information on Each Instance
Proportions Sections 10.1 and 10.2	Yes/No
Means Sections 10.3 and 10.4	Quantitative

LO❶ 10.1 Modelling Sample Proportions

If we could take many random samples of 1000 cardholders, we'd find the proportion of each sample who spent more than $800 and collect all of those proportions into a histogram. Where would you expect the centre of that histogram to be? Of course, we don't *know* the answer, but it's reasonable to think that it will be at the true proportion in the population. We'll probably never know the value of the true proportion. But it's important to us, so we'll give it a label, p, for "true proportion."

We can't really take all those different random samples of size 1000, but we can use a computer to pretend to draw random samples of 1000 individuals from some population of values over and over. In this way, we can model the process of drawing many samples from a real population. A *simulation* can help us understand how sample proportions vary due to random sampling.

When we have only two possible outcomes for an event, the convention in Statistics is to arbitrarily label one of them "success" and the other "failure." Here, a "success" would be that a customer increased card charges by at least $800, and a

Imagine
We see only the sample we actually drew, but if we *imagine* the results of all the other possible samples we could have drawn (by modelling or simulating them), we can learn more.

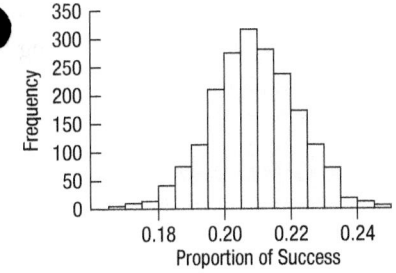

Figure 10.1 The distribution of 2000 sample values of $\hat{p}$, from simulated samples of size 1000 drawn from a population in which the true p is 0.21.

"failure" would be that the customer didn't. In the simulation, we'll set the true proportion of successes to a known value, draw random samples, and then record the sample proportion of successes, which we'll denote by $\hat{p}$, for each sample. Figure 10.1 shows a histogram of the proportions of cardholders who increased spending by at least \$800 in 2000 independent samples of 1000 cardholders, when the true

---

FOR EXAMPLE **The distribution of a sample proportion of retail customers**

A supermarket has installed "self-checkout" stations that allow customers to scan and bag their own groceries. These are popular, but because customers occasionally encounter a problem, a staff member must be available to help out. The manager wants to estimate what proportion of customers need help so that he can optimize the number of self-check stations per staff monitor. He collects data from the stations for 60 days, recording the proportion of customers on each day who need help, and makes a histogram of the observed proportions.

QUESTIONS

1. If the proportion needing help is independent from day to day, what shape would you expect his histogram to follow?

2. Is the assumption of independence reasonable?

ANSWERS

1. Approximately Normal, centred at the true proportion.

2. Possibly not. For example, shoppers on weekends might be less experienced than regular weekday shoppers and would then need more help. Also, over time, people get used to the machines and need less help.

Statistics Trumps Intuition

A company in New Brunswick sells natural medicine from its website. Its products fall into two categories: "vitamins and supplements" (VS), which accounts for 180 orders per day on average, and "herbal remedies" (HR), which accounts for 30 orders per day on average. Customers request express shipping on an average of 20% of orders, whether they are VS or HR orders. Of course, some days it is more than 20% and other days it is less. The company wants to monitor how much variability there is in the percentage of orders requiring express shipping, and records that percentage for VS and HR separately each day for a month.

Do you think the probability of getting over 30% express shipping orders is higher for VS or for HR?

When I asked my students this question:

- 20% of students thought the probability of >30% express shipping orders would be higher for VS
- 15% of students thought the probability of >30% express shipping orders would be higher for HR
- 65% of students thought the probability of >30% express shipping orders would be about the same for VS and HR.

Psychologists[1] who have asked large numbers of people similar questions get similar results. The correct answer is that it is higher for HR.

The VS samples (180 per day on average) are larger than the HR samples (30 per day on average). The key point here is, "Does the variability in a sample proportion depend on the size of the sample?" The answer is Yes, and it's higher for small samples. In Section 10.2, we'll see why.

[1]Tversky, A., and Kahneman, D. (1974). "Judgement under Uncertainty: Heuristics and Biases," *Science*, Vol. 185.

proportion $p = 0.21$. (We know this is the true value of p because in a simulation we can control it.) It looks bell-shaped and in fact is approximately Normally distributed.

10.2 The Sampling Distribution for Proportions

The distribution of proportions over many independent samples from the same population is called the **sampling distribution** of the proportions. Section 10.1 showed a simulation in which that distribution was bell-shaped and centred at the true proportion, p. In order to model it using the Normal distribution, we need to know its mean and standard deviation, and we know only that the mean is p, the true proportion. What about the standard deviation?

An amazing fact about proportions is that once we know the mean, p, and the sample size, n, we also know the standard deviation of the sampling distribution, as you can see from its formula:

$$SD(\hat{p}) = \sqrt{\frac{p(1 - p)}{n}} = \sqrt{\frac{pq}{n}}$$

If the true proportion of credit card holders who increased their spending by more than \$800 is 0.21, then for samples of size 1000 we expect the distribution of sample proportions to have a standard deviation of

$$SD(\hat{p}) = \sqrt{\frac{p(1 - p)}{n}} = \sqrt{\frac{0.21(1 - 0.21)}{1000}} = 0.0129, \text{ or about } 1.3\%.$$

The Sampling Distribution Model for a Proportion

Provided that the sampled values are independent and the sample size is large enough, the sampling distribution of $\hat{p}$ is modelled by a Normal model with mean $\mu(\hat{p}) = p$ and standard deviation $SD(\hat{p}) = \sqrt{\frac{pq}{n}}$.

Remember that the two samples of size 1000 had proportions of 21.1% and 20.2%. Since the standard deviation of proportions is 1.3%, these two proportions aren't even a full standard deviation apart. In other words, the two samples don't really disagree. Proportions of 21.1% and 20.2% from samples of 1000 are both *consistent* with a true proportion of 21%. We know from Chapter 3 that this difference between sample proportions is referred to as a *sampling error*. But it's not really an *error*; it's the variability you'd expect to see from one sample to another. A better term is **sampling variability**.

We have now answered the question raised at the start of the chapter. To discover how variable a sample proportion is, we need to know the true proportion and the size of the sample. That's all.

Look back at Figure 10.1 to see how well the model worked in our simulation. If $p = 0.21$, we now know that the standard deviation should be about 0.013. The 68-95-99.7 Rule from the Normal model says that 68% of the samples will have proportions within one SD of the mean of 0.21. How closely does our simulation match the predictions? The actual standard deviation of our 2000 *sample* proportions is 0.0129, or 1.29%. And, of the 2000 simulated samples, 1346 of them had proportions between 0.197 and 0.223 (one standard deviation on either side of 0.21). The 68-95-99.7 Rule predicts 68%—the actual number is 1346/2000, or 67.3%.

Now we know everything we need to know to model the sampling distribution. We know the mean and standard deviation of the sampling distribution of proportions: They're p, the true population proportion, and $\sqrt{\frac{pq}{n}}$.

Effect of Sample Size

Because n is in the denominator of $SD(\hat{p})$, the larger the sample, the smaller the standard deviation. We need a small standard deviation to make sound business decisions, but larger samples cost more. That tension is a fundamental issue in Statistics.

We saw this worked well in a simulation, but can we rely on it in all situations? It turns out that this model can be justified theoretically with just a little mathematics; it's based on the Normal approximation to the Binomial distribution that we saw in Chapter 9 (see Optional Math Box). It won't work for *all* situations, but it works for most situations that you'll encounter in practice. We'll provide conditions to check so you'll know when the model is useful.

The sampling distribution model for $\hat{p}$ is valuable for a number of reasons. First, because it is known from mathematics to be a good model (and one that gets better and better as the sample size gets larger), the standard deviation tells us how accurately our sample mean represents the true population mean.

Optional Math Box

Sampling Distribution for Proportions and the Normal Approximation to the Binomial

If the true population proportion is $p = 0.21$, we've seen that the probability of getting $n\hat{p} = 202$ successes out of $n = 1000$ (i.e., $\hat{p} = 0.202$) comes from the Normal distribution with mean $p = 0.21$ and standard deviation $SD = \sqrt{\dfrac{pq}{n}} = \sqrt{\dfrac{0.21 \times 0.79}{1000}} = 0.0129$.

$$z = \frac{\hat{p} - p}{\sqrt{\dfrac{pq}{n}}} = \frac{0202 - 0.21}{0.0129} = -0.621$$

Alternatively, we could look at this as an example of the Binomial distribution. The probability of getting 202 successes out of 1000 is Binomial and can be approximated by the Normal distribution with mean $np = 210$ and standard deviation $SD = \sqrt{npq} = \sqrt{10000 \times 0.21 \times 0.79} = 12.9$.

$$z = \frac{n\hat{p} \pm 0.5 - np}{\sqrt{npq}} = \frac{202 \pm 0.5 - 210}{12.9} \approx -0.621$$

The only difference is that, in the case of the Normal approximation to the Binomial, we add or subtract 0.5 depending on whether we're interested in the probability of getting a value below or above 202. This deals with the fact that the Binomial is a discrete distribution with only integer values, whereas our approach in this chapter based on the sampling distribution for proportions uses the Normal distribution, which is continuous.

The sampling distribution for proportions can therefore be regarded as equivalent to the Normal approximation to the Binomial distribution. Both approaches require the same assumptions and conditions, in particular $np > 10$ and $nq > 10$.

JUST CHECKING

1 You want to poll a random sample of 100 shopping mall customers about whether they like the proposed location for the new coffee shop on the third floor, with a panoramic view of the food court. Of course, you'll get just one number, your sample proportion $\hat{p}$. But if you imagined all the possible samples of 100 customers you could draw and imagined the histogram of all the sample proportions from these samples, what shape would it have?

2 Where would the centre of that histogram be?

3 If you think that about half the customers are in favour of the plan, what would the standard deviation of the sample proportions be?

Answers are found in Appendix A.

How Good Is the Normal Model?

We've seen that the simulated proportions follow the 68-95-99.7 Rule well. But do all sample proportions really work like this? Stop and think for a minute about what we're claiming. We've said that if we draw repeated random samples of the same size, n, from some population and measure the proportion, $\hat{p}$, we get for each sample, then the collection of these proportions will pile up around the underlying population proportion, p, in such a way that a histogram of the sample proportions can be modelled well by a Normal model.

There must be a catch. Suppose the samples were of size two, for example. Then the only possible numbers of successes could be zero, one, or two, and the

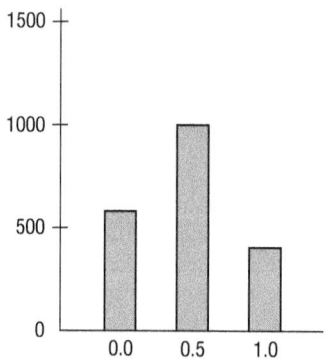

Figure 10.2   Proportions from samples of size two can take on only three possible values. A Normal model does not work well here.

proportion values would be 0, 0.5, and 1. There's no way the histogram could ever look like a Normal model with only three possible values for the variable (Figure 10.2).

Well, there *is* a catch. The claim is only approximately true. (But that's fine. Models are *supposed* to be only approximately true.) And the model becomes a better and better representation of the distribution of the sample proportions as the sample size gets bigger.[2] Samples of size one or two just aren't going to work very well, but the distributions of proportions of many larger samples do have histograms that are remarkably close to a Normal model.

FOR EXAMPLE   Sampling distribution for proportions of telecommunications customers

Rogers provides cable, phone, and internet services to customers, some of whom subscribe to "packages" including several services. Nationwide, suppose that 30% of Rogers customers are "package subscribers" and subscribe to all three types of service. A local representative in Toronto wonders if the proportion in his region is the same as the national proportion.

QUESTIONS   If the same proportion holds in his region and he takes a survey of 100 customers at random from his subscriber list:

1. What proportion of customers would you expect to be package subscribers?
2. What is the standard deviation of the sample proportion?
3. What shape would you expect the sampling distribution of the proportion to have?
4. Would you be surprised to find out that in a sample of 100, 49 of the customers are package subscribers? Explain. What might account for this high percentage?

ANSWERS

1. Because 30% of customers nationwide are package subscribers, we would expect the same for the sample proportion.

2. The standard deviation is $SD(\hat{p}) = \sqrt{\dfrac{pq}{n}} = \sqrt{\dfrac{(0.3)(0.7)}{100}} = 0.046$.

3. Normal.

4. Forty-nine customers results in a sample proportion of 0.49. The mean is 0.30 with a standard deviation of 0.046. This sample proportion is more than four standard deviations higher than the mean: $\dfrac{(0.49 - 0.30)}{0.046} = 4.13$. It would be very unusual to find such a large proportion in a random sample. Either it's a very unusual sample, or the proportion in the representative's region isn't the same as the national average.

Assumptions and Conditions

Most models are useful only when specific assumptions are true. In the case of the model for the distribution of sample proportions, there are two assumptions:

> **Independence Assumption**: The sampled values must be *independent* of each other.
> **Sample Size Assumption**: The sample size, *n*, must be *large* enough.

Of course, the best we can do with assumptions is to think about whether they're likely to be true, and we should do so. However, we can often check corresponding

---

[2]Formally, we say the claim is true in the limit as the sample size (*n*) grows.

conditions that provide information about the assumptions as well. Think about the Independence Assumption and check the following corresponding conditions before using the Normal model to model the distribution of sample proportions:

> **Randomization Condition:** If your data come from an experiment, subjects should have been randomly assigned to treatments. If you have a survey, your sample should be a simple random sample of the population. If some other sampling design was used, be sure the sampling method was not biased and that the data are representative of the population.
>
> **10% Condition:** The sample size, n, must be no larger than 10% of the population.
>
> **Success/Failure Condition:** The Success/Failure Condition says that the sample size must be big enough so that both the number of "successes," np, and the number of "failures," nq, are expected to be at least 10.[3] Expressed without the symbols, this condition says simply that we need to expect at least 10 successes and at least 10 failures to have enough data for sound conclusions. For the bank's credit card promotion example, we labelled as a "success" a cardholder who increases monthly spending by at least $800 during the trial. The bank observed 211 successes and 789 failures. Both are at least 10, so there are certainly enough successes and enough failures for the condition to be satisfied.[4]

These last two conditions seem to contradict each other. The Success/Failure Condition wants a big sample size. How big depends on p. If p is near 0.5, we need a sample of only 20 or more. If p is only 0.01, however, we'd need at least 1000. But the 10% Condition says that the sample size can't be too large a fraction of the population. Fortunately, the tension between them isn't usually a problem in practice. Often, as in polls that sample from all adults, or industrial samples from a day's production, the populations are much larger than 10 times the sample size.

FOR EXAMPLE   **Assumptions and conditions for sample proportions in a customer survey**

The analyst conducting the Rogers survey in For Example: "Sampling distribution for proportions of telecommunications customers" says that, unfortunately, only 20 of the customers he tried to contact actually responded, but that of those 20, 8 are package subscribers.

QUESTIONS

1. If the proportion of package subscribers in his region is 0.30, how many package subscribers, on average, would you expect in a sample of 20?
2. Would you expect the shape of the sampling distribution of the proportion to be Normal? Explain.

ANSWERS

1. You would expect $0.30 \times 20 = 6$ package subscribers.
2. No. Because 6 is less than 10, we should be cautious in using the Normal as a model for the sampling distribution of proportions. (The number of *observed* successes, 8, is also less than 10.)

---

[3] Why 10? We'll discuss this when we discuss confidence intervals.

[4] The Success/Failure Condition is about the number of successes and failures we *expect*, but if the number of successes and failures that *occurred* is $\geq$ 10, then you can use that.

GUIDED EXAMPLE   Foreclosures

Galina Barskaya/Shutterstock

An analyst at a home-loan lender was looking at a package of 90 mortgages that the company had recently purchased in central New Brunswick. The analyst was aware that in that region about 13% of the homeowners with current mortgages will default on their loans in the next year and that the houses will go into foreclosure. In deciding to buy the collection of mortgages, the finance department assumed that no more than 15 of the mortgages would go into default. Any amount above that will result in losses for the company. In the package of 90 mortgages, what's the probability that there will be more than 15 foreclosures?

PLAN	**Setup** State the objective of the study.	We want to find the probability that in a group of 90 mortgages more than 15 will default. Since 15 out of 90 is 16.7%, we need the probability of finding more than 16.7% defaults out of a sample of 90, if the proportion of defaults is 13%.
	Model Check the conditions.	✓ **Independence Assumption** If the mortgages come from a wide geographical area, one homeowner defaulting should not affect the probability that another does. However, if the mortgages come from the same neighbourhood(s), the Independence Assumption may fail and our estimates of the default probabilities may be wrong.
		✓ **Randomization Condition** The 90 mortgages in the package can be considered as a random sample of mortgages in the region.
		✓ **10% Condition** The 90 mortgages are less than 10% of the population.
		✓ **Success/Failure Condition** $np = 90(0.13) = 11.7 \geq 10$ $np = 90(0.87) = 78.3 \geq 10$
	State the parameters and the sampling distribution model.	The population proportion is $p = 0.13$. The conditions are satisfied, so we'll model the sampling distribution of $\hat{p}$ with a Normal model, with mean 0.13 and standard deviation $$SD(\hat{p}) = \sqrt{\frac{pq}{n}} = \sqrt{\frac{(0.13)(0.87)}{90}} = 0.035.$$
	Plot Make a picture. Sketch the model and shade the area we're interested in—in this case the area to the right of 16.7%.	We want to find $P(\hat{p} > 0.167)$. 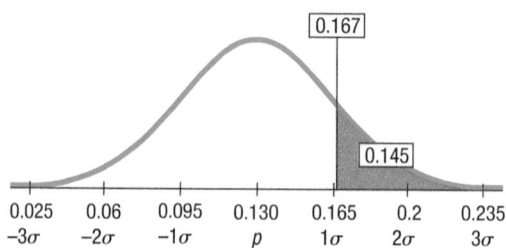
DO	**Mechanics** Use the standard deviation as a ruler to find the z-score of the cutoff proportion. Find the resulting probability from a table, a computer program, or a calculator.	$$z = \frac{\hat{p} - p}{SD(\hat{p})} = \frac{0.167 - 0.13}{0.035} = 1.06$$ $$P(\hat{p} > 0.167) = P(z > 1.06) = 0.1446$$

REPORT	Conclusion Interpret the probability in the context of the question.	MEMO **Re: Mortgage Defaults** Assuming that the 90 mortgages we recently purchased are a random sample of mortgages in this region, there's about a 14.5% chance that we'll exceed the 15 foreclosures that Finance has determined as the breakeven point.

LO❸ **10.3**

The Central Limit Theorem—The Fundamental Theorem of Statistics

Type of Sampling Distribution	Information on Each Instance
Proportions Sections 10.1 and 10.2	Yes/No
Means Sections 10.3 and 10.4	Quantitative

When we sample proportions at random, the results we get will vary from sample to sample. The Normal model seems an incredibly simple way to summarize all that variation. Could something that simple work for means? We won't keep you in suspense. It turns out that means also have a sampling distribution that we can model with a Normal model. And it turns out that there's a theoretical result that proves it to be so. As we did with proportions, we can get some insight from a simulation.

Simulating the Sampling Distribution of a Mean

Here's a simple simulation with a quantitative variable. Let's start with one fair die. If we toss this die 10,000 times, what should the histogram of the numbers on the face of the die look like? Figure 10.3 shows the results of a simulated 10,000 tosses.

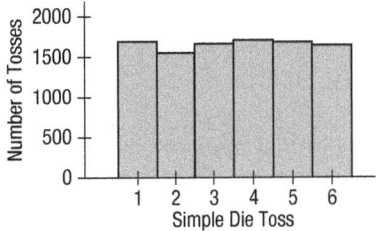

Figure 10.3   Simple die toss.

That's called the *uniform distribution*, and it's certainly not Normal. Now let's toss a *pair* of dice and record the average of the two. If we repeat this (or at least simulate repeating it) 10,000 times, recording the average of each pair, what will the histogram of these 10,000 averages look like? Before you look, think a minute. Is getting an average of 1 on *two* dice as likely as getting an average of 3 or 3.5? Let's look at the results in Figure 10.4.

We're much more likely to get an average near 3.5 than we are to get one near 1 or 6. Without calculating those probabilities exactly, it's fairly easy to see that the *only* way to get an average of 1 is to get two 1s. To get a total of 7 (for an average of 3.5), though, there are many more possibilities. This distribution even has a name—the *triangular distribution*.

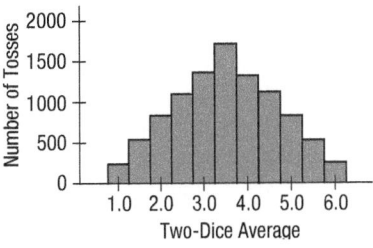

Figure 10.4   Two-dice average.

What if we average three dice? We'll simulate 10,000 tosses of three dice and take their average in Figure 10.5.

What's happening? First notice that it's getting harder to have averages near the ends. Getting an average of 1 or 6 with three dice requires all three to come up 1 or 6, respectively. That's less likely than for two dice to come up both 1 or both 6. The distribution is being pushed toward the middle. But what's happening to the shape?

Let's continue this simulation to see what happens with larger samples. Figure 10.6 shows a histogram of the averages for 10,000 tosses of five dice.

The pattern is becoming clearer. Two things are happening. The first fact we know already from the Law of Large Numbers, which we saw in Chapter 8. It says that as the sample size (number of dice) gets larger, each sample average tends to become closer to the population mean. So we see the shape continuing to tighten around 3.5. But the shape of the distribution is the surprising part. It's becoming bell-shaped. In fact, it's approaching the Normal model.

Are you convinced? Let's skip ahead and try 20 dice. The histogram of averages for 10,000 throws of 20 dice is shown in Figure 10.7.

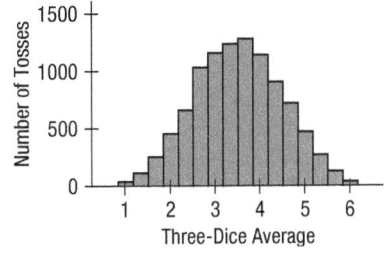

Figure 10.5   Three-dice average.

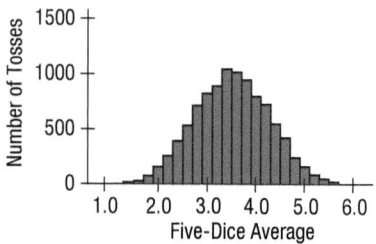

Figure 10.6   Five-dice average.

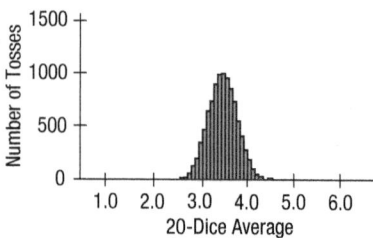

Figure 10.7   Twenty-dice average.

> **The Central Limit Theorem (CLT)**
>
> The mean of a random sample has a sampling distribution whose shape can be approximated by a Normal model. The larger the sample, the better the approximation will be.

The theory of probabilities is at bottom nothing but common sense reduced to calculus.

—Laplace, in *Théorie Analytique des Probabilités*, 1812

Laplace was one of the greatest scientists and mathematicians of his time. In addition to his contributions to probability and statistics, he published many new results in mathematics, physics, and astronomy (where his nebular theory was one of the first to describe the formation of the solar system in much the same way it is understood today). He also played a leading role in establishing the metric system of measurement.

His brilliance, though, sometimes got him into trouble. A visitor to the Académie des Sciences in Paris reported that Laplace let it be known widely that he considered himself the best mathematician in France. The effect of this on his colleagues was not eased by the fact that Laplace was right.

Now we see the Normal shape again (and notice how much smaller the spread is). But can we count on this happening for situations other than dice throws? What kinds of sample means have sampling distributions that we can model with a Normal model? It turns out that Normal models work well amazingly often.

The Central Limit Theorem

The dice simulation may look like a special situation. But it turns out that what we saw with dice is true for means of repeated samples for almost every situation. When we looked at the sampling distribution of a proportion, we had to check only a few conditions. For means, the result is even more remarkable. There are almost no conditions at all.

Let's say that again: The sampling distribution of almost *any* mean becomes Normal as the sample size grows. All we need is for the observations to be independent and collected with randomization. We don't even care about the shape of the population distribution![5] This surprising fact was proven in a fairly general form in 1810 by Pierre-Simon Laplace, and it caused quite a stir (at least in mathematics circles) because it is so unintuitive. Laplace's result is called the **Central Limit Theorem (CLT)**.[6]

Not only does the distribution of means of many random samples get closer and closer to a Normal model as the sample size grows, but *this is true regardless of the shape of the population distribution!* Even if we sample from a skewed or bimodal population, the Central Limit Theorem tells us that means of repeated random samples will tend to follow a Normal model as the sample size grows. Of course, you won't be surprised to learn that it works better and faster the closer the population distribution is to a Normal model. And it works better for larger samples. If the data come from a population that's exactly Normal to start with, then the observations themselves are Normal. If we take samples of size one, their "means" are just the observations—so of course they have a Normal sampling distribution. But now suppose the population distribution is very skewed (like the CEO data from Chapter 5, for example). The CLT works, although it may take a sample size of dozens or even hundreds of observations for the Normal model to work well.

For example, think about a real bimodal population, one that consists of only 0s and 1s. The CLT says that even means of samples from this population will follow a Normal sampling distribution model. But wait. Suppose we have a categorical variable and we assign a 1 to each individual in the category and a 0 to each individual not in the category. Then we find the mean of these 0s and 1s. That's the same as counting the number of individuals who are in the category and dividing by n. That mean will be the *sample proportion*, $\hat{p}$, of individuals who are in the category (a "success"). So maybe it wasn't so surprising that proportions, like means, have Normal sampling distribution models; proportions are actually just a special case of Laplace's remarkable theorem. Of course, for such an extremely bimodal population, we need a reasonably large sample size—and that's where the Success/Failure Condition for proportions comes in.

Be careful. We've been slipping smoothly between the real world, in which we draw random samples of data, and a magical mathematical-model world, in which we describe how the sample means and proportions we observe in the real world might behave if we could see the results from every random sample we might have drawn. Now we have *two* distributions to deal with. The first is the real-world distribution of the sample, which we might display with a histogram (for quantitative

---

[5]Technically, the data must come from a population with a finite variance.

[6]The word "central" in the name of the theorem means "fundamental." It doesn't refer to the centre of a distribution.

data) or with a bar chart or table (for categorical data). The second is the math-world *sampling distribution* of the statistic, which we model with a Normal model based on the Central Limit Theorem. Don't confuse the two.

For example, don't mistakenly think the CLT says that the *data* are Normally distributed as long as the sample is large enough. In fact, as samples get larger, we expect the distribution of the data to look more and more like the distribution of the population from which it is drawn—skewed, bimodal, whatever—but not necessarily Normal. You can collect a sample of CEO salaries for the next 1000 years, but the histogram will never look Normal. It will be skewed to the right. The Central Limit Theorem doesn't talk about the distribution of the data from the sample. It talks about the sample *means* and sample *proportions* of many different random samples drawn from the same population. Of course, we never actually draw all those samples, so the CLT is talking about an imaginary distribution—the sampling distribution model.

When the population shape is not unimodal and symmetric, it takes longer for the sampling distribution to resemble the Normal. But with a large enough sample, the CLT applies to means of almost any data set.

FOR EXAMPLE   **The Central Limit Theorem for retail customers**

The manager in For Example: "The distribution of a sample proportion of retail customers" also examines the amount spent by customers using the self-checkout stations. He finds that the distribution of these amounts is unimodal but skewed to the high end because some customers make unusually expensive purchases. He finds the mean spent on each of the 60 days studied and makes a histogram of those values.

QUESTIONS

1. What shape would you expect for this histogram?
2. If, instead of averaging all customers on each day, the manager selects the first 10 for each day and just averages those, how would you expect his histogram of the means to differ from the one in (1)?

ANSWERS

1. Approximately Normal. It doesn't matter that the sample is drawn from a skewed distribution; the CLT tells us that the means will follow a Normal model.
2. The CLT requires large samples. Samples of 10 are not large enough.

LO❸   10.4   ## The Sampling Distribution of the Mean

The CLT says that the sampling distribution of any mean or proportion is approximately Normal. But which Normal? We know that any Normal model is specified by its mean and standard deviation. For proportions, the sampling distribution is centred at the population proportion. For means, it's centred at the population mean. What else would we expect?

What about the standard deviations? We noticed in our dice simulation that the histograms got narrower as the number of dice we averaged increased. This shouldn't be surprising. Means vary less than the individual observations. Think about it for a minute. Which would be more surprising: having *one* person in your Statistics class who is over two metres tall, or having the *mean* of 100 students taking the course be over two metres? The first event is fairly rare. You may have seen somebody this tall in one of your classes sometime. But finding a class of 100

For the sample mean, $\bar{y}$, the standard error is

$$SE(\bar{y}) = \frac{s}{\sqrt{n}}.$$

You may see a "standard error" reported by a computer program in a summary or offered by a calculator. It's safe to assume that if no statistic is specified, what was meant is $SE(\bar{y})$, the standard error of the mean.

JUST CHECKING

4 The entrance exam for business schools, the GMAT, given to 100 students had a mean of 520 and a standard deviation of 120. What was the standard error for the mean of this sample of students?

5 As the sample size increases, what happens to the standard error, assuming the standard deviation of the samples remains constant?

6 If the sample size is doubled, what is the impact on the standard error?

Answers are found in Appendix A.

To keep track of how the concepts we've seen combine, we can draw a diagram relating them. At the heart is the idea that *the statistic itself (the proportion or the mean) is a random quantity*. We can't know what our statistic will be because it comes from a random sample. A different random sample would have given a different result. This sample-to-sample variability is what generates the sampling distribution, the distribution of all the possible values that the statistic could have had.

We could simulate that distribution by pretending to take lots of samples. Fortunately, for the mean and the proportion, the CLT tells us that we can model their sampling distribution directly with a Normal model.

The two basic truths about sampling distributions are as follows:

1. Sampling distributions arise because samples vary. Each random sample will contain different cases, and so a different value of the statistic.
2. Although we can always simulate a sampling distribution, the Central Limit Theorem saves us the trouble for means and proportions.

Figure 10.8 diagrams the process.

Figure 10.8   We start with a population model, which can have any shape. It can even be bimodal or skewed (as this one is). We label the mean of this model μ and its standard deviation σ.

We draw one real sample (solid line) of size *n* and show its histogram and summary statistics. We imagine (or simulate) drawing many other samples (dotted lines), which have their own histograms and summary statistics.

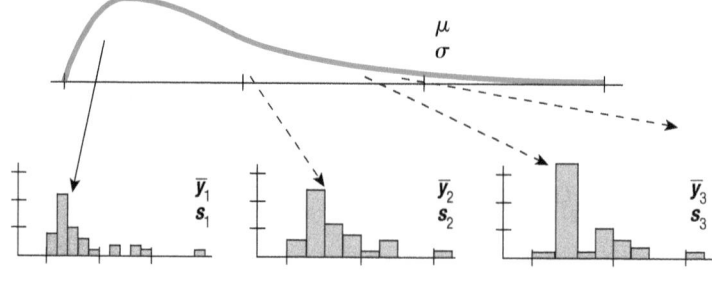

We imagine gathering all the means into a histogram.

The CLT tells us that we can model the shape of this histogram with a Normal model. The mean of this Normal is μ, and the standard deviation is $SD(\bar{y}) = \dfrac{\sigma}{\sqrt{n}}$. When we don't know σ, we estimate it with the standard deviation of the one real sample. That gives us the standard error $SE(\bar{y}) = \dfrac{s}{\sqrt{n}}$.

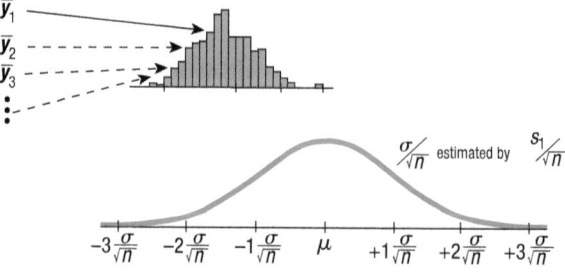

WHAT CAN GO WRONG?

- **Don't confuse the sampling distribution with the distribution of the sample.** When you take a sample, you always look at the distribution of the values, usually with a histogram, and you may calculate summary statistics. Examining the distribution of the sample like this is wise. But that's not the sampling distribution. The sampling distribution is an imaginary collection of the values that a statistic, such as a proportion or a mean, might have taken for all the random samples—the one you got and the ones you didn't get. Use the sampling distribution model to make statements about how the statistic varies.

- **Beware of observations that are not independent.** The CLT depends crucially on the assumption of independence. Unfortunately, this isn't something you can check in your data. You have to think about how the data were gathered. Good sampling practice and well-designed randomized experiments ensure independence.

- **Watch out for small samples when dealing with proportions.** The Success/Failure Condition tells us to make sure the sample size is large enough that $np > 10$ and $nq > 10$. That's okay if we know p (and hence $q = 1 - p$), but the reason we are taking a sample from our population is to estimate p and q. We need to choose n large enough for any reasonable p and q that we might expect to find, and then when we have an estimate of p and q from our sample, go back and check whether n was in fact large enough.

- **Watch out for small samples from skewed populations when dealing with means.** The CLT assures us that the sampling distribution model is Normal if n is large enough. If the population is nearly Normal, even small samples may work. If the population is very skewed, then n will have to be large before the Normal model will work well. Unfortunately, there's no good rule to handle this. It just depends on how skewed the data distribution is.

ETHICS IN ACTION

A national retailer of contemporary furniture and home decor has recently received customer complaints about the delivery of its products. This retailer uses different carriers depending on the order destination. Its policy with regard to most items it sells and ships is to simply deliver to the customer's doorstep. However, its policy with regard to furniture is to "deliver, unpack, and place furniture in the intended area of the home." Most of the recent complaints have been from customers who were dissatisfied because their furniture deliveries were not unpacked and placed in their homes. Since the retailer uses different carriers, it's important for it to label its packages correctly so the delivery company can distinguish between furniture and nonfurniture deliveries. The retailer sets as a target "1% or less" for incorrect labelling of packages. Joe Zangard, V.P. Logistics, was asked to look into the problem. The retailer's largest warehouse prepares about 1000 items per week for shipping. Joe's initial attention was directed at this facility, not only because of its large volume, but also because he had some reservations about the newly hired warehouse manager, Brent Mossir. Packages at the warehouse were randomly selected and examined over a period of several weeks. Out of 1000 packages, 13 were labelled incorrectly. Since Joe had expected the count to be 10 or fewer, he was confident that he had now pinpointed the problem. His next step was to set up a meeting with Brent in order to discuss the ways in which he can improve the labelling process at his warehouse.

Ethical Issue *Joe is treating the sample proportion as if it were the true fixed value. By not recognizing that this sample proportion varies from sample to sample, he has unfairly judged*

(continued)

> *the labelling process at Brent's warehouse. This is consistent with his initial misgivings about Brent being hired as warehouse manager (related to Item A, ASA Ethical Guidelines; see Appendix C, the American Statistical Association's Ethical Guidelines for Statistical Practice, also available online at www.amstat.org/about/ethicalguidelines.cfm).*

> **Ethical Solution**　*Joe Zangard needs to use the Normal distribution to model the sampling distribution for the sample proportion. In this way, he would realize that the sample proportion observed is less than one standard deviation away from 1% (the upper limit of the target) and thus not conclusively larger than the limit.*

WHAT HAVE WE LEARNED?

Learning Objectives

❶ We know that no sample fully and exactly describes the population; sample proportions and means will vary from sample to sample. That's sampling variability. We know it will always be present—indeed, the world would be a boring place if variability didn't exist. You might think sampling variability would prevent us from learning anything reliable about a population by looking at a sample, but that's just not so. The fortunate fact is that sampling variability is not just unavoidable—it's predictable!

❷ We've learned how to describe the behaviour of sample proportions—shape, centre, and spread—as long as certain conditions are met. The sample must be random, of course, and large enough that we expect at least 10 successes and 10 failures. Then,
- The sampling distribution (the imagined histogram of the proportions from all possible samples) is shaped like a Normal model.
- The mean of the sampling model is the true proportion in the population.
- The standard deviation of the sample proportions is $\sqrt{\dfrac{pq}{n}}$.

❸ We've learned to describe the behaviour of sample means based on the Central Limit Theorem—the fundamental theorem of Statistics. Again the sample must be random and needs to be larger if our data come from a population that's not roughly unimodal and symmetric. Then,
- Regardless of the shape of the original population, the shape of the distribution of the means of all possible samples can be described by a Normal model, provided the samples are large enough.
- The centre of the sampling model will be the true mean of the population from which we took the sample.
- The standard deviation of the sample means is the population's standard deviation divided by the square root of the sample size, $\dfrac{\sigma}{\sqrt{n}}$.

Terms

Central Limit Theorem (CLT)	The Central Limit Theorem (CLT) states that the sampling distribution model of the sample mean (and proportion) is approximately Normal for large n, regardless of the distribution of the population, as long as the observations are independent.
Sampling distribution	The distribution of a statistic over many independent samples of the same size from the same population.
Sampling distribution model for the mean	If the Independence Assumption and Randomization Condition are met and the sample size is large enough, the sampling distribution of the sample mean is well modelled by a Normal model with a mean equal to the population mean, μ, and a standard deviation equal to $\dfrac{\sigma}{\sqrt{n}}$.
Sampling distribution model for a proportion	If the Independence Assumption and Randomization Condition are met and we expect at least 10 successes and 10 failures, then the sampling distribution of a proportion is well modelled by a Normal model with a mean equal to the true proportion value, p, and a standard deviation equal to $\sqrt{\dfrac{pq}{n}}$.

Sampling variability	The variability we expect to see from sample to sample.
Standard error (SE)	When the standard deviation of the sampling distribution of a statistic is estimated from the data.

Skills

Plan
- Understand that the variability of a statistic (as measured by the standard deviation of its sampling distribution) depends on the size of the sample. Statistics based on larger samples are less variable.
- Understand that the Central Limit Theorem gives the sampling distribution model of the mean for sufficiently large samples regardless of the underlying population.

Do
- Be able to use a sampling distribution model to make simple statements about the distribution of a proportion or mean under repeated sampling.

Report
- Be able to interpret a sampling distribution model as describing the values taken by a statistic in all possible realizations of a sample or randomized experiment under the same conditions.

MINI case studies

MBNA Canada

MBNA Canada's affiliates program allows other organizations to offer credit cards to their members. The Toronto Blue Jays and the Edmonton Eskimos both use MBNA's affiliates program, as does the Canadian Automobile Association. Whenever a member of one of these organizations makes a purchase using the card, MBNA processes the transaction and gives a certain percentage of the value of the transaction to the organization.

Pat Crowe II/AP Images

Suppose you're working for a sports club that's considering joining MBNA's affiliates program. You know that many of your members would be proud to use a card with your logo on it, but you also know that many of them already have other credit cards, and you don't want to annoy them by offering them another one if they don't want it. The president of the club decides to become an MBNA affiliate only if the proportion of members signing on for the new card is over 3%. You know from a colleague in another club that they had a take-up rate for affiliate cards of 4.3%. You think the other club is similar to yours and decide to survey 100 of your members to find out how many would accept the new card.

What is the probability that more than 3% of your sample would accept the new card? State your assumptions clearly. Indicate on a graph how this probability changes if you increase your sample size in increments of 100 from 100 to 1000. Approximately what sample size do you recommend?

Real Estate Simulation

Many variables important to the real estate market are skewed, limited to only a few values or considered as categorical variables. Yet marketing and business decisions are often made based on means and proportions calculated over many homes. One reason these statistics are useful is the Central Limit Theorem.

(continued)

Data on 1063 houses sold recently in the Saratoga, New York, area are in the file **ch10_MCSP_Real_Estate**. Let's investigate how the CLT guarantees that the sampling distribution of proportions approaches Normal and that the same is true for means of a quantitative variable even when samples are drawn from populations that are far from Normal.

Part 1: Proportions

The variable *Fireplace* is a dichotomous variable, where 1 = *has a fireplace* and 0 = *does not have a fireplace*.

- Calculate the proportion of homes that have fireplaces for all 1063 homes. Using this value, calculate what the standard error of the sample proportion would be for a sample of size 50.

- Using the software of your choice, draw 100 samples of size 50 from this population of homes, find the proportion of homes with fireplaces in each of these samples, and make a histogram of these proportions.

- Compare the mean and standard deviation of this (sampling) distribution to what you previously calculated.

Part 2: Means

- Select one of the quantitative variables and make a histogram of the entire population of 1063 homes. Describe the distribution (including its mean and SD).

- Using the software of your choice, draw 100 samples of size 50 from this population of homes, find the means of these samples, and make a histogram of these means.

- Compare the (sampling) distribution of the means to the distribution of the population.

- Repeat the exercise with samples of sizes 10 and 30. What do you notice about the effect of the sample size?

Some statistics packages make it easier than others to draw many samples and find means. Your instructor can provide advice on the path to follow for your package. If you're using Excel, you'll need to use the DDXL add-in to make your histograms.

An alternative approach is to have each member of the class draw one sample to find the proportion and mean and then combine the statistics for the entire class.

EXERCISES

SECTION 10.1

1. An investment website can tell what devices are used to access the site. The site managers wonder whether they should enhance the facilities for trading via smart phones, so they want to estimate the proportion of users who access the site that way (even if they also use their computers sometimes). They draw a random sample of 200 investors from their customers. Suppose that the true proportion of smart phone users is 36%.

a) What would you expect the shape of the sampling distribution for the sample proportion to be?
b) What would be the mean of this sampling distribution?
c) If the sample size were increased to 500, would your answers change? Explain. **LO ❶**

2. The proportion of adult women in Canada is approximately 51%. A marketing survey telephones 400 people at random.

a) What proportion of women in the sample of 400 would you expect to see?

b) How many women, on average, would you expect to find in a sample of that size? (*Hint:* Multiply the expected proportion by the sample size.) **LO ❶**

SECTION 10.2

3. The investment website in Exercise 1 draws a random sample of 200 investors from its customers. Suppose that the true proportion of smart phone users is 36%.

a) What would be the standard deviation of the sampling distribution of the proportion of smart phone users?

b) What is the probability that the sample proportion of smart phone users is greater than 0.36?

c) What is the probability that it's between 0.30 and 0.40?

d) What is the probability that it's less than 0.28?

e) What is the probability that it's greater than 0.42? **LO ❷**

4. The proportion of adult women in Canada is approximately 51%. A marketing survey telephones 400 people at random.

a) What is the sampling distribution of the observed proportion that are women?

b) What is the standard deviation of that proportion?

c) Would you be surprised to find 53% women in a sample of size 400? Explain.

d) Would you be surprised to find 41% women in a sample of size 400? Explain.

e) Would you be surprised to find that there were fewer than 160 women in the sample? Explain. **LO ❷**

5. A real estate agent wants to know how many owners of homes worth over $1,000,000 might be considering putting their home on the market in the next 12 months. He surveys 40 of them and finds that 10 are considering such a move. Are all the assumptions and conditions for finding the sampling distribution of the proportion satisfied? Explain briefly. **LO ❷**

6. A tourist agency wants to know what proportion of visitors to the Eiffel Tower are from Asia. To find out, the agency surveys 100 people in the line to purchase tickets to the top of the tower one Sunday afternoon in May. Are all the assumptions and conditions for finding the sampling distribution of the proportion satisfied? Explain briefly. **LO ❷**

SECTION 10.3

7. Games for the iPad have a distribution of prices that is skewed to the high end.

a) Explain why this is what you would expect.

b) Members of the iPad gamers club each own about 50 games. Pat is one such member. What would you expect the shape of the distribution of game prices on her iPad to be?

c) Each club member computes the average price of his or her games. What shape would you expect the distribution of these averages to have? **LO ❸**

8. For a sample of 36 houses, what would you expect the distribution of the sale prices to be? A real estate agent has been assigned 10 houses at random to sell this month. She wants to know whether the mean price of those houses is typical. What, if anything, does she need to assume about the distribution of prices to be able to use the Central Limit Theorem? Are those assumptions reasonable? **LO ❸**

SECTION 10.4

9. According to a Gallup poll, 27% of adults have high levels of cholesterol. According to recent studies, cholesterol levels in healthy adults average about 215 mg/dL with a standard deviation of about 30 mg/dL and are roughly Normally distributed. If the cholesterol levels of a sample of 42 healthy adults are taken,

a) What shape should the sampling distribution of the mean have?

b) What would the mean of the sampling distribution be?

c) What would its standard deviation be?

d) If the sample size were increased to 100, how would your answers to (a) to (c) change? **LO ❸**

10. As in Exercise 9, cholesterol levels in healthy adults average about 215 mg/dL with a standard deviation of about 30 mg/dL and are roughly Normally distributed. If the cholesterol levels of a sample of 42 healthy adults are taken, what is the probability that the mean cholesterol level of the sample

a) Will be no more than 215?

b) Will be between 205 and 225?

c) Will be less than 200?

d) Will be greater than 220? **LO ❸**

SECTION 10.5

11. A marketing researcher for a phone company surveys 100 people and finds that the proportion of clients who are likely to switch providers when their contract expires is 0.15.

a) What is the standard deviation of the sampling distribution of the proportion?

b) If the researcher wants to reduce the standard deviation by half, how large a sample would she need? **LO ❷, ❸**

12. A market researcher for a provider of iPod accessories wants to know the proportion of customers who own cars in order to assess the market for a new iPod car charger. A survey of 500 customers indicates that 76% own cars.

a) What is the standard deviation of the sampling distribution of the proportion?

b) How large would the standard deviation have been if the researcher had surveyed only 125 customers (assuming the proportion is about the same)? **LO ❷, ❸**

CHAPTER EXERCISES

13. Send money, part 1. When it sends out its fundraising letter, a philanthropic organization typically gets a return from about 5% of the people on its mailing list. To see what the response rate might be for future appeals, it did a simulation using samples of size 20, 50, 100, and 200. For each sample size, it simulated 1000 mailings with success rate $p = 0.05$ and constructed the histogram of the 1000 sample proportions shown below. Explain how these histograms demonstrate what the Central Limit Theorem says about the sampling distribution model for sample proportions. Be sure to talk about shape, centre, and spread. **LO ❶**

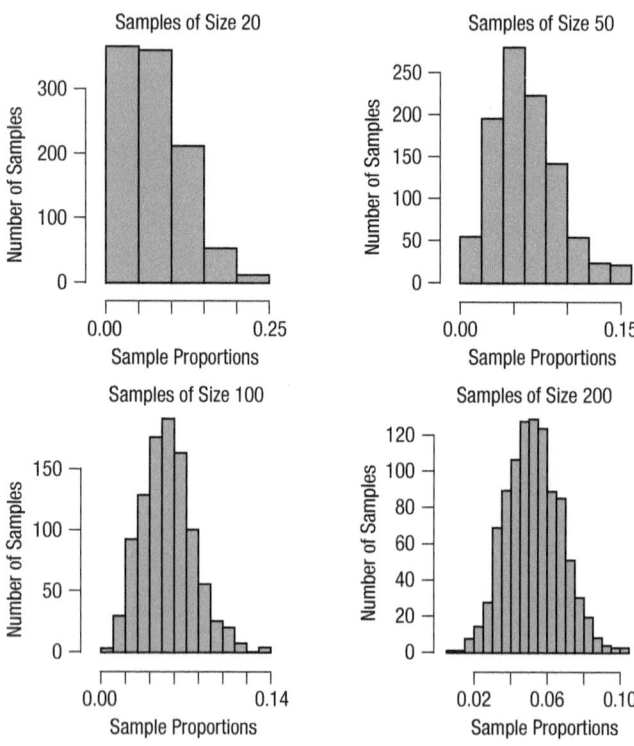

14. Send money, part 2. The philanthropic organization in Exercise 13 expects about a 5% success rate when it sends fundraising letters to the people on its mailing list. In Exercise 13 you looked at the histograms showing distributions of sample proportions from 1000 simulated mailings for samples of size 20, 50, 100, and 200. The sample statistics from each simulation were as follows:

n	mean	st. dev.
20	0.0497	0.0479
50	0.0516	0.0309
100	0.0497	0.0215
200	0.0501	0.0152

a) According to the Central Limit Theorem, what should the theoretical mean and standard deviations be for these sample sizes?

b) How close are those theoretical values to what was observed in these simulations?

c) Looking at the histograms in Exercise 13, at what sample size would you be comfortable using the Normal model as an approximation for the sampling distribution?

d) What does the Success/Failure Condition say about the choice you made in (c)? **LO ❷**

15. Stock picking, part 1. A professor asks a student to select stocks by throwing 16 darts at pages of *The Wall Street Journal*. They then check to see whether their stock picks rose or fell the next day and report their proportion of "successes." As a lesson, the professor has selected pages of the *Journal* for which exactly half the publicly traded stocks went up and half went down. The professor then makes a histogram of the reported proportions.

a) What shape would you expect this histogram to be? Why?

b) Where do you expect the histogram to be centred?

c) How much variability would you expect among these proportions?

d) Explain why a Normal model should not be used here.

16. Quality management, part 1. Manufacturing companies strive to maintain production consistency, but it's often difficult for outsiders to tell whether they've succeeded. Sometimes, however, we can find a simple example. The candy company that makes M&M'S claims that 10% of the candies it produces are green and that bags are packed randomly. We can check on its production controls by sampling bags of candies. Suppose we open bags containing about 50 M&M'S and record the proportion of green candies.

a) If we plot a histogram showing the proportions of green candies in the various bags, what shape would you expect it to have?

b) Can that histogram be approximated by a Normal model? Explain.

c) Where should the centre of the histogram be?

d) What should the standard deviation of the proportion be? **LO ❷**

17. Stock picking, part 2. The class in Exercise 15 expands its stock-picking experiment.

a) The students use computer-generated random numbers to choose 25 stocks each. Use the 68-95-99.7 Rule to describe the sampling distribution model.

b) Confirm that you can use a Normal model here.

c) The students increase the number of stocks picked to 64 each. Draw and label the appropriate sampling distribution model. Check the appropriate conditions to justify your model.

d) Explain how the sampling distribution model changes as the number of stocks picked increases. **LO ❷**

18. Quality management, part 2. Would a bigger sample help us assess manufacturing consistency? Suppose that instead of the 50-candy bags in Exercise 16, we work with bags that contain 200 M&M'S each. Again we calculate the proportion of green candies found.

a) Explain why it's appropriate to use a Normal model to describe the distribution of the proportion of green M&M'S we might expect.

b) Use the 68-95-99.7 Rule to describe how this proportion might vary from bag to bag.

c) How would this model change if the bags contained even more candies? **LO ❷**

19. Stock picking, part 3. One student in the class from Exercise 15 claims to have found a winning strategy. He watches a cable news show about investing and *during the show* throws his darts at the pages of the *Journal*. He claims that of 200 stocks picked in this manner, 58% were winners.

a) What do you think of his claim? Explain.

b) If there are 100 students in the class, are you surprised that one was this successful? Explain. **LO ❷**

20. Quality management, part 3. In a really large bag of M&M'S, we found that 12% of 500 candies were green. Is this evidence that the manufacturing process is out of control and has made too many greens? Explain. **LO ❷**

21. Speeding. Police believe that 70% of the drivers travelling on a major highway exceed the speed limit. They plan to set up a radar trap and check the speeds of 80 cars.

a) Using the 68-95-99.7 Rule, draw and label the distribution of the proportion of these cars the police will observe speeding.

b) Do you think the appropriate conditions necessary for your analysis are met? Explain. **LO ❷**

22. Smoking. Public health statistics indicate that 20.6% of adults smoke cigarettes. Using the 68-95-99.7 Rule, describe the sampling distribution model for the proportion of smokers among a randomly selected group of 50 adults. Be sure to discuss your assumptions and conditions. **LO ❷**

23. Vision. It is generally believed that nearsightedness affects about 12% of all children. A school district has registered 170 incoming kindergarten children.

a) Can you apply the Central Limit Theorem to describe the sampling distribution model for the sample proportion of children who are nearsighted? Check the conditions and discuss any assumptions you need to make.

b) Sketch and clearly label the sampling model, based on the 68-95-99.7 Rule.

c) How many of the incoming students might the school expect to be nearsighted? Give a range two standard deviations either side of the mean. **LO ❷**

24. Contacts. The campus representative for Lens.com wants to know what percentage of students at a university currently wear contact lenses. Suppose the true proportion is 30%.

a) We randomly pick 100 students. Let $\hat{p}$ represent the proportion of students in this sample who wear contacts. What's the appropriate model for the distribution of $\hat{p}$? Specify the name of the distribution, the mean, and the standard deviation. Be sure to verify that the conditions are met.

b) What's the approximate probability that more than one-third of this sample wear contacts? **LO ❷**

25. Back to school, part 1 Best known for its testing program, ACT Inc. also compiles data on a variety of issues in education. In 2004 the company reported that the national college freshman-to-sophomore retention rate held steady at 74% over the previous four years. Consider colleges with freshman classes of 400 students. Use the 68-95-99.7 Rule to describe the sampling distribution model for the percentage of those students we expect to return to that school for their sophomore years. Do you think the appropriate conditions are met? **LO ❷**

26. Back to school, part 2. Based on the 74% national retention rate described in Exercise 25, does a college where 522 of the 603 freshman returned the next year as sophomores have a right to brag that it has an unusually high retention rate? Explain. **LO ❷**

27. Polling. Just before a referendum on a school budget, a local newspaper polls 400 voters in an attempt to predict whether the budget will pass. Suppose that the budget actually has the support of 52% of the voters. What's the probability that the newspaper's sample will lead it to predict defeat? Be sure to verify that the assumptions and conditions necessary for your analysis are met. **LO ❷**

28. Seeds. Information on a packet of seeds claims that the germination rate is 92%. What's the probability that more than 95% of the 160 seeds in the packet will germinate? Be sure to discuss your assumptions and check the conditions that support your model. **LO ❷**

29. Apples. When a truckload of apples arrives at a packing plant, a random sample of 150 is selected and examined for bruises, discolouration, and other defects. The whole truckload will be rejected if more than 5% of the sample is unsatisfactory. Suppose that in fact 8% of the apples on the truck do not meet the desired standard. What's the probability that the shipment will be accepted anyway? **LO ❷**

30. Genetic defect. It's believed that 4% of children have a gene that may be linked to juvenile diabetes. Researchers hoping to track 20 of these children for several years test 732 newborns for the presence of this gene. What's the probability that they find enough subjects for their study?

31. Sampling, part 1. A sample is chosen randomly from a population that can be described by a Normal model.

a) What's the sampling distribution model for the sample mean? Describe shape, centre, and spread.

b) If we choose a larger sample, what's the effect on this sampling distribution model? **LO ❸**

32. Sampling, part 2. A sample is chosen randomly from a population that was strongly skewed to the left.

a) Describe the sampling distribution model for the sample mean if the sample size is small.

b) If we make the sample larger, what happens to the sampling distribution model's shape, centre, and spread?

c) As we make the sample larger, what happens to the expected distribution of the data in the sample? **LO ❸**

33. Waist size, part 1. A study commissioned by a clothing manufacturer measured the *Waist Size* of 250 men, finding a mean of 36.33 inches and a standard deviation of 4.02 inches. Here's a histogram of these measurements:

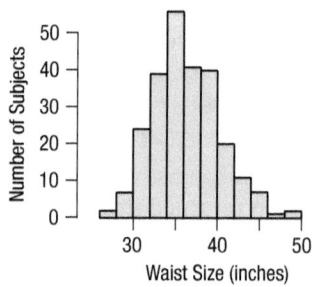

a) Describe the histogram of *Waist Size*.

b) To explore how the mean might vary from sample to sample, the manufacturer simulated by drawing many samples of sizes 2, 5, 10, and 20, with replacement, from the 250 measurements. Here are histograms of the sample means for each simulation. Explain how these histograms demonstrate what the Central Limit Theorem says about the sampling distribution model for sample means. **LO ❸**

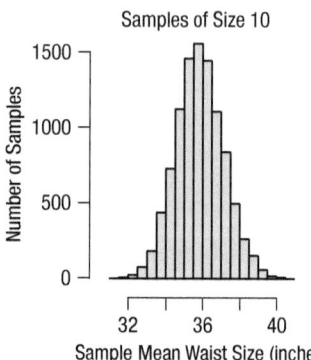

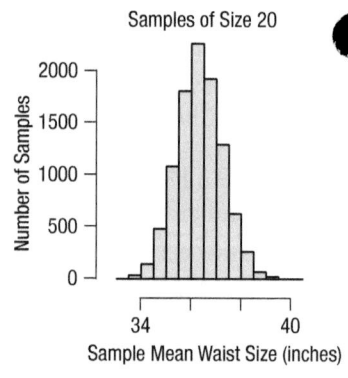

34. CEO compensation, part 1. The average total annual compensation for CEOs of the 800 largest U.S. companies (in $1000) is 10,307.31 and the standard deviation is 17,964.62. Here's a histogram of their annual compensations (in $1000):

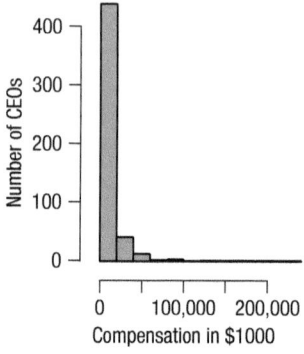

a) Describe the histogram of *Total Compensation*. A research organization simulated sample means by drawing samples of sizes 30, 50, 100, and 200, with replacement, from the 800 CEOs. The histograms below show the distributions of means for many samples of each size.

b) Explain how these histograms demonstrate what the Central Limit Theorem says about the sampling distribution model for sample means. Be sure to talk about shape, centre, and spread.

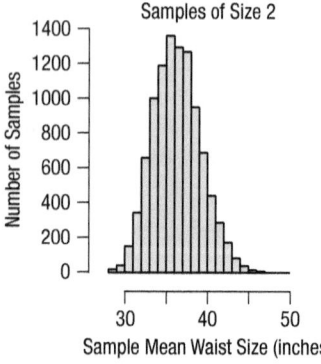

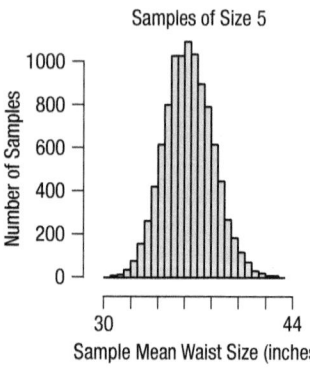

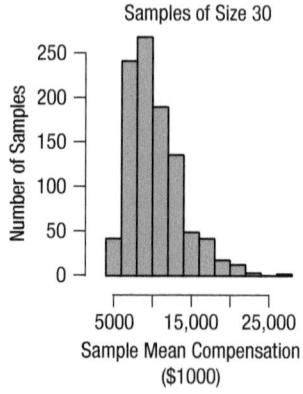

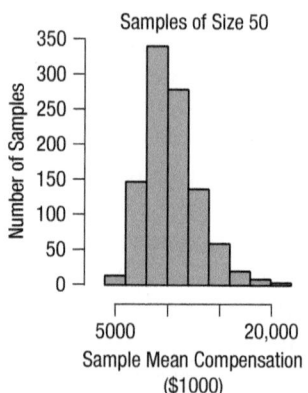

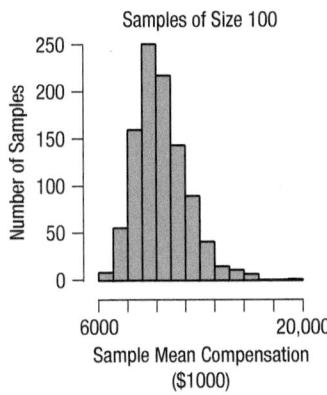

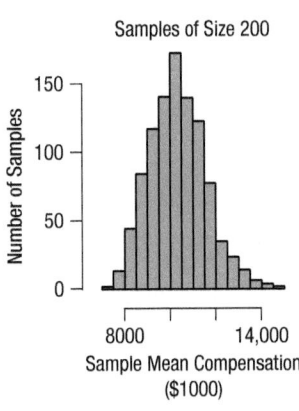

n	mean	st. dev.
30	10,251.73	3359.64
50	10,343.93	2483.84
100	10,329.94	1779.18
200	10,340.37	1230.79

c) Comment on the rule of thumb whereby "With a sample size of at least 30, the sampling distribution of the mean is Normal." **LO ❸**

35. Waist size, part 2. A study commissioned by a clothing manufacturer measured the *Waist Sizes* of a random sample of 250 men. The mean and standard deviation of the *Waist Sizes* for all 250 men are 36.33 inches and 4.019 inches, respectively. In Exercise 33 you looked at the histograms of simulations that drew samples of sizes 2, 5, 10, and 20 (with replacement). The summary statistics for these simulations were as follows:

n	mean	st.dev.
2	36.314	2.855
5	36.314	1.805
10	36.341	1.276
20	36.339	0.895

a) According to the Central Limit Theorem, what should the theoretical mean and standard deviation be for each of these sample sizes?
b) How close are the theoretical values to what was observed in the simulation?
c) Looking at the histograms in Exercise 33, at what sample size would you be comfortable using the Normal model as an approximation for the sampling distribution?
d) What is it about the shape of the *Waist Size* distribution that explains your choice of sample size in part (c)? **LO ❸**

36. CEO compensation, part 2. In Exercise 34 you looked at the annual compensation for 800 CEOs, for which the true mean and standard deviation were (in thousands of dollars) 10,307.31 and 17,964.62, respectively. A simulation drew samples of sizes 30, 50, 100, and 200 (with replacement) from the total annual compensations of the Fortune 800 CEOs. The summary statistics for these simulations were as follows:

a) According to the Central Limit Theorem, what should the theoretical mean and standard deviation be for each of these sample sizes?
b) How close are the theoretical values to what was observed from the simulation?
c) Looking at the histograms in Exercise 34, at what sample size would you be comfortable using the Normal model as an approximation for the sampling distribution?
d) What is it about the shape of the *Total Compensation* distribution that explains your answer in (c)? **LO ❸**

37. Grade point averages (GPAs). A university's data about its incoming first years indicate that the mean of their high school GPAs was 3.4, with a standard deviation of 0.35; the distribution was roughly mound-shaped and only slightly skewed. The students are randomly assigned to first-year writing seminars in groups of 25. What might the mean GPA of one of these seminar groups be? Describe the appropriate sampling distribution model—shape, centre, and spread—with attention to assumptions and conditions. Make a sketch using the 68-95-99.7 Rule. **LO ❸**

38. The trial of the pyx. In 1150, it was recognized in England that coins should have a standard weight of precious metal as the basis for their value. A guinea, for example, was supposed to contain 128 grains of gold. (There are 360 grains in an ounce.) In the "trial of the pyx," coins minted under contract to the Crown were weighed and compared to standard coins (which were kept in a wooden box called the pyx). Coins were allowed to deviate by no more than 0.28 grains—roughly equivalent to specifying that the standard deviation should be no greater than 0.09 grains (although they didn't know what a standard deviation was in 1150). In fact, the trial was performed by weighing 100 coins at a time and requiring the *sum* to deviate by no more than 100 × 0.28 = 28 or 28 grains—equivalent to the sum having a standard deviation of about 9 grains.

a) In effect, the trial of the pyx required that the mean weight of the sample of 100 coins have a standard deviation of 0.09 grains. Explain what was wrong with performing the trial in this manner.
b) What should the limit have been on the standard deviation of the mean? **LO ❸**

Note: Because of this error, the Crown was exposed to being cheated by private mints that could mint coins with greater variation and then, after their coins passed the trial, select out the heaviest ones and recast them at the proper weight, retaining the excess gold for themselves. The error persisted for over 600 years, until sampling distributions became better understood.

39. Safe cities. An insurance company identified the 10 safest and 10 least-safe cities from among the 200 largest cities in the country, based on the mean number of years drivers went between automobile accidents. The cities on both lists were all smaller than the 10 largest cities. Using facts about the sampling distribution model of the mean, explain why this is not surprising. **LO ❸**

40. Steak special. A restaurateur anticipates serving about 180 people on a Friday evening and believes that about 20% of the patrons will order the chef's steak special.

a) How many of those meals should he plan on serving in order to be pretty sure of having enough steaks on hand to meet customer demand?

b) Justify your answer, including an explanation of what "pretty sure" means to you. **LO ❷**

41. Common-law couples in Quebec. Suppose that, according to a recent census, 29% of all families in the province of Quebec are common-law couples. You survey 100 families in the city of Montreal in order to assess the purchasing preferences of common-law couples.

a) What is the probability that the percentage of common-law couples in your Montreal sample is higher than 30%? State your assumptions clearly.

b) You need to find 100 common-law couples in Montreal to interview in detail. Would a sample size of 400 families be sufficient for you to be confident of finding these 100 couples? State your assumptions and reasons clearly. **LO ❷**

42. Fishing tournament. Organizers of a fishing tournament believe that the lake holds a sizable population of large-mouth bass. They assume that the weights of these fish have a model that's skewed to the right with a mean of 3.5 pounds and a standard deviation of 2.32 pounds.

a) Explain why a skewed model makes sense here.

b) Explain why you can't determine the probability that a largemouth bass randomly selected ("caught") from the lake weighs over 3 pounds.

c) Each contestant catches five fish each day. Can you determine the probability that someone's catch averages over 3 pounds? Explain.

d) The 12 contestants competing each caught the limit of five fish. What's the standard deviation of the mean weight of the 60 fish caught?

e) Would you be surprised if the mean weight of the 60 fish caught in the competition was more than 4.5 pounds? **LO ❷, ❸**

43. Canadian property and casualty insurance. Intact is the leading property and casualty (P&C) insurer in Canada and claimed 17% of the market in its "Quick Facts" report for 3Q14. The top five P&C insurers have 38% of the market. Suppose you work for a P&C insurer not currently in the top five, and you'd like to arrange focus groups with at least 75 customers of the top five companies, including at least 25 customers of Intact. You call at random a sample of 220 people in the market for P&C insurance.

a) What is the probability that your sample will contain at least 75 customers of the top five companies?

b) What is the probability that your sample will contain at least 25 customers of Intact?

c) What would be the effect of using a sample size of 20 and aiming to get smaller focus groups? **LO ❷**

44. Canadian income per capita. Suppose that, according to a recent census, the income per capita measured in U.S. dollars was $41,287 in Canada and $43,298 in Norway. Let's assume that income per capita is Normally distributed with a standard deviation equal to 31% of the mean for each country. You select a random sample of six people in Norway and six people in Canada.

a) What is the probability that the mean income of your Canadian sample is above $43,298?

b) What is the probability that the mean income of your Norwegian sample is above $41,287?

c) What would be the effect of not assuming that the income per capita is Normally distributed? (*Source:* Norean Sharpe, Richard D De Veaux, Paul Velleman, David Wright, Business Statistics, Third Canadian Edition, 3e, © 2018, Pearson Education, Inc.) **LO ❸**

45. Cod farming in Atlantic Canada. Young cod are transferred from a hatchery to sea cages, and it then takes an average of 26 months for cod to reach market size, with a standard deviation of one month. The average weight of market-size cod is 3.75 kilograms with a standard deviation of 0.38 kilograms, and we'll assume that it's Normally distributed. You have developed a new feeding program for cod in sea cages, and your first sample of 52 cod has reached market size in an average of 25.6 months and weighs an average of 3.9 kilograms.

a) What is the probability of a random sample of 52 cod reaching market size in an average of 25.6 months or less without your new feeding program?

b) What is the probability of a random sample of 52 market-size cod weighing an average of 3.9 kilograms or more without your new feeding program?

c) You want to examine 20 market-size cod that have achieved a weight of over 4.25 kilograms without your new feeding program. You take a random sample of 250 market-sized cod. What is the probability that this sample will contain enough cod for your purposes? **LO ❸**

46. Loans. Based on past experience, a bank believes that 7% of the people who receive loans will not make payments on time. The bank has recently approved 200 loans.

a) What are the mean and standard deviation of the proportion of clients in this group who may not make timely payments?

b) What assumptions underlie your model? Are the conditions met? Explain.

c) What's the probability that over 10% of these clients will not make timely payments? **LO ❷**

47. At work. Some business analysts estimate that the length of time people work at a job has a mean of 6.2 years and a standard deviation of 4.5 years.

a) Explain why you suspect this distribution may be skewed to the right.
b) Explain why you could estimate the probability that 100 people selected at random had worked for their employers an average of 10 years or more, but you could not estimate the probability that an individual had done so. **LO ❶, ❸**

48. Store receipts. Grocery store receipts show that customer purchases have a skewed distribution with a mean of $32 and a standard deviation of $20.

a) Explain why you cannot determine the probability that the next customer will spend at least $40.
b) Can you estimate the probability that the next 10 customers will spend an average of at least $40? Explain.
c) Is it likely that the next 50 customers will spend an average of at least $40? Explain. **LO ❶, ❸**

49. Quality control. The weight of cement in a medium-size bag is stated to be 10 kilograms. The amount that the packaging machine puts in these bags is believed to have a Normal model with a mean of 10.2 kilograms and a standard deviation of 0.12 kilograms.

a) What fraction of all bags sold are underweight?
b) Some of the cement is sold in "bargain packs" of three bags. What's the probability that none of the three is underweight?
c) What's the probability that the mean weight of the three bags is below the stated amount?
d) What's the probability that the mean weight of a 24-bag case of cement is below 10 kilograms? **LO ❸**

50. Milk production. Although most of us buy milk by the litre, quart, or gallon, farmers measure daily production in pounds. Ayrshire cows average 47 pounds of milk a day, with a standard deviation of 6 pounds. For Jersey cows, the mean daily production is 43 pounds, with a standard deviation of 5 pounds. Assume that Normal models describe milk production for these breeds.

a) We select an Ayrshire at random. What's the probability that she averages more than 50 pounds of milk a day?
b) What's the probability that a randomly selected Ayrshire gives more milk than a randomly selected Jersey?
c) A farmer has 20 Jerseys. What's the probability that the average production for this small herd exceeds 45 pounds of milk a day? **LO ❸**

51. Computers in Canada. The Economist Intelligence Unit says there were 132.6 computers per 100 people in Canada in 2012. We ask 1000 randomly selected Canadian adults how many computers they have; 100 of them say none; 500 of them say one; 200 of them say two, and 100 say three.

a) Calculate the mean number of computers per person in the sample.

b) Estimate the mean number of computers per person in Canada, stating your assumptions.
c) Calculate the standard deviation of the number of computers in the sample.
d) What is the standard error of the estimate in (b).
e) Can this question be answered using (i) the sampling distribution for proportions, or (ii) the sampling distribution for means? Give your reasons. **LO ❸**

52. Canadian Real Estate Association (CREA). CREA puts the average price at which a house was sold in Canada in 2014 at $415,100. Let's assume that the standard deviation of the house prices is $134,216. Suppose you'd done a survey of a random selection of 36 house sale prices in 2014 and obtained an average house price of $368,533. What's the chance that such a survey would have resulted in an average price this low or lower? **LO ❸**

53. A popular tax in B.C. When the British Columbia government introduced a carbon tax in 2008, it didn't want to lose votes, as might easily happen with a new tax. It therefore guaranteed that revenue from the carbon tax would be channelled back into reducing income taxes. In 2011 Environics asked 1023 British Columbians whether they supported the tax and found 54% in favour. Politicians could therefore claim that "most people support the tax." What's the probability of getting this survey result (or higher) if in fact only 48% of British Columbians support the tax? **LO ❷**

54. Families in Nova Scotia. Statistics Canada divides families into two groups: couple families and lone-parent families. According to Statistics Canada's Table 1110009 "Family Characteristics, Summary," in 2012 in Nova Scotia, the data were as follows:

	Couple Families	Lone-Parent Families
Number of families	219,030	46,960
Number of people	616,370	118,420
Median total income	$76,580	$34,370

A surveyor calls 1000 families in Nova Scotia at random in order to market products of different types to the two types of family. For each of the following questions, either answer the question or state why it is not possible to answer it with the information provided and the methods given in this chapter. Give answers to four significant figures.

a) What is the expected proportion of lone-parent families in this sample?
b) What is the probability that the proportion of lone-parent families in the sample will be greater than 0.19?
c) What is the expected average number of people per couple family in the sample?
d) What is the probability that the average number of people per couple family is less than 2.5?

e) What is the expected median total income of couple families in the sample?

f) What is the probability that the median total income of lone-parent families in the sample is less than $30,000? (*Source:* Norean Sharpe, Richard D De Veaux, Paul Velleman, David Wright, Business Statistics, Third Canadian Edition, 3e, © 2018, Pearson Education, Inc.) **LO ❷, ❸**

55. Families in Alberta. Statistics Canada divides families into two groups: couple families and lone-parent families. According to Statistics Canada's Table 1110009 "Family Characteristics, Summary," in 2012 in Alberta, the data were as follows:

	All Families	Lone-Parent Families
Number of families	1,066,610	145,010
Number of people per family	2.969033	2.61644
Median total income	$94,460	$44,380

A surveyor calls 2000 families in Alberta at random in order to market products of different types to the two types of family. For each of the following questions, either answer the question or state why it is not possible to answer it with the information provided and the methods given in this chapter. Give answers to four significant figures.

a) What is the expected proportion of lone-parent families in this sample?

b) The surveyor needs at least 300 lone-parent families in the sample. What is the probability of achieving this objective?

c) What is the expected average number of people per couple family in the sample?

d) What is the probability that the average number of people per couple family is greater than 2.5?

e) What is the expected median total income of couple families in the sample?

f) What is the probability that the median total income of couple families in the sample is less than $100,000? (*Source:* Norean Sharpe, Richard D De Veaux, Paul Velleman, David Wright, Business Statistics, Third Canadian Edition, 3e, © 2018, Pearson Education, Inc.) **LO ❷, ❸**

56. Families in Nova Scotia and Alberta. Using the data in Exercises 54 and 55, what is the probability that a random sample of 1500 families from Nova Scotia contains more lone-parent families than a random sample of 1500 families from Alberta? (*Hint:* Consider the difference between the proportions of lone-parent families in the two provinces. The variance of this difference is the sum of the variances.) **LO ❸**

57. Hepatitis C in British Columbia. On World Hepatitis Day, July 28, 2014, the BC Centre for Disease Control stated that 3% of British Columbians (about 130,000 people) were infected with hepatitis C. Although there is no vaccination against hepatitis C, it can be cured with a daily combination pill that cures 95% of patients.

a) In a survey of 2500 randomly selected British Columbians, what is the expected number that have hepatitis C? What is the probability that the proportion in the sample with hepatitis C is less than 2%?

b) Suppose the average age of people in the survey is 45.2 years and the standard deviation is 12.5 years. Calculate the standard error of the average age.

c) Suppose 80 people in your sample have hepatitis C. What is the probability that they can all be cured using the daily combination pill?

d) If it is not possible to answer any of the above questions in (a) to (c) because the sample size is too small, how large would the sample size need to be in order to answer the question? **LO ❷, ❸**

58. Large families in Canada. According to the Canadian Census, the proportion of families with three or more children (aged less than 25) declined from 42% in 1961 to 19% in 2011. Suppose we estimate that this proportion is 17.5% this year. In order to market products to large families, we randomly select 1600 Canadian families for a survey.

a) What is the expected proportion of families with three or more children in our sample?

b) In our sample, we find 19.3% of the families have three or more children. What is the probability of a proportion as high as 19.3% or higher in the sample if our estimate of 17.5% in the population is correct?

c) Comment on whether the survey result casts doubt on the population estimate.

d) Suppose we had surveyed a random sample of only 400 families instead of 1600 and had gotten the same result: 19.3% of the sample had three or more children. Comment on whether this result from a smaller survey casts doubt on the population estimate. **LO ❷**

59. Canadian earnings. According to a survey from Statistics Canada (Table 2020107, "Earnings of Individuals, by Selected Characteristics and North American Industry Classification System (NAICS), 2011 Constant Dollars"), in 2011, the average earnings in manufacturing in Alberta were $66,700 and in Ontario were $53,700.

a) What additional information do we need in order to calculate the standard error of the estimate for Ontario?

b) What additional information do we need in order to calculate the standard deviation of the estimate for Alberta? **LO ❸**

60. Earnings in Vancouver, B.C. According to a survey from Statistics Canada (Table 2020107, "Earnings of Individuals, by Selected Characteristics and North American Industry Classification System (NAICS), 2011 Constant Dollars"), in 2011, the average earnings in Vancouver were $42,800 in Educational Services and $78,600 in the Financial Services industry.

a) Suppose the standard deviation of earnings in Educational Services for the whole of Vancouver was $12,500, and we want the standard deviation of average earnings in our survey to be $1000. What sample size do we need to take?

b) Suppose we used a sample of size 360 for our estimate of average earnings in Financial Services, and the standard deviation of earnings in our survey was $15,200. What is the standard error of the average earnings in Financial Services? **LO ❸**

61. Broadband in Canada. The Economist Intelligence Unit says there were 32.5 broadband subscribers per 100 people in Canada in 2012.

a) We ask 1000 randomly selected Canadian adults whether they have broadband internet access to their homes. In response, 325 of them say yes and 675 say no, so that the proportion of people having broadband is 0.325. What is the standard error of this estimate?

b) We ask 1000 people how many broadband internet access lines they have to their homes. In response, 325 of them say one and 675 say none, so that the mean number of broadband lines is 0.325. What is the standard error of this estimate? (*Hint:* First calculate the standard deviation of the number of broadband lines in the sample.)

c) Comment on the relationship between (a) and (b). **LO ❷, ❸**

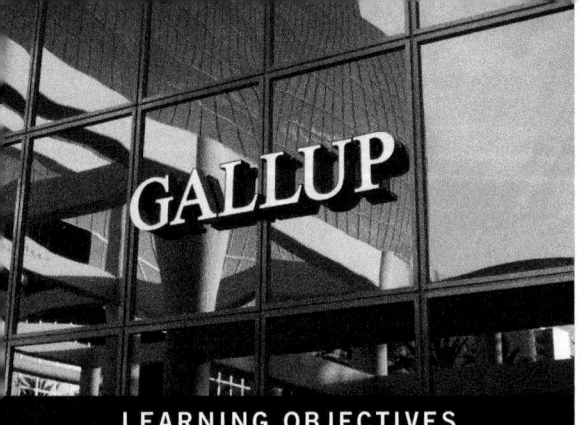

11

LEARNING OBJECTIVES

In this chapter we show you how to calculate confidence intervals when estimating the proportion of a population that has a certain characteristic. After reading and studying this chapter, you should be able to:

❶ Calculate a confidence interval for a proportion

❷ Trade off certainty of precision

❸ Choose the appropriate size for a sample

❹ Calculate a confidence interval for the difference between two proportions

Confidence Intervals for Proportions

The Gallup Organization

Dr. George Gallup was working as a market research director at an advertising agency in the 1930s when he founded the Gallup Organization to measure and track the public's attitudes toward political, social, and economic issues. Today, the Gallup Poll is a household name. During the late 1930s, he founded the Gallup International Research Institute to conduct polls across the globe. International businesses use the Gallup polls to track how consumers in over 150 countries think about such issues as corporate behaviour, government policies, and executive compensation. Gallup Canada, headquartered in Toronto, regularly surveys Canadians' opinions on issues such as clean energy, the economy, health care, and the North American trade agreements.

During the late 20th century, the Gallup Organization partnered with CNN and *USA Today* to conduct and publish public opinion polls. As Gallup once said, "If politicians and special interests have polls to guide them in pursuing their interests, the voters should have polls as well."[1]

Gallup's web-based data storage system now holds data from polls taken over the past 65 years on a variety of topics, including consumer confidence, household savings, stock market investment, and unemployment.

---

[1]Based on The Gallup Organization, Princeton, NJ. Retrieved from www.gallup.com

ROADMAP FOR STATISTICAL INFERENCE					
Number of Variables	Objective	Large Sample or Normal Population		Small Sample and Non-normal Population or Non-numeric Data	
		Chapter	Parametric Method	Chapter	Nonparametric Method
1	Calculate confidence interval for a proportion	11			
1	Compare a proportion with a given value	12	z-test		
1	Calculate a confidence interval for a mean and compare it with a given value	13	t-test	17.2	Wilcoxon Signed-Rank Test
2	Compare two proportions	12.8	z-test		
2	Compare two means for independent samples	14.1–14.5	t-test	17.4, 17.5	Wilcoxon Rank-Sum (Mann-Whitney) Test Tukey's Quick Test
2	Compare two means for paired samples	14.6, 14.7	Paired t-test	17.2	Wilcoxon Signed-Rank Test
≥3	Compare multiple means	15	ANOVA: ANalysis Of VAriance	17.3 17.6	Friedman Test Kruskal-Wallis Test
≥3	Compare multiple counts (proportions)	16	χ^2 test		
2	Investigate the relationship between two variables	18	Correlation Regression	17.7, 17.8	Kendall's tau Spearman's rho
≥3	Investigate the relationship between multiple variables	20	Multiple Regression		

WHO   Adults

WHAT   Proportion who think the economy is getting better

WHEN   April 2013

WHY   To measure expectations about the economy

In order to plan their inventory and production needs, businesses use a variety of forecasts about the economy. One important attribute is consumer confidence in the overall economy. Tracking changes in consumer confidence over time can help businesses gauge whether the demand for their products is on an upswing or about to experience a downturn. The Gallup Poll periodically asks a random sample of adults whether they think economic conditions are getting better, getting worse, or staying about the same. When Gallup polled 3559 respondents in April 2013 (during the week ending April 21), only 1495 thought economic conditions in the United States were getting better—a sample proportion of $\hat{p} = 1495/3559 = 42\%$. We (and Gallup) hope that this observed proportion is close to the population proportion, p, but we know that a second sample of 3559 adults wouldn't have a sample proportion of exactly 42.0%. In fact, Gallup did sample another group of adults just a few days later and found a slightly different sample proportion.

From Chapter 10, we know it isn't surprising that two random samples give slightly different results. We'd like to say something, not about different random *samples*, but about the proportion of *all* adults who thought economic conditions in the United States were getting better in April 2013.

Notice that the kind of survey question we're dealing with in this chapter is the Yes/No type. "Do you think economic conditions are getting better?" is a simple situation in which we get the proportion of people answering "Yes." In

Chapters 13 and 14, we'll deal with the more complex situation in which we ask a question with a numerical answer, for example, "By how much did your income increase during the past year?" The statistical analysis of numerical answers is more complex than for Yes/No answers, which is why we deal with proportions first, in Chapters 11 and 12, and numerical results later, in Chapters 13 and 14. The sampling distribution will be the key to our ability to generalize from our sample to the population.

LO❶ 11.1 A Confidence Interval

NOTATION ALERT

Remember that $\hat{p}$ is our sample estimate of the true proportion, p. Recall also that q is just shorthand for $1 - p$, and $\hat{q} = 1 - \hat{p}$.

What do we know about our sampling distribution model? We know that it's centred at the true proportion, p, of all adults who think the economy is improving. But we don't know p. It may not be 42.0%. That's the $\hat{p}$ from our sample. What we do know is that the sampling distribution model of $\hat{p}$ is centred at p, and we know that the standard deviation of the sampling distribution is $\sqrt{\dfrac{pq}{n}}$. We also know, from the Central Limit Theorem, that the shape of the sampling distribution is approximately Normal when the sample is large enough.

We don't know p, so we can't find the true standard deviation of the sampling distribution model. But we'll use $\hat{p}$ and find the standard error (SE):

$$SE(\hat{p}) = \sqrt{\frac{\hat{p}\hat{q}}{n}} = \sqrt{\frac{(0.42)(1 - 0.42)}{3559}} = 0.008$$

Since the Gallup sample of 3559 is large, we know that the sampling distribution model for $\hat{p}$ should look approximately like the one shown in Figure 11.1.

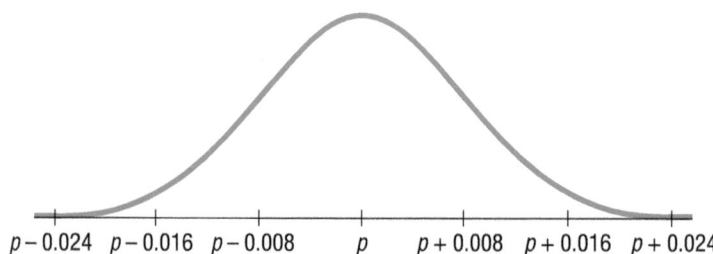

$p-0.024 \quad p-0.016 \quad p-0.008 \qquad p \qquad p+0.008 \quad p+0.016 \quad p+0.024$

Figure 11.1 The sampling distribution of sample proportions is centred at the true proportion, p, with a standard deviation of 0.008.

The sampling distribution model for $\hat{p}$ is Normal with a mean of p and a standard deviation we estimate to be $\sqrt{\dfrac{\hat{p}\hat{q}}{n}}$. Using the 68-95-99.7 Rule for Normal distributions, we'd expect that about 68% of all samples of 3559 U.S. adults taken in April 2013 would have had sample proportions within one standard deviation of p. And about 95% of all these samples will have proportions within $p \pm$ two SEs. But where is *our* sample proportion in this picture? And what value does p have? We still don't know!

We do know that for 95% of random samples, $\hat{p}$ will be no more than two SEs away from p. So let's reverse it and look at it from $\hat{p}$'s point of view. For 95% of the $\hat{p}$'s, p is no more than two SEs away. If we reach out two SEs, or 2×0.008, away

Figure 11.2   Reaching out two SEs on either side of $\hat{p}$ makes us 95% confident that we'll trap the true proportion, p.

from us on both sides, we'll be 95% sure that p will be within our grasp, as shown in Figure 11.2. Of course, we won't know, and even if our interval does catch p, we still don't know its true value. The best we can do is state a level of confidence that we've covered the true value in our interval.

What Can We Say About a Proportion?

So what can we really say about p? Here's a list of things we'd like to be able to say and the reasons we can't say most of them:

1. **"42.0% of *all* adults thought the economy was improving."** It would be nice to be able to make absolute statements about population values, but we just don't have enough information to do that. There's no way to be sure that the population proportion is the same as the sample proportion; in fact, it almost certainly isn't. Observations vary. Another sample would yield a different sample proportion.

2. **"It's *probably* true that 42.0% of all adults thought the economy was improving."** No. In fact, we can be pretty sure that whatever the true proportion is, it's not exactly 42.0%, so the statement is not true.

3. **"We don't know exactly what proportion of adults thought the economy was improving, but we *know* that it's within the interval 42.0% $\pm$ 2 $\times$ 0.8%. That is, it's between 40.4% and 43.6%."** This is getting closer, but we still can't be certain. We can't know for sure that the true proportion is in this interval—or in any particular range.

4. **"We don't know exactly what proportion of adults thought the economy was improving, but we are reasonably sure that the interval from 40.4% to 43.6% contains the true proportion."** We've now fudged twice—first by giving an interval and second by admitting that we only think the interval "probably" contains the true value.

That last statement may be true, but it's a bit wishy-washy. We can tighten it up by quantifying what we mean by "reasonably sure." We saw that 95% of the time when we reach out two SEs from $\hat{p}$ we capture p, *so we can be 95% confident that this is one of those times*. After putting a number on the level of confidence that this interval covers the true proportion, we've given our best guess of where the parameter is and how confident we are that it's within some range.

Far better an approximate answer to the right question ... than an exact answer to the wrong question.

—John W. Tukey

5. **"We're 95% confident that between 40.4% and 43.6% of adults thought the economy was improving."** This is now an appropriate interpretation of our confidence intervals. It's not perfect, but it's about the best we can do. When survey results are reported in the media, they're typically phrased differently, for example, "42% of adults surveyed think the economy is improving. This result is accurate to 1.6%, 19 times out of 20." Statisticians prefer a phrasing that uses the word "confident," but the phrasing used in the media is equivalent.

Each **confidence interval** discussed in the book has a name. You'll see many different kinds of confidence intervals in the following chapters. Some will be about more than *one* sample, some will be about statistics other than *proportions*, and some will use models other than the Normal. The interval calculated and interpreted here is an example of a **one-proportion z-interval**.[2] We'll lay out the formal definition in the next few pages.

What Does "95% Confidence" Really Mean?

What do we mean when we say we have 95% confidence that our interval contains the true proportion? Formally, what we mean is that "95% of samples of this size will produce confidence intervals that capture the true proportion." This is correct but a little long-winded, so we sometimes say, "We're 95% confident that the true proportion lies in our interval." Our uncertainty is about whether the particular sample we have at hand is one of the successful ones or one of the 5% that fail to produce an interval that captures the true value. In Chapter 10 we saw how proportions vary from sample to sample. If other pollsters had selected their own samples of adults, they would have found some who thought the economy was getting better, but each sample proportion would almost certainly differ from ours. When they each tried to estimate the true proportion, they'd centre their confidence intervals at the proportions they observed in their own samples. Each would have ended up with a different interval.

Figure 11.3 shows the confidence intervals produced by simulating 20 samples. The purple dots are the simulated proportions of adults in each sample who thought the economy was improving, and the orange segments show the confidence intervals found for each simulated sample. The green line represents the true percentage of adults who thought the economy was improving. You can see

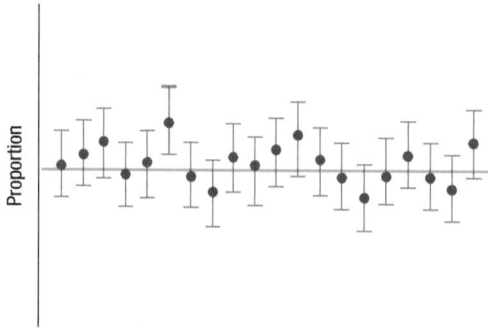

Figure 11.3   The horizontal green line shows the true proportion of people in April 2013 who thought the economy was improving. Most of the 20 simulated samples shown here produced 95% confidence intervals that captured the true value, but one missed.

---

[2]In fact, this confidence interval is so standard for a single proportion that you may see it simply called a "confidence interval for the proportion."

that most of the simulated confidence intervals include the true value—but one missed. (Note that it's the *intervals* that vary from sample to sample; the green line doesn't move.)

Of course, a huge number of possible samples *could* be drawn, each with its own sample proportion. This simulation approximates just some of them. Each sample can be used to make a confidence interval. That's a large pile of possible confidence intervals, and ours is just one of those in the pile. Did *our* confidence interval "work"? We can never be sure because we'll never know the true proportion of all adults who thought in April 2013 that the economy was improving. However, the Central Limit Theorem assures us that 95% of the intervals in the pile are winners, covering the true value, and only 5%, on average, miss the target. That's why we're 95% *confident* that our interval is a winner.

FOR EXAMPLE   Finding a 95% confidence interval for a proportion of voters

The Chamber of Commerce of a mid-sized city has supported a proposal to change the zoning laws for a new part of town. The new regulations would allow for mixed commercial and residential development. The vote on the measure is scheduled for three weeks from today, and the president of the Chamber of Commerce is concerned that they may not have the majority of votes they'll need to pass the measure. She commissions a survey that asks likely voters if they plan to vote for the measure. Of the 516 people selected at random from likely voters, 289 said they would likely vote for the measure.

QUESTIONS

1. Find a 95% confidence interval for the true proportion of voters who will vote for the measure. (Use the 68-95-99.7 Rule.)
2. What would you report to the president of the Chamber of Commerce?

ANSWERS

1. $\hat{p} = \dfrac{289}{516} = 0.56$. So, $SE(\hat{p}) = \sqrt{\dfrac{\hat{p}\hat{q}}{n}} = \sqrt{\dfrac{(0.56)(0.44)}{516}} = 0.022$

   A 95% confidence interval for p can be found from $\hat{p} \pm 2\ SE(\hat{p}) = 0.56 \pm 2(0.022)$

   $= (0.516,\ 0.604)$ or 51.6% to 60.4%.

2. We're 95% confident that the true proportion of voters who plan to vote for the measure is between 51.6% and 60.4%. This assumes that the sample we have is representative of all likely voters.

LO❷   11.2   Margin of Error: Certainty vs. Precision

We've just claimed that at a certain confidence level we've captured the true proportion of all adults who thought the economy was improving in April 2013. Our confidence interval stretched out the same distance on either side of the estimated proportion with the form

$$\hat{p} \pm 2\ SE(\hat{p}).$$

The *extent* of that interval on either side of $\hat{p}$ is called the **margin of error (ME)**. In general, confidence intervals look like this:

$$Estimate \pm ME$$

Confidence Intervals

We'll see many confidence intervals in this book. All have the form

   Estimate $\pm$ ME.

For proportions at 95% confidence:

   $ME \approx 2SE(\hat{p})$

The margin of error for our 95% confidence interval was two SEs. What if we wanted to be more confident? To be more confident, we'd need to capture p more often, and to do that we'd need to make the interval wider. For example, if we want to be 99.7% confident, the margin of error will have to be three SEs, as shown in Figure 11.4.

$\hat{p} - 3\ SE$ ────────── $\hat{p}$ ────────── $\hat{p} + 3\ SE$

Figure 11.4 Reaching out three SEs on either side of $\hat{p}$ makes us 99.7% confident that we'll trap the true proportion, p. Compare the width of this interval with the interval in Figure 11.2.

The more confident we want to be, the larger the margin of error must be. We can be 100% confident that any proportion is between 0% and 100%, but that's not very useful. Or we could give a narrow confidence interval, say, from 40.4% to 43.6% as in the example on pages 339-340. But we would be less confident about a statement this precise. Every confidence interval is a balance between certainty and precision.

The tension between certainty and precision is always there. There is no simple answer to the conflict. Fortunately, in most cases we can be both sufficiently certain and sufficiently precise to make useful statements. The choice of confidence level is somewhat arbitrary, but you must choose the level yourself. The data can't do it for you. The most commonly chosen confidence levels are 90%, 95%, and 99%, but any percentage can be used. (In practice, though, using something like 92.9% or 97.2% might be viewed with suspicion.)

LO❶ 11.3 Critical Values

In our opening example, our margin of error was two SEs, which produced a 95% confidence interval. To change the confidence level, we'll need to change the *number* of SEs to correspond to the new level. A wider confidence interval means more confidence. For any confidence level, the number of SEs we must stretch out on either side of $\hat{p}$ is called the **critical value**. Because it's based on the Normal model, we denote it z^*. For any confidence level, we can find the corresponding critical value from a computer, a calculator, or a Normal probability table, such as Table Z at the back of the book.

For a 95% confidence interval, the precise critical value is $z^* = 1.96$. That is, 95% of a Normal model is found within ± 1.96 standard deviations of the mean. We've been using $z^* = 2$ from the 68-95-99.7 Rule because 2 is very close to 1.96

NOTATION ALERT

We put an asterisk on a letter to indicate a critical value. We usually use "z" when we talk about Normal models, so z^* is always a critical value from a Normal model.

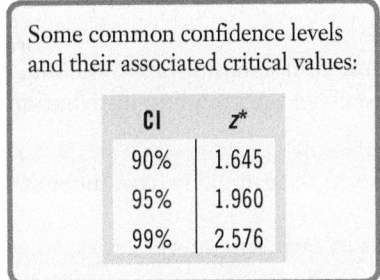

Some common confidence levels and their associated critical values:

CI	z^*
90%	1.645
95%	1.960
99%	2.576

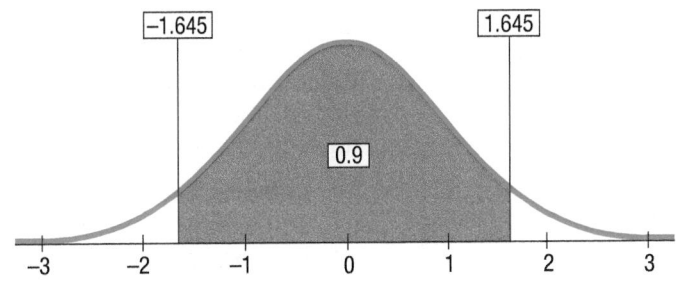

Figure 11.5 For a 90% confidence interval the critical value is 1.645, because for a Normal model, 90% of the values fall within 1.645 standard deviations of the mean.

and is easier to remember. Usually the difference is negligible, but if you want to be precise, use 1.96.[3]

Suppose we could be satisfied with 90% confidence. What critical value would we need? We can use a smaller margin of error. Our greater precision is offset by our acceptance of being wrong more often (i.e., having a confidence interval that misses the true value). Specifically, for a 90% confidence interval, the critical value is only 1.645, because for a Normal model, 90% of the values are within 1.645 standard deviations from the mean, as shown in Figure 11.5. By contrast, suppose your boss demands more confidence. If she wants an interval in which she can have 99% confidence, she'll need to include values within 2.576 standard deviations, creating a wider confidence interval.

FOR EXAMPLE | Finding confidence intervals for proportions of voters with different levels of confidence

The president of the Chamber of Commerce is worried that 95% confidence is too low and wants a 99% confidence interval.

QUESTION Find a 99% confidence interval. Would you reassure her that the measure will pass? Explain.

ANSWER In For Example: "Finding a 95% confidence interval for a proportion of voters" we used 2 as the value of z^* for 95% confidence. A more precise value would be 1.96 for 95% confidence. For 99% confidence, the critical z-value is 2.576. So, a 99% confidence interval for the true proportion is $\hat{p} \pm 2.576\ SE(\hat{p}) = 0.56 \pm 2.576(0.022)$ $= (0.503,\ 0.617)$.

The confidence interval is now wider: 50.3% to 61.7%.

The Chamber of Commerce needs at least 50% for the vote to pass. At a 99% confidence level, it looks now as if the measure will pass. However, we must assume that the sample is representative of the voters in the actual election and that people vote in the election as they said they would when they took the survey.

---

[3] It's been suggested that since 1.96 is both an unusual value and so important in Statistics, you can recognize someone who's taken a Statistics course just by saying "1.96" and seeing whether he or she reacts.

LO❶   11.4   Assumptions and Conditions

Calculating confidence intervals requires the same four assumptions and conditions that we saw in Chapter 10 when we first discussed the sampling distribution for proportions:

- **Independence Assumption:** The individuals in the sample behave independently of each other.
- **Randomization Condition:** The individuals in each sample were selected at random.
- **10% Condition:** The sample is less than 10% of the population.
- **Success/Failure Condition for $\hat{p}$ and $\hat{q}$:**

$$n\hat{p} > 10$$
$$n\hat{q} > 10$$

> **One-Proportion z-Interval**
>
> When the conditions are met, we are ready to find the confidence interval for the population proportion, p. The confidence interval is $\hat{p} \pm z^* \times SE(\hat{p})$, where the standard deviation of the proportion is estimated by
>
> $SE(\hat{p}) = \sqrt{\dfrac{\hat{p}\hat{q}}{n}}$, and z^* is the
>
> critical value discussed in Section 11.3.

FOR EXAMPLE   **Assumptions and conditions for a confidence interval for proportions of voters**

In For Example: "Finding confidence intervals for proportions with different levels of confidence of voters," we previously reported a confidence interval to the president of the Chamber of Commerce.

QUESTION   Were the assumptions and conditions for making this interval satisfied?

ANSWER   Because the sample was randomized, we assume that the responses of the people surveyed were independent, so the Independence Assumption and the Randomization Condition are met. We assume that 516 people represent fewer than 10% of the likely voters in the town, and so the 10% Condition is met. Because 289 people said they were likely to vote for the measure and thus 227 said they were not, $n\hat{p} = 289$ and $n\hat{q} = 227$. Both are much larger than 10, so the Success/Failure Condition is also met.

All the conditions to make a confidence interval for the proportion appear to have been satisfied.

GUIDED EXAMPLE   Alberta Oil Sands

In 2014, musician Neil Young said of the Alberta oil sands project: "It's the greediest, most destructive and disrespectful demonstration of something run amok that you can ever see." The Canadian government continued to support the project, however, and no doubt took public opinion into account in making that commitment. In 2014, Nanos Research interviewed 1000 adult Canadians as to whether they had a favourable attitude toward the oil sands and found that 46% had either favourable or somewhat favourable attitudes. It is important to estimate how accurate this information is by providing a 95% confidence interval.

PLAN	**Setup** State the context of the question.	We want to find an interval that is likely with 95% confidence to contain the true proportion, p, of Canadian adults who have either a favourable or somewhat favourable attitude toward the oil sands project. We have a random sample of 1000 Canadian adults, with a sample proportion of 46%.
	Identify the parameter you wish to estimate.	

Identify the *population* about which you wish to make statements. Choose and state a confidence level. **Model** Specify the assumptions and check the conditions to decide whether we can use the Normal model. State the sampling distribution model for the statistic. Choose your method.	✓ **Independence Assumption:** Nanos Research contacted a random sample of Canadian adults. It's unlikely that any respondent influenced another. ✓ **Randomization Condition:** Nanos Research drew a random sample from all Canadian adults. We don't have details of their randomization, but we assume that we can trust it. ✓ **10% Condition:** The sample is certainly less than 10% of the population. ✓ **Success/Failure Condition:** $$n\hat{p} = 1000 \times 0.46 = 460 > 10$$ $$n\hat{q} = 1000 \times 0.54 = 540 > 10$$ The conditions are satisfied, so we can use a Normal model to find a one-proportion z-interval.

Mechanics Construct the confidence interval. First, find the standard error. (*Remember:* It's called the "standard error" because we don't know p and have to use $\hat{p}$ instead.) Next, find the margin of error. We could informally use 2 for our critical value, but 1.96 is more accurate. Write the confidence interval.	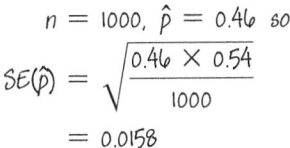 $$n = 1000, \hat{p} = 0.46 \text{ so}$$ $$SE(\hat{p}) = \sqrt{\frac{0.46 \times 0.54}{1000}}$$ $$= 0.0158$$ Because the sampling model is Normal, for a 95% confidence interval, the critical value is $z^* = 1.96$. The margin of error is $$ME = z^* \times SE(\hat{p}) = 1.96 \times 0.0158 = 0.0309.$$ So the 95% confidence interval is $$0.46 \pm 0.03, \text{ i.e., between } 0.43 \text{ and } 0.49$$

 **Conclusion** Interpret the confidence interval in the proper context.	MEMO Nanos Research surveyed 1000 Canadian adults and asked how favourable they were toward the Alberta oil sands project, finding that 46% of those surveyed were either favourable or somewhat favourable toward the project. Although we can't know the true proportion of all Canadian adults who were favourable or somewhat favourable, based on Nanos's results, we can be 95% confident that between 43% and 49% were either favourable or somewhat favourable toward the project.

JUST CHECKING

Think some more about the 95% confidence interval we just created for the proportion of adults who have either a favourable or somewhat favourable attitude toward the oil sands project.

1 If we wanted to be 98% confident, would our confidence interval need to be wider or narrower?

2 Our margin of error was about ± 3%. If we wanted to reduce it to ± 2% without increasing the sample size, would our level of confidence be higher or lower?

3 If Nanos Research had polled more people, would the interval's margin of error likely have been larger or smaller?

Answers are found in Appendix A.

LO❸ **11.5** **Choosing the Sample Size**

Every confidence interval must balance precision—the width of the interval—against confidence. Although it's good to be precise and comforting to be confident, there's a trade-off between the two. A confidence interval that says the percentage is between 10% and 90% wouldn't be of much use, although you could be quite confident that it covered the true proportion. An interval from 43% to 44% is reassuringly precise, but not if it carries a confidence level of 35%. It's a rare study that reports confidence levels lower than 80%. Levels of 95% or 99% are more common.

The time to decide whether the margin of error is small enough to be useful is when you design your study. Don't wait until you compute your confidence interval. To get a narrower interval without giving up confidence, you need to have less variability in your sample proportion. How can you do that? Choose a larger sample.

Consider a company planning to offer a new service to its customers. Product managers want to estimate the proportion of customers who are likely to purchase this new service to within 3% with 95% confidence. How large a sample do they need? Usually about half the customers purchase new services.

> **What $\hat{p}$ Should We Use?**
>
> Often you'll have an estimate of the population proportion based on experience or perhaps on a previous study. If so, use that value as $\hat{p}$ in calculating what size sample you need. If not, the cautious approach is to use $\hat{p} = 0.5$. The graph below shows that $\hat{p} = 0.5$ gives the largest value of $\hat{p}\hat{q}$, and hence will determine the largest sample necessary regardless of the true proportion. It's the *worst-case* scenario.
>
>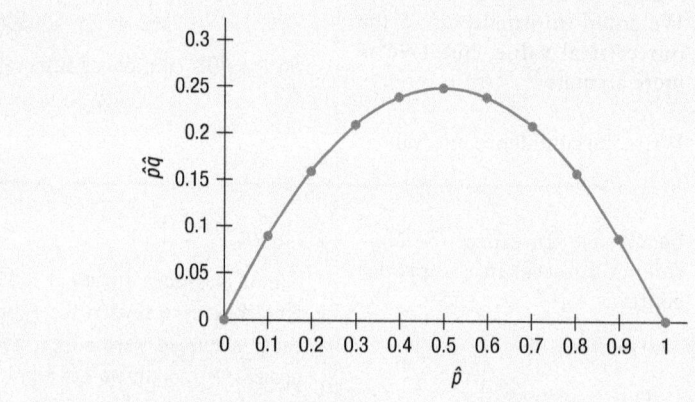

Let's look at the margin of error:

$$ME = z^* \sqrt{\frac{\hat{p}\hat{q}}{n}}$$

$$0.03 = 1.96 \sqrt{\frac{\hat{p}\hat{q}}{n}}$$

They want to find n, the sample size. To find n, they need a value for $\hat{p}$. They don't know $\hat{p}$ because they don't have a sample yet, but they can probably guess a value. The worst case—the value that makes the SD (and therefore n) largest—is 0.50, so if they use that value for $\hat{p}$, they'll certainly be safe.

The company's equation, then, is

$$0.03 = 1.96 \sqrt{\frac{(0.5)(0.5)}{n}}.$$

To solve for n, just multiply both sides of the equation by $\sqrt{n}$ and divide by 0.03:

$$0.03\sqrt{n} = 1.96\sqrt{(0.5)(0.5)}$$

$$\sqrt{n} = \frac{1.96\sqrt{(0.5)(0.5)}}{0.03} \approx 32.67$$

Then square the result to find n:

$$n \approx (32.67)^2 \approx 1067.1$$

That method will probably give a value with a fraction. To be safe, always round up. The company will need at least 1068 respondents to keep the margin of error as small as 3% with a confidence level of 95%.

Unfortunately, bigger samples cost more money and require more effort. Because the standard error declines only with the *square root* of the sample size, to cut the standard error (and thus the ME) in half you must *quadruple* the sample size.

Generally, a margin of error of 5% or less is acceptable, but different circumstances call for different standards. The size of the margin of error may be a marketing decision or one determined by the amount of financial risk you (or the company) are willing to accept. Drawing a large sample to get a smaller ME, however, can run you into trouble. It takes time to survey 2400 people, and a survey that extends over a week or more may be trying to hit a target that moves during the time of the survey. A news event or new product announcement can change opinions in the middle of the survey process.

Keep in mind that the sample size for a survey is the number of respondents, not the number of people to whom questionnaires were sent or whose phone numbers were dialled. Also keep in mind that a low response rate turns any study essentially into a voluntary response study, which is of little value for inferring population values. It's almost always better to spend resources on increasing the response rate than on surveying a larger group. A complete or nearly complete response by a modest-size sample can yield useful results.

Surveys aren't the only place where proportions pop up. Credit card banks sample huge mailing lists to estimate what proportion of people will accept a credit card offer. Even pilot studies may be mailed to 50,000 customers or more. Most of these customers don't respond. But in this case, that doesn't make the sample smaller. In fact, they did respond in a way—they just said, "No thanks." To the bank, the response rate[4] is $\hat{p}$. With a typical success rate below 1%, the bank needs a very small margin of error—often as low as 0.1%—to make a sound business decision. That calls for a large sample, and the bank should take care when estimating the size needed. For our company offering a new service, we worked with $p = 0.5$, both because it's safe and because we honestly believed p to be near 0.5. If the bank used 0.5, it would get an absurd answer. Instead, it bases its calculation on a value of p that it expects to find from its experience.

When Angus Reid Strategies conducts a survey in Canada, it typically uses a sample size of around 1000. Does that mean it should use a larger sample in the United States, which has a population about 10 times that of Canada? Can it get by with a smaller sample in Iceland, which has a population about 1% of Canada's? Intuitively, many people would answer "Yes" to these questions, but our calculations show that the answer is no. The population size, N, does not appear in our formulas. The sample size, n, depends on $\hat{p}$, the confidence level, and the margin of error, but not on N.

> Public opinion polls often use a sample size of 1000, which gives an ME of about 3% (at 95% confidence) when p is near 0.5. But businesses and nonprofit organizations often use much larger samples to estimate the response to a direct mail campaign. Why? Because the proportion of people who respond to these mailings is very low, often 5% or even less. An ME of 3% may not be precise enough if the response rate is that low. Instead, an ME like 0.1% would be more useful, and that requires a very large sample size.

---

[4]Be careful. In marketing studies like this, *every* mailing yields a response—"yes" or "no"—and response rate means the success rate, the proportion of customers who accept the offer. That's a different use of the term "response rate" from the one used in survey response.

How Much Difference Can It Make?

A credit card company is about to send out a mailing to test the market for a new credit card. From that sample, it wants to estimate the true proportion of people who will sign up for the card nationwide. To be within one-tenth of a percentage point, or 0.001, of the true acquisition rate with 95% confidence, how big does the test mailing have to be? Similar mailings in the past lead the company to expect that about 0.5% of the people receiving the offer will accept it. Using those values, it finds

$$ME = 0.001 = z^*\sqrt{\frac{\hat{p}\hat{q}}{n}} = 1.96\sqrt{\frac{(0.005)(0.995)}{n}}$$

$$(0.001)^2 = 1.96^2\frac{(0.005)(0.995)}{n} \Rightarrow n = \frac{1.96^2(0.005)(0.995)}{(0.001)^2}$$

$$= 19{,}111.96 \; or \; 19{,}112.$$

That's a perfectly reasonable size for a trial mailing. But if the company had used 0.50 for its estimate of p, it would have found

$$ME = 0.001 = z^*\sqrt{\frac{\hat{p}\hat{q}}{n}} = 1.96\sqrt{\frac{(0.5)(0.5)}{n}}$$

$$(0.001)^2 = 1.96^2\frac{(0.5)(0.5)}{n} \Rightarrow n = \frac{1.96^2(0.5)(0.5)}{(0.001)^2} = 960{,}400.$$

That's quite a different result!

This shows the power of statistical analysis. From a sample of 1000 people we can make conclusions about a population of 100 million just as accurately as we can about a population of 1 million. Of course, our sample must be randomly chosen from that larger population, but the size of our sample doesn't need to be larger. This is good news for survey companies, since the cost of conducting a survey is closely related to the number of people surveyed.

FOR EXAMPLE   Sample size calculations for a confidence interval for a proportion of voters

The president of the Chamber of Commerce in the previous For Example boxes is worried that the 99% confidence interval is too wide. Recall that it was (0.503, 0.617), which has a width of 0.114.

QUESTION   How large a sample would she need in order to have a 99% interval half as wide? One-quarter as wide? What if she wanted a 99% confidence interval that was plus or minus three percentage points? How large a sample would she need?

ANSWER   Because the formula for the confidence interval is dependent on the inverse of the square root of the sample size:

$$\hat{p} \pm z^*\sqrt{\frac{\hat{p}\hat{q}}{n}},$$

a sample size four times as large will produce a confidence interval *half* as wide. The original 99% confidence interval had a sample size of 516. If the president wants it half as wide, she'd need about $4 \times 516 = 2064$ respondents. To get it a quarter as wide, she'd need $4^2 \times 516 = 8192$ respondents!

If she wants a 99% confidence interval that's plus or minus three percentage points, she must calculate

$$\hat{p} \pm z^* \sqrt{\frac{\hat{p}\hat{q}}{n}} = \hat{p} \pm 0.03.$$

So

$$2.576\sqrt{\frac{(0.5)(0.5)}{n}} = 0.03.$$

Which means that

$$n \approx \left(\frac{2.576}{0.03}\right)^2 (0.5)(0.5) = 1843.27.$$

Rounding up, she'd need 1844 respondents. We used 0.5 because we didn't have any information about the election before taking the survey. Using $p = 0.56$ instead would give $n = 1817$.

MyStatLab
A Confidence Interval for Small Samples, this advanced section can be located on MyStatLab.

LO❹   **11.6**   ## Confidence Interval for the Difference Between Two Proportions

Up to now in this chapter we've dealt with a single proportion from a single population, but we often need to compare two populations. For instance, Statistics Canada's Survey of Household Spending reports that 66.5% of households in Ontario spend money on gambling, whereas the figure for Manitoba is 75.2%. We might well ask how large the difference is between these two provinces. A quick answer is $75.2 - 66.5 = 8.7$, but that's the difference in the survey results, which represent the populations in those provinces only to a certain degree of accuracy. What we really need is the confidence interval around 8.7%. Like the other confidence intervals we've discussed, the width of the confidence interval depends on the number of households surveyed. Statistics Canada surveyed 10,811 households across Canada, and we can assume the number in Ontario and Manitoba was in proportion to the populations of those provinces: 38.4% in Ontario and 3.6% in Manitoba. That gives $0.384 \times 10811 = 4151$ households in Ontario and $0.036 \times 10811 = 389$ in Manitoba.

We know that the standard error for Ontario is $\sqrt{\frac{\hat{p}_1\hat{q}_1}{n_1}} = \sqrt{\frac{0.665 \times 0.335}{4151}} = 0.007326$. Similarly, for Manitoba it's $\sqrt{\frac{\hat{p}_2\hat{q}_2}{n_2}} = \sqrt{\frac{0.752 \times 0.248}{389}} = 0.02190$. But we can't just add or subtract these standard errors to get the standard error for the difference between Ontario and Manitoba. When dealing with the difference between random variables, we add the variances, so that the standard error for the difference in the proportion of gambling households between Ontario and Manitoba is

$$SE(\hat{p}_1 - \hat{p}_2) = \sqrt{SE(\hat{p}_1)^2 + SE(\hat{p}_2)^2}$$
$$= \sqrt{\frac{\hat{p}_1\hat{q}_1}{n_1} + \frac{\hat{p}_2\hat{q}_2}{n_2}} = \sqrt{\frac{0.665 \times 0.335}{4151} + \frac{0.752 \times 0.248}{389}} = 0.02309.$$

The 95% confidence interval for the difference in the proportion of gambling households is therefore

$$(\hat{p}_1 - \hat{p}_2) \pm 1.96 \times SE(\hat{p}_1 - \hat{p}_2) = -0.087 \pm 0.0453$$

i.e., between −0.132 and −0.042.

FOR EXAMPLE | Any friends for the Alberta oil sands project?

Nanos Research's survey of opinion about the Alberta oil sands project showed a difference among the provinces for the percentage of people who were favourable or somewhat favourable toward the project. In the Atlantic provinces they surveyed 100 people and found the percentage to be 35.4%, whereas in Ontario they surveyed 300 people and found it to be 46.1%.

QUESTION   Construct a 99% confidence interval for the difference in support for the Alberta oil sands project between the Atlantic provinces and Ontario. What does this confidence interval tell us about whether opinions differ on this issue?

ANSWER

$$SE(\hat{p}_1 - \hat{p}_2) = \sqrt{\frac{\hat{p}_1\hat{q}_1}{n_1} + \frac{\hat{p}_2\hat{q}_2}{n_2}} = \sqrt{\frac{0.354 \times 0.646}{100} + \frac{0.461 \times 0.539}{300}} = 0.0558$$

The critical value for a 99% confidence interval is $z^* = 2.58$. The confidence interval for the difference between two proportions is

$$(\hat{p}_1 - \hat{p}_2) \pm z \times SE(\hat{p}_1 - \hat{p}_2) = 0.354 - 0.461 \pm 2.58 \times 0.0558 = -0.107 \pm 0.144$$

i.e., between –0.251 and 0.037.

Since this interval includes zero, we can't conclude that there's a difference in the percentages of people who are favourable or somewhat favourable toward the Alberta oil sands project between the Atlantic provinces and Ontario at the 99% level.

Confidence Interval for the Difference Between Two Proportions

The confidence interval for the difference between two proportions is

$$(\hat{p}_1 - \hat{p}_2) \pm z^* \times SE(\hat{p}_1 - \hat{p}_2),$$

where z^* is the critical value and

$$SE(\hat{p}_1 - \hat{p}_2) = \sqrt{\frac{\hat{p}_1\hat{q}_1}{n_1} + \frac{\hat{p}_2\hat{q}_2}{n_2}}.$$

In Section 11.5, we chose the sample size in order to achieve a given margin of error, ME. When comparing two proportions, we have two sample sizes. To simplify things, let's assume we can choose the same size for each of our samples, that is, $n_1 = n_2 = n$. Since ME = z^* SE, we can switch around our SE formula to find:

$$n = \frac{(z^*)^2(\hat{p}_1\hat{q}_1 + \hat{p}_2\hat{q}_2)}{ME^2}.$$

WHAT CAN GO WRONG?

Confidence intervals are powerful tools. Not only do they tell us what is known about the parameter value, but—more important—they also tell us what we *don't* know. In order to use confidence intervals effectively, you must be clear about what you say about them. Don't misstate what the interval means.

- **Don't suggest that the parameter varies.** A statement like "There's a 95% chance that the true proportion is between 40.4% and 43.6%" sounds as though you think the population proportion wanders around and sometimes happens to fall between 40.4% and 43.6%. When you interpret a confidence interval, make it clear that you know the population parameter is fixed and that it's the interval that varies from sample to sample.

What *Can* I Say?

Confidence intervals are based on random samples, so the interval is random, too. The Central Limit Theorem tells us that 95% of the random samples will yield intervals that capture the true value. That's what we mean by being 95% confident.

Technically, we should say, "I am 95% confident that the interval from 40.4% to 43.6% captures the true proportion of adults who thought the economy was improving in April 2013." That formal phrasing emphasizes that *our confidence (and our uncertainty) is about the interval, not the true proportion.* But you may choose a more casual phrasing, like "I am 95% confident that between 40.4% and 43.6% of adults thought the economy was improving in April 2013." Because you've made it clear that the uncertainty is yours and you didn't suggest that the randomness is in the true proportion, this is okay. Keep in mind that it's the interval that's random. It's the focus of both our confidence and our doubt.

- **Don't claim that other samples will agree with yours.** Keep in mind that the confidence interval makes a statement about the true population proportion. An interpretation such as "In 95% of samples of adults, the proportion who thought the economy was improving in April 2013 will be between 40.4% and 43.6%" is just wrong. The interval isn't about sample proportions, but about the population proportion. There is nothing special about the sample we happen to have; it doesn't establish a standard for other samples.

- **Don't be certain about the parameter.** Saying, "Between 40.4% and 43.6% of adults thought the economy was improving in April 2013" asserts that the population proportion cannot be outside that interval. Of course, you can't be absolutely certain of that (just pretty sure).

- **Don't forget: It's about the parameter.** Don't say, "I'm 95% confident that $\hat{p}$ is between 40.4% and 43.6%." Of course, you are—in fact, we calculated that our sample proportion was 42.0%. So we already *know* the sample proportion. The confidence interval is about the (unknown) population parameter, p.

- **Don't claim to know too much.** Don't say, "I'm 95% confident that between 40.4% and 43.6% of all adults think the economy is improving." Gallup sampled adults during April 2013, and public opinion shifts over time.

- **Do take responsibility.** Confidence intervals are about *un*certainty. *You* are the one who is uncertain, not the parameter. You have to accept the responsibility and consequences of the fact that not all the intervals you compute will capture the true value. In fact, about 5% of the 95% confidence intervals you find will fail to capture the true value of the parameter. You *can* say, "I'm 95% confident that between 40.4% and 43.6% of adults thought the economy was improving in April 2013."

- **Watch out for biased sampling.** Don't forget about the potential sources of bias in surveys, which we discussed in Chapter 3. Just because we have more statistical machinery now doesn't mean we can forget what we've already learned. A questionnaire that finds that 85% of people enjoy filling out surveys still suffers from nonresponse bias, even though we're now able to put confidence intervals around this (biased) estimate.

- **Think about independence.** The assumption that the values in a sample are mutually independent is one that you can't usually check. It always pays to think about it, though.

- **Be careful of sample size.** The validity of the confidence interval for proportions may be affected by sample size. Avoid using the confidence interval on "small" samples.

- **Don't think you need a larger sample just because you've got a larger population.** The sample size depends on $\hat{p}$, the confidence level, and the margin of error only.

ETHICS IN ACTION

One of Tim Solsby's major responsibilities at NS East Credit Union is managing online services and website content. In an effort to better serve NS East members, Tim routinely visits the websites of other financial institutions to get ideas about how he can improve NS East's online presence. One of the features that catches his attention is a "teen network" that focuses on educating teenagers about personal finances. He thinks this is a novel idea and one that could help build a stronger online community among NS East's members. The executive board of NS East is meeting next month to consider proposals for improving credit union services, and Tim is eager to present his idea for adding an online teen network. To strengthen his proposal, he decides to poll current credit union members. On the NS East Credit Union website, he posts an online survey. Among the questions he asks are "Do you have teenage children in your household?" and "Would you encourage your teenage children to learn more about managing personal finances?" Based on 850 responses, Tim constructs a 95% confidence interval and is able to estimate (with 95%

confidence) that between 69% and 75% of members have teenage children at home and that between 62% and 68% would encourage their teenagers to learn more about managing personal finances. Tim believes these results will help convince the executive board that NS East should add this feature to its website.

Ethical Issue *The sampling method introduces bias because it's a voluntary response sample and not a random sample. Customers who do have teenagers are more likely to respond than those who do not (related to Item A, ASA Ethical Guidelines; see Appendix C, the American Statistical Association's Ethical Guidelines for Statistical Practice, also available online at www.amstat.org/about/ethicalguidelines.cfm).*

Ethical Solution *Tim should revise his sampling methods. He might draw a simple random sample of credit union customers and try to contact them by mail or telephone. Whatever method he uses, Tim needs to disclose the sampling procedure to the board and discuss possible sources of bias.*

WHAT HAVE WE LEARNED?

Learning Objectives ┆ ❶ We've learned to use the sample we have at hand to say something about the *world at large*. This process, called *statistical inference*, is based on our understanding of sampling models and is a key contribution of statistics to management decision making.

As our first step in statistical inference, we've learned to use our sample to make a *confidence interval* that estimates what proportion of a population has a certain characteristic.

There are important assumptions and conditions we must check before using this (or any) statistical inference procedure.

We've learned to interpret a confidence interval by reporting what we believe is true in the entire population from which we took our random sample. Of course, we can't be *certain*. We've learned not to overstate or misinterpret what the confidence interval says.

Our best estimate of the true population proportion is the proportion we observed in the sample, so we centre our confidence interval there.

Samples don't represent the population perfectly, so we create our interval with a *margin of error*. This method successfully captures the true population proportion most of the time, providing us with a level of confidence in our interval.

❷ For a given sample size, the higher the level of confidence we want, the *wider* our confidence interval becomes.

For a given level of confidence, the larger the sample size we have, the *narrower* our confidence interval can be.

❸ When designing a study, we can calculate the sample size we'll need to enable us to reach conclusions that have a desired margin of error and level of confidence.

If our sample is very small, we've learned how to adjust the calculation of the confidence interval.

❹ We've learned how to compare two proportions by calculating the confidence interval for the difference between them.

Terms

Confidence interval
An interval of values, usually of the form *Estimate* ± *Margin of error*, found from data in such a way that a percentage of all random samples can be expected to yield intervals that capture the true parameter value.

Critical value
The number of standard errors to move away from the mean of the sampling distribution to correspond to the specified level of confidence. The critical value, denoted z^*, is usually found from a table or with technology.

Margin of error (ME)
In a confidence interval, the extent of the interval on either side of the estimated parameter. A margin of error is typically the product of a critical value from the sampling distribution and a standard error from the data. A small margin of error corresponds to a confidence interval that pins down the parameter precisely. A large margin of error corresponds to a confidence interval that gives relatively little information about the estimated parameter.

One-proportion z-interval
A confidence interval for the true value of a proportion. The confidence interval is

$$\hat{p} \pm z^* SE(\hat{p}),$$

where z^* is a critical value from the standard Normal model corresponding to the specified confidence level.

Skills

Plan
- Understand confidence intervals as a balance between the precision and the certainty of a statement about a model parameter.
- Understand that the margin of error of a confidence interval for a proportion changes with the sample size and the level of confidence.
- Know how to examine your data for violations of conditions that would make an inference about a population proportion unwise or invalid.

Do
- Be able to construct a one-proportion z-interval.

Report
- Know how to interpret a one-proportion z-interval in a simple sentence or two. Be able to write such an interpretation so that it doesn't state or suggest that the parameter of interest is itself random, but rather that the bounds of the confidence interval are the random quantities about which we state our degree of confidence.

MINI case studies

Alberta Oil Sands

In 2014, Nanos Research conducted a survey of 1000 adult Canadians to determine their favourability toward the Alberta oil sands project. The responses were "favourable," "somewhat favourable," "somewhat unfavourable," "unfavourable," and "unsure." Grouping "favourable" and "somewhat favourable" together, the percentages vary by geography, gender, and age group and are given in the data file **ch11_MCSP_Alberta_Oil_Sands**.

Construct 95% confidence intervals for each geographical region and compare them graphically. Give a 99% confidence interval for the difference between the Prairies (where favourability is highest) and the Atlantic provinces (where favourability is lowest), and interpret its meaning. Conduct a similar analysis for the age groups. Are you 99% confident that there is a difference between men and women? Write a report summarizing what this survey indicates about differences in favourability to the Alberta oil sands project by geography, gender, and age group.

Nuclear Power in Canada

Fred Lum/The Canadian Press

Suppose you're working for Gallup Canada on a survey to estimate how many people believe that Canada should increase the amount of electric power generated by nuclear power stations. You conduct an initial survey of 250 adults, and 12.7% state that they support an increase in nuclear power. Your boss asks how accurate this estimate is, and goes on to say that the 95% confidence interval shouldn't be spread more than 10% either side of the mean. To ensure a narrow enough spread, you get funding to increase your sample from 250 people, and get the figures in the following table:

Sample Size	250	500	750	1000
Proportion supporting nuclear power	0.127	0.149	0.131	0.134

Write a brief report presenting your results graphically, with recommendations for the next step in this project.

Forecasting Demand

Utilities must forecast the demand for energy use far into the future, because it takes decades to plan and build new power plants. Ron Bears, who worked for a Maritime utility company, had the job of predicting the proportion of households that would choose to use electricity to heat their homes. Although he was prepared to report a confidence interval for the true proportion, after seeing his preliminary report, his manager demanded a single number as his prediction.

Help Ron explain to his manager why a confidence interval for the desired proportion would be more useful for planning purposes. Explain how the precision of the interval and the confidence we can have in it are related to each other. Discuss the business consequences of an interval that is too narrow and the consequences of an interval with too low a confidence level.

Technology Help: Confidence Intervals for Proportions

EXCEL

Inference methods for proportions are not part of the standard Excel tool set, but you can compute a confidence interval using Excel's equations.

For example, suppose you have 100 observations in cells A1:A100 and each cell is "yes" or "no."

- In cell B2, enter = countif(A1:A100,"yes")/100 to compute the proportion of "yes" responses. (The 100 here represents 100 observations. Replace it with the number of observations you actually have.)

- In cell B3, enter = sqrt(B2*(1 -B2)/100) to compute the standard error.

- In cell B4, enter = NORM.S.INV (.975) for a 95% confidence interval.

- In cell B5, enter = B2-B4*B3 as the lower end of the CI.

- In cell B6, enter = B2+B4*B3 as the upper end of the CI.

Comments

For summarized data, compute the proportion in cell B2 according to whether your summaries are counts, percentages, or already proportions, and continue with the example, using total count in place of the "100" in the second step.

MINITAB

Choose **Basic Statistics** from the **Stat** menu.

- Choose **1 Proportion** from the Basic Statistics submenu.

- If the data are category names in a variable, assign the variable from the variable list box to the samples in the **Columns** box. If you have summarized data, click the **Summarized Data** button and fill in the number of trials and the number of successes.

- Click the **Options** button and specify the remaining details.

- If you have a large sample, check **Use test and interval based on normal distribution.**

- Click the **OK** button.

Comments

When working from a variable that names categories, MINITAB treats the last category as the "success" category. You can specify how the categories should be ordered.

SPSS

SPSS does not find confidence intervals for proportions.

JMP

For a categorical variable that holds category labels, the **Distribution** platform includes tests and intervals for proportions. For summarized data, put the category names in one variable and the frequencies in an adjacent variable. Designate the frequency column to have the **Role** of **Frequency**. Then use the **Distribution** platform.

Comments

JMP uses slightly different methods for proportion inferences from those discussed in this text. Your answers are likely to be slightly different, especially for small samples.

EXERCISES

SECTION 11.1

1. For each situation below, identify the population and the sample and identify p and $\hat{p}$ if appropriate, and what the value of $\hat{p}$ is. Would you trust a confidence interval for the true proportion based on these data? Explain briefly why or why not.

a) As concertgoers enter a stadium, a security guard randomly inspects their backpacks for alcoholic beverages. Of the 130 backpacks checked so far, 17 contained alcoholic beverages of some kind. The guards want to estimate the percentage of all backpacks of concertgoers at this concert that contain alcoholic beverages.

b) The website of the English newspaper *The Guardian* asked visitors to the site to say whether they approved of recent "bossnapping" actions by British workers who were outraged over being fired. Of those who responded, 49.2% said "Yes. Desperate times call for desperate measures."

c) An airline wants to know the weight of carry-on baggage that customers take on their international routes, so it takes a random sample of 50 bags and finds that the average weight is 17.3 pounds. **LO ❶**

2. For each situation below, identify the population and the sample and explain what p and $\hat{p}$ represent and what the value of $\hat{p}$ is. Would you trust a confidence interval for the true proportion based on these data? Explain briefly why or why not.

a) A marketing analyst conducts a large survey of her customers to find out how much money they plan to spend at the company website in the next six months. The average amount reported from the 534 respondents is $145.34.

b) A campus survey on a large campus (40,000 students) is trying to find out whether students approve of a new parking policy allowing them to park in previously inaccessible parking lots, but for a small fee. Surveys are sent out by mail and email. Of the 243 surveys returned, 134 are in favour of the change.

c) The Human Resources department of a large Fortune 100 company wants to find out how many employees would take advantage of an on-site day-care facility. They send out an email to 500 employees and receive responses from 450 of them. Of those responding, 75 say that they would take advantage of such a facility. **LO ❶**

3. A survey of 200 students is selected randomly on a large university campus. They're asked if they use a laptop in class to take notes. Suppose that based on the survey, 70 of the 200 students responded "yes."

a) What is the value of the sample proportion, $\hat{p}$?

b) What is the standard error of the sample proportion?

c) Construct an approximate 95% confidence interval for the true proportion p by taking ±2 SEs from the sample proportion. **LO ❶**

4. From a survey of 250 co-workers, you find that 155 would like the company to provide on-site day care.

a) What is the value of the sample proportion, $\hat{p}$?

b) What is the standard error of the sample proportion?

c) Construct an approximate 95% confidence interval for the true proportion by taking ±2 SEs from the sample proportion. **LO ❶**

5. From a survey of 200 co-workers, you find that 48% have already received this year's flu vaccine. An approximate 95% confidence interval is (0.409, 0.551). Which of the following are true? If not, explain briefly.

a) 95% of the co-workers fall in the interval (0.409, 0.551).

b) We're 95% confident that the proportion of co-workers who have received this year's flu vaccine is between 40.9% and 55.1%.

c) There's a 95% chance that a random selected co-worker has received the vaccine.

d) There's a 48% chance that a random selected co-worker has received the vaccine.

e) We're 95% confident that between 40.9% and 55.1% of the samples will have a proportion near 48%. **LO ❶, ❷**

6. A sample of 200 students is selected randomly on a large university campus. They are asked if they use a laptop in class to take notes. The result of the survey is that 70 of the 200 students responded "yes." You construct an approximate 95% confidence interval for the true proportion p by taking plus/minus two SEs from the sample proportion and obtain (0.283, 0.417). Which of the following are true? If a statement is not true, explain briefly why not.

a) 95% of the 200 students are in the interval (0.283, 0.417).

b) The true proportion of students who use laptops to take notes is captured in the interval (0.283, 0.417) with probability 0.95.

c) There is a 35% chance that a student uses a laptop to take notes.

d) There is a 95% chance that the student uses a laptop to take notes 35% of the time.

e) We are 95% confident that the true proportion of students who use laptops to take notes is captured in the interval (0.283, 0.417). **LO ❶**

SECTIONS 11.2 AND 11.3

7. From the survey in Exercise 6,

a) How would the confidence interval change if the confidence level had been 90% instead of 95%?

b) How would the confidence interval change if the sample size had been 300 instead of 200? (Assume the same sample proportion.)

c) How would the confidence interval change if the confidence level had been 99% instead of 95%?

d) How large would the sample size have to be to make the margin of error half as big in the 95% confidence interval? **LO ❶, ❷**

8. As in Exercise 5, from a survey of co-workers you find that 48% of 200 have already received this year's flu vaccine. An approximate 95% confidence interval is (0.409, 0.551).

a) How would the confidence interval change if the sample size had been 800 instead of 200?

b) How would the confidence interval change if the confidence level had been 90% instead of 95%?

c) How would the confidence interval change if the confidence level had been 99% instead of 95%? **LO ❶, ❷**

SECTION 11.4

9. Consider each situation in the descriptions that follow. Identify the population and the sample, explain what p and $\hat{p}$ represent, and tell whether the methods of this chapter can be used to create a confidence interval.

a) A consumer group hoping to assess customer experiences with auto dealers surveys 167 people who recently bought new cars; 3% of them expressed dissatisfaction with the salesperson.

b) A cell phone service provider wants to know what percentage of university students have cell phones. A total of 2883 students were asked as they entered a football stadium, and 2243 indicated they had phones with them. **LO ❶**

10. Consider each situation described below. Identify the population and the sample, explain what p and $\hat{p}$ represent, and tell whether the methods of this chapter can be used to create a confidence interval.

a) A total of 240 potato plants in a field in Prince Edward Island are randomly checked, and only seven show signs of blight. How severe is the blight problem for the Canadian potato industry?

b) Concerned about workers' compensation costs, a small company decided to investigate on-the-job injuries. The company reported that 12 of its 309 employees suffered an injury on the job last year. What can the company expect in future years? **LO ❶**

SECTION 11.5

11. Suppose you want to estimate the proportion of students on your campus who own their own car. You have no preconceived idea of what that proportion might be.

a) What sample size is needed if you wish to be 95% confident that your estimate is within 0.02 of the true proportion?

b) What sample size is needed if you wish to be 99% confident that your estimate is within 0.02 of the true proportion?

c) What sample size is needed if you wish to be 95% confident that your estimate is within 0.05 of the true proportion? **LO ❶, ❸**

12. As in Exercise 11, you want to estimate the proportion of students on your campus who own their own car. However, from some research on other university campuses, you believe the proportion will be near 20%.

a) What sample size is needed if you wish to be 95% confident that your estimate is within 0.02 of the true proportion?

b) What sample size is needed if you wish to be 99% confident that your estimate is within 0.02 of the true proportion?

c) What sample size is needed if you wish to be 95% confident that your estimate is within 0.05 of the true proportion? **LO ❶, ❸**

13. It's believed that as many as 25% of adults over age 50 never graduated from high school. We wish to see if this percentage is the same among the 25 to 30 age group.

a) How many of this younger age group must we survey in order to estimate the proportion of non-graduates to within 6% with 90% confidence?

b) Suppose we want to cut the margin of error to 4%. What's the necessary sample size?

c) What sample size would produce a margin of error of 3%? **LO ❶, ❸**

14. In preparing a report on the economy, we need to estimate the percentage of businesses that plan to hire additional employees in the next 60 days.

a) How many randomly selected employers must we contact in order to create an estimate in which we're 98% confident with a margin of error of 5%?

b) Suppose we want to reduce the margin of error to 3%. What sample size will suffice?

c) Why might it not be worth the effort to try to get an interval with a margin of error of 1%? **LO ❶, ❸**

SECTION 11.6

15. In a Nanos Research survey of 1000 Canadian adults about how favourable they were toward the Alberta oil sands project, 19.5% were favourable and 25.6% were somewhat favourable. Of those who were favourable, 15.4% agreed that the oil sands project creates jobs, whereas the corresponding percentage for those who were somewhat favourable was 9.4%. Construct a 99% confidence interval for the difference between those who were favourable and those who were somewhat favourable as to whether the oil sands project creates jobs. **LO ❹**

16. In a Nanos Research survey of 1000 Canadian adults about how favourable they were toward the Alberta oil sands project, 30.5% were unfavourable and 16.9% were somewhat unfavourable. Of those who were unfavourable, 72.0% agreed that the oil sands project was bad for the environment, whereas the corresponding percentage for those who were somewhat unfavourable was 53.3%. Construct a 90% confidence interval for the difference between those who were unfavourable and those who were somewhat unfavourable as to whether the oil sands project is bad for the environment. **LO ❹**

CHAPTER EXERCISES

17. Margin of error, part 1. A corporate executive reports the results of an employee satisfaction survey, stating that 52% of employees say they are either "satisfied" or "extremely satisfied" with their jobs. The executive then says, "The margin of error is plus or minus 4%." Explain carefully what that means. **LO ❶**

18. Margin of error, part 2. A market researcher estimates that the percentage of adults between the ages of 21 and 39 who will see a particular television ad is 15%, adding that he believes his estimate has a margin of error of about 3%. Explain what the margin of error means. **LO ❶**

19. Conditions, part 1. Consider each situation described below. Identify the population and the sample, explain what p and $\hat{p}$ represent, and tell whether the methods of this chapter can be used to create a confidence interval.

a) Police set up an auto checkpoint at which drivers are stopped and their cars inspected for safety problems. They find that 14 of the 134 cars stopped have at least one safety violation. They want to estimate the proportion of all 52,000 cars in this area that may be unsafe.

b) A CBC show asks viewers to register their opinions on corporate corruption by logging on to a website. Of the 602 people who voted, 488 thought corporate corruption was "worse" this year than last year. The show wants to estimate the level of support among the general public. **LO ❶**

20. Conditions, part 2. Consider each situation described below. Identify the population and the sample, explain what p and $\hat{p}$ represent, and tell whether the methods of this chapter can be used to create a confidence interval.

a) A large company with 10,000 employees at its main research site is considering moving its day-care centre off-site to save money. Human Resources gathers employees' opinions by sending a questionnaire home with all employees; 380 surveys are returned, with 228 employees in favour of the change.

b) A company sold 1632 MP3 players last month, and within a week, 1388 of the customers had registered their products online at the company website. The company wants to estimate the percentage of all its customers who enrol their products. **LO ❶**

21. Catalogue sales. A catalogue sales company promises to deliver orders placed on the internet within three days. Follow-up calls to a few randomly selected customers show that a 95% confidence interval for the proportion of all orders that arrive on time is 88% ±6%. What does this mean? Are the conclusions in (a) to (e) correct? Explain.

a) Between 82% and 94% of all orders arrive on time.
b) 95% of all random samples of customers will show that 88% of orders arrive on time.
c) 95% of all random samples of customers will show that 82% to 94% of orders arrive on time.
d) The company is 95% sure that between 82% and 94% of the orders placed by the customers in this sample arrived on time.
e) On 95% of the days, between 82% and 94% of the orders will arrive on time. **LO ❶**

22. Belgian euro. Recently, two students made worldwide headlines by spinning a Belgian euro 250 times and getting 140 heads—that's 56%. That makes the 90% confidence interval (51%, 61%). Can we draw any conclusions about Belgian euros in general from this information? **LO ❶**

23. Confidence intervals, part 1. Several factors are involved in the creation of a confidence interval. Among them are the sample size, the level of confidence, and the margin of error. Which statements are true?

a) For a given sample size, higher confidence means a smaller margin of error.
b) For a specified confidence level, larger samples provide smaller margins of error.
c) For a given confidence level, halving the margin of error requires a sample twice as large. **LO ❶, ❷**

24. Confidence intervals, part 2. Several factors are involved in the creation of a confidence interval. Among them are the sample size, the level of confidence, and the margin of error. Which statements are true?

a) For a certain confidence level, you can get a smaller margin of error by selecting a bigger sample.
b) For a given confidence level, a sample nine times as large will make a margin of error one-third as big. **LO ❶**

25. Cars. A student is considering publishing a new magazine aimed directly at owners of Japanese automobiles. He wants to estimate the fraction of cars in Canada that are made in Japan. The computer output summarizes the results of a random sample of 50 autos. Explain carefully what it tells you. **LO ❶**

z-interval for proportion
With 90.00% confidence
0.29938661 < p(japan) < 0.46984416

26. Quality control. For quality control purposes, 900 ceramic tiles were inspected to determine the proportion of defective (e.g., cracked, uneven finish) tiles. Assuming that these tiles are representative of all tiles manufactured by an Italian tile company, what can you conclude from the computer output? **LO ❶**

z-interval for proportion
With 95.00% confidence
0.025 < p(defective) < 0.035

27. Email. A small company involved in ecommerce is interested in statistics concerning the use of email. A poll found that 38% of a random sample of 1012 adults who use a computer at their home, work, or school said that they do not send or receive email.

a) Find the margin of error for this poll if we want 90% confidence in our estimate of the percentage of adults who do not use email.
b) Explain what that margin of error means.
c) If we want to be 99% confident, will the margin of error be larger or smaller? Explain.
d) Find that margin of error.
e) In general, if all other aspects of the situation remain the same, will smaller margins of error involve greater or less confidence in the interval? **LO ❶, ❷**

28. Biotechnology. A biotechnology firm is planning its investment strategy for research into human cloning. A poll found that only 8% of a random sample of 1012 Canadian adults approved of attempts to clone a human.

a) Find the margin of error for this poll if we want 95% confidence in our estimate of the percentage of Canadian adults who approve of cloning humans.

b) Explain what that margin of error means.

c) If we only need to be 90% confident, will the margin of error be larger or smaller? Explain.

d) Find that margin of error.

e) In general, if all other aspects of the situation remain the same, would smaller samples produce smaller or larger margins of error? **LO ❶**

29. Teenage drivers. An insurance company checks police records on 582 accidents selected at random and notes that teenagers were at the wheel in 91 of them.

a) Create a 95% confidence interval for the percentage of all auto accidents that involve teenage drivers.

b) Explain what your interval means.

c) Explain what "95% confidence" means.

d) A politician urging tighter restrictions on drivers' licences issued to teens says, "In one of every five auto accidents, a teenager is behind the wheel." Does your confidence interval support or contradict this statement? Explain. **LO ❶**

30. Advertisers. Direct mail advertisers send solicitations ("junk mail") to thousands of potential customers in the hope that some will buy the company's product. The response rate is usually quite low. Suppose a company wants to test the response to a new flyer and sends it to 1000 people randomly selected from its mailing list of over 200,000 people. The company gets orders from 123 of the recipients.

a) Create a 90% confidence interval for the percentage of people the company contacts who may buy something.

b) Explain what this interval means.

c) Explain what "90% confidence" means.

d) The company must now decide whether to do a mass mailing. The mailing won't be cost-effective unless it produces at least a 5% return. What does your confidence interval suggest? Explain. **LO ❶**

31. Retailers. Some food retailers propose subjecting food to a low level of radiation in order to improve safety, but the sale of such "irradiated" food is opposed by many people. Suppose a grocer wants to find out what his customers think. He has cashiers distribute surveys at the checkout and ask customers to fill them out and drop them in a box near the front door. He gets responses from 122 customers, of whom 78 oppose the radiation treatments. What can the grocer conclude about the opinions of all his customers? **LO ❶**

32. Local news. The mayor of a small city has suggested that the province locate a new prison there, arguing that the construction project and resulting jobs will be good for the local economy. A total of 183 residents show up for a public hearing on the proposal, and a show of hands finds 31 in favour of the prison project. What can the city council conclude about public support for the mayor's initiative? **LO ❶**

33. Internet music. In a survey on downloading music, the Gallup Poll asked 703 internet users if they "ever downloaded music from an internet site that was not authorized by a record company," and 18% responded "yes." Construct a 95% confidence interval for the true proportion of internet users who have downloaded music from an internet site that was not authorized. **LO ❶**

34. Economy worries. In 2008, a Gallup Poll asked 2335 Americans aged 18 or over how they rated economic conditions. In a poll conducted January 27–February 1, 2008, only 24% rated the economy as "Excellent/Good." Construct a 95% confidence interval for the true proportion of Americans who rated the U.S. economy as "Excellent/Good." **LO ❶**

35. Environmental certification in North America. In Canada, the vast majority (90%) of companies in the chemical industry are ISO 14001 certified. The ISO 14001 is an international standard for environmental management systems. An environmental group wished to estimate the percentage of U.S. chemical companies that are ISO 14001 certified. Of the 550 chemical companies sampled, 385 are certified.

a) What proportion of the sample reported being certified?

b) Create a 95% confidence interval for the proportion of U.S. chemical companies with ISO 14001 certification. Compare this with the Canadian proportion. **LO ❶, ❷**

36. Acquiring wealth. GfK Roper surveyed people worldwide, asking them, "How important is acquiring wealth to you?" Of 1535 respondents in India, 1168 said that it was of more than average importance. In the United States, of 1317 respondents, 596 said it was of more than average importance.

a) What proportion thought acquiring wealth was of more than average importance in each country's sample?

b) Create a 95% confidence interval for the proportion who thought it was of more than average importance in India. Compare this with a confidence interval for the U.S. population.

c) Create a 95% confidence interval for the difference in the proportions who thought acquiring wealth was of more than average importance between India and the United States. **LO ❶, ❹**

37. Business ethics. In a survey on corporate ethics, a poll split a sample of 1076 at random, asking 538 faculty and corporate recruiters the question, "Generally speaking, do you believe that MBAs are more or less aware of ethical issues in business today than five years ago?" The other 538 were asked, "Generally speaking, do you believe that

MBAs are less or more aware of ethical issues in business today than five years ago?" These may seem like the same questions, but sometimes the order of the choices matters. In response to the first question, 53% thought MBA graduates are more aware of ethical issues, but when the question was phrased differently, this proportion dropped to 44%.

a) What kind of bias may be present here?
b) Each group consisted of 538 respondents. If we combine them, considering the overall group to be one larger random sample, what is a 95% confidence interval for the proportion of the faculty and corporate recruiters who believe MBAs are more aware of ethical issues today?
c) How does the margin of error based on this pooled sample compare with the margins of error from the separate groups? Why? **LO ❶**

38. **Pharmaceutical company.** A pharmaceutical company is considering investing in a "new and improved" vitamin D supplement for children. Vitamin D, whether ingested as a dietary supplement or produced naturally when sunlight falls upon the skin, is essential for strong, healthy bones. The bone disease rickets was largely eliminated in England during the 1950s, but now there's concern that a generation of children more likely to watch TV or play computer games than spend time outdoors is at increased risk. A recent study of 2700 children randomly selected from all parts of England found 20% of them deficient in vitamin D.

a) Find a 98% confidence interval for the proportion of children in England who are deficient in vitamin D.
b) Explain carefully what your interval means.
c) Explain what "98% confidence" means.
d) Does the study show that computer games are a likely cause of rickets? Explain. **LO ❶**

39. **Funding.** A survey developed by Babson College and the Association of Women's Business Centers (WBCs) was distributed to WBCs in the United States. Of a representative sample of 20 WBCs, 40% reported that they had received funding from the national Small Business Association (SBA).

a) Check the assumptions and conditions for inference on proportions.
b) If it's appropriate, find a 90% confidence interval for the proportion of WBCs that received SBA funding. **LO ❶**

40. **Real estate in Toronto.** A real estate agent looks over the 15 listings she has in a particular postal code in Toronto and finds that 80% of them have swimming pools.

a) Check the assumptions and conditions for inference on proportions.
b) If it's appropriate, find a 90% confidence interval for the proportion of houses in this postal code that have swimming pools. **LO ❶**

41. **Canada Revenue Agency.** In a random survey of 226 self-employed individuals, 20 reported having had their tax returns audited by the Canada Revenue Agency in the past year. Estimate the proportion of self-employed individuals nationwide who've been audited in the past year.

a) Check the assumptions and conditions (to the extent you can) for constructing a confidence interval.
b) Construct a 95% confidence interval.
c) Interpret your interval.
d) Explain what "95% confidence" means in this context. **LO ❶**

42. **ACT Inc.** ACT Inc. reported that 74% of 1644 randomly selected first-year college students returned to college the next year. Estimate the national first-year student retention rate.

a) Check that the assumptions and conditions are met for inference on proportions.
b) Construct a 98% confidence interval.
c) Interpret your interval.
d) Explain what "98% confidence" means in this context. **LO ❶**

43. **Politics.** A poll of 1005 U.S. adults split the sample into four age groups: ages 18–29, 30–49, 50–64, and 65+. In the youngest age group, 62% said that they thought the United States was ready for a woman president, as opposed to 35% who said no, the country was not ready (3 percent were undecided). The sample included 250 18-to-29-year-olds.

a) Do you expect the 95% confidence interval for the true proportion of all 18-to-29-year-olds who think the United States is ready for a woman president to be wider or narrower than the 95% confidence interval for the true proportion of all U.S. adults? Explain.
b) Find the 95% confidence interval for the true proportion of all 18-to-29-year-olds who believe the United States is ready for a woman president. **LO ❶**

44. **Trade agreement.** Results from a January 2008 telephone survey conducted by Gallup showed that 57% of urban Colombian adults support a free trade agreement (FTA) with the United States. Gallup used a cluster sample in which the cities of Bogotá, Cali, Barranquilla, and Medellín provided a representative sample of 1000 urban Colombians aged 15 and older.

a) What is the parameter being estimated? What is the population? What is the sample size?
b) Check the conditions for making a confidence interval.
c) Construct a 95% confidence interval for the fraction of Colombians in agreement with the FTA.
d) Explain what this interval means. **LO ❶**

45. **Graduation.** As in Exercise 13, we hope to estimate the percentage of adults aged 25 to 30 who never graduated from high school. What sample size would allow us to increase our confidence level to 95% while reducing the margin of error to only 2%? **LO ❸**

46. Better hiring info. Editors of the business report in Exercise 14 are willing to accept a margin of error of 4% but want 99% confidence. How many randomly selected employers will they need to contact? LO ❸

47. Pilot study. An environmental agency worries that a large percentage of cars may be violating clean air emissions standards. The agency hopes to check a sample of vehicles in order to estimate that percentage with a margin of error of 3% and 90% confidence. To gauge the size of the problem, the agency first picks 60 cars and finds 9 with faulty emissions systems. How many should be sampled for a full investigation? LO ❸

48. Another pilot study. During routine conversations, the CEO of a new startup reports that 22% of adults between the ages of 21 and 39 will purchase her new product. Hearing this, some investors decide to conduct a large-scale study, hoping to estimate the proportion to within 4% with 98% confidence. How many randomly selected adults between the ages of 21 and 39 must they survey? LO ❸

49. Approval rating. A newspaper reports that the premier's approval rating stands at 65%. The article adds that the poll is based on a random sample of 972 adults and has a margin of error of 2.5%. What level of confidence did the pollsters use? LO ❷

50. Amendment. The board of directors of a publicly traded company says that a proposed amendment to their bylaws is likely to win approval in the upcoming election because a poll of 1505 stock owners indicated that 52% would vote in favour. The board goes on to say that the margin of error for this poll was 3%.
a) Explain why the poll is actually inconclusive.
b) What confidence level did the pollsters use? LO ❷

T 51. Customer spending. The data set provided contains last month's credit card purchases of 500 customers randomly chosen from a segment of a major credit card issuer. The marketing department is considering a special offer for customers who spend more than $1000 per month on their card. From these data, construct a 95% confidence interval for the proportion of customers in this segment who will qualify. LO ❶

T 52. Advertising. A philanthropic organization knows that its donors have an average age near 60 and is considering taking out an ad in the *Canadian Association of Retired Persons* (CARP) magazine. An analyst wonders what proportion of the donors are actually 50 years old or older. He takes a random sample of the records of 500 donors. From the data provided, construct a 95% confidence interval for the proportion of donors who are 50 or older. LO ❶

53. Abortion in Canada. Abortion is legal in Canada, but public opinion is divided on the circumstances in which it should be publicly funded. According to a survey of 1002 randomly selected Canadian adults, 43% said the health-care system should fund abortions whenever they're requested and 41% said the health-care system should only fund abortions in the event of medical emergencies. Calculate 95% confidence intervals for these percentages and interpret the meaning of these intervals. LO ❶

54. Climate change opinion in Canada. A survey of 1013 randomly selected Canadian adults asked whether they thought the government will impose a carbon tax on the oil sands in Alberta; only 12% thought that it would. Calculate a 90% confidence interval on this percentage and interpret the meaning of this interval. LO ❶

55. Black Friday in Canada. Ipsos surveyed 1005 Canadian adults just after the Black Friday sale in 2014 and found that 24.7% of them had bought something during the Black Friday sales promotions.
a) Calculate a 95% confidence interval for the proportion of Canadian adults buying something during the Black Friday sales promotions in 2014 and interpret its meaning.
b) How many Canadian adults would Ipsos need to survey in order to reduce the width of this confidence interval by 50%?
c) How much wider is the 99% confidence interval than the 95% interval you calculated in (a)? Give your answer as the ratio between the widths of the two confidence intervals.
d) A similar survey by Ipsos of 1010 Canadian adults in 2013 found 27.2% of them had purchased something during the Black Friday sales promotions that year. Calculate a 95% confidence interval for the difference in this proportion between 2013 and 2014 and interpret its meaning. Did the proportion decline between 2013 and 2014? LO ❶, ❷, ❸, ❹

56. Carbon tax in British Columbia. It's not often that taxes are popular, but when Environics surveyed 1023 adult British Columbians in 2011, it found 54% in favour of the carbon tax in that province. At $25/tonne of carbon, the tax adds only 5¢ to the price of a litre of gasoline.
a) Calculate a 90% confidence interval for the percentage of British Columbians in favour of the carbon tax in 2011 and interpret the meaning of your interval in words.
b) Phrase your confidence interval in the form commonly used by the media. For example, "*x*% of Ontarians support the *X* political party. This result is accurate to plus or minus *y*%, *n* times out of *N*."
c) How many British Columbian adults would Environics need to survey in order to reduce the width of this confidence interval by 25%?
d) How much wider is the 95% confidence interval than the 90% interval you calculated in (a)? Give your answer as the ratio between the widths of the two confidence intervals. LO ❶, ❷, ❸

57. Canadian Senate, part 1. Suppose we surveyed 1000 adult Canadians about reform of the Canadian Senate and 34% answered "Yes" to the question, "Do you support abolishing the Senate of Canada?"

a) Construct a 95% confidence interval for this proportion and give a verbal explanation of what your interval means.
b) Phrase your confidence interval in the form commonly used by the media. For example, "*x*% of Ontarians support the *X* political party. This result is accurate to plus or minus *y*%, *n* times out of *N*." **LO ❶**

58. Soybeans in Manitoba. Research at the University of Manitoba has resulted in the development of high yielding, high protein soybeans particularly suited to the local climate. There has been rapid growth in the land area planted with these soybeans, many of which are not genetically modified (non-GMO), making them suitable for export to the European Union. A survey of 420 soybean farmers found 85% of them grew non-GMO soybeans.

a) Calculate a 90% confidence interval for this proportion, stating your assumptions clearly. Interpret its meaning.
b) How much wider would this confidence interval have been if we had only surveyed 210 soybean farmers?
c) How many times wider would a 99% confidence interval be?
d) Five years later, a survey of 285 soybean farmers found that 80% of them grew non-GMO soybeans. Are we 95% confident that the proportion of farmers growing non-GMO soybeans is going down?

59. Canadian Senate, part 2. Suppose we surveyed 1000 adult Canadians about reform of the Canadian Senate. We found that 32% of people in Ontario supported abolishing the Senate of Canada, whereas the percentage in Quebec was 43%. Construct a 90% confidence interval for the difference in support for abolishing the Senate between Quebec and Ontario. (Assume that 38.4% of the people surveyed were in Ontario and 23.6% were in Quebec.) **LO ❹**

60. The Canadian nickel coin. Suppose we surveyed 1016 Canadian adults (assume half men and half women) and found that 65% of men and 45% of women support scrapping the five-cent coin (the nickel).

a) Construct a 90% confidence interval for the difference in support for scrapping the nickel between men and women.
b) Construct a 99% confidence interval for the difference in support for scrapping the nickel between men and women.
c) Interpret the meaning of the fact that one of these confidence intervals is wider than the other.

d) If we wanted the 90% confidence interval in (a) to be one-quarter as wide (narrower by 75%), how many more people would we need to survey? Answer the same question for the 99% confidence interval in (b). **LO ❷, ❸, ❹**

61. Canadian values. Suppose we surveyed 1006 Canadian adults and found that 41% believed that Canadian values were more right wing than 10 years previously.

a) A newspaper reporting these results stated, "Canadian opinion on this issue ranges from 33% agreement for 18-to-34-year-olds to 48% agreement for those over 54 years of age. These results are accurate to within plus or minus 3.1%, 19 times out of 20." Comment on the ethics of this statement as it relates to the ASA Ethical Guidelines in Appendix C.
b) Ontario has 39% of the Canadian population, whereas British Columbia has only 13%. Should we survey three times as many people in Ontario as in British Columbia in order for the confidence intervals on our results to be of similar width in the two provinces? **LO ❶, ❸**

62. Online music in Canada. Ipsos-Reid asked 900 Canadian adults whether they approve of using illegal or unauthorized online methods to access online music. In their responses, 12% of men said they completely approve, whereas the corresponding percentage for women was 6%.

a) Construct a 90% confidence interval for the percentage of Canadian adult men who completely approve of using illegal or unauthorized online methods to access online music and interpret what this interval means. State your assumptions clearly and check the conditions.
b) Are you 99% confident that there is a difference between men and women on this issue? Suppose Ipsos-Reid had interviewed 2000 Canadian adults. How much narrower would the confidence interval in (a) be? Give your answer as a percentage of the answer in (a).
c) The population of Ontario is 10 times as large as the population of Manitoba. Should we survey 10 times as many people in Ontario as in Manitoba in order for the confidence intervals on our results to be of similar width in the two provinces? **LO ❶, ❷, ❸, ❹**

63. Stroke treatment. The University of Calgary's Hotchkiss Brain Institute has developed a new procedure for treating stroke using a retrievable stent. Initial trials indicate a positive outcome in 55% of patients compared to 30% with the previous treatment. Suppose they want to be 90% confident of a difference in the procedures in a trial with the same number of patients treated by each method. How many patients would they need? **LO ❸, ❹**

Darryl Dyck/The Canadian Press

12

Testing Hypotheses About Proportions

Rogers

Ted Rogers started his business career in 1960 by buying the CHFI radio station, but with his philosophy that "The best is yet to come," it's no surprise that he quickly broadened his outlook and by 1979 owned the largest cable company in Canada, and in 1989 was already investing in mobile communications when that industry was only in its infancy. Telephone service and high speed internet followed in the 1990s, and today Rogers is a recognized brand in all forms of communications services, including mobile payments.

Telecommunications, particularly wireless, is an energy-intensive business, and Rogers' transmission sites consume more power than other aspects of its operations. Energy use is growing, and so is business, however the amount of energy required to generate each dollar of Rogers' revenue is also growing. To deal with this situation, Rogers has declared two long-term energy targets. By 2025, Rogers aims to reduce greenhouse gas emissions by 25% and energy use by 10% to below 2011 levels.

		Large Sample or Normal Population		Small Sample and Non-normal Population or Non-numeric Data	
Number of Variables	**Objective**	Chapter	Parametric Method	Chapter	Nonparametric Method
1	Calculate confidence interval for a proportion	11			
1	Compare a proportion with a given value	12	z-test		
1	Calculate a confidence interval for a mean and compare it with a given value	13	t-test	17.2	Wilcoxon Signed-Rank Test
2	Compare two proportions	12.8	z-test		
2	Compare two means for independent samples	14.1–14.5	t-test	17.4, 17.5	Wilcoxon Rank-Sum (Mann-Whitney) Test Tukey's Quick Test
2	Compare two means for paired samples	14.6, 14.7	Paired t-test	17.2	Wilcoxon Signed-Rank Test
≥3	Compare multiple means	15	ANOVA: ANalysis Of VARiance	17.3 17.6	Friedman Test Kruskal-Wallis Test
≥3	Compare multiple counts (proportions)	16	χ^2 test		
2	Investigate the relationship between two variables	18	Correlation Regression	17.7, 17.8	Kendall's tau Spearman's rho
≥3	Investigate the relationship between multiple variables	20	Multiple Regression		

ROADMAP FOR STATISTICAL INFERENCE

Video is very important on Rogers' networks, and it is a very competitive business. One way to increase revenue and at the same time retain customers is to monitor each customer's viewing habits and generate a profile of the types of videos the customer likes in order to make recommendations for future viewing. Many factors come into play in a customer's choice of video. It is not just the genre of video, but also the time of day and day of the week. Many people like multiple types of videos, and may prefer drama on a TV and sports on a mobile phone. Rogers and its competitors have developed sophisticated algorithms for analyzing preferences and making recommendations, and they are forever tweaking their algorithms to gain a competitive advantage of recommending "just the video I was in the mood for."

Suppose a video provider knows that 67% of its current customers are satisfied with the video recommendations it provides. It then launches a trial of a new recommendation algorithm for some customers and surveys 1000 of those customers selected at random. It finds that 71% are satisfied with the recommendations. Is the new algorithm better than the previous one? This chapter gives you a precise statistical methodology for answering that type of question. We start by formulating the situation in terms of hypotheses.

LO❶   ## 12.1   Hypotheses

Null Hypothesis

How can we state and test a hypothesis about the proportion of customers who are satisfied with our new algorithm for video recommendations? Hypotheses are working models that we adopt temporarily. So, our starting hypothesis,

> **Hypothesis** *n.*;
> pl. {Hypotheses}.
>   A supposition; a proposition or principle which is supposed or taken for granted, in order to draw a conclusion or inference for proof of the point in question; something not proved, but assumed for the purpose of argument.
>
> —*Webster's Revised Unabridged Dictionary, Merriam-Webster, Inc.*

NOTATION ALERT

Capital H is the standard letter for hypotheses. H_0 labels the null hypothesis, and H_A labels the alternative.

They make things admirably plain,
But one hard question will remain:
If one hypothesis you lose,
Another in its place you choose . . .

—JAMES RUSSELL LOWELL,
CREDIDIMUS JOVEM REGNARE

The Three Alternative Hypotheses

Two-sided:
$H_0: p = p_0$
$H_A: p \neq p_0$
One-sided:
$H_0: p = p_0$
$H_A: p < p_0$
One-sided:
$H_0: p = p_0$
$H_A: p > p_0$

---

called the **null hypothesis**, is that the proportion of satisfied customers has not changed. Notice that our hypothesis is about the proportion of *all* our customers, not just the 1000 that we sampled. We already know that 71% of them are satisfied with the new algorithm. Can we deduce anything about the whole population? Our hypothesis is therefore about a *parameter*, *p*, the proportion of *the whole population* of customers that are satisfied. We usually express it in the form:

$$H_0: p = p_0$$

This is a concise way to specify the two things we need most: the identity of the parameter we hope to learn about (the true proportion, *p*) and a specific hypothesized value for that parameter, p_0. Because the original algorithm yielded 67% satisfied customers, the null hypothesis is:

$$H_0: p = 0.67$$

Our null hypothesis essentially says "there's nothing new." That is, the new algorithm gives the same customer satisfaction as the current algorithm. It is a pessimistic hypothesis that all our work developing a new algorithm amounts to nothing. (Don't get too depressed about the null hypothesis. We'll soon come to the alternative hypothesis.)

We need a hypothesized value so that we can compare our survey results to it. Which value to use for the null hypothesis is not a statistical question but a business question: What were we hoping to change by developing our new algorithm? Answer: We wanted to change the current customer satisfaction proportion, *p*, so that is the *parameter* to use in the hypothesis. What would be the value if it didn't change? Answer: 0.67, so that is the *value* to use in the hypothesis.

Alternative Hypothesis

The **alternative hypothesis**, which we denote H_A, contains the range of proportions that we consider plausible if the null hypothesis is not true. This depends on our original business question: "Is the new algorithm *better* than the previous one?" In this case, we are hoping that the proportion of satisfied customers is *greater* than 0.67, so our alternative hypothesis is:

$$H_A: p > 0.67$$

Additional Examples

An index on the Toronto Stock Exchange, the S&P/TSX Composite Index, tracks the behaviour of the market. Some days it goes up, and others it goes down. Some analysts believe that the up and down days are split 50/50. In order to test this out, we collect data for 1000 days and find that the proportion of up days is 0.515. Note how this example differs from the previous example about customer satisfaction. In the previous example, we were looking specifically for an *improvement* in customer satisfaction. In the TSX case, we are interested in whether the proportion of up days is 0.5 or not. We don't care whether it is higher or lower. In this case, our hypotheses are:

$$H_0: p = 0.5$$
$$H_A: p \neq 0.5$$

A supplier of stainless steel kitchen utensils is having 0.86% of its merchandise returned as a result of corrosion of the steel. The company improves the quality control on the production process, monitors 2000 shipments chosen at random, and has 0.53% of the merchandise returned for corrosion issues. In this example, we are hoping that the proportion of merchandise returned will *go down*. We are not specifically told this, but our understanding of the business situation makes it pretty clear, so the hypotheses are:

$$H_0: p = 0.0086$$

$$H_A: p < 0.0086$$

In each of these three examples, we give the results of a survey: 71% satisfied customers for video recommendations, 51.5% up days on the TSX, and 0.53% returned merchandise. These results do not appear in the hypotheses themselves, but we will use them later to test whether the hypotheses are true. The numerical values in the null and alternative hypotheses are always the same and represent the situation where nothing has changed. The null hypothesis says this default numerical value of our parameter has not changed and the alternative hypothesis is that it has changed.

In our example about the TSX, we were equally interested in proportions that deviate from 50% in *either* direction. So we wrote our alternative hypothesis as $H_A: p \neq 0.5$. Such an alternative hypothesis is known as a **two-sided alternative**, because we are equally interested in deviations on either side of the null hypothesis value.

In our example about video recommendations we expected an increase, and in our example about returned merchandise we expected a decrease in the proportion we were measuring. This led to an alternative hypothesis that focuses on deviations from the null hypothesis value in only one direction, which is called a **one-sided alternative**.

Be sure to set the parameter in the null hypothesis to represent the status quo or current situation; that is, nothing has changed. The issue that we are investigating goes in the alternative hypothesis. Be sure to choose an alternative hypothesis that represents the business question we are asking. We wanted to know whether the number of up days on the TSX is 50% or not. That is different from wanting to know whether the number of up days is more than 50%.

What NOT to Do

Don't fudge the null hypothesis so that you can prove something you want to prove. The difference between the current video recommendation algorithm and the new one doesn't seem like much: Customer satisfaction only changed from 67% to 71%. Maybe that's not enough to prove that the new algorithm is better. If we make our null hypothesis $H_0: p = 0.5$ instead of $p = 0.67$, we will have a good chance of proving that the new algorithm satisfies more than half the customers. But that was not the business issue we were addressing. We wanted to know whether the new algorithm is *better* than the current one. The null hypothesis should represent the business issue, not something an analyst has dreamed up.

Don't fudge the alternative hypothesis so that you can prove something you want to prove. In the TSX example, we thought there would be 50% up days and wondered whether in fact it was something different. We found a sample with 51.5% up days, so maybe the number of up days is higher than 50% and our alternative hypothesis should be $H_A: p > 0.5$. Not so! The alternative hypothesis represents our original business question: Is the percentage of up days 50%? We can and should frame our hypotheses even before we collect data and discover the 51.5% figure. Our alternative hypothesis should not be influenced by the data we collect. It should only reflect the business issue we are addressing.

Don't put the issue that you are investigating into the null hypothesis. It should go in the alternative hypothesis. The null hypothesis says that the issue you are investigating is NOT true. We want to know whether the new algorithm is better, whether the proportion of up days is different from 0.5, whether we have less returned merchandise. It is those issues that determined the sign ($>$, $\neq$, or $<$) in the alternative hypothesis. The null hypothesis represents the status quo.

Don't have different numbers in the null and alternative hypotheses. The numerical values are always the same.

JUST CHECKING

1 Formulate hypotheses for each of the following situations.

  a) Your stockbroker claims to be able to recommend stocks that will rise over the next month. You think that he will get it right for half the stocks he recommends. In fact, out of 40 recommendations, he gets it right 60% of the time.

  b) A car manufacturer tests engine cylinder blocks for microscopic cracks and is able to detect 92% of cracks. An entrepreneur approaches the manufacturer with a new ultrasound technology that is claimed to perform better. The car manufacturer tests the ultrasound technology and finds that it can detect 98% of cracks.

  c) Twenty years ago, the percentage of homes in a city with unsafe levels of lead in the tap water was 17%. The mayor believes that lead is less of a problem now.

Answers are found in Appendix A.

FOR EXAMPLE   Framing hypotheses about website customers

SmartWool, an online vendor of fancy woolen ski mitts, recently redesigned its website, and analysts at SmartWool want to know if the proportion of visits resulting in a sale has changed since the new site went online.

QUESTION   If the old site's proportion was 20%, frame appropriate null and alternative hypotheses for the proportion.

ANSWER   For the proportion, let p = proportion of visits that result in a sale.

$$H_0: p = 0.2 \text{ vs. } H_A: p \neq 0.2$$

LO❶   **12.2   A Trial as a Hypothesis Test**

We started by assuming that the proportion of customers satisfied with our video recommendations stayed the same and then formulated an alternative hypothesis that it increased. This chapter is about whether we have sufficient evidence to prove that it has increased. You've seen this reasoning before in a different context. This is the logic of jury trials.

Let's suppose a defendant has been accused of robbery. In British common law and those systems derived from it (including Canadian and U.S. law), the null hypothesis is that the defendant is innocent. Instructions to juries are quite explicit about this.

The evidence takes the form of facts that seem to contradict the presumption of innocence. For us, this means collecting data. In the trial, the prosecutor presents evidence. ("If the defendant were innocent, wouldn't it be remarkable that the police found him at the scene of the crime with a bag full of money in his hand, a mask on his face, and the keys to a getaway car parked outside?") The next step

William Manning/Alamy Stock Photo

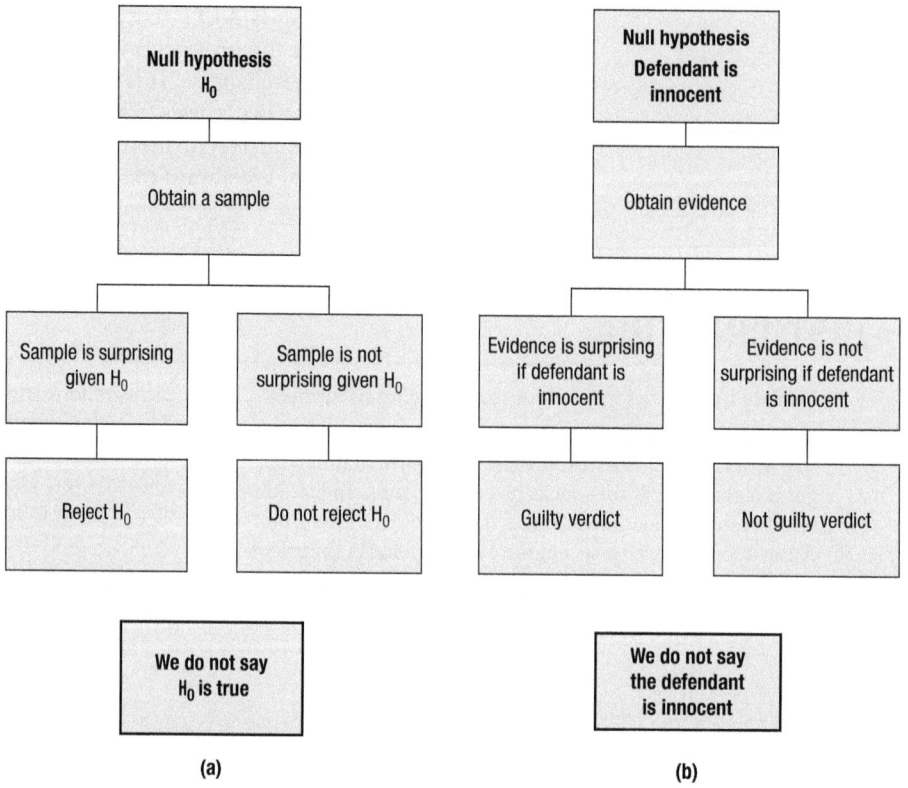

Figure 12.1   (a) Hypothesis testing. (b) Court case.

is to judge the evidence. Evaluating the evidence is the responsibility of the jury in a trial, but it falls on your shoulders in hypothesis testing. The jury considers the evidence in light of the *presumption* of innocence and judges whether the evidence against the defendant would be plausible *if the defendant were in fact innocent.*

Like the jury, we ask, "Could these data plausibly have happened by chance if the null hypothesis were true?" (See Figure 12.1.) If they're very unlikely to have occurred, then the evidence raises a reasonable doubt about the null hypothesis. Ultimately, *you* must make a decision. The standard of "beyond a reasonable doubt" is purposely ambiguous, because it leaves the jury to decide the degree to which the evidence contradicts the hypothesis of innocence. No analogy is perfect, and juries don't explicitly use probability to help them decide whether to reject that hypothesis. But when you ask the same question of your null hypothesis, you have the advantage of being able to quantify exactly how surprising the evidence would be if the null hypothesis were true.

Another difference between a trial and a hypothesis test is that in Statistics, we are always estimating a quantitative value (e.g., the proportion of satisfied customers). By contrast, much of the evidence presented in court is qualitative. Also, judges and juries are making subjective decisions, whereas in statistical hypothesis testing we have a quantitative procedure, described in the rest of this chapter. In Section 12.10, we calculate the "power" of our statistical test—that is, how good it is. Such a measure is not available for courtroom decisions. A final difference is that, in a courtroom, lawyers for the two sides seek actively to *persuade* the judge and jury about the merits of their case. We must be very careful to avoid that in statistical hypothesis testing. Whatever pressure we are under from the CEO of our pharmaceutical company to prove that the new medication is better than those currently available, we must conduct an objective analysis. It is an infringement of Item H of the ethical guidelines in Appendix C for management to put pressure on statistical analysts to come up with a result that the company wants.

LO❶   12.3

P-Values

The fundamental step in our reasoning is the question, "Are the data surprising, given the null hypothesis?" And the key calculation is to determine exactly how likely the data we observed would be if the null hypothesis were the true model of the world. So we need a *probability*. Specifically, we want to find the probability of seeing data like these (or something even less likely) *given* that we accept the null hypothesis. This probability is the value on which we base our decision, so statisticians give this probability a special name, the **P-value**, or "plausibility value."

A low enough P-value says that the data we've observed would be very unlikely if our null hypothesis were true, that is, the null hypothesis has a low "plausibility." We started with a model, and now that same model tells us that the data we have are unlikely to have happened. That's surprising. In this case, the model and data are at odds with each other, so we have to make a choice: Either the null hypothesis is correct and we've just seen something remarkable, or the null hypothesis is wrong. If you believe in data more than in assumptions, then, given that choice, when you see a low P-value you should reject the null hypothesis.

When the P-value is *high* (or just not low *enough*), what do we conclude? In that case, we haven't seen anything unlikely or surprising at all. The data are consistent with the model from the null hypothesis, and we have no reason to reject the null hypothesis. Events that have a high probability of happening happen all the time. So when the P-value is high, does that mean we've proven that the null hypothesis is true? No! We realize that many other similar hypotheses could also account for the data we've seen. The most we can say is that it doesn't appear to be false. Formally, we say that we "fail to reject" the null hypothesis. That may seem to be a pretty weak conclusion, but it's all we can say when the P-value isn't low enough. All that means is that the data are consistent with the model we started with.

What would convince you that the proportion of up days on the TSX was not 50%? If, on 95 out of 100 days, the TSX closed up, most people would be convinced that up and down days were not equally likely. But if the sample proportion of up days were only slightly higher than 50%, you'd be skeptical. After all, observations do vary, so we wouldn't be surprised to see some difference. How different from 50% must the proportion be before we *are* convinced that it has changed? Whenever we ask about the size of a statistical difference, we naturally think of the standard deviation. So let's start by finding the standard deviation of the sample proportion of days on which the TSX increased.

We've seen 51.5% up days out of 1000 trading days, and we have a hypothesis that the proportion of up days is 0.5. To test a null hypothesis, we (temporarily) *assume* it's true so that we can see whether that description of the world is plausible. If we assume that the TSX increases or decreases with equal likelihood, we'll need to centre our Normal sampling model at a mean of 0.5. Then we can find the standard deviation of the sampling model using the results of Chapter 10:

$$SD(\hat{p}) = \sqrt{\frac{p_0 q_0}{n}} = \sqrt{\frac{0.5 * (1 - 0.5)}{1000}} = 0.0158$$

Now we know both parameters of the Normal sampling distribution model for our null hypothesis. For the mean, μ, we use $p = 0.50$, and for σ we use the standard deviation of the sample proportions, $SD(\hat{p}) = 0.0158$. We want to know how likely it would be to see the observed value $\hat{p}$ as far away from 0.5 as the value of 0.515 that we've actually observed. Looking first at a picture (Figure 12.2), we can see that 0.515 doesn't look very surprising. The more exact answer (from software, or the Normal table) is obtained from the Normal distribution:

$$z = \frac{x - \mu}{\sigma} = \frac{0.515 - 0.5}{0.0158} = 0.949$$

Beyond a Reasonable Doubt

We ask whether the data were unlikely beyond a reasonable doubt. The probability that the observed statistic value (or an even more extreme value) could occur if the null hypothesis were true is the P-value.

Conditional Probability

Did you notice that a P-value results from what we referred to as a conditional probability in Chapter 8? A P-value is a conditional probability because it's based on—or is conditional on—another event being true: It's the probability that the observed results could have happened *if the null hypothesis is true.*

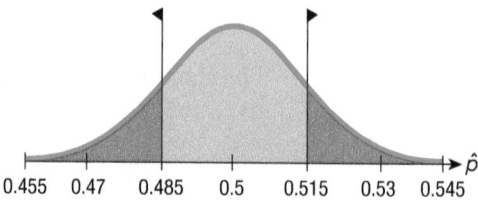

Figure 12.2   How likely is a proportion of more than 51.5% or less than 48.5% when the true mean is 50%? This is what it looks like. Each red area is 0.171 of the total area under the curve.

which we can look up in Table Z of Appendix B to obtain a probability of 0.829. This is the probability of being to the left of 0.515 in Figure 12.2. But from Section 12.1, our hypotheses are:

$$H_0: p = 0.5$$

$$H_A: p \neq 0.5$$

We have a two-sided alternative hypothesis, so we must add the probabilities in the red areas in Figure 12.2. We are interested in the probability of observing a proportion of up days as extreme as 0.515 or more extreme in both directions. The probability in one of those red regions is $1 - 0.829 = 0.171$, so the total area in both of them is $2 \times 0.171 = 0.342$.

This is the probability of observing more than 51.5% up days (or more than 51.5% down days) if the null model were true. In other words, if the chance of an up day for the TSX is 50%, we'd expect to see stretches of 1000 trading days with as many as 51.5% up days about 17.1% of the time, and with as many as 51.5% down days about 17.1% of the time. That's not terribly unusual, so there's really no convincing evidence that the market did not have a 50/50 ratio of up and down days.

It may surprise you that even during a bull market, the probability that any given day will end up or down appears to be about 0.5. When the stock market has a long run up (or down), it does so not by having more days of increasing or decreasing value, but by the dollar amounts of the increases or decreases being unequal.

For two-sided alternatives, the P-value is the probability of deviating in *either* direction from the null hypothesis value (see Figure 12.3).

For one-sided alternative hypotheses, like our example of the proportion of returned merchandise, the P-value is the probability of deviating *only in the direction of the alternative* away from the null hypothesis value (see Figure 12.4). In Figures 12.2, 12.3, and 12.4, the red area represents the probability of getting a survey result as extreme as the result we got or more extreme than that.

Imagine a test of whether a company's new website design encourages a higher percentage of visitors to make a purchase (as compared with the site it's used for years). The null hypothesis is that the new site is no more effective at stimulating purchases than the old one. The test sends visitors randomly to one version of the website or the other. Of course, some will make a purchase, and others won't. If we compare the

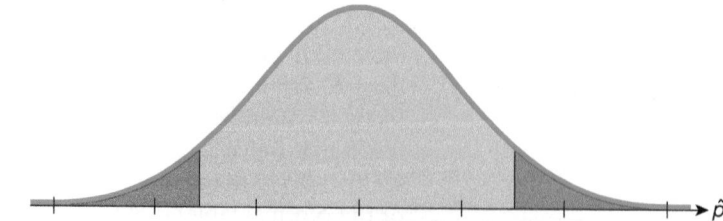

Figure 12.3   The P-value for a two-sided alternative adds the probabilities in both tails of the sampling distribution model outside the value that corresponds to the test statistic.

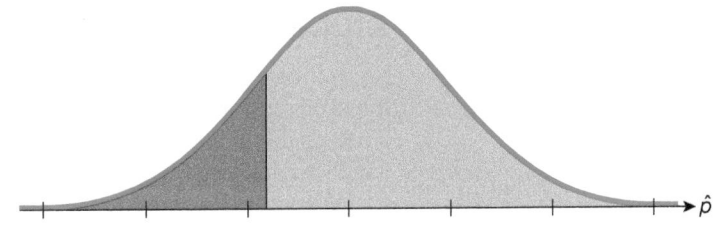

Figure 12.4 The P-value for a one-sided alternative considers only the probability of values beyond the test statistic value in the specified direction.

Don't We Want to Reject the Null?

Often the people who collect the data or perform the experiment hope to reject the null. They hope the new drug is better than the placebo; they hope the new ad campaign is better than the old one; or they hope their candidate is ahead of the opponent. But when we practise Statistics, we can't allow that hope to affect our decision. The essential attitude for a hypothesis tester is skepticism. Until we become convinced otherwise, we cling to the null's assertion that there's nothing unusual, nothing unexpected, no effect, no difference, etc. As in a jury trial, the burden of proof rests with the alternative hypothesis—innocent until proven guilty. When you test a hypothesis, you must act as judge and jury; you're not the prosecutor.

Conclusion

If the P-value is "low," reject H_0 and conclude H_A.

If the P-value isn't "low enough," then fail to reject H_0 and the test is inconclusive.

two websites on only 10 customers each, the results are likely *not to be clear*, and we'll be unable to reject the null hypothesis. Does this mean the new design is a complete bust? Not necessarily. It simply means that we don't have enough evidence to reject our null hypothesis. That's why we don't start by assuming that the new design is *more* effective. If we were to do that, then we could test just a few customers, find that the results aren't clear, and claim that since we've been unable to reject our original assumption, the redesign must be effective. The board of directors is unlikely to be impressed by that argument. If the results of a hypothesis test are inconclusive, the one thing we can do is to increase our sample size. That will narrow down the width of the distributions in Figures 12.2, 12.3, and 12.4. But we can't just keep on increasing it and stop when we find a result that we like, or one that pleases our boss.

FOR EXAMPLE   **Conclusions about website customers from P-values**

The SmartWool analyst (see For Example: "Framing hypotheses about website customers") is now testing hypotheses about whether the proportion of website visitors who make a purchase has *increased* from 0.2 since the redesign of the website. H_0: $p = 0.2$; H_A: $p > 0.2$. She collects a random sample of 50 visits since the new website has gone online and finds that 24% of them made purchases.

QUESTION   What conclusions can she draw?

ANSWER   Assuming the null hypothesis is true until it is proven false, we have $p = 0.2$, so that the standard deviation of the Normal sampling model is:

$SD(\hat{p}) = \sqrt{\dfrac{0.2 * 0.8}{50}} = 0.0566$. We then calculate $z = \dfrac{x - \mu}{\sigma}$

$= \dfrac{0.24 - 0.2}{0.0566} = 0.707$. From software, we find a probability of 0.760, so that the

P-value (that is, the probability of getting a result as extreme as 24% or more extreme) is $1 - 0.760 = 0.240$, which is not very low. The sample result is not surprising given the null hypothesis that nothing has changed. Although we have some information that the new website design may be more effective, our data could easily (with a probability of 0.24) have occurred by chance.

JUST CHECKING

2 A pharmaceutical firm wants to know whether aspirin helps to thin blood. The null hypothesis says that it doesn't. The firm's researchers test 12 patients, observe the proportion with thinner blood, and get a P-value of 0.32. They proclaim that aspirin doesn't work. What would you say?

3 An allergy drug has been tested and found to give relief to 75% of the patients in a large clinical trial. Now the scientists

want to see whether an "improved" version works even better. What would the null hypothesis be?

4 The new allergy drug above is tested on 2500 patients and found to give relief to 78% of them. What would you conclude about the drug?

Answers are found in Appendix A.

LO❶   12.4   Alpha Levels and Significance

Sometimes we need to make a firm decision about whether to reject the null hypothesis. A jury must *decide* whether the evidence reaches the level of "beyond a reasonable doubt." A business must *select* a website design. You need to decide which section of a Statistics course to enrol in.

When the P-value is small, it tells us that our data are rare *given the null hypothesis*. As humans, we're suspicious of rare events. If the data are "rare enough," we just don't think that could have happened due to chance. Since the data *did* happen, something must be wrong. All we can do now is reject the null hypothesis.

But how rare is "rare"? How low does the P-value have to be?

We can define "rare event" arbitrarily by setting a threshold for our P-value. If our P-value falls below that point, we'll reject the null hypothesis. We call such results *statistically significant*. Data are *statistically significant* if they have a low probability of occurring when the null hypothesis is true. The threshold is called an **alpha level**. Not surprisingly, it's labelled with the Greek letter α. Common α-levels are 0.10, 0.05, and 0.01. You have the option—almost the *obligation*—to consider your alpha level carefully and choose an appropriate one for the situation. If you're assessing the safety of air bags, you'll want a low alpha level; even 0.01 might not be low enough. If you're just wondering whether folks prefer their pizza with or without pepperoni, you might be happy with $\alpha = 0.10$. It can be hard to justify your choice of α, though, so we often arbitrarily choose 0.05.

Where did the value 0.05 come from? In 1931, in a famous book called *The Design of Experiments*, Sir Ronald Fisher discussed the amount of evidence needed to reject a null hypothesis. He said that it was situation dependent, but remarked, somewhat casually, that for many scientific applications, 1 out of 20 might be a reasonable value, especially in a first experiment—one that will be followed by confirmation. Since then, some people—indeed some entire disciplines—have acted as if the number 0.05 were sacrosanct.

The alpha level is also called the **significance level**. When we reject the null hypothesis, we say that the test is "significant at that level." For example, we might say that we reject the null hypothesis that the TSX goes up on 50% of days "at the 5% level of significance." Some people prefer to say that their result is significant at the 95% level instead of at the 5% level. It sounds more significant. We will use 95% and 5% equivalently. Also, 99% significance is equivalent to 1%, and 90% is equivalent to 10%. There is no confusion since we are using either numbers around 5% or numbers around 95%. The alpha value is always around 5%, but it sometimes sounds better to talk of a significance around 95%. You must select the alpha level *before* you look at the data. Otherwise, you can be accused of finagling the conclusions by tuning the alpha level to the results after you've seen the data.

What can you say if the P-value does not fall below α? When you haven't found sufficient evidence to reject the null according to the standard you've established, you should say, "The data have failed to provide sufficient evidence to reject the null hypothesis." Don't say, "We accept the null hypothesis." You certainly haven't proven or established the null hypothesis; it was assumed to begin with. You *could* say that you have *retained* the null hypothesis, but it's better to say that you've failed to reject it.

NOTATION ALERT

The first Greek letter α is used in Statistics for the threshold value of a hypothesis test. You'll hear it referred to as the alpha level. Common values are 0.10, 0.05, 0.01, and 0.001.

> **It Could Happen to You!**
>
> Of course, if the null hypothesis *is* true, no matter what alpha level you choose, you still have a probability α of rejecting the null hypothesis by mistake. When we do reject the null hypothesis, no one ever thinks that *this* is one of those rare times. As statistician Stuart Hunter notes, "The statistician says 'rare events do happen—but not to me!'"

Conclusion

If the P-value $< \alpha$, then reject H_0.
If the P-value $\geq \alpha$, then fail to reject H_0.

The evidence against H_0 is:
Good (*) if $0.01 \leq P < 0.05$
Very good (**) if
$0.001 \leq P < 0.01$
Super (***) if $P < 0.001$

If the P-value is close to α, then report the P-value together with your recommendation about rejecting the null hypothesis

Statistical vs. Business Significance

Statistical significance measures how sure we are that things have changed from the null hypothesis. Business significance depends on whether the change is large enough to increase profits.

The automatic nature of the reject/fail-to-reject decision when we use an alpha level may make you uncomfortable. If your P-value falls just slightly above your alpha level, you're not allowed to reject the null. Yet a P-value just barely below the alpha level leads to rejection. If this bothers you, you're in good company. Many statisticians think it better to report the P-value than to choose an alpha level and carry the decision through to a final reject/fail-to-reject verdict. So when you declare your decision, it's always a good idea to report the P-value as an indication of the strength of the evidence.

It's in the stars. Some disciplines carry the idea further and code P-values by their size. In this scheme, a P-value between 0.05 and 0.01 gets highlighted by a single asterisk (*). A P-value between 0.01 and 0.001 gets two asterisks (**), and a P-value less than 0.001 gets three (***). This can be a convenient summary of the weight of evidence against the null hypothesis, but it isn't wise to take the distinctions too seriously and make black-and-white decisions near the boundaries. The boundaries are a matter of tradition, not science; there is nothing special about 0.05. A P-value of 0.051 should be looked at seriously and not casually thrown away just because it's larger than 0.05, and one that's 0.009 is not very different from one that's 0.011.

The importance of P-values is also clear in the common situation in which the person performing the statistical analysis isn't the decision maker. In many organizations, statistical results are reported to management, which then makes the decision on whether to accept the alternative hypothesis. Pharmaceutical companies developing drugs spend millions of dollars testing whether a new drug is more effective than existing drugs, and their reports are filled with P-values. But the decision on whether a new drug is better and whether to manufacture it is made by management taking into account all those P-values plus numerous other factors. Suppose management wants to be 95% sure the new drug is better. A statistical report shouldn't simply do a hypothesis test with $\alpha = 0.05$ and state that the hypothesis test shows the new drug is better. It should also give the P-value. A P-value of 0.01 leads to the same hypothesis test result as a P-value of 0.045, but it gives the decision maker more confidence in the results.

What do we mean when we say that a test is statistically significant? All we mean is that the test statistic had a P-value lower than our alpha level. The P-value is the smallest value of α for which we can reject the null hypothesis.

Business Significance

For large samples, even small deviations from the null hypothesis can be statistically significant. On the other hand, if the sample isn't large enough, even large, financially or scientifically important differences may not be statistically significant.

It's good practice to report the magnitude of the difference between the observed statistic value and the null hypothesis value (in the data units) along with the P-value on which you've based your decision about statistical significance. For instance, you might say: "Our data about the new website design indicate that it has increased the proportion of visitors who make purchases from 0.2 to 0.24 and this is significant at the 5% level with a P-value of 0.043."

A result may have statistical significance, but no business significance. A large insurance company mined its data and found a statistically significant ($P = 0.04$) difference between the mean incomes from policies sold last year and those sold this year. The difference in the mean values was $4.25. Even though it was statistically significant, management did not see this as an important difference since the income from a typical policy is more than $1000. This is known as the **effect size**. The effect size in this case is very small, only $4.25. A very small change can be statistically significant if we have a very large sample size.

On the other hand, a result may have business significance but not be statistically significant. A marketable improvement of 10% in the relief rate for a new pain medicine was not supported by a statistical test using $\alpha = 0.001$. The P-value was 0.009. The effect might not be statistically significant for two reasons. First, we might not have had a sufficiently large sample. Second, we were aiming for a very high level of significance with $\alpha = 0.001$. If we want to use a very low value of α, then we are going to need a very large sample size. The effect may or may not have business significance. Even if the Marketing Department tells us that a 10% improvement (the effect size) is marketable, we still need to consider the cost of manufacturing the new drug, and then figure out whether it will improve profits.

FOR EXAMPLE   Setting the α level for website customers

QUESTION   Following from For Example: "Conclusions about website customers from P-values," the manager of the analyst at SmartWool wants her to compare an α level of 0.05 with an α level of 0.01 for her hypothesis tests. What would her conclusion be if the P-value comes to (a) 0.06; (b) 0.03; or (c) 0.003? (d) Should SmartWool use the new website if the P-value is 0.003?

ANSWER

(a) There is insufficient evidence as to whether the proportion of site visits resulting in a sale has changed from 0.2. This conclusion applies if $\alpha = 0.05$ or if $\alpha = 0.01$.

(b) If $\alpha = 0.05$ we have sufficient evidence of a change, but if $\alpha = 0.01$ we do not.

(c) There is sufficient evidence of a change in the proportion of site visits resulting in a sale. This conclusion applies if $\alpha = 0.05$ or if $\alpha = 0.01$.

(d) We cannot make the business decision as to which website to use until we have information on the costs of maintaining the two sites, whether the proportion of sales increased or decreased, and what change in profits comes from that increase or decrease.

LO❷   ## 12.5   The Reasoning of Hypothesis Testing

The null hypothesis is never proved or established, but is possibly disproved, in the course of experimentation. Every experiment may be said to exist only in order to give the facts a chance of disproving the null hypothesis.

—From The Design of Experiments by Sir Ronald Aylmer Fisher. Published by Oliver and Boyd, © 1935.

Hypothesis tests follow a carefully structured path. To avoid getting lost as we navigate down it, we divide that path into a sequence of eight steps, grouped into the three major stages used in our Guided Examples: PLAN, DO, REPORT. We now list those eight steps, illustrating them with the example of testing a new video recommendation algorithm that we described at the start of this chapter.

Hypothesis Testing in a Nutshell

Plan

1. Hypotheses (formulate them)
2. Alpha (choose it)
3. Assumptions (check them)

Do

4. Data (collect it)
5. Statistical test (calculate the P-value)

Report

6. Statistical significance (how significant?)
7. Hypotheses (reject the null or don't)
8. Business significance (e.g., how can we figure out the impact on profits?)

GUIDED EXAMPLE   The Eight Steps of Hypothesis Testing: Testing the Video Recommendation Algorithm

 PLAN   1. Interpret the business situation in terms of hypotheses.

General Principle	New Video Recommendation Algorithm
Choose a numerical parameter that is important to the business context.	We want to know the proportion, p, of customers satisfied with our video recommendations.
Decide whether the business situation needs you to investigate whether this parameter has increased, decreased, or changed in either direction.	We want to see whether p has increased.
Formulate the null hypothesis related to this parameter: $H_0: p = p_0$	$H_0: p = 0.67$
Formulate the alternative hypothesis. The sign depends on whether we are investigating an increase ($H_A: p > p_0$), a decrease ($H_A: p < p_0$), or a change in either direction ($H_A: p \neq p_0$).	$H_A: p > 0.67$

2. Interpret the business situation in terms of a significance level, α.

General Principle	New Video Recommendation Algorithm
Choose a value of α that corresponds to the business context. Here is one way of doing that. $\alpha = 0.001$ for a life/death business where we need to be super sure of getting things right. $\alpha = 0.01$ for a business situation in which things can be measured pretty accurately. $\alpha = 0.05$ for behavioural situations where parameters are open to interpretation. Other ways of choosing α may also be used.	$\alpha = 0.05$ since we are surveying customers and they may interpret "satisfied" in different ways.

3. Check the assumptions and conditions for using the Normal model.

General Principle (these allow us to use a Normal distribution for our statistical test)	New Video Recommendation Algorithm
Independence Assumption	We survey customers who do not know each other.
Randomization Condition	We choose our sample of customers at random.
10% Condition	We surveyed 1000 customers, which is less than 10% of our total number of customers.
Success/Failure Condition for the parameter value in the null hypothesis, p_0	$p_0 = 0.67$ and $n = 1000$ Therefore, $np_0 = 670 > 10$ Also $n(1 - p_0) = 330 > 10$

(continued)

DO 4. Gather data.

General Principle	New Video Recommendation Algorithm
Do a survey or collect measurements from a production line or from company records.	We surveyed $n = 1000$ customers and found $\hat{p} = 0.71$.

5. Apply the statistical test, calculating a P-value.

General Principle (we are using the "one-sample test for proportions" also known as the "one-proportion z-test")	New Video Recommendation Algorithm
$$SD(\hat{p}) = \sqrt{\frac{p_0(1 - p_0)}{n}}$$	$$SD(\hat{p}) = \sqrt{\frac{0.67 \times (1 - 0.67)}{1000}}$$ $$= 0.0149$$
$$z = \frac{x - \mu}{\sigma}$$	$$z = \frac{0.71 - 0.67}{0.0149} = 2.69$$
Look up the probability, P_{Tab}, in Table Z, Appendix B. For (H_A: $p > p_0$), P-value $= 1 - P_{Tab}$ For (H_A: $p < p_0$), P-value $= P_{Tab}$ For (H_A: $p \neq p_0$), P-value $= 2 \times (1 - P_{Tab})$	From the table, the probability of being lower than 0.71 is $P_{Tab} = 0.996$. We have H_A: $p > 0.67$. Therefore: P-value $= 1 - 0.996 = 0.004$.

REPORT 6. Interpret the P-value in terms of statistical significance.

General Principle	New Video Recommendation Algorithm
If P-value $< \alpha$, then we have a result that is statistically significant at the level α.	P-value $= 0.004 < \alpha = 0.05$ Our survey results are statistically significant at the 5% level.

7. Interpret the P-value in terms of your original hypotheses.

General Principle	New Video Recommendation Algorithm
If the results are statistically significant, we can reject the null hypothesis.	We reject the null hypothesis that the proportion of customers satisfied with our video recommendation algorithm remained unchanged at 0.67.

8. Interpret these results in the business context.

General Principle	New Video Recommendation Algorithm
State what the P-value and your decision about the null hypothesis mean in the business context.	For this type of situation, we would have been happy with a 5% significance level. In fact, our P-value is 0.4%, indicating a result that is even more significant. The increase in the proportion of satisfied customers is very significant. We are very sure that the new video recommendation algorithm has increased customer satisfaction.

General Principle	New Video Recommendation Algorithm
What other factors should be taken into account before taking a business decision, including the statistical significance, the cost, and the revenue implications of the size of effect we have observed from our data?	Before implementing the new algorithm for all customers, we need to assess its costs and also the impact on revenue of an increase of 4% (71% − 67%) in customer satisfaction.

When you do a hypothesis test, you don't have to spell out this list of eight points with their various sub-points. Treat them as a guide to be sure you cover all your bases.

FOR EXAMPLE **The reasoning of hypothesis tests about website customers**

QUESTION   The analyst at SmartWool (see For Example: "Setting the α level for website customers") makes another change to the website, puts it online, selects 200 recent web visits at random, and finds that 29% of them have resulted in a sale. Would this be a surprising proportion of sales if the true proportion of sales were 20%? We are interested in whether the proportion of visits resulting in a sale has changed since the new website went live. Comment on the statistical and business significance of this result.

ANSWER   We are going to follow the eight steps described above and number them to illustrate clearly what we have just covered. You don't always have to number them precisely like that, but you must be sure to cover all the eight steps within the context of the business situation you are analyzing.

1. We want to investigate whether the proportion, p, of customers making a purchase has changed. The baseline proportion is $p_0 = 0.2$, therefore our hypotheses are: $H_0: p = 0.2$; $H_A: p \neq 0.2$.

2. Since this is a situation where quantitative data is accurate, we choose $\alpha = 0.01$.

3. Customers behave independently of each other and were chosen at random. $n = 200$ and we assume the company has more than 2000 customers. $np_0 = 40 > 10$. $n(1 - p_0) = 160 > 10$.

4. We surveyed $n = 200$ customers and found a proportion $\hat{p} = 0.29$ made a purchase.

5. $SD(\hat{p}) = \sqrt{\dfrac{p_0 q_0}{n}} = \sqrt{\dfrac{(0.2)(0.8)}{200}} = 0.02828$.

$$z = \frac{\hat{p} - p_0}{SD(\hat{p})} = \frac{0.29 - 0.20}{0.02828} = 3.182.$$

From Table Z in Appendix B, we find $P_{Tab} = 0.9993$. Therefore the P-value (for our two-sided test) is $2 \times (1 - 0.9993) = 0.0014$.

6. Our P-value $= 0.0014$ is a lot less than our $\alpha = 0.01$. We therefore have a result that is statistically significant at the 1% level.

7. We can therefore reject the null hypothesis that $p = 0.2$.

8. We have very good evidence that the proportion of website visitors who make purchases has changed from 0.2. The P-value is 0.0014, indicating a probability of 0.0014 that this result could have occurred by chance. Before going ahead with the new website, we should assess the costs of operating it and also the additional revenues from the increased proportion ($0.29 - 0.2 = 0.09$) of purchasing customers in order to assess its profitability.

GUIDED EXAMPLE   Home Field Advantage

Nathan Denette/The Canadian Press/AP Images

Major league sports are big business. And the fans are more likely to come out to root for the team if the home team has a good chance of winning. Anyone who follows or plays sports has heard of the "home field advantage." It is said that teams are more likely to win when they play at home. That *would* be good for encouraging the fans to come to the games. But is it true?

Suppose that, last season, the home team won 1263 of 2429 games, or 52.0% of the time. If there were no home field advantage, the home teams would win about half of all games played. Could this deviation from 50% be explained just from natural sampling variability, or does this evidence suggest that there really is a home field advantage, at least in professional baseball?

PLAN	**Setup** State what we want to know. Define the variables and discuss their context.	We want to know whether the home team in professional baseball is more likely to win. The data are all 2429 games from last season. The parameter of interest is the proportion of home team wins.

$$H_0 : p = 0.50$$
$$H_A : p > 0.50$$

Hypotheses The null hypothesis makes the claim of no home field advantage.

We're interested only in a home field *advantage*, so the alternative hypothesis is one-sided.

Model Think about the assumptions and check the appropriate conditions.

Consider the time frame carefully.

This is a situation where everything is well quantified, so we choose $\alpha = 0.01$.

✓ **Independence Assumption.** Generally, the outcome of one game has no effect on the outcome of another game. But this may not always be strictly true. For example, if a key player is injured, the probability that the team will win in the next couple of games may decrease slightly, but independence is still roughly true.

✓ **Randomization Condition.** We have results for all 2429 games from last season. While these games were not randomly selected, they may be reasonably representative of all recent professional baseball games.

✓ **10% Condition.** 2429 games are fewer than 10% of all games played over the years.

✓ **Success/Failure Condition.** Both
$np_0 = 2429(0.50) = 1214.5$ and
$nq_0 = 2429(0.50) = 1214.5$ are at least 10.

Specify the sampling distribution model.

Tell what test you plan to use.

Because the conditions are approximately satisfied, we'll use a Normal model for the sampling distribution of the proportion and do a one-proportion z-test using our data of 52.0% home wins.

DO	**Mechanics** The null model gives us the mean, and (because we're working with proportions) the mean gives us the standard deviation.	The null model is a Normal distribution with a mean of 0.50. Since this is a hypothesis test, the standard deviation is calculated from p_0 (in the null hypothesis).

$$SD(\hat{p}) = \sqrt{\frac{p_0 q_0}{n}} = \sqrt{\frac{(0.5)(1 - 0.5)}{2429}} = 0.01015$$

The observed proportion $\hat{p}$ is 0.52.

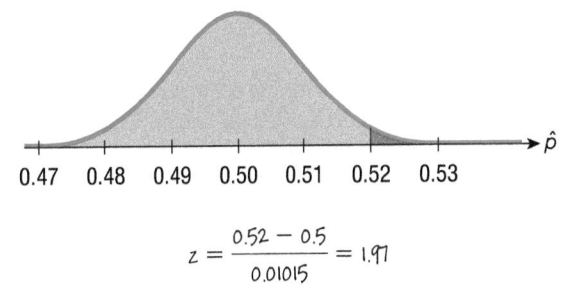

From technology or numerical calculation and the Normal distribution table, we can find the P-value, which tells us the probability of observing a value that extreme (or more).

$$z = \frac{0.52 - 0.5}{0.01015} = 1.97$$

The corresponding P-value is 0.0244.

REPORT

Conclusion State your conclusion about the parameter—in context.

MEMO:

Re: Home Field Advantage

Our analysis of outcomes during the last baseball season did not show a statistically significant advantage to the home team at the 1% level. Our data does not allow us to be 99% sure that the home team has an advantage.

In Guided Example: "Home Field Advantage," we never even considered home field disadvantage. Some statisticians build this into the null hypothesis and write

$$H_0: p \leq 0.50$$

$$H_A: p > 0.50,$$

which spells out the fact that there's a possibility of a home field disadvantage. The calculations are exactly the same; the only difference is the way the null hypothesis is written. In this book, we'll always use an exact value in our null hypotheses, since that corresponds to most practical situations. We usually have a number, p_0, and we're testing whether our proportion is different from that number. Table 12.1 summarizes the three types of hypothesis tests.

Notice that the null hypothesis always has an "equals" sign. The alternative hypothesis involves "less than," "greater than," or "not equal to."

	Two-Sided	**One-Sided**	**One-Sided**
How we write it	$H_0 : p = p_0$ $H_A : p \neq p_0$	$H_0 : p = p_0$ $H_A : p > p_0$	$H_0 : p = p_0$ $H_A : p < p_0$
How some people write it to spell out the details	No change, i.e., $H_0 : p = p_0$ $H_A : p \neq p_0$	$H_0 : p \leq p_0$ $H_0 : p > p_0$	$H_0 : p \geq p_0$ $H_0 : p < p_0$
Practical example	Is the proportion of "up" days on the stock market different from the proportion of "down" days?	Is there a home field advantage?	Are customers returning fewer items this year than the 3% they returned last year?
p_0 in the example	0.5	0.5	0.03

Table 12.1   Three types of hypothesis test.

JUST CHECKING

5 A car manufacturer tests engine cylinder blocks for microscopic cracks and is able to detect 92% of cracks. The manufacturer provides a 10-year warranty on its cylinder heads. If the crack leads to a failure of the cylinder head, the manufacturer incurs the costs of replacing the cylinder head, plus some bad publicity. An entrepreneur approaches the manufacturer with a new ultrasound technology that allegedly performs better. The car manufacturer tests the ultrasound technology on a random sample of 500 cracked cylinder blocks and finds that it can detect 94% of cracks. Should the car manufacturer adopt the new technology? Investigate two significance levels that give different results.

Answers are found in Appendix A.

LO❷ **12.6** ## Critical Values

When building a confidence interval in Chapter 11, Section 3, we found a **critical value**, z^*, to correspond to our selected confidence level. Critical values can also be used as a shortcut for hypothesis tests. Any z-score larger in magnitude (i.e., more extreme) than a particular critical value has to be less likely, so it will have a P-value smaller than the corresponding alpha.

If we were willing to settle for a flat reject/fail-to-reject decision, comparing an observed z-score with the critical value for a specified alpha level would give a shortcut path to that decision. Let us take the case of our supplier of stainless steel kitchen utensils, which is receiving 0.86% of its merchandise returned as a result of corrosion of the steel. The company improves the quality control on the production process, monitors 2000 shipments chosen at random, and receives 0.53% of the merchandise returned for corrosion issues. The null hypothesis is that there is no improvement: $H_0: p = 0.0086$. A quick calculation shows: $SD(\hat{p}) = 0.002065$ and $z = -1.598$. If we want to test the significance of this result at the 1% level, then we can find the critical value corresponding to 1% by looking up $1\% = 0.01$ in the body of the Normal distribution table in Appendix B. The corresponding z value (at the edge of the table) is the critical value and comes to -2.33. (We are essentially using the Normal distribution table backwards.) This situation is illustrated in Figure 12.5. Since our value of z (-1.598) is not more extreme than the critical value (-2.33), we cannot reject the null hypothesis.

The critical value approach differs from the P-value approach described in Section 12.3, in that it does not calculate a P-value. This saves some time, but it provides less information and we do not have a measure of how plausible our data is. The P-value measures the plausibility of our data.

Table 12.2 gives the traditional z^* critical values from the Normal model, as illustrated in Figures 12.5 and 12.6.[1]

> If you need to make a quick decision with no technology, remember "2." That's our old friend from the 68-95-99.7 Rule. It's roughly the critical value for testing a hypothesis against a two-sided alternative at $\alpha = 0.05$. The exact critical value is 1.96, but 2 is close enough for most decisions.

α	One-Sided	Two-Sided
0.10	1.28	1.645
0.05	1.645	1.96
0.01	2.33	2.576
0.001	3.09	3.29

Table 12.2 Critical values, z^*, for different types of hypothesis test.

---

[1]In a sense, these are the flip side of the 68-95-99.7 Rule. There we chose simple statistical distances from the mean and recalled the areas of the tails. Here we select convenient tail areas (0.05, 0.01, and 0.001, either on one side or adding the two together) and record the corresponding statistical distances.

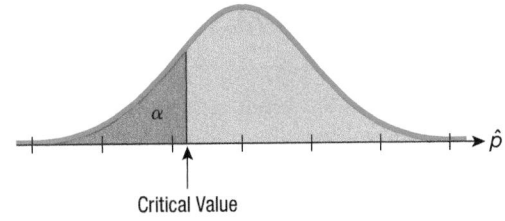

Figure 12.5 When the alternative is one-sided, the critical value puts all of α on one side.

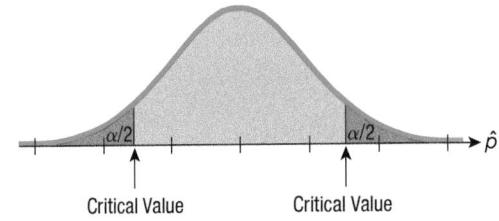

Figure 12.6 When the alternative is two-sided, the critical value splits α equally into two tails.

FOR EXAMPLE

Tests about website customers using critical values

QUESTION Find the critical z value for the SmartWool hypothesis (see For Example: "The reasoning of hypothesis tests about website customers") using $\alpha = 0.05$ and show that the same decision would have been made using critical values.

ANSWER For the two-sided test of proportions, we refer to Figure 12.6. Since $\alpha = 0.05$, $\alpha/2 = 0.025$, so that $1 - \alpha/2 = 0.975$. Looking up this value in the body of Table Z in Appendix B gives a critical z value of 1.96. This is also the value given in Table 12.2. Because the z value was 3.182, much larger than 1.96, we reject the null hypothesis.

LO❸   12.7   Confidence Intervals and Hypothesis Tests

Watch out for a subtle difference between the calculations for hypothesis tests and confidence intervals. Although they're very similar, they're not identical. An easy way to remember this difference is to focus on what information is available. For a confidence interval, all we have available is the proportion from our sample, whereas for a hypothesis test we *also* have the hypothesized value for the population.

For a confidence interval, we estimate the standard deviation of $\hat{p}$ from $\hat{p}$ itself, making it a *standard error*,

$$SE(\hat{p}) = \sqrt{\frac{\hat{p}\hat{q}}{n}}.$$

For the corresponding hypothesis test, we use the model's *standard deviation* for $\hat{p}$ based on the null hypothesis value p_0,

$$SD(\hat{p}) = \sqrt{\frac{p_0 q_0}{n}}.$$

When $\hat{p}$ and p_0 are close, these calculations give similar results. When they differ, you're likely to reject H_0 (because the observed proportion is far from your hypothesized value). In that case, you're better off building your confidence interval with a standard error estimated from the data rather than relying on the model you just rejected. Because confidence intervals are naturally two-sided, they correspond to two-sided tests. For example, a 95% confidence interval corresponds to a two-sided hypothesis test at $\alpha = 5\%$. In general, a confidence interval with a confidence level of $C\%$ corresponds to a two-sided hypothesis test with an α level of $100 - C\%$. For a one-sided hypothesis test, we use a one-sided confidence interval, extending to infinity on the other side.

NOTATION ALERT

We've attached symbols to many of the p's. Let's keep them straight.

p is a population parameter—the true proportion in the population.

p_0 is a hypothesized value of p.

$\hat{p}$ is an observed proportion.

Calculating $\sqrt{\dfrac{pq}{n}}$

Use Whatever Proportions You've Got

If you know the population proportion, p, as in Chapter 10, use that.
If you are testing a hypothesis about p, use p_0.
For a confidence interval, use $\hat{p}$.

> **Checking Success/Failure Condition** $np > 10$ and $n(1 - p) > 10$
>
> **Use Whatever Proportions You've Got**
>
> If you know the population proportion, p, as in Chapter 10, use that.
>
> If you are testing a hypothesis about p, use p_0.
>
> For a confidence interval, use $\hat{p}$.

One-Sided Confidence Intervals

For a one-sided test with $\alpha = 1\%$, you could construct a one-sided confidence interval, leaving 1% in one tail and extending to infinity on the other side. A one-sided confidence interval leaves one side unbounded. For example, in the home field scenario, we wondered whether the home field gave the home team an *advantage*, so our test was naturally one-sided. The standard error is calculated from the proportion from the sample, which is 0.52:

$$SE(\hat{p}) = \sqrt{\frac{\hat{p}\hat{q}}{n}} = \sqrt{\frac{0.52 \times (1 - 0.52)}{2429}} = 0.01014$$

This is very slightly different from the standard deviation of 0.01015 that we calculated in Guided Example: "Home Field Advantage," based on the proportion 0.5 in the null hypothesis. The lower limit of the 99% confidence interval is shown in Figure 12.7(a) and is calculated from the critical z value for a one-sided test in Table 12.2, which is 2.33:

$$0.52 - 2.33 \times 0.01014 = 0.496$$

In order to leave 1% on one side, we used the z^* value 2.33, which leaves 1% in one tail. Writing the one-sided interval as $(0.496, \infty)$ allows us to say with 99% confidence that we know the home team will win, on average, at least 49.6% of the time. To test the hypothesis $H_0: p = 0.50$, we note that the value 0.50 is in this interval. We cannot therefore reject the hypothesis that $p = 0.50$.

Two-Sided Confidence Intervals

Now, let's change the example so that we are not looking for a home field *advantage*, but instead a home field *difference*. Looking for a difference either

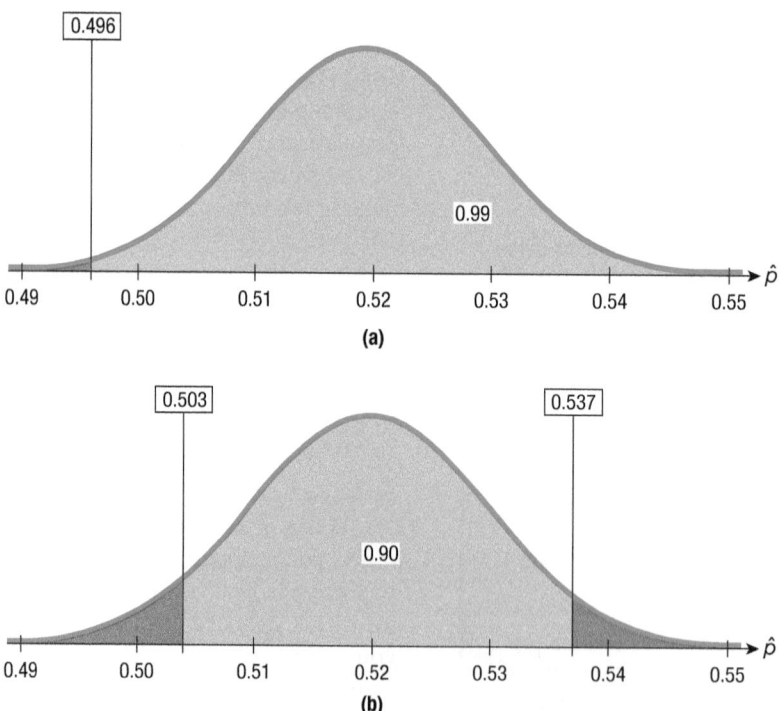

Figure 12.7   (a) The one-sided 95% confidence interval (top) leaves 5% on one side (in this case the left), but leaves the other side unbounded. (b) The 90% confidence interval is symmetric.

way from a 0.5 proportion of wins implies a two-sided hypothesis test with $H_A: p \neq 0.5$. Let us calculate a 90% confidence interval for the proportion of wins. Using the critical value from Table 12.2 of 1.645, the confidence interval is shown in Figure 12.7(b) and is calculated as:

$$0.52 \pm 1.645 \times 0.01014 = (0.503, 0.537)$$

The value 0.5 is not in this interval, so we can reject the null hypothesis of $p = 0.5$ at the 10% significance level.

There's another good reason for finding a confidence interval along with a hypothesis test. Although the test can tell us whether the observed statistic differs from the hypothesized value, it doesn't say by how much. Often, business decisions depend not only on whether there's a statistically significant difference, but also on whether the difference is meaningful. The range of the confidence interval, from 0.503 to 0.537, shows how much difference there might be. For some fans, that's enough for them to buy tickets when their team plays at home.

Extraordinary claims require extraordinary proof.

—*CARL SAGAN*

JUST CHECKING

Last year, 21% of customers at our grocery store purchased gluten-free (GF) products. We expect the proportion to increase this year, and a random sample of 300 of this year's customers indicates that 25% purchased GF products.

6 Construct a 95% confidence interval for this year's proportion.

7 State appropriate hypotheses and calculate the P-value at the 5% significance level.

8 Comment on the standard deviation or standard error that you used in Questions 6 and 7.

9 What do the above results tell us about whether the proportion has increased this year? Comment on these conclusions.

Answers are found in Appendix A.

GUIDED EXAMPLE   Credit Card Promotion

A credit card company found that, last year, 25% of customers charged more than $500 per month to their cards. Due to changing economic conditions, the company expects that this year the proportion will be higher. A random sample of 500 customers this year indicates that 29.6% of them charged over $500 to their cards. Does this indicate an increase this year compared to last year?

PLAN	**Setup** State the problem and discuss the variables and the context.	We want to know whether more than 25% of customers will charge over $500 per month to their credit cards this year. The statistic is $\hat{p} = 0.296$, the proportion of customers who charged $500 or more.

Hypotheses The null hypothesis is that the proportion is 25%. The alternative is that it's higher. It's clearly a one-sided test, so we will use a one-sided confidence interval.

$$H_0: p = 0.25$$
$$H_A: p > 0.25$$

✓ **Independence Assumption.** Customers aren't likely to influence one another when it comes to spending on their credit cards.

✓ **Randomization Condition.** This is a random sample from the company's database.

✓ **10% Condition.** The sample is less than 10% of all customers.

(continued)

	Model Check the conditions. State your method. Here we're using a confidence interval to test a hypothesis.	✓ **Success/Failure Condition.** $$np_0 = 500 \times 0.25 = 125$$ $$np_0 = 500 \times 0.75 = 375$$ Since both are > 10, our sample size is large enough. Under these conditions, the sampling model is Normal. We'll create a one-proportion z-interval.
DO	**Mechanics** To use a confidence interval, we need a confidence level that corresponds to the alpha level of the test. If we use $\alpha = 0.05$, we should use a critical value of 1.645 from Table 12.2. Determine the standard error of the sample proportion and the margin of error.	Since we're calculating a confidence interval, the standard error is obtained from $\hat{p}$. Contrast the hypothesis test in Guided Example: "Home Field Advantage." $$SE(\hat{p}) = \sqrt{\frac{\hat{p}\hat{q}}{n}} = \sqrt{\frac{(0.296)(0.704)}{500}} = 0.0204$$ $$ME = z^* \times SE(\hat{p})$$ $$= 1.645(0.0204) = 0.034$$ The 95% one-sided confidence interval starts at $0.296 - 0.034$ and can be written: $(0.262, \infty)$.
REPORT	**Conclusion** Link the confidence interval to your decision about the null hypothesis, then state your conclusion in context.	MEMO: **Re: Credit Card Promotion** Our study of a sample of customer records indicates that over 26.2% of customers charge $500 or more. We are 95% confident that this interval includes the true value. Because last year's value of 25% is below this interval, we conclude that it's not a plausible value, and so we reject the null hypothesis that only 25% of customers charge more than $500 a month.

To address this credit card question using hypothesis testing, the main difference is the way we calculate $SD(\hat{p})$ based on the value in the null hypothesis, $p = 0.25$, instead of being based on $\hat{p} = 0.296$ for the SE in the calculation of the confidence interval.

$$SD(\hat{p}) = \sqrt{\frac{0.25 \times (1 - 0.25)}{500}} = 0.0194$$

$$z = \frac{0.296 - 0.25}{0.0194} = 2.38$$

The corresponding P-value is 0.00876, which is significant at the 5% level. We therefore can reject the null hypothesis and claim at the 5% significance level that the proportion of customers charging more than $500 per month is higher this year than last year. This confirms the conclusion from the confidence interval analysis in Guided Example: "Credit Card Promotion." The only situation where we would get a different result is if $SD(\hat{p})$ used in the hypothesis test and calculated from the value of p_0 in H_0 is very different from $SE(\hat{p})$ used in the confidence interval and calculated from the estimated value $\hat{p}$. In our case, $SD(\hat{p}) = 0.0194$, which is not very different from $SE(\hat{p}) = 0.0204$.

QUESTION Construct an appropriate confidence interval for testing the earlier hypothesis (see For Example: "Framing hypotheses about website customers" and For Example: "The reasoning of hypothesis tests about website customers") and show how we could have reached the same conclusion from this interval.

ANSWER The test of proportion was two-sided, so we construct a 99% confidence interval for the true proportion: $\hat{p} \pm 2.576 \times SE(\hat{p}) = 0.29 \pm 2.576 \times \sqrt{\dfrac{(0.29)(0.71)}{200}}$

$= (0.207, 0.373)$. Since 0.20 is not inside this interval, 29% sales is a surprisingly large value. We reject the null hypothesis.

LO⑤ 12.8 Comparing Two Proportions

Nanos Research conducts a weekly survey of which federal political parties Canadians would consider voting for. Suppose that this week's survey of 1002 adults indicated that 36% would consider voting NDP, and that a year ago it was 41% in a survey of 1980 adults. Has there been a change in NDP support over the past year? We can formulate a hypothesis test to address this question:

H_0: There is no difference between the proportions of adults who would consider voting NDP this week and a year ago.

H_A: There is a difference between the proportions of adults who would consider voting NDP this week and a year ago.

This is a different type of hypothesis test from the one we dealt with earlier about whether the percentage of up days for the TSX was equal to 50% or whether there's a home team advantage. In those cases, we were comparing sample results with a fixed number of 50%. In the case of NDP support, there is no fixed number. Instead, we're comparing one sample with another sample. At first sight, this may seem tough. We want to know whether the percentage who would consider voting NDP this week is different from what it was a year ago, but we don't know what the percentage support was a year ago. In fact, we can resolve this problem pretty fast by thinking instead about the *difference* in the percentage support over the past year. Now we're comparing the percentage support a year ago *minus* the percentage support this week with a fixed number: zero.

If p_1 and p_2 are the population proportions who would consider voting NDP this week and a year ago, respectively, our original null hypothesis was:

$$H_0: p_1 = p_2$$

Now we have rephrased it as:

$$H_0: p_1 - p_2 = 0$$

The alternative hypothesis is:

$$H_A: p_1 - p_2 \neq 0$$

Our estimate of p_1 is $\hat{p}_1$ (in our case, 0.36) and our estimate of p_2 is $\hat{p}_2$ (in our case, 0.41). So, using the approach described in Section 12.5, we calculate:

$$z = \frac{\hat{p}_1 - \hat{p}_2}{SE(\hat{p}_1 - \hat{p}_2)}$$

The standard error of the difference between $\hat{p}_1$ and $\hat{p}_2$ is obtained from the fact that these are independent random variables and that we can therefore add their variances:

$$SE(\hat{p}_1 - \hat{p}_2) = \sqrt{SE(\hat{p}_1)^2 + SE(\hat{p}_2)^2}$$

$$= \sqrt{\frac{\hat{p}_1 \hat{q}_1}{n_1} + \frac{\hat{p}_2 \hat{q}_2}{n_2}}$$

This is known as the "Two-Proportion z-Test," and it can be used to test whether the difference between two proportions is any number, K:

$$H_0: p_1 - p_2 = K$$

In our case, $K = 0$, meaning that we're testing whether the two proportions are equal. This is a special case. Since the null hypothesis is $p_1 = p_2$, we don't really have two estimates $\hat{p}_1$ and $\hat{p}_2$ of different proportions. They're two estimates of the same proportion. We can "pool" these two estimates into a single estimate. Suppose x_1 people out of n_1 would consider voting NDP this week (giving $p_1 = x_1/n_1$) and x_2 people out of n_2 would consider voting NDP a year ago (giving $p_2 = x_2/n_2$), and our null hypothesis says the support is the same. Then we should use a "pooled" estimate of the support from both surveys:

$$\bar{p} = \frac{x_1 + x_2}{n_1 + n_2}$$

Our standard error is now

$$SE(\hat{p}_1 - \hat{p}_2) = \sqrt{\frac{\bar{p}\bar{q}}{n_1} + \frac{\bar{p}\bar{q}}{n_2}} = \sqrt{\bar{p}\bar{q}\left(\frac{1}{n_1} + \frac{1}{n_2}\right)}$$

where $\bar{q} = 1 - \bar{p}$.

We now have two z-tests for two proportions, as summarized in the boxes in the margin. One of them tests whether the difference between two proportions is any number, K, and the other is specific to testing whether the two proportions are the same—i.e., $K = 0$.

These tests require the same four assumptions and conditions that we used in the case of the **one-proportion z-test:**

- **Independence Assumption:** The two samples are independent of each other.
- **Randomization Condition:** The people in each sample were selected at random.
- **10% Condition:** The sample is less than 10% of Canada's population.
- **Success/Failure Condition:**

$$n_1 p_1 > 10; \; n_1 q_1 > 10;$$

$$n_2 p_2 > 10; \; n_2 q_2 > 10.$$

We can be confident that the first two conditions are satisfied, since Nanos Research is a professional survey company. A quick calculation shows that the other two conditions are also satisfied.

Returning to our question about whether there's a difference between the proportions who would consider voting NDP this week and a year ago, we have:

$$H_0: p_1 = p_2$$

$$\bar{p} = \frac{x_1 + x_2}{n_1 + n_2} = \frac{0.36 \times 1002 + 0.41 \times 1980}{1002 + 1980} = 0.3932$$

$$z = \frac{0.36 - 0.41}{\sqrt{0.3932 \times 0.6068 \times \left(\frac{1}{1002} + \frac{1}{1980}\right)}} = -2.64$$

Looking this z value up in Table Z, Appendix B, we find a probability of 0.0041. Since this is a two-sided test, the corresponding P-value is 0.0082, which is less than 0.05. Clearly there *is* a difference between the proportions who would consider voting NDP this week and a year ago at the 5% significance level.

FOR EXAMPLE	The effect of sample size when comparing two proportions of voting preferences

Survey companies like Nanos Research often survey about 1000 people in order to get a narrow standard deviation on their results and hence significant results. To see the effect of using a much smaller sample, let's suppose that only 30 people had been surveyed.

QUESTION If the survey of whether people would consider voting NDP had been done on only 30 people this week and on only 30 people a year ago, and resulted in 61% and 36%, respectively, would this indicate a significant difference over the past year on this issue at the 5% level?

ANSWER Although 61% is very different from 36%, these are percentages of very small samples (size $n = 30$). Considering the entire population of Canada, it is possible that the overall proportion who would consider voting NDP was actually higher a year ago. We therefore formulate a two-sided hypothesis test.

H_0: There is no difference between the proportions who would consider voting NDP this week and a year ago, i.e., $p_1 - p_2 = 0$.

H_A: There is a difference between the proportions who would consider voting NDP this week and a year ago, i.e., $p_1 - p_2 \neq 0$.

Checking the conditions, the Independence Assumption and Randomization Condition are assumed true if this is a professionally designed survey. Certainly these small samples are less than 10% of the population of Canada. The Success/Failure Condition is only just satisfied, indicating that these samples are really only just large enough for us to use a test based on the Normal distribution:

$$n_1 p_1 = 30 \times 0.61 = 18.3 > 10;$$

$$n_1 q_1 = 30 \times 0.39 = 11.7 > 10;$$

$$n_2 p_2 = 30 \times 0.36 = 10.8 > 10;$$

$$n_2 q_2 = 30 \times 0.64 = 19.2 > 10.$$

First we calculate the pooled proportion:

$$\bar{p} = \frac{x_1 + x_2}{n_1 + n_2} = \frac{0.36 \times 30 + 0.61 \times 30}{30 + 30} = 0.485$$

Our test statistic is

$$z = \frac{0.61 - 0.36}{\sqrt{0.485 \times 0.515 \times \left(\dfrac{1}{30} + \dfrac{1}{30}\right)}}$$

$$= 1.94$$

The corresponding P-value is 0.053, indicating that the difference is *not* significant at the 5% level.

This example shows that a difference that looks large may not be significant if the sample sizes are small.

LO❹   **12.9**   # Two Types of Error

Nobody's perfect. Even with lots of evidence, we can still make the wrong decision. In fact, when we perform a hypothesis test, we can make mistakes in *two* ways:

I. The null hypothesis is true, but we mistakenly reject it.
II. The null hypothesis is false, but we fail to reject it.

These are known as a **Type I error** and **Type II error**, respectively. One way to keep the names straight is to remember that we start by assuming the null hypothesis is true, so a Type I error is the first kind of error we could make.

In medical disease testing, the null hypothesis is usually the assumption that a person is healthy. The alternative is that he or she has the disease we're testing for. So a Type I error is a *false positive*—a healthy person is diagnosed with the disease. A Type II error, in which an ill person is diagnosed as disease free, is a *false negative*. These errors have other names, depending on the particular discipline and context.

Which type of error is more serious depends on the situation. In a jury trial, a Type I error occurs if the jury convicts an innocent person. A Type II error occurs if the jury fails to convict a guilty person. Which seems more serious? In medical diagnosis, a false negative could mean that a sick patient goes untreated. A false positive might mean that a healthy person must undergo treatment.

In business planning, a false positive result could mean that money will be invested in a project that turns out not to be profitable. A false negative result might mean that money won't be invested in a project that would have been profitable. Which error is worse, the lost investment or the lost opportunity? The answer always depends on the situation, the cost, and your point of view.

Figure 12.8 gives an illustration of the situations:

How often will a Type I error occur? It happens when the null hypothesis is true but we've had the bad luck to draw an unusual sample. To reject H_0, the P-value must fall below α. When H_0 is true, that happens *exactly* with probability α. The α level that you choose is the maximum probability of a Type I error that you are prepared to tolerate.

What if H_0 is not true? Then we can't possibly make a Type I error. You can't get a false positive from a sick person. A Type I error can happen only when H_0 is true.

When H_0 is false and we reject it, we've done the right thing. A test's ability to detect a false hypothesis is called the **power** of the test. In a jury trial, power is a measure of the ability of the criminal justice system to convict people who are guilty. We'll have a lot more to say about power in Section 12.10.

When H_0 is false but we fail to reject it, we've made a Type II error. We assign the letter β to the probability of this mistake. What's the value of β? That's harder to assess than α because we don't know what the value of the parameter really is. When

NOTATION ALERT

In Statistics, α is the probability of a Type I error and β is the probability of a Type II error.

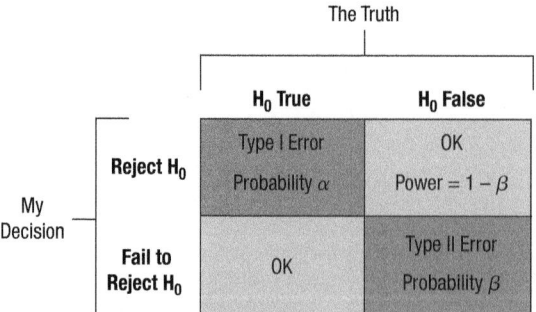

Figure 12.8   The two types of errors occur on the diagonal, where the truth and decision don't match. Remember that we start by assuming H_0 to be true, so an error made (rejecting it) when H_0 is true is called a Type I error. A Type II error is made when H_0 is false (and we fail to reject it).

The null hypothesis specifies a single value for the parameter. So it's easy to calculate the probability of a Type I error. But the alternative gives a whole range of possible values, and we may want to find a β for several of them.

We've seen ways to find a sample size by specifying the margin of error. Choosing the sample size to achieve a specified β (for a particular alternative value) is sometimes more appropriate, but the calculation is more complex and lies beyond the scope of this book.

H_0 is true, it specifies a single parameter value. But when H_0 is false, we don't have a specific one; we have many possible values. We can compute the probability β for any parameter value in H_A, but the choice of which one to pick is not always clear.

One way to focus our attention is by thinking about the *effect size*. That is, ask, "How big a difference would matter?" Suppose a charity wants to test whether placing personalized address labels in an envelope along with a request for a donation increases the response rate above the baseline of 5%. If the minimum response that would pay for the address labels is 6%, the charity would calculate β for the alternative $p = 0.06$.

Of course, we could reduce β for *all* alternative parameter values by increasing α. By making it easier to reject the null, we'd be more likely to reject it whether it's true or not. The only way to reduce *both* types of error is to collect more evidence or, in statistical terms, to collect more data. Otherwise, we just wind up trading off one kind of error against the other. Whenever you design a survey or experiment, it's a good idea to calculate β (for a reasonable α level). Use a parameter value in the alternative that corresponds to an effect size you want to be able to detect. Too often, studies fail because their sample sizes are too small to detect the change they're looking for.

Table 12.3 gives a summary of Type I and Type II errors:

Name	Also Known As:	Probability	Statistical Terminology	Business Example
Type I error	False positive	α	Reject a true null hypothesis	Invest in a project that is not successful
Type II error	False negative	β	Fail to reject a false null hypothesis	Fail to invest in a project that would have been successful

Table 12.3 Type I and II errors.

FOR EXAMPLE   Type I and Type II errors for website visits

QUESTION Suppose that a year later, a full accounting of all the SmartWool transactions (see For Example: "The reasoning of hypothesis tests about website customers") finds that 26.5% of visits resulted in sales. Have any errors been made?

ANSWER We rejected the null hypothesis that $p = 0.20$ and in fact $p = 0.265$, so we did not make a Type I error (the only error we could have made when rejecting the null hypothesis).

FOR EXAMPLE   Type I and Type II errors for quality control

A company manufactures ceramic ball bearings, but customers complain that some of them are cracked. Some cracking is inevitable and the company accepts 0.2% cracked product. A random sample of ball bearings is collected from the manufacturing plant and tested to determine whether more than 0.2% are cracked. The P-value comes to 0.075, so management concludes that there is no cracking problem and continues to operate the plant as in the past. A month later, a major customer complains that 1.1% of the ball bearings in the last shipment were cracked.

QUESTION Did the company make a Type I or Type II error? How does this example illustrate the importance of Type I and/or Type II errors? Is it possible to make a Type I error and a Type II error at the same time?

(continued)

> **ANSWER** The null hypothesis is that 0.2% are cracked and they failed to reject this hypothesis even though 1.1% are cracked. This is a Type II error. Making this error has caused a major customer to complain about the quality of the product. Type I errors are made when the null hypothesis is true. Type II errors are made when the null hypothesis is false. It is therefore not possible to make both types of error at the same time.

LO❹ **12.10 Power**

Remember, we can never prove a null hypothesis true. We can only fail to reject it. But when we fail to reject a null hypothesis, it's natural to wonder whether we looked hard enough. Might the null hypothesis actually be false and our test too weak to tell?

When the null hypothesis actually *is* false, we hope our test is strong enough to reject it. We'd like to know how likely we are to succeed. The power of the test gives us a way to think about that. The power of a test is the probability that it correctly rejects a false null hypothesis. When the power is high, we can be confident that we've looked hard enough. We know that β is the probability that a test *fails* to reject a false null hypothesis, so the power of the test is the complement, $1 - \beta$. We might have just written $1 - \beta$, but power is such an important concept that it gets its own name.

> Power is the probability of correctly rejecting the null hypothesis.

Let's take the case of a pharmaceutical company that has invested millions of dollars in developing a new drug. The company wouldn't just test this drug on a few patients; it might not work on those patients, even though it's a good drug in general. So drug companies typically conduct a large trial involving thousands of patients in order to be pretty sure of spotting an effective drug when they have one. By using more patients, they're increasing the *power* of their test, so as to reduce the risk of failing to market an effective drug (Type II error).

The Canadian natural gas company Encana holds approximately 1 million acres of mineral rights in the Cutbank Ridge area of northeast British Columbia and northwest Alberta. When Encana explores for sites that are going to be productive for natural gas, it wants to be pretty sure of finding the gas if it's there. Encana doesn't want to commit a Type II error and fail to find gas available in the land for which it owns the mineral rights. The statistical design behind its exploration technique therefore aims for *high-power* tests so that the chance of a false negative is low.

Whenever a study fails to reject its null hypothesis, the test's power comes into question. Was our sample size big enough to detect an effect, had there been one? Might we have missed an effect large enough to be interesting just because we failed to gather sufficient data or because there was too much variability in the data we could gather?

When we calculate power, we imagine that the null hypothesis is false. The value of the power depends on how far the truth lies from the null hypothesis value. We call the distance between the null hypothesis value, p_0, and the truth, p, the effect size. The power depends directly on the effect size. It's easier to see larger effects, so the farther p_0 is from p, the greater the power.

How can we decide what power we need? Choice of power is more a financial or scientific decision than a statistical one, because to calculate the power, we need to specify the "true" parameter value we're interested in. In other words, power is calculated for a particular effect size, and it changes depending on the size of the effect we want to detect.

JUST CHECKING

Last year, 21% of customers at our grocery store purchased gluten-free (GF) products. We expect the proportion to increase this year, and a random sample of 300 of this year's customers indicates that 25% purchased GF products.

10 What could we do to increase the power of this test?

11 Suppose that, in fact, 27% of all this year's customers are purchasing GF products. Will the power of our test be higher or lower than if the true percentage is 29%?

Answers are found in Appendix A.

NOTATION ALERT

Now we have four different types of proportion, p.

p is a population parameter—the true proportion in the population.

p_0 is a hypothesized value of p.

$\hat{p}$ is an observed proportion.

p^* is a critical value of a proportion corresponding to a specified α (see Figures 12.5 and 12.6).

For a given sample size, there's a trade-off between α and β

Calculating the Power of a Test From Figure 12.9

$$SD(\hat{p}) = \sqrt{\frac{p_0(1 - p_0)}{n}}$$

Use α to get z^* from Table Z of Appendix B.

$$p^* = p_0 + z^* \times SD(\hat{p})$$

$$z = (p^* - p)/SD(\hat{p})$$

Get β from looking up z in Table Z of Appendix B.

Power = $1 - \beta$

Graph It!

It makes intuitive sense that the larger the effect size, the easier it should be to see it. Obtaining a larger sample size decreases the probability of a Type II error, so it increases the power. It also makes sense that the more we're willing to accept a Type I error, the less likely we'll be to make a Type II error.

Figure 12.9 may help you visualize the relationships among these concepts. Suppose we're testing $H_0: p = p_0$ against the alternative $H_A: p > p_0$. We'll reject the null if the observed proportion, $\hat{p}$, is big enough. By *big enough*, we mean $\hat{p} > p^*$ for some critical value p^* (shown as the red region in the right tail of the upper curve). The upper model shows a picture of the sampling distribution model for the proportion when the null hypothesis is true. If the null were true, then this would be a picture of that truth. We'd make a Type I error whenever the sample gave us $\hat{p} > p^*$ because we would reject the (true) null hypothesis. Unusual samples like that would happen only with probability α.

In reality, though, the null hypothesis is rarely *exactly* true. The lower probability model supposes that H_0 is not true. In particular, it supposes that the true

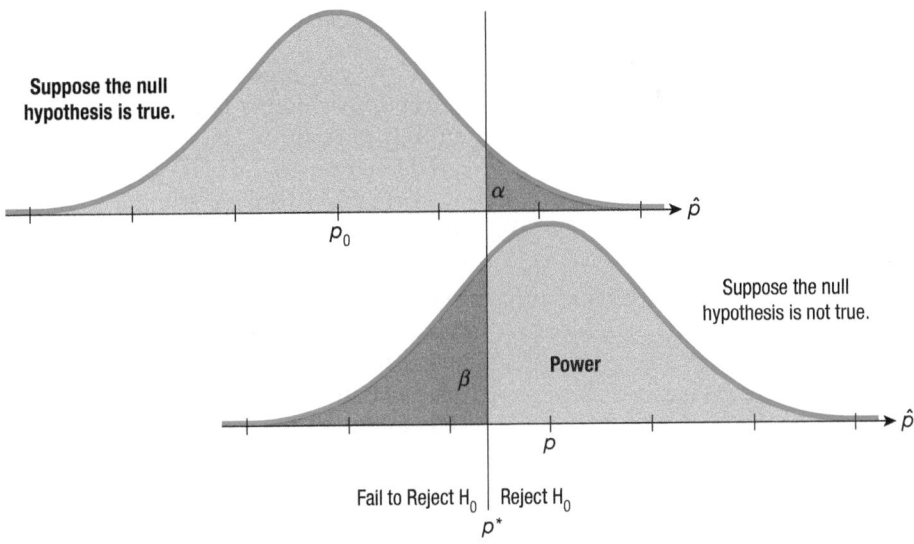

Figure 12.9   The power of a test is the probability that it rejects a false null hypothesis. The upper figure shows the null hypothesis model. We'd reject the null in a one-sided test if we observed a value in the red region to the right of the critical value, p^*. The lower figure shows the true model. If the true value of p is greater than p_0, then we're more likely to observe a value that exceeds the critical value and to make the correct decision to reject the null hypothesis. The power of the test is the green region on the right of the lower figure. Of course, even drawing samples whose observed proportions are distributed around p, we'll sometimes get a value in the red region on the left and make a Type II error of failing to reject the null.

value is p, not p_0. It shows a distribution of possible observed $\hat{p}$ values around this true value. Because of sampling variability, sometimes $\hat{p} < p*$ and we fail to reject the (false) null hypothesis. Then we'd make a Type II error. The area under the curve to the left of $p*$ in the bottom model in Figure 12.9 represents how often this happens. The probability is β. In this picture, β is less than half, so most of the time we *do* make the right decision. The *power* of the test—the probability that we make the right decision—is shown as the region to the right of $p*$. It's $1 - \beta$.

We calculate $p*$ based on the upper model because $p*$ depends only on the null model and the alpha level. No matter what the true proportion, $p*$ doesn't change. After all, we don't *know* the truth, so we can't use it to determine the critical value. But we always reject H_0 when $\hat{p} > p*$.

How often we reject H_0 when it's *false* depends on the effect size. We can see from the picture that if the true proportion were farther from the hypothesized value, the bottom curve would shift to the right, making the power greater. Suppose you buy a bag of candies which allegedly has a 50/50 split of red and green candies. Just glancing at the bag, it would be tough to spot a bag that had 55% red candies. Our test (glancing at bags) isn't powerful enough. But if a bag in fact had 90% red candies, you would notice it easily. The power of our test has been increased because the *effect size*, $0.9 - 0.5 = 0.4$, is very large.

We can see several important relationships from Figure 12.9:

- Power = $1 - \beta$.
- Moving the critical value, $p*$, to the right reduces α, the probability of a Type I error, but increases β, the probability of a Type II error. It correspondingly reduces the power.
- The larger the true effect size—the real difference between the hypothesized value, p_0, and the true population value, p—the smaller the chance of making a Type II error and the greater the power of the test.

If the two proportions are very far apart, the two models will barely overlap, and we wouldn't be likely to make any Type II errors at all—but then, we're unlikely to really need a formal hypothesis testing procedure to see such an obvious difference.

Let's take a banking example to illustrate the calculation of the power of a statistical test. Banks make money on commissions selling financial products—including student loans, mortgages, and mutual funds—to retail customers. In order to attract customers, they offer financial planning advice. The industry norm is that 37% of bank customers get financial planning advice from their bank. Suppose Bank of Montreal wants to increase its percentage above the industry norm this year, and halfway through the year tracks progress with a random sample of 500 customers, finding that 44% of them get such advice from Bank of Montreal. When all customers are analyzed at the end of the year, it turns out that in fact the true percentage was 43%.

The first point to notice about this example is that it does not contain enough information to calculate the power of the test. We need the bank's significance level, α, in order to calculate $p*$ in the top graph in Figure 12.9. Then we will be able to calculate the power from the lower graph.

The second point to notice is that our description contains superfluous information. We don't actually need to know the sample proportion, $\hat{p} = 0.44$. That value is important in conducting the test and figuring out whether our proportion is higher than the industry average, but it does not determine the power of the test.

The power of a test is an attribute of the test itself. It is not about the results of the test. A statistician asks, "Have I got a powerful enough test?" If not, let's not waste time conducting the test, getting sample data, and analyzing it. A more powerful test can be planned up front by increasing the sample size.

To calculate the power of the test for Bank of Montreal, let's take a significance level of $\alpha = 0.01$. We first get the characteristics of the top graph in Figure 12.9:

$$H_0: p = 0.37, \ H_A: p > 0.37, \ p_0 = 0.37$$

$$SD(\hat{p}) = \sqrt{\frac{0.37 \times 0.63}{500}} = 0.02159$$

For a significance level of $\alpha = 0.01$, the critical z value is 2.33 from Table Z in Appendix B or from Table 12.2:

$$p^* = 0.37 + 2.33 \times 0.02159 = 0.4203$$

Now we move to the lower graph in Figure 12.9, which corresponds to the situation with $p = 0.43$. In this case:

$$SD(\hat{p}) = \sqrt{\frac{0.43 \times 0.57}{500}} = 0.02214$$

We can now calculate the power of the test:

$$z = (0.4203 - 0.43)/0.02214 = -0.4377$$

From Table Z in Appendix B, we find the power of the test is $1 - 0.331 = 0.669$. The probability of making a Type II error, failing to spot the increased percentage of customers seeking financial planning advice, is 0.331.

Reducing Both Type I and Type II Errors

Figure 12.9 seems to show that if we reduce Type I error, we must automatically increase Type II error. But there is a way to reduce both. Can you think of it?

If we can make both curves narrower, as shown in Figure 12.10, then the probabilities of both Type I errors and Type II errors will decrease, and the power of the test will increase.

> We can reduce both α and β by increasing the sample size.

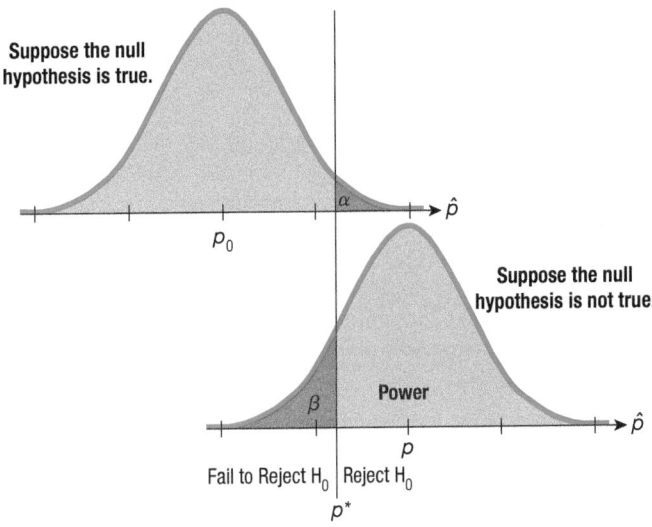

Figure 12.10 Making the standard deviations smaller increases the power without changing the alpha level or the corresponding z-critical value. The means are just as far apart as in Figure 12.9, but the error rates are reduced.

How can we do that? The only way is to reduce the standard deviations by increasing the sample size. (Remember, these are pictures of sampling distribution models, not of data.) Increasing the sample size works regardless of the true population parameters. But recall the curse of diminishing returns. The standard deviation of the sampling distribution model decreases only as the *square root* of the sample size, so to halve the standard deviations we must *quadruple* the sample size.

FOR EXAMPLE   The power of a quality control test

A company manufactures ceramic ball bearings, but customers complain that some of them are cracked. Some cracking is inevitable and the company accepts 0.2% cracked product. A random sample of 5000 ball bearings is collected from the manufacturing plant and tested to determine whether more than 0.2% are cracked. The sample has 0.28% cracked and the company uses a 5% significance level.

QUESTION Calculate the critical value p^*. Supposing the true percentage cracked is 0.32%, calculate the power of the test.

ANSWER For a one-sided 5% significance test, $z = 1.645$ (from Table Z in Appendix B, or from Table 12.2).

$$SD(\hat{p}) = \sqrt{\frac{0.002 \times 0.998}{5000}} = 0.000632$$

So the critical value is $p^* = 0.002 + 1.645 \times 0.000632 = 0.00304$.

The power of the test is calculated from the distribution with

$$SD(\hat{p}) = \sqrt{\frac{0.0032 \times 0.9968}{5000}} = 0.000799$$

$$z = \frac{0.00304 - 0.0032}{0.000799} = -0.201$$

The corresponding probability from Table Z in Appendix B is $\beta = 0.420$, so the power of the test is 0.580.

JUST CHECKING

Last year, 21% of customers at our grocery store purchased gluten-free (GF) products. We expect the proportion to increase this year to 28%, and a random sample of 300 of this year's customers indicates that 25% purchased GF products. We apply a statistical test with a 10% significance level.

12 Find the critical value p^*.

13 Calculate the power of the test, based on the expected increase.

14 Supposing the results of our survey of 300 customers were that 23% purchased GF products, would the power of our test be higher?

15 Supposing we sampled more than 300 customers, would the power be higher?

16 Supposing we used a 5% significance level, would the power of our test be higher?

Answers are found in Appendix A.

WHAT CAN GO WRONG?

- **Don't base your null hypotheses on what you see in the data.** You're not allowed to look at the data first and then adjust your null hypothesis so that it will be rejected. If your sample value turns out to be $\hat{p} = 51.8\%$ with a standard deviation of 1%, don't form a null hypothesis as $H_0: p = 49.8\%$, knowing that this will enable you to reject it. Your null hypothesis describes the "nothing interesting" or "nothing has changed" scenario and should not be based on the data you collect.

- **Don't base your alternative hypothesis on the data, either.** You should always think about the situation you're investigating and base your alternative hypothesis on that. Are you interested only in knowing whether something has *increased*? Then write a one-tail (upper tail) alternative. Or would you be equally interested in a change in either direction? Then you want a two-tailed alternative. You should decide whether to do a one- or two-tailed test based on what results would be of interest to you, not on what you might see in the data.

- **Don't make your null hypothesis what you want to show to be true.** Remember, the null hypothesis is the status quo, the nothing-is-strange-here position that a skeptic would take. You wonder whether the data cast doubt on that. You can reject the null hypothesis, but you can never "accept" or "prove" the null.

- **Don't forget to check the conditions.** The reasoning of inference depends on randomization. No amount of care in calculating a test result can save you from a biased sample. The probabilities you compute depend on the Independence Assumption. And your sample must be large enough to justify your use of a Normal model.

- **Don't believe too strongly in arbitrary alpha levels.** There's not really much difference between a P-value of 0.051 and a P-value of 0.049, but sometimes it's regarded as the difference between night (having to retain H_0) and day (being able to shout to the world that your results are "statistically significant"). It may just be better to report the P-value and a confidence interval and let the world (perhaps your manager or client) decide along with you.

- **Don't confuse practical and statistical significance.** A large sample size can make it easy to discern even a trivial change from the null hypothesis value. On the other hand, you could miss an important difference if your test lacks sufficient power.

- **Don't forget that despite all your care, you might make a wrong decision.** No one can ever reduce the probability of a Type I error (α) or a Type II error (β) to zero (but increasing the sample size helps).

ETHICS IN ACTION

Shellie Cooper, longtime owner of a small organic food store in New Brunswick, specializes in locally produced organic foods and products. Over the years Shellie's customer base has been quite stable, consisting mainly of health-conscious individuals who tend not to be very price-sensitive, opting to pay higher prices for better-quality local, organic products. However, faced with increasing competition from grocery chains offering more organic choices, Shellie is now thinking of offering coupons. She needs to decide between the newspaper and the internet. She recently read that the percentage of consumers who use printable internet coupons is on the rise but, at 15%, is much less than the 40% who clip and redeem newspaper coupons. Nonetheless, she's interested in learning more about the internet and sets up a meeting with Jack Kasor, a web consultant. She discovers that for an initial investment and continuing monthly fee, Jack would design Shellie's website, host it on his server, and broadcast internet coupons to her customers at regular intervals. While she was concerned about the difference in redemption rates for internet coupons and newspaper coupons, Jack assured her that internet coupon redemptions are continuing to rise and that she should expect between 15% and 40% of her customers to redeem them. Shellie agreed to give it a try.

After the first six months, Jack informed Shellie that the proportion of her customers who redeemed internet coupons was significantly greater than 15%. He determined this by selecting several broadcasts at random and finding the number redeemed (483) out of the total number sent (3000). Shellie thought that this was positive and made up her mind to continue the use of internet coupons.

Ethical Issue *Statistical vs. practical significance. While it's true that the percentage of Shellie's customers redeeming internet coupons is significantly greater than 15% statistically, in fact the percentage is just over 16%. This difference amounts to about 33 customers, or more than 15%, which may not be of practical significance to Shellie (related to Item A, ASA Ethical Guidelines; see Appendix C, the American Statistical Association's Ethical Guidelines for Statistical Practice, also available online at www.amstat.org/about/ethicalguidelines.cfm). Mentioning a range of 15% to 40% may mislead Shellie into expecting a value somewhere in the middle.*

Ethical Solution *Jack should report the difference between the observed value and the hypothesized value to Shellie, especially since there are costs associated with continuing internet coupons. Perhaps he should recommend that she reconsider using the newspaper.*

WHAT HAVE WE LEARNED?

Learning Objectives

❶ We've learned to use what we see in a random sample to test a particular hypothesis about the world. This is our second step in statistical inference, complementing our use of confidence intervals. We've learned that testing a hypothesis involves proposing a model and then seeing whether the data we observe are consistent with that model or so unusual that we must reject it. We do this by finding a P-value—the probability that data like ours could have occurred if the model is correct.

❷ If the data are out of line with the null hypothesis model, the P-value will be small, and we'll reject the null hypothesis. If the data are consistent with the null hypothesis model, the P-value will be large, and we won't reject the null hypothesis.

We've learned that:

- We start with a *null hypothesis* specifying the parameter of a model we'll test using our data.
- Our *alternative hypothesis* can be one- or two-sided, depending on what we want to learn.
- We must check the appropriate *assumptions* and *conditions* before proceeding with our test.
- The *significance level* of the test establishes the level of proof we'll require. That determines the critical value of z that will lead us to reject the null hypothesis.

❸ *Hypothesis tests* and *confidence intervals* are really two ways of looking at the same question. The hypothesis test gives us the answer to a decision about a parameter; the confidence interval tells us the plausible values of that parameter.

❹ If the null hypothesis is really true and we reject it, that's a *Type I error*; the alpha level of the test is the probability that this happens.

If the null hypothesis is really false but we fail to reject it, that's a *Type II error*.

The *power* of the test is the probability that we reject the null hypothesis when it's false. The larger the size of the effect we're testing for, the greater the power of the test in detecting it. Tests with a greater likelihood of Type I error have more power and less chance of a Type II error. We can increase power while reducing the chances of both kinds of error by increasing the sample size.

❺ If we have independent samples from two different populations, we construct a hypothesis test to compare the two populations with each other.

Terms

Alpha level
The threshold P-value that determines when we reject a null hypothesis. Using an alpha level of α, if we observe a statistic whose P-value based on the null hypothesis is less than α, we reject that null hypothesis.

Alternative hypothesis
The hypothesis that proposes what we should conclude if we find the null hypothesis to be unlikely.

Critical value
The value in the sampling distribution model of the statistic whose P-value is equal to the alpha level. Any statistic value farther from the null hypothesis value than the critical value will have a smaller P-value than α and will lead to rejecting the null hypothesis. The critical value is often denoted with an asterisk, as z^*, for example.

Effect size
The difference between the null hypothesis value and the true value of a model parameter.

Null hypothesis
The claim being assessed in a hypothesis test. Usually, the null hypothesis is a statement of "no change from the traditional value," "no effect," "no difference," or "no relationship." For a claim to be a testable null hypothesis, it must specify a value for some population parameter that can form the basis for assuming a sampling distribution for a test statistic.

One-proportion z-test
A test of the null hypothesis that the proportion of a single sample equals a specified value ($H_0: p = p_0$) by comparing the statistic $z = \dfrac{\hat{p} - p_0}{SD(\hat{p})}$ to a standard Normal model.

One-sided alternative
An alternative hypothesis is one-sided (e.g., $H_A: p > p_0$ or $H_A: p < p_0$) when we're interested in deviations in *only one* direction away from the hypothesized parameter value.

P-value
If the null hypotheses is true, the P-value is the probability of observing a value for a test statistic at least as far from the hypothesized value as the statistic value actually observed. A small P-value indicates that the observation obtained is improbable given the null hypothesis and thus provides evidence against the null hypothesis.

Power
The probability that a hypothesis test will correctly reject a false null hypothesis. To find the power of a test, we must specify a particular alternative parameter value as the "true" value. For any specific value in the alternative, the power is $1 - \beta$.

Significance level
Another term for the alpha level, used most often in a phrase such as "at the 5% significance level."

Two-sided alternative
An alternative hypothesis is two-sided ($H_A: p \neq p_0$) when we're interested in deviations in *either* direction away from the hypothesized parameter value.

Type I error
The error of rejecting a null hypothesis when in fact it is true (also called a "false positive"). The probability of a Type I error is α.

Type II error
The error of failing to reject a null hypothesis when in fact it is false (also called a "false negative"). The probability of a Type II error is commonly denoted β and depends on the effect size.

Skills

Plan
- Be able to state the null and alternative hypotheses for a one-proportion z-test and the z-test for comparing two proportions.
- Know how to think about the assumptions and their associated conditions. Examine your data for violations of those conditions.
- Be able to identify and use the alternative hypothesis when testing hypotheses. Understand how to choose between a one-sided and two-sided alternative hypothesis and be able to explain your choice.

Do

- Know how to perform a one-proportion z-test and the z-test for comparing two proportions.

Report

- Be able to interpret the results of a one-proportion z-test and the z-test for comparing two proportions.
- Be able to interpret the meaning of a P-value in nontechnical language, making clear that the probability claim is about computed values under the assumption that the null model is true and not about the population parameter of interest.
- Be able to comment on business significance using the effect size.

Hypothesis Tests in a Nutshell

Plan

Hypotheses (formulate them)   Alpha (choose it)   Assumptions (check them)

Do

Data (collect it)   Statistical test (calculate the P-value)

Report

Statistical significance (how significant?)   Hypotheses (reject the null or don't)
Business significance (e.g., how can we figure out the impact on profits?)

MINI case studies

Common-Law Couples in Quebec

According to a recent census, 29% of all families in Quebec were common-law couples. In order to test-market products to common-law couples, you need to select a city with a large percentage of this type of family. Suppose you survey 100 randomly selected families in Montreal and find that 35% of them are common-law couples. After completing your survey, you read in a newspaper about another survey done in Montreal by a reputable survey company that used a sample size of 400 families and found that 33% of them are common-law couples. Using hypothesis tests *and* confidence intervals, estimate the proportion of common-law couples in Montreal and whether it's higher than the provincial average at the 5% significance level. Comment on the different results from the two surveys.

Metal Production

Maksym Dragunov/Fotolia

Ingots are huge pieces of metal, often weighing in excess of 9000 kilograms, made in a giant mould. They must be cast in one large piece for use in fabricating large structural parts for cars and planes. If they crack while being made, the crack may propagate into the zone required for the part, compromising its integrity. Airplane manufacturers insist that metal for their planes be defect-free, so the ingot must be made over if any cracking is detected.

Even though the metal from the cracked ingot is recycled, the scrap cost runs into the tens of thousands of dollars. Metal manufacturers would like to avoid cracking if at all possible. But the casting process is complicated, and not everything can be controlled completely. In one plant, only about 75% of the ingots have been free of cracks. So, in an attempt to reduce the cracking proportion, the plant engineers and chemists made changes to the casting process. The data from 5000 ingots produced since the changes can be found in the file **ch12_MCSP_Ingots**. The variable *Crack* indicates whether a crack was found (1) or not (0). Select a random sample of 100 ingots and test the claim that the cracking rate has decreased from 25%. Find a confidence interval for the cracking rate as well. Now select a random sample of 1000 ingots, test the claim, and find the confidence interval again. Compare the two tests and intervals and prepare a short report about your findings, including the differences (if any) you see in the two samples.

Loyalty Program

An airline marketing manager sent out 10,000 mail pieces to a random sample of customers to test a new web-based loyalty program. The customers received either nothing (No Offer), a free companion airline ticket (Free Flight), or free flight insurance on their next flight (Free Insurance). The person in charge of selecting the 10,000 customers has assured the marketing manager that the sample is representative of the various marketing segments in the customer base. However, the manager is worried that the offer wasn't sent out to enough customers in the *Travel* segment, which represents 25% of the entire customer base (variable *Spending Segment*). In addition, he's worried that fewer than one-third of customers in that segment actually received no offer. Using the data found in the file **ch12_MCSP_Loyalty_Program,** write a short report to the manager testing the appropriate hypotheses and summarizing your findings. Include in your report a 95% confidence interval for the proportion of customers who responded to the offer by signing up for the loyalty program. (The variable *Response* indicates a 1 for responders and 0 for nonresponders.)

MyStatLab   Students! Save time, improve your grades with MyStatLab. Questions marked in ▇ can be found on MyStatLab. You can practise them as often as you want, and most feature step-by-step guided solutions to help you find the right answer. You'll find a personalized study plan available to you too!

Technology Help: Testing Hypotheses About Proportions

Hypothesis tests for proportions are so easy and natural that many statistics packages don't offer special commands for them. Most statistics programs want to know the "success" and "failure" status for each case. Usually these are given as 1 or 0, but they might be category names like "yes" and "no." Often we just know the proportion of successes, $\hat{p}$, and the total count, n. Computer packages don't usually deal naturally with summary data like this, but see below for the option available in Minitab.

In some programs you can reconstruct the original values. But even when you've reconstructed (or can reconstruct) the raw data values, often you won't get *exactly* the same test statistic from a computer package as you would from working by hand. The reason is that when the packages treat the proportion as a mean, they make some approximations. The result is very close, but not exactly the same. If you use a computer package, you may notice slight discrepancies between your answers and the answers in the back of the book, but they're not important.

Reports about hypothesis tests generated by technologies don't follow a standard form. Most will name the test and provide the test statistic value, its standard deviation, and the P-value. But these elements may not be labelled clearly. For example, the expression "Prob > |z|" means the probability (the "Prob") of observing a test statistic whose magnitude (the absolute value tells us this) is larger than that of the one (the "z") found in the data (which, because it's written as "z," we know follows a Normal model). That is a fancy (and not very clear) way of saying P-value. In some packages, you can specify that the test be one-sided. Others might report three P-values, covering the ground for both one-sided tests and two-sided tests.

Sometimes a confidence interval and hypothesis test are automatically given together. The confidence interval ought to be for the corresponding confidence level: $1 - \alpha$.

(continued)

We get the standard deviation for a proportion from the null hypothesis value. Nevertheless, you may see the standard deviation called a "standard error," even for tests with proportions.

Here are the kinds of results you might see in typical computer output:

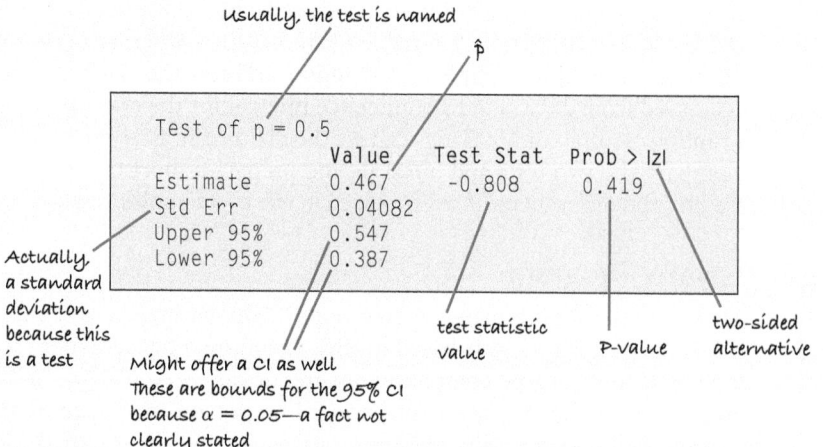

<hr>

EXCEL

Inference methods for proportions are not part of the standard Excel tool set.

To calculate a *z*-test of a proportion in Excel:

	A	B	C	D	E
1	z-Test of a Proportion				
2					(Expression for Column D)
3	Sample proportion	0.467	z Stat	-0.81	=(B3-B5)/((B5*(1-B5)/B4)^0.5)
4	Sample size	150	P(Z<=z) one-tail	0.2094	=(1-NORM.S.DIST(ABS(D3),TRUE))
5	Hypothesized proportion	0.5	z Critical one-tail	1.6449	=NORM.S.INV(1-B6)
6	Alpha	0.05	P(Z<=z) two-tail	0.4189	=2*D4
7			z Critical two-tail	1.9600	=NORM.S.INV(1-B6/2)

- To calculate the values in cells D3–D7, type the formulas in cells E3 through E7.

- After the formulas are set in column D, enter information for any *z*-test for a proportion in cells B3 through B6, and the results will show in column D. Note that the one- and two-tail critical values given are for the upper end of the distribution. If a lower one-tail test is being conducted, the critical value will be negative, and for a two-tail test the lower tail critical value will be negative.

XLSTAT

To find a one-proportion *z* interval:

- Select **Parametric Tests**, and then choose **Tests for one proportion**.

- Under the **General** tab, choose the **Data format** to be either **Frequency** or **Proportion** depending on the form of your data.

- Enter the **frequency** of your variable (or **proportion**) and the **sample size**.

- Enter the **test proportion**.

- Under **Data format** choose the appropriate button.

- Under the **Options** tab choose the **Alternative hypothesis** of **Proportion – Test proportion ≠ D**. Enter 0 for the **Hypothesized difference (D)**.

- Enter 5 under **Significance Level**. The output will show the 95% confidence interval.

MINITAB

- Choose **Basic Statistics** from the **Stat** menu.

- Choose **1 Proportion** from the Basic Statistics submenu.

- If the data are category names in a variable, assign the variable from the variable list box to the **Samples in columns** box.

- If you have summarized data, click the **Summarized Data** button and fill in the number of trials and the number of successes.

- Click the **Options** button and specify the remaining details.

- If you have a large sample, check **Use test and interval based on Normal distribution**.

- Click the **OK** button.

  Comments

When working from a variable that names categories, Minitab treats the last category as the "success" category. You can specify how the categories should be ordered.

SPSS

SPSS does not find hypothesis tests for proportions.

JMP

For a categorical variable that holds two categories, go to **Analyze > Distribution.** Put the variable containing the categories in the **Y, Columns** box and press **OK**.

- Click the red triangle next to the column name and select **Test Probabilities**.

- Put both p_0 and $1 - p_0$ into the probabilities and click **Done**.

  Comments

JMP does not use the Normal distribution to test the proportions, so your answers will differ slightly from the book. For summarized data, you will need to have the frequencies in another column and designate that column as the **Frequencies**.

EXERCISES

SECTIONS 12.1 AND 12.2

1. For each of the following, write out the null and alternative hypothesis, making sure to state whether it's one-sided or two-sided.

a) A company reports that last year 40% of its reports in accounting were on time. From a random sample this year, it wants to know if that proportion has changed.

b) Last year, 42% of the employees enrolled in at least one wellness class at the company's site. Using a survey, the company wants to know if a greater percentage is planning to take a wellness class this year.

c) A political candidate wants to know from recent polls if she's going to garner a majority of votes in next week's election. **LO ❶**

2. For each of the following, write out the alternative hypothesis, being sure to indicate whether it is one-sided or two-sided.

a) *Consumer Reports* discovered that 20% of a certain computer model had warranty problems over the first three months. From a random sample, the manufacturer wants to know if a new model has improved that rate.

b) The last time a philanthropic agency requested donations, 4.75% of people responded. From a recent pilot mailing, it wonders if that rate has increased.

c) A student wants to know if other students on her campus prefer Coke or Pepsi. **LO ❶**

SECTION 12.3

3. Which of the following are true? If false, explain briefly.

a) A very high P-value is strong evidence that the null hypothesis is false.

b) A very low P-value proves that the null hypothesis is false.

c) A high P-value shows that the null hypothesis is true.

d) A P-value below 0.05 is always considered sufficient evidence to reject a null hypothesis. **LO ❶**

4. Which of the following are true? If false, explain briefly.

a) A very low P-value provides evidence against the null hypothesis.

b) A high P-value is strong evidence in favour of the null hypothesis.

c) A P-value above 0.10 shows that the null hypothesis is true.

d) If the null hypothesis is true, you can't get a P-value below 0.01. **LO ❶**

SECTION 12.4

5. Which of the following statements are true? If false, explain briefly.

a) Using an alpha level of 0.05, a P-value of 0.04 results in rejecting the null hypothesis.

b) The alpha level depends on the sample size.

c) With an alpha level of 0.01, a P-value of 0.10 results in rejecting the null hypothesis.

d) Using an alpha level of 0.05, a P-value of 0.06 means the null hypothesis is true. **LO ❶**

6. Which of the following statements are true? If false, explain briefly.

a) It's better to use an alpha level of 0.05 than an alpha level of 0.01.

b) If we use an alpha level of 0.01, then a P-value of 0.001 is statistically significant.

c) If we use an alpha level of 0.01, then we reject the null hypothesis if the P-value is 0.001.

d) If the P-value is 0.01, we reject the null hypothesis for any alpha level greater than 0.01. **LO ❶**

SECTION 12.5

7. A consulting firm had predicted that 35% of the employees at a large firm would take advantage of a new company credit union, but management is skeptical. They doubt the rate is that high. A survey of 300 employees shows that 138 of them are currently taking advantage of the credit union. Apply the eight steps of hypothesis testing with a 1% significance level and indicate any steps that are not relevant. **LO ❷**

8. A survey of 100 CEOs finds that 60 think the economy will improve next year. Is there evidence that the rate is higher among all CEOs than the 55% reported by the public at large?

a) Find the standard deviation of the sample proportion based on the null hypothesis.

b) Find the z-statistic.

c) Does the z-statistic seem like a particularly large or small value? **LO ❷**

SECTION 12.6

9. For each of the following situations, find the critical value(s) for z.

a) $H_0: p = 0.5$ vs. $H_A: p \neq 0.5$ at $\alpha = 0.05$.
b) $H_0: p = 0.4$ vs. $H_A: p > 0.4$ at $\alpha = 0.05$.
c) $H_0: p = 0.5$ vs. $H_A: p > 0.5$ at $\alpha = 0.01$; $n = 345$.

LO ❷

10. For each of the following situations, find the critical value for z.

a) $H_0: p = 0.5$ vs. $H_A: p > 0.5$ at $\alpha = 0.05$.
b) $H_0: p = 0.6$ vs. $H_A: p \neq 0.6$ at $\alpha = 0.01$.

c) $H_0: p = 0.5$ vs. $H_A: p < 0.5$ at $\alpha = 0.01$; $n = 500$.
d) $H_0: p = 0.2$ vs. $H_A: p < 0.2$ at $\alpha = 0.01$. **LO ❷**

SECTION 12.7

11. Suppose you're testing the hypotheses $H_0: p = 0.20$ vs. $p \neq 0.20$. A sample size of 250 results in a sample proportion of 0.25.

a) Construct a 95% confidence interval for p.
b) Based on the confidence interval, at $\alpha = 0.05$ can you reject H_0? Explain.
c) What's the difference between the standard error and standard deviation of the sample proportion?
d) Which is used in computing the confidence interval? **LO ❸**

12. Suppose you're testing the hypotheses $H_0: p = 0.40$ vs. $H_A: p > 0.40$. A sample size of 200 results in a sample proportion of 0.55.

a) Construct a 90% confidence interval for p.
b) Based on the confidence interval, at $\alpha = 0.05$ can you reject H_0? Explain.
c) What's the difference between the standard error and standard deviation of the sample proportion?
d) Which is used in computing the confidence interval? **LO ❸**

SECTION 12.8

13. In an Angus Reid survey of opinions regarding same-sex marriage, 13% of a sample of 1003 Canadian adults said that same-sex couples should not have any legal recognition. The corresponding percentage for a survey of 1980 Britons was 15%. Does a greater percentage of Britons hold this view than Canadians at the 5% significance level? **LO ❺**

14. An Angus Reid survey of 1003 Canadian adults and 1980 British adults found that 59% of the Canadian sample and 56% of the British sample thought that homosexuality is something people are born with as opposed to being a preference they have chosen. Does a smaller percentage of Britons hold this view than Canadians at the 5% significance level? **LO ❺**

SECTIONS 12.9

15. For each of the following situations, state whether a Type I, a Type II, or neither error has been made. Explain briefly.

a) A bank wants to know if the enrollment on its website is above 30% based on a small sample of customers. It tests H_0: $p = 0.3$ vs. $H_A: p > 0.3$ and rejects the null hypothesis. Later it finds out that actually 28% of all customers enrolled.
b) A student tests 100 students to determine whether other students on her campus prefer Coke or Pepsi and finds no evidence that preference for Coke is not 0.5. Later, a marketing company tests all students on campus and finds no difference.
c) A human resource analyst wants to know if the applicants this year score, on average, higher on their placement

exam than the 52.5 points the candidates averaged last year. She samples 50 recent tests and finds the average to be 54.1 points. She fails to reject the null hypothesis that the mean is 52.5 points. At the end of the year, they find that the candidates this year had a mean of 55.3 points.
d) A pharmaceutical company tests whether a drug lifts the headache relief rate from the 25% achieved by the placebo. It fails to reject the null hypothesis because the P-value is 0.465. Further testing shows that the drug actually relieves headaches in 38% of people. **LO ❹**

16. For each of the following situations, state whether a Type I, a Type II, or neither error has been made.

a) A test of $H_0: p = 0.8$ vs. $H_A: p < 0.08$ fails to reject the null hypothesis. Later it's discovered that $p = 0.9$.
b) A test of $H_0: p = 0.5$ vs. $H_A: p \neq 0.5$ rejects the null hypothesis. Later it's discovered that $p = 0.65$.
c) A test of $H_0: p = 0.7$ vs. $H_A: p < 0.7$ fails to reject the null hypothesis. Later it's discovered that $p = 0.6$. **LO ❹**

SECTION 12.10

17. Last year, a luxury hotel chain operating across the Caribbean attracted 14% of Canadian snowbirds travelling to the Caribbean during February and found that 56% were "very satisfied" with their stay. This year, the chain has upgraded its properties, with the aim of achieving 70% "very satisfied" guests. Pollsters randomly select 100 guests to express their satisfaction level and find that 66% are "very satisfied."

a) State the hypotheses.
b) What is the power of this test if a 1% significance level is used in interpreting the results? Interpret the meaning of "power."
c) If the result of the survey was higher than 66% "very satisfied," would the power be higher?
d) If the significance level was higher, would the power be higher?
Give reasons for your answers to (c) and (d) without actually doing the calculations. **LO ❹**

18. In 2012, 14.8% of medium-sized businesses in Canada were foreign-controlled, according to Statistics Canada Table 1790005: "Corporations Returns Act (CRA), enterprise characteristics by country of control and operating revenue size." These data are based on corporate tax returns and are therefore a few years old when published. A financial services company wants to offer financial services to foreign-controlled medium-sized businesses in Canada and, using market projections, estimates that the percentage of such businesses has by now increased to 17.5%. In order to check this out, it plans to survey 400 medium-sized businesses selected at random.

a) State the hypotheses.
b) What is the power of this test if a 10% significance level is used in interpreting the results?

c) If the company is only able to survey a smaller number of businesses, would the power be lower?

d) If the significance level was lower, would the power be lower?

Give reasons for your answers to (c) and (d) without actually doing the calculations. **LO❹**

CHAPTER EXERCISES

19. **Hypotheses, part 1.** Write the null and alternative hypotheses to test each of the following situations.

a) An online clothing company is concerned about the timeliness of the delivery of its products. The VP of Operations and Marketing recently stated that she wanted the percentage of products delivered on time to be more than 90%, and she wants to know if the company has succeeded.

b) A realty company recently announced that the proportion of houses taking more than three months to sell is now greater than 50%.

c) A financial firm's accounting reports have an error rate below 2%. **LO❶**

20. **Hypotheses, part 2.** Write the null and alternative hypotheses to test each of the following situations.

a) A business magazine article reports that, in 1990, 35% of CEOs had an MBA degree. Has the percentage changed?

b) Recently, 20% of cars of a certain model have needed costly transmission work after being driven between 50,000 and 100,000 miles. The car manufacturer hopes that the redesign of a transmission component has solved this problem.

c) A market researcher for a cola company decides to field-test a new-flavour soft drink, planning to market it only if he's sure that over 60% of the people like the flavour. **LO❶**

21. **Deliveries.** The clothing company in Exercise 19(a) looks at a sample of delivery reports. The company tests the hypothesis that 90% of the deliveries are on time against the alternative that greater than 90% are on time and finds a P-value of 0.22. Which of these conclusions is appropriate?

a) There's a 22% chance that 90% of the deliveries are on time.

b) There's a 78% chance than 90% of the deliveries are on time.

c) There's a 22% chance that the sample the company drew shows the correct percentage of on-time deliveries.

d) There's a 22% chance that natural sampling variation could produce a sample of on-time deliveries at least as extreme as the one obtained if, in fact, 90% of deliveries are on time. **LO❶**

22. **House sales.** The realty company in Exercise 19(b) looks at a recent sample of houses that have sold. On testing the null hypothesis that 50% of the houses take more than three months to sell against the hypothesis that more than 50% of the houses take more than three months to sell, the company finds a P-value of 0.034. Which of these conclusions is appropriate?

a) There's a 3.4% chance that 50% of the houses take more than three months to sell.

b) If 50% of the houses take more than three months to sell, there's a 3.4% chance that a random sample would produce a sample proportion as high as the one obtained.

c) There's a 3.4% chance that the null hypothesis is correct.

d) There's a 96.6% chance that 50% of the houses take more than three months to sell. **LO❶**

23. **P-value, part 1.** Have harsher penalties and ad campaigns increased seatbelt use among drivers and passengers? Observations of commuter traffic have failed to find evidence of a significant change compared with three years ago. Explain what the study's P-value of 0.17 means in this context. **LO❶**

24. **P-value, part 2.** A company developing scanners to search for hidden weapons at airports has concluded that a new device is significantly better than the current scanner. The company made this decision based on a P-value of 0.03. Explain the meaning of the P-value in this context. **LO❶**

25. **Ad campaign.** An information technology analyst believes that her company is losing customers on its website who find the checkout and purchase system too complicated. She adds a one-click feature to the website to make it easier, but finds that only about 10% of the customers are using it. She decides to launch an ad awareness campaign to tell customers about the new feature in the hope of increasing the percentage. She doesn't see much of a difference, so she hires a consultant to help her. The consultant selects a random sample of recent purchases, tests the hypothesis that the ads produced no change against the alternative (that the percentage who use the one-click feature is now greater than 10%), and finds a P-value of 0.22. Which conclusion is appropriate? Explain.

a) There's a 22% chance that the ads worked.

b) There's a 78% chance that the ads worked.

c) There's a 22% chance that the null hypothesis is true.

d) There's a 22% chance that natural sampling variation could produce poll results at least as extreme as these if the use of the one-click feature has increased.

e) There's a 22% chance that natural sampling variation could produce poll results at least as extreme as these if there's really no change in website use. **LO❶**

26. **Mutual funds.** A mutual fund manager claims that at least 70% of the stocks she selects will increase in price over the next year. We examined a sample of 200 of her selections over the past three years. Our P-value turns out to be 0.03. Test an appropriate hypothesis. Which conclusion is appropriate? Explain.

a) There's a 3% chance that the fund manager is correct.

b) There's a 97% chance that the fund manager is correct.

c) There's a 3% chance that a random sample could produce results at least as extreme as we observed if $p = 0.7$, so it's reasonable to conclude that the fund manager is correct.

d) There's a 3% chance that a random sample could produce results at least as extreme as we observed if $p = 0.7$, so it's reasonable to conclude that the fund manager is not correct.

e) There's a 3% chance that the null hypothesis is correct. **LO ❶**

27. Product effectiveness. A pharmaceutical company's old antacid formula provided relief for 70% of the people who used it. The company tests a new formula to see if it's better and gets a P-value of 0.27. Is it reasonable to conclude that the new formula and the old one are equally effective? Explain. **LO ❶**

28. Stocks. A young investor is concerned that investing in the stock market is actually gambling, since the chance of the stock market going up on any given day is 50%. She decides to track her favourite stock for 250 days and finds that on 140 days, the stock was "up."

a) Find a 95% confidence interval for the proportion of days the stock was "up." Don't forget to check the conditions first.

b) Does your confidence interval provide any evidence that the market is not random? Explain.

c) What is the significance level of this test? Explain. **LO ❸**

29. Economy, part 1. In 2008, a Gallup Poll asked 2336 U.S. adults aged 18 or over how they rated economic conditions. In a poll conducted from January 27 through February 1, 2008, 24% rated the economy as "Excellent/Good." A recent media outlet claimed that the percentage of Americans who felt the economy was in "Excellent/Good" shape was, in fact, 28%. Does the Gallup Poll support this claim?

a) Find a 95% confidence interval for the sample proportion of U.S. adults who rated the economy as "Excellent/Good." Check conditions.

b) Does your confidence interval provide evidence to support the claim?

c) What is the significance level of the test in part (b)? Explain. **LO ❸**

30. Economy, part 2. The same Gallup Poll data from Exercise 29 also reported that 33% of those surveyed rated the economy as "Poor." The same media outlet claimed the true proportion to be 30%. Does the Gallup Poll support this claim?

a) Find a 95% confidence interval for the sample proportion of U.S. adults who rated the economy as "Poor." Check conditions.

b) Does your confidence interval provide evidence to support the claim?

c) What is the significance level of the test in part (b)? Explain. **LO ❸**

31. Convenient alpha. An enthusiastic junior executive has run a test of his new marketing program. He reports that it resulted in a "significant" increase in sales. A footnote on his report explains that he used an alpha level of 7.2% for his test. Presumably, he performed a hypothesis test against the null hypothesis of no change in sales.

a) If instead he had used an alpha level of 5%, is it more or less likely that he would have rejected his null hypothesis? Explain.

b) If he chose the alpha level 7.2% so that he could claim statistical significance, explain why this is not an ethical use of statistics. **LO ❷**

32. Safety. The manufacturer of a new sleeping pill suspects that it may increase the risk of sleepwalking, which could be dangerous. A test of the drug fails to reject the null hypothesis of no increase in sleepwalking when tested at $\alpha = 0.01$.

a) If the test had been performed at $\alpha = 0.05$, would the test have been more or less likely to reject the null hypothesis of no increase in sleepwalking?

b) Which alpha level do you think the company should use? Why? **LO ❷**

33. Product testing. Since many people have trouble assembling furniture, a supplier has developed what it hopes will be easier instructions. The goal is to have at least 96% of customers assemble their furniture correctly on the first attempt. The company tests the new system on 200 people, 188 of whom were successful. Is this strong evidence that the new system fails to meet the company's goal? A student's test of this hypothesis is shown here. Identify 7 mistakes.

$$H_0: \hat{p} = 0.96$$

$$H_A: \hat{p} \neq 0.96$$

$$SRS, 0.96(200) > 10$$

$$\frac{188}{200} = 0.94; \ SD(\hat{p}) = \sqrt{\frac{(0.94)(0.06)}{200}} = 0.017$$

$$z = \frac{0.96 - 0.94}{0.017} = 1.18$$

$$P = P(z > 1.18) = 0.12$$

There is strong evidence that the new system doesn't work. **LO ❷**

34. Marketing. A newsletter reported that 90% of adults drink milk. A regional farmers' organization planning a new marketing campaign across its multicounty area polls a random sample of 750 adults living there. In this sample, 657 people said that they drink milk. Do these responses provide strong evidence that the 90% figure isn't accurate for this region? Correct the mistakes you find in a student's following attempt to test an appropriate hypothesis:

$H_0: \hat{p} = 0.9$

$H_A: \hat{p} < 0.9$

SRS, $750 > 10$

$\dfrac{657}{750} = 0.876; SD(\hat{p}) = \sqrt{\dfrac{(0.88)(0.12)}{750}} = 0.012$

$z = \dfrac{0.876 - 0.94}{0.012} = -2$

$P = P(z > -2) = 0.977$

There is more than a 97% chance that the stated percentage is correct for this region. **LO❷**

35. Environment. In the 1980s, it was generally believed that congenital abnormalities affected about 5% of the nation's children. Some people believe that the increase in the number of chemicals in the environment has led to an increase in the incidence of abnormalities. A recent study examined 384 children and found that 46 of them showed signs of an abnormality. Is this strong evidence that the risk has increased at the 5% significance level?

a) Write appropriate hypotheses.
b) Check the necessary assumptions.
c) Perform the mechanics of the test. What is the P-value?
d) Explain carefully what the P-value means in this context.
e) What's your conclusion?
f) Do environmental chemicals cause congenital abnormalities? **LO❷**

36. Spike poll. In a telephone poll of 1302 randomly selected men, only 39 said that their most important measure of success was their work.

a) Estimate the percentage of all males who measure success primarily by their work. Use a 98% confidence interval. Don't forget to check the conditions first.
b) Some believe that few contemporary men judge their success primarily by their work. Suppose we wished to conduct a hypothesis test to see if the fraction has fallen below the 5% mark. What does your confidence interval indicate? Explain.
c) What is the significance level of this test? Explain. **LO❸**

37. Education. In 2006, 34% of students had not been absent from school even once during the previous month. In a 2011 survey, responses from 8302 students showed that this figure had slipped to 33%. Officials would be concerned if student attendance were declining. Do these figures give evidence of a decrease in student attendance?

a) Write appropriate hypotheses.
b) Check the assumptions and conditions.
c) Perform the test and find the P-value.

d) State your conclusion.
e) Do you think this difference is meaningful? Explain. **LO❷**

38. Customer satisfaction. A company hopes to improve customer satisfaction, setting as a goal no more than 5% negative comments. A random survey of 350 customers found only 10 with complaints.

a) Create a 95% confidence interval for the true level of dissatisfaction among customers.
b) Does this provide evidence that the company has reached its goal? Using your confidence interval, test an appropriate hypothesis, and state your conclusion. **LO❸**

39. Maintenance costs. A limousine company is concerned with increasing costs of maintaining its fleet of 150 cars. After testing, the company found that the emissions systems of 7 out of the 22 cars it tested failed to meet pollution control guidelines. The company had forecasted costs assuming that a total of 30 cars would need updating to meet the latest guidelines. Is this strong evidence that more than 20% of the fleet might be out of compliance? Test an appropriate hypothesis and state your conclusion. Be sure the appropriate assumptions and conditions are satisfied before you proceed. **LO❷**

40. Damaged goods. An appliance manufacturer stockpiles washers and dryers in a large warehouse for shipment to retail stores. Sometimes in handling the appliances get damaged. Even though the damage may be minor, the company must sell those machines at drastically reduced prices. The company goal is to keep the proportion of damaged machines below 2%. One day an inspector randomly checks 60 washers and finds that 5 of them have scratches or dents. Is this strong evidence that the warehouse is failing to meet the company's goal? Test an appropriate hypothesis and state your conclusion. Be sure the appropriate assumptions and conditions are satisfied before you proceed. **LO❷**

41. Defective products. An internal report from a manufacturing company indicated that about 3% of all products were defective. Data from one batch found only 4 defective products out of 233 products. Is this consistent with the report? Test an appropriate hypothesis using a 5% significance level. Also calculate a confidence interval and state your conclusion. Be sure the appropriate assumptions and conditions are satisfied before you proceed. **LO❷, ❸**

42. Jobs. The accounting department of a major Canadian university would like to advertise that more than 50% of its graduates obtained a job offer prior to graduation. A sample of 240 recent graduates indicated that 138 of these graduates had a job offer prior to graduation. Test an appropriate hypothesis at the 5% significance level and state your conclusion. Be sure the appropriate assumptions and conditions are satisfied before you proceed. **LO❷**

43. WebZine. A magazine called *WebZine* is considering the launch of an online edition. The magazine plans to go ahead only if it's convinced that more than 25% of current readers would subscribe. The magazine contacts a simple random sample of 500 current subscribers, and 137 of those surveyed expressed interest. What should the magazine do? Test an appropriate hypothesis at the 10% significance level and state your conclusion. Be sure the appropriate assumptions and conditions are satisfied before you proceed. Supposing the true proportion of readers who would subscribe to an online edition is 0.27, calculate the power of the test and interpret its meaning. **LO❷**, **❹**

44. Truth in advertising. A garden centre wants to store leftover packets of vegetable seeds for sale the following spring, but the centre is concerned that the seeds may not germinate at the same rate a year later. The manager finds a packet of last year's green bean seeds and plants them as a test. Although the packet claims a germination rate of 92%, only 171 of 200 test seeds sprout. Is this evidence that the seeds have lost viability during a year in storage? Test an appropriate hypothesis at the 1% significance level and state your conclusion. Be sure the appropriate assumptions and conditions are satisfied before you proceed. **LO❷**

45. Women executives. A company is criticized because only 13 of 43 people in executive-level positions are women. The company explains that although this proportion is lower than it might wish, it's not surprising given that only 40% of its employees are women. What do you think? Test an appropriate hypothesis at the 5% significance level and state your conclusion. Be sure the appropriate assumptions and conditions are satisfied before you proceed. **LO❷**

46. Jury. Census data for a certain county show that 19% of the adult residents are Hispanic. Suppose 72 people are called for jury duty, and only 9 of them are Hispanic. Does this apparent underrepresentation of Hispanics call into question the fairness of the jury selection system? Explain using a 5% significance level. **LO❷**

47. Nonprofit. A nonprofit company concerned with high school dropout rates has designed a tutoring program aimed at students between 16 and 18 years of age. Nationally, the high school dropout rate for the year 2013 was 10.9%. One school district, which adopted the use of the nonprofit's tutoring program and has always had a dropout rate very close to the national average, reported in 2013 that 175 of its 1782 students dropped out. Is their experience evidence that the tutoring program has been effective? Explain using a 5% significance level. **LO❷**

48. Real estate. A national real estate magazine advertised that 15% of first-home buyers have a family income below $40,000. A national real estate firm believes this percentage is too low and samples 100 of its records. The firm finds that 25 of its first-home buyers did have a family income below $40,000. Does the sample suggest that the proportion of first-home buyers with an income less than $40,000 is more than 15%? Comment and write up your own con-

clusions based on an appropriate confidence interval as well as a hypothesis test using a 5% significance level. Include any assumptions you made about the data. **LO❷**, **❸**

49. Public relations. An airline's public relations department says that the airline rarely loses luggage. Furthermore, it claims that when it does, 90% of the time the bags are recovered and delivered within 24 hours. A consumer group surveys a large number of air travellers and finds that 103 of 122 people who lost luggage were reunited with their missing items within 24 hours. Does this cast doubt on the airline's claim? Explain using a 5% significance level. **LO❷**

50. TV ads. A startup company is about to market a new computer printer. It decides to gamble by running commercials during the Super Bowl. The company hopes that name recognition will be worth the high cost of the ads. The goal of the company is that over 40% of the public recognize its brand name and associate it with computer equipment. The day after the game, a pollster contacts 420 randomly chosen adults and finds that 181 of them know that this company manufactures printers. Would you recommend that the company continue to advertise during the Super Bowl? Explain using a 1% significance level. **LO❷**, **❹**

51. Business ethics. A study reports that 30% of newly hired MBAs are confronted with unethical business practices during their first year of employment. One business school dean wondered if her MBA graduates had had similar experiences. She surveyed a random sample of 120 out of 1400 recent graduates and found that 27% of them claim to have encountered unethical business practices in the workplace. Can she conclude that her graduates' experiences are different at the 5% significance level? **LO❷**

52. Stocks. A young investor believes he can beat the market by picking stocks that will increase in value. Assume that, on average, 50% of the stocks selected by a portfolio manager will increase over 12 months. Of the 25 stocks that the young investor bought over the past 12 months, 14 have increased. Can he claim that he's better at predicting increases than the typical portfolio manager? Explain using a 5% significance level. **LO❷**

53. Testing cars, part 1. A clean air standard requires that vehicle exhaust emissions not exceed specified limits for various pollutants. Suppose government regulators double-check a random sample of cars that a suspect repair shop has certified as okay. They will revoke the shop's licence if they find significant evidence that the shop is certifying vehicles that don't meet standards.

a) State the hypotheses.
b) In this context, what is a Type I and what is a Type II error?
c) Which type of error would the shop's owner consider more serious?
d) Which type of error might environmentalists consider more serious? **LO❶**, **❹**

54. Quality control, part 1. Production managers on an assembly line must monitor the output to be sure that the level of defective products remains small. They periodically inspect a random sample of the items produced. If they find a significant increase in the proportion of items that must be rejected, they'll halt the assembly process until the problem can be identified and repaired.

a) Write null and alternative hypotheses for this problem.
b) What are the Type I and Type II errors in this context?
c) Which type of error would the factory owner consider more serious?
d) Which type of error might customers consider more serious? **LO❶, ❹**

55. Testing cars, part 2. As in Exercise 53, regulators are checking up on repair shops to see if they're certifying vehicles that don't meet pollution standards.

a) In this context, what is meant by the power of the test the regulators are conducting?
b) Will the power be greater if they test 20 or 40 cars? Why?
c) Will the power be greater if they use a 5% or a 10% level of significance? Why?
d) Will the power be greater if the repair shop's inspectors are only a little out of compliance or a lot? Why? **LO❹**

56. Quality control, part 2. Consider again the task of the quality control inspectors in Exercise 54.

a) In this context, what is meant by the power of the test the inspectors conduct?
b) They're currently testing 5 items each hour. Someone has proposed that they test 10 items each hour instead. What are the advantages and disadvantages of such a change?
c) Their test currently uses a 5% level of significance. What are the advantages and disadvantages of changing to a significance level of 1%?
d) Suppose that as a day passes one of the machines on the assembly line produces more and more items that are defective. How will this affect the power of the test? **LO❹**

57. Statistics software. A Statistics professor has observed that for several years about 13% of the students who initially enrol in his Introductory Statistics course withdraw before the end of the semester. A salesperson suggests that he try a statistics software package that gets students more involved with computers, predicting that it will cut the dropout rate. The software is expensive, and the salesperson offers to let the professor use it for a semester to see if the dropout rate goes down significantly. The professor will have to pay for the software only if he chooses to continue using it.

a) Is this a one-tailed or two-tailed test? Explain.
b) Write the null and alternative hypotheses.
c) In this context, explain what would happen if the professor makes a Type I error.

d) In this context, explain what would happen if the professor makes a Type II error.
e) What is meant by the power of this test? **LO❶, ❹**

58. Radio ads. A company is willing to renew its advertising contract with a local radio station only if the station can prove that more than 20% of the residents of the city have heard the ad and recognize the company's product. The radio station conducts a random phone survey of 400 people.

a) What are the hypotheses?
b) The station plans to conduct this test using a 10% level of significance, but the company wants the significance level lowered to 5%. Why?
c) What is meant by the power of this test?
d) For which level of significance will the power of this test be higher? Why?
e) The station finally agrees to use $\alpha = 0.05$, but the company proposes that the station call 600 people instead of the 400 initially proposed. Will that make the risk of a Type II error higher or lower? Explain. **LO❶, ❹**

❶ 59. Customer spending. The data set provided contains last month's credit card purchases of 500 customers randomly chosen from a segment of a major credit card issuer. The Marketing Department is considering a special offer for customers who spend more than $1000 per month on their card. Historically, the percentage has been 11%, and the Finance Department wonders if it has increased. Test the appropriate hypothesis and write your conclusions. **LO❷**

❶ 60. Fundraising. A philanthropic organization knows that its donors have an average age near 60, and so is considering taking out an ad in the *Canadian Association of Retired Persons* (CARP) magazine. The head of Finance says that the CARP advertisement won't be worth the money unless more than two-thirds of the donors are 50 or older. Using the data set provided, test the appropriate hypothesis and write up a few sentences with your conclusions. **LO❷**

61. Drugs in Canada, part 1. The Liberal government that decriminalized the possession of small quantities of marijuana was replaced by a Conservative government in the 2006 federal election. The new government considered scrapping the legislation, and in 2007 Angus Reid conducted a survey of 1028 adult Canadians and found that only 38% would support that move. However, pollsters also found that 59% of Conservative voters supported scrapping the legislation. Suppose the Conservative government wanted to adopt policies supported by more than 50% of its own voters. Should it have scrapped the legislation in 2007? Assume 40% of the people surveyed were Conservative voters. (*Source:* Based on Angus Reid Strategies. [2007]. Illegal drugs: Drugs a national problem—Canadians would mix Grit and Tory policies. Retrieved from http://juror.ca/Angus_Reid_55%25.pdf.) **LO❷**

62. Drugs in Canada, part 2. In 2002, the Liberal government introduced "harm reduction" programs for drug users, such as supervised injection sites and needle-exchange programs. However, a Conservative government was elected in 2006. The new government considered eliminating the harm reduction programs, and in 2007 Angus Reid conducted a survey of 1028 adult Canadians and found that only 37% would support that move. Fifty-four percent of Conservative voters supported eliminating the programs, however. Suppose the Conservative government wanted to adopt policies supported by more than 50% of its own voters. Should it have eliminated the harm reduction programs in 2007? Assume 40% of the people surveyed were Conservative voters. (*Source:* Angus Reid Strategies. [2007]. Illegal drugs: Drugs a national problem—Canadians would mix Grit and Tory policies. Retrieved from http://juror.ca/Angus_Reid_55%25.pdf.) **LO ❷**

63. Canadian head of state, part 1. Angus Reid Strategies regularly surveys Canadians as to whether they prefer an elected head of state instead of a monarch. The percentage preferring an elected head of state was 43% in November 2009, 30% in July 2010, and 40% in April 2013 based on surveys of 1005 Canadian adults each year. (*Source:* Angus Reid Public Opinion. [2013]. Canadians lukewarm on monarchy. Retrieved April 30, 2013, from http://www.angusreidglobal.com/wp-content/uploads/2013/04/2013.04.30_Monarchy_CAN.pdf.)

a) Test whether support for an elected head of state in 2013 was lower than 43% at the 1% significance level, and interpret the result.

b) Suppose support among all Canadians for an elected head of state in 2013 was in fact 41%. Calculate the power of the test in part (a). Interpret the result, explaining what makes the test powerful or not powerful.

c) Test whether support for an elected head of state in 2013 was more than 5% higher than it had been in 2010 at the 5% significance level, and interpret the result. **LO ❶, ❷, ❹, ❺**

64. Sex offenders in Canada. In May 2010, Public Safety Minister Vic Toews introduced a bill in Parliament proposing that sex offenders who have abused children should not be able to get a government pardon. Angus Reid conducted a survey of 1013 Canadian adults and found that 81% supported the bill. (*Source:* Angus Reid Strategies. [2010]. Crime: Canadians support proposed new regulations for pardons. Retrieved from http://www.angus-reid.com/polls/43065/canadians-support-proposed-new-regulations-for-pardons.)

a) How sure can we be that the percentage of Canadian adults supporting the bill was in fact more than 80%?

b) The survey found that 76% of Liberal Party voters supported the bill. How sure can we be that the percentage of Liberal voters supporting the bill is in fact less than 80%? Assume that 40% of the survey respondents were Liberal voters. **LO ❷**

65. Canadian Aboriginals, part 1. Aboriginals make up 3.9% of the Canadian population, and in 2015, 7 out of the 308 federal Members of Parliament were Aboriginal. Using the methods given in this chapter, compare these pieces of information to answer the question "Are Aboriginals underrepresented in Parliament?" State your assumptions clearly. **LO ❷**

66. Canadian Aboriginals, part 2. During the entire history of Canada, 0.74% of the 4201 federal Members of Parliament have been Aboriginals. In 2015, 7 out of the 308 federal Members of Parliament were Aboriginal. Using the methods given in this chapter, compare these pieces of information to answer the question "Were Aboriginals better represented in Parliament in 2015 than previously?" State your assumptions clearly. **LO ❷**

67. Canadian Senate, part 1. In 2013, Angus Reid surveyed 1000 adult Canadians about reform of the Canadian Senate.

a) 72% answered "Yes" to the question "Do you support allowing Canadians to directly elect their senators?" Does this indicate that the proportion of the adult Canadian population who would answer "Yes" to this question is over 70% at the 95% significance level?

b) 71% said that a referendum should be held to determine the future of the Canadian Senate. Does this indicate that the proportion of Canadians who favour a referendum is over 70% at the 90% significance level?

c) A statistician commented to the press: "Over 70% of Canadians want a referendum on Senate reform and want to elect their senators directly." Comment on the ethics of this statement in relation to the ASA Ethical Guidelines summarized in Appendix C. **LO ❷**

68. Molson. Molson has been in business in Canada for over two and a quarter centuries, a fact that speaks to the consistent quality of the beer. Suppose Molson's aim is that at least 98% of customers say the taste hasn't changed. One way to ensure consistency is to run taste tests with a random selection of customers. Ninety-nine percent of a random sample of 850 customers say the taste hasn't changed in the past 10 years. Is that sufficient for Molson's purposes? **LO ❷**

69. The BC carbon tax. British Columbia introduced a carbon tax of $10 per tonne of carbon in 2008, rising by $5 per tonne each year until 2012. In 2011, with the tax at $25 per tonne, Environics surveyed 1025 British Columbians about the tax and found that 54% supported it. A politician claimed, "Over half of British Columbians support the carbon tax."

a) At what significance level is this statement statistically sound?

b) Comment on the ethics of this statement in relation to the ASA Ethical Guidelines summarized in Appendix C. How could the statement be improved?

c) In 2013, Environics surveyed 250 British Columbians and found that 52% supported the tax. Has support for the tax gone down between 2011 and 2013 at the 10% significance level? **LO❷**

70. **The Canadian nickel coin, part 1.** Suppose a professional survey of 1016 Canadian adults found that 55% were in favour of scrapping the nickel and a reporter commented, "Over half of Canadian adults want to scrap the nickel."

a) Analyze the statistical validity of this statement.
b) Comment on the ethics of this statement as it relates to the ASA Ethical Guidelines in Appendix C. **LO❶, ❷**

71. **The Canadian nickel coin, part 2.** Suppose a professional survey of 1016 Canadian adults found that support for scrapping the nickel was high in British Columbia (62%) and Ontario (55%). Do these survey results lead to the conclusion that a greater percentage of British Columbian adults support scrapping the nickel than Ontarian adults? (Assume that 13.3% of the people surveyed were in British Columbia and 38.8% were in Ontario.) **LO❶, ❺**

72. **The Canadian nickel coin, part 3.** Suppose a professional survey of 1016 Canadian adults (assume a 50/50 split between men and women) found that 65% of men and 45% of women support scrapping the nickel.

a) At what level of significance can we conclude that more Canadian men than women support scrapping the nickel?
b) If we wanted to check out the conclusion in part (a) at the 95% level without going to the expense of surveying 1000 people, how many people would we need to survey? **LO❶, ❺**

73. **Canadian Senate, part 2.** An Angus Reid survey of 1000 adult Canadians about reform of the Canadian Senate found that 32% of people in Ontario supported abolishing the Senate of Canada, whereas the percentage in Quebec was 43%. Do more people in Quebec support abolishing the Canadian Senate than in Ontario? (Assume that 38.4% of the people surveyed were in Ontario and 23.6% were in Quebec.) **LO❶, ❺**

74. **Single-parent families in Canada.** A random sample of 1000 families in Alberta reported 14% single-parent families. Another random sample of 700 families in Nova Scotia reported 17% single-parent families. Is there a lower percentage of single-parent families in Alberta than in Nova Scotia at the 95% level of significance? **LO❺**

75. **Adults living with parents in Canada.** A random survey of 1000 Canadians aged 20–24 in 2008 found that 61.4% lived with their parents. In 2013 a similar survey found 65.3% of Canadians aged 20–24 lived with their parents. Is there a difference between the percentages of Canadians aged 20–24 living with their parents in 2008 and 2013 at the 95% level of significance? **LO❺**

76. **Mature middle class in India.** The National Sample Survey identifies a segment of Indian households as the "Mature Middle Class" with an income of around 170,000 rupees per year. The rapid growth of the Indian economy has resulted in an increase in the proportion of households in this group, and the survey estimates that it increased from 27% in 2005 to 50% in 2011. What sample size is necessary in order to conclude that the proportion of the Indian population in this group increased between 2005 and 2011 at the 99% significance level? You can assume that the size of the sample is the same in 2005 and in 2011. **LO❺**

77. **Canadian head of state, part 2.** Angus Reid Strategies surveys Canadians as to whether they prefer an elected head of state instead of a monarch. The percentages preferring an elected head of state were 54% for men and 33% for women in a 2013 survey of 1008 Canadian adults. Test whether the percentage of men with this view was more than 10% higher than the percentage of women at the 1% significance level and interpret the result. Assume half of the people surveyed were men and half were women. **LO❶, ❺**

78. **Canadian solar.** Ontario is the Canadian centre for solar panel manufacturing, with companies like Canadian Solar exporting around the world. A competing company manufactures 250 watt solar panels, but the manufacturing process does not guarantee that the panels will produce exactly 250 watts of electric power. Some 8.5% of panels are classified as "underpowered," producing less than 240 watts and can be sold, but for a lower price. The company improves its manufacturing process with the aim of reducing the percentage of underpowered panels from 8.5% to 4%. Workers take a random sample of 200 panels and find that 4.3% of them are under 240 watts. They wish to conduct a statistical test, at the 10% significance level, to establish whether the proportion of underpowered panels has been reduced. Calculate the power of the test assuming that the true proportion after the improvement in the manufacturing process is 0.04. (You are not asked to actually conduct the test.) **LO❹**

79. **Canada–United States energy/environment cooperation.** A Nanos Research survey for the *Globe and Mail* on energy and the environment in December 2014 asked whether Canadians believe cooperation between Canada and the United States on these issues is important. The percentages saying this is important or somewhat important were 87.3% for the 497 men surveyed and 90.5% for the 503 women. Is there a difference between men and women on this point at the 1% significance level? **LO❶, ❺**

80. **Oil transport across Canada.** A Nanos Research survey for the *Globe and Mail* on energy and the environment in December 2014 asked what is the most environmentally responsible way to transport oil. Of 205 Canadian adults in the age group 18–29, 50.8% answered "pipeline" as opposed to rail, road, etc. But for 178 people in the age group 50–59, the corresponding percentage was 66.3%. Is there a difference between these age groups on this issue at the 1% significance level? **LO❶, ❺**

81. Bearings Canada. A company manufactures ceramic ball bearings, but customers complain that some of them are cracked. Some cracking is inevitable and the company accepts 0.2% cracked product. A random sample of ball bearings is collected from the manufacturing plant and tested to determine whether more than 0.2% are cracked. The P-value comes to 0.165, and management concludes that there is no cracking problem and continues to operate the plant as in the past.

a) Comment on how the P-value has been interpreted by the company.
b) Give possible reasons for the P-value if in fact more than 0.2% are cracked. **LO❶, ❷**

82. Tangerine. Tangerine gives its banking customers a commission if they refer new people to open bank accounts at Tangerine. As a result, 55% of new customers at Tangerine came from referrals in 2014. Another Canadian bank had 14% referrals last year (out of a total of 65,000 new customers) and has increased the commission this year. They expect to achieve 20% referrals this year and pick a random selection of 400 new customers and find that 18% of them came from referrals.

a) Can we claim that the proportion of referrals has increased from last year at the 1% significance level?
b) Calculate a confidence interval in order to confirm the result in part (a). Does your confidence interval confirm that result?
c) Calculate the power of the test, based on the expected increase.

For (d)–(h), you are not asked to do the calculation, just to answer the question with reasons.

d) Supposing the result of our survey of 400 customers was that 21% came from referrals, would the answer to part (a) be different?
e) Supposing the result of our survey of 400 customers was that 21% came from referrals, would the power of our test be higher?

f) Supposing we used a 5% significance level, would the answer to part (a) be different?
g) Supposing we used a 5% significance level, would the power of our test be higher?
h) Supposing we sampled more than 400 customers, would the power be higher? **LO❶, ❷, ❸, ❹, ❺**

83. Road accidents in Ontario. Many fatal road accidents are due to preventable driver-related causes including drugs, alcohol, cell phone use, speeding, and failure to use a seatbelt or helmet. In 2014, 230 out of 265 fatal accidents were due to these driver-related causes. The deputy commissioner of the Ontario Provincial Police published this data so that people would know the seriousness of their actions and be more careful in future. "Most of the people who have died on our roads did not have to die," he said.

a) Suppose that, during January of this year, 67% of fatal accidents were due to these driver-related causes. Is this year going to have a lower proportion of driver-related fatalities than 2014?
b) Suppose that, during the first half of this year, 82% of fatal accidents were due to these driver-related causes. Is this year going to have a lower proportion of driver-related fatalities than 2014? **LO❶, ❷**

84. Savings for retirement in Canada. McKinsey & Co. surveyed 12,000 Canadian households equally divided among low, middle, and high incomes as to whether they would be able to maintain their lifestyle after they stopped working, taking into account savings, pensions, and government payments. The results were that 93% of low income households would be able to do this and that 77% of middle and high income households (combined) would be able to. Calculate 90% confidence intervals on these percentages. **LO❶**

Bert Hardy/Hulton Archive/Getty Images

13

Confidence Intervals and Hypothesis Tests for Means

Guinness & Co.

In 1759, when Arthur Guinness was 34 years old, he took an incredible gamble, signing a 9000-year lease on a run-down, abandoned brewery in Dublin. The brewery covered four acres and consisted of a mill, two malt houses, stabling for 12 horses, and a loft that could hold 200 tonnes of hay. At the time, brewing was a difficult and competitive market. Gin, whisky, and the traditional London porter were the drinks of choice.

In addition to the lighter ales that Dublin was known for, Guinness began to brew dark porters to compete directly with those of the English brewers. Forty years later, Guinness stopped brewing light Dublin ales altogether to concentrate on his stouts and porters. Upon his death in 1803, his son Arthur Guinness II took over the business, and a few years later the company began to export Guinness stout to other parts of Europe. By the 1830s, the Guinness St. James's Gate Brewery had become the largest in Ireland. In 1886, the Guinness Brewery, with an annual production of 1.2 million barrels, was the first major brewery to be incorporated as a public company on the London Stock Exchange. During the 1890s, the company began to employ scientists. One of those, William S. Gosset, was hired as a chemist to test the quality of the brewing process. Gosset wasn't only an early pioneer of quality control method in industry; his statistical work also made modern statistical inference possible.[1]

[1]Guinness & Co. (2006). Retrieved from www.guinness.com/global/story/history

Number of Variables	Objective	Large Sample or Normal Population		Small Sample and Non-normal Population or Non-numeric Data	
		Chapter	Parametric Method	Chapter	Nonparametric Method
1	Calculate confidence interval for a proportion	11			
1	Compare a proportion with a given value	12	z-test		
1	Calculate a confidence interval for a mean and compare it with a given value	13	t-test	17.2	Wilcoxon Signed-Rank Test
2	Compare two proportions	12.8	z-test		
2	Compare two means for independent samples	14.1–14.5	t-test	17.4, 17.5	Wilcoxon Rank-Sum (Mann-Whitney) Test Tukey's Quick Test
2	Compare two means for paired samples	14.6, 14.7	Paired t-test	17.2	Wilcoxon Signed-Rank Test
≥3	Compare multiple means	15	ANOVA: ANalysis Of VAriance	17.3 17.6	Friedman Test Kruskal-Wallis Test
≥3	Compare multiple counts (proportions)	16	χ^2 test		
2	Investigate the relationship between two variables	18	Correlation Regression	17.7, 17.8	Kendall's tau Spearman's rho
≥3	Investigate the relationship between multiple variables	20	Multiple Regression		

ROADMAP FOR STATISTICAL INFERENCE

As a chemist at the Guinness Brewery in Dublin, William S. Gosset was in charge of quality control. His job was to make sure that the stout (a thick, dark beer) leaving the brewery was of high enough quality to meet the standards of the brewery's many discerning customers. It's easy to imagine why testing a large amount of stout might be undesirable, not to mention dangerous to one's health. So to test for quality, Gosset often used a sample of only three or four observations per batch. But he noticed that with samples of this size, his tests for quality weren't quite right. He knew this because when the batches he rejected were sent back to the laboratory for more extensive testing, too often the test results turned out to be wrong. As a practising statistician, Gosset knew he had to be wrong *some* of the time, but he hated being wrong more often than the theory predicted. One result of Gosset's frustrations was the development of a test to handle small samples, the main subject of this chapter.

LO❶,❷   **13.1**   **The Sampling Distribution for the Mean**

As discussed in Chapter 11, for *proportions*, the confidence interval is

$$\hat{p} \pm \text{ME}.$$

The margin of error, ME, is equal to a critical value, z^*, times $SE(\hat{p})$. Our confidence interval for *means* will be

$$\bar{y} \pm \text{ME},$$

and our ME will be a critical value times $SE(\bar{y})$. So let's put the pieces together. What the Central Limit Theorem told us in Chapter 10 is exactly what we need.

The Central Limit Theorem

When a random sample is drawn from *any* population with mean μ and standard deviation σ, its sample mean, $\bar{y}$, has a sampling distribution whose *shape* is approximately Normal as long as the sample size is large enough. The larger the sample used, the more closely the Normal approximates the sampling distribution for the mean. The mean of the sampling distribution is μ, and its standard deviation is $SD(\bar{y}) = \dfrac{\sigma}{\sqrt{n}}$.

This gives us a sampling distribution and a standard deviation for the mean. All we need is a random sample of quantitative data and the true value of the population standard deviation, σ.

But wait. That could be a problem. To compute $\sigma/\sqrt{n}$, we need to know σ. How are we supposed to know σ? Suppose we told you that for 25 young executives the mean value of their stock portfolios is \$125,672. Would that tell you the value of σ? No, the standard deviation depends on how similarly the executives invest, not on how well they invested (the mean tells us that). But we need σ because it's the numerator of the standard deviation of the sample mean: $SD(\bar{y}) = \dfrac{\sigma}{\sqrt{n}}$.

So what can we do? The obvious answer is to use the sample standard deviation, s, from the data instead of σ. The result is the standard error: $SE(\bar{y}) = \dfrac{s}{\sqrt{n}}$.

A century ago, people like Gosset just plugged the standard error into the Normal model, assuming it would work. And for large sample sizes it *did* work pretty well. But they began to notice problems with smaller samples. The extra variation in the standard error was wreaking havoc with the P-values and margins of error.

William S. Gosset was the first to investigate this phenomenon. He realized that not only do we need to allow for the extra variation with larger margins of error and P-values, but we also need a new sampling distribution model. In fact, we need a whole *family* of models, depending on the sample size, n. These models are unimodal, symmetric, and bell-shaped, but the smaller our sample, the more we must stretch out the tails. Gosset's work transformed Statistics, but most people who use his work don't even know his name.

Gosset's *t*

Gosset checked the stout's quality at Guinness by performing hypothesis tests. He knew that if he set $\alpha = 0.05$, the test would make some Type I errors by rejecting about 5% of the good batches of stout. However, the lab told him that he was in fact rejecting about 15% of the good batches. Gosset knew something was wrong, and it bugged him.

Gosset took time off from his job to study the problem and to earn a graduate degree in the emerging field of Statistics. He figured out that when he used the standard error $\dfrac{s}{\sqrt{n}}$, the shape of the sampling model was no longer Normal. He even figured out what the new model was and called it a *t*-distribution.

The Guinness Company didn't give Gosset a lot of support for his work. In fact, it had a policy against publishing results. Gosset had to convince the company that he wasn't publishing an industrial secret and, as part of getting permission to publish, he had to use a pseudonym. The pseudonym he chose was "Student," and ever since, the model he found has been known as **Student's *t***.

Gosset's model is always bell-shaped, but the details change with the sample sizes. So the Student's *t*-models form a family of related distributions that depend on a parameter known as **degrees of freedom (df)**. We often denote degrees of freedom as df and the model as t_{df}, with the numerical value of the degrees of freedom as a subscript.

LO❶   13.2   A Confidence Interval for Means

To make confidence intervals or to test hypotheses for means, we need to use Gosset's model. Which one? Well, for means, it turns out that the right value for degrees of freedom is df = $n - 1$.

Practical Sampling Distribution Model for Means

When certain conditions are met, the standardized sample mean,

$$t = \frac{\bar{y} - \mu}{SE(\bar{y})},$$

follows a Student's *t*-model with $n - 1$ degrees of freedom. We find the standard error from

$$SE(\bar{y}) = \frac{s}{\sqrt{n}}.$$

NOTATION ALERT

Ever since Gosset, the letter *t* has been reserved in Statistics for his distribution.

z or t?

If you know σ, use z. (That's rare!) Whenever you use s to estimate σ, use t.

When Gosset corrected the Normal model for the extra uncertainty, the margin of error got bigger, as you might have guessed. When you use Gosset's model instead of the Normal model, your confidence intervals will be just a bit wider and your P-values just a bit larger (Figure 13.1). That's just the correction you need. By using the *t*-model, you've compensated for the extra variability in precisely the right way.

NOTATION ALERT

When we found critical values from a Normal model in Chapter 12, we called them z^*. When we use a Student's *t*-model, we denote the critical values t^*.

One-Sample *t*-Interval

When the assumptions and conditions are met, we're ready to find the **confidence interval for the population mean, μ**. The confidence interval extends on either side of the mean by an amount known as the margin of error, ME, and can be calculated as:

$$\bar{y} \pm ME = \bar{y} \pm t^*_{n-1} \times SE(\bar{y}),$$

where the standard error of the mean is

$$SE(\bar{y}) = \frac{s}{\sqrt{n}}.$$

The critical value t^*_{n-1} depends on the particular confidence level, C, that you specify and on the number of degrees of freedom, $n - 1$, which we get from the sample size.

Student's *t*-models are unimodal, symmetric, and bell-shaped, just like the Normal model. But *t*-models with only a few degrees of freedom have a narrower peak than the Normal model and have much fatter tails. (That's what makes the margin of error bigger.) As the degrees of freedom increase, the *t*-models look more and more like the Normal model. In fact, the *t*-model with infinite degrees

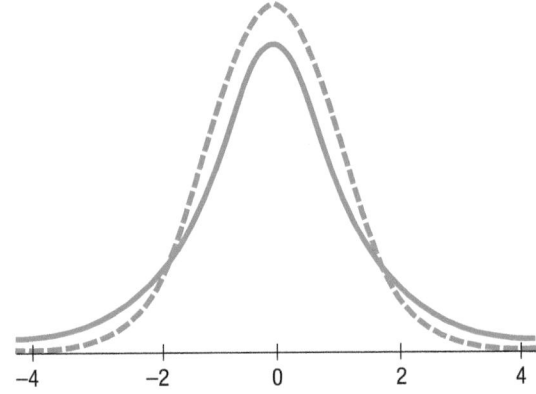

Figure 13.1 The *t*-model (solid curve) with two degrees of freedom has fatter tails than the Normal model (dashed curve). So the 68-95-99.7 Rule doesn't work for *t*-models with only a few degrees of freedom.

of freedom is exactly Normal.[2] This is great news if you happen to have an infinite number of data values. Unfortunately, that's not practical. Fortunately, above a few hundred degrees of freedom it's very hard to tell the difference. Of course, in the rare situation that we *know* σ, it would be foolish not to use that information. If we don't have to estimate σ, we can use the Normal model. Typically, that value of σ would be based on (lots of) experience, or on a theoretical model. Usually, however, we estimate σ by s from the data and use the *t*-model.

FOR EXAMPLE **Finding a confidence interval for the mean contaminant levels in fish**

In a widely cited study of contaminants in farmed salmon, fish from many sources were analyzed for 14 organic contaminants.[3] One of those was the insecticide Mirex, which has been shown to be carcinogenic and is suspected of being toxic to the liver, kidneys, and endocrine system. Summaries for 150 Mirex concentrations (in parts per million) from a variety of farmed salmon sources were reported as:

$$n = 150; \bar{y} = 0.0913 \text{ ppm}; s = 0.0495 \text{ ppm}.$$

QUESTION   The Environmental Protection Agency (EPA) recommends to recreational fishers as a "screening value" that Mirex concentrations be no larger than 0.08 ppm. What does the 95% confidence interval say about that value?

ANSWER   Because $n = 150$, there are 149 df. From Table T in Appendix B, for a 95% confidence level in the last row of the table, we find $t^*_{149} = 1.977$ (from technology, $t^*_{149} = 1.976$), so a 95% confidence interval can be found from:

$$\bar{y} + t^*_{149} \times SE(\bar{y}) = \bar{y} \pm 1.976 \times \frac{s}{\sqrt{n}} = 0.0913 \pm 1.976\frac{0.0495}{\sqrt{150}} = (0.0833, 0.0993)$$

If this sample is representative (as the authors claim it is), we can be 95% confident that our confidence interval contains the true value of the mean Mirex concentration. Because the interval from 0.0833 to 0.0993 ppm is entirely above the recommended value set by the EPA, we have reason to believe that the true Mirex concentration exceeds the EPA guidelines.

LO❶, ❷   **13.3**   Assumptions and Conditions

Gosset found the *t*-model by simulation. Years later, when Sir Ronald Fisher showed mathematically that Gosset was right, he needed to make some assumptions to make the proof work. These are the assumptions we need in order to use the Student's *t*-models:

- **Independence Assumption:** The data values should be independent. There's really no way to check independence of the data by looking at the sample, but we should think about whether the assumption is reasonable from the business context.

---

[2]Formally, in the limit as the number of degrees of freedom goes to infinity.
[3]Hites, R. A., Foran, J. A., Carpenter, D. O., Hamilton, M. C., Knuth, B. A., and Schwager, S. J. (2004, January). Global assessment of organic contaminants in farmed salmon. *Science, 303*(5655), 226–229.

- **Randomization Condition:** The data arise from a random sample or suitable randomized experiment.
- **10% Condition:** The sample size should be no more than 10% of the population. When we made inferences about proportions, this condition was crucial. But for means there's a correction formula we could use if the condition does not apply.

Student's *t*-models won't work for populations that are badly skewed. How skewed is too skewed? Well, formally, we assume that the data are from a population that follows a Normal model. Practically speaking, there's no way to be certain this is true.

And it's almost certainly *not* true. Models are idealized; real data are, well, real. The good news, however, is that even for small samples, it's sufficient to check a condition:

- **Nearly Normal Condition:** The data come from a distribution that is unimodal and symmetric. This is a much more practical condition and one we can check by making a histogram and using the Normal probability plot described in Section 9.10. For small samples, it can be hard to see any distribution shape in the histogram. Unfortunately, the condition matters most when it's hardest to check.[4]

For very small samples ($n < 15$ or so), the data should follow a Normal model pretty closely. Of course, with so little data it's rather hard to tell. But if you do find outliers or strong skewness, use the Wilcoxon Signed-Rank Test (Section 17.2).

For moderate sample sizes (*n* between 15 and 40 or so), the *t* methods will work well as long as the data are unimodal and reasonably symmetric. Make a histogram to check.

When the sample size is larger than 40 or 50, the *t* methods are safe to use unless the data are extremely skewed. Make a histogram anyway. If you find outliers in the data and they aren't errors that are easy to fix, it's always a good idea to perform the analysis twice, once with and once without the outliers, even for large samples. The outliers may hold additional information about the data, so they deserve special attention. If you find multiple modes, you may have different groups that should be analyzed and understood separately.

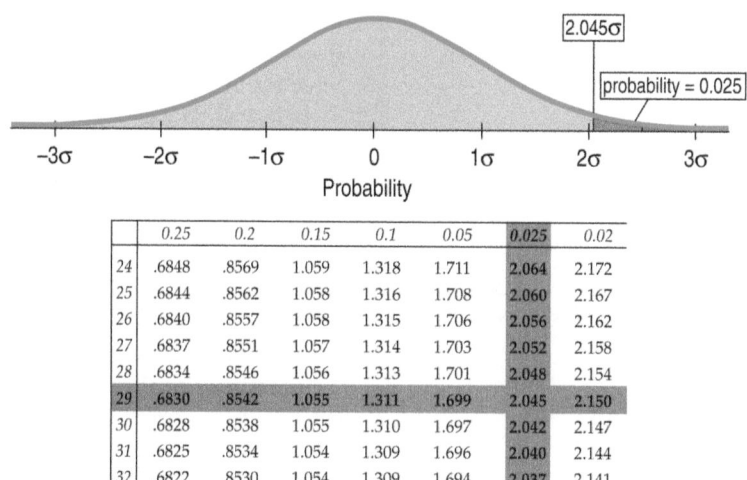

Figure 13.2   Using the Student's *t* to look up the critical value *t** for a 95% confidence level with 29 degrees of freedom.

[4]There are formal tests of Normality, but they don't really help. When we have a small sample—just when we really care about checking Normality—these tests have very little power. So it doesn't make much sense to use them in deciding whether to perform a *t*-test.

FOR EXAMPLE	Checking the assumptions and conditions for analyzing contaminant levels in fish

Researchers purchased whole farmed salmon at random from 51 farms in eight regions in six countries (see For Example: "Finding a confidence interval for the mean contaminant levels in fish"). The histogram shows the concentrations of the insecticide Mirex in the 150 samples of farmed salmon we examined previously:

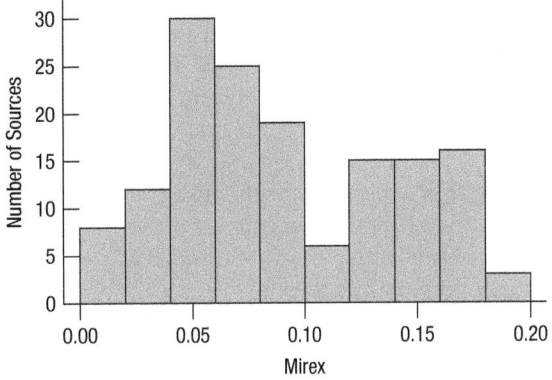

QUESTION Are the assumptions and conditions for making a confidence interval for the mean Mirex concentration satisfied?

ANSWER

✓ **Independence Assumption:** The fish were raised in many different places, and samples were purchased independently from several sources.
✓ **Randomization Condition:** The fish were selected randomly from those available for sale.
✓ **10% Condition:** There are lots of fish in the sea (and at the fish farms); 150 is certainly far fewer than 10% of the population.
✓ **Nearly Normal Condition:** The histogram of the data looks bimodal. While it might be interesting to learn the reason for that and possibly identify the subsets, we can proceed because the sample size is large.

It's okay to use these data about farm-raised salmon to make a confidence interval for the mean.

JUST CHECKING

Every five years, Statistics Canada takes a census that includes every resident of Canada. In addition, the census collects information on gender, age, family type, and languages spoken. Businesses of all types use the census data to plan sales and marketing strategies and to understand the underlying demographics of the areas they serve. StatsCan also conducts a number of surveys of samples of the population, for example, the monthly Labour Force Survey and the annual Survey of Household Spending.

1 Why does StatsCan need a confidence interval for reporting results from surveys, but not for the results of the census?

2 Why must StatsCan base these confidence intervals on t-models?

3 Why are the confidence intervals wider for surveys that use smaller sample sizes? How does the formula for the one-sample t-interval show that this will happen?

4 Suppose StatsCan decided to report on geographic areas from which only 50 people were surveyed. What effect would that have on a 95% confidence interval for, say, the mean annual spending on housing? Specifically, which values used in the formula for the margin of error would change? Which values would change a lot, and which values would change only slightly? Approximately how much wider would that confidence interval based on 50 people be than the one based on 200 people?

Answers are found in Appendix A.

GUIDED EXAMPLE   Insurance Profits

Sapsiwai/Shutterstock

Life insurance companies take risks. When they insure a life, they must price the policy in such a way that their expected profit covers the risk. They can base their projections on actuarial tables, but the reality of the insurance business often demands that they discount policies to a variety of customers and situations. Managing this risk is made even more difficult by the fact that until the policy expires, the company won't know if it's made a profit, no matter what premium it charges.

A manager wanted to see how well one of her sales representatives was doing, so she selected a random sample of 30 mature policies that had been sold by the sales rep and computed the (net) profit (premium charged minus paid claims) for each of the 30 policies.

The manager would like you, as a consultant, to construct a 95% confidence interval for the mean profit of the policies sold by this sales rep.

Profit (in $) from 30 Policies		
222.80	463.35	2089.40
1756.23	−66.20	2692.75
1100.85	57.90	2495.70
3340.66	833.95	2172.70
1006.50	1390.70	3249.65
445.50	2447.50	−397.70
3255.60	1847.50	−397.31
3701.85	865.40	186.25
−803.35	1415.65	590.85
3865.90	2756.34	578.95

PLAN

Setup State what we want to know. Identify the variables and their context.

Make a picture. Check the distribution shape and look for skewness, multiple modes, and outliers.

We wish to find a 95% confidence interval for the mean profit of policies sold by this sales rep. We have data for 30 mature policies.

Here's a boxplot, histogram, and Normal probability plot of these values:

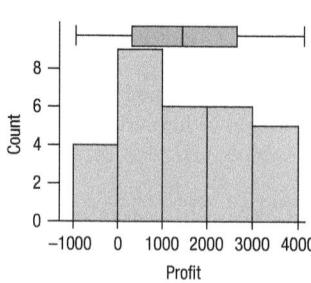
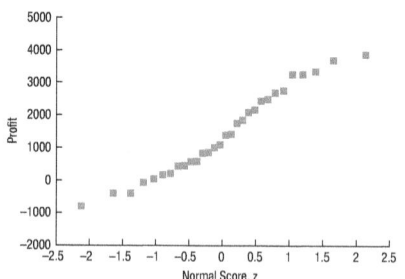

Model Think about the assumptions and check the conditions.

State the sampling distribution model for the statistic.

The sample appears to be unimodal and fairly symmetric, with profit values between −$1000 and $4000 and no outliers, and the Normal probability plot is fairly straight.

✓ **Independence Assumption.** This is a random sample, so observations should be independent.

✓ **Randomization Condition.** This sample was selected randomly from the mature policies sold by the sales representative of the company.

✓ **10% Condition.** We assume that the sales rep has sold more than 300 policies.

✓ **Nearly Normal Condition.** The distribution of profits is unimodal and fairly symmetric, without strong skewness.

Since we can calculate the *sample* standard deviation, but the *population* standard deviation is unknown, we will use a Student's t-model with $n - 1 = 30 - 1 = 29$ degrees of freedom and find a one-sample t-interval for the mean.

DO

Mechanics Compute basic statistics and construct the confidence interval.

Remember that the standard error of the mean is equal to the standard deviation divided by the square root of *n*.

The critical value we need to make a 95% confidence interval comes from a Student's *t* table, a computer program, or a calculator. We have $30 - 1 = 29$ degrees of freedom. The selected confidence level says that we want 95% of the probability to be caught in the middle, so we exclude 2.5% in each tail, for a total of 5%. The degrees of freedom and 2.5% tail probability are all we need to know to find the critical value. Here it's 2.045.

Using software, we obtain the following basic statistics:

$$n = 30$$
$$\bar{y} = 1438.90$$
$$s = \$1329.60$$

The standard error of the mean is

$$SE(\bar{y}) = \frac{s}{\sqrt{n}} = \frac{1329.60}{\sqrt{30}} = 242.751.$$

There are $30 - 1 = 29$ degrees of freedom. The manager has specified a 95% level of confidence, so the critical value (from Table T in Appendix B) is 2.045.

The margin of error is

$$ME = 2.045 \times SE(\bar{y})$$
$$= 2.045 \times 242.751$$
$$= 496.43.$$

The 95% confidence interval for the mean profit is

$$\$1438.90 \pm \$496.43 = (\$942.47, \$1935.33).$$

REPORT

Conclusion Interpret the confidence interval in the proper context.

When we construct confidence intervals in this way, we expect 95% of them to cover the true mean and 5% to miss the true value. That's what "95% confident" means.

MEMO

Re: Profit from Policies

From our analysis of the selected policies, we are 95% confident that the true mean profit of policies sold by this sales rep is contained in the interval from $942.47 to $1935.33.

Caveat: Insurance losses are notoriously subject to outliers. One very large loss could influence the average profit substantially. However, there were no such cases in this data set.

The critical value in Guided Example: "Insurance Profits" was found in the Student's *t* table (Table T in Appendix B). To find the critical value, locate the row of the table corresponding to the degrees of freedom and the column corresponding to the probability you want; see Figure 13.2. Since a 95% confidence interval leaves 2.5% of the values on either side, we look for 0.025 at the top of the column or look for 95% confidence directly in the bottom row of the table. The value in the table at that intersection is the critical value we need. In Guided Example: "Insurance Profits," the number of degrees of freedom was $30 - 1 = 29$, so we located the value of 2.045, as shown in Figure 13.2.

LO❶   13.4   Cautions About Interpreting Confidence Intervals

Confidence intervals for means offer tempting wrong interpretations. Here are some ways to keep from going astray:

- *Don't say,* "*95% of all the policies* sold by this sales rep have profits between $942.47 and $1935.33." The confidence interval is about the *mean*, not about the measurements of individual policies.

- *Don't say,* "We are 95% confident that *a randomly selected policy* will have a net profit between $942.47 and $1935.33." This false interpretation is also about individual policies rather than about the *mean* of the policies. We're 95% confident that the *mean* profit of all (similar) policies sold by this sales rep is between $942.47 and $1935.33.
- *Don't say,* "The mean profit is $1438.90 95% *of the time.*" That's about means, but still wrong. It implies that the true mean varies, when in fact it's the confidence interval that would have been different had we gotten a different sample.
- Finally, *don't say,* "95% *of all samples* will have mean profits between $942.48 and $1935.33." That statement suggests that *this* interval somehow sets a standard for every other interval. In fact, this interval is no more (or less) likely to be correct than any other. You could say that 95% of all possible samples would produce intervals that contain the true mean profit. (The problem is that because we'll never know what the true mean profit is, we can't know if our sample was one of those 95%.)

LO❷   ## 13.5   Hypothesis Test for Means

If you are new to hypothesis testing and haven't read Chapter 12, you might like to take a look at Sections 12.1, 12.2, and 12.4 before reading this section.

P-Value Method

The manager from Guided Example: "Insurance Profits" has a more specific concern. Company policy states that if a sales rep's mean profit is below $1500, the sales rep has been discounting too much and will have to adjust his or her pricing strategy. Is there evidence from this sample that the mean is really less than $1500? This question calls for a hypothesis test called the **one-sample *t*-test for the mean**.

You already know enough to construct this test. The test statistic looks just like the others we've seen. We've always compared the difference between the observed statistic and a hypothesized value with the standard error. For means, that looks like $\frac{\bar{y} - \mu_0}{SE(\bar{y})}$. We already know that the appropriate probability model to use is Student's *t* with $n - 1$ degrees of freedom.

One-Sample *t*-Test for the Mean

The conditions for the one-sample *t*-test for the mean are the same as for the one-sample *t*-interval. We test the hypothesis $H_0: \mu = \mu_0$ using the statistic

$$t_{n-1} = \frac{\bar{y} - \mu_0}{SE(\bar{y})},$$

where the standard error of $\bar{y}$ is $SE(\bar{y}) = \frac{s}{\sqrt{n}}$.

We choose a significance level, α, usually 0.01, 0.05, or 0.1, as we did in Chapter 12.

When the conditions are met and the null hypothesis is true, this statistic follows a Student's *t*-model with $n - 1$ degrees of freedom. We use that model to obtain a P-value from Table T in Appendix B or from statistical software.

GUIDED EXAMPLE   Insurance Profits Revisited

Let's apply the one-sample t-test to the 30 mature policies sampled by the manager in Guided Example: "Insurance Profits." From these 30 policies, the management would like to know if there's evidence that the mean profit of policies sold by this sales rep is less than $1500.

PLAN	**Setup** State what we want to know. Make clear what the population and parameter are. Identify the variables and context.	We want to test whether the mean profit of the sales rep's policies is less than $1500. We have a random sample of 30 mature policies from which to judge.

$$H_0: \mu = \$1500$$

$$H_A: \mu < \$1500$$

Hypotheses The null hypothesis is that the true mean profit is equal to $1500. Because we're interested in whether the profit is less, the alternative is one-sided.

Model Check the conditions.

State the sampling distribution model.

Let us choose a significance level $\alpha = 0.05$.

We checked the assumptions and conditions in Guided Example: "Insurance Profits."

The conditions are satisfied, so we'll use a Student's t-model with $n - 1 = 29$ degrees of freedom and a one-sample t-test for the mean.

DO

Mechanics Compute the sample statistics. Be sure to include the units when you write down what you know from the data.

Using software, we obtain the following basic statistics:

$$n = 30$$

$$\text{Mean} = \$1438.90$$

$$\text{StDev} = \$1329.60$$

$$t = \frac{1438.90 - 1500}{1329.60/\sqrt{30}} = -0.2517$$

The t-statistic calculation is just a standardized value.

We assume the null model is true to find the P-value. Make a picture of the t-model, centred at μ_0. Since this is a lower-tail test, shade the region to the left of the observed average profit.

(The negative value of t implies that the observed mean is less than the hypothesized value. Since this is what we are investigating in our alternative hypothesis, we can ignore the minus sign, below, when we look t up in Table T in Appendix B.)

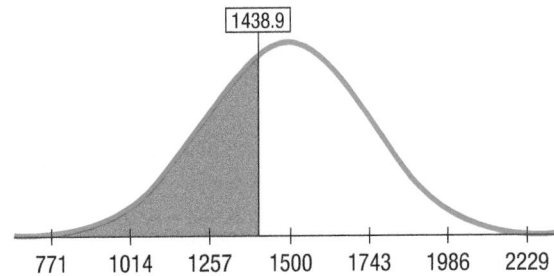

The P-value is the probability of observing a sample mean as small as $1438.90 (or smaller) *if the* true mean were $1500, as the null hypothesis states. We can determine this P-value from a table, calculator, or computer program.

Using software, we obtain:

$$\text{P-value} = P(t_{29} < -0.2517) = 0.4015$$

Alternatively, we can look up 0.2517 in Table T in Appendix B and find $P > 0.1$.

Comparing the P-value with our significance level, $\alpha = 0.05$, we conclude that P-value $> \alpha$, so that we do not have enough evidence to conclude that the sample mean is less than $1500 at the 5% significance level.

(continued)

REPORT   **Conclusion** Link the P-value to your decision about H_0, and state your conclusion in context.

MEMO

Re: Sales Performance

The mean profit on 30 sampled policies closed by the sales rep in question has fallen below our standard of $1500, but there isn't enough evidence in this sample of policies to indicate that the true mean is below $1500. If the mean were $1500, we would expect a sample size of 30 to have a mean this low about 40.15% of the time.

Two tail probability		0.20	0.10	0.05
One tail probability		0.10	0.05	0.025
Table T	df			
Values of t_α	1	3.078	6.314	12.706
	2	1.886	2.920	4.303
	3	1.638	2.353	3.182
	4	1.533	2.132	2.776
	5	1.476	2.015	2.571
	6	1.440	1.943	2.447
	7	1.415	1.895	2.365
	8	1.397	1.860	2.306
	9	1.383	1.833	2.262
	10	1.372	1.812	2.228
	11	1.363	1.796	2.201
	12	1.356	1.782	2.179
	13	1.350	1.771	2.160
	14	1.345	1.761	2.145
	15	1.341	1.753	2.131
	16	1.337	1.746	2.120
	17	1.333	1.740	2.110
	18	1.330	1.734	2.101
	19	1.328	1.729	2.093
	⋮	⋮	⋮	⋮
	∞	1.282	1.645	1.960
Confidence levels		80%	90%	95%

Figure 13.3   Part of Table T in Appendix B.

The Student's t-model is different for each value of degrees of freedom. We might print a table like Table Z in Appendix B for each degrees of freedom value, but that's a lot of pages and not likely to be a bestseller. One way to shorten it is to limit ourselves to 80%, 90%, 95%, and 99% confidence levels. So Statistics books usually have one table of t-model critical values for a selected set of confidence levels. (See Table T in Appendix B.)

The t-tables run down the page for as many degrees of freedom as can fit (Figure 13.3). Then they get to the bottom of the page and run out of room. Of course, for *enough* degrees of freedom, the t-model gets closer and closer to the Normal, so the tables give a final row with the critical values from the Normal model and label it "∞ df."

For example, suppose we've performed a one-sample t-test finding $t = 1.639$ with 19 df, and we want the upper-tail P-value. From the table we see that 1.639 falls between 1.328 and 1.729. All we can say is that the P-value is in the range $0.05 < P < 0.10$.

Or we can use technology. Calculators or statistics programs can give critical values for a t-model for any number of degrees of freedom and for any confidence level you need. And they can go straight to P-values when you test a hypothesis. With tables, we can only approximate P-values by pinning them down between two of the columns. Usually that's good enough. More precision won't necessarily help make a good business decision.

We can summarize the P-value method of hypothesis testing in the following flow diagram:

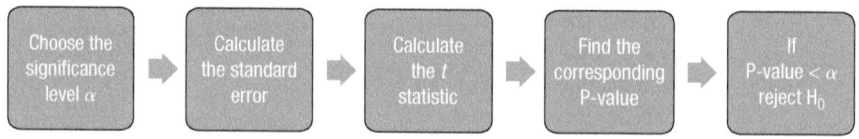

JUST CHECKING

When Statistics Canada conducts a survey based on random samples of the population, it is sometimes possible to compare the results of the survey with the results of the census that includes every resident of Canada. For instance, the respondent's age is often recorded and this is also one of the pieces of information recorded in the census. Estimates of average age in a given geographic region from a survey may not match the "true" values from the census.

5 Suppose we take 100 random samples from the responses to a survey to make one hundred 95% confidence intervals for

the mean age of residents. How many of these hundred intervals should we expect will *fail* to include the true mean age (as determined from the census data)?

6 Based on a survey, we might test the null hypothesis that the mean household income in a region was the same as in the previous census. Would the standard error for such a test be likely to increase or decrease if we used a survey with more respondents?

Answers are found in Appendix A.

For large degrees of freedom, the shape of Student's t-models changes more gradually. Table T in Appendix B includes degrees of freedom between 100 and 1000, so you can pin down the P-value for just about any df. If your dfs aren't listed, take the cautious approach by using the next-lower value or use technology to find the exact value.

FOR EXAMPLE   Testing a mean for retail sales

QUESTION   From 58 randomly selected retail sales, an analyst finds that the mean amount spent is $26.05 with a standard deviation of $10.20 and is approximately Normally distributed. Test the hypothesis that the mean is still $24.85, as it was last year, against the alternative that it has increased.

ANSWER   We can write: $H_0: \mu = \$24.85$ *vs.* $H_A: \mu > \$24.85$.

The assumptions and conditions are satisfied.

Then $t = \dfrac{(26.05 - 24.85)}{10.2/\sqrt{58}} = 0.896.$

Because the alternative is *one-sided*, we find $P(t > 0.896)$ with 57 degrees of freedom. From technology, $P(t > 0.896) = 0.1870$, a large P-value. This isn't a surprising value, given the hypothesized mean of $24.85. Therefore we *fail to reject* the null hypothesis and conclude that there isn't sufficient evidence to suggest that the mean has increased from $24.85.

The advantage of this method is that it tells us how strong the evidence is for rejecting the null hypothesis. The smaller the value of P, the stronger the evidence. If P = 0.0001, the null hypothesis is totally crushed by the weight of evidence our data provides. If P = 0.001, the evidence is less strong but still overwhelming. For these tiny values of P, we don't even need to use the last box in our diagram on the previous page since no one ever chooses α this small. If P = 0.01 or 0.1, we are in the realm of value judgements as to how strong we would like the evidence to be. This is where the last box in the diagram becomes essential and α comes into play. It tells us how strong we need the evidence to be in our particular business situation.

Critical Value Method

The critical value method of hypothesis testing is an alternative to the P-value method and can be summarized by the following flow diagram:

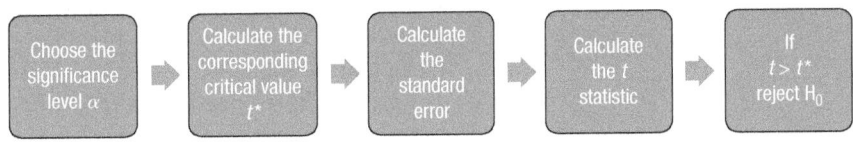

Both methods allow us to decide whether to reject the null hypothesis. The decision will be the same, whichever method we use. Some people prefer the critical value method since it avoids calculating a P-value. Other people prefer the P-value method because the P-value gives extra information about how extreme a sample is.

The key step in the critical value method is calculating the critical value, t^* from the significance level, α. For this we can use software or Table T in Appendix B. We choose a column corresponding to the significance level, α, and a row corresponding to the number of degrees of freedom. The cell at the intersection of this row and column gives the critical value t^*. The only point to watch out for is whether we have a one-sided or a two-sided hypothesis test, since that determines which row to use at the top of the table.

We illustrate the critical value method on the example (Guided Example: "Insurance Profits") that we used for the P-value method.

We have $H_0: \mu = 1500$; $H_A: \mu < 1500$ (one-sided test); $\alpha = 0.5$, and the number of insurance policies in our sample is $n = 30$ so that the degrees of freedom, df $= n - 1 = 29$.

Using Table T in Appendix B, we choose the row for df $= 29$. Since we have a one-sided test we choose the column for a "one-tail probability" with $\alpha = 0.5$. We read off $t^* = 1.699$.

The calculation of the standard error and the t statistic is the same as in the P-value method, giving $t = -0.2517$. The negative value of t confirms that our sample is less than the value in the null hypothesis. Since this is what we are investigating in the alternative hypothesis, we can ignore the minus sign on the value of t and compare $t = 0.2517$ with $t^* = 1.699$. Clearly $t^* > t$, so we cannot reject the null hypothesis, confirming the same conclusion we reached with the P-value method.

Type I and Type II Errors

If you are new to hypothesis testing and haven't read Chapter 12, you should take a look at Section 12.9, about two types of error that can occur.

- A Type I error is another name for a false positive: we reject a null hypothesis which is in fact true. The probability of a Type I error is α, the significance level.
- A Type II error is another name for a false negative: we fail to reject a null hypothesis which is in fact false. We denote the probability of a Type II error by β.

There is a trade-off between Type I and Type II errors. For a given sample size, a smaller α results in an increased β.

Another important concept is the power of a test, which is the probability of correctly rejecting the null hypothesis and is equal to $1 - \beta$. You can take a look at Section 12.10 for a full description of the power of a hypothesis test.

LO❸ 13.6 Sample Size

How large a sample do we need? The simple answer is always "larger." But more data cost money, effort, and time. So how much is enough? As we make plans to collect data, we should have some idea of the size of the difference we want to see. If the size of the effect we're studying is large, then we may be able to tolerate a wide confidence interval or a big difference between the hypothesized value of the mean and the value we get from our sample. This will allow us to go with a small sample size. If we need great precision, however, we'll want a narrow confidence interval and we will want to be able to detect a small difference between hypothesized and sample means. Of course, that means a larger sample size.

The difference between the hypothesized and sample means comes from the same formula that determines the margin of error, ME (half the width of the confidence interval). So the previous paragraph is really saying that we should choose a margin of error, and that will lead us to a sample size that we should use. The t^* in the formula for ME is obtained from the confidence level we want for a confidence interval, or from the significance level we want for a hypothesis test together with whether that test is one-sided or two-sided.

$$\text{ME} = t^*_{n-1} \times \frac{s}{\sqrt{n}}$$

Therefore:

$$n = \left(\frac{t^*_{n-1}s}{\text{ME}}\right)^2$$

The good news is that we have an equation; the bad news is that we won't know most of the values we need to compute it. We don't know s until we get some data, but we want to calculate the sample size *before* collecting the data. We might be able to make a good guess, and that's often good enough for this purpose. If we have no idea what the standard deviation might be or if the sample size really matters (e.g., because each additional individual is very expensive to sample or experiment on), it might be a good idea to run a small *pilot study* to get some feeling for the size of the standard deviation.

That's not all. Without knowing n, we don't know the degrees of freedom, and we can't find the critical value, t^*_{n-1}. One common approach is to use the corresponding z^* value from the Normal model. If you've chosen a 95% confidence level, then just use 2, following the 68-95-99.7 Rule, or 1.96 to be more precise. If your estimated sample size is 60 or more, it's probably okay—z^* was a good guess. If it's smaller than that, you may want to add a step, using z^* at first, finding n, and then replacing z^* with the corresponding t^*_{n-1} and calculating the sample size once more.

Sample size calculations are *never* exact. The margin of error you find *after* collecting the data won't match exactly the one you used to find n. The sample size formula depends on quantities that you won't have until you collect the data, but using it is an important first step. Before you collect data, it's always a good idea to know whether the sample size is large enough to give you a good chance of being able to tell you what you want to know.

FOR EXAMPLE   Finding the sample size for a confidence interval for mean contaminant levels in fish

In the 150 samples of farmed salmon (see For Example: "Checking the assumptions and conditions for analyzing contaminant levels in fish"), the mean concentration of Mirex was 0.0913 ppm with a standard deviation of 0.0495 ppm. A 95% confidence interval for the mean Mirex concentration was found to be (0.0833, 0.0993).

QUESTION   How large a sample would be needed to produce a 95% confidence interval with a margin of error of 0.004?

ANSWER   We will assume that the standard deviation is 0.0495 ppm. The margin of error is equal to the critical value times the standard error. Using z^*, we find:

$$0.004 = 1.96 \times \frac{0.0495}{\sqrt{n}}$$

Solving for n, we find:

$$\sqrt{n} = 1.96 \times \frac{0.0495}{0.004}$$

or

$$n = \left(1.96 \times \frac{0.0495}{0.004}\right)^2 = 588.3$$

The t^* critical value with 400 df is 1.966 instead of 1.960. Using that value, the margin of error is:

$$1.966 \times \frac{0.0495}{\sqrt{589}} = 0.00401$$

You could go back and use 1.966 instead of 1.960 in the equation for n above, and you'd find that n should be 592. That will give a margin of error of 0.004, but the uncertainty in the standard deviation is likely to make such differences unimportant.

JUST CHECKING

Weights of fish caught by a trawler over the past few years have been approximately Normally distributed, with a mean of 2.1 kg and a standard deviation of 0.25 kg. A Fisheries and Oceans researcher thinks that foreign trawlers have been illegally overfishing the stock so that fish are no longer as big as previously. She wants to take a sample of fish to test whether this is true and will accept a 95% confidence interval with ME = 0.125 kg, half the population standard deviation from previous years.

7 What sample size should she use? Use two iterations.

Answers are found in Appendix A.

WHAT CAN GO WRONG?

First, you must decide when to use Student's t methods.

- **Don't confuse proportions and means.** When you treat your data as categorical, counting successes and summarizing with a sample proportion, make inferences using the Normal model methods. When you treat your data as quantitative, summarizing with a sample mean and standard deviation, make your inferences using Student's t methods.

- **Be careful of interpretation when confidence intervals overlap.** If confidence intervals for the means from two groups overlap, don't jump to the conclusion that the means are equal. Use the methods of Chapter 14.

    Student's t methods work only when the Normal population assumption is true. Naturally, many of the ways things can go wrong turn out to be ways that the Normal population assumption can fail. It's always a good idea to look for the most common kinds of failure. It turns out that you can even fix some of them.

- **Beware of multimodality.** The Nearly Normal Condition clearly fails if a histogram of the data has two or more modes. When you see this, look for the possibility that your data come from two groups. If so, your best bet is to try to separate the data into groups. Then you can analyze each group separately.

- **Beware of skewed data.** Make a histogram of the data. If the data are severely skewed, you might try re-expressing the variable. Re-expressing may yield a distribution that is unimodal and symmetric, making it more appropriate for the inference methods for means.

- **Investigate outliers.** The Nearly Normal Condition also fails if the data have outliers. If you find outliers in the data, you need to investigate them. Sometimes, it's obvious that a data value is wrong and the justification for removing or correcting it is clear. When there's no clear justification for removing an outlier, you might want to run the analysis both with and without the outlier and note any differences in your conclusions. Any time data values are set aside, you *must* report on them individually. Often they will turn out to be the most informative part of your report on the data.[5]

---

[5]This suggestion may be controversial in some disciplines. Setting aside outliers is seen by some as unethical because the result is likely to be a narrower confidence interval or a smaller P-value. But an analysis of data with outliers left in place is *always* wrong. The outliers violate the Nearly Normal Condition and also the implicit assumption of a homogeneous population, so they invalidate inference procedures. An analysis of the non-outlying points, along with a separate discussion of the outliers, is often much more informative and can reveal important aspects of the data.

Of course, Normality issues aren't the only risks you face when doing inferences about means.

- **Watch out for bias.** Measurements of all kinds can be biased. If your observations differ from the true mean in a systematic way, your confidence interval may not capture the true mean. And there is no sample size that will save you. A bathroom scale that's five kilograms off will be five kilograms off even if you weigh yourself 100 times and take the average. We've seen several sources of bias in surveys, but measurements can be biased, too. Be sure to think about possible sources of bias in your measurements.

- **Make sure data are independent.** Student's t methods also require the sampled values to be mutually independent. We check for random sampling and the 10% Condition. You should also think hard about whether there are likely violations of independence in the data collection method. If there are, be very cautious about using these methods.

- **Make sure that data are from an appropriately randomized sample.** Ideally, all data we analyze are drawn from a simple random sample or generated by a randomized experiment. When they're not, be careful about making inferences from them. You may still compute a confidence interval correctly or get the mechanics of the P-value right, but this can't save you from making a serious mistake in inference.

ETHICS IN ACTION

The Fraser Institute's 2014 report on hospital waiting lists in Canada indicated that the waiting time between referral from a general practitioner and treatment, averaged across Canada, was 18.2 weeks in 2014. Ontario had the shortest wait time of 14.1 weeks and New Brunswick the longest at 37.3 weeks. Ontario's wait time was 55% longer than it had been in 1993 and New Brunswick's 203% longer. In Quebec, where the wait time is 16.9 weeks, a hospital monitors its wait time in order to demonstrate that it's shorter than an average hospital in the province. A survey of 30 patients gave an average wait time of 12.3 weeks with a standard deviation of 1.4 weeks.

Francis Vachon/Alamy Stock Photo

Further statistical analysis yielded a 95% confidence interval of 11.8 to 12.8 weeks, a clear indication that patients wait less than 16 weeks to get treatment. The hospital issued a press release stating, "Ninety-five percent of our patients wait four weeks less than the provincial average to get treatment."

Ethical Issue *Interpretation of the confidence interval is incorrect and misleading (related to Item C, ASA Ethical Guidelines; see Appendix C, the American Statistical Association's Ethical Guidelines for Statistical Practice, also available online at www.amstat.org/about/ethicalguidelines. cfm). The confidence interval does not provide results for individual patients. So it's incorrect to state that 95% of individual patients wait less (or can expect to wait less) than 13 weeks to get treatment.*

Ethical Solution *Interpret the results of the confidence interval correctly, in terms of the mean waiting time and not individual patients. Also use a one-sided confidence interval if you want a one-sided conclusion. "We are 97.5% sure the average wait time is four weeks less than the provincial average."*

Source: Based on Esmail, N., & Hazel, M., with Walker, M. A. (2008). Waiting your turn: Hospital waiting lists in Canada. Vancouver: Fraser Institute Studies in Health Care Policy.

WHAT HAVE WE LEARNED?

Learning Objectives

❶ We've learned that what we can say about a population mean is inferred from data, using the mean and standard deviation of a representative random sample.

We've learned to describe the sampling distribution of sample means using a model we select from the Student's t family based on our degrees of freedom.

We've learned that our ruler for measuring the variability in sample means is the standard error:

$$SE(\bar{y}) = \frac{s}{\sqrt{n}}.$$

We've learned to find the margin of error for a confidence interval using that standard error ruler and a critical value based on a Student's t-model.

❷ We've also learned to use that ruler to test hypotheses about the population mean.

❸ We've learned how to choose a large enough sample in order to get a desired width of confidence interval.

Terms

Confidence interval for the population mean

$$\bar{y} \pm t^*_{n-1} \times SE(\bar{y}), \text{ where } SE(\bar{y}) = \frac{s}{\sqrt{n}}.$$

The critical value, t^*_{n-1}, depends on the particular confidence level, C, you specify and on the number of degrees of freedom, $n - 1$.

Degrees of freedom (df)   A parameter of the Student's t-distribution that depends on the sample size, df $= n - 1$. Typically, more degrees of freedom reflects increasing information from the sample.

One-sample t-test for the mean   The one-sample t-test for the mean tests the hypothesis $H_0 : \mu = \mu_0$ using the statistic $t_{n-1} = \dfrac{\bar{y} - \mu_0}{SE(\bar{y})}$, where $SE(\bar{y}) = \dfrac{s}{\sqrt{n}}$.

Student's t   A family of distributions is indexed by its degrees of freedom. The t-models are unimodal, symmetric, and bell-shaped, but generally have fatter tails and a narrower centre than the Normal model. As the degrees of freedom increase, t-distributions approach the Normal model.

Skills

Plan
- Be able to state the assumptions required for t-tests and t-based confidence intervals.
- Know to examine your data for violations of conditions that would make inference about the population mean unwise or invalid.
- Understand that a hypothesis test can be performed with an appropriately chosen confidence interval.

Do
- Know how to compute and interpret a t-test for the population mean using a statistics software package or by working from summary statistics for a sample.
- Know how to compute and interpret a t-based confidence interval for the population mean using a statistics software package or by working from summary statistics for a sample.

Report
- Be able to explain the meaning of a confidence interval for a population mean. Make clear that the randomness associated with the confidence level is a statement about the interval bounds and not about the population parameter value.
- Understand that a 95% confidence interval does not trap 95% of the sample values.
- Be able to interpret the result of a test of a hypothesis about a population mean.
- Know that we don't "accept" a null hypothesis if we can't reject it. We say that we fail to reject it.
- Understand that the P-value of a test doesn't give the probability that the null hypothesis is correct.

MINI case studies

Citizens Bank of Canada

Citizens Bank of Canada operates a credit card program that supports not-for-profit initiatives aimed at effecting positive environmental and social change. The Shared Interest VISA card has no annual fee, and each time it's used 10 cents is donated to a pool of not-for-profits.

Suppose you work for another credit card issuer and your vice-president is considering launching a competing "enviro-social" credit card. You're assigned to assess the market for such a card. Evidently a card of this type doesn't appeal to everyone, so you decide to focus initially on just one market, "Young Technocrats," for which you have some demographic information. Made up of recent graduates like yourself, this group is motivated to support issues like the environment, which they learned more about while at university. Moreover, they've postponed starting a family and can therefore afford to support causes they believe in with the high disposable income from their median $82,000 earnings.

You test-market the "enviro-social" card to 25 Young Technocrats who already use another of your company's cards. Some of them sign up for the new card, and in the next three months average $526 per month in spending on the new card and $89 on their other card(s). Young Technocrats as a whole, when previously using other cards, averaged $496 per month. These results look good for the new card, but the words of your vice-president at the end of the last meeting echo in your ears: "I don't want cardholders to reduce the total money they put through our cards, and I don't want test-market results spread more than 10% on either side of the mean, but I do want numbers on spending." In order to get a narrow spread in the test-market results, you get funding to increase your sample from 25 people, monitor their spending for three months, and get the figures in the following table:

Sample Size	25	50	75	100
Total monthly spending				
New "enviro-social" card	526	591	497	576
Other card(s)	89	56	132	79
Total	615	647	629	655
Standard Deviation of Total	318	341	311	322

Your manager wants a report so that she can give the vice-president an update on progress. "He's getting impatient, and he wants a look at some graphs, not vast tables of numbers," she says. Give a clear statistical interpretation (based on 95% confidence intervals) of what you think the vice-president means by "[not] spread more than 10% on either side of the mean," and write a brief report indicating whether the new card should be introduced. Criticize the method of successively increasing the sample size to get the confidence interval narrow enough. Choose the sample size by another method based on the results from the initial sample of size 25.

(continued)

Megapress/Alamy Stock Photo

Sparton Resources of Toronto

Craig Hanson/Shutterstock

Climate-change concerns are resulting in investment in fuels that don't produce greenhouse gases. Although solar and wind power garner a lot of attention, nuclear power from uranium is also a possibility. China is investing in nuclear power, and even countries such as Sweden that previously banned nuclear power are also building reactors. The world has limited uranium ores, which has prompted Sparton Resources of Toronto to look for alternatives. Coal contains small concentrations of uranium, and the ash that's left when coal is burned in a coal-fired power station contains uranium at a higher concentration. Sparton has developed technology for extracting uranium from coal ash, with initial implementation at Lincang in Yunnan Province in China.

The coal used in Lincang has an exceptionally high uranium concentration, making it more economical to extract uranium from the ash than in most other parts of the world. However, the concentration is also very variable, ranging from 20 to 315 parts per million. The average concentration in the ash is 0.46 pounds of uranium oxide per tonne.

Suppose the data file (**ch13_MCSP_Sparton_Resources**) gives concentrations of uranium oxide in the coal ash from random samples taken in eight different locations. In order to be economic, on the basis of long-term contract prices of uranium oxide, Sparton requires an average concentration of at least 0.32 pounds per tonne. Suppose Sparton can fund two extraction plants. Use hypothesis testing to recommend which locations it should choose. Which third location should management investigate, even though the hypothesis test isn't significant? Give a reason for your choice.

Real Estate

A real estate agent is trying to understand the pricing of homes in her area, a region in the United States comprising small to midsize towns and a small city. For each of 1200 homes recently sold in the region, the file **ch13_MCSP_Real_Estate** holds the following variables:

- *Sale Price* (in $)
- *Lot Size* (size of the lot in acres)
- *Waterfront* (Yes, No)
- *Age* (in years)
- *Central Air* (Yes, No)
- *Fuel Type* (Wood, Oil, Gas, Electric, Propane, Solar, Other)
- *Condition* (1 to 5; 1 = Poor, 5 = Excellent)
- *Living Area* (in square feet)
- *Pct College* (% in zip code who attend a four-year college)
- *Full Baths* (number of full bathrooms)
- *Half Baths* (number of half bathrooms)
- *Bedrooms* (number of bedrooms)
- *Fireplaces* (number of fireplaces)

The agent has a family interested in a four-bedroom house. Using confidence intervals, how should she advise the family on what the average price of a four-bedroom house might be in this area? Compare that with a confidence interval for two-bedroom homes. How does the presence of central air conditioning affect the mean price of houses in this area? Use confidence intervals and graphics to help answer that question.

Explore other questions that might be useful for the real estate agent in knowing how different categorical factors affect the sale price, and write up a short report on your findings.

Donor Profiles

A philanthropic organization collects and buys data on its donor base. The full database contains about 4.5 million donors and over 400 variables collected on each, but the data set **ch13_MCSP_Donor_Profiles** is a sample of 916 donors and includes the following variables:

- *Age* (in years)
- *Homeowner* (H = Yes, U = Unknown)
- *Gender* (F = Female, M = Male, U = Unknown)
- *Wealth* (ordered categories of total household wealth from 1 = Lowest to 9 = Highest)
- *Children* (number of children)
- *Donated Last* (0 = Did not donate to last campaign, 1 = Did donate to last campaign)
- *Amt Donated Last* ($ amount of contribution to last campaign)

The analysts at the organization want to know how much people donate on average to campaigns, and what factors might influence that amount. Compare the confidence intervals for the mean *Amt Donated Last* by those known to own their homes with those whose homeowner status is unknown. Perform similar comparisons for *Gender* and two of the *Wealth* categories. Write up a short report using graphics and confidence intervals for what you've found. (Be careful not to make inferences directly about the differences between groups. We'll discuss that in Chapter 14. Your inference should be about single groups.)

(The distribution of *Amt Donated Last* is highly skewed to the right, so the median might be thought to be the appropriate summary. But the median is $0.00, so the analysts must use the mean. From simulations, they've ascertained that the sampling distribution for the mean is unimodal and symmetric for samples larger than 250 or so. Note that small differences in the mean could result in millions of dollars of added revenue nationwide. The average cost of their solicitation is $0.67 per person to produce and mail.)

MyStatLab Students! Save time, improve your grades with MyStatLab. Questions marked in ▉ can be found on MyStatLab. You can practise them as often as you want, and most feature step-by-step guided solutions to help you find the right answer. You'll find a personalized study plan available to you too!

Technology Help: Inference for Means

Statistics packages offer convenient ways to make histograms of data. That means you have no excuse for skipping the check that the data are nearly Normal.

Any standard statistics package can compute a hypothesis test. Here's what the package output might look like in general (although no package we know gives the results in exactly this form):

(continued)

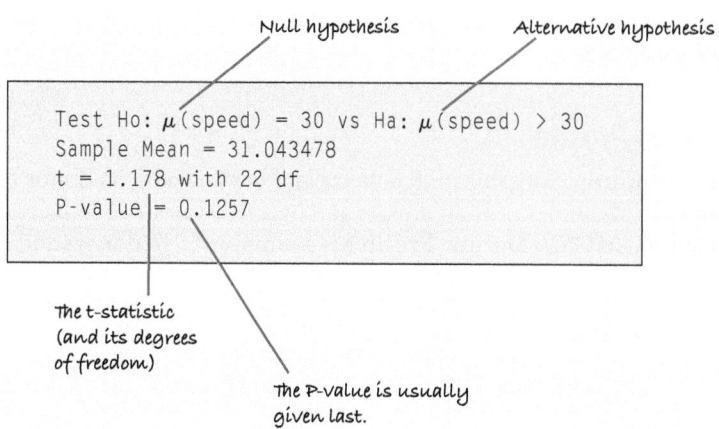

The package computes the sample mean and sample standard deviation of the variable and finds the P-value from the t-distribution based on the appropriate number of degrees of freedom. All modern statistics packages report P-values. The package may also provide additional information such as the sample mean, the sample standard deviation, the t-statistic value, and the degrees of freedom. These are useful for interpreting the resulting P-value.

Inference results are also sometimes reported in a table. You may have to read carefully to find the values you need. Often, test results and the corresponding confidence interval bounds are given together. And often you must read carefully to find the alternative hypothesis. Here's an example of that kind of output:

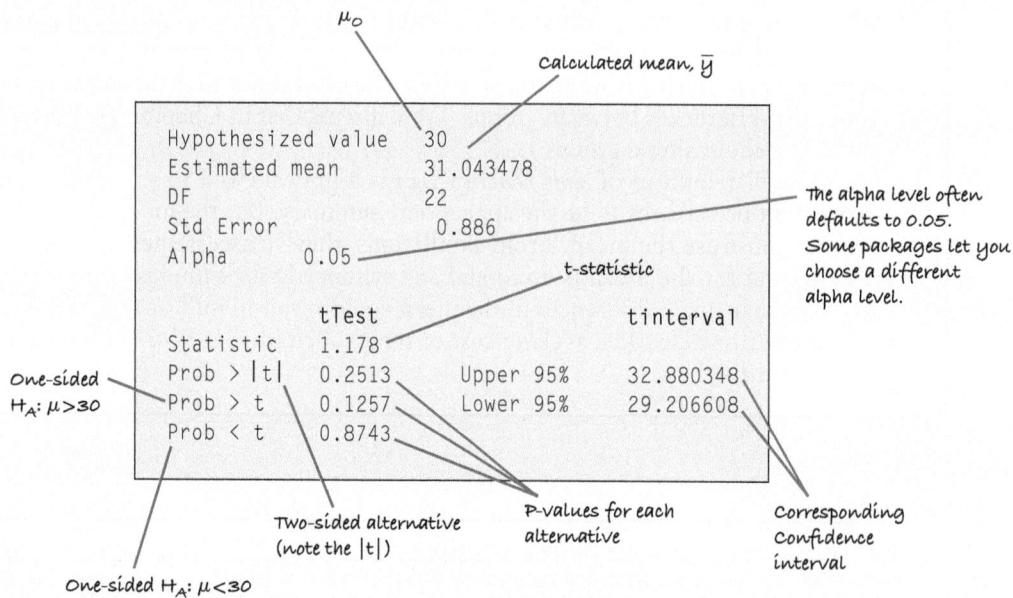

EXCEL

To find a one-sample t-interval and one-sample t-test for the mean using Excel, follow these examples:

	A	B	C	D	E	F
1	t-Estimate of a Mean					
2						
3	Sample mean	15.02	Confidence Interval Estimate			Syntax for Column E
4	Sample standard deviation	8.31	15.02	±	1.81	=ABS(T.INV((1-B6)/2,(B5-1))*(B4/B5^0.5))
5	Sample size	83	Lower confidence limit		13.21	=B3-E4
6	Confidence level	0.95	Upper confidence limit		16.83	=B3+E4

▲	A	B	C	D	E
1	t-Test of a Mean				
2					Syntax for Column D
3	Sample mean	460.38	t Stat	1.89	=(B3-B6)/(B4/B5^0.5)
4	Sample standard deviation	38.83	P(T<=t) one-tail	0.0323	=1-(T.DIST(ABS(D3),(B5-1),1))
5	Sample size	50	t Critical lower one-tail	-1.6766	=T.INV(B7,B5-1)
6	Hypothesized mean	450	t Critical upper one tail	1.6766	=ABS(T.INV(B7,B5-1))
7	Alpha	0.05	P(T<=t) two-tail	0.0646	=2*D4
8			t Critical two-tail	± 2.0096	=T.INV(B7/2,B5-1)

XLSTAT

To find a one-sample z-interval or a one-sample t-interval:

- Choose **Parametric Tests**, and then **One-sample t-test and z-test**.
- Under the **General** tab, enter your data cell range and choose either **z-test** or **Student's t test**.
- On the **Options** tab, choose the **Alternative hypothesis** of **Mean 1 ≠ Theoretical mean**.
- For calculating just a confidence interval, you can leave the **Theoretical mean** field blank. If you are also conducting a hypothesis test, enter in the theoretical mean here.
- Under **Significance Level**, enter in the desired level of significance. The output will yield the $(1 - a)100\%$ confidence level.

　　To conduct a one-mean z-test or a one-mean t-test:

- Choose **Parametric Tests**, and then **One-sample t-test and z-test**.
- Complete the dialogue box as you did for a confidence interval.
- Fill in the field for **Theoretical mean** with the population mean from your null hypothesis.

MINITAB

To perform a z-test and z-interval or t-test and t-interval in Minitab:

From the Stat menu, choose the **Basic Statistics** submenu.

From that menu, choose:

- **1-sample Z**… for a z-interval or z-test
- **1-sample t**… for a t-interval or t-test

Then fill in the dialog:

- If a hypothesis test is desired, check **Perform hypothesis test** and enter the population mean.
- Click **Options** and set confidence level and alternative hypothesis.

Comments

The dialogue offers a clear choice between confidence interval and hypothesis test. Notice that Minitab also offers the opportunity to calculate the test or confidence interval by entering summarized data.

JMP

To find a confidence interval and perform a hypothesis test using JMP:

- From the **Analyze** menu, select **Distribution**.
- Drag the column containing the data into the **Y, Columns** box and press **OK**.
- The upper and lower limits of the 95% confidence interval can be found in the "Summary Statistics" section. (Be sure that your variables are "Continuous" type so that this section will be available.)
- To perform a t-test for the mean, click the arrow next to the variable name and choose **Test Mean**.

Comments

Choosing **Confidence Interval** in the expanded menu under the arrow next to the variable name allows for confidence levels other than 95%. In **Test Mean**, one can also run a z-test for the mean by providing a known standard deviation.

SPSS

To find a t-interval in SPSS:

- From the Analyze Menu, choose **Descriptive Statistics**.
- Choose **Explore**.
- Click the **Statistics** button to change confidence level and choose **Statistics** only if no plots are desired.

To perform a t-test in SPSS:

- From the Analyze menu, choose the **Compare Means** submenu.
- Choose the **One-Sample t-test** command.
- Select the column containing data and enter the test value for the mean.

EXERCISES

SECTION 13.1

1. A survey of 25 randomly selected customers at an internet music site found the following ages (in years):

20	32	34	29	30
30	30	14	29	11
38	22	44	48	26
25	22	32	35	32
35	42	44	44	48

The mean is 31.84 years and the standard deviation is 9.84 years.
a) What is the standard error of the mean?
b) How would the standard error change if the sample size had been 100 instead of 25? (Assume that the sample standard deviation didn't change.) **LO ❶, ❷**

2. A random sample of 20 purchases at the internet music site in Exercise 1 shows the following amounts (in $):

39.05	2.73	32.92	47.51
37.91	34.35	64.48	51.96
56.95	81.58	47.80	11.72
21.57	40.83	38.24	32.98
75.16	74.30	47.54	65.62

The mean is $45.26 and the standard deviation is $20.67.
a) What is the standard error of the mean?
b) How would the standard error change if the sample size had been 5 instead of 20? (Assume that the sample standard deviation didn't change.) **LO ❶, ❷**

3. For the data in Exercise 1:
a) How many degrees of freedom does the t-statistic have?
b) How many degrees of freedom would the t-statistic have if the sample size had been 100? **LO ❶, ❷**

4. For the data in Exercise 2:
a) How many degrees of freedom does the t-statistic have?
b) How many degrees of freedom would the t-statistic have if the sample size had been 5? **LO ❶, ❷**

SECTION 13.2

5. For the ages in Exercise 1:
a) Construct a 95% confidence interval for the mean age of all customers, assuming that the assumptions and conditions for the confidence interval have been met.
b) How large is the margin of error?

c) How would the confidence interval change if you had assumed that the standard deviation was known to be 10.0 years? **LO ❶**

6. For the purchase amounts in Exercise 2:
a) Construct a 90% confidence interval for the mean purchases of all customers, assuming that the assumptions and conditions for the confidence interval have been met.
b) How large is the margin of error?
c) How would the confidence interval change if you had assumed that the standard deviation was known to be $20? **LO ❶**

SECTION 13.3

7. For the confidence intervals of Exercise 5, a histogram of the data looks like this:

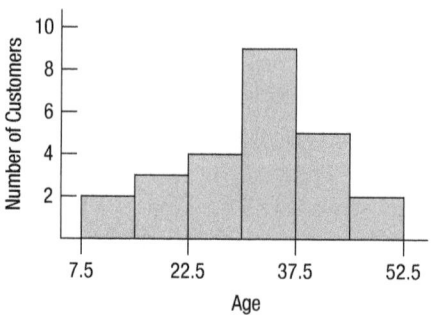

Check the assumptions and conditions for your inference. **LO ❶, ❷**

8. For confidence intervals of Exercise 6, a histogram of the data looks like this:

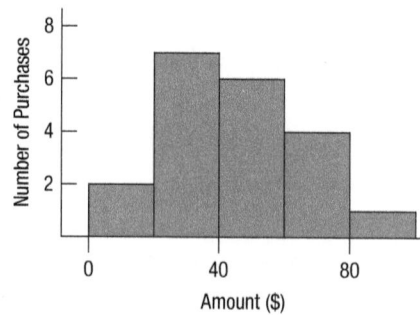

Check the assumptions and conditions for your inference. **LO ❶, ❷**

SECTION 13.4

9. A feed supply company has developed a special feed supplement to see if it will promote weight gain in livestock. Its researchers report that the 77 cows studied gained an average of 56 pounds and that a 95% confidence interval for the mean weight gain this supplement produces has a margin of error of ±11 pounds. Staff in the company's Marketing Department wrote the following conclusions. Did anyone interpret the interval correctly? Explain any misinterpretations.

a) 95% of the cows studied gained between 45 and 67 pounds.
b) We're 95% sure that a cow fed this supplement will gain between 45 and 67 pounds.
c) We're 95% sure that the average weight gain among the cows in this study was between 45 and 67 pounds.
d) The average weight gain of cows fed this supplement is between 45 and 67 pounds 95% of the time.
e) If this supplement is tested on another sample of cows, there's a 95% chance that their average weight gain will be between 45 and 67 pounds. **LO ❶**

10. A company is interested in estimating the costs of lunch in its cafeteria. After surveying employees, the staff calculated that a 95% confidence interval for the mean amount of money spent for lunch over a period of six months is ($780, $920). Now the organization is trying to write its report and is considering the following interpretations. Comment on each.

a) 95% of all employees pay between $780 and $920 for lunch.
b) 95% of the sampled employees pay between $780 and $920 for lunch.
c) We're 95% sure that employees in this sample average between $780 and $920 for lunch.
d) 95% of all samples of employees have average lunch costs between $780 and $920.
e) We're 95% sure that the average amount all employees pay for lunch is between $780 and $920. **LO ❶**

SECTION 13.5

11. The owner of the internet music site from Exercise 1 wants to know if the mean age of all customers is 25 years old.

a) What is the null hypothesis?
b) Is the alternative one- or two-sided?
c) What is the value of the test statistic?
d) What is the P-value of the test statistic?
e) What do you conclude at $\alpha = 0.05$?
f) Given the confidence interval you found in Exercise 5, what might you have concluded? Explain. **LO ❶, ❷**

12. The analyst in Exercise 2 wants to know if the mean purchase amount of all transactions is at least $40.

a) What is the null hypothesis?
b) Is the alternative one- or two-sided?
c) What is the value of the test statistic?

d) What is the P-value of the test statistic?
e) What do you conclude at $\alpha = 0.05$?
f) Given the confidence interval you found in Exercise 6, what might you have concluded? Explain. **LO ❶, ❷**

SECTION 13.6

13. For the confidence interval in Exercise 5:

a) How large would the sample size have to be to cut the margin of error in half?
b) About how large would the sample size have to be to cut the margin of error by a factor of 10? **LO ❸**

14. For the confidence interval in Exercise 6:

a) To reduce the margin of error to about $4, how large would the sample size have to be?
b) How large would the sample size have to be to reduce the margin of error to $0.80? **LO ❸**

CHAPTER EXERCISES

15. *t*-models, part 1. Using the *t* tables, software, or a calculator, estimate the following:

a) The critical value of *t* for a 90% confidence interval with df = 17.
b) The critical value of *t* for a 98% confidence interval with df = 88.
c) The P-value for $t \geq 2.09$ with 4 degrees of freedom.
d) The P-value for $t > 1.78$ with 22 degrees of freedom. **LO ❶**

16. *t*-models, part 2. Using the *t* tables, software, or a calculator, estimate the following:

a) The critical value of *t* for a 95% confidence interval with df = 7.
b) The critical value of *t* for a 99% confidence interval with df = 102.
c) The P-value for $t \leq 2.19$ with 41 degrees of freedom.
d) The P-value for $t > 2.33$ with 12 degrees of freedom. **LO ❶**

17. Confidence intervals, part 1. Describe how the width of a 95% confidence interval for a mean changes as the standard deviation (*s*) of a sample increases, assuming sample size remains the same. **LO ❶**

18. Confidence intervals, part 2. Describe how the width of a 95% confidence interval for a mean changes as the sample size (*n*) increases, assuming the standard deviation remains the same. **LO ❶**

19. Confidence intervals and sample size, part 1. A confidence interval for the price of gasoline from a random sample of 30 gas stations in a region gives the following statistics:

$$\bar{y} = \$1.49 \quad s = \$0.18$$

a) Find a 95% confidence interval for the mean price of regular gasoline in that region.
b) Find the 90% confidence interval for the mean.
c) If we had the same statistics from a sample of 60 stations, what would the 95% confidence interval be? **LO ❶**

20. Confidence intervals and sample size, part 2. A confidence interval for the price of gasoline from a random sample of 30 gas stations in a region gives the following statistics:

$$\bar{y} = \$1.29 \quad SE(\bar{y}) = \$0.06$$

a) Find a 95% confidence interval for the mean price of regular gasoline in that region.
b) Find the 90% confidence interval for the mean.
c) If we had the same statistics from a sample of 60 stations, what would the 95% confidence interval be? **LO ❶**

21. CEO compensation. A sample of 20 CEOs from the Forbes 500 shows total annual compensations ranging from a minimum of $0.1 million to $62.24 million. The average for these 20 CEOs is $7.946 million. The histogram and boxplot are as follows:

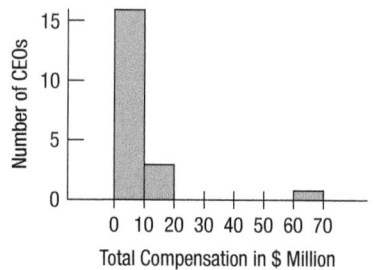

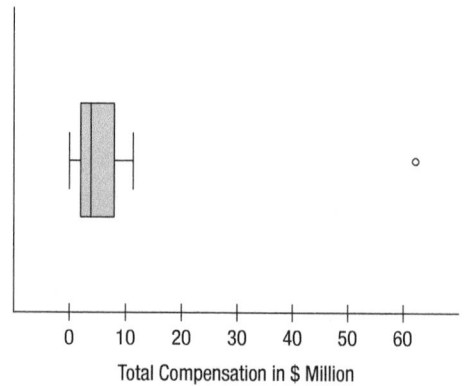

Based on these data, a computer program found that a 95% confidence interval for the mean annual compensation of all Forbes 500 CEOs is (1.69, 14.20) $ million. Why should you be hesitant to trust this confidence interval? **LO ❶**

22. Credit card charges. A credit card company takes a random sample of 100 cardholders to see how much they charged on their card last month. A histogram and boxplot are as follows:

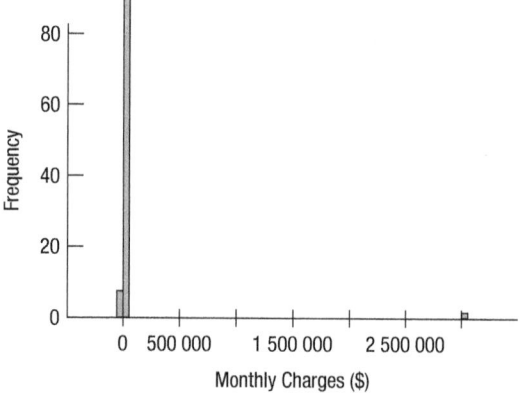

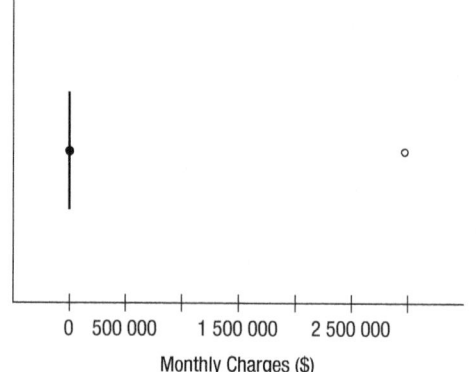

A computer program found that the 95% confidence interval for the mean amount spent last month is (–$28,366.84, $90,691.49). Explain why the analysts didn't find the confidence interval useful, and explain what went wrong. **LO ❶**

23. Parking, part 1. Hoping to attract more shoppers downtown, a city builds a new public parking garage in the central business district. The city plans to pay for the structure through parking fees. For a random sample of 44 weekdays, daily fees collected averaged $12,600 with a standard deviation of $1500.

a) What assumptions must you make in order to use these statistics for inference?
b) Find a 90% confidence interval for the mean daily income this parking garage will generate.
c) Explain in context what this confidence interval means.
d) Explain what 90% confidence means in this context.
e) The consultant who advised the city on this project predicted that parking revenues would average $12,800 per day. Based on your confidence interval, what do you think of the consultant's prediction? Why? **LO ❶**

24. Housing, part 1. When homeowners fail to make mortgage payments, the bank forecloses and sells the home, often at a loss. In one large community, realtors randomly sampled 36 bids from potential buyers to determine the average loss in home value. The sample showed that the average loss was $11,560 with a standard deviation of $1500.

a) What assumptions and conditions must be checked before finding a confidence interval? How would you check them?

b) Find a 95% confidence interval for the mean loss in value per home.

c) Interpret this interval and explain what 95% confidence means.

d) Suppose that, nationally, the average loss in home values at this time was $10,000. Do you think the loss in the sampled community differs significantly from the national average? Explain. **LO ❶**

25. Parking, part 2. Suppose that for budget planning purposes the city in Exercise 23 needs a better estimate of the mean daily income from parking fees.

a) Someone suggests that the city use its data to create a 95% confidence interval instead of the 90% interval first created. How would this interval be better for the city? (You need not actually create the new interval.)

b) How would the 95% confidence interval be worse for the planners?

c) How could the city achieve a confidence interval estimate that would better serve its planning needs? **LO ❶**

26. Housing, part 2. In Exercise 24, we found a 95% confidence interval to estimate the loss in home values.

a) Suppose the standard deviation of the losses was $3000 instead of the $1500 used for that interval. What would the larger standard deviation do to the width of the confidence interval (assuming the same level of confidence)?

b) Your classmate suggests that the margin of error in the interval could be reduced if the confidence level were changed to 90% instead of 95%. Do you agree with this statement? Why or why not?

c) Instead of changing the level of confidence, would it be more statistically appropriate to draw a bigger sample? **LO ❶**

27. Provincial budgets, part 1. Provinces that rely on sales tax for revenue to fund education, public safety, and other programs often end up with budget surpluses during economic growth periods (when people spend more on consumer goods) and budget deficits during recessions (when people spend less on consumer goods). Fifty-one small retailers in a province with a growing economy were recently sampled. The sample showed a mean increase of $2350 in additional sales tax revenue collected per retailer compared with the previous quarter. The sample standard deviation = $425.

a) Find a 95% confidence interval for the mean increase in sales tax revenue.

b) What assumptions have you made in this inference? Do you think the appropriate conditions have been satisfied?

c) Explain what your interval means and provide an example of what it doesn't mean. **LO ❶**

28. Provincial budgets, part 2. Suppose the province in Exercise 27 sampled 16 small retailers instead of 51, and for the sample of 16, the sample mean increase again equalled $2350 in additional sales tax revenue collected per retailer compared with the previous quarter. Also assume the sample standard deviation = $425.

a) What is the standard error of the mean increase in sales tax revenue collected?

b) What happens to the accuracy of the estimate when the interval is constructed using the smaller sample size?

c) Find and interpret a 95% confidence interval.

d) How does the margin of error for the interval constructed in Exercise 27 compare with the margin of error constructed in this exercise? Explain statistically how sample size changes the accuracy of the constructed interval. Which sample would you prefer if you were a provincial budget planner? Why? **LO ❶**

29. Ecommerce, part 1. A market researcher at a major clothing company decides to investigate whether the amount of online sales has increased. She compares the mean monthly online sales of a random selection of recent months with a historical figure for mean monthly sales for online purchases. She gets a P-value of 0.01. Explain in this context what the 1% represents. **LO ❷**

Ⓣ **30.** Math education: Canada and OECD. The OECD conducts the Program for International Student Assessment and in 2012 tested 510,000 15-year-old high school students in 65 countries to assess their performance in math, reading, and science. The results are in the data file for the countries whose average score was 500 or more in math. We wish to test whether Canada's score of 518 in math is significantly above 500.

a) Check the assumptions and conditions for performing a hypothesis test on these data.

b) State the hypotheses.

c) What additional information do you need in order to perform the test? **LO ❶, ❷**

31. Ecommerce, part 2. The average age of online consumers a few years ago was 23.3 years. As older individuals gain confidence with the internet, it is believed that the average age has increased. We would like to test this belief.

a) Write appropriate hypotheses.

b) We plan to test the null hypothesis by selecting a random sample of 40 individuals who made an online purchase during 2017. Do you think the necessary assumptions for inference are satisfied? Explain.

c) The online shoppers in our sample had an average age of 24.2 years with a standard deviation of 5.3 years. What's the P-value for this result?

d) Explain (in context) what this P-value means.

e) What's your conclusion? **LO ❷**

Ⓣ **32.** Popcorn. Pop's Popcorn, Inc. needs to determine the optimum power and time settings for its new licorice-flavoured microwave popcorn. Management wants to find a combination of power and time that delivers high-quality popcorn with less than 10% of the kernels left unpopped, on average—a value that market research says is demanded by the company's customers. Its research department experiments with several settings and determines that power nine at four minutes is optimum. Its tests confirm that this setting meets the less-than-10% requirement. The company changes the instructions on the box and promotes a new money-back guarantee of less than 10% unpopped kernels.

a) If, in fact, the setting results in more than 10% kernels unpopped, what kind of error has the company made? What will the consequence be for the company?

b) To reduce the risk of making an error, the president (Pop himself) tells the researchers to test eight more bags of popcorn (selected at random) at the specified setting. They find the following percentage of unpopped kernels: 7, 13.2, 10, 6, 7.8, 2.8, 2.2, 5.2. Does this provide evidence that the setting meets the goal of less than 10% unpopped? Explain. **LO❷**

T 33. Chips Ahoy. In 1998, as an advertising campaign, the Nabisco Company announced a "1000 Chips Challenge," claiming that every 18-ounce bag of its Chips Ahoy cookies contained at least 1000 chocolate chips. Dedicated Statistics students at the Air Force Academy (no kidding) purchased some randomly selected bags of cookies and counted the chocolate chips. Some of their data are given below (**Source:** *Chance, 12*, no. 1 [1999]).

1219	1214	1087	1200	1419	1121	1325	1345
1244	1258	1356	1132	1191	1270	1295	1135

a) Check the assumptions and conditions for inference. Comment on any concerns you have.

b) Create a 95% confidence interval for the average number of chips in bags of Chips Ahoy cookies.

c) What does this evidence say about Nabisco's claim? **LO❶**

T 34. Consumer Reports. *Consumer Reports* tested 14 brands of vanilla yogurt and found the following numbers of calories per serving: 160, 200, 220, 230, 120, 180, 140, 130, 170, 190, 80, 120, 100, and 170.

a) Check the assumptions and conditions for inference.

b) Create a 95% confidence interval for the average calorie content of vanilla yogurt.

c) A diet guide claims that you'll get 120 calories from a serving of vanilla yogurt. What does this evidence indicate? Use your confidence interval to test an appropriate hypothesis and state your conclusion. **LO❶**

T 35. Investment. Investment style plays a role in constructing a mutual fund. Many individual stocks can be grouped into two distinct categories: growth and value. A growth stock is one with high earning potential and often pays little or no dividends to shareholders. Conversely, value stocks are commonly viewed as steady or more conservative stocks with a lower earning potential. A family is

trying to decide what type of funds to invest in. An independent advisor claims that value mutual funds provided an annualized return of greater than 8% over a recent five-year period. Below are the summary statistics for the five-year return for a random sample of such value funds:

Variable	N	Mean	SE Mean	StDev
5-yr Return	35	8.418	0.493	2.916

	Minimum	Q1	Median	Q3	Maximum
	2.190	6.040	7.980	10.840	14.320

Test the hypothesis that the mean five-year return for value funds is greater than 8%, assuming a significance level of 5%. What does this evidence say about the independent advisor's claim that the annualized five-year return was greater than 8%? State your conclusion. **LO❷**

T 36. Manufacturing. A tire manufacturer is considering a newly designed tread pattern for its all-weather tires. Tests have indicated that these tires will provide better fuel efficiency and longer tread life. The last remaining test is for braking effectiveness. The company hopes the tire will allow a car travelling at 80 kilometres per hour to come to a complete stop within an average of 35 metres after the brakes are applied. It will adopt the new tread pattern unless there is strong evidence that the tires do not meet this objective. The distances (in metres) for 10 stops on a test track were 41.5, 41, 37, 36.5, 38.2, 39.1, 40.2, 39.3, 37.1, and 38.0. Should the company adopt the new tread pattern? Test an appropriate hypothesis and state your conclusion. Explain why you made the recommendation you did. **LO❷**

37. Collections, part 1. Credit card companies lose money on cardholders who fail to pay their minimum payments. They use a variety of methods to encourage their delinquent cardholders to pay their credit card balances, such as letters, phone calls, and eventually, the hiring of a collection agency. To justify the cost of using the collection agency, the agency must collect an average of at least $200 per customer. After a trial period during which the agency attempted to collect from a random sample of 100 delinquent cardholders, the 90% confidence interval on the mean collected amount was reported as ($190.25, $250.75). Given this, what recommendation(s) would you make to the credit card company about using the collection agency? **LO❶**

38. Free gift, part 1. A philanthropic organization sends out "free gifts" to people on its mailing list in the hope that the receiver will respond by sending back a donation. Typical gifts are mailing labels, greeting cards, or postcards. The organization wants to test out a new gift that costs $0.50 per item to produce and mail. It mails the gift to a "small" sample of 2000 customers and finds a 90% confidence interval of the mean donation to be ($0.489, $0.879). As a consultant, what recommendation(s) would you make to the organization about using this gift? **LO❶**

39. Collections, part 2. The owner of the collection agency in Exercise 37 is quite certain that the agency can collect more than $200 per customer on average. He urges that the credit card company run a larger trial. Do you think a larger trial might help the company make a better decision? Explain. **LO ❸**

40. Free gift, part 2. The philanthropic organization of Exercise 38 decided to go ahead with the new gift. In mailings to 98,000 prospects, the new mailing yielded an average of $0.78. If the company had decided based on its initial trial *not* to use this gift, what kind of error would it have made? What aspects of the initial trial might have suggested to you (as the consultant) that a larger trial would be worthwhile?

41. Batteries. A battery company claims that its batteries last an average of 100 hours under normal use. There have been several complaints that the batteries don't last that long, so an independent testing agency is engaged to test them. For the 16 batteries the agency tested, the mean lifetime was 97 hours with a standard deviation of 12 hours.

a) What are the null and alternative hypotheses?
b) A consumer advocate (who does not know Statistics) says that 97 hours is a lot less than the advertised 100 hours, so we should reject the company's claim. Explain to him the problem with doing that.
c) What assumptions must we make in order to proceed with inference?
d) At a 5% level of significance, what do you conclude?
e) Suppose that, in fact, the average life of the company's batteries is only 98 hours. Has an error been made in (d)? If so, what kind? **LO ❷**

42. Pet breeding. Fancy pets are big business, so a young entrepreneur (age 12) decided to breed golden hamsters, a type well known to pet stores and collectors. (Oddly enough, nearly all the golden hamsters in captivity are descendants of one litter found in Syria in 1930.) Of 47 recent litters, there were an average of 7.27 baby hamsters with a standard deviation of 2.5 hamsters per litter.

a) Find and interpret a 90% confidence interval for the mean litter size.
b) How much smaller or larger would the margin of error be for a 99% confidence interval? Explain.
c) Based on these statistics, how many litters would we need to estimate the mean litter size to within one baby hamster with 95% confidence? **LO ❶, ❸**

43. Fish production. Farmed salmon is much cheaper to bring to market than salmon caught in the wild, but consumers are concerned about several issues recently publicized about farmed salmon, including the type of food they are fed and the contaminants found in their meat (see www.healthcastle.com). Among the contaminants are such compounds as polychlorinated biphenyls (PCBs), dioxins, toxaphene, dieldrin, hexachlorobenzene, lindane, heptachlor epoxide, cis-nonachlor, trans-nonachlor, gamma-chlordane, alpha-chlordane, Mirex, endrin, and DDT.

The EPA recommends that salmon contain no more than 0.08 ppm of the insecticide Mirex. A local environmental group is considering a boycott of salmon if it exceeds 0.08 ppm. A 95% confidence interval based on a sample of farmed salmon from a random sample of 150 different salmon farms (*Source: Science, 9*, January 2004) is found to be 0.0834 to 0.0992 ppm. The data were unimodal and symmetric, with no outliers.

a) Is there evidence that the farms are producing salmon with mean Mirex contamination higher than the EPA recommended amount? Your explanation should discuss the confidence level, the P-value, and the decision.
b) Discuss the two types of errors that can be made in the context of a business decision of whether to prohibit the producers from selling their salmon. **LO ❶, ❷**

Ⓣ 44. Cell phone batteries. A company that produces cell phones claims its standard phone battery lasts longer on average than other batteries in the market. To support this claim, the company publishes an ad reporting the results of a recent experiment showing that under normal usage, its batteries last at least 35 hours. To investigate this claim, a consumer advocacy group asked the company for the raw data. The company sends the group the following results:

$$35, 34, 32, 31, 34, 34, 32, 33, 35, 55, 32, 31$$

Test an appropriate hypothesis and state your conclusion:
a) including the outlier,
b) excluding the outlier. What should be done about the outlier? **LO ❷**

45. Growth and air pollution. Government officials have difficulty attracting new business to communities with troubled reputations. Nevada has been one of the fastest-growing states in the United States for a number of years. Accompanying the rapid growth are massive new construction projects. Since Nevada has a dry climate, the construction creates visible dust pollution. High pollution levels may paint a less than attractive picture of the area, and can also result in fines levied by the U.S. federal government. As required by government regulation, researchers continually monitor pollution levels. In the most recent test of pollution levels, 121 air samples were collected. The dust particulate levels must be reported to the federal regulatory agencies. In the report sent to the federal agency, it was noted that the mean particulate level = 57.6 micrograms/cubic litre of air, and the 95% confidence interval estimate is 52.06 mg to 63.07 mg. A graph of the distribution of the particulate amounts was also included and is shown below:

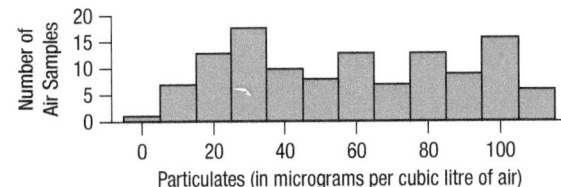

a) Discuss the assumptions and conditions for using Student's *t*-inference methods with these data.

b) Do you think the confidence interval noted in the report is valid? Briefly explain why or why not. **LO ❷**

46. **Convention revenues.** At one time, Nevada was the only U.S. state that allowed gambling. Although gambling continues to be one of the major industries in Nevada, the proliferation of legalized gambling in other areas of the country has required state and local governments to look at other growth possibilities. The convention and visitors' authorities in many Nevada cities actively recruit national conventions that bring thousands of visitors to the state. Various demographic and economic data are collected from surveys given to convention attendees. One statistic of interest is the amount visitors spend on slot machine gambling. Nevada often reports the slot machine expenditure as amount spent per hotel guest room. A recent survey of 500 visitors asked how much they spent on gambling. The average expenditure per room was $180.

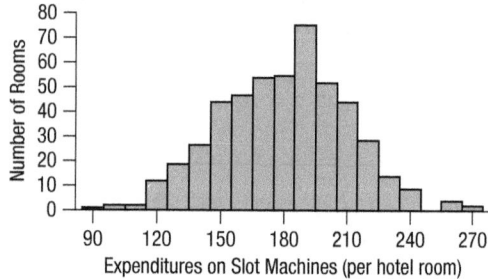

Casinos will use the information reported in the survey to estimate slot machine expenditure per hotel room. Do you think the estimates produced by the survey will accurately represent expenditures? Explain, using the statistics reported and the graph shown. **LO ❶**

47. **Traffic speed, part 1.** Police departments often try to control traffic speed by using speed-measuring machines that tell motorists how fast they're driving. Traffic safety experts must determine where machines should be placed. In one recent test, police recorded the average speed clocked by cars driving on one busy street close to an elementary school. For a sample of 25 speeds, it was determined that the average amount over the speed limit for the 25 clocked speeds was 11.6 kilometres per hour with a standard deviation of 8 kilometres per hour. The 95% confidence interval estimate for this sample is 8.30 to 14.90 kilometres per hour.

a) What is the margin of error for this problem?

b) The researchers commented that the interval was too wide. Explain specifically what should be done to reduce the margin of error to no more than ±2 kilometres per hour. **LO ❶, ❸**

48. **Traffic speed, part 2.** The speed-measuring machines must measure accurately to maximize effectiveness in slowing traffic. The accuracy of the machines will be tested before placement on city streets. To ensure that error rates are estimated accurately, the researchers want to take a large enough sample that will ensure usable and accurate interval estimates of how much the machines may be off in measuring actual speeds. Specifically, the researchers want the margin of error for a single speed measurement to be no more than ±1.5 kilometres per hour.

a) Discuss how the researchers may obtain a reasonable estimate of the standard deviation of error in the measured speeds.

b) Suppose the standard deviation for the error in the measured speeds equals 4 kilometres per hour. At 95% confidence, what sample size should be taken to ensure that the margin of error is no larger than ±1.0 kilometre per hour? **LO ❶, ❸**

49. **Canada Revenue Agency, part I.** Certified public accountants are often required to appear with clients if the Canada Revenue Agency audits a client's tax return. Some accounting firms give the client an option to pay a fee when the tax return is completed that guarantees tax advice and support from the accountant if the client is audited. The fee is charged up front like an insurance premium and is less than the amount that would be charged if the client were later audited and then decided to ask the firm for assistance during the audit. A large accounting firm is trying to determine what fee to charge for next year's returns. In previous years, the actual mean cost to the firm for attending a client audit session was $650. To determine if this cost has changed, the firm randomly samples 32 client audit fees. The sample mean audit cost was $680 with a standard deviation of $75.

a) Develop a 95% confidence interval estimate for the mean audit cost.

b) Perform the appropriate test to determine if the mean audit cost is now different from the historical mean of $650. Use a 0.05 level of significance.

c) Comment on how the confidence interval estimate supports the results of the hypothesis test. **LO ❶, ❷**

ⓣ 50. **Canada Revenue Agency, part 2.** While reviewing the sample of audit fees, a senior accountant for the firm notes that the fee charged by the firm's accountants depends on the complexity of the return. A comparison of actual charges therefore might not provide the information needed to set next year's fees. To better understand the fee structure, the senior accountant requests a new sample that measures the time the accountants spent on the audit. Last year, the average hours charged per client audit were 3.25 hours. A new sample of 10 audit times shows the following times in hours:

4.2, 3.7, 4.8, 2.9, 3.1, 4.5, 4.2, 4.1, 5.0, 3.4

a) Assume that the conditions necessary for inference are met. Find a 90% confidence interval estimate for the mean audit time.

b) Perform the appropriate test to determine if the mean audit time for this year's audits is significantly different from last year's 3.25 hours. Use $\alpha = 0.10$.

c) Comment on how the confidence interval estimate supports the results of the hypothesis test. **LO ❶, ❷**

51. Wind power in Ontario. Ontario has installed a lot of wind turbines compared to other provinces, but should a landowner build some more? To produce enough energy, the site should have an annual average wind speed of at least 8 kilometres per hour. One candidate site was monitored for a year, with wind speeds recorded every six hours. A total of 1114 readings of wind speed averaged 8.019 kilometres per hour with a standard deviation of 3.813 kilometres per hour. You've been asked to make a statistical report to help the landowner decide whether to place a wind turbine at this site.

a) Discuss the assumptions and conditions for using Student's t-inference methods with these data. Here are some plots that may help you decide whether the methods can be used:

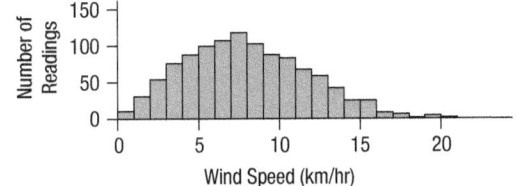

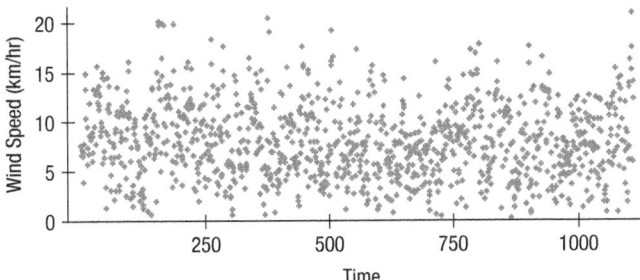

b) What would you tell the landowner about whether this site is suitable for a wind turbine? Explain. **LO ❷**

52. Real estate in Manitoba. During a recent peak period for house prices, the average selling price of homes in a region of Manitoba was $191,300. A real estate agency wants to know how much the prices have fallen since then. It collects a sample of 1231 homes in the region and finds the average asking price to be $178,613.50 with a standard deviation of $92,701.56. You have been retained by the real estate agency to report on the current situation.

a) Discuss the assumptions and conditions for using t methods for inference with these data. Here is a plot that may help you decide what to do:

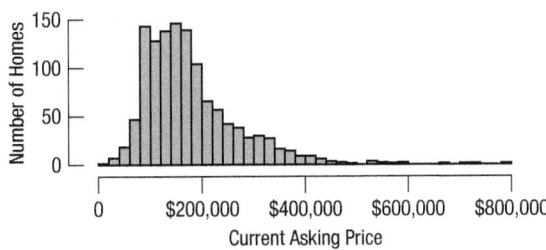

b) What would you report to the real estate agency about the current situation? **LO ❷**

53. Science education: Canada and OECD. The OECD conducts the Program for International Student Assessment and in 2012 tested 510,000 15-year-old high school students in 65 countries to assess their performance in math, reading, and science. The results are in the data file for the countries whose average score was 500 or more in science. Assume that the number of students who took the test is greater than 3000 in each country.

a) Which countries' science scores are above the OECD average of 501 but not significantly above at the 0.5% level?

b) What is the 95% confidence interval for Canada's score of 525?

c) Is Japan's score significantly less than 550 at the 0.05 level? **LO ❶, ❷**

54. Canadian house sizes. The Organisation for Economic Co-operation and Development (OECD) produces a "Better Life Index" based in part on a survey of 1000 homes in each member country. They found that the number of rooms per person in Canadian homes was 2.5 on average, whereas for the average OECD country it was 1.6. Assume that the standard deviation for the Canadian sample was 1.7 rooms. Would you say that Canadian homes have more than 1.6 rooms per person on average? State your hypotheses and calculate a P-value. State conditions and assumptions clearly, and indicate whether they are likely to be true. **LO ❷**

55. Canadian hours of work. The Organisation for Economic Co-operation and Development (OECD) produces a "Better Life Index" based in part on a survey of 1000 people in each member country. They found that the number of hours worked by Canadians was 1710 hours per year on average, whereas for the average OECD country it was 1765. Assume that the standard deviation for the Canadian sample was 486 hours. Would you say that, in Canada, people work less than 1765 hours per year? State your hypotheses and calculate a P-value. State conditions and assumptions clearly, and indicate whether they're likely to be true. **LO ❷**

56. Via Rail improvements. Via Rail recently installed new passing tracks and a Centralized Traffic Control system on the line between Kingston and Ottawa in order to reduce delays. Suppose that, before the improvements, trains between Kingston and Ottawa were on average 12.4 minutes late. After the improvements, a consumer group monitored delays during a period of three months. For a random sample of 35 trains, it found the average delay to be 6.2 minutes with a standard deviation of 8 minutes. "The improvements reduced delays by half," they claimed.

a) Have average delays been reduced? State your hypotheses and calculate a P-value. State any assumptions you're making and whether they're likely to be true.

b) Calculate the 95% confidence interval for the delays after the improvements, assuming the conditions are satisfied. Comment on the validity of your confidence interval.

c) Comment on the ethics of the consumer group's statement. **LO ❶**, **❷**

57. Canadian house prices. The average house price in Canada in 2010 was $339,100, according to the Canadian Real Estate Association (CREA). Today, a consumer group randomly selected a sample of 54 house prices and found an average price of $418,200 with a standard deviation of $94,300. The group put out a press release saying: "House prices have gone up by over 20% compared with 2010."

a) Have average house prices increased? State your hypotheses and calculate a P-value. State any assumptions you're making and whether they're likely to be true.

b) Calculate the 95% confidence interval for the house prices today, assuming the conditions are satisfied. Comment on the validity of your confidence interval.

c) Comment on the ethics of the consumer group's statement. **LO ❶**, **❷**

58. Canadian lawyers' salaries. It's tough to find out how much people earn, but on September 3, 2011, *The Economist* reported that the average lawyer's salary in Canada was $64,000. Suppose that today you interview a random sample of 35 lawyers in Canada and find that the average salary is $75,293 with a standard deviation of $83,278. Do you think the average lawyer's salary today is higher than that reported by *The Economist* in 2011? **LO ❷**

59. Nurses' schedules in Newfoundland. A major hospital in Newfoundland is dealing with complaints that some nurses feel their schedules are worse than they were last year. A survey of 75 randomly selected nurses found an average satisfaction score of 6.5 for scheduling (on a scale of 1 to 10) with a standard deviation of 2.6, compared to an average score last year for all nurses of 7.1.

a) Calculate a 99% confidence interval for the survey result.

b) What can you say from this confidence interval about whether the score is different from last year?

c) If you wanted the confidence interval to have a width of 1, how many nurses should you survey? **LO ❶**, **❸**

Mario Beauregard/The Canadian Press

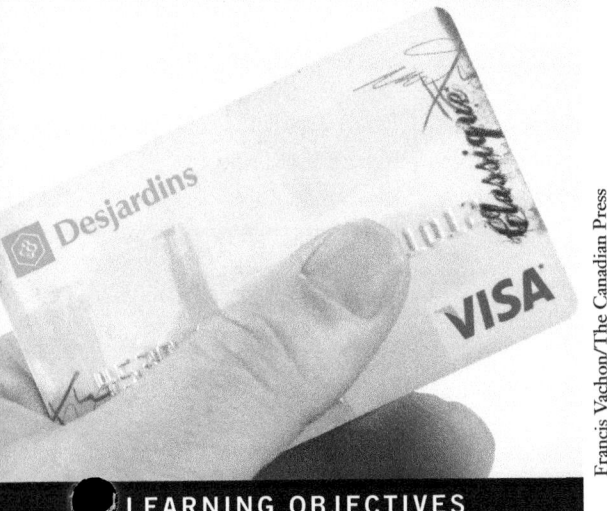

Francis Vachon/The Canadian Press

14

Comparing Two Means

Visa Canada

In Canada, Visa and MasterCard have issued about twice as many credit cards as the Canadian population, and about the same number have been issued by other companies. Visa operates the world's largest retail electronic payments network, capable of handling over 10,000 transactions per second.

Visa's origins go back to 1958, when Bank of America issued a credit card program called BankAmericard in Fresno, California. During the 1960s it expanded to other U.S. states and to Canada, where Toronto-Dominion Bank, Canadian Imperial Bank of Commerce, Royal Bank of Canada, Banque Canadienne Nationale, and Bank of Nova Scotia issued credit cards under the Chargex name. Other names were used in other countries, but in 1975, they united under the name "Visa."

Although Visa employs 6000 people worldwide, it did not become a publicly traded company until 2008. At that time, Visa Canada, Visa International, and Visa USA merged to form Visa Inc., which had the largest IPO in U.S. history, raising $17.9 billion.

Today, Visa cards are issued in Canada by a number of banks, including CIBC, Desjardins, Laurentian Bank, Royal Bank of Canada, Scotiabank, and TD Canada Trust.

Visa supports the Olympic and Paralympic Games, and in return is the only form of electronic payment accepted at Olympic venues. In Canada, it has a similar deal with the NHL, being an official partner and the official payment card.

ROADMAP FOR STATISTICAL INFERENCE					
Number of Variables	**Objective**	**Large Sample or Normal Population**		**Small Sample and Non-normal Population or Non-numeric Data**	
		Chapter	Parametric Method	Chapter	Nonparametric Method
1	Calculate confidence interval for a proportion	11			
1	Compare a proportion with a given value	12	z-test		
1	Calculate a confidence interval for a mean and compare it with a given value	13	t-test	17.2	Wilcoxon Signed-Rank Test
2	Compare two proportions	12.8	z-test		
2	Compare two means for independent samples	14.1–14.5	t-test	17.4, 17.5	Wilcoxon Rank-Sum (Mann-Whitney) Test Tukey's Quick Test
2	Compare two means for paired samples	14.6, 14.7	Paired t-test	17.2	Wilcoxon Signed-Rank Test
≥3	Compare multiple means	15	ANOVA: ANalysis Of VAriance	17.3 17.6	Friedman Test Kruskal-Wallis Test
≥3	Compare multiple counts (proportions)	16	χ^2 test		
2	Investigate the relationship between two variables	18	Correlation Regression	17.7, 17.8	Kendall's tau Spearman's rho
≥3	Investigate the relationship between multiple variables	20	Multiple Regression		

A re some credit card promotions more effective than others? For example, do customers spend more using their credit card if they know they'll be given "double miles" or "double points" toward flights, hotel stays, or store purchases? To answer questions such as this, credit card issuers often perform experiments on a sample of customers, making them an *offer* of an incentive, while other customers receive no offer. Promotions cost the company money, so the company needs to estimate the size of any increased revenue to judge whether it's sufficient to cover expenses. By comparing the performance of the offer on the sample, the company can decide whether the new offer would provide enough potential profit if it were to be "rolled out" and offered to the entire customer base.

Experiments that compare two groups are common throughout both science and industry. Other applications include comparing the effects of a new drug with the traditional therapy, the fuel efficiency of two car engine designs, or the sales of new products on two different customer segments. Usually the experiment is carried out on a sample that is a very small percentage of the total population, thus saving costs. Using statistics, we can make statements about whether the means of the two groups differ in the population at large, and how large that difference might be.

LO❶   14.1   Comparing Two Means

The natural display for comparing the means of two groups is side-by-side boxplots (see Figure 14.1). For the credit card promotion, the company judges performance by comparing the *mean* spend lift (the change in spending from before receiving the promotion to after receiving it) for the two samples. If the difference in spend lift between the group that received the promotion and the group that didn't is high enough, this will be viewed as evidence that the promotion worked. Looking at the two boxplots, it's not obvious that there's much of a difference. Can

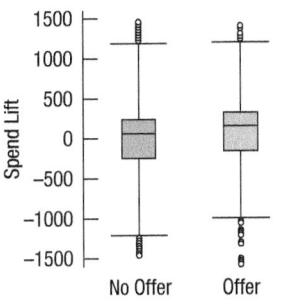

Figure 14.1 Side-by-side boxplots show a small increase in spending for the group that received the promotion.

we conclude that the slight increase seen for those who received the promotion is more than just random fluctuation? We'll need statistical inference.

For two groups, the statistic of interest is the difference in the observed means of the offer and no offer groups: $\bar{y}_1 - \bar{y}_2$. We've offered the promotion to a random sample of cardholders, and used another sample of cardholders who got no special offer as a control group. We know what happened in our samples, but what we'd really like to know is the difference of the means in the population at large, $\mu_1 - \mu_2$.

We compare two means in much the same way as we compared a single mean to a hypothesized value in Chapter 13. But now the population model parameter of interest is the *difference* between the means. In our example, it's the true difference between the mean spend lift for customers offered the promotion and for customers for whom no offer was made. We estimate the difference with $\bar{y}_1 - \bar{y}_2$. How can we tell if a difference we observe in the sample means indicates a real difference in the underlying population means? We'll need to know the sampling distribution model and standard deviation of the difference. Once we know those, we can build a confidence interval and test a hypothesis just as we did for a single mean.

We have data on 500 randomly selected customers who were offered the promotion and another randomly selected 500 who were not. It's easy to find the mean and standard deviation of the spend lift for each of these groups. From these, we can find the standard deviations of the means, but that's not what we want. We need the standard deviation of the *difference* in their means.

As long as the two groups are independent, we saw in Section 9.3 that we can find the standard deviation of the *difference* between the two sample means by adding their variances and then taking the square root:

$$SD(\bar{y}_1 - \bar{y}_2) = \sqrt{Var(\bar{y}_1) + Var(\bar{y}_2)}$$

$$= \sqrt{\left(\frac{\sigma_1}{\sqrt{n_1}}\right)^2 + \left(\frac{\sigma_2}{\sqrt{n_2}}\right)^2} \text{ (from Section 10.4)}$$

$$= \sqrt{\frac{\sigma_1^2}{n_1} + \frac{\sigma_2^2}{n_2}}$$

Of course, usually we don't know the true standard deviations of the two populations, σ_1 and σ_2, so we substitute the estimates, s_1 and s_2, and find a *standard error*:

$$SE(\bar{y}_1 - \bar{y}_2) = \sqrt{\frac{s_1^2}{n_1} + \frac{s_2^2}{n_2}}$$

Just as we did for one mean, we'll use the standard error to see how big the difference really is. You shouldn't be surprised that, just as for a single mean, the ratio of the difference in the means to the standard error of that difference has a sampling model that follows a Student's t-distribution.

A Sampling Distribution for the Difference Between Two Means

When the conditions are met (see Section 14.3), the standardized sample difference between the means of two independent groups,

$$t = \frac{(\bar{y}_1 - \bar{y}_2) - (\mu_1 - \mu_2)}{SE(\bar{y}_1 - \bar{y}_2)},$$

can be modelled by a Student's t-model with a number of degrees of freedom found with a special formula. We estimate the standard error with

$$SE(\bar{y}_1 - \bar{y}_2) = \sqrt{\frac{s_1^2}{n_1} + \frac{s_2^2}{n_2}}.$$

An Easier Rule?

The formula for the degrees of freedom of the sampling distribution of the difference between two means is complicated. So some books teach an easier rule: The number of degrees of freedom is always at *least* the smaller of $n_1 - 1$ and $n_2 - 1$ and at most $n_1 + n_2 - 2$. The problem is that if you need to perform a two-sample *t*-test and don't have the formula at hand to find the correct degrees of freedom, you have to be conservative and use the lower value. And *that* approximation can be a poor choice because it can give fewer than *half* the degrees of freedom you're entitled to from the correct formula.

What else do we need? Only the degrees of freedom for the Student's *t*-model. Unfortunately, *that* formula isn't as simple as $n - 1$. The problem is that the sampling model isn't *really* Student's *t*, but something close. The reason is that we estimated two different variances (s_1^2 and s_2^2), and they may be different. That extra variability makes the distribution even more variable than the Student's *t* for either of the means. But by using a special, adjusted degrees of freedom value, we can find a Student's *t*-model that is so close to the right sampling distribution model that nobody can tell the difference. The adjustment formula is straightforward but doesn't help our understanding much, so we leave it to the computer or calculator. (If you're curious and really want to see the formula, look in the footnote.[1])

FOR EXAMPLE   Sampling distribution of the difference of two mean car discounts

The owner of a large car dealership wants to understand the negotiation process for buying a new car. Cars are given a "sticker price," but a potential buyer may negotiate a better price. The owner wonders if there's a difference in how men and women negotiate and who, if either, obtains the larger discount.

He takes a random sample of 100 customers from the last six months' sales and finds that 54 were men and 46 were women. On average, the 54 men received a discount of $962.96 with a standard deviation of $458.95; the 46 women received an average discount of $1262.61 with a standard deviation of $399.70.

QUESTION   What is the mean difference of the discounts received by men and women? What is its standard error?

ANSWER   The mean difference is $1262.61 - $962.96 = $263.65. The women received, on average, a discount that was larger by $263.65. The standard error is

$$SE(\bar{y}_{Women} - \bar{y}_{Men}) = \sqrt{\frac{s_{Women}^2}{n_{Women}} + \frac{s_{Men}^2}{n_{Men}}} = \sqrt{\frac{(399.70)^2}{46} + \frac{(458.95)^2}{54}} = \$85.87.$$

Women receive a higher discount by $263.65 much larger than its standard error of $85.87.

LO❶   **14.2**   The Two-Sample *t*-Test

NOTATION ALERT

Δ_0 (pronounced "delta sub zero") isn't so standard that you can assume everyone will understand it. We use Delta because it's the capital Greek letter "D" for "difference."

Now we've got everything we need to construct the hypothesis test, and you already know how to do it. It's the same idea we used when testing one mean against a hypothesized value. Here, we start by hypothesizing a value for the true difference of the means. We'll call that hypothesized difference Δ_0. (It's so common for that hypothesized difference to be zero that we often just assume $\Delta_0 = 0$.) We then

---

[1] The result is due to Satterthwaite and Welch.

Satterthwaite, F. E. (1946). An approximate distribution of estimates of variance components. *Biometrics Bulletin, 2,* 110–114.

Welch, B. L. (1947). The generalization of "Student's" problem when several different population variances are involved. *Biometrika, 34,* 28–35.

$$df = \frac{\left(\dfrac{s_1^2}{n_1} + \dfrac{s_2^2}{n_2}\right)^2}{\dfrac{1}{n_1 - 1}\left(\dfrac{s_1^2}{n_1}\right)^2 + \dfrac{1}{n_2 - 1}\left(\dfrac{s_2^2}{n_2}\right)^2}$$

This approximation formula usually doesn't even give a whole number. If you're using a table, you'll need a whole number, so round down to be safe. If you're using technology, the approximation formulas that computers and calculators use for the Student's *t*-distribution can deal with fractional degrees of freedom.

take the ratio of the difference in the means from our samples to its standard error and compare that ratio with a critical value from a Student's t-model. The test is called the **two-sample t-test**.

Two-Sample t-Test

When the appropriate assumptions and conditions are met, we test the hypothesis

$$H_0: \mu_1 - \mu_2 = \Delta_0,$$

where the hypothesized difference Δ_0 is almost always 0. We use the statistic

$$t = \frac{(\bar{y}_1 - \bar{y}_2) - \Delta_0}{SE(\bar{y}_1 - \bar{y}_2)}.$$

The standard error of $\bar{y}_1 - \bar{y}_2$ is

$$SE(\bar{y}_1 - \bar{y}_2) = \sqrt{\frac{s_1^2}{n_1} + \frac{s_2^2}{n_2}}.$$

When the null hypothesis is true, the statistic can be closely modelled by a Student's t-model with a number of degrees of freedom given by a special formula. We use that model to compare our t-ratio with a critical value for t or to obtain a P-value.

FOR EXAMPLE | The t-test for the difference of two mean car discounts

QUESTION   We saw (in For Example: "Sampling distribution of the difference of two mean car discounts") that the difference between the average discount obtained by men and women appeared to be large if we assume that there is no true difference. Test the hypothesis, find the P-value, and state your conclusions.

ANSWER   The null hypothesis is: $H_0: \mu_{Women} - \mu_{Men} = 0$ vs. $H_A: \mu_{Women} - \mu_{Men} \neq 0$. The difference $\bar{y}_{Women} - \bar{y}_{Men}$ is $263.65 with a standard error of $84.26. The t-statistic is the difference divided by the standard error:

$$t = \frac{\bar{y}_{Women} - \bar{y}_{Men}}{SE(\bar{y}_{Women} - \bar{y}_{Men})} = \frac{263.65}{85.87} = 3.07.$$ The approximation formula gives 97.94

degrees of freedom (which is close to the maximum possible of $n_1 + n_2 - 2 = 98$). The P-value (from technology) for $t = 3.07$ with 97.94 df in a two-sided test is 0.0028. We reject the null hypoythesis. Comparing with the P-values discussed in section 12.4, this is very good evidence to suggest that the difference in mean discount received by men and women is not 0.

LO❶ **14.3** **Assumptions and Conditions**

Before we can perform a two-sample t-test, we have to check the assumptions and conditions, which are similar to those in Sections 10.4 and 13.3 plus a new condition that the two groups should be independent of each other.

Independence Assumption

The data in each group must be drawn independently and at random from each group's own homogeneous population or generated by a randomized comparative experiment. We can't expect that the data, taken as one big group, come from a homogeneous population because that's what we're trying to test. But without randomization of some sort, there are no sampling distribution models and no inference. We should think about whether the Independence Assumption is reasonable. We can also check two conditions:

- **Randomization Condition:** Were the data collected with suitable randomization? For surveys, are they a representative random sample? For experiments, was the experiment randomized?
- **10% Condition:** We check this condition if we have a very small population or an extremely large sample. We needn't worry about it at all for randomized experiments.

Normal Population Assumption

As we did before with Student's t-models, we need the assumption that the underlying populations are *each* Normally distributed. So we check one condition:

- **Nearly Normal Condition:** We must check this for *both* groups; a violation by either one violates the condition. As we saw for single sample means, the Normality assumption matters most when sample sizes are small. When either group is small ($n < 15$), you should not use these methods if the histogram or Normal probability plot shows skewness. For n-values closer to 40, a mildly skewed histogram is okay, but you should remark on any outliers you find and not work with severely skewed data. When both groups are bigger than that, the Central Limit Theorem (Section 10.3) starts to work unless the data are severely skewed or there are extreme outliers, so the Nearly Normal Condition for the data matters less. Even in large samples, however, you should still be on the lookout for outliers, extreme skewness, and multiple modes.

Independent Groups Assumption

To use the two-sample t methods, the two groups we're comparing must be independent of each other. In fact, the test is sometimes called the two *independent samples t*-test. No statistical test can verify that the groups are independent. You have to think about how the data were collected. The assumption would be violated, for example, if one group comprised husbands and the other their wives. Whatever we measure on one might naturally be related to the other. Similarly, if we compared subjects' performances before some treatment with their performances afterward, we'd expect a relationship of each "before" measurement with its corresponding "after" measurement. In these situations, we may be able to use the methods described in Sections 14.6 and 14.7 instead.

GUIDED EXAMPLE	**Scotiabank Credit Card Promotion**

Richard Lam/The Canadian Press

Suppose Scotiabank wants to evaluate the effectiveness of offering an incentive on one of its Visa cards. The preliminary market research has suggested that a new incentive may increase customer spending. However, before the bank invests in this promotion on the entire population of cardholders, it tests it for six months on a random sample of 1000 and obtains the data you'll find in the file **ch14_GE_Credit_Card_Promo**. We are hired as statistical consultants to analyze the results. To judge whether the incentive works, we will examine the change in spending (called the *spend lift*) over a six-month period. We'll see whether the spend lift for the group that received the offer was greater than that for the group that received no offer.

PLAN

Setup State what we want to know.

Identify the parameter we wish to estimate. Here our parameter is the difference in the means, not the individual group means.

Identify the population(s) about which we wish to make statements.

Identify the variables and context.

Make a graph to compare the two groups and check the distribution of each group. For completeness, we should report any outliers. If any outliers are extreme enough, we should consider performing the test both with and without the outliers and reporting the difference.

Model Check the assumptions and conditions.

For large samples like these with quantitative data, we often don't worry about the 10% Condition.

State the sampling distribution model for the statistic. Here the degrees of freedom will come from the approximation formula in Footnote 1.

Specify your method.

We want to know if cardholders who are offered a promotion spend more on their credit card. We have the spend lift (in $) for a random sample of 500 cardholders who were offered the promotion and for a random sample of 500 customers who were not.

H_0: The mean spend lift for the population that receives the offer is the same as for the population that does not:

$H_0: \mu_{Offer} = \mu_{No\ Offer}$

or $H_0: \mu_{Offer} - \mu_{No\ Offer} = 0$

H_A: The mean spend lift for the population that receives the offer is higher:

$H_A: \mu_{Offer} > \mu_{No\ Offer}$

or $H_A: \mu_{Offer} - \mu_{No\ Offer} > 0$

The boxplots and histograms show the distribution of both groups. It looks like the distribution for each group is fairly symmetric. The boxplots indicate several outliers in each group, but we have no reason to delete them, and their impact is minimal.

✓ **Independence Assumption.** We have no reason to believe that the spending behaviour of one customer would influence the spending behaviour of another customer in the same group. The data report the "spend lift" for each customer for the same time period.

✓ **Randomization Condition.** The customers who were offered the promotion were selected at random.

✓ **Nearly Normal Condition.** The samples are large, so we're not overly concerned with this condition, and the boxplots and histograms show symmetric distributions for both groups.

✓ **Independent Groups Assumption.** Customers were assigned to groups at random. There's no reason to think that those in one group can affect the spending behaviour of those in the other group. Under these conditions, it's appropriate to use a Student's *t*-model.

We will use a two-sample *t*-test.

(*continued*)

DO **Mechanics** List the summary statistics. Be sure to include the units along with the statistics. Use meaningful subscripts to identify the groups.

Use the sample standard deviations to find the standard error of the sampling distribution.

Use the approximation formula for the degrees of freedom and find the P-value.

We know $n_{\text{No Offer}} = 500$ and $n_{\text{Offer}} = 500$.

From technology, we find:

$$\bar{y}_{\text{No Offer}} = \$7.69 \quad \bar{y}_{\text{Offer}} = \$127.61$$

$$s_{\text{No Offer}} = \$611.62 \quad s_{\text{Offer}} = \$566.05$$

The observed difference in the two means is

$$\bar{y}_{\text{Offer}} - \bar{y}_{\text{No Offer}} = \$127.61 - \$7.69 = \$119.92.$$

The groups are independent, so

$$SE(\bar{y}_{\text{Offer}} - \bar{y}_{\text{No Offer}}) = \sqrt{\frac{(611.62)^2}{500} + \frac{(566.05)^2}{500}}$$

$$= \$37.27.$$

The observed t-value is

$$t = 119.92/37.27 = 3.218.$$

The degrees of freedom, df, comes from technology or from the formula in Footnote 1:

$$df = \frac{\left(\dfrac{611.62^2}{500} + \dfrac{566.05^2}{500}\right)^2}{\dfrac{1}{499}\left(\dfrac{611.62^2}{500}\right)^2 + \dfrac{1}{499}\left(\dfrac{566.05^2}{500}\right)^2}$$

$$= 992.$$

(To use critical values, we could find that the one-sided 0.05 critical value for a t with 992 df is $t^* = 1.646$.

Our observed t-value is larger than this, so we could reject the null hypothesis at the 0.05 level. In fact, since our t-value of 3.218 is a lot higher than 1.646, we can reject the null hypothesis at an even-higher significance level—for example, for $P = 0.01$, the critical value is $t^* = 2.33$.)

Using software to obtain the P-value, we get:

One-sided P-value $= 0.0006669$

REPORT **Conclusion** Interpret the test results in the proper context.

MEMO

Re: Credit Card Spending

Our analysis of the credit card promotion experiment found that customers offered the promotion spent more than those not offered the promotion. The difference was statistically significant, with a P-value<0.001. So we conclude that this promotion will increase spending. The difference in spend lift averaged $119.92, but our analyses so far haven't determined how much income this will generate for the company and thus whether the estimated increase in spending is worth the cost of the offer. Also we don't know whether the spend lift will be maintained beyond the 6 months trial period.

JUST CHECKING

Ron Rowan Photography/Shutterstock

Chaoss/Fotolia

Iko/Fotolia

Juliet Photography/Shutterstock

Many office "coffee stations" collect voluntary payments for the food consumed. Researchers at the University of Newcastle upon Tyne performed an experiment to see whether the image of eyes watching would change employee behaviour.[2] They alternated pictures of eyes looking at the viewer with pictures of flowers each week on the cupboard behind the "honesty box." The researchers then measured the consumption of milk to approximate the amount of food consumed and recorded the contributions (in £) each week per litre of milk. The table summarizes their results:

	Eyes	Flowers
n(# weeks)	5	5
$\bar{y}$	0.417£/litre	0.151£/litre
s	0.1811	0.067

1 What null hypothesis were the researchers testing?

2 Check the assumptions and conditions needed to test whether there really is a difference in behaviour due to the difference in pictures.

Answers are found in Appendix A.

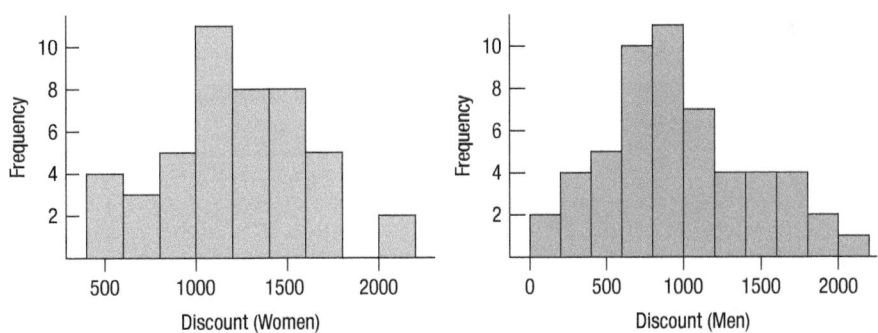

FOR EXAMPLE   **Checking assumptions and conditions for car discounts**

QUESTION In For Example: "The t-test for the difference of two mean car discounts," we rejected the null hypothesis that the mean discount received by men and women is the same. Here are the histograms of the discounts for both women and men. Check the assumptions and conditions and state any concerns you might have about the conclusion we reached.

ANSWER We were told that the sample was random, so the Randomiazation Condition is satisfied. There's no reason to think that the men's and women's responses are related (as they might be if they were husband and wife pairs), so the Independent Group Assumption is plausible. Because both groups have more than 40 observations, the discounts can be mildly skewed, which is the case. There are no obvious outliers (there's a small gap in the women's distribution, but the observations aren't far from the centre), so all the assumptions and conditions seem to be satisfied. We have no real concerns about the conclusion we reached that the mean difference is not 0.

[2]Bateson, M., Nettle, D., & Roberts, G. (2006.) Cues of being watched enhance cooperation in a real-world setting. *Biology Letters, 2,* 412–414. doi:10.1098/rsbl.2006.0509

LO❷   14.4   A Confidence Interval for the Difference Between Two Means

We rejected the null hypothesis that credit card customers' mean spending wouldn't change when offered a promotion. Because the company took a random sample of customers for each group, and our P-value was convincingly small, we concluded that this difference is not zero for the population. Does this mean we should offer the promotion to all customers?

A hypothesis test really says nothing about the size of the difference. All it says is that the observed difference is large enough that we can be confident it isn't zero. That's what the term "statistically significant" means. It doesn't say that the difference is important, financially significant, or interesting. Rejecting a null hypothesis simply says that the observed statistic is unlikely to have been observed if the null hypothesis were true.

So, what recommendations can we make to the company? Almost every business decision will depend on looking at a range of likely scenarios—precisely the kind of information a confidence interval gives. We construct the confidence interval for the difference in means in the usual way, starting with our observed statistic, in this case $(\bar{y}_1 - \bar{y}_2)$. We then add and subtract a multiple of the standard error $SE(\bar{y}_1 - \bar{y}_2)$ where the multiple is based on the Student's t-distribution with the same df formula we saw before.

Confidence Interval for the Difference Between Two Means

When the conditions are met, we're ready to find a **two-sample t-confidence interval** for the difference between means of two independent groups, $\mu_1 - \mu_2$. The confidence interval is

$$(\bar{y}_1 - \bar{y}_2) \pm t^*_{df} \times SE(\bar{y}_1 - \bar{y}_2),$$

where the standard error of the difference of the means is

$$SE(\bar{y}_1 - \bar{y}_2) = \sqrt{\frac{s_1^2}{n_1} + \frac{s_2^2}{n_2}}.$$

The critical value t^*_{df} depends on the particular confidence level and on the number of degrees of freedom.

GUIDED EXAMPLE   Scotiabank Credit Card Spending

Francis Vachon/ The Canadian Press

Let's assume that Scotiabank accepts our advice that the group of customers who received the offer increased their credit card spending by more than the group who didn't receive any offer. In statistical terms, we rejected the null hypothesis that the mean spending in the two groups was equal. From Scotiabank's perspective, it now knows that there's an increase in spending. We next need to estimate the magnitude and variability of the spend lift.

 PLAN   **Setup** State what we want to know. | We want to find a 95% confidence interval for the mean difference in spending between those who are offered a promotion and those who aren't.

Identify the *parameter* we wish to estimate. Here our parameter is the difference in the means, not the individual group means.

Identify the *population(s)* about which we wish to make statements.

Identify the variables and context.

Specify the method.

We looked at the boxplots and histograms of the groups and checked the conditions before. The same assumptions and conditions are appropriate here, so we can proceed directly to the confidence interval.

We will use a two-sample t-interval.

DO

Mechanics Construct the confidence interval. Be sure to include the units along with the statistics. Use meaningful subscripts to identify the groups.

Use the sample standard deviations to find the standard error of the sampling distribution.

Use the approximation formula for the degrees of freedom and find the confidence interval.

In our previous analysis, we found:

$$\bar{y}_{Offer} = \$7.69 \quad \bar{y}_{Offer} = \$127.61$$
$$s_{No\ Offer} = \$611.62 \quad s_{Offer} = \$566.05$$

The observed difference in the two means is

$$\bar{y}_{Offer} - \bar{y}_{No\ Offer} = \$127.61 - \$7.69 = \$119.92,$$

and the standard error is

$$SE(\bar{y}_{Offer} - \bar{y}_{No\ Offer}) = \$37.27.$$

From technology, the df is 992.007, and the 0.025 critical value for t with 992.007 df is 1.96. So the 95% confidence interval is

$$119.92 \pm 1.96(37.27) = (\$46.87, \$192.97).$$

REPORT

Conclusion Interpret the test results in the proper context.

MEMO

Re: Credit Card Promotion Experiment

In our experiment, the promotion resulted in an increased spend lift of $119.92 on average. Further analysis gives a 95% confidence interval of ($46.79, $193.06). In other words, we expect with 95% confidence that under similar conditions, the mean spend lift we achieve when we roll out the offer to all similar customers will be in this interval. We recommend that the company consider whether the values in this interval will justify the cost of the promotion program.

FOR EXAMPLE   **A confidence interval for the difference between car discounts**

QUESTION We concluded in For Example: "The t-test for the difference of two mean car discounts" that, on average, women receive a larger discount than men at the car dealership. How big is the difference, on average? Find a 95% confidence interval for the difference.

(continued)

> **ANSWER** We've seen that the difference from our sample is $263.65 with a standard error of $85.84 and that it has 97.94 degrees of freedom. The 95% critical value for a t with 97.94 degrees of freedom is 1.984.
>
> $$\bar{y}_{Women} - \bar{y}_{Men} \pm t^*_{97.97}SE\,(\bar{y}_{Women} - \bar{y}_{Men}) = 263.65 \pm 1.984 \times 85.87$$
> $$= (\$93.28, \$434.02)$$
>
> We are 95% confident that, on average, women received a discount that's between $93.28 and $434.02 larger than the men at this dealership.

LO❶   14.5   The Pooled t-Test

Lenaer/Shutterstock

If you bought a used camera in good condition from a friend, would you pay the same as you would if you bought the same item from a stranger? A researcher at Cornell University[3] wanted to know how friendship might affect simple sales such as this. She randomly divided subjects into two groups and gave each group descriptions of items they might want to buy. One group was told to imagine buying from a friend whom they expected to see again. The other group was told to imagine buying from a stranger.

Table 14.1 gives the prices they offered for a used camera in good condition.

The researcher who designed the friendship study was interested in testing the impact of friendship on negotiations. Previous theories had doubted that friendship had a measurable effect on pricing, but she hoped to find such an effect. The usual null hypothesis is that there's no difference in means, and that's what we'll use for the camera purchase prices.

When we performed the t-test earlier in the chapter, we used an approximation formula that adjusts the degrees of freedom to a lower value. When $n_1 + n_2$ is only 15, as it is here, we don't really want to lose any degrees of freedom. Because this is an experiment, we might be willing to make another assumption. The null hypothesis says that whether people buy from a friend or a stranger should have no

Price Offered for a Used Camera ($)	
Buying from a Friend	**Buying from a Stranger**
275	260
300	250
260	175
300	130
255	200
275	225
290	240
300	

Table 14.1   Prices offered for a used camera.

[3]Halpern, J. J. (1997). The transaction index: A method for standardizing comparisons of transaction characteristics across different contexts. *Group Decision and Negotiation* 6(6), 557–572.

effect on the mean amount they're willing to pay for a camera. If it has no effect on the means, should it affect the variance of the transactions?

If we're willing to *assume* that the variances of the groups are equal (at least when the null hypothesis is true), then we can save some degrees of freedom. To do that, we have to pool the two variances that we estimate from the groups into one common, or *pooled*, estimate of the variance:

$$s^2_{pooled} = \frac{(n_1 - 1)s_1^2 + (n_2 - 1)s_2^2}{(n_1 - 1) + (n_2 - 1)}$$

(If the two sample sizes are equal, this is just the average of the two variances.)

Now we just substitute this pooled variance for each of the variances in the standard error formula. Remember, the standard error formula for the difference of two independent means is

$$SE(\bar{y}_1 - \bar{y}_2) = \sqrt{\frac{s_1^2}{n_1} + \frac{s_2^2}{n_2}}.$$

We substitute the common pooled variance for each of the two variances in this formula, making the pooled standard error formula simpler:

$$SE_{pooled}(\bar{y}_1 - \bar{y}_2) = \sqrt{\frac{s^2_{pooled}}{n_1} + \frac{s^2_{pooled}}{n_2}} = s_{pooled}\sqrt{\frac{1}{n_1} + \frac{1}{n_2}}$$

The formula for degrees of freedom for the Student's *t*-model is simpler, too. It was so complicated for the two-sample *t* that we stuck it in a footnote on page 446. Now it's just df $= (n_1 - 1) + (n_2 - 1)$.

Substitute the pooled *t* estimate of the standard error and its degrees of freedom into the steps of the confidence interval or hypothesis test and you'll be using pooled *t* methods. Of course, if you decide to use a pooled *t* method, you must defend your assumption that the variances of the two groups are equal.

To use the pooled *t* methods, you'll need to add the Equal Variance Assumption that the variances of the two populations from which the samples have been drawn are equal; that is, $\sigma_1^2 = \sigma_2^2$. (Of course, we can think about the standard deviations being equal instead.)

Pooled *t*-Test and Confidence Interval for the Difference Between Means

The conditions for the **pooled *t*-test** for the difference between the means of two independent groups are the same as for the two-sample *t*-test, with the additional assumption that the variances of the two groups are the same. We test the hypothesis

$$H_0: \mu_1 - \mu_2 = \Delta_0,$$

where the hypothesized difference Δ_0 is almost always 0, using the statistic

$$t = \frac{(\bar{y}_1 - \bar{y}_2) - \Delta_0}{SE_{pooled}(\bar{y}_1 - \bar{y}_2)}.$$

The standard error of $\bar{y}_1 - \bar{y}_2$ is

$$SE_{pooled}(\bar{y}_1 - \bar{y}_2) = s_{pooled}\sqrt{\frac{1}{n_1} + \frac{1}{n_2}},$$

where the pooled variance is

$$s^2_{pooled} = \frac{(n_1 - 1)s_1^2 + (n_2 - 1)s_2^2}{(n_1 - 1) + (n_2 - 1)}.$$

(continued)

When the conditions are met and the null hypothesis is true, we can model this statistic's sampling distribution with a Student's t-model with $(n_1 - 1) + (n_2 - 1)$ degrees of freedom. We use that model to obtain a P-value for a test or a margin of error for a confidence interval.

The corresponding **pooled t-confidence interval** is

$$(\bar{y}_1 - \bar{y}_2) \pm t^*_{df} \times SE_{pooled}(\bar{y}_1 - \bar{y}_2),$$

where the critical value t^* depends on the confidence level and is found with $(n_1 - 1) + (n_2 - 1)$ degrees of freedom.

GUIDED EXAMPLE   Role of Friendship in Negotiations

We have data on the prices two randomly selected groups of people would offer for a used camera. The first group think they're buying from a friend and the second think they're buying from a stranger. Our samples are quite small, but we wish to see whether they're large enough to establish whether friendship has an impact on the price people are prepared to offer.

Monkey Business Images/Shutterstock

PLAN	Setup State what we want to know.	We want to know whether people are likely to offer a different amount for a used camera when buying from a friend than when buying from a stranger. We wonder whether the difference between mean amounts is zero. We have bid prices from eight subjects buying from a friend and seven subjects buying from a stranger, found in a randomized experiment.

Identify the *parameter* we wish to estimate. Here our parameter is the difference in the means, not the individual group means. Identify the variables and context.

Hypotheses   State the null and alternative hypotheses.

The research claim is that friendship changes what people are willing to pay.[4] The natural null hypothesis is that friendship makes no difference.

H_0: The difference in mean price offered to friends and the mean price offered to strangers is zero:

$$\mu_F - \mu_S = 0$$

We didn't start with any knowledge of whether friendship might increase or decrease the price, so we choose a two-sided alternative.

H_A: The difference in mean prices is not zero:

$$\mu_F - \mu_S \neq 0$$

---

[4]This claim is a good example of what is called a "research hypothesis" in many social sciences. The only way to check it is to deny that it's true and see where the resulting null hypothesis leads us.

Make a graph. Boxplots are the display of choice for comparing groups. We'll also want to check the distribution of each group. Histograms may do a better job.

Looks like the prices are higher if you buy from a friend. The two ranges barely overlap, so we'll be pretty surprised if we don't reject the null hypothesis.

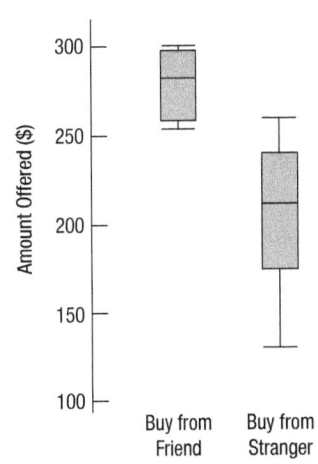

Model   Think about the assumptions and check the conditions. (Because this is a randomized experiment, we haven't sampled at all, so the 10% Condition doesn't apply.)

✓ **Independence Assumption**. There is no reason to think that the behaviour of one person will influence the behaviour of another.

✓ **Randomization Condition**. The experiment was randomized. Subjects were assigned to treatment groups at random.

✓ **Independent Groups Assumption**. Randomizing the experiment gives independent groups.

✓ **Nearly Normal Condition**. Histograms of the two sets of prices show no evidence of skewness or extreme outliers:

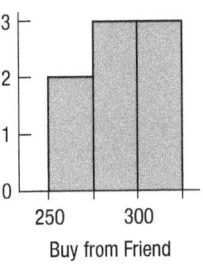

Buy from Friend

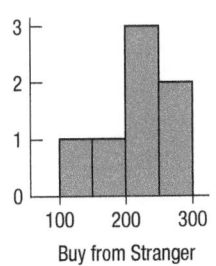

Buy from Stranger

State the sampling distribution model.

Specify the method.

Because this is a randomized experiment with a null hypothesis of no difference in means, we can make the Equal Variance Assumption. If, as we're assuming from the null hypothesis, the treatment doesn't change the means, then it's reasonable to assume that it also doesn't change the variances. Under these assumptions and conditions, we can use a Student's *t*-model to perform a pooled *t*-test.

DO   **Mechanics**   List the summary statistics. Be sure to use proper notation.

Use the null model to find the P-value. First determine the standard error of the difference between sample means.

From the data:

$$n_F = 8 \qquad n_S = 7$$
$$\bar{y}_F = \$281.88 \qquad \bar{y}_S = \$211.43$$
$$s_F = \$18.31 \qquad s_S = \$46.43$$

The pooled variance estimate is

$$s_p^2 = \frac{(n_F - 1)\, s_F^2 + (n_S - 1)\, s_S^2}{n_F + n_S - 2}$$

$$= \frac{(8 - 1)(18.31)^2 + (7 - 1)(46.43)^2}{8 + 7 - 2}$$

$$= 1175.48.$$

(continued)

Make a graph. Sketch the *t*-model centred at the hypothesized difference of zero. Because this is a two-tailed test, shade the region to the right of the observed difference and the corresponding region in the other tail.

Find the *t*-value.

A statistics program can find the P-value.

The standard error of the difference becomes

$$SE_{pooled}(\bar{y}_F - \bar{y}_S) = \sqrt{\frac{s_p^2}{n_F} + \frac{s_p^2}{n_S}}$$

$$= 17.744.$$

The observed difference in means is

$$(\bar{y}_F - \bar{y}_S) = 281.88 - 211.43 = \$70.45,$$

which results in a *t*-ratio:

$$t = \frac{(\bar{y}_F - \bar{y}_S) - (0)}{SE_{pooled}(\bar{y}_F - \bar{y}_S)} = \frac{70.45}{17.744} = 3.97.$$

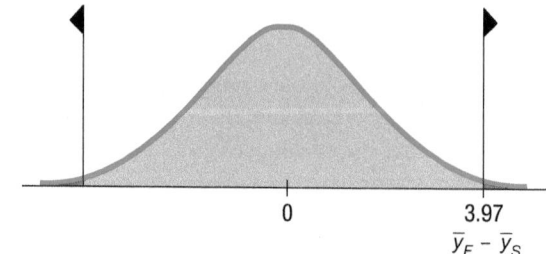

The pooled *t*-test gives df = 13, P-value = 0.001600
We conclude that the difference in means is not equal to 0.

To obtain a 95 percent confidence interval, we check for a 2-sided test with df=13 in Table T of Appendix B an get *t* = 2.16. The confidence interval is:

$$70.45 \pm 2.16 \times 17.74 = (32.11, \quad 108.78)$$

which does not include 0, confirming the result of the hypothesis test.

REPORT

Conclusion Link the P-value to your decision about the null hypothesis and state the conclusion in context.

The confidence interval can reveal more detailed information about the size of the difference. In the original article (referenced in Footnote 3 in this chapter), the researcher tested several items and proposed a model relating the size of the difference to the price of the items.

MEMO

Re: Role of Friendship in Negotiations

Results of a small experiment show that people buying from a friend are likely to offer a different amount for a used camera than people buying from a stranger. The difference in mean offers was statistically significant (P = 0.0016).

The confidence interval suggests that people buying from a friend tend to offer more than people buying from a stranger. For the camera, the 95% confidence interval for the mean difference in price was $32.11 to $108.78, but we suspect that the actual difference may vary with the price of the item purchased.

JUST CHECKING

Recall the test in the previous Just Checking box to see whether pictures of eyes would change compliance in voluntary contributions at an office coffee station.

3 What alternative hypothesis would you test?

4 The P-value of the test was less than 0.05. State a brief conclusion.

Answers are found in Appendix A.

When Should You Use the Pooled *t*-Test?

When the variances of the two groups are in fact equal, the two methods (pooled *t*-test and the *t*-test described in Section 14.2) give pretty much the same result. Pooled methods have a small advantage (slightly narrower confidence intervals, slightly more powerful tests) mostly because they usually have a few more degrees of freedom, but the advantage is slight. When the variances are *not* equal, the pooled methods are just not valid and can give poor results. You have to use the two-sample methods instead.

As the sample sizes get bigger, the advantages that come from a few more degrees of freedom make less and less difference. So the advantage (such as it is) of the pooled method is greatest when the samples are small—just when it's hardest to check the conditions. And the difference in the degrees of freedom is greatest when the variances are not equal—just when you can't use the pooled method anyway.

Pooled methods are actually very important in Statistics for designed experiments, where we start by assigning subjects to treatments at random. We know that at the start of the experiment each treatment group is a random sample from the same population,[5] so each treatment group begins with the same population variance. In this case, assuming the variances are equal after we apply the treatment is the same as assuming that the treatment doesn't change the variance. When we test whether the true means are equal, we may be willing to go a bit further and say that the treatments made no difference *at all*. That's what we did in the friendship and bargaining experiment. Then it's not much of a stretch to assume that the variances have remained equal.

> For *t*-tests, the advantages of **pooling** are small, and you're allowed to pool only rarely (when the Equal Variance Assumption is met).

FOR EXAMPLE   The pooled *t*-test for car discounts

QUESTION   Would the owner of the car dealership in For Example: "The *t*-test for the difference of two mean car discounts" have reached a different conclusion had he used the pooled *t*-test for the difference in mean discounts?

ANSWER   The difference in the pooled *t*-test is that it assumes that the variances of the two groups are equal, and pools those two estimates to find the standard error of the difference. The pooled estimate of the common standard deviation is

$$s_{pooled} = \sqrt{\frac{(n_{Women} - 1)s^2_{Women} + (n_{Men} - 1)s^2_{Men}}{n_{Women} + n_{Men} - 2}}$$

$$= \sqrt{\frac{(46 - 1)(399.70)^2 + (54 - 1)(458.95)^2}{46 + 54 - 2}} = 432.75.$$

We use that to find the *SE* of the difference:

$$SE_{pooled}(\bar{y}_{Women} - \bar{y}_{Men}) = s_{pooled}\sqrt{\frac{1}{n_{Women}} + \frac{1}{n_{Men}}} = 432.75\sqrt{\frac{1}{46} + \frac{1}{54}} = \$86.83.$$

(Without pooling, our estimate was $85.87.) This pooled *t* has $46 + 54 - 2 = 98$ degrees of freedom.

$$t_{98} = \frac{\bar{y}_{Women} - \bar{y}_{Men}}{SE_{pooled}(\bar{y}_{Women} - \bar{y}_{Men})} = \frac{263.65}{86.83} = 3.04$$

The P-value for a *t* of 3.04 with 98 degrees of freedom is (from technology) 0.0030. The two-sample *t*-test value gave P = 0.0028.

There is no practical difference between these, and we reach the same conclusion that the difference is not 0. The assumption of equal variances did not affect the conclusion.

---

[5]That is, the population of experimental subjects. Remember that to be valid, experiments don't need a representative sample drawn from a population, because we're not trying to estimate a population model parameter.

LO❸   *14.6*   **Paired Data**

The two-sample *t*-test depends crucially on the assumption that the cases in the two groups are independent of each other. When is that assumption violated? Most commonly, it's when we have data on the *same* cases in two different circumstances. For example, we might want to compare *the same* customers' spending at our website last January with this January, or we might have *each participant* in a focus group rate two different product designs. Data such as these are called **paired data** because we have two items of data from the same subject.

Pairing isn't a problem; it's an opportunity. If you know the data are paired, you can take advantage of the pairing—in fact, you *must* take advantage it. You *should not* use the two-sample (or pooled two-sample) method when the data are paired. Be careful. There is no statistical test to determine whether the data are paired. You must decide whether the data are paired from understanding how they were collected and what they mean (check the Five W's).

Once we recognize that our data are matched pairs, it makes sense to concentrate on the *difference* between the two measurements for each individual. That is, we look at the collection of pairwise differences in the measured variable. For example, if studying customer spending, we would analyze the *difference* between this January's and last January's spending for each customer. Because it's the *differences* we care about, we can treat them as if there was a single variable of interest holding those differences. With only one variable to consider, we can use a simple one-sample *t*-test. A **paired *t*-test** is just a one-sample *t*-test (see Section 13.5) for the mean of the pairwise differences. The sample size is the number of pairs.

Paired Data Assumption

The data must actually be paired. You can't just decide to pair data from independent groups. When you have two groups with the same number of observations, it may be tempting to match them up, but that's not valid. You can't pair data just because they "seem to go together." To use paired methods, you must determine from knowing how the data were collected whether the two groups are paired or independent. Usually the context will make it clear.

Be sure to recognize paired data when you have it. Remember, two-sample *t* methods aren't valid unless the groups are independent, and paired groups aren't independent.

Independence Assumption

For these methods, it's the *differences* that must be independent of each other. This is just the one-sample *t*-test assumption of independence, now applied to the differences. In the well-known Coke vs. Pepsi challenge, one rater's opinion shouldn't affect how another person rated the colas. As always, randomization helps to ensure independence.

Randomization Condition

Randomness can arise in many ways. The *pairs* may be a random sample. For example, we may be comparing opinions of husbands and wives from a random selection of couples. In an experiment, the order of the two treatments may be randomly assigned, or the treatments may be randomly assigned to one member of each pair. In a before-and-after study like this one, we may believe that the observed differences are a representative sample from a population of interest. If we have any doubts, we'll need to include a control group to be able to draw conclusions. What we want to know usually focuses our attention on where the randomness should be.

10% Condition

When we sample from a finite population, we should be careful not to sample more than 10% of that population. Sampling too large a fraction of the population calls the Independence Assumption into question. Here, we can regard our sample customers as representative of the (potentially very large) population of all customers.

Normal Population Assumption

We need to assume that the population of *differences* follows a Normal model. We don't need to check the data in each of the two individual groups. In fact, the data from each group can be quite skewed, but the differences can still be unimodal and symmetric.

- **Nearly Normal Condition** This condition can be checked with a histogram of the differences. As with the one-sample *t* methods, this assumption matters less as we have more pairs to consider. You may be pleasantly surprised when you check this condition. Even if your original measurements are skewed or bimodal, the *differences* may be nearly Normal. After all, the individual who was way out in the tail on an initial measurement is likely to still be out there on the second one, giving a perfectly ordinary difference.

FOR EXAMPLE   Paired data for car discounts

QUESTION   The owner of the car dealership is curious about the maximum discount his salespeople are willing to give to customers. In particular, two of his salespeople, Frank and Nikita, seem to have very different ideas about how much discount to allow. To test his suspicion, he selects 30 cars from the lot and asks Frank and Nikita to each say how much discount they would allow a customer. If we want to test whether the mean discount they each give is the same, what test would we use? Explain.

ANSWER   A paired *t*-test. The responses (maximum discount in $) aren't independent between the two salespeople because they're evaluating the same 30 cars.

LO❸   14.7   The Paired *t*-Test

The paired *t*-test is mechanically a one-sample *t*-test from Section 13.5. We treat the differences as our variable. We simply compare the mean difference to its standard error. If the *t*-statistic is large enough, we reject the null hypothesis.

Paired *t*-Test

When the conditions are met, we're ready to test whether the mean paired difference is significantly different from a hypothesized value (called Δ_0). We test the hypothesis

$$H_0 : \mu_d = \Delta_0,$$

where the *d*'s are the pairwise differences and Δ_0 is almost always 0.

We use the statistic

$$t_{n-1} = \frac{\bar{d} - \Delta_0}{SE(\bar{d})},$$

where s_d is the mean of the pairwise differences, *n* is the number of pairs, and

$$SE(\bar{d}) = \frac{s_d}{\sqrt{n}},$$

where s_d is the standard deviation of the pairwise differences.

When the conditions are met and the null hypothesis is true, the sampling distribution of this statistic is a Student's *t*-model with $n - 1$ degrees of freedom, and we use that model to obtain the P-value.

Similarly, we can construct a confidence interval for the true difference. As in a one-sample *t*-interval (Section 13.2), we centre our estimate at the mean difference in our data. The margin of error on either side is the standard error multiplied by a critical *t*-value (based on our confidence level and the number of pairs we have).

> **Paired *t*-Confidence Interval**
>
> When the conditions are met, we're ready to find the confidence interval for the mean of the paired differences. The confidence interval is
>
> $$\bar{d} \pm t^{*}_{n-1} \times SE(\bar{d}),$$
>
> where the standard error of the mean difference is $SE(\bar{d}) = \dfrac{s_d}{\sqrt{n}}$.
>
> The critical value t^{*} from the Student's *t*-model depends on the particular confidence level you specify and on the degrees of freedom, $n - 1$, which is based on the number of pairs, *n*.

When data are paired, the *t*-test can sometimes see differences that a two-sample *t*-test can't. A paired design has roughly half the degrees the freedom of the two-sample *t*-test. Typically, we'd want *more* degrees of freedom, but usually pairing more than compensates for this by reducing the variation.

JUST CHECKING

Think about each of the following situations. Would you use a two-sample *t* or paired *t* method (or neither)? Why?

5 Random samples of 50 men and 50 women are surveyed on the amount they invest on average in the stock market on an annual basis. We want to estimate any gender difference in how much they invest.

6 A single random sample of 500 students was surveyed on their perception of ethical and community service issues in both their first year and their fourth year at a university. The university wants to know whether its required programs in ethical decision making and service learning change student perceptions.

7 A random sample of work groups within a company was identified. Within each work group, one male and one female worker were selected at random. Each was asked to rate the secretarial support that their work group received. When rating the same support staff, do men and women rate them equally, on average?

8 A total of 50 companies are surveyed about business practices. They are categorized by industry, and we wish to investigate differences across industries.

9 These same 50 companies are surveyed again one year later to see if their perceptions, business practices, and R&D investment have changed.

GUIDED EXAMPLE   Seasonal Spending in Canada

Ariel Skelley/Blend Images/Getty Images

In Canada, it is well known that retail sales are higher than average in December and drop substantially in January. In 2014, December sales were 12.5% higher than the average of the previous 11 months, but there was a drop of 24.8% in January 2015. This sudden drop in January impacts credit card companies, since they receive a percentage of the amount spent on each card. But how much is the drop for our credit card—say, Scotiabank Visa? The answer depends on the demographics.

For any particular group of cardholders, we could select two random samples—one for each month—and simply compare the average amount spent in January with that in December. A more sensible approach might be to select a single random sample and compare the spending between the two months for *each cardholder* in that sample. Designing the study in this way and examining the paired differences gives a more precise estimate of the actual change in spending.

We have a sample of 911 cardholders aged 25–30 and the amount they charged on their cards last December and January. We plan to use a paired *t*-confidence interval to estimate the mean difference in spending for all our cardholders in that demographic group.

WHO	Cardholders in a particular market segment of a major credit card issuer
WHAT	Amount charged on their credit cards
WHEN	Last December and January
WHERE	Canada
WHY	To estimate the amount of decrease in spending one could expect after the holiday shopping season

Source: Based on Statistics Canada. (2015). Table 800020: Retail trade, sales by the North American Industry Classification System (NAICS).

PLAN

Setup State what we want to know.

Identify the *parameter* we wish to estimate and the sample size.

Model Check the conditions.

State why the data are paired. Simply having the same number of individuals in each group or displaying them in side-by-side columns doesn't make them paired.

Think about what we hope to learn and where the randomization comes from.

Make a picture of the differences. Don't plot separate distributions of the two groups—that would entirely miss the pairing. For paired data, it's the Normality of the differences that we care about. Treat those paired differences as you would a single variable, and check the Nearly Normal Condition.

Specify the sampling distribution model.

Choose the method.

We want to know how much we can expect credit card charges to change, on average, from December to January for cardholders aged 25–30, and we have data for a random sample of 911 cardholders for their spending last December and January. We want to find a confidence interval for the true mean difference in charges between these two months for all cardholders in this segment. Because we know that people tend to spend more in December, we'll look at the difference: *December spend–January spend*. A positive difference will mean a decrease in spending.

✓ **Paired Data Assumption.** The data are paired because they are measurements on the same cardholders in two different months.

✓ **Independence Assumption.** The behaviour of any individual is independent of the behaviour of the others, so the differences are mutually independent.

✓ **Randomization Condition.** This was a random sample from a large market segment.

✓ **Nearly Normal Condition.** The distribution of the differences is unimodal and symmetric. Although there are many observations nominated by the boxplot as outliers, the distributions are symmetric. (This is typical of the behaviour of credit card spending.) There are no isolated cases that would unduly dominate the mean difference, so we'll leave all observations in the study.

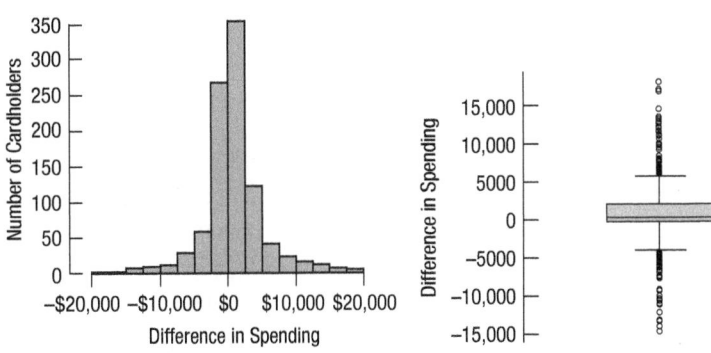

The conditions are met, so we'll use a Student's *t*-model with $(n - 1) = 910$ degrees of freedom and find a **paired *t*-confidence interval.**

DO

Mechanics *n* is the number of *pairs*—in this case, the number of cardholders.

$\bar{d}$ is the mean difference.

The computer output tells us:

$n =$ 911 pairs

$\bar{d} =$ 788.18

$s_d =$ 3740.22

(continued)

s_d is the standard deviation of the differences.

Make a picture. Sketch a t-model centred at the observed mean of 788.18.

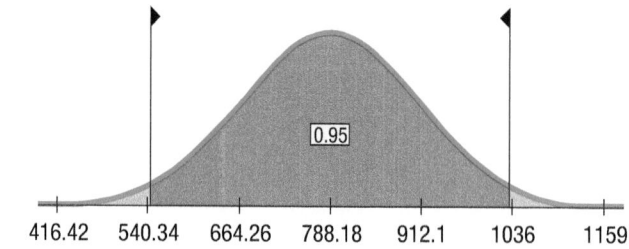

Find the standard error and the t-score of the observed mean difference. There is nothing new in the mechanics of the paired t methods. These are the mechanics of the t-interval for a mean applied to the differences.

We estimate the standard error of $\bar{d}$ using:

$$SE(\bar{d}) = \frac{s_d}{\sqrt{n}} = \frac{3740.22}{\sqrt{911}} = \$123.919$$

$$t^*_{910} = 1.96$$

The margin of error is $ME = t^*_{910} \times SE(\bar{d})$

$$= 1.96 \times 123.919 = 242.88$$

So a 95% CI is $\bar{d} \pm ME = (\$545.30, \$1031.06)$.

REPORT

Conclusion Link the results of the confidence interval to the context of the problem.

MEMO

Re: Credit Card Expenditure Changes
In the sample of cardholders studied, the change in expenditures between December and January averaged \$788.18, which means that, on average, card-holders spend \$788.18 *less* in January than the month before. Although we didn't measure the change for all cardholders in the segment, we can be 95% confident that the true *mean* decrease in spending is between \$545.30 and \$1031.06.

FOR EXAMPLE   The paired t-test for car discounts

Here are some summary statistics from the study undertaken by the car dealership owner (see For Example: "Paired data for car discounts"):

$$\bar{y}_{Frank} = \$414.48 \quad \bar{y}_{Nikita} = \$478.88$$
$$SD_{Frank} = \$87.33 \quad SD_{Nikita} = \$175.12$$
$$\bar{y}_{Diff} = \$64.40 \quad SD_{Diff} = \$146.74$$

QUESTION Test the hypothesis that the mean maximum discount that Frank and Nikita would give is the same. Give a 95% confidence interval for the mean difference.

ANSWER We use a paired t-test because Frank and Nikita were asked to give opinions about the same 30 cars:

$$t_{n-1} = \frac{\bar{d}}{SE(\bar{d})}$$

$$SE(\bar{d}) = \frac{s_d}{\sqrt{n}} = \frac{146.74}{\sqrt{30}} = \$26.79$$

$$t_{29} = \frac{64.40}{26.79} = 2.404$$

which has a (two-sided) P-value of 0.0228. We reject the null hypothesis that the mean difference is 0 at the 95% level and conclude that there's strong evidence to suggest that they're not the same.

A 95% confidence interval,

$$t_{29}^* = 2.045 \text{ at } 95\% \text{ confidence}$$

$$\bar{d} \pm t_{29}^* \times SE(\bar{d}) = 64.40 \pm 2.045 \times 26.79$$

$$= (\$9.61, \ \$119.19),$$

shows that Nikita gives, on average, somewhere between $9.61 and $119.19 more for her maximum discount than Frank does.

WHAT CAN GO WRONG?

- **Watch out for paired data.** The Independent Groups Assumption deserves special attention. Some researchers deliberately violate this assumption. For example, suppose you wanted to test a diet program. You select 10 people at random to take part in your diet. You measure their weights at the beginning of the diet and after 10 weeks of the diet. So you have two columns of weights, one for *before* and one for *after*. The data are related; each "*after*" weight goes naturally with the "before" weight for the *same* person. So we should use the paired *t*-test.

- **Don't use individual confidence intervals for each group to test the difference between their means.** If you make 95% confidence intervals for the means of two groups separately and you find that the intervals don't overlap, you can reject the hypothesis that the means are equal (at the corresponding α level). But if the intervals do overlap, it doesn't mean that you *can't* reject the null hypothesis. The margin of error for the difference between the means is smaller than the sum of the individual confidence interval margins of error. Comparing the individual confidence intervals is like adding the standard deviations. But we know that it's the variances that we add, and when we do it right, we actually get a more powerful test. So don't test the difference between group means by looking at separate confidence intervals. Always make a two-sample *t*-interval or perform a two-sample *t*-test.

- **Look at the plots.** The usual (by now) cautions about checking for outliers and non-Normal distributions apply. The simple defence is to make and examine boxplots. You may be surprised at how often this simple step saves you from the wrong or even absurd conclusions that can be generated by a single undetected outlier. You don't want to conclude that two methods have very different means just because one observation is atypical.

- **Don't forget outliers.** The outliers we care about now are in the differences. A subject who is extraordinary both before and after a treatment may still have a perfectly typical difference. But one outlying difference can completely distort your conclusions. Be sure to plot the differences (even if you also plot the data).

- **Don't use a paired *t* method when the samples aren't paired.** When two groups don't have the same number of values, it's easy to see that they can't be paired. But just because two groups have the same number of observations doesn't mean they can be paired, even if they're shown side by side in a table. We might have 25 men and 25 women in our study, but they might be completely independent of one another. If they were siblings or spouses, we might consider them paired. Remember that you can't *choose* which method to use based on your preferences. Only if the data are from an experiment or study in which observations were paired can you use a paired method.

ETHICS IN ACTION

Anthony Meehan/Mediacorp Canada

The Canada's Best Diversity Employers program recognizes employers that have exceptional diversity and inclusiveness programs covering (a) women, (b) members of visible minorities, (c) persons with disabilities, (d) Aboriginal peoples, and (e) lesbian, gay, bisexual, and transgendered/transsexual (LGBT) peoples.

Advocacy groups for equity and diversity in the workplace often cite middle managers as an obstacle to many organizations' efforts to be more inclusive. In response to this concern, Li Xue, the CEO for a mining company, asked Mohammed Mehri, VP of Human Resources, to look into the possibility of instituting some type of diversity training for the company's middle managers. One option under consideration was an online education program that focused on cultural diversity, gender equity, and disability awareness. Mohammed suspected that an online program, although cost-effective, would not be as effective as traditional training for middle managers. In order to evaluate the program under consideration, 20 middle managers were selected to participate. Before beginning, they were given a test to assess their knowledge of and sensitivity to various diversity and equity issues. Out of a possible perfect score of 100, the test average was 63.65. Each of the 20 managers then completed the six-week online diversity education program and was retested. The average on the test after completing the online program was 69.15. Although the group achieved a higher mean test score after completing the program, the two-sample t-test revealed that this average test score wasn't significantly higher than the average prior to completing the online program ($t = -0.94$, P-value $= 0.176$). Mohammed wasn't surprised, and began to explore more traditional diversity education programs.

Ethical Issue: *The pre-test and post-test designs violate independence, and therefore the two-sample t-test is not appropriate (related to Item A, ASA Ethical Guidelines; see Appendix C, the American Statistical Association's Ethical Guidelines for Statistical Practice, also available online at www.amstat.org/about/ethicalguidelines.cfm).*

Ethical Solution: *Using the correct test, the paired t-test, may show that the online diversity education program was effective.*

WHAT HAVE WE LEARNED?

Learning Objectives

❶ We've learned how to test whether the difference in the means of two independent groups is equal to some hypothesized value.
- The two-sample t-test is appropriate for independent groups. It uses a special formula for degrees of freedom.
- The assumptions and conditions are the same as for one-sample inferences for means, with the addition of assuming that the groups are independent of each other.
- The most common null hypothesis is that the means are equal.

❷ We've learned how to construct and interpret a confidence interval for the difference between the means of two independent groups.
- The confidence interval inverts the t-test in the natural way.

We've learned how and when to use pooled t-inference methods.
- There is an additional assumption that the variances of the two groups are equal.
- This may be a plausible assumption in a randomized experiment.

❸ We've learned to recognize when you have paired or matched samples and to use an appropriate inference method.
- Paired t methods are the same as one-sample t methods applied to the pairwise differences.
- If data are paired they cannot be independent, so two-sample t and pooled t methods would not be applicable.

Terms

Paired data
    Data are paired when the observations are collected in pairs or the observations in one group are naturally related to observations in the other. The simplest form of pairing is to measure each subject twice—often before and after a treatment is applied.

Paired t-confidence interval	A confidence interval for the mean of the pairwise differences between paired groups found as $\bar{d} \pm t^*_{n-1} \times SE(\bar{d})$, where $SE(\bar{d}) = \dfrac{s_d}{\sqrt{n}}$ and n is the number of pairs.
Paired t-test	A hypothesis test for the mean of the pairwise differences of two groups. It tests the null hypothesis $H_0 : \mu_d = \Delta_0$, where the hypothesized difference is almost always 0, using the statistic $t = \dfrac{\bar{d} - \Delta_0}{SE(\bar{d})}$ with $n - 1$ degrees of freedom, where $SE(\bar{d}) = \dfrac{s_d}{\sqrt{n}}$ and n is the number of pairs.
Pooled t-confidence interval	A confidence interval for the difference in the means of two independent groups used when we are willing and able to make the additional assumption that the variances of the groups are equal. It is found as: $$(\bar{y}_1 - \bar{y}_2) \pm t^*_{df} \times SE_{pooled}(\bar{y}_1 - \bar{y}_2),$$ where $$SE_{pooled}(\bar{y}_1 - \bar{y}_2) = s_{pooled}\sqrt{\dfrac{1}{n_1} + \dfrac{1}{n_2}},$$ and the pooled variance is $$s^2_{pooled} = \dfrac{(n_1 - 1)S^2_1 + (n_2 - 1)S^2_2}{(n_1 - 1) + (n_2 - 1)}.$$ The number of degress of freedom is $(n_1 - 1) + (n_2 - 1)$.
Pooled t-test	A hypothesis test for the difference in the means of two independent groups when we are willing and able to assume that the variances of the groups are equal. It tests the null hypothesis $$H_0 : \mu_1 - \mu_2 = \Delta_0$$ where the hypothesized difference Δ_0 is almost always 0, using the statistic $$t_{df} = \dfrac{(\bar{y}_1 - \bar{y}_2) - \Delta_0}{SE_{pooled}(\bar{y}_1 - \bar{y}_2)},$$ where the pooled standard error is defined as for the pooled t-confidence interval and the degrees of freedom is $(n_1 - 1) + (n_2 - 1)$.
Pooling	Combining data from two or more populations to estimate a statistic (typically a pooled variance) when we're willing to assume that the estimated value is the same in both populations. The resulting larger sample size may lead to an estimate with lower sample variance.
Two-sample t-confidence interval	A confidence interval for the difference in the means of two independent groups found as $$(\bar{y}_1 - \bar{y}_2) \pm t^*_{df} \times SE(\bar{y}_1 - \bar{y}_2), \text{ where}$$ $$SE(\bar{y}_1 - \bar{y}_2) = \sqrt{\dfrac{s^2_1}{n_1} + \dfrac{s^2_2}{n_2}}$$ and the number of degrees of freedom is given by the approximation formula in Footnote 1 of this chapter, or with technology.
Two-sample t-test	A hypothesis test for the difference in the means of two independent groups. It tests the null hypothesis $$H_0 : \mu_1 - \mu_2 = \Delta_0,$$ where the hypothesized difference Δ_0 is almost always 0, using the statistic $$t_{df} = \dfrac{(\bar{y}_1 - \bar{y}_2) - \Delta_0}{SE(\bar{y}_1 - \bar{y}_2)},$$ with the number of degrees of freedom given by the approximation formula in Footnote 1 of this chapter, or with technology.

Skills

Plan

- Be able to recognize situations in which we want to do inference on the difference between the means of two independent groups.
- Know how to examine your data for violations of conditions that would make inference about the difference between two population means unwise or invalid.

Do
- Be able to recognize when a pooled t procedure might be appropriate, and be able to explain your reasons if you decide to use a two-sample method anyway.
- Recognize whether a design that compares two groups is paired or not.
- Be able to perform a two-sample t-test using a statistics package or calculator (at least for finding the degrees of freedom).
- Know how to find a paired confidence interval, recognizing that it is mechanically equivalent to doing a one-sample t-interval applied to the differences.
- Be able to perform a paired t-test, recognizing that it is mechanically equivalent to a one-sample t-test applied to the differences.

Report
- Be able to interpret a test of the null hypothesis that the means of two independent groups are equal. (If the test is a pooled t-test, your interpretation should include a defence of your assumption of equal variances.)
- Know how to interpret a paired t-test, recognizing that the hypothesis tested is about the mean of the differences between paired values rather than about the differences between the means of two independent groups.
- Know how to interpret a paired t-interval, recognizing that it gives an interval for the mean difference in the pairs.

MINI case studies

Real Estate

Larger homes generally fetch a higher price than smaller homes. How much can we learn about a house from the fact that it has a fireplace or more than the average number of bedrooms? Data for a random sample of 1047 homes can be found in the file **ch14_MCSP_Real_Estate**. There are six quantitative variables: *Price* (\$), *Living Area* (sq. ft.), *Bathrooms* (#), *Bedrooms* (#), *Lot Size* (acres), and *Age* (years), and one categorical variable, *Fireplace?* (1 = Yes; 0 = No), denoting whether the house has at least one fireplace. We can use t methods to see, for example, whether homes with fireplaces sell for more, on average, and by how much. For the quantitative variables, create new categorical variables by splitting them at the median or some other splitting point of your choice, and compare home prices above and below this value. For example, the median number of *Bedrooms* of these homes is two. You might compare the prices of homes with one or two bedrooms to those with more than two. Write up a short report summarizing the differences in mean price based on the categorical variables you created.

Rate Your Professors in Canada

Rate My Professors[6] records the opinions of students about their professors according to three criteria: clarity, easiness, and helpfulness. You and your friend want to choose between two professors for your Statistics class, and you see that the average ratings of these professors are as follows, together with the number of students who have provided those ratings:

	Number of Students	Clarity	Easiness	Helpfulness
Professor X	12	4.2	4.5	3.3
Professor Y	47	4.0	4.1	3.6

Like many organizations providing ratings and evaluations, Rate My Professors provides an average rating without any measure of the extent of variation among the students from which that average was calculated. You estimate the standard deviations in the ratings as

---
[6]www.RateMyProfessors.com

10% of the averages in the table (e.g., you estimate the standard deviation of Prof X's Clarity rating to be $0.1 < 4.2 = 0.42$), whereas your friend estimates them as 20% of the average. (a) Do these different assumptions result in you and your friend coming to different conclusions (at the 0.05 significance level) about which professor is better on the three criteria given? (Give three answers, one for each criterion.) (b) Does it make any difference if you pool your estimates of the standard deviations? (Give three answers, one for each criterion.) (c) What percentage would the standard deviation need to be in relation to the mean for you to be just unable to distinguish between the professors at the 90% level? (Give six answers, with two significant figures of accuracy: one for each criterion in the pooled and not pooled situations. *Hint:* Use a trial-and-error approach with software.)

Consumer Spending Patterns

You're on the financial planning team for monitoring a high-spending segment of a credit card. You know that customers tend to spend more during December before the holidays, but you're not sure about the pattern of spending in the months after the holidays. Look at the data set **ch14_MCSP_Consumer_Spending**. It contains the monthly credit card spending of 1200 customers during the months December, January, February, and March. Report on the spending differences between the months. If you'd failed to realize that these are paired data, what difference would that have made in your reported confidence intervals and tests?

Technology Help: Comparing Two Means

Here's some typical computer package output with comments:

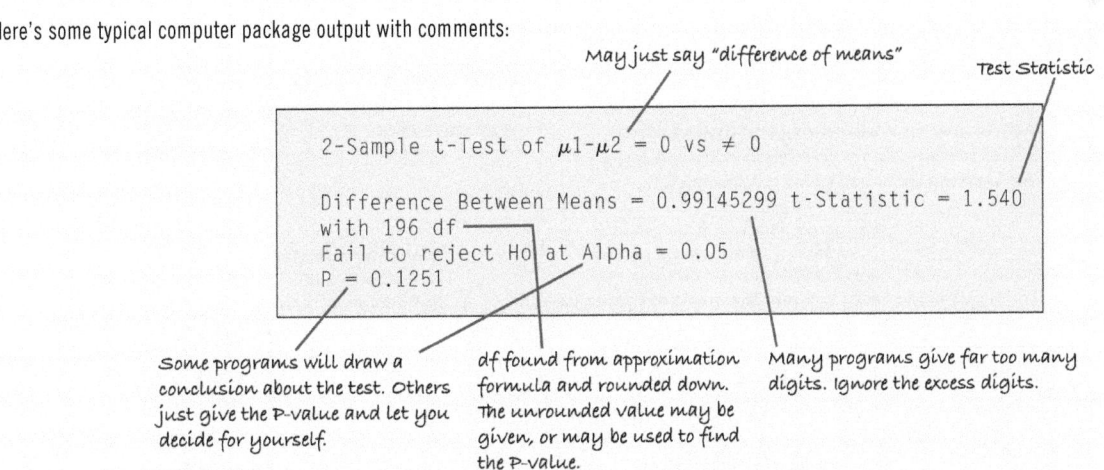

Some statistics software packages automatically try to test whether the variances of the two groups are equal, and some software packages automatically offer both the two-sample *t* and pooled *t* results. Ignore the test for the variances; it has little power in any situation in which its results could matter. If the pooled and two-sample methods differ in any important way, you should stick with the two-sample method. Most likely, the Equal Variance Assumption needed for the pooled method has failed.

The degrees of freedom approximation usually gives a fractional value. Most packages seem to round the approximate value down to the

next smallest integer (although they may actually compute the P-value with the fractional value, gaining a tiny amount of power).

There are two ways to organize data when we want to compare two independent groups. The first, called *unstacked data*, lists the data in two columns, one for each group. Each list can be thought of as a variable. In this method, the variables in the credit card example would be "Offer" and "No Offer." Graphing calculators usually prefer this form, and some computer programs can use it as well.

The alternative way to organize the data is as *stacked data*. What is the response variable for the credit card experiment? It's the "Spend

(continued)

Lift"—the amount by which customers increased their spending. But the values of this variable in the unstacked lists are in both columns, and actually there's an experiment factor here, too—namely, whether the customer was offered the promotion or not. So we could put the data into two different columns, one with the "Spend Lifts" in it and one with a "Yes" for those who were offered the promotion and a "No" for those who weren't. The stacked data would look like this:

Spend Lift	Offer
969.74	Yes
915.04	Yes
197.57	No
77.31	No
196.27	Yes
…	…

The commands to do inference for two independent groups on common statistics technology are not always found in obvious places. Here are some starting guidelines.

Most statistics programs can compute paired *t* analyses. Some may want you to find the differences yourself and use the one-sample *t* methods. Those that perform the entire procedure will need to know the two variables to compare. The computer, of course, can't verify that the variables are naturally paired. Most programs will check whether the two variables have the same number of observations, but some stop there, and that can cause trouble. Most programs will automatically omit any pair that's missing a value for either variable. You must look carefully to see whether that has happened.

Below is a generic example with comments:

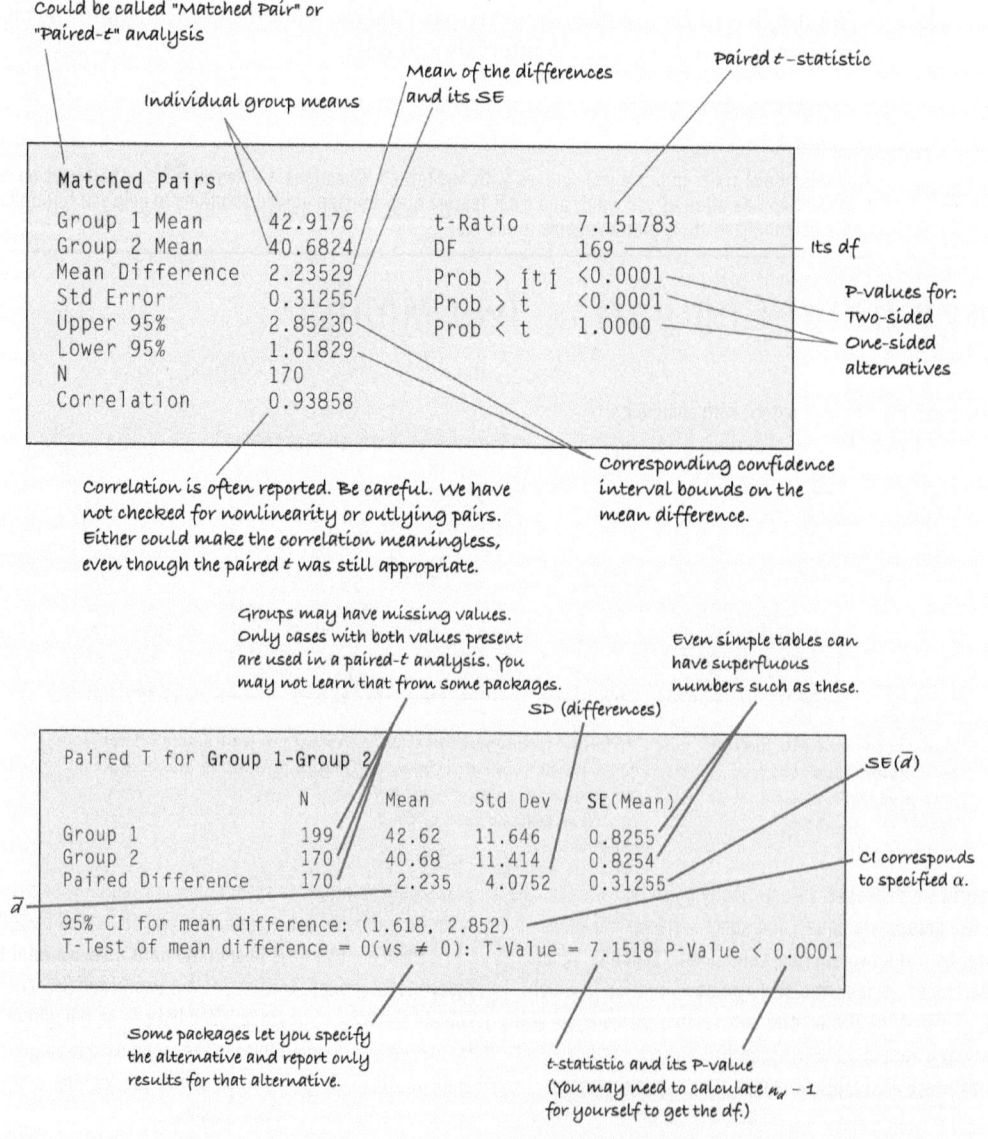

Could be called "Matched Pair" or "Paired-*t*" analysis

Individual group means

Mean of the differences and its SE

Paired *t*-statistic

```
Matched Pairs

Group 1 Mean      42.9176      t-Ratio    7.151783
Group 2 Mean      40.6824      DF         169
Mean Difference    2.23529     Prob > |t| <0.0001
Std Error          0.31255     Prob > t   <0.0001
Upper 95%          2.85230     Prob < t    1.0000
Lower 95%          1.61829
N                170
Correlation        0.93858
```

Its df

P-values for:
Two-sided
One-sided alternatives

Correlation is often reported. Be careful. We have not checked for nonlinearity or outlying pairs. Either could make the correlation meaningless, even though the paired *t* was still appropriate.

Corresponding confidence interval bounds on the mean difference.

Groups may have missing values. Only cases with both values present are used in a paired-*t* analysis. You may not learn that from some packages.

SD (differences)

Even simple tables can have superfluous numbers such as these.

SE($\bar{d}$)

```
Paired T for Group 1-Group 2

                N      Mean    Std Dev   SE(Mean)
Group 1        199    42.62    11.646     0.8255
Group 2        170    40.68    11.414     0.8254
Paired Difference  170    2.235     4.0752     0.31255

95% CI for mean difference: (1.618, 2.852)
T-Test of mean difference = 0(vs ≠ 0): T-Value = 7.1518 P-Value < 0.0001
```

$\bar{d}$

CI corresponds to specified α.

Some packages let you specify the alternative and report only results for that alternative.

t-statistic and its P-value (You may need to calculate $n_d - 1$ for yourself to get the df.)

EXCEL

To perform a two-sample *t*-test in Excel using Data Analysis Tool Pack:

- In the **Data** menu, Choose **Data Analysis** (found under Analysis).
- Choose the appropriate *t*-test from the menu.
- Identify the following:
  - The cell range for the data in the two samples (for testing independent groups) or the difference data (for a paired *t*-test).
  - The hypothesized difference.
- Check the box next to Labels if the first row of the data contains labels, and identify where you would like the results to be placed.

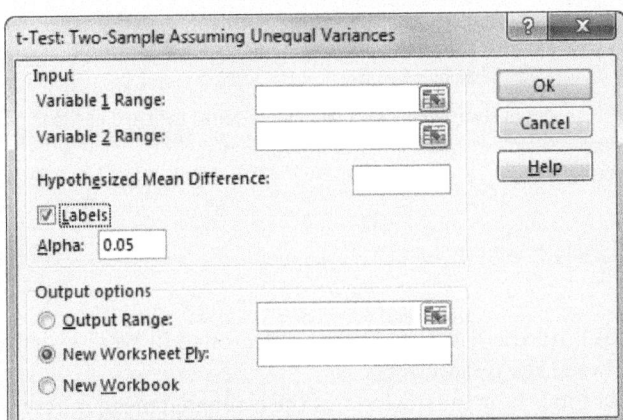

To perform a two-sample *t*-test using built-in formulas:

- From Formulas, choose **More functions** > **Statistical** > **T.TEST**, and specify:
  - Array 1 and Array 2 = Location in the spreadsheet of the two groups to compare.
  - Tails of the distribution = 1 for one-tailed test and 2 for two-tailed test.
- Type = 1 for a paired test, 2 for equal variance *t*-test, and 3 for un-equal variance *t*-test.

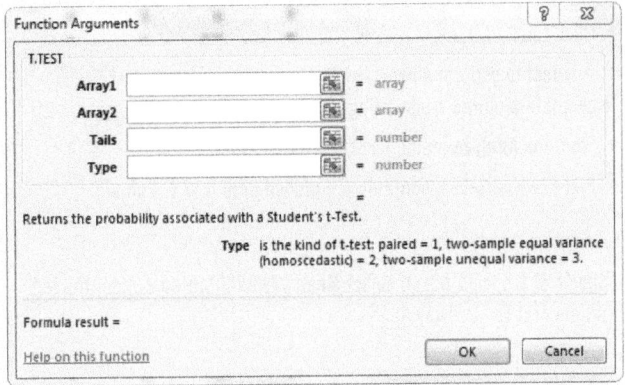

To perform a paired *t*-test in Excel:

- Enter paired data into two columns with one pair in each row.
- In another column, calculate the difference of the values in the two columns.
- Analyze the difference column using a one-sample *t*-test. An example is shown below:

	A	B	C	D	E
1	t-Test of a Mean				
2					**Syntax for Column D**
3	Sample mean	460.38	t Stat	1.89	=(B3-B6)/(B4/B5^0.5)
4	Sample standard deviation	38.83	P(T<=t) one-tail	0.0323	=1-(T.DIST(ABS(D3),(B5-1),1))
5	Sample size	50	t Critical lower one-tail	-1.6766	=T.INV(B7,B5-1)
6	Hypothesized mean	450	t Critical upper one tail	1.6766	=ABS(T.INV(B7,B5-1))
7	Alpha	0.05	P(T<=t) two-tail	0.0646	=2*D4
8			t Critical two-tail	± 2.0096	=T.INV(B7/2,B5-1)

XLSTAT

To conduct a *t*-test for the difference between two means:

- Choose **Parametric tests**, and then **Two-sample *t*-test and *z*-test**.
- If the two samples are in two separate columns in your workbook, choose the option **One column per sample**.
- If your data are *stacked* (one column lists the data, and the other the group identifier), choose the option **One column per variable**.
- If the data are paired, choose the option **Paired samples**.
- Enter the range of cell data.
- On the **Options** tab, for a test that is not pooled uncheck the box next to **Assume equality**.

The output yields the results of a hypothesis test and a confidence interval for the difference between means.

MINITAB

To perform a two-sample *t*-test in Minitab:

- From the **Stat** menu, choose the **Basic Statistics** submenu.
- Choose **2t 2-sample t**… and fill in the dialogue for:
  - Data in "one column" (unstacked data)
  - Data in "two columns" (stacked data) or
  - Summarized data

To conduct a paired *t*-test using Minitab:

- From the **Stat** menu, choose the **Basic Statistics** submenu.
- Choose **t-t Paired t** and fill in the dialogue for:
  - Data in "two columns" or
  - Summarized data

Note: For two-sample *t*-tests, the **Graphs** button creates boxplots of your two samples and the **Options** button allows you to conduct either a one-sided or two-sided test or change the confidence level.

(*continued*)

To conduct a two-sample *t*-test in JMP:

- From the **Analyze** menu, select **Fit X by Y**.
- Select variables: a **Y, Response** variable that holds the data and an **X, Factor** variable that holds the group names. Click OK, and JMP will make a dotplot. Be sure that the variable type for the **X, Factor** variable is set to nominal or ordinal.
- Click the Red triangle next to "Oneway Analysis…" and select:
  - *t* **Test** to perform a two-sample *t*-test.

To compute a paired *t*-test using JMP:

- From the **Analyze** menu, select **Matched Pairs**.
- Place two variables containing matched data into **Y, Column**.

Comments

To perform a pooled *t*-test, select **Means/ANOVA/Pooled** *t* under the red triangle next to "Oneway Analysis…"

To conduct a two-sample *t*-test in SPSS:

- From the **Analyze** menu, choose the **Compare Means** submenu.
- Choose **Independent-Samples t-test**.
- Specify the data variable and grouping variable, click the button under the grouping variable, and identify numerical codes for groups.

Note: SPSS offers both the two-sample and pooled-*t* results in the same table. SPSS expects the data in one variable and group names in the other. If there are more than two group names in the group variable, only the two that are named in the dialogue box will be compared.

To perform a paired *t*-test in SPSS:

- From the **Analyze** menu, choose the **Compare Means** submenu.
- Choose **Paired Samples t-test**.
- Highlight the two variables containing the paired data and add to the list.

EXERCISES

SECTION 14.1

1. A developer wants to know if the houses in two different neighbourhoods were built at roughly the same time. She takes a random sample of houses from each neighbourhood and finds that the summary statistics for the two neighbourhoods look as follows:

Neighbourhood 1	Neighbourhood 2
$n_1 = 30$	$n_2 = 35$
$\bar{y}_1 = 57.2$ yrs	$\bar{y}_2 = 47.6$ yrs
$S_1 = 7.51$ yrs	$S_2 = 7.85$ yrs

a) Find the estimated mean age difference between the two neighbourhoods.
b) Find the standard error of the estimated mean difference.
c) Calculate the *t*-statistic for the observed difference in mean ages, assuming that the true mean difference is 0. **LO ❶**

2. A market analyst wants to know if the new website he designed is showing increased page views per visit. A customer is randomly sent to one of two different websites, which offer the same products but with different designs. He takes a random sample of customers from each website and records their page views. Here are the data:

Website 1	Website 2
$n_1 = 80$	$n_2 = 95$
$\bar{y}_1 = 7.7$ pages	$\bar{y}_2 = 7.3$ pages
$S_1 = 4.6$ pages	$S_2 = 4.3$ pages

a) Find the estimated mean difference in page visits between the two websites.
b) Find the standard error of the estimated mean difference.
c) Calculate the *t*-statistic for the observed difference in mean page visits, assuming that the true mean difference is 0. **LO ❶**

SECTIONS 14.2 AND 14.3

3. Using the data in Exercise 1, test the hypothesis that the mean ages of houses in the two neighbourhoods are the same. You may assume that the ages of houses in each neighbourhood follow a Normal distribution.

a) Calculate the P-value of the statistic, knowing that the approximation formula gives 53.4 df (you'll need to round or to use technology).
b) Calculate the P-value of the statistic using the rule that df is at least $\min(n_1 - 1, n_2 - 1)$.
c) What do you conclude at $\alpha = 0.05$? **LO ❶**

4. Using the data in Exercise 2, test the hypothesis that the mean numbers of page views from the two websites are the same. You may assume that the number of page views from each website follows a Normal distribution.

a) Calculate the P-value of the statistic, knowing that the approximation formula gives 148.0 df.
b) Calculate the P-value of the statistic using the rule that df is at least $\min(n_1 - 1, n_2 - 1)$.
c) What do you conclude at $\alpha = 0.05$? **LO ❶**

SECTION 14.4

5. Using the summary statistics in Exercise 1, and assuming that the data come from a distribution that is Normally distributed,

a) Find a 95% confidence interval for the mean difference in ages of houses in the two neighbourhoods using the df given in Exercise 3.
b) Is 0 within the confidence interval?
c) What does it say about the null hypothesis that the mean difference is 0? **LO ❷**

6. Using the summary statistics in Exercise 2, and assuming that the data come from a distribution that's Normally distributed,

a) Find a 95% confidence interval for the mean difference in page views from the two websites.
b) Is 0 within the confidence interval?
c) What does it say about the null hypothesis that the mean difference is 0? **LO ❷**

SECTION 14.5

7. For the data in Exercise 1,

a) Test the null hypothesis $\alpha = 0.05$ using the pooled t-test. (Show the t-statistic, P-value, and conclusion.)
b) Find a 95% confidence interval using the pooled degrees of freedom.
c) Are your answers different from what you previously found in Exercise 5? Explain briefly why or why not. **LO ❷**

8. For the data in Exercise 2,

a) Test the null hypothesis $\alpha = 0.05$ using the pooled t-test. (Show the t-statistic, P-value, and conclusion.)
b) Find a 95% confidence interval using the pooled degrees of freedom.
c) Are your answers different from what you previously found in Exercise 6? Explain briefly why or why not. **LO ❷**

SECTION 14.6

9. For each of the following scenarios, say whether the data should be treated as independent or paired samples. Explain briefly. If paired, explain what the pairing involves.

a) An efficiency expert claims that a new ergonomic desk chair makes typing at a computer terminal easier and faster. To test it, 15 volunteers are selected. Using both the new chair and their old chair, each volunteer types a randomly selected passage for two minutes and the number of correct words typed is recorded.
b) A developer wants to know if the houses in two different neighbourhoods have the same mean price. She selects 10 houses from each neighbourhood at random and tests the null hypothesis that the means are equal.

c) A manager wants to know if the mean productivity of two workers is the same. For a random selection of 30 hours in the past month, he compares the number of items produced by each worker in that hour. **LO ❸**

10. For each of the following scenarios, say whether the data should be treated as independent or paired samples. Explain briefly. If paired, explain what the pairing involves.

a) An efficiency expert claims that a new ergonomic desk chair makes typing at a computer terminal easier and faster. To test it, 30 volunteers are selected. Half of the volunteers will use the new chair and half will use their old chairs. Each volunteer types a randomly selected passage for two minutes and the number of correct words typed is recorded.
b) A real estate agent wants to know how much extra a fireplace adds to the price of a house. She selects 25 city blocks. In each block she randomly chooses a house with a fireplace and one without and records the assessment value.
c) A manager wants to know if the mean productivity of two workers is the same. For each worker he randomly selects 30 hours in the past month and compares the number of items produced. **LO ❸**

SECTION 14.7

11. A supermarket chain wants to know if its "buy one, get one free" campaign increases customer traffic enough to justify the cost of the program. For each of 10 stores it selects two days at random to run the test. For one of those days (selected by a coin flip), the program will be in effect. The chain wants to test the hypothesis that there is no mean difference in traffic against the alternative that the program increases the mean traffic. Here are the results in number of customer visits to the 10 stores:

Store #	With Program	Without Program
1	140	136
2	233	235
3	110	108
4	42	35
5	332	328
6	135	135
7	151	144
8	33	39
9	178	170
10	147	141

a) Are the data paired? Explain.
b) Compute the mean of the differences.
c) Compute the standard deviation of the differences.
d) Compute the standard error of the mean difference.

e) Find the value of the *t*-statistic.
f) How many degrees of freedom does the *t*-statistic have?
g) Is the alternative one- or two-sided? Explain.
h) What is the P-value associated with this *t*-statistic? (Assume that the other assumptions and conditions for inference are met.)
i) At $\alpha = 0.05$, what do you conclude? **LO ❸**

12. A city wants to know if a new advertising campaign to make citizens aware of the dangers of driving after drinking has been effective. It counts the number of drivers who have been stopped with more alcohol in their system than the law allows for each day of the week in the week before and a month after the campaign starts. Here are the results:

Day of Week	Before	After
M	5	2
T	4	0
W	2	2
Th	4	1
F	6	8
S	14	7
Su	6	7

a) Are the data paired? Explain.
b) Compute the standard deviation of the differences.
c) Compute the standard error of the mean difference.
d) Find the value of the *t*-statistic.
e) How many degrees of freedom does the *t*-statistic have?
f) Is the alternative one- or two-sided? Explain.
g) What is the P-value associated with this *t*-statistic? (Assume that the other assumptions and conditions for inference are met.)
h) At $\alpha = 0.05$, what do you conclude? **LO ❸**

13. In order to judge whether the program is successful, the manager of the supermarket chain in Exercise 11 wants to know the plausible range of values for the mean increase in customers using the program. Construct a 90% confidence interval. **LO ❸**

14. A new operating system is installed in every workstation at a large company. The claim of the operating system manufacturer is that the time to shut down and turn on the machine will be much faster. To test it, an employee selects 36 machines and tests the combined shutdown and restart time of each machine before and after the new operating system has been installed. The mean and standard deviation of the differences (before – after) is 23.5 seconds with a standard deviation of 40 seconds.

a) What is the standard error of the mean difference?
b) How many degrees of freedom does the *t*-statistic have?

c) What is the 90% confidence interval for the mean difference?
d) What do you conclude at $\alpha = 0.05$? **LO ❸**

CHAPTER EXERCISES

15. Trucking company. A trucking company would like to compare two different routes for efficiency. Truckers are randomly assigned to two different routes. Twenty truckers following Route A report an average of 40 minutes with a standard deviation of 3 minutes. Twenty truckers following Route B report an average of 43 minutes with a standard deviation of 2 minutes. Histograms of travel times for the routes are roughly symmetric and show no outliers.

a) Find a 95% confidence interval for the difference in average time for the two routes.
b) Will the company save time by always driving one of the routes? Explain. **LO ❷**

16. Western Canada retail sales. A specialty food chain wants to compare the changes in sales across different regions. An examination of the differences in sales over a 37-week period in a recent year for 8 stores in Alberta compared with 12 stores in British Columbia reveals the following descriptive statistics for relative increase in sales. (If these means are multiplied by 100, they show % increase in sales.)

Province	N	Mean	StDev
Alberta	8	0.0738	0.0666
B.C.	12	0.0559	0.0503

a) Find the 90% confidence interval for the difference in relative increase in sales over this time period.
b) Is there a significant difference in increase in sales between these two groups of stores? Explain.
c) What would you like to see to check the conditions? **LO ❷**

17. Cereal company. A food company is concerned about recent criticism that the sugar content of its children's cereals is high compared with that of adults' cereals. The data show the sugar content (as a percentage of weight) of several national brands of children's and adults' cereals:

Children's cereals: 40.3, 55, 45.7, 43.3, 50.3, 45.9, 53.5, 43, 44.2, 44, 47.4, 44, 33.6, 55.1, 48.8, 50.4, 37.8, 60.3, 46.6

Adults' cereals: 20, 30.2, 2.2, 7.5, 4.4, 22.2, 16.6, 14.5, 21.4, 3.3, 6.6, 7.8, 10.6, 16.2, 14.5, 4.1, 15.8, 4.1, 2.4, 3.5, 8.5, 10, 1, 4.4, 1.3, 8.1, 4.7, 18.4

a) Write the null and alternative hypotheses.
b) Check the conditions.
c) Find the 95% confidence interval for the difference in means.

d) Is the sugar content of children's cereals significantly higher than that of adults' cereals? **LO ❶, ❷**

18. **Foreclosure rates.** According to reports, home foreclosures were up 47% in March 2008 compared with the previous year (http://realestate.msn.com, April 2008). The data show home foreclosure rates (as % change from the previous year) for a sample of cities in two regions of the United States: the Northeast and the Southwest:

Northeast: 2.99, −2.36, 3.03, 1.01, 5.77, 9.95, −3.52, 7.16, −3.34, 4.75, 5.25, 6.21, 1.67, −2.45, −0.55, 3.45, 4.50, 1.87, −2.15, −0.75

Southwest: 10.15, 23.05, 18.95, 21.16, 17.45, 12.67, 13.75, 29.42, 11.45, 16.77, 12.67, 13.69, 25.81, 21.16, 19.67, 11.88, 13.67, 18.00, 12.88

a) Write the null and alternative hypotheses.
b) Check the conditions.
c) Test the hypothesis and find the P-value.
d) Is there a significant difference in the mean home foreclosure rates between these two regions of the United States? Explain. **LO ❶**

19. **Herbs from Halifax.** The owner of a small organic food store was concerned about her sales of a line of herbal products from Nova Scotia. As a result of increasing fuel costs, she recently had to increase its price. To help boost sales, she decided to place the product on a different shelf (near eye level for most consumers) and in a location near other popular products. She kept track of sales (number of containers sold per week) for six months after she made the change. These values are shown in the following table, along with the sales numbers for the six months prior to making the change, in stem-and-leaf displays:

After Change		Before Change	
3	2	2	0
3	9	2	899
4	23	3	224
4	589	3	7789
5	0012	4	0000223
5	55558	4	5567
6	00123	5	0
6	67	5	6
7	0		

Do these results suggest that sales are better after the change in product placement? Test an appropriate hypothesis and state your conclusion. Be sure to check assumptions and conditions. **LO ❶**

20. **Named tropical cyclones 2012.** It has been suggested that global climate change may be affecting the frequency of tropical storms. The data here show the number of tropical cyclones (including hurricanes) assigned official names by the National Hurricane Center. Is there evidence of a change?

1995–2001	2002–2012
19, 13, 7, 14, 12, 14, 15	12, 16, 15, 27, 9, 15, 16, 9, 19, 18, 19

a) Write the null and alternative hypotheses.
b) Are the conditions for hypothesis testing satisfied?
c) If so, test the hypothesis. **LO ❶**

❶ 21. Designated hitter 2012, part 1. American League baseball teams play their games with the designated hitter rule, meaning that pitchers do not bat. The league believes that replacing the pitcher, traditionally a weak hitter, with another player in the batting order produces more runs and generates more interest among fans. The data provided in the table below include the average numbers of runs scored per game (*Runs per game*) by American League and National League teams for the 2012 season (www.baseball-reference.com).

American League			National League		
Team	R/G	HR	Team	R/G	HR
Los Angeles Angels	4.73	187	Colorado Rockies	4.68	166
Texas Rangers	4.99	200	St. Louis Cardinals	4.72	159
Detroit Tigers	4.48	163	San Francisco Giants	4.43	103
Kansas City Royals	4.17	131	Washington Nationals	4.51	194
New York Yankees	4.96	245	Milwaukee Brewers	4.79	202
Boston Red Sox	4.53	165	Arizona Diamondbacks	4.53	165
Minnesota Twins	4.33	131	Philadelphia Phillies	4.22	158
Chicago White Sox	4.62	211	Los Angeles Dodgers	3.93	116
Cleveland Indians	4.12	136	Cincinnati Reds	4.13	172
Baltimore Orioles	4.40	214	New York Mets	4.01	139
Toronto Blue Jays	4.42	198	Atlanta Braves	4.32	149
Tampa Bay Rays	4.30	175	San Diego Padres	4.02	121
Oakland Athletics	4.40	195	Miami Marlins	3.76	137
Seattle Mariners	3.82	149	Pittsburgh Pirates	4.02	170
			Chicago Cubs	3.78	137
			Houston Astros	3.60	146

a) Create an appropriate display of these data. What do you see?
b) With a 95% confidence interval, estimate the mean number of runs scored by American League teams.
c) With a 95% confidence interval, estimate the mean number of runs scored by National League teams.

d) Explain why you should not use two separate confidence intervals to decide whether the two leagues differ in average number of runs scored. (*Source:* Norean Sharpe, Richard D De Veaux, Paul Velleman, David Wright, Business Statistics, Third Canadian Edition, 3e, © 2018, Pearson Education, Inc.) **LO ❷**

22. Productivity. A factory hiring people to work on an assembly line gives job applicants a test of manual agility. This test counts how many strangely shaped pegs the applicant can fit into matching holes in a one-minute period. The table summarizes the data by gender of the job applicant. Assume that all conditions necessary for inference are met.

	Male	Female
Number of Subjects	50	50
Pegs Placed:		
Mean	19.39	17.91
SD	2.52	3.39

a) Find 95% confidence intervals for the average number of pegs that males and females can each place.
b) The intervals in (a) overlap. What does this suggest about any gender-based difference in manual agility?
c) Find a 95% confidence interval for the difference in the mean number of pegs that could be placed by men and women.
d) What does the interval in (c) suggest about any gender-based difference in manual agility?
e) The two results seem contradictory. Which method is correct: doing two-sample inference, or doing one-sample inference twice?
f) Why don't the results agree? **LO ❷**

23. Online shopping. Online shopping statistics are routinely reported by www.shop.org. Of interest to many online retailers are gender-based differences in shopping preferences and behaviours. The average monthly online expenditures are reported for males and females:

Group		Male	Female
	n	45	45
	Mean	$352	$310
	StDev	$95	$80

a) Find 95% confidence intervals for the average monthly online expenditures for males and females.
b) These intervals overlap. What does this suggest about any gender-based difference in monthly online expenditures?
c) Find a 95% confidence interval for the *difference* in average monthly online expenditures between males and females.
d) The two results seem contradictory. Which method is correct: doing two-sample inference, or doing one-sample inference twice? **LO ❷**

T 24. Designated hitter 2012, part 2. Do the data in Exercise 21 suggest that the American League's designated hitter rule may lead to more runs per game scored?

a) Write the null and alternative hypotheses.
b) Find a 95% confidence interval for the difference in mean runs per game, and interpret your interval.
c) Test the hypothesis stated above in part (a) and find the P-value.
d) Interpret the P-value and state your conclusion. Does the test suggest that the American League scores more runs on average? **LO ❶, ❷**

25. Delivery time. A small appliance company is interested in comparing delivery times of its products during two months. The company is concerned that the summer slowdowns in August cause delivery times to be different during this month. Given the following delivery times (in days) of appliances to customers for a random sample of six orders each month, test if delivery times differ across these two months. **LO ❶**

June	54	49	68	66	62	62
August	50	65	74	64	68	72

26. ERP effectiveness. When implementing a packaged enterprise resource planning (ERP) system, many companies report that the module they first install is Financial Accounting. Among the measures used to gauge the effectiveness of their ERP system implementation is acceleration of the financial close process. Below is a sample of eight companies that report their average time (in weeks) to financial close before and after the implementation of their ERP system:

Company	Before	After
1	6.5	4.2
2	7.0	5.9
3	8.0	8.0
4	4.5	4.0
5	5.2	3.8
6	4.9	4.1
7	5.2	6.0
8	6.5	4.2

Which type of *t*-test is appropriate for this data? You're not asked to actually conduct the *t*-test, but rather just to say which type you would use. **LO ❶, ❸**

27. Advertisements. Ads for many products use sexual images to try to attract attention to the product, but do these ads bring people's attention to the item being advertised? A company wants to design an experiment to see if the presence of sexual images in an advertisement affects people's ability to remember the product.

a) Describe an experimental design that would require a paired t procedure to analyze the results.
b) Describe an experimental design that would require an independent sample procedure to analyze the results. **LO ❶, ❸**

28. Pizza sales, part 1. A national food product company believes that it sells more frozen pizza during the winter months than during the summer months. Average weekly sales for a sample of stores over a three-year period provided the following data for sales volume (in kilograms) during the two seasons:

Season	n	Mean	StDev	Minimum	Maximum
Winter	38	31,234	13,500	15,312	73,841
Summer	40	22,475	8442	12,743	54,706

a) How much difference is there between the mean amount of this brand of frozen pizza sold (in kilograms) between the two seasons? (Assume that this time frame represents typical sales in the area.)
b) Construct and interpret a 95% confidence interval for the difference between weekly sales during the winter and summer months.
c) Suggest factors that might have influenced sales of the frozen pizza during the winter months. **LO ❷**

29. Pizza sales, part 2. Here's some additional information about the pizza sales data presented in Exercise 28. It is generally thought that pizza sales spike during the weeks leading up to football championship games, as well as during the weeks leading up to the Super Bowl at the end of January each year. If we omit those six weeks of sales from this three-year period of weekly sales, the summary statistics look like this. Do sales appear to be higher during the winter months after omitting those weeks most influenced by football championship games?

Season	n	Mean	StDev	Minimum	Maximum
Winter	32	28,995	9913	15,312	48,354
Summer	40	22,475	8442	12,743	54,706

a) Write the null and alternative hypotheses.
b) Test the null hypothesis and state your conclusion.
c) Suggest additional factors that may influence pizza sales. **LO ❶**

30. Marketing slogan, part 1. A company is considering marketing its classical music as "music to study by." Is this a valid slogan? In a study conducted by some Statistics students, 62 people were randomly assigned to listen to rap music, music by Mozart, or no music while attempting to memorize objects pictured on a page. They were then asked to list all the objects they could remember. Here are summary statistics for each group:

	Rap	Mozart	No Music
Count	29	20	13
Mean	10.72	10.00	12.77
SD	3.99	3.19	4.73

a) Does it appear that it's better to study while listening to Mozart than to rap music? Test an appropriate hypothesis and state your conclusion.
b) Create a 90% confidence interval for the mean difference in memory score between students who study to Mozart and those who listen to no music at all. Interpret your interval. **LO ❶**

31. Marketing slogan, part 2. Using the results of the experiment described in Exercise 30, is it better to study without music at all than to listen to rap music?

a) Test an appropriate hypothesis and state your conclusion at the 95% significance level.
b) If you concluded that there is a difference, estimate the size of that difference with a 90% confidence interval and explain what your interval means. **LO ❶**

Ⓣ 32. Kitchener vs. Waterloo, part 1. Residents of Kitchener and Waterloo, Ontario, have an ongoing disagreement over who lays claim to the higher average price of a single-family home. You decide to obtain a random sample of homes listed for sale with a major local realtor to investigate if there's actually any difference in the average home price.

a) Using the data provided, check the conditions for this test.
b) Write the null and alternative hypotheses for this test.
c) Test the hypotheses and find the P-value.
d) What is your conclusion? **LO ❶**

Ⓣ 33. Kitchener vs. Waterloo, part 2. Residents of one of the cities discussed in Exercise 32 claim that since their city is much smaller, the sample size should be increased. Instead of random-sampling 30 homes, you decide to sample 42 homes from the database to test the difference in the mean prices of single-family homes in Kitchener and Waterloo.

a) Using the data provided, check the conditions for this test.
b) Write the null and alternative hypotheses for this test.
c) Test the hypotheses and find the P-value.
d) What is your conclusion? Did the sample size make a difference? **LO ❶**

34. Productivity and music. Some offices pipe in background music. The vendor claims this improves productivity, but might it cause more distraction? A firm's HR department wants to learn whether productivity is affected by background music. The company hires a research firm to conduct an experiment. The researchers will time some volunteers to see how long it takes them to complete some relatively easy crossword puzzles. During some of the trials, the room will be quiet; during other trials in the same room, background music will be piped in.

a) Design an experiment that will require a two-sample *t* procedure to analyze the results.
b) Design an experiment that will require a paired *t* procedure to analyze the results.
c) Which experiment would you consider the stronger design? Why? **LO ❶, ❸**

❶ **35.** Friday the 13th, part 1. The *British Medical Journal* published an article titled "Is Friday the 13th Bad for Your Health?" Researchers in Britain examined how Friday the 13th affects human behaviour. One question was whether people tend to stay at home more on such a date. The data show the number of cars passing Junctions 9 and 10 on the M25 motorway for consecutive Fridays (6th and 13th) for five different time periods:

Year	Month	6th	13th
1990	July	134,012	132,908
1991	September	133,732	131,843
1991	December	121,139	118,723
1992	March	124,631	120,249
1992	November	117,584	117,263

Here are summaries of two possible analyses:

Paired *t*-Test of $\mu 1 = \mu 2$ vs. $\mu 1 > \mu 2$
Mean of Paired Differences: 2022.4
t-Statistic = 2.9377w/4 df
P = 0.0212
2-Sample *t*-Test of $\mu 1 = \mu 2$ vs. $\mu 1 > \mu 2$
Difference Between Means: 2022.4
t-Statistic = 0.4237 w/7.998 df
P = 0.3402

a) Which of the tests is appropriate for these data? Explain.
b) Using the test you selected, state your conclusion.
c) Are the assumptions and conditions for inference met? **LO ❶, ❸**

36. All you can eat. Some sports arenas and ballparks are offering "all you can eat" sections where, for a higher ticket price, fans can feast on all the hot dogs and popcorn they want. (Alcohol and desserts are extra.) But, of course, the teams want to price those tickets appropriately. They want to design an experiment to determine how much fans are likely to eat in an "all you can eat" section and whether it's more or less than they might ordinarily eat in similar regular seats.

Juan Silva/The Image Bank/Getty Images

a) Design an experiment that would require a two-sample *t* procedure for analysis.
b) Design an experiment that would require a paired *t* procedure for analysis. **LO ❶, ❸**

❶ **37.** Online insurance, part 1. After seeing countless commercials claiming one can get cheaper car insurance from an online company, a local insurance agent was concerned that he might lose some customers. To investigate, he randomly selected profiles (type of car, coverage, driving record, etc.) for 10 of his clients and checked online price quotes for their policies. The comparisons are shown in the table. His statistical software produced the following summaries (where *PriceDiff = Local − Online*)

Variable	Count	Mean	StdDev
Local	10	799.200	229.281
Online	10	753.300	256.267
PriceDiff	10	45.9000	175.663

Local	Online	PriceDiff
568	391	177
872	602	270
451	488	−37
1229	903	326
605	677	−72
1021	1270	−249
783	703	80
844	789	55
907	1008	−101
712	702	10

At first, the insurance agent wondered whether there was some kind of mistake in this output. He thought the Pythagorean Theorem of Statistics should work for finding the standard deviation of the price differences—in other words, that $SD(Local - Online) = \sqrt{SD^2(Local) + SD^2(Online)}$. But when he checked, he found that $\sqrt{(229.281)^2 + (256.267)^2} = 343.864$, not 175.663, as given by the software. Tell him where his mistake is. **LO ❸**

❶ 38. Friday the 13th, part 2. The researchers in Exercise 35 also examined the number of people admitted to emergency rooms for vehicular accidents on 12 Friday evenings (six each on the 6th and 13th):

Year	Month	6th Group 1	13th Group 2
1989	October	9	13
1990	July	6	12
1991	September	11	14
1991	December	11	10
1992	March	3	4
1992	November	5	12

Based on these data, is there evidence that more people are admitted on average on Friday the 13th? Here are two possible analyses of the data:

Paired t-Test of $\mu1 = \mu2$ vs. $\mu1 < \mu2$

Mean of Paired Differences = 3.333

t-Statistic = 2.7116w/5 df

P = 0.0211

2-Sample t-Test of $\mu1 = \mu2$ vs. $\mu1 < \mu2$

Difference Between Means = 3.333

t-Statistic = 1.6644w/9.940 df

P = 0.0636

a) Which of these tests is appropriate for these data? Explain.
b) Using the test you selected, state your conclusion.
c) Are the assumptions and conditions for inference met?
LO ❶, ❸

39. Online insurance, part 2. In Exercise 37, we saw summary statistics for 10 drivers' car insurance premiums quoted by a local agent and an online company. Here are displays for each company's quotes and for the difference (*Local – Online*):

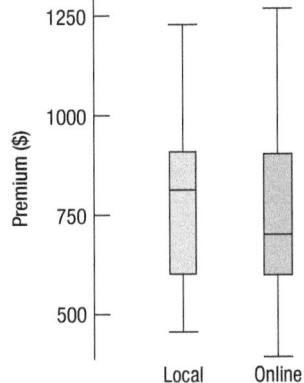

a) Which of the summaries would help you decide whether the online company offers cheaper insurance? Why?
b) The standard deviation of *PriceDiff* is quite a bit smaller than the standard deviation of prices quoted by either the local or the online companies. Discuss why.
c) Using the information you have, discuss the assumptions and conditions for inference with these data. **LO ❸**

40. Wind energy by Lake Ontario, part 1. Alternative sources of energy are of increasing interest throughout the energy industry. Wind energy has great potential, but appropriate sites must be found for the turbines. To select the site for an electricity-generating wind turbine, wind speeds were recorded at several potential sites every six hours for a year. Two sites on the shore of Lake Ontario looked good. Each had a mean wind speed high enough to qualify, but we should choose the site with a higher average daily wind speed. Because the sites are near each other and the wind speeds were recorded at the same times, we should view the speeds as paired. Here are the summaries of the speeds (in kilometres per hour):

Variable	Count	Mean	StdDev
site2	1114	7.452	3.586
site4	1114	7.248	3.421
site2 – site4	1114	0.204	2.551

Is there a mistake in this output? Why doesn't the Pythagorean Theorem of Statistics work here? In other words, shouldn't $SD(site2 - site4) = \sqrt{SD^2(site2) + SD^2(site4)}$? But $\sqrt{(3.586)^2 + (3.421)^2} = 4.956$, not 2.551 as given by the software. Explain why this happened. **LO ❸**

41. Online insurance, part 3. Exercises 37 and 39 give summaries and displays for car insurance premiums quoted by a local agent and an online company. Test an appropriate hypothesis to see if there's evidence that drivers might save money by switching to the online company. **LO ❶**

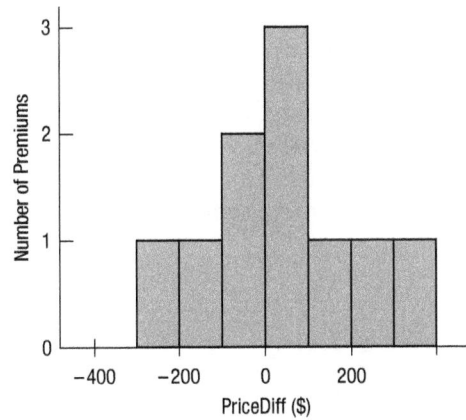

42. Wind energy by Lake Ontario, part 2. In Exercise 40, we saw summary statistics for wind speeds at two sites near each other, both being considered as locations for an electricity-generating wind turbine. The data, recorded every six hours for a year, showed that each of the sites had a mean wind speed high enough to qualify, but how can we tell which site is best? Here are some displays:

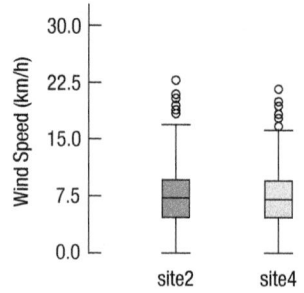

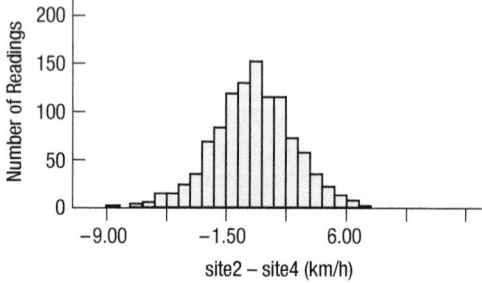

a) The boxplots show outliers for each site, yet the histogram shows none. Discuss why.
b) Which of the summaries would you use to select between these sites? Why?
c) Using the information you have, discuss the assumptions and conditions for paired t inference for these data. (*Hint:* Think hard about the Independence Assumption in particular.) **LO ❸**

43. Wheelchair marathon. The Boston Marathon has had a wheelchair division since 1977. Who do you think is typically faster, the men's marathon winner on foot or the women's wheelchair marathon winner? Because the conditions differ year to year and speeds have improved over the years, it seems best to treat these as paired measurements. Here are summary statistics for the pairwise differences in finishing time (in minutes):

Summary of wheelchair F – run M

$n = 31$

Mean $= -2.12097$

SD $= 33.4434$

a) Comment on the assumptions and conditions.
b) Assuming that these times are representative of such races and the differences appeared acceptable for inference,

construct and interpret a 95% confidence interval for the mean difference in finishing times.
c) Would a hypothesis test at $\alpha = 0.05$ reject the null hypothesis of no difference? What conclusion would you draw? **LO ❸**

44. Wind energy by Lake Ontario, part 3. Exercises 40 and 42 give summaries and displays for two potential sites for a wind turbine. Test an appropriate hypothesis to see if there's evidence that either of these sites has a higher average wind speed. **LO ❶**

45. Employee athletes, part 1. An ergonomics consultant is engaged by a large consumer products company to see what it can do to increase productivity. The consultant recommends an "employee athlete" program, encouraging every employee to devote five minutes an hour to physical activity. The company worries that the gains in productivity will be offset by the loss in time on the job. Management would like to know if the program increases or decreases productivity. To measure it, the company monitors a random sample of 145 employees who word-process, measuring their hourly keystrokes both before and after the program is instituted. Here are the data:

	Keystrokes per Hour		
	Before	**After**	**Difference (After − Before)**
Mean	1534.2	1556.9	22.7
SD	168.5	149.5	113.6
n	145	145	145

a) What are the null and alternative hypotheses?
b) What can you conclude? Explain.
c) Give a 95% confidence interval for the mean change in productivity (as measured by keystrokes per hour). **LO ❸**

46. Boston startup years. When we considered the Boston Marathon in Exercise 43, we were unable to check the Nearly Normal Condition. Here's a histogram of the differences:

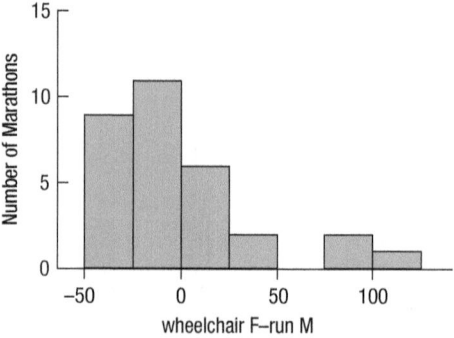

Those three large differences are the first three years of wheelchair competition: 1977, 1978, and 1979. Often the startup years of new events are different; later on more athletes train and compete. If we omit those three years, the summary statistics change as follows:

Summary of wheelchair F − run M

$n = 28$

Mean = 12.1780

SD = 19.5116

a) Comment on the assumptions and conditions.
b) Assuming that these times are representative of such races, construct and interpret a 95% confidence interval for the mean difference in finishing time.
c) Would a hypothesis test at $\alpha = 0.05$ reject the null hypothesis of no difference? What conclusion would you draw? LO ❸

47. Employee athletes, part 2. A small company, on hearing about the employee athlete program (see Exercise 45) at the large company down the street, decides to try it as well. To measure the difference in productivity, the company measures the average number of keystrokes per hour of 23 employees before and after the five-minutes-per-hour program is instituted. The data follow:

| | Keystrokes per Hour | | |
	Before	After	Difference (After − Before)
Mean	1497.3	1544.8	47.5
SD	155.4	136.7	122.8
n	23	23	23

a) Is there evidence to suggest that the program increases productivity? State your hypotheses clearly.
b) Give a 95% confidence interval for the mean change in productivity (as measured by keystrokes per hour).
c) Explain the difference between the results of (a) and (b). LO ❸

48. Productivity, part 1. A national fitness firm claims that a company may increase employee productivity by implementing one of the firm's fitness programs at the job site. As evidence of this, the fitness firm reports that one company was able to increase job productivity of a random sample of 30 employees from 57 to 70 (on a scale of 100). The standard deviation of the increases was 7.9. The national fitness firm wants to estimate the mean increase a company could expect after implementing the fitness program.

a) Check the assumptions and conditions for inference.
b) Find a 95% confidence interval.
c) Explain what your interval means in this context. LO ❸

49. Productivity, part 2. After implementing the fitness program described in Exercise 48, another company found that a random sample of 48 employees increased their productivity score from 49 to 56 with a standard deviation of 6.2.

This company believes that the fitness firm may have exaggerated the potential results of its program. Is there evidence that the mean improvement seen by this company is less than the one claimed by the fitness company? Be sure to check the assumptions and conditions for inference. LO ❸

❶ 50. Market value. Real estate agents want to set the price of a house that's about to go on the real estate market correctly. They must choose a price that strikes a balance between one that's so high that the house takes too long to sell and one that's so low that not enough value will go to the homeowner. One appraisal method is the "Comparative Market Analysis" approach, by which the market value of a house is based on recent sales of similar homes in the neighbourhood. Because no two houses are exactly the same, appraisers have to adjust comparable homes for such features as extra square footage, bedrooms, fireplaces, upgrading, parking facilities, swimming pool, lot size, location, and so on. The data file contains the appraised market values and the selling prices of 45 homes from the same region.

a) Test the hypothesis that, on average, the market value and the sale price of homes from this region are the same.
b) Find a 95% confidence interval for the mean difference.
c) Explain your findings in a sentence or two. LO ❸

51. BST, part 1. Many dairy cows now receive injections of BST, a hormone intended to spur greater milk production. After the first injection, a test herd of 60 Ayrshire cows increased their mean daily production from 47 pounds to 61 pounds of milk. The standard deviation of the increases was 5.2 pounds. We want to estimate the mean increase a farmer could expect in his own cows.

a) Check the assumptions and conditions for inference.
b) Write a 95% confidence interval.
c) Explain what your interval means in this context.
d) Given the cost of BST, a farmer believes he can't afford to use it unless he's sure of attaining at least a 25% increase in milk production. Based on your confidence interval, what advice would you give him? LO ❸

52. BST, part 2. In the experiment about hormone injections in cows described in Exercise 51, a group of 52 Jersey cows increased average milk production from 43 pounds to 52 pounds per day, with a standard deviation of 4.8 pounds. Is this evidence that the hormone may be more effective in one breed than in the other? Test an appropriate hypothesis and state your conclusion. Be sure to discuss any assumptions you make. LO ❸

53. European temperatures. The table on the next page gives the average high temperatures in January and July for several European cities. Find a 90% confidence interval for the mean temperature difference between summer and winter in Europe. Be sure to check conditions for inference, and clearly explain what your interval means within the context of the situation. LO ❸

Mean High Temperatures (°C)		
City	January	July
Vienna	1.1	23.9
Copenhagen	2.2	22.2
Paris	5.6	24.4
Berlin	1.7	23.3
Athens	12.2	32.2
Rome	12.2	31.1
Amsterdam	4.4	20.6
Madrid	8.3	30.6
London	6.7	22.8
Edinburgh	6.1	18.3
Moscow	−6.1	24.4
Belgrade	2.8	28.9

⊕ 54. Summer school. Having done poorly on their final math exams in June, six students repeat the course in summer school and take another exam in August. If we consider these students to be representative of all students who might attend this summer school in other years, do these results provide evidence that the program is worthwhile?

June	54	49	68	66	62	62
August	50	65	74	64	68	72

a) Identify the procedure you would use to assess whether this program is worthwhile, and check to see if the conditions allow for the use of that procedure.
b) Test an appropriate hypothesis and state your conclusion. **LO ❸**

55. Job satisfaction. A company institutes an exercise break for its workers to see if this will improve job satisfaction, as measured by a questionnaire that assesses workers' satisfaction. Scores for 10 randomly selected workers before and after the implementation of the exercise program are shown in the following table:

Worker Number	Job Satisfaction Index	
	Before	After
1	34	33
2	28	36
3	29	50
4	45	41
5	26	37
6	27	41
7	24	39
8	15	21
9	15	20
10	27	37

a) Identify the procedure you would use to assess the effectiveness of the exercise program and check to see if the conditions allow for the use of that procedure.
b) Test an appropriate hypothesis and state your conclusion. **LO ❸**

56. Advertising. A company developing an ad campaign for its cola is investigating the impact of caffeine on studying in hopes of finding evidence of its claim that caffeine helps memory. The firm asked 30 subjects, randomly divided into two groups, to take a memory test. The subjects then each drank two cups of regular (caffeinated) cola or caffeine-free cola. Thirty minutes later they each took another version of the memory test, and the changes in their scores were noted. Among the 15 subjects who drank caffeine, scores fell an average of −0.933 points with a standard deviation of 2.988 points. Among the no-caffeine group, scores went up an average of 1.429 points with a standard deviation of 2.441 points. Assumptions of Normality were deemed reasonable based on histograms of differences in scores.

a) Did scores change significantly for the group who drank caffeine? Test an appropriate hypothesis and state your conclusion.
b) Did scores change significantly for the no-caffeine group? Test an appropriate hypothesis and state your conclusion.
c) Does this indicate that some mystery substance in non-caffeinated cola may aid memory? What other explanation is plausible? **LO ❸**

⊕ 57. Efficiency. Many drivers of cars that can run on regular gas actually buy premium gas in the belief that they'll get better gas mileage. To test that belief, a consumer research group evaluated the use of 10 cars in a company fleet in which all the cars run on regular gas. Each car was filled first with either regular or premium gasoline, decided by a coin toss, and the mileage for that tankful was recorded. Then the mileage was recorded again for the same cars with a tankful of the other kind of gasoline. The consumer research group did not let the drivers know about this experiment. Here are the results (miles per gallon):

Car No.	1	2	3	4	5	6	7	8	9	10
Regular	16	20	21	22	23	22	27	25	27	28
Premium	19	22	24	24	25	25	26	26	28	32

a) Is there evidence that cars get better gas mileage on average with premium gasoline?
b) How big might that difference be? Check a 90% confidence interval.
c) Even if the difference is significant, why might the car fleet company choose to stick with regular gasoline?

d) Suppose you had mistakenly treated these data as two independent samples instead of matched pairs. What would the significance test have found? Carefully explain why the results are so different. **LO ❸**

T 58. Quality control, part 1. In an experiment on braking performance, a tire manufacturer measured the stopping distance for one of its tire models. On a test track, a car made repeated stops from 60 miles per hour. Twenty tests were run, 10 each on both dry and wet pavement, with results shown in the following table. (Note that actual *braking distance*, which takes into account the driver's reaction time, is much longer, typically nearly 300 feet at 60 miles per hour!)

Stopping Distance (ft.)	
Dry Pavement	Wet Pavement
145	211
152	191
141	220
143	207
131	198
148	208
126	206
140	177
135	183
133	223

a) Find a 95% confidence interval for the mean dry pavement stopping distance. Be sure to check the appropriate assumptions and conditions, and explain what your interval means.
b) Find a 95% confidence interval for the mean increase in stopping distance on wet pavement. Be sure to check the appropriate assumptions and conditions, and explain what your interval means. **LO ❷**

T 59. Advertising claims. Advertisements for an instructional video claim that the techniques will improve the ability of Little League pitchers to throw strikes and that, after undergoing the training, players will be able to throw strikes on more than 60% of their pitches. To test this claim, we have 20 Little Leaguers throw 50 pitches each, and we record the number of strikes. After the players participate in the training program, we repeat the test. The table in the next column shows the number of strikes each player threw before and after the training.

a) Is there evidence that after training players can throw strikes more than 60% of the time?
b) Is there evidence that the training is effective in improving a player's ability to throw strikes? **LO ❶, ❸**

Number of Strikes (out of 50)			
Before	After	Before	After
28	35	33	33
29	36	33	35
30	32	34	32
32	28	34	30
32	30	34	33
32	31	35	34
32	32	36	37
32	34	36	33
32	35	37	35
33	36	37	32

T 60. Quality control, part 2. For another test of the tires in Exercise 58, the company tried them on 10 different cars, recording the stopping distance for each car on both wet and dry pavement. Results are shown in the following table:

Car #	Stopping Distance (ft.)	
	Dry Pavement	Wet Pavement
1	150	201
2	147	220
3	136	192
4	134	146
5	130	182
6	134	173
7	134	202
8	128	180
9	136	192
10	158	206

a) Find a 95% confidence interval for the mean dry pavement stopping distance. Be sure to check the appropriate assumptions and conditions, and explain what your interval means.
b) Find a 95% confidence interval for the mean increase in stopping distance on wet pavement. Be sure to check the appropriate assumptions and conditions, and explain what your interval means. **LO ❷, ❸**

T 61. Yogurt. Do the data in the table on the next page suggest that there is a significant difference in calories between servings of strawberry and vanilla yogurt? Test an appropriate hypothesis and state your conclusion, including a check of assumptions and conditions. **LO ❸**

Brand		Calories per Serving	
		Strawberry	Vanilla
	America's Choice	210	200
	Breyer's Lowfat	220	220
	Columbo	220	180
	Dannon Light'n Fit	120	120
	Dannon Lowfat	210	230
	Dannon la Crème	140	140
	Great Value	180	80
	La Yogurt	170	160
	Mountain High	200	170
	Stonyfield Farm	100	120
	Yoplait Custard	190	190
	Yoplait Light	100	100

62. Store profits. The managers for a sample of stores maintain that their businesses are doing better this year, despite relatively flat sales. Their argument is that they've been able to reduce costs through more efficient staffing and inventory management. Using the data provided in the file, determine if the average weekly profits for one quarter increased for these stores over the past year (from year 1 to year 2). Do your results support the claim of the store managers? **LO ❸**

63. Canadian house sizes. The Organisation for Economic Co-operation and Development (OECD) surveyed 1000 homes at random in each of its member countries in 2014 and found that the number of rooms per person in Canadian homes was 2.5 on average, whereas in the United States it was 2.3. Assume that the standard deviation is 35% of these average values.

Do Canadian homes in general have more rooms per person than homes in the United States? Answer this question:

a) Without pooling the estimates of the standard deviation.
b) With a pooled estimate of the standard deviation.
c) Why is it not possible to use the "paired samples" approach for this question?
d) At which significance level (0.01, 0.05, or 0.1) would your answers to (a) and (b) be different if the OECD had surveyed only 100 homes in each country instead of 1000? **LO ❶, ❸**

64. Auto repair shops. Certain businesses and professions have reputations for being somewhat dishonest when dealing with customers. One area of concern is the honesty of auto repair shops. Many provinces require emissions checks; a vehicle that doesn't pass the check must be repaired. In one province, the Department of Transport (DT) has been receiving numerous complaints about a particular auto repair chain. The province decided to check the shops to determine whether they were unlawfully issuing "no pass" reports in order to charge customers unnecessary repair fees. The province procured eight vehicles. Each was first tested on department emissions equipment, and then the eight vehicles were randomly sent to auto repair shops for testing on emissions. As part of the check for accuracy, the hydrocarbon (HC) emissions in parts per million (ppm) were compared:

Vehicle	1	2	3	4	5	6	7	8
DT HC Level	7	10	3	1	5	8	30	7
Auto Shop HC Level	20	11	5	10	5	7	42	15

a) Is there a difference between the measured HC levels taken from the auto shop and the DT measurements? Find a suitable confidence interval.
b) Do you think the DT has evidence that the auto shop readings differ from the department readings? Perform the appropriate test.
c) If you found the test results to be significant, can the DT automatically assume the auto shop is cheating its customers? What other possible explanations could cause the differences in readings? **LO ❸**

65. Ipsos' Canadian media landscape. In order to assist advertisers in targeting advertising to the appropriate age groups, Ipsos surveyed 9700 Canadian adults to record the amount of time they spent consuming media and obtained the following results:

Age Group	Birth Years	Time Spent (hrs)
Boomers	1947–65	6.2
Generation Xers	1966–81	5.3
Leading Millennials	1982–89	5.2
Trailing Millennials	1990–96	6.6

Assume that the number of people surveyed is proportional to the age range of each age group, rounded to the nearest integer. (For example, number of Boomers surveyed = $9700 \times (66 - 47)/(97 - 47) = 3686$.) Also assume that the standard deviation is 35% of the time spent (e.g., SD for Boomers $= 0.35 \times 6.2 = 1.86$ hrs).

a) Is the time spent consuming media by the Generation Xers higher than for the Leading Millennials? Give the P-value for the level of significance.

b) Is the time spent consuming media by the Trailing Millennials higher than for the Boomers? Give the P-value for the level of significance. LO ❶, ❸

66. Life satisfaction in Canada. According to the OECD, life satisfaction measures how people evaluate their life as a whole rather than their current feelings. It captures a reflective assessment of which life circumstances and conditions are important for subjective well-being. In 2014, they asked a random sample of 1000 Canadians to rate their general satisfaction with life on a scale from 0 to 10, and the average result was 7.6. A similar survey of 1000 people in Switzerland gave an average result of 7.8. We are interested in whether people in Switzerland are more satisfied with life than people in Canada.

a) What missing information do you need in order to conduct a statistical test to answer this question?
b) State the hypotheses that you would test.
c) Explain whether this is a case of paired samples. LO ❶, ❸

67. Math education: Canada and OECD. The OECD conducts the Program for International Student Assessment and in 2012 tested 510,000 15-year-old high school students in 65 countries to assess their performance in math, reading, and science. We are interested in how Canada compares to Germany and Japan.

a) What missing information do you need in order to conduct a statistical test to answer this question?
b) State the hypotheses that you would test.
c) Explain whether this is a case of paired samples. LO ❶, ❸

68. Hot Ontario summers. Ontario is a world leader in the installation of smart electricity meters on residences. This has allowed the province to charge different rates for electricity at different times of day and has also resulted in the accumulation of a vast database of the amount of electricity (in kilowatt-hours) consumed by each residence during each hour of each day for the past several years. Peak electricity demand in Ontario usually occurs between 3:00 P.M. and 5:00 P.M. in July, when air conditioning use is at a maximum. Hydro One, the largest electricity transmission and distribution company in Ontario, wants to test the effectiveness of its "Peaksaver PLUS" program, which supplies customers with a free thermostat that Hydro One can control remotely to reduce air conditioning use during peak times. They take a random sample of 40 customers with Peaksaver PLUS today and 40 customers without it today to compare their consumption (in kilowatt-hours) of electricity between 3:00 P.M. and 5:00 P.M. in July for the past five years (2 hours × 31 days × 5 years = 310 measurements for each customer).

For the analyses in (a) and (b) below, state (i) the sample you would use from the database; (ii) the hypotheses you would test; (iii) which statistical test you would use,

with a reason; and (iv) how you would check the conditions for using that test.

a) Comparison of electricity consumption between 3:00 P.M. and 4:00 P.M. and electricity consumption between 4:00 P.M. and 5:00 P.M.
b) Analysis of whether 3:00 P.M. to 5:00 P.M. electricity consumption of customers with Peaksaver PLUS is less than that of customers without it.
c) Suppose we want to analyze whether 3:00 P.M. to 5:00 P.M. electricity consumption of customers with Peaksaver PLUS today is less than before they subscribed to it. (i) Is this sample of customers satisfactory? (ii) If the sample is satisfactory, which statistical test is appropriate?

69. Snowy Ontario winters. Partly as a result of a government incentive program, several businesses and residences in Ontario have installed solar panels so as to reduce their electricity bills. The amount of electricity (in kilowatt-hours) generated by each of these installations is recorded in a database each hour of each day for four years together with the size of installation (in peak kilowatt-hours that could be generated in ideal conditions). Ottawa is a particularly good city for generating solar power because of its year-round clear skies and cold winters (solar panels generate more power at lower temperatures). However, a problem is that snow may accumulate on the panels and prevent them from generating electricity. Snow tends to slide off panels that are steeply sloped but may accumulate on others.

An installer wants to analyze the effect of snow on electricity generation to figure out whether she should focus on steeply sloped projects in the future to obtain maximum profits over the 25-year life of the panels. She takes a random sample of 30 installations in Ottawa that have a steep slope (>45 degrees) and another sample of 30 that have a shallow slope (<45 degrees). The total number of installations in Ottawa is 1248. Since some installations are larger than others, she scales the amount of electricity generated by the size of the installation, calculating (kilowatt-hours/peak kilowatt-hours) as a measure of the "effectiveness" of the installation at generating power.

For the analyses in (a) and (b) below, state (i) the sample you would use from the database; (ii) the hypotheses you would test; (iii) which statistical test you would use, with a reason; and (iv) how you would check the conditions for using that test.

a) Analyze whether the average effectiveness in January of solar installations with a steep slope is higher than for those that have a shallow slope.
b) Compare the amount of electricity generated during three days immediately before the first major snowfall (accumulation >5 cm) of the season with the amount of electricity generated during three days immediately after that first major snowfall.

70. **Hours of work in Canada.** The Organisation for Economic Co-operation and Development (OECD) surveyed 1000 people at random in each of its member countries in 2014 and found that the number of hours worked by Canadians was 1710 hours per year on average, whereas in the United States it was 1790. Assume that the standard deviation is 30% of these average values. In Canada, do people work fewer hours per year than people in the United States? Answer this question:

a) Without pooling the estimates of the standard deviation.

b) With a pooled estimate of the standard deviation.

c) Why is it not possible to use the "paired samples" approach for this question?

d) At which significance level (0.01, 0.05, or 0.1) would your answers to (a) and (b) be different if the OECD had surveyed only 100 people in each country instead of 1000? **LO❶, ❸**

Glyn Thomas/Alamy Stock Photo

15

Design of Experiments and Analysis of Variance (ANOVA)

LEARNING OBJECTIVES

In this chapter we show you how to design statistical experiments and analyze the results using ANOVA: ANalysis Of VAriance. After reading and studying this chapter, you should be able to:

❶ Distinguish between an observational study and a statistical experiment

❷ Apply the principles of experimental design

❸ Analyze the results using ANOVA: ANalysis Of VAriance

Capital One

Not everyone graduates first in their class at a prestigious business school. But even if you do, it won't guarantee that the first company you start will become a Fortune 500 company within a decade. Richard Fairbank managed to do both. When he graduated from Stanford Business School in 1981 he wanted to start his own company, but, as he said in an interview with *Stanford Business* magazine, he had no experience, no money, and no business ideas. So he went to work for a consulting firm. Wanting to be on his own, he left in 1987 and landed a contract to study the operations of a large credit card company in New York. It was then that he realized that the secret lay in data. He and his partner, Nigel Morris, asked themselves, "Why not use the mountains of data that credit cards produce to design cards with prices and terms to satisfy different customers?" But they had a hard time selling this idea to the large credit card issuers. At the time, all cards carried the same interest rate—19.8% with a $20 annual fee—and almost half the population didn't even qualify for a card. As well, credit issuers were naturally resistant to new ideas.

Finally, Fairbank and Morris signed on with Signet, a regional bank that hoped to expand its modest credit card operation. Using demographic and financial data about Signet's customers, they designed and tested combinations of card features that allowed the bank to offer credit to customers who previously hadn't qualified. Signet's credit card business grew and, by 1994, was spun off as Capital One with a market capitalization of $1.1 billion.

Capital One started its Canadian operation in 1996 with offices in Toronto and Halifax, and introduced a Platinum MasterCard. Today, it offers a range of MasterCards, including the Aspire suite of rewards cards. In Canada it also co-brands cards with Hudson's Bay Company, Inter-Continental Hotels Group, and Costco.

Capital One reduces its environmental footprint by using 100% recycled paper in its offices and for 95% of its direct marketing. It encourages Canadian youth to be financially responsible and entrepreneurial by supporting a youth entrepreneurship fund and a national competition for post-secondary students called the Financial Education Challenge.

ROADMAP FOR STATISTICAL INFERENCE

Number of Variables	Objective	Large Sample or Normal Population		Small Sample and Non-normal Population or Non-numeric Data	
		Chapter	Parametric Method	Chapter	Nonparametric Method
1	Calculate confidence interval for a proportion	11			
1	Compare a proportion with a given value	12	z-test		
1	Calculate a confidence interval for a mean and compare it with a given value	13	t-test	17.2	Wilcoxon Signed-Rank Test
2	Compare two proportions	12.8	z-test		
2	Compare two means for independent samples	14.1–14.5	t-test	17.4, 17.5	Wilcoxon Rank-Sum (Mann-Whitney) Test Tukey's Quick Test
2	Compare two means for paired samples	14.6, 14.7	Paired t-test	17.2	Wilcoxon Signed-Rank Test
≥ 3	Compare multiple means	15	ANOVA: ANalysis Of VARiance	17.3 17.6	Friedman Test Kruskal-Wallis Test
≥ 3	Compare multiple counts (proportions)	16	χ^2 test		
2	Investigate the relationship between two variables	18	Correlation Regression	17.7, 17.8	Kendall's tau Spearman's rho
≥ 3	Investigate the relationship between multiple variables	20	Multiple Regression		

LO❶　15.1　Observational Studies

Fairbank started by analyzing the data that had already been collected by the credit card company. These data weren't from designed studies of customers. He simply *observed* the behaviour of customers from the data that were already there. Such a study is called an **observational study**. Many companies collect data from customers with "frequent shopper" cards, which allow the companies to record each purchase. A company might study that data to identify associations between customer behaviour and demographic information. For example, customers with pets might tend to spend more. The company can't conclude that owning a pet *causes* these customers to spend. People who have pets may also have higher incomes on average or be more likely to own their own homes. Nevertheless, the company may decide to make special offers targeted at pet owners.

Observational studies are used widely in public health and marketing because they can reveal trends and relationships. An observational study that examines an outcome in the present by delving into historical records is called a **retrospective study**. When Fairbank looked at the accumulated experiences of Signet bank's credit card customers, he started with information about which customers earned the bank the most money and sought facts about these customers that could identify others like them. Such retrospective studies often generate testable hypotheses because, although they can't demonstrate a causal link, they can identify interesting relationships.

When it's practical, a somewhat better approach is to observe individuals over time, recording the variables of interest and seeing how things turn out. For example, if we thought pet ownership might be a way to identify profitable customers, we might start by selecting a random sample of new customers and asking whether they have a pet. We could then track their performance and compare those who own pets to those who don't. Identifying subjects in advance and collecting data as events unfold would make this a **prospective study**. Prospective studies are often used in public health, where by following, say, smokers or runners over a period of time, we may find that one group or the other develops emphysema or arthritic knees (as you might expect), or dental cavities (which you might not expect).

Although an observational study may identify important variables related to the outcome we're interested in, there's no guarantee that it will find the right or the most important related variables. People who own pets may differ from the other customers in ways that we failed to observe. It may be this difference—whether we know what it is or not—rather than owning a pet in itself that leads pet owners to be more profitable customers. Again, it's just not possible for observational studies, whether prospective or retrospective, to demonstrate a causal relationship. That's why we need experiments.

FOR EXAMPLE   Observational studies for Ottawa–Toronto flights

Porter offers flights to and from the Island airport in Toronto, providing faster access to the downtown area than Pearson International Airport, which is farther from the city centre. Porter's fare structure focuses on business passengers; it also provides complimentary refreshments and internet access in its Toronto and Ottawa airport lounges. As a new member of Porter's Marketing Department, you want to boost the number of student passengers on the Ottawa–Toronto route. Suppose you examine last year's sample of passengers and find that 6% of them were students. Of those, 92% used the free internet service, as opposed to only 61% of the other passengers.

QUESTION What kind of study is this? Can you conclude that internet use is a factor in deciding to fly with Porter?

ANSWER This is a retrospective observational study. Although we can compare rates of internet use between students and non-students, we can't come to any conclusions about why they chose to fly with Porter.

JUST CHECKING

In early 2007, a larger-than-usual number of cats and dogs developed kidney failure. Many died. Initially, researchers didn't know why, so they used an observational study to investigate.

1 Suppose that, as a researcher for a pet food manufacturer, you are called on to plan a study seeking to identify factors related to this problem. Specify how you might proceed. Would your study be prospective or retrospective?

Answers are found in Appendix A.

LO❶ **15.2** **Randomized, Comparative Experiments**

Fairbank also introduced "scientific testing." Capital One designs experiments to gather data about customers. For example, customers who hear about a better deal than the one their current card offers may phone, saying they will switch to another company unless they get a better deal. To help identify which potential card-hoppers were serious, Fairbank designed an experiment. When a card-hopper called, the customer service agent's computer randomly ordered one of three actions: Match the claimed offer, split the difference in rates or fees, or just say no. In that way the company could gather data on who switched, who stayed, and how they behaved. Now when a potential card-hopper phones, the computer can give the operator a script specifying the terms to offer—or instruct the operator to bid the card-hopper a pleasant goodbye.

Fairbank attributes the phenomenal success of Capital One to its use of such experiments. According to Fairbank, "Anyone in the company can propose a test and, if the results are promising, Capital One will rush the new product or approach into use immediately." Why does this work for Capital One? Because, as Fairbank says, "We don't hesitate, because our testing has already told us what will work."

Experiments are the only way to show cause-and-effect relationships convincingly, so they're a critical tool for understanding what products and ideas will work in the marketplace. An **experiment** is a study in which the experimenter *manipulates* attributes of what is being studied and observes the consequences. Usually, the attribute, called a **factor**, is manipulated by being set to a particular **level** and then allocated or assigned to individuals. An experimenter identifies at least one factor to manipulate and at least one response variable to measure. Often the observed **response** is a quantitative measurement, such as the amount of a product sold. However, responses can be categorical ("customer purchased"/"customer didn't purchase"). The combination of factor levels assigned to a subject is called that subject's **treatment**.

Humans who are experimented on are commonly called **subjects or participants**. Other individuals (rats, products, fiscal quarters, company divisions) are commonly referred to by the more generic term **experimental units**.

You've been the subject of marketing experiments. Every credit card offer you receive is actually a combination of various factors that specify your "treatment"— the specific offer you get. For example, the factors might be *Annual Fee, Interest Rate*, and *Communication Channel* (email, direct mail, phone, etc.). The particular treatment you receive might be a combination of *no Annual Fee* and a *moderate Interest Rate* with the offer being sent by *email*. Other customers receive different treatments. The response might be categorical (Do you accept the offer of that card?) or quantitative (How much do you spend with that card during the first three months you have it?).

Two key features distinguish an experiment from other types of investigations. First, the experimenter actively and deliberately manipulates the factors to specify the treatment. Second, the experiment assigns the subjects to those treatments at *random*, using the methods described in Chapter 3. The importance of **random assignment** may not be immediately obvious. Experts, such as business executives and physicians, may think they know how different subjects will respond to various treatments. In particular, marketing executives may want to send what they consider the best offer to their best customers. But this makes fair comparisons of treatments impossible and thus invalidates the inference from the test. Without random assignment, we can't perform the hypothesis tests that allow us to conclude that differences among the treatments were responsible for any differences we observed in the responses. By using random assignment to ensure that the groups receiving different treatments are comparable, the experimenter can be sure that these differences are *due to* the differences in treatments.

FOR EXAMPLE   **A marketing experiment for Ottawa–Toronto flights**

Having discovered that most student passengers on the Porter Ottawa–Toronto route use the free internet service in the airport lounges (see For Example: "Observational studies for Ottawa–Toronto flights"), you decide to find out how best to attract more students to fly the route. After purchasing a mailing list of 16,000 students, you decide to randomly send one-quarter a coupon worth 10% off their next trip (*Coupon*), one-quarter a bonus card (*Card*), and one-quarter a free Netflix download during their next trip (*Movie*). The remaining 4000 students will receive no offer (*No Offer*). You plan to monitor the four groups to see which group travels most during the 12 months after sending the offer.

QUESTION What kind of study is this, an observational study or an experiment? What are the factors and levels? What are the subjects? What is the response variable?

ANSWER This is an experiment because the factor (type of offer) has been manipulated. The four levels arc *Coupon*, *Card*, *Movie*, and *No Offer*. The subjects are 16,000 students. The response variable is *Miles Travelled* during the next 12 months on Porter.

LO❷   **15.3   The Four Principles of Experimental Design**

There are four **principles of experimental design**:

1. **Randomize.** In any true experiment, subjects are assigned treatments at random. Randomization allows us to equalize the effects of unknown or uncontrollable sources of variation. Although randomization can't eliminate the effects of these sources, it spreads them out across the treatment levels so that we can see past them. Randomization also makes it possible to use the powerful methods of inference to draw conclusions from your study. In addition, it protects us even from effects we didn't know about. Perhaps women are more likely to respond to a credit card offer. We don't need to test equal numbers of men and women—our mailing list may not have that information. But if we randomize, that tendency won't contaminate our results. There's an adage that says, "Control what you can, and randomize the rest."

2. **Control.** We **control** sources of variation other than the factors we're testing by making conditions as similar as possible for all treatment groups. In a test of a new credit card, all alternative offers are sent to customers at the same time and in the same manner. Otherwise, if gas prices soar, the stock market drops, or interest rates spike dramatically during the study, those events could influence customers' responses, making it difficult to assess the effects of the treatments. So an experimenter tries to make any other variables that are not manipulated as similar as possible. Controlling extraneous sources of variation reduces the variability of the responses, making it easier to discern differences among the treatment groups.

> **Experimental Design**
>
> **Randomize:** Assign treatments to subjects at random.
>
> **Control:** Make the factors that we are not testing as similar as possible for all treatment groups.
>
> **Replicate:** Repeat observations for each treatment.
>
> **Block:** Group together experimental subjects that are similar to each other.

There is a second meaning of control in experiments. A bank testing the new creative idea of offering a card with special discounts on chocolate to attract more customers will want to compare its performance against one of its standard cards. Such a baseline measurement is called a control treatment, and the group that receives it is called the **control group**.

3. **Replicate.** Replication shows up in different ways in experiments. Because we need to estimate the variability of our measurements, we must make more than one observation at each level of each factor. Sometimes that just means making repeated observations. But, as we'll see later, some experiments combine two or more factors in ways that may permit a single observation for each *treatment*—that is, each combination of factor levels. When such an experiment is repeated in its entirety, it is said to be *replicated*. Repeated observations at each treatment are called *replicates*. If the number of replicates is the same for each treatment combination, we say that the experiment is *balanced*.

A second kind of replication is to repeat the entire experiment for a different group of subjects, under different circumstances, or at a different time. Experiments don't require, and often can't obtain, representative random samples from an identified population. Experiments study the consequences of different levels of their factors. They rely on the random assignment of treatments to the subjects to generate the sampling distributions and to control for other possibly contaminating variables. When we detect a significant difference in response among treatment groups, we can conclude that it's due to the difference in treatments. However, we should take care in generalizing that result too broadly if we've only studied a specialized population. A special offer of accelerated checkout lanes for regular customers may attract more business in December, but it may not be effective in July. Replication in a *variety of circumstances* can increase our confidence that our results apply to other situations and populations.

4. **Block.** Sometimes we can identify a factor not under our control, but which we suspect might have an effect either on our response variable or on the ways in which the factors we're studying affect that response. Perhaps men and women will respond differently to our chocolate offer. Or maybe customers with young children at home behave differently than those without. Platinum card members may be much more tempted by a premium offer than standard card members are. Factors like these can account for some of the variation in our observed responses because subjects at different levels respond differently. But we can't *assign* them at random to subjects. So we deal with them by grouping, or **blocking**, our subjects together and, in effect, analyzing the experiment separately for each block. Such factors are called *blocking factors*, and their levels are called *blocks*. Blocking in an experiment is like stratifying in a survey design. Blocking reduces variation by comparing subjects within these more homogenous groups. That makes it easier to discern any differences in response due to the factors of interest. In addition, we may want to study the effect of the blocking factor itself. Blocking is an important compromise between randomization and control. However, unlike the first three principles, blocking is not required in all experiments.

FOR EXAMPLE | **Experimental design principles for Ottawa–Toronto flights**

QUESTION Explain how the four principles of experimental design are used in the Porter experiment described For Example: "A marketing experiment for Ottawa–Toronto flights."

ANSWER Randomization: Although we can't control the other factors that may influence a person's decision, by randomizing which students receive which offer, we hope that the influences of all those other factors will average out, enabling us to see the effect of the four treatments.

Control: It is impossible to control other factors that may influence a person's decision to fly. However, a control group—one that receives no offer—will be used to compare with the other three treatment levels.

Replication: We'll send each type of offer to 4000 students. We hope that the response is high enough that we'll be able to see differences in *Miles Travelled* among the groups. This experiment is balanced, since the number of subjects is the same for all four treatments.

Blocking: We haven't blocked the experiment. Possible blocking factors might include demographic variables such as the region of the students' home or university, their gender, or their parents' income.

JUST CHECKING

Following concerns about the contamination of its pet foods by melamine, which had led to kidney failure, a manufacturer now claims its products are safe. You are called on to design the study to demonstrate the safety of the new formulation.

2 Identify the treatment and response.

3 How would you implement control, randomization, and replication?

Answers are found in Appendix A.

LO❷   15.4   Experimental Designs

Completely Randomized Designs

When each of the possible treatments is assigned to at least one subject at random, the design is called a **completely randomized design**. This design is the simplest and easiest to analyze of all experimental designs. A diagram of the procedure (Figure 15.1) can help in thinking about experiments. In this experiment, the subjects are assigned at random to the two treatments.

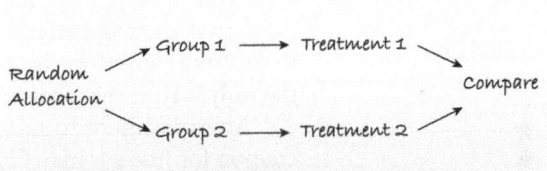

Figure 15.1   The simplest randomized design has two groups randomly assigned to two different treatments.

Randomized Block Designs

When one of the factors is a blocking factor, complete randomization isn't possible. We can't randomly assign factors based on people's behaviour, age, gender, or other attributes. But we may want to block these factors in order to reduce variability and to understand their effect on the response. When we have a blocking factor, we randomize the subject to the treatments *within each block*. This is called a **randomized block design**. In the following experiment, a marketer wanted to know the effect of two types of offers in each of two segments: a high-spending group and a low-spending group. The marketer selected 12,000 customers *from each group* at random and then randomly assigned the three treatments (including the Control treatment) to the 12,000 customers *in each group* so that 4000 customers in each segment received one of the three treatments. A display (Figure 15.2) makes the process clearer.

Factorial Designs

An experiment with more than one manipulated factor is called a **factorial design**. A full factorial design contains treatments that represent all possible combinations of all levels of all factors. That can be a lot of treatments. With only three factors, one at three

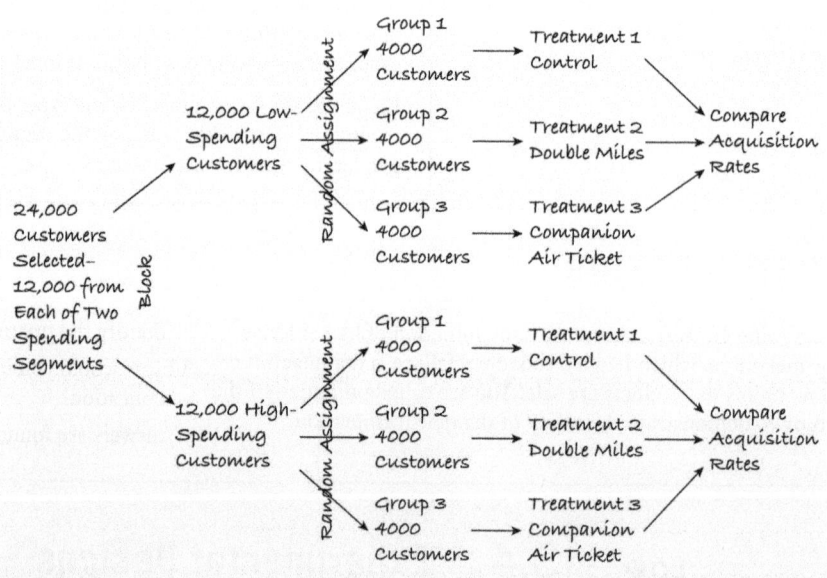

Figure 15.2   This example of a randomized block design shows that customers are randomized to treatments within each segment, or block.

levels, one at four, and one at five, there would be $3 \times 4 \times 5 = 60$ different treatment combinations. So researchers typically limit the number of levels to just a few.

It may seem that the added complexity of multiple factors isn't worth the trouble. In fact, just the opposite is true. First, if each factor accounts for some of the variation in responses, having the important factors in the experiment makes it *easier* to discern the effects of each. Testing multiple factors in a single experiment makes more efficient use of the available subjects. And testing factors together is the only way to see what happens at *combinations* of the levels.

An experiment to test the effectiveness of offering credit card holders a $50 coupon for free gas may find that the coupon increases credit card customer spending by 1%. Another experiment finds that lowering the interest rate increases spending by 2%. But unless some customers were offered *both* the $50 free gas coupon *and* the lower interest rate, the analyst can't learn whether offering both together would lead to still greater spending or less.

When the combination of two factors has a different effect than you would expect by adding the effects of the two factors together, that phenomenon is called an **interaction**. If the experiment does not contain both factors, it is impossible to see interactions. That can be a major omission because such effects can have the most important and surprising consequences in business.

FOR EXAMPLE   **Designing an experiment for Ottawa–Toronto flights**

Continuing from For Example: "Experimental design principles for Ottawa–Toronto flights," you're considering splitting up the students into two groups before mailing the offers: those who live or go to school in Montreal, and those who live or go to school in Ottawa or Toronto. Using home and school postal codes, you split the original 16,000 students into those groups and find that they split 8000 in Ottawa or Toronto and 8000 in Montreal. You plan to randomize the treatments within those two groups, and you'll monitor them to see if this factor, *City*, affects their *Miles Travelled* as well as the type of offer they receive.

QUESTION What kind of design would this be? Diagram the experiment.

ANSWER This is a randomized block experiment with *City* as the blocking factor.

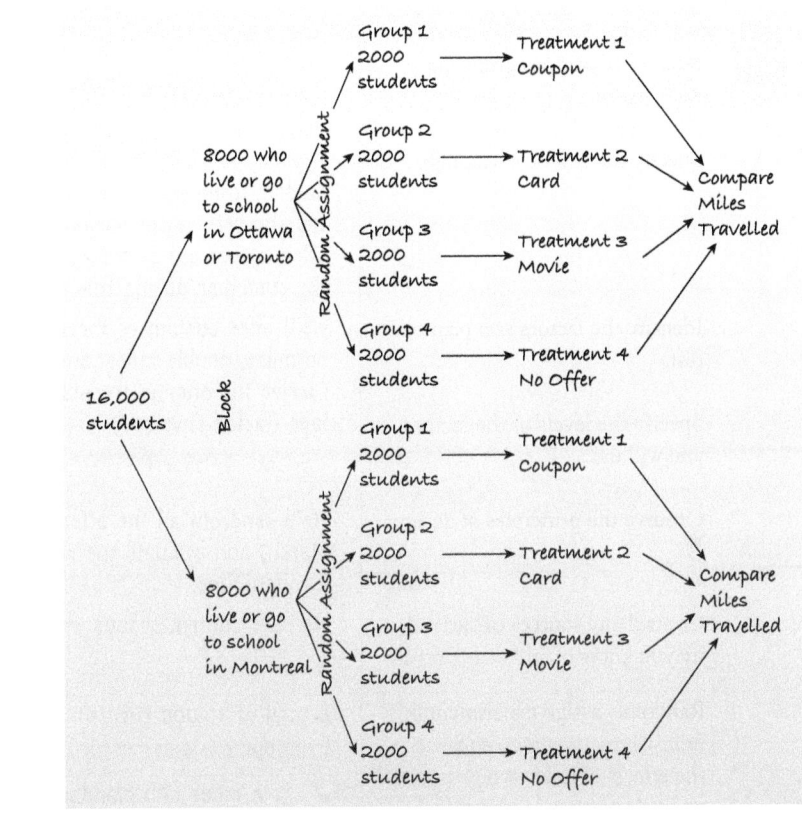

GUIDED EXAMPLE   Designing a Direct Mail Experiment

Michael Blann/PhotoDisc/Getty Images

At a major credit card company, management has been pleased with the success of a recent campaign to cross-sell Silver card customers with the new WestJet card. But you, as a marketing analyst, think the revenue of the card can be increased by adding three months of double miles on WestJet to the offer, and you think the additional gain in charges will offset the cost of the double miles. You want to design a marketing experiment to find out what the difference will be in revenue if you offer the double miles. You've also been thinking about offering a new version of the miles called "use anywhere miles," which can be transferred to other airlines, so you want to test that version as well.

You also know that customers receive so many offers that they tend to disregard most of their direct mail. So you'd like to see what happens if you send the offer in a shiny gold envelope with the WestJet logo prominently displayed on the front. How can we design an experiment to see whether either of these factors has an effect on charges?

(continued)

PLAN	**Setup** State the problem.	We want to design an experiment to study two factors to see their effect on the revenue generated for a new credit card offer.
DO	**Mechanics** For designing an experiment:	
	Specify the response variable.	Revenue is a percentage of the amount charged to the card by the cardholder. To measure the success, we'll use the monthly charges of customers who receive the various offers. We'll use the three months after the offer is sent out as the collection period and use the total amount charged per customer during this period as the response.
	Identify the factors you plan to test.	We'll offer customers three levels of the factor miles for the WestJet card: no miles, double miles, and double "use anywhere miles." Customers will receive the offer in the standard envelope or the new WestJet logo envelope (factor envelope).
	Specify the levels of the factors you will use.	
	Observe the principles of design:	We'll send out all the offers to customers at the same time (in mid-March) and evaluate the response as total charges in the period April through June.
	Control any sources of variability you know of and can control.	We have control groups who are offered no miles.
	Randomly assign experimental units to treatments to equalize the effects of unknown or uncontrollable sources of variation.	A total of 30,000 current Silver card customers will be randomly selected from our customer records to receive one of the six offers:
		✓ No miles with standard envelope
		✓ Double miles with standard envelope
		✓ Double "anywhere miles" with standard envelope
		✓ No miles with logo envelope
	Replicate results by placing more than one customer (usually many) in each treatment group.	✓ Double miles with logo envelope
		✓ Double "anywhere miles" with logo envelope
	Make a Picture A diagram of your design can help you think about it.	

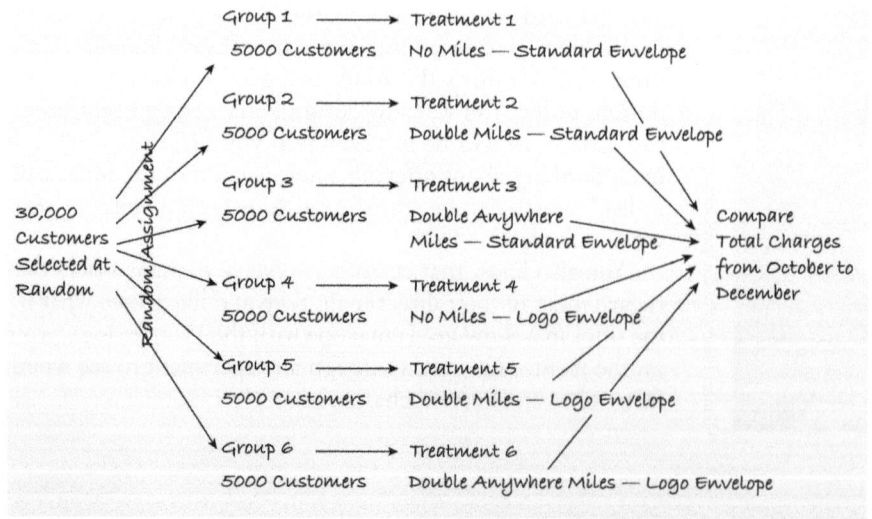

| Specify how to measure the response. | On July 15, we will examine the total card charges for each customer for the period April 1 through June 30. |

REPORT **Conclusion** Relate your design to the original objectives.

MEMO

Re: Test Mailing for Creative Offer and Envelope

We have designed an experiment that will see whether:

✓ offering double miles is worth the cost of the miles

✓ the "use anywhere miles" are worth the cost

✓ the logo envelope increased spending enough to justify the added expense

LO❷ **15.5** **Blinding and Placebos**

Humans are notoriously susceptible to errors in judgment—all of us. When we know what treatment is assigned, it's difficult not to let that knowledge influence our response or our assessment of the response, even when we try to be careful.

Suppose you were trying to sell your new brand of cola to be stocked in a school's vending machines. You might hope to convince the committee designated to make the choice that students prefer your less expensive cola, or at least that they can't taste the difference. You could set up an experiment to see which of the three competing brands students prefer (or whether they can tell the difference at all). But people have brand loyalties. If they know which brand they're tasting, it might influence their rating. To avoid this bias, it would be better to disguise the brands as much as possible. This strategy is called **blinding** the participants to the treatment. Even professional taste testers in food industry experiments are blinded to the treatment to reduce any prior feelings that might influence their judgment.

But it isn't just the subjects who should be **blind**. Experimenters themselves often subconsciously behave in ways that favour what they believe. It wouldn't be appropriate for you to run the study yourself if you have an interest in the outcome. People are so good at picking up subtle cues about treatments that the best (in fact, the only) defence against such biases in experiments on human subjects is to keep anyone who could affect the outcome or the measurement of the response from knowing which subjects have been assigned to which treatments. So, not only should your cola-tasting subjects be blinded, but also you, as the experimenter, shouldn't know which drink is which—at least until you're ready to analyze the results.

There are two main classes of individuals who can affect the outcome of the experiment:

- those who could influence the results (the subjects, treatment administrators, or technicians)
- those who evaluate the results (judges, experimenters, etc.)

When all the individuals in either one of these classes are blinded, an experiment is said to be **single-blind**. When everyone in both classes is blinded, we call the experiment **double-blind**. Double-blinding is the gold standard for any experiment involving both human subjects and human judgment about the response.

Often simply applying *any* treatment can induce an improvement. Every parent knows the medicinal value of a kiss to make a toddler's scrape or bump stop hurting. Some of the improvement seen with a treatment—even an effective

Blinding by Misleading

Social science experiments can sometimes blind subjects by misleading them about the purpose of a study. One of the authors participated as an undergraduate volunteer in a (now infamous) psychology experiment using such a blinding method. The subjects were told that the experiment was about three-dimensional spatial perception and were assigned to draw a model of a horse. While they were busy drawing, a loud noise and then groaning were heard coming from the room next door. The *real* purpose of the experiment was to see how people reacted to the apparent disaster. The experimenters wanted to see whether the social pressure of being in groups made people react to the disaster differently. Subjects had been randomly assigned to draw either in groups or alone. The experimenter had no interest in how well the subjects could draw the horse, and made the subjects blind to the treatment because they were misled.

> The placebo effect is stronger when placebo treatments are administered with authority or by a figure who appears to be an authority. "Doctors" in white coats generate a stronger effect than salespeople in polyester suits. But the placebo effect isn't reduced much, even when subjects know the effect exists. People often suspect that they've gotten the placebo if nothing at all happens. So, recently, drug manufacturers have gone so far in making placebos realistic that they cause the same side effects as the drug being tested! Such "active placebos" usually induce a stronger placebo effect.

treatment—can be due simply to the act of treating. To separate these two effects, we can sometimes use a control treatment that mimics the treatment itself. A "fake" treatment that looks just like the treatments being tested is called a **placebo**. Placebos are the best way to blind subjects so they don't know whether they've received the treatment or not. One common version of a placebo in drug testing is a "sugar pill." Especially when psychological attitude can affect the results, control group subjects treated with a placebo may show an improvement.

The fact is that subjects treated with a placebo sometimes improve. It's not unusual for 20% or more of subjects given a placebo to report reduction in pain, improved movement, or greater alertness, or even to demonstrate improved health or performance. This **placebo effect** highlights both the importance of effective blinding and the importance of comparing treatments with a control. Placebo controls are so effective that you should use them as an essential tool for blinding whenever possible.

The best experiments are usually

- randomized, comparative
- double-blind
- placebo-controlled

JUST CHECKING

The pet food manufacturer we've been following hires you to perform the experiment to test whether its new formulation is safe and nutritious for cats and dogs.

4 How would you establish a control group?

5 Would you use blinding? How?

6 Both cats and dogs are to be tested. Should you block? Explain.

Answers are found in Appendix A.

LO❷   **15.6   Confounding and Lurking Variables**

A credit card company wanted to test the sensitivity of the market to two factors: the annual fee charged for a card and the annual percentage interest rate charged. The company selected 100,000 people at random from a mailing list and sent out 50,000 offers with a low rate and no fee and 50,000 offers with a higher rate and a $50 annual fee. It discovered that people preferred the low-rate, no-fee card. No surprise. In fact, customers signed up for that card at over twice the rate of the other offer. But the question the company really wanted to answer was "How much of the change was due to the rate, and how much was due to the fee?" Unfortunately, there's simply no way to separate out the two effects with that experimental design.

If the company had followed a factorial design in the two factors and sent out all four possible different treatments—low rate with no fee, low rate with $50 fee, high rate with no fee, and high rate with $50 fee—each to 25,000 people, it could have learned about both factors and could have also learned about the interaction between rate and fee. But we can't tease apart these two effects because the people who were offered the low rate were also offered the no-fee card. When the levels of one factor are associated with the levels of another factor, we say that the two factors are **confounded**.

Confounding can also arise in well-designed experiments. If some other variable not under the experimenter's control but associated with a factor has an effect on the response variable, it can be difficult to know which variable is really responsible for the effect. For example, a shock to the economic or political situation that occurs during a marketing experiment can overwhelm the effects of the factors being tested. Randomization will usually take care of confounding by distributing uncontrolled factors over the treatments at random. But be sure to watch out for potential confounding effects even in a well-designed experiment.

Confounding may remind you of the problem of lurking variables that we discussed in Chapter 6. Confounding variables and lurking variables are alike in that they interfere with our ability to interpret our analyses simply. Each can mislead us, but they're not the same. A lurking variable is associated with two variables in such a way that it creates an apparent, possibly causal relationship between them. By contrast, confounding arises when a variable associated with a factor has an effect on the response variable, making it impossible to separate the effect of the factor from the effect of the confounder. Both confounding and lurking variables are outside influences that make it harder to understand the relationship we're modelling.

LO❸   15.7   Analyzing a Completely Randomized Design: The One-Way Analysis of Variance

The most common experimental design used in business is the single-factor experiment with two levels. Often these are known as champion/challenger designs because typically they're used to test a new idea (the challenger) against the current version (the champion). In this case, the customers offered the champion are the control group, and the customers offered the challenger (a special deal, a new offer, a new service, etc.) are the test group. As long as the customers are randomly assigned to the two groups, we already know how to analyze data from experiments like these. When the response is quantitative, we can test whether the means are equal with a two-sample t-test (see Chapter 14), and if the response is 0/1 (yes/no), we would test whether the two proportions are equal using a two-proportion z-test (see Section 12.8). In this chapter, we are dealing with quantitative responses and the analysis uses an F-test. When we have only two groups to compare, $F = t^2$ so that the t-test and the F-test give exactly the same results.

But those methods can compare only two groups. What happens when we introduce a third level into our single-factor experiment? Suppose an associate in a percussion music supply company, Tom's Tom-Toms, wants to test ways to increase the amount purchased from the catalogue the company sends out every three months. He decides on three treatments: a coupon for free drum sticks with any purchase, a free practice pad, and a $50 discount on any purchase. The response will be the dollar amount of sales per customer. He decides to keep some customers as a control group by sending them the catalogue without any special offer. The experiment is a single-factor design with four levels: no coupon, coupon for free drum sticks, coupon for the practice pad, and $50 coupon. He assigns the same number of customers to each treatment randomly.

Now the hypothesis to test isn't quite the same as when we tested the difference in means between two independent groups. To test whether all k means are equal, the hypothesis becomes:

$$H_0: \mu_1 = \mu_2 = \ldots = \mu_k$$

$$H_A: \text{At least one mean is different}$$

The test statistic compares the variance of the means with what we'd expect that variance to be based on the variance of the individual responses.

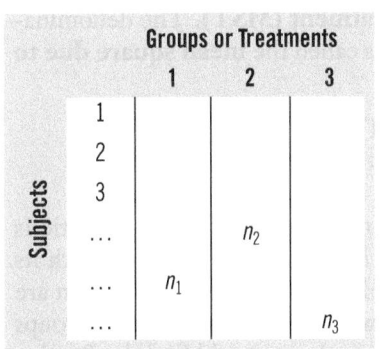

Data layout for completely randomized design with three groups and different numbers of subjects in each group.

Thor Jorgen Udvang/Shutterstock

Remarkably (and this is Fisher's real contribution), these two variances estimate the *same* variance when the null hypothesis is true. When it's false (and the group means differ), the MST gets larger.

The *F*-statistic tests the null hypothesis by taking the ratio of these two mean squares:

$$F_{k-1,\,N-k} = \frac{\text{MST}}{\text{MSE}} \text{ and rejecting the hypothesis if the ratio is too large.}$$

The critical value and P-value depend on the two degrees of freedom $k-1$ and $N-k$.

Let's look at an example. For the summer catalogue of the percussion supply company Tom's Tom-Toms, 4000 customers were selected at random to receive one of four offers:[2] *No Coupon*, *Free Sticks* with purchase, *Free Pad* with purchase, or *Fifty Dollars* off next purchase. All the catalogues were sent out on March 15 and sales data for the month following the mailing were recorded.

The first step is to plot the data. Figure 15.4 shows boxplots of the spending of the four groups for the month after the mailing:

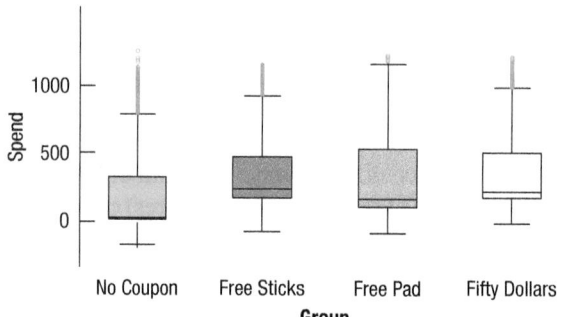

Figure 15.4 Boxplots of the spending of the four groups show that the coupons seem to have stimulated spending.

Here are summary statistics for the four groups:

	Group			
	No Coupon	Free Sticks	Free Pad	Fifty Dollars
Median	$0.00	$233.00	$157.50	$232.00
Mean	$216.68	$385.87	$339.54	$399.95
SD	$390.58	$331.10	$364.17	$337.07

The ANOVA table (Table 15.2) shows the components of the calculation of the **F-test**.

The very small P-value is an indication that the differences we saw in the boxplots are not due to chance, so we reject the null hypothesis of equal means and conclude that the four means are not equal.

---

[2]Realistically, companies often select equal (and relatively small sizes) for the treatment groups and consider all other customers as the control. To make the analysis easier, we'll assume that this experiment just considered 4000 "control" customers. Adding more controls wouldn't increase the power very much.

Source	df	Sum of Squares	Mean Square	F-Ratio	Prob > F
Groups (Between)	3	20,825,966	6,941,988.66	54.6169	<0.0001
Error (Within)	3996	507,905,263	127,103.42		
Total	3999	528,731,229			

Table 15.2 The ANOVA table shows that the F-statistic has a very small P-value, so we can reject the null hypothesis that the means of the four treatments are equal.

FOR EXAMPLE Analyzing a one-way design for Ottawa–Toronto flights

You decide to implement the simple one-factor completely randomized design, sending out four offers (*Coupon, Card, Movie,* or *No Offer*) to 4000 students each (see For Example: "Designing an experiment for Ottawa–Toronto flights"). A year later you collect the results and find the following table of means and standard deviations:

Level	Number	Mean	Std Dev	Std Err Mean	Lower 95%	Upper 95%
Coupon	4000	15.17	72.30	1.14	12.93	17.41
Card	4000	11.53	62.62	0.99	9.59	13.47
Movie	4000	13.29	66.51	1.05	11.22	15.35
No Offer	4000	9.03	50.99	0.81	7.45	10.61

An ANOVA table shows:

Source	df	Sum of Squares	Mean Square	F-Ratio	Prob > F
Offer	3	81,922.26	27,307.42	6.75	0.0002
Error	15,996	64,669,900.04	4,042.88		
Total	15,999	64,751,822.29			

QUESTION What conclusions can you draw from these data?

ANSWER From the ANOVA table, the null hypothesis that all the means are equal is strongly rejected since the P-value is very small. The average number of miles travelled seems to have increased 2.5 miles (=11.53 − 9.03) for students receiving the *Card*, 4.26 miles for students receiving the free *Movie*, and 6.14 miles for those students receiving the *Coupon*. See Section 15.9 for more on these comparisons.

LO❸ **15.8 Assumptions and Conditions for ANOVA**

Whenever we compute P-values and make inferences about a hypothesis, we need to make assumptions and check conditions to see if the assumptions are reasonable. The ANOVA is no exception. Because it's an extension of the two-sample t-test, many of the same assumptions apply.

Independence Assumption

The groups must be independent of each other. No test can verify this assumption. You have to think about how the data were collected. The individual observations must be independent as well.

We check the Randomization Condition. Did the experimental design incorporate suitable randomization? We were told that the customers were assigned to each treatment group at random.

Equal Variance Assumption

ANOVA assumes that the true variances of the treatment groups are equal. We can check the corresponding Similar Variance Condition in various ways:

- Look at side-by-side boxplots of the groups to see whether they have roughly the same spread. It can be easier to compare spreads across groups when they have the same centre, so consider making side-by-side boxplots of the residuals. If the groups have differing spreads, it can make the pooled variance—the MSE—larger, reducing the F-statistic value and making it less likely that we can reject the null hypothesis. So the ANOVA will usually fail on the "safe side," rejecting H_0 less often than it should. Because of this, we usually require the spreads to be quite different from each other before we become concerned about the condition failing. If you've rejected the null hypothesis, this is especially true.

- Look at the original boxplots of the response values again. In general, do the spreads seem to change systematically with the centres? One common pattern is for the boxes with bigger centres to have bigger spreads. This kind of systematic trend in the variances is more of a problem than random differences in spread among the groups and should not be ignored. Fortunately, such systematic violations are often helped by re-expressing the data. If, in addition to spreads that grow with the centres, the boxplots are skewed with the longer tail stretching off to the high end, then the data are pleading for a re-expression. Try taking logs of the response variable for a start. You'll likely end up with a much cleaner analysis.

- Look at the residuals plotted against the predicted values. Often, larger predicted values lead to larger magnitude residuals. This is another sign that the condition is violated. If the residual plot shows more spread on one side or the other, it's usually a good idea to consider re-expressing the response variable. Such a systematic change in the spread is a more serious violation of the Equal Variance Assumption than slight variations of the spreads across groups. However none of these problems occur with our data shown in Figure 15.5.

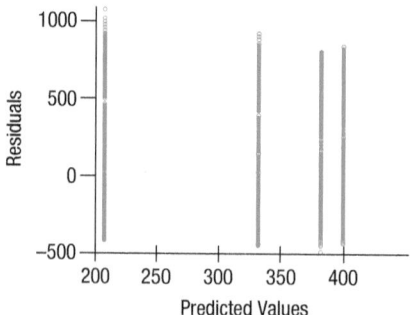

Figure 15.5 A plot of the residuals against the predicted values from the ANOVA shows no sign of unequal spread.

Normal Population Assumption

Like Student's t-tests, the F-test requires that the underlying errors follow a Normal model. As before when we faced this assumption, we'll check a corresponding Nearly Normal Condition.

Technically, we need to assume that the Normal model is reasonable for the populations underlying each treatment group. We can (and should) look at the side-by-side boxplots for indications of skewness. Certainly, if they're all (or mostly) skewed in the same direction, the Nearly Normal Condition fails (and re-expression is likely to help).

However, in many business applications, sample sizes are quite large, and when that's true, the Central Limit Theorem implies that the sampling distribution of the means may be nearly Normal in spite of skewness. Fortunately, the *F*-test is conservative. That means that if you see a small P-value, it's probably safe to reject the null hypothesis for large samples even when the data are non-Normal.

Check Normality with a histogram or a Normal probability plot of all the residuals together. Because we really care about the Normal model within each group, the Normal population assumption is violated if there are outliers in any of the groups. Check for outliers in the boxplots of the values for each treatment.

The Normal probability plot for the Tom's Tom-Toms residuals (Figure 15.6) holds a surprise. Investigating further with a histogram (Figure 15.7), we see the problem.

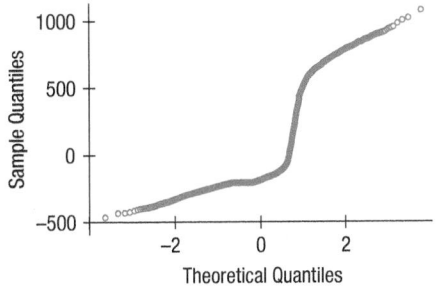

Figure 15.6 A Normal probability plot shows that the residuals from the ANOVA of the Tom's Tom-Toms data are clearly not Normal.

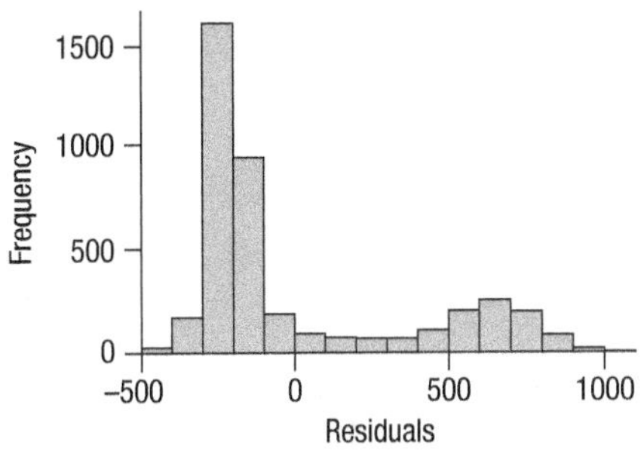

Figure 15.7 A histogram of the residuals reveals bimodality.

The histogram shows clear bimodality of the residuals. If we look at the histograms of the spending of each group, in Figure 15.8 we can see that the boxplots failed to reveal the bimodal nature of the spending.

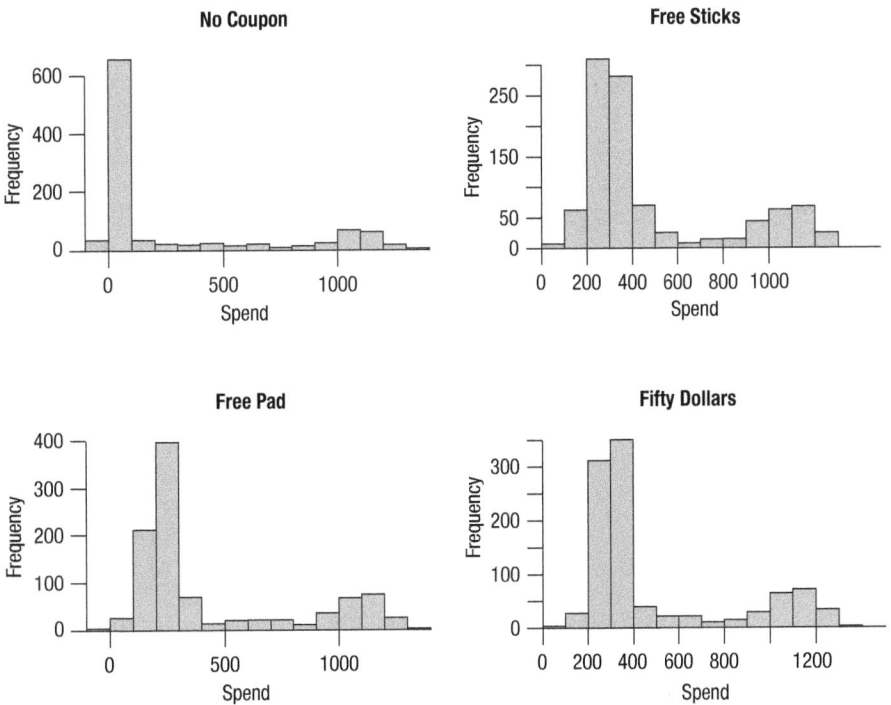

Figure 15.8 The spending appears to be bimodal for all the treatment groups. There is one mode near $1000 and another larger mode between $0 and $200 for each group.

The manager of the company wasn't surprised to hear that the spending is bimodal. In fact, he said, "We typically have customers who either order a complete new drum set or buy accessories. And, of course, we have a large group of customers who choose not to purchase anything during a given quarter."

These data (and the residuals) clearly violate the Nearly Normal Condition. Does that mean we can't say anything about the null hypothesis? No. Fortunately, the sample sizes are large, and there are no individual outliers that have undue influence on the means. With sample sizes this large, we can appeal to the Central Limit Theorem and still make inferences about the means. In particular, we're safe in rejecting the null hypothesis. When the Nearly Normal Condition isn't satisfied, the F-test will tend to fail on the safe side and be less likely to reject the null. Since we have a very small P-value, we can be fairly sure that the differences we saw were real.

FOR EXAMPLE   Assumptions and conditions for ANOVA for Ottawa–Toronto flights

Closer examination of the miles data from the Porter project (see For Example: "Analyzing a one-way design for Ottawa–Toronto flights") shows that only about 5% of the students overall actually flew, so the *Miles Travelled* are about 95% zeros and the other values are highly skewed to the right.

QUESTION   Are the assumptions and conditions for ANOVA satisfied?

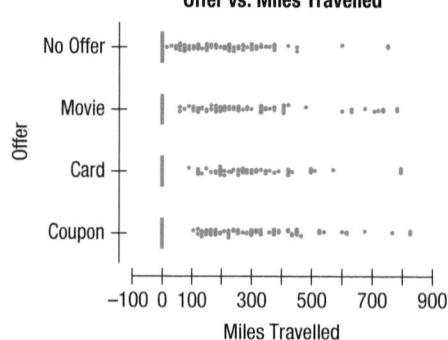

ANSWER   The responses are independent since the offer was randomized to the students on the mailing list. The distributions of *Miles Travelled* by *Offer* are highly right-skewed. Most of the entries are zeros. This could present a problem, but because the sample size is so large (4000 per group), the inference is valid (a simulation shows that the averages of 4000 are Normally distributed). Although the distributions are right-skewed, there are no extreme outliers influencing the group means. The variances in the four groups also appear to be similar. Thus, the assumptions and conditions appear to be met. (An alternative analysis might be to focus on the *Miles Travelled* only of those who actually took Porter. The conclusion of the ANOVA would remain the same).

JUST CHECKING

Your experiment to test the new pet food formulation has been completed. One hypothesis you've tested is whether the new formulation is different in safety and nutritional value (measured by having veterinarians evaluate the test animals) from a standard food known to be safe and nutritious. The ANOVA has an F-statistic of 1.2, which (for the degrees of freedom in your experiment) has a P-value of 0.87. Now you need to make a report to the company.

7 Write a brief report. Can you conclude that the new formulation is safe and nutritious?

Answers are found in Appendix A.

We have now covered all the topics needed for a one-way ANOVA. Let's summarize them as a sequence of steps.

Step	Procedure	Example: Tom's Tom-Toms
1	Design an experiment in which you assign subjects at random to a number of different groups (or treatments).	Four offers: *Nothing* (control); *Free Sticks; Free Pad; Fifty Dollars*
2	Specify the response variable and α.	Sales during one month, $\alpha = 0.05$
3	State hypotheses.	H_0: average sales is the same independent of the offer
4	Check conditions: independence of groups; equal variances of each group; each group Normally distributed or large sample size. If the conditions are not met, go to Section 17.6.	Randomization implies independence; similar box plots; skewed histograms but large sample size
5	Calculate SST, SSE, MST, MSE, and F. Look up the P-value from the F-table.	Table 15.2; $P < 0.0001$
6	If $P < \alpha$, reject null hypothesis.	At least one of the groups has average sales significantly different from the others.
7	State a business conclusion.	We need to evaluate the costs of these offers before deciding which to use in future.

Steps 5, 8, and 9 are typically handled by software, but some human judgment is needed for the others.

LO❸ 15.9 ANOVA on Observational Data

So far we've applied ANOVA only to data from designed experiments, which is appropriate for several reasons. The primary one is that randomized comparative experiments are specifically designed to compare the results for different treatments. The overall null hypothesis, and the subsequent tests on pairs of treatments in ANOVA, address such comparisons directly. In addition, the Equal Variance Assumption (which we need for all of the ANOVA analyses) is often plausible in a randomized experiment because when we randomly assign subjects to treatments, all the treatment groups start out with the same underlying variance of the experimental units.

Sometimes, though, we just can't perform an experiment. When ANOVA is used to test equality of group means from *observational* data, there's no reason to think the group variances might be equal at all. Even if the null hypothesis of equal means were true, the groups might easily have different variances. But you can use ANOVA on observational data if the side-by-side boxplots of responses for each group show roughly equal spreads and symmetric, outlier-free distributions.

Observational data tend to be messier than experimental data. If you aren't assigning subjects to treatment groups, it's harder to guarantee the same number of subjects in each group. The only way we know to avoid the effects of possible lurking variables is with control and randomized assignment to treatment groups, and for observational data, we have neither.

ANOVA is often applied to observational data when an experiment would be impossible or unethical. (We can't randomly break some subjects' legs, but we *can* compare pain perception among those with broken legs, those with sprained ankles, and those with stubbed toes by collecting data on subjects who have already suffered those injuries.) In such data, subjects are already in groups, but not by random assignment.

Be careful: If you haven't assigned subjects to treatments randomly, you can't draw *causal* conclusions even when the *F*-test is significant. You have no way to control for lurking variables or confounding, so you can't be sure whether any differences you see among groups are due to the grouping variable or to some other unobserved variable that may be related to the grouping variable.

LO❸   15.10   Analyzing a Randomized Block Design

	Groups or Treatments		
	1	...	T
Blocks 1			
2			
3			
...			
B			

Data layout for randomized block design with T treatments and B blocks

So far we have dealt with one-way ANOVA in which we investigate the effect of one single variable on another variable. For example: "How does the type of offer we give our customers affect the revenue that they bring us?" But we all know that life is not one-dimensional and there are many other factors (age group, income level) that come into play in addition to the one we are investigating (the type of offer). We may not be able to control these other factors, but we know they are there. We call them blocking factors.

Agriculture, forestry, and fishing are very important in the Canadian economy, contributing $30 billion to exports in 2014, a figure that has been growing at over 10% per year. Government and industry researchers are continuously developing new varieties and new ways of maximizing their productivity. Let us take an example of the impact of fertilizer treatment on pine tree growth. Different fertilizer treatments are applied to different groups of trees, and the increase in tree volume is measured after four years. Sounds simple enough, but obviously local conditions like the type of soil in which the trees are planted can also have a major impact on tree growth. We really need a block of trees in one area divided into smaller plots that are then given the different fertilizer treatments, and then other blocks in other areas divided up and treated the same way. The part of each block (e.g., the northeast quadrant) that gets a certain fertilizer treatment is selected at random. This example shows the meaning of the word "block" in a randomized block design. We are blocking for local conditions by taking a block of trees growing in a certain area. It also shows the meaning of the word "treatment," since we are testing alternative fertilizer treatments. Here are some results of tree growth in cubic metres per hectare four years after fertilizer treatment:

m³/hectare	Fertilizer Treatment			
Block	None	A	B	C
1	139	157	168	177
2	152	160	168	175
3	178	192	190	201
4	193	205	213	202

You don't have to be a forestry expert to know that some trees grow faster than others, and that we are not interested in the growth of individual trees. Instead we are interested in the average growth of a hectare of forest and that is what is recorded in the table. This is obvious when we are talking about trees and forests, but it is an important point that distinguishes a randomized block design from the factorial design discussed in the next section. Another point to note about a randomized block design is that each treatment is applied to each block. In the completely randomized design in Section 15.7, we can have different numbers of observations, n_i, for each treatment.

Our experiment shows quite a lot of variability in tree growth, from 139 to 213 m³/ha. However, we can also see that some of that variability is due to blocks 3 and 4 being better at growing trees than blocks 1 and 2. We don't know why that is (it might be the soil type or the microclimate or something else) and we don't care, because ultimately we need to apply fertilizer to a whole forest of trees covering a range of different local conditions. It is important that we can attribute some of the variability to the blocking, since that means there is less variability remaining for our analysis of the effect of fertilizer. Blocking gives us more accuracy in the analysis of the fertilizer treatment, which is what we are really interested in. Mathematically we can see this by comparing the equation for a completely randomized design in Section 15.7:

$$\text{SSTotal} = \text{SST} + \text{SSE}$$

with the equation for a randomized block design:

$$\text{SSTotal} = \text{SST} + \text{SSB} + \text{SSE}$$

The sum of squares error, SSE, in the completely randomized design has been split into two parts, one due to blocking, SSB, leaving a reduced SSE in the randomized block design. The lower the SSE, the more accurate our analysis will be. The principle of the analysis is the same as for the completely randomized design: we calculate how much variability there is due to the treatments compared to how much is due to errors, MST/MSE, and look it up in an F-table. The details of the equations are slightly different:

$$\text{SST} = B\sum_{j=1}^{T}(\bar{y}_{*j} - \bar{y})^2 \qquad\qquad \text{MST} = \frac{\text{SST}}{T - 1}$$

$$\text{SSB} = T\sum_{i=1}^{B}(\bar{y}_{i*} - \bar{y})^2 \qquad\qquad \text{MSB} = \frac{\text{SSB}}{B - 1}$$

$$\text{SSE} = \sum_{i=1}^{B}\sum_{j=1}^{T}(y_{ij} - \bar{y}_{*j} - \bar{y}_{i*} + \bar{y})^2 \qquad\qquad \text{MSE} = \frac{\text{SSE}}{N - T - B - 1}$$

$$F_T = \frac{\text{MST}}{\text{MSE}} \qquad\qquad F_B = \frac{\text{MSB}}{\text{MSE}}$$

where:
y_{ij} = the result for treatment j on block i
$\bar{y}_{*j}$ = the average of all blocks for treatment j
$\bar{y}_{i*}$ = the average of all treatments for block i
$\bar{y}$ = the average of all treatments and all blocks
B = the number of blocks
T = the number of treatments

$N = BT =$ the total number of results
$df_T = T - 1$
$df_B = B - 1$
$df_E = N - B - T - 1$

The analysis for the fertilizer treatment data gives:

Source of Variation	SS	df	MS	F	P-value	F critical $\alpha = 0.05$
Blocks	5297.5	3	1765.8	48.10	0.00001	3.86
Treatments	1237.6	3	412.5	11.24	0.00213	3.86
Error	330.4	9	36.7			
Total	6865.5	15				

We can interpret these results in two ways. First, we can compare the actual value of F for fertilizer treatment, 11.24, with the critical value of 3.86 from Table F in Appendix B with $\alpha = 0.05$, and degrees of freedom $= (3, 9)$. The fact that it is larger indicates that the fertilizer treatment has a very significant impact on tree growth per hectare. Alternatively, we can compare the P-value of 0.00213 with $\alpha = 0.05$ and come to the same conclusion. In order to find out which fertilizer treatment improves tree growth most, we could use the Bonferroni method described in the online supplement; however, that is beyond the scope of the current example.

We also see that the blocking is very significant since it has a large F and a small P-value.

Here is a step-by-step procedure for randomized block analysis:

Step	Procedure	Example: Fertilizer treatment of pine trees
1	Design an experiment in which you assign treatments at random within a number of blocks.	Four fertilizer treatments are assigned at random to plots of land within different blocks.
2	Specify the response variable and α.	Tree growth (m^3/ha) after four years, $\alpha = 0.05$
3	State hypotheses.	H_0: average tree growth is the same independent of the fertilizer treatment H_A: at least one fertilizer treatment results in different average tree growth than the others
4	Check conditions: independence of treatment groups; equal variances of each group; each group Normally distributed or large sample size. If the conditions are not met, go to Section 17.3.	Randomization implies independence; we don't have enough data to check the other conditions, but there is no evidence that they are violated.
5	Calculate SST, SSE, MST, MSE, x, and hence F. Look up the P-value from the *F*-table.	Table of results given in text: $P = 0.00213$
6	If P $< \alpha$, reject null hypothesis.	At least one of the fertilizer treatments gives significantly different tree growth than the others.
7	State a business conclusion.	Fertilizer treatment significantly affects tree growth four years after application. The optimal fertilizer treatment to use requires further analysis, which would include the cost of fertilizer application and the value of the increased tree growth.

LO❸   15.11   Analyzing a Factorial Design—Two-Way Analysis of Variance

In our direct mail example, we looked at two factors: *Miles* and *Envelope*. *Miles* had three levels: *no miles, double miles,* and *double anywhere miles.* The factor *Envelope* had two levels: *standard* and new *logo.* The three levels of *Miles* and the two levels of *Envelope* resulted in six treatment groups. Because this was a completely randomized design, the 30,000 customers were selected at random, and 5000 were assigned at random to each treatment.

Three months after the offer was mailed out, the total charges on the card were recorded for each of the 30,000 cardholders in the experiment. Figure 15.9 shows boxplots of the treatment groups' responses, plotted against each factor.

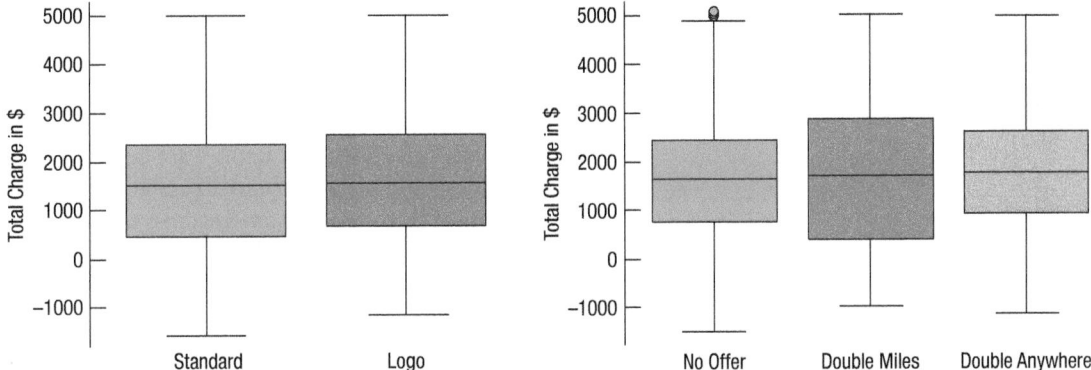

Figure 15.9   Boxplots of *Total Charge* by each factor. It's difficult to see the effects of the factors for two reasons. First, the other factor hasn't been accounted for, and second, the effects are small compared with the overall variation in charges.

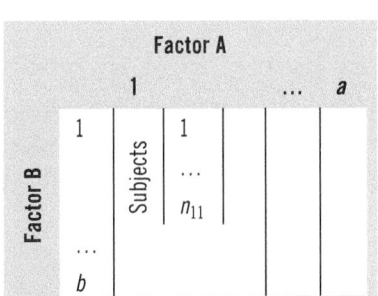

Data layout for a factorial design with *a* levels for factor A, *b* levels for factor B, and n_{ij} subjects at levels *i, j*

If you look closely, you may be able to discern a very slight increase in the *Total Charges* for some levels of the factors, but it's very difficult to see. There are two reasons for this. First, the variation due to each factor gets in the way of seeing the effect of the other factor. For example, some of the customers in the boxplot for the *logo Envelope* got each of the offers. If those offers had an effect on spending, then that increased the variation within the *logo* treatment group. Second, as is typical in a marketing experiment of this kind, the effects are very small compared with the variability in people's spending. That's why companies use such a large sample size.

The analysis of variance for two factors removes the effects of each factor from consideration of the other. It can also model whether the factors interact, increasing or decreasing the effect. In our example, it will separate out the effect of changing the levels of *Miles* and the effect of changing the levels of *Envelope.* It will also test whether the effect of the *Envelope* is the same for the three different *Miles* levels. If the effect is different, it's called an interaction effect between the two factors.

The details of the calculations[3] for the two-way ANOVA with interaction are less important than understanding the summary, the model, and the assumptions and conditions under which it's appropriate to use the model. For a one-way ANOVA, we calculated three sums of squares (SS): the total SS, the treatment SS, and the error SS. For this model, we'll calculate five: the total SS, the SS due to factor A, the SS due to factor B, the SS due to the interaction, and the error SS.

---

[3]See Optional Math Box online.

Let's suppose we have *a* levels of factor A, *b* levels of factor B, and *r* replicates at each treatment combination. In our case, $a = 2$, $b = 3$, $r = 5000$, and $a \times b \times r = N$ is 30,000. Then the ANOVA table will look like Table 15.3.

Source	df	Sum of Squares	Mean Square	F-Ratio	Prob > F
Factor A	$a-1$	SSA	MSA	MSA/MSE	P-value
Factor B	$b-1$	SSB	MSB	MSB/MSE	P-value
Interaction	$(a-1) \times (b-1)$	SSAB	MSAB	MSAB/MSE	P-value
Error	$ab(r-1)$	SSE	MSE		
Total	$N-1$	SSTotal			

Table 15.3   An ANOVA table for a replicated two-factor design with a row for each factor's sum of squares, interaction sum of square, error, and total.

There are now three null hypotheses:

H_0: the means of the levels of factor A are equal,
H_0: the means of the levels of factor B are equal, and
H_0: the effects of factor A are *constant* across the levels of factor B (or vice versa).

Each of the corresponding P-values is used to test the corresponding hypothesis.

Table 15.4 is the ANOVA table for the marketing experiment.

Source	df	Sum of Squares	Mean Square	F-Ratio	Prob > F
Miles	2	201,150,000	100,575,000	66.20	<0.0001
Envelope	1	203,090,000	203,090,000	133.68	<0.0001
Miles × Envelope	2	1,505,200	752,600	0.50	0.61
Error	29,994	45,568,000,000	1,519,237		

Table 15.4   The ANOVA table for the marketing experiment. The effects of both *Miles* and *Envelope* are highly significant, but the interaction term is not.

From the ANOVA table, we can see that both the *Miles* and the *Envelope* effects are highly significant, but that the interaction term is not. An **interaction plot**, a plot of means for each treatment group, is essential for sorting out what these P-values mean (Figure 15.10).

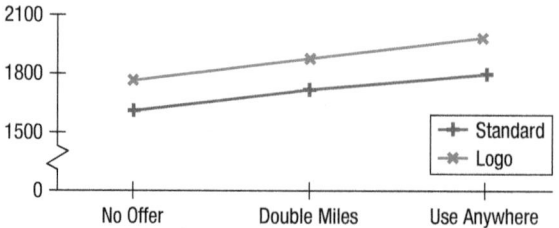

Figure 15.10   An interaction plot of the *Miles* and *Envelope* effects. The parallel lines show that the effects of the three *Miles* offers are roughly the same over the two different *Envelopes* and therefore that the interaction effect is small.

The interaction plot shows the mean *charges* at all six treatment groups. The levels of one of the factors, in this case *Miles*, are shown on the *x*-axis, and the mean charges of the groups for each *Envelope* level are shown at *each Miles level*. The means of each level of *Envelope* are connected for ease of understanding. Notice that the effect of *double miles* over *no offer* is about the same for both the *standard* and *logo Envelopes*. And the same is true for the *use anywhere* miles. This indicates that the effect of *Miles* is constant for the two different *Envelopes*. The lines are parallel, which indicates that there is no interaction effect.

We reject the null hypothesis that the mean *charges* at the three different levels of *Miles* are equal (with P-values < 0.0001), and we also reject that the mean *charges* for *standard* and *logo* are the same (with P-value < 0.0001). We have no evidence, however, to suggest that there's an interaction between the factors.

After rejecting the null hypotheses, we can create a confidence interval for any particular treatment mean or perform a hypothesis test for the difference between any two means. If we want to do several tests or confidence intervals, we'll need to use a multiple comparisons method that adjusts the size of the confidence interval or the level of the test to keep the *overall* Type I error rate at the level we desire. One such method is the Bonferroni method described in the online supplement.

When the interaction term isn't significant, we can talk about the overall effect of either factor as we did in Section 15.9. Because the effect of *Envelope* is roughly the same for all three *Miles* offers (as we know by virtue of not rejecting the hypothesis that the interaction effect is zero), we can calculate and interpret an overall *Envelope* effect. The means of the two *Envelope* levels are

$$Logo\ 1871.75\ Standard\ 1707.19,$$

so the *logo* envelope generated a difference in average charge of $\$1871.75 - \$1707.19 = \$164.56$. A confidence interval for this difference is ($\$136.66$, $\$192.45$), which the analysts can use to decide whether the added cost of the *logo* envelope is worth the expense.

But when an interaction term is significant, we must be very careful not to talk about the effect of a factor on *average*, because the effect of one factor *depends* on the level of the other factor. In that case, we always have to talk about the factor effect at a specific level of the other factor, as we'll see in the next example.

FOR EXAMPLE | **Factorial designs for Ottawa–Toronto flights**

QUESTION Suppose that you'd run the randomized block design (see For Example: "Designing an experiment for Ottawa–Toronto flights"). You would have had two levels of the (blocking) factor *City* and the same four levels of *Offer* (*Coupon*, *Card*, *Movie*, and *No Offer*). The ANOVA shows a significant interaction effect between *City* and *Offer*. Explain what that means. An analysis of the two groups separately shows that for the Ottawa/Toronto group, the P-value for testing the four offers is < 0.0001, but for the Montreal group, the P-value is 0.2354. Is this consistent with a significant interaction effect? What would you tell the marketing group?

ANSWER A significant interaction effect implies that the effect of one factor isn't the same for the levels of another. Thus, it's saying that the effect of the four offers isn't the same for those in Ottawa/Toronto as it is for those in Montreal. The separate analysis explains this further. For those in Montreal, the offers don't significantly change the average number of miles they travel. However, for those in Ottawa/Toronto, the offers do have an effect. This could influence where Porter decides to advertise its offers, or to whom it decides to send them.

GUIDED EXAMPLE   A Follow-Up Experiment

After analyzing the data, the credit card company decided to go with the *Logo* envelope, but a marketing special-ist thought that more *Miles* might increase spending even more. A new test was designed to test both the type of *Miles* and the amount. Again, total *charge* in three months is the response.

PLAN	**Setup** State the problem.	We want to study the two factors *Miles* and *Amount* to see their effect on the revenue generated for a new credit card offer.
	Specify the response variable.	To measure the success, we'll use the monthly charges of customers who receive the various offers during the three months after the offer is sent out.
	Identify the factors you plan to test.	We'll offer each customer one of the two levels of the factor *Miles* for the WestJet card: WestJet *miles* or *use anywhere* miles. Customers are offered three levels of *Miles*: *regular miles, double miles,* and *triple miles.*
	Specify the levels of the factors you will use.	
	Specify the design.	A total of 60,000 current customers will be randomly selected from our customer records to receive one of the six offers.

Make a Picture A diagram of your design can help you think about it. We could also draw this diagram like the one in the Guided Example at the end of Section 15.4 with six treatment groups, but now we're think-ing of the design as having two distinct factors that we wish to evaluate individually, so this form gives the right impression.

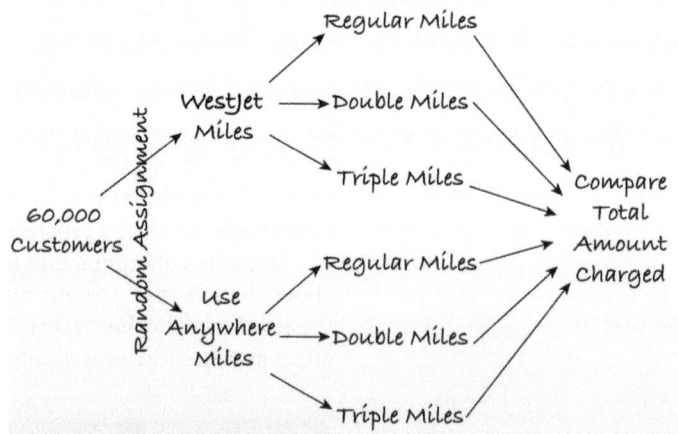

Specify how to measure the response and your hypotheses.

The three null hypotheses are:

H_0: The mean charges for WestJet *miles* and *use anywhere* miles are the same (the means for *Miles* are equal).

H_0: The mean charges for *no miles, double miles,* and *triple miles* are the same (the means for *Amount* are equal).

H_0: The effect of *Miles* is the same for all levels of *Amount* (and vice versa) (no interaction effect).

The alternative for the first hypothesis is that the mean charges for the two levels of *Miles* are different.

The alternative for the second hypothesis is that at least one of the mean charges for the three levels of *Amount* is different.

DO   Examine the boxplots and interaction plots.

The alternative for the third hypothesis is that there is an interaction effect.

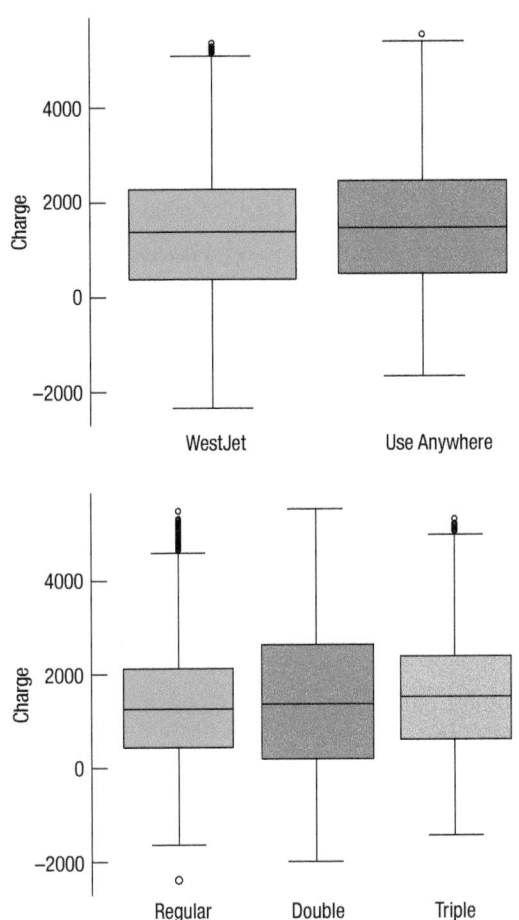

Boxplots by each factor show that there may be a slight increase in charges due to the *use anywhere miles* and the *Amount* of miles offered, but the differences are hard to see because of the intrinsic variation in charges.

There are some outliers apparent in the boxplots, but none exerts a large influence on its group mean, so we'll leave them in.

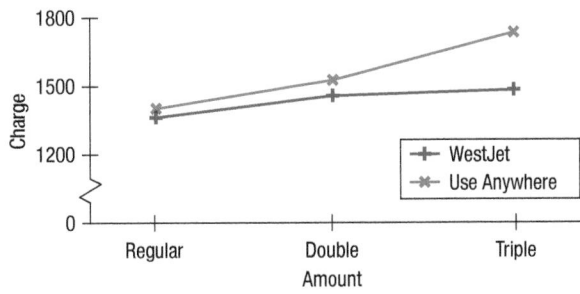

(*continued*)

The interaction plot shows that offering *triple miles* may have a much larger effect for *use anywhere miles* than for *WestJet miles*.

Assumptions and Conditions
Think about the assumptions and check the conditions.

✓ **Independence Assumption, Randomization Condition.** The experiment was randomized to current cardholders.

✓ **Similar Variance Condition.** The boxplots show that the variances across all groups are similar. (We can recheck with a residual plot after fitting the ANOVA model.)

✓ **Outlier Condition.** There are some outliers, but none appear to be exerting undue influence on the group means.

Check the remaining conditions on the residuals.

✓ **Nearly Normal Condition.** A histogram of the residuals shows that they are reasonably unimodal and symmetric:

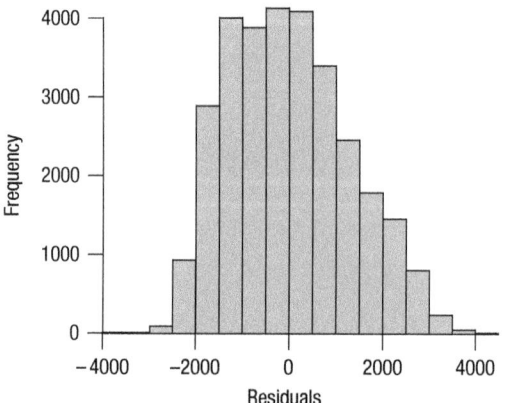

Under these conditions, it's appropriate to interpret the *F*-ratios and their P-values.

	Source	df	SS	MS	*F*-Ratio	P-Value
	Miles	1	103,576,768	103,576,768	61.6216	<0.0001
	Amount	2	253,958,660.1	126,979,330	75.5447	<0.0001
	Miles × Amount	2	64,760,963.01	32,380,481.51	19.2643	<0.0001
	Error	29,994	50,415,417,459	1,680,850		
	Total	29,999	50,837,713,850			

Discuss the results of the ANOVA table.

Show a table of means, possibly with confidence intervals or tests from an appropriate multiple comparisons method.

The *F*-ratios are all large, and the P-values are all very small, so we reject all three null hypotheses. Because the interaction effect is significant, we can't talk about the overall effect of the amount of miles but must make the discussion specific to the type of miles offered.

Level					Mean
Use Anywhere, Triple	A				1732.21
Use Anywhere, Double		B			1526.93
WestJet, Triple		B			1484.34
WestJet, Double		B	C		1460.20
Use Anywhere, Regular			C	D	1401.89
WestJet, Regular				D	1363.94

REPORT

Conclusion To answer the initial question, we ask whether the differences we observe in the means of the groups are meaningful.

Be sure to make recommendations based on the context of your business decision.

MEMO

Re: Test Mailing for Creative Offer and Envelope

The mailing for testing the triple miles initiative went out in March, and results on charges from April through June were available in early July. We found that *use anywhere miles* performed better than the standard *WestJet miles*, but that the amount they increased charges depended on the amount offered.

Triple miles for the WestJet miles didn't increase *Charge* significantly and is probably not worth the added expense. However, triple miles for the use anywhere miles generated an average $205 more in average *Charge* (with a confidence interval from $131 to $279).

Dependent on a satisfactory cost analysis, we recommend offering triple miles for the use anywhere miles offers but would keep the double miles offer for the WestJet miles.

WHAT CAN GO WRONG?

- **Don't give up just because you can't run an experiment.** Sometimes we can't run an experiment because we can't identify or control the factors. Sometimes it would simply be unethical to run the experiment. If we can't perform an experiment, often an observational study is a good choice.

- **Beware of confounding.** Use randomization whenever possible to ensure that the factors not in your experiment are not confounded with your treatment levels. Be alert to confounding that can't be avoided, and report it along with your results.

- **Bad things can happen even to good experiments.** Protect yourself by recording additional information. An experiment in which the air conditioning failed for two weeks, affecting the results, was saved by recording the temperature (although that wasn't originally one of the factors) and estimating the effect the higher temperature had on the response.[4] It's generally good practice to collect as much information as possible about your experimental units and the circumstances of the experiment. For example, in the direct mail experiment, it would be wise to record details of the general economy and any global events (such as a sharp downturn in the stock market) that might affect customer behaviour.

- **Don't spend your entire budget on the first run.** Just as it's a good idea to pretest a survey, it's always wise to try a small pilot experiment before running the full-scale experiment. You may learn, for example, about how to choose factor levels more effectively, about effects you forgot to control, and about unanticipated confounding.

- **Watch out for outliers.** One outlier in a group can change both the mean and the spread of that group. It will also inflate the error mean square, which can influence the F-test. The good news is that ANOVA fails on the safe side by losing power when there are outliers. That is, you're less likely to

---

[4]DeVeaux, R. D., & Szelewski, M. (1989). Optimizing automatic splitless injection parameters for gas chromatographic environmental analysis. *Journal of Chromatographic Science, 27*(9), 513–518.

reject the overall null hypothesis if you have (and leave) outliers in your data, so they're not likely to cause you to make a Type I error.

- **Watch out for changing variances.** The conclusions of the ANOVA depend crucially on the assumptions of independence and constant variance and (somewhat less seriously as *n* increases) on Normality. If the conditions on the residuals are violated, it may be necessary to re-express the response variable to approximate these conditions more closely. ANOVA benefits so greatly from a judiciously chosen re-expression that the choice of a re-expression might be considered a standard part of the analysis.

- **Be wary of drawing conclusions about causality from observational studies.** ANOVA is often applied to data from randomized experiments for which causal conclusions are appropriate. If the data aren't from a designed experiment, however, the analysis of variance provides no more evidence for causality than any other method we've studied.

- **Be wary of generalizing to situations other than the one at hand.** Think hard about how the data were generated to understand the breadth of conclusions you're entitled to draw.

- **Watch for multiple comparisons.** When rejecting the null hypothesis, you can conclude that the means are not *all* equal. But you can't start comparing every pair of treatments in your study with a *t*-test. You'll run the risk of inflating your Type I error rate. Use a multiple comparisons method when you want to test many pairs.

- **Be sure to fit an interaction term when it exists.** When the design is replicated, it's always a good idea to fit an interaction term. If it turns out not to be statistically significant, you can then fit a simpler two-factor main effects model instead.

- **When the interaction effect is significant, don't interpret the main effects.** Main effects can be very misleading in the presence of interaction terms. Look at the interaction plot in Figure 15.11:

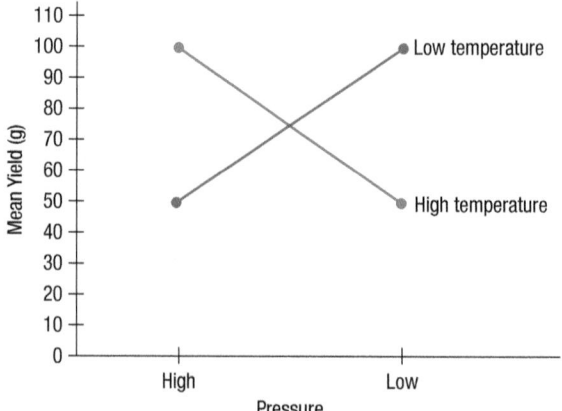

Figure 15.11 An interaction plot of *Yield* by *Temperature* and *Pressure*. The main effects are misleading. There is no (main) effect of *Pressure* because the average *Yield* at the two pressures is the same. That doesn't mean that *Pressure* has no effect on the *Yield*. In the presence of an interaction effect, be careful when interpreting the main effects.

The experiment was run at two temperatures and two pressure levels. High amounts of material were produced at high pressure with high temperature and at low pressure with low temperature. What's the effect of *Temperature*? Of *Pressure*? Both main effects are zero, but it would be silly (and wrong) to say that neither *Temperature* nor *Pressure* was important. The real story is in the interaction.

ETHICS IN ACTION

Professors at many universities belong to a faculty union. The unionized faculty members at one university are preparing for contract negotiations. Ryma McCrady, recently elected union president, has long been concerned about the salary differential between male and female faculty. As union president, she now has access to faculty salary information and decides to run some analyses. After consulting with a few colleagues who regularly use statistics, she settles on using analysis of variance to determine if differences in salary can be attributed to gender, accounting for faculty rank (assistant professor, associate professor, and full professor). She's not surprised by the results. While there is no significant interaction effect of gender and rank, she does find that both gender and rank are significant factors in explaining salary differences. Given that discrimination based on gender is a serious issue, she plans to raise it during the contract negotiations.

ETHICAL ISSUE *This is an observational study lacking the control of an experimental study. Confounding variables are likely to exist, but are not discussed. For instance, lower-paid disciplines (e.g., Education) tend to have more female faculty than higher-paid disciplines (e.g., Engineering) (related to Item A, ASA Ethical Guidelines; see Appendix C, the American Statistical Association's Ethical Guidelines for Statistical Practice, also available online at www.amstat.org/about/ethicalguidelines.cfm). She should also check for outliers. Special cases, such as a star football coach or Nobel Prize winner, may command unusually large salaries but not be relevant to the pay of ordinary faculty members.*

ETHICAL SOLUTION *Make all caveats explicit. This is a complex issue that should not be treated simply.*

WHAT HAVE WE LEARNED?

Learning Objectives

❶ Recognize observational studies.

- A retrospective study looks at an outcome in the present and looks for facts in the past that relate to it.
- A prospective study selects subjects and follows them as events unfold.

Know the elements of a designed randomized experiment.

- *Experimental units* (sometimes called *subjects* or *participants*) are assigned at random to *treatments*.
- The experimenter manipulates *factors*, setting them to specified *levels* to establish the treatments.
- A quantitative *response variable is* measured or observed for each experimental unit.
- We can attribute differences in the response to the differences among the treatments.

❷ State and apply the four principles of experimental design.

- *Randomize* the assignment of subjects to treatments. *Balance* the design by assigning the same number of subjects to each treatment.
- *Control* sources of variation other than the factors being tested. Make the conditions as similar as possible for all treatment groups, except for differences among the treatments.
- *Replicate* the experiment on more than one subject.
- *Block* the experiment by grouping together subjects who are similar in important ways that you can't control.

Work with *blinding* and *control groups*.

- A *single-blind* study is one in which either all those who can affect the results or all those who evaluate the results are kept ignorant of which subjects receive which treatments.
- A *double-blind* study is one in which both those classes of actors are ignorant of the treatment assignment.
- A *control group* is assigned to a null or placebo treatment or to the best available alternative treatment.

❸ Understand how to use analysis of variance (ANOVA).

We test whether the means of two groups are equal using a t-test. Now we've extended that to testing whether the means of several groups are equal. A good first step in looking at the relationship between a quantitative response and a categorical grouping variable is to look at side-by-side boxplots. It's still a good first step before formally testing the null hypothesis.

We've learned that the F-test is a generalization of the t-test that we used for testing two groups. We've seen that although this makes the mechanics familiar, there are new conditions to check. We've also learned that when the null hypothesis is rejected and we conclude that there are differences, we need to adjust the confidence intervals for the pairwise differences between means. We also need to adjust the alpha levels of tests we perform once we've rejected the null hypothesis.

- We've learned that under certain assumptions, the statistic used to test whether the means of k groups are equal is distributed as an F-statistic with $k-1$ and $N-k$ degrees of freedom.
- We've learned to check four conditions to verify the assumptions before we proceed with inference, and we've seen that most of the checks can be made by graphing the data and the residuals.
- We've learned that if the F-statistic is large enough, we reject the null hypothesis that all the means are equal.
- We've also learned to create and interpret confidence intervals for the differences between each pair of group means, recognizing that we need to adjust the confidence interval for the number of comparisons we make.
- We've learned that sometimes factors can interact with each other. When we have at least two observations at each combination of factor levels, we can add an interaction term to our model to account for the possible interaction.
- Finally, we've learned to recognize the problems posed by confounding variables in experiments and lurking variables in observational studies.

Terms	
Analysis of variance (ANOVA)	An analysis method for testing equality of means across treatment groups.
ANOVA table	The ANOVA table is convenient for showing the degrees of freedom, treatment mean square, error mean square, their ratio the F-statistic, and its P-value. There are usually other quantities of lesser interest included as well.
Blind, blinding	Any individual associated with an experiment who is not aware of how subjects have been allocated to treatment groups is said to be blinded.
Blocking	When groups of experimental units are similar, it's often a good idea to gather them together into blocks. By blocking we isolate the variability attributable to the differences between the blocks so that we can see the differences in the means due to the treatments more clearly.
Confounded	When the levels of one factor are associated with the levels of another factor so that their effects cannot be separated, we say that these two factors are confounded.
Control	When we limit the levels of a factor not explicitly part of the experiment design, we have controlled that factor. (By contrast, the factors we are testing are said to be *manipulated*.)
Control group	The experimental units assigned to a baseline treatment level, typically either the default treatment, which is well understood, or a null, placebo treatment. Their responses provide a basis for comparison.
Designs	• **Randomized block design:** The randomization occurs only within blocks. • **Completely randomized design:** All experimental units have an equal chance of receiving any treatment. • **Factorial design:** Includes more than one factor in the same design and includes every combination of all the levels of each factor.
Double-blind, single-blind	There are two classes of individuals who can affect the outcome of an experiment: • those who could *influence the results* (subjects, treatment administrators, or technicians) • those who *evaluate the results* (judges, treating physicians, etc.)

When every individual in *either* of these classes is blinded, an experiment is said to be single-blind. When everyone in *both* classes is blinded, we call the experiment double-blind.

Experiment	An experiment *manipulates* factor levels to create treatments, *randomly assigns* subjects to these treatment levels, and then *compares* the responses of the subject groups across treatment levels.
Experimental units	Individuals on whom an experiment is performed. Usually called subjects or participants when they are human.
Factor	A variable whose levels are controlled by the experimenter. Experiments attempt to discover the effects that differences in factor levels may have on the responses of the experimental units.
***F*-statistic**	The *F*-statistic is the ratio MST/MSE. When the *F*-statistic is sufficiently large, we reject the null hypothesis that the group means are equal.
***F*-test**	The *F*-test tests the null hypothesis that all the group means are equal against the one-sided alternative that they are not all equal. We reject the hypothesis of equal means if the *F*-statistic exceeds the critical value from the *F*-distribution corresponding to the specified significance level and degrees of freedom.
Interaction	When the effects of the levels of one factor change depending on the level of the other factor, the two factors are said to interact. When interaction terms are present, it's misleading to talk about the main effect of one factor because how large it is *depends* on the level of the other factor.
Interaction plot	A plot that shows the means at each treatment combination, highlighting the factor effects and their behaviour at all the combinations.
Level	The specific value that the experimenter chooses for a factor.
Mean square	A sum of squares divided by its associated degrees of freedom. • **Mean square due to error (MSE):** The estimate of the error variance obtained by pooling the variance of each treatment group. • **Mean square due to treatment (MST):** The estimate of the error variance under the null hypothesis that the treatment means are all equal. If the null hypothesis is not true, the MST will be larger than the error variance.
Observational study	A study based on data in which no manipulation of factors has been employed.
Placebo	A treatment known to have no effect, administered so that all groups experience the same conditions. Only by comparing with a placebo can we be sure that the observed effect of a treatment is not due simply to the placebo effect.
Placebo effect	The tendency of many human subjects (often 20% or more of experiment subjects) to show a response even when administered a placebo.
Principles of experimental design	• *Randomize* subjects to treatments to even out effects we cannot control. • *Control* aspects of the experiment that we know may have an effect on the response but that are not the factors being studied. • *Replicate* over as many subjects as possible. Results for a single subject are just anecdotes. • *Block* to reduce the effects of identifiable attributes of the subjects that cannot be controlled.
Prospective study	An observational study in which subjects are followed to observe future outcomes.
Random assignment	Assigning experimental units to treatment groups at random. Random assignment is necessary for an experiment to be valid.
Response	A variable whose values are compared across different treatments. In a randomized experiment, large response differences can be attributed to the effect of differences in treatment level.
Retrospective study	An observational study in which subjects are selected and then their previous conditions or behaviours are determined.
Single-blind	See *double-blind, single-blind*.
Subjects or participants	Experimental units that are people.

| Treatment | The process, intervention, or other controlled circumstance applied to randomly assigned experimental units. Treatments are the different levels of a single factor or are made up of combinations of levels of two or more factors. |

Skills

Plan

- Recognize when an observational study would be appropriate.
- Be able to identify observational studies as retrospective or prospective and understand the strengths and weaknesses of each method.
- Know the four basic principles of sound experimental design—randomize, control, replicate, and block—and be able to explain each.
- Be able to recognize the factors, treatments, and response variable in a description of a designed experiment.
- Understand the essential importance of randomization in assigning treatments to experimental units.
- Understand the importance of replication to move from anecdotes to general conclusions.
- Understand the value of blocking so that variability due to differences in attributes of the subjects can be removed.
- Understand the importance of a control group and the need for a placebo treatment in some studies.
- Understand the importance of blinding and double-blinding in studies on human subjects and be able to identify blinding and the need for blinding in experiments.
- Understand the value of a placebo in experiments with human participants.
- Recognize situations for which ANOVA is the appropriate analysis.
- Know how to examine your data for violations of conditions that would make ANOVA unwise or invalid.
- Recognize when a further analysis of differences between group means would be appropriate.
- Understand the advantages of an experiment in two factors.
- Be able to design a completely randomized experiment to test the effect of a single factor.

Do

- Be able to design an experiment in which blocking is used to reduce variation.
- Know how to use graphical displays to compare responses for different treatment groups.
- Be able to perform an ANOVA using a statistics package or calculator for one response variable and one factor with any number of levels.
- Be able to perform several subsequent tests using a multiple comparisons procedure.
- Be able to use a statistics package to compute a two-way ANOVA.
- Know how to interpret an interaction plot for replicated data with two factors.

Report

- Know how to report the results of an observational study. Identify the subjects, how the data were gathered, and any potential biases or flaws you may be aware of. Identify the factors known and those that might have been revealed by the study.
- Know how to report the results of an experiment. Tell who the subjects are and how their assignment to treatments was determined. Report on how the response variable was measured and in what measurement units.
- Understand that your description of an experiment should be sufficient for another researcher to replicate the study with the same methods.
- Be able to explain the contents of an ANOVA table, in particular the role of the MST, MSE, and P-value.
- Be able to interpret a test of the null hypothesis that the true means of several independent groups are equal. (Your interpretation should include a defence of your assumption of equal variances.)
- Be able to interpret the results of tests that use multiple comparisons methods.
- Be able to interpret main effects in a two-way ANOVA.
- Be able to use an interaction plot to explain an interaction effect.
- Be able to distinguish when a discussion of main effects is appropriate in the presence of a significant interaction.

MINI case studies

Choosing a Statistics Professor

Four professors teach Statistics at your university in classes of about 85 students each, and you need to choose a good one. You can check them out on Ratemyprofessors.com, but some professors don't receive many ratings and you'd prefer a larger sample of opinions. And although your university publishes teaching evaluations given by students in previous years, it publishes only the average evaluation without showing the standard deviation. You know that students have very different opinions about Statistics professors, and you want to take that into account! Your student association therefore conducts its own survey and publishes the rating given by each student for each professor who taught last year on a scale of zero to five. The results for those students who filled out the online questionnaire are given in the file **ch15_MCSP_StatsProfs**. Your friend analyzes the results and finds that Prof A has a larger number of evaluations, a higher average rating, and a lower standard deviation than any of the other professors. "I'm going to register with Prof A," she says. Use ANOVA to check out whether she's right. Which professor would you choose?

Do It Yourself

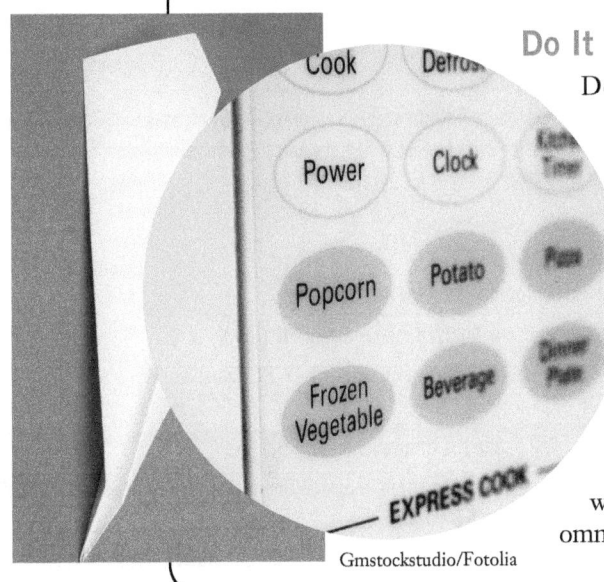

Design, carry out, and analyze your own multifactor experiment. The experiment doesn't have to involve human subjects. In fact, an experiment designed to find the best settings for microwave popcorn, the best paper airplane design, or the optimal weight and placement of coins on a toy car to make it travel farthest and fastest down an incline are all fine ideas. Be sure to define your response variable of interest before you start the experiment and detail how you'll perform the experiment, specifically including the elements you control, how you use randomization, and how many times you replicate the experiment. Analyze the results of your experiment and write up your analysis and conclusions including any recommendations for further testing.

Furo Felix/Fotolia

Gmstockstudio/Fotolia

MyStatLab Students! Save time, improve your grades with MyStatLab. Questions marked in ■ can be found on MyStatLab. You can practise them as often as you want, and most feature step-by-step guided solutions to help you find the right answer. You'll find a personalized study plan available to you too!

Technology Help: ANOVA

Most analyses of variance are performed with computers, and all statistics packages present the results in an ANOVA table much like the ones in this chapter. Technology also makes it easy to examine the side-by-side boxplots and check the residuals for violations of the assumptions and conditions. Statistics packages offer different choices among possible multiple comparisons methods. This is a specialized area. Get advice or read further if you need to choose a multiple comparisons method.

There are two ways to organize data recorded for several groups. We can put all the response values in a single variable and use a second, "factor," variable to hold the group identities. This is sometimes called stacked format. The alternative is an unstacked format, placing the data for each group in its own column or variable. Then the variable identities become the group identifiers. Stacked format is necessary for experiments with more than one factor. Each factor's levels are named in a variable. Some packages can work

(continued)

with either format for simple one-factor designs, and some use one format for some things and the other for others. (Be careful, for example, when you make side-by-side boxplots; be sure to give the appropriate version of that command to correspond to the structure of your data.) Most packages offer to save residuals and predicted values and make them available for further tests of conditions. In some packages, you may have to request them specifically.

Some statistics packages have different commands for models with one factor and those with two or more factors. You must be alert to these differences when analyzing a two-factor ANOVA. It's not unusual to find ANOVA models in several different places in the same package. (Look for terms like "Linear Models.")

EXCEL

To compute a single-factor ANOVA:

- From the Data Ribbon select **Data Analysis**.
- Select **Anova Single Factor** from the list of analysis tools.
- Click the **OK** button.
- Enter the data range in the box provided.
- Check the **Labels in First Row** box, if applicable.
- Enter an alpha level for the *F*-test in the box provided.
- Click the **OK** button.

Comments

The data range should include two or more columns of data to compare. Unlike statistics packages, Excel expects each column of the data to represent a different level of the factor. However, it offers no way to label these levels. The columns need not have the same number of data values, but the selected cells must make up a rectangle large enough to hold the column with the most data values.

The Excel Data Analysis add-in offers a two-way ANOVA "with and without replication." That command requires the data to be in a special format and can't deal with unbalanced (i.e., unequal counts in treatment groups) data. For a randomized block design, you can use a two-way ANOVA without replication.

MINITAB

- Choose **ANOVA** from the Stat menu.
- Choose **One-way...** or **Two-way...** from the **ANOVA** submenu.
- In the dialogue, assign a quantitative Y-variable to the Response box and assign the categorical X-factor(s) to the Factor box.
- In a two-way ANOVA, specify interactions.
- Check the **Store Residuals** check box.
- Click the **Graphs** button.
- In the ANOVA-Graphs dialogue, select **Standardized residuals**, and check **Normal plot of residuals** and **Residuals versus fits**.
- Click the **OK** button to return to the ANOVA dialogue.
- Click the **OK** button to compute the ANOVA.

Comments

If your data are in unstacked format, with separate columns for each treatment level, Minitab can compute a one-way ANOVA directly. Choose

One-way (unstacked) from the **ANOVA** submenu. For two-way ANOVA, you must use the stacked format.

SPSS

To compute a one-way ANOVA:

- Choose **Compare Means** from the **Analyze** menu.
- Choose **One-way ANOVA** from the **Compare Means** submenu.
- In the One-Way ANOVA dialogue, select the Y-variable and move it to the dependent target. Then move the X-variable to the independent target.
- Click the **OK** button.

To compute a two-way ANOVA:

- Choose **Analyze** > **General Linear Model** > **Univariate**.
- Assign the response variable to the **Dependent Variable** box.
- Assign the two factors to the **Fixed Factor(s)** box. This will fit the model with interactions by default.
- To omit interactions, click on **Model**. Select **Custom**. Highlight the factors. Select **Main Effects** under the **Build Terms** arrow and click the arrow.
- Click **Continue** and **OK** to compute the model.

Comments

SPSS expects data in stacked format. The **Contrasts** and **Post Hoc** buttons offer ways to test contrasts and perform multiple comparisons. See your SPSS manual for details.

JMP

To compute a one-way ANOVA:

- From the **Analyze** menu, select **Fit Y by X**.
- Select variables: a quantitative Y, Response variable, and a categorical X, Factor variable.
- JMP opens the **Oneway** window.
- Click on the red triangle beside the heading, select **Display Options**, and choose **Boxplots**.
- From the same menu, choose the **Means/ANOVA t-test** command.
- JMP opens the one-way ANOVA output.

To compute a two-way ANOVA:

- From the **Analyze** menu, select **Fit Model**.
- Select variables and **Add** them to the **Construct Model Effects** box.
- To specify an interaction, select both factors and press the **Cross** button.
- Click **Run Model**.
- JMP opens a **Fit Least Squares** window.
- Click on the red triangle beside each effect to see the means plots for that factor. For the interaction term, this is the interaction plot.
- Consult JMP documentation for information about other features.

Comments

JMP expects data in "stacked" format with one continuous response and two nominal factor variables.

EXERCISES

SECTION 15.1

1. For the following observational studies, indicate whether they are prospective or retrospective.

a) A company looked at a sample of returned registration cards to estimate the income level of households that purchased its product.
b) A retail outlet encouraged customers to join its "frequent buyers" program and studied whether those who joined were more likely to make use of discount coupons than those who were not members. **LO❶**

2. For the following observational studies, indicate whether they are prospective or retrospective.

a) An airline was concerned that new security measures might discourage air travellers. A year after the new security restrictions were put into place, the airline compared the miles travelled by its frequent fliers before and after the change.
b) Does giving children a flu shot protect parents? Researchers questioned a random sample of families at the end of a flu season. They asked whether the children had been immunized, whether the parents had received flu shots, and who in the family had contracted the flu. **LO❶**

SECTION 15.2

3. For the following experiment, identify the experimental units, the treatments, the response, and the random assignment.

A commercial food lab compared recipes for chocolate chip cookies. It baked cookies with different kinds of chips (milk chocolate, dark chocolate, and semi-sweet). All other ingredients and amounts were the same. Ten trained tasters rated the cookies on a scale of 1 to 10. The cookies were presented to the tasters in a random order. **LO❶**

4. For the following experiment, identify the experimental units, the treatments, the response, and the random assignment.

An investment club decided to compare investment strategies. Starting with nine equal investment amounts, three invested in the "dogs of the Dow"—stocks in the Dow Jones Industrial Average that had been underperforming relative to the rest of the Dow average. The relative amounts to invest in each of the stocks were chosen randomly and differently for each fund. Three funds invested following the advice of a TV investment show host, again choosing the specific stocks and allocations randomly for the three funds. And three funds invested by throwing darts at a page from *The Wall Street Journal* that listed stocks on the NYSE, investing in each of the stocks hit by a dart, and throwing a different set of darts for each of the three funds. At the end of six months the funds were compared. **LO❶**

SECTION 15.3

5. For the cookie recipe experiment of Exercise 3, identify how control, randomization, and replication were used. **LO❷**

6. For the investment experiment of Exercise 4, identify how control, randomization, and replication were used. **LO❷**

SECTION 15.4

7. An internet sale site randomly sent customers to one of three versions of its welcome page. It recorded how long each visitor stayed at the site.

Here is a diagram of that experiment. Fill in the parts of the experiment. **LO❷**

8. The internet company in question 7 was concerned that customers who came directly to its site (by typing its URL into a browser) might respond differently than those referred to the site from other sites (such as search engines). It decided to block according to how the customer arrived at the site.

Here is a diagram of that experiment. Fill in the parts. **LO❷**

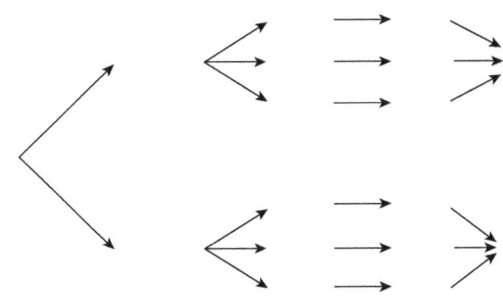

SECTIONS 15.5 AND 15.6

9. For the following experiment, indicate whether it was single-blind, double-blind, or not blinded at all. Explain your reasoning.

Makers of a new frozen entree arranged for it to be served to randomly selected customers at a restaurant in place of the equivalent entree ordinarily prepared in the kitchen. The customers were unaware of the substitution. After their meal, the customers were asked about the quality of the food. **LO➋**

10. For the following experiment, indicate whether it was single-blind, double-blind, or not blinded at all. Explain your reasoning.

Does a "stop smoking" program work better if it costs more? Smokers responding to an advertisement offering to help them stop smoking were randomly offered a program costing $100 or the same program costing $250. The offer was made individually to each client by presenting a sealed envelope so that the clerk providing the offer wouldn't know the offer's details. At the end of the program (a course and films along with diet and smoking cessation aids), clients were followed for six months to see if they had indeed quit smoking. **LO➋**

SECTIONS 15.7 AND 15.9

11. In a completely randomized design, 10 subjects were assigned to each of four treatments of a factor. Below is the partially completed ANOVA table:

Source	Sum of Squares	Mean Square	F-Ratio	P-Value
Treatment (Between)	856.07			
Error (Within)				
Total	1177.97			

a) What are the degrees of freedom for treatment, error, and total?
b) What is SSE?
c) What is MST?
d) What is MSE? **LO➌**

12. Refer to Exercise 11.

a) State the null and alternative hypotheses.
b) Calculate the F-ratio.
c) What is the P-value?
d) State your conclusion at $\alpha = 0.05$. **LO➌**

SECTION 15.10

⊕ 13. Salmon farms in Atlantic Canada have a problem of sea lice that attack the fish. Three alternative pesticides have been developed to kill the lice and are being tested on three different farms. We want to select a single pesticide for use on all three farms since pesticide can be carried in the water from one farm to another. Four different sections of each farm are randomly selected and used to test the three pesticides (one per section) together with a no-treatment option in the fourth section for comparison. After the treatment, the number of salmon attacked by sea lice per cubic metre of water is recorded:

Farm	Pesticides None	A	B	C
1	2.5	1.1	1.7	2
2	2.8	2.3	1.6	1.3
3	3.7	2.4	2.5	2.6

a) State the hypotheses.
b) Perform an ANOVA analysis with $\alpha = 0.05$.
c) State the conclusions in business terms, including recommending the next step in the analysis. **LO➌**

14. A wind farm is being proposed for the shore of Lake Superior to supply power to Thunder Bay and nearby mining operations. The farm operator is testing turbines from five different manufacturers and wants to select a single supplier for the whole wind farm. Wind conditions vary along the shore, and three sites are selected for testing. A turbine from each supplier is randomly positioned within each of those sites. The energy output (in gigawatt-hours) over a year is recorded for each turbine:

Site	Supplier A	B	C	D	E
1	0.96	1.12	1.23	0.87	0.76
2	1.11	1.78	1.37	0.99	1.08
3	1.24	1.36	1.87	1.97	1.62

a) State the hypotheses.
b) Perform an ANOVA analysis with $\alpha = 0.05$.
c) State the conclusions in business terms, including recommending the next step in the analysis. **LO➌**

SECTION 15.11

15. In the experiment described in Exercise 3, the study also compared the use of butter and margarine in the recipes. The design was balanced, with each combination of chip type and oil type tested.

a) What were the factors and factor levels?
b) What were the treatments?
c) If an interaction was found to be significant, what would that mean? **LO➌**

16. The investment club described in Exercise 4 decided to repeat its experiment in a different way. Three members of the club took responsibility for one of each of the three investment "strategies," making the final choices and allocations of investment dollars. For this new experiment:

a) What were the subjects?
b) What were the factors and factor levels?
c) What were the treatments? **LO➌**

CHAPTER EXERCISES

17. **Laundry detergents, part 1.** A consumer group wants to test the efficacy of a new laundry detergent. Researchers take 16 white shirts and stain each with the same amount of grease. They decide to try it using both hot- and cold-water settings and at both short and long washing times. Half of the 16 shirts will get the new detergent, and half will get a standard detergent. They'll compare the shirts by using an optical scanner to measure whiteness.

a) What are the factors they're testing?
b) Identify all the factor levels.
c) What is/are the response(s)? **LO ❶**

18. **Sales scripts.** An outdoor products company wants to test a new website design where customers can get information about their favourite outdoor activity. The company randomly sends half of the customers coming to the website to the new design. It wants to see whether the web visitors spend more time at the site and whether they make a purchase.

a) What are the factors the company is testing?
b) Identify all the factor levels.
c) What is/are the response(s)? **LO ❶**

19. **Laundry detergents, part 2.** One member of the consumer group in Exercise 17 is concerned that the experiment will take too long and makes some suggestions to shorten it. Comment briefly on each idea.

a) Cut the runs to eight by testing only the new detergent. Compare the results to results on the standard detergent published by the manufacturer.
b) Cut the runs to eight by testing only in hot water.
c) Keep the number of runs at 16, but save time by running all the standard detergent runs first to avoid swapping detergents back and forth. **LO ❷**

20. **Swimsuits.** A swimsuit manufacturer wants to test the speed of its newly designed $550 suit. It designs an experiment by having six randomly selected Olympic swimmers swim as fast as they can with their old swimsuit first and then swim the same event again with the new, expensive swimsuit. The manufacturer will use the difference in times as the response variable. Criticize the experiment and point out some of the problems with generalizing the results. **LO ❷**

21. **Mozart, part 1.** Will listening to a Mozart piano sonata make you smarter? In a 1995 study, Rauscher, Shaw, and Ky reported that when students were given a spatial reasoning section of a standard IQ test, those who listened to Mozart for 10 minutes improved their scores more than those who simply sat quietly.

a) These researchers said the differences were statistically significant. Explain what that means in this context.
b) Steele, Bass, and Crook tried to replicate the original study. The subjects were 125 students who participated in the experiment for course credit. Subjects first took

the test. Then they were assigned to one of three groups: listening to a Mozart piano sonata, listening to music by Philip Glass, and sitting for 10 minutes in silence. Three days after the treatments, they were retested. Draw a diagram displaying the design of this experiment.
c) The boxplots show the differences in score before and after treatment for the three groups. Did the Mozart group show improvement?
d) Do you think the results prove that listening to Mozart is beneficial? Explain. **LO ❷**

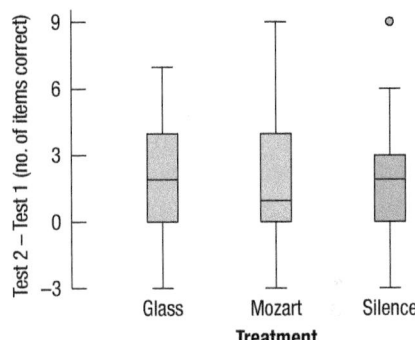

22. **Mozart, part 2.** An advertisement selling specially designed CDs of Mozart's music because they will "strengthen your mind, heal your body, and unlock your creative spirit" claims that "in Japan, a brewery actually reported that their best sake is made when Mozart is played near the yeast." Suppose you wished to design an experiment to test whether this is true. Assume you have the full cooperation of the sake brewery. Specify how you would design the experiment. Indicate factors and response and how they would be measured, controlled, or randomized. **LO ❷**

23. **Cereal marketing.** The makers of Frumpies, "the breakfast of rug rats," want to improve their marketing, so they consult you.

a) They first want to know what fraction of children, aged 10 to 13, like their celery-flavoured cereal. What kind of study should they perform?
b) They're thinking of introducing a new flavour, maple-marshmallow Frumpies, and want to know whether children will prefer the new flavour to the old one. Design a completely randomized experiment to investigate this question.
c) They suspect that children who regularly watch the Saturday-morning cartoon show starring Frump, the flying teenage warrior rabbit who eats Frumpies in every episode, may respond differently to the new flavour. How would you take that into account in your design? **LO ❶, ❷**

24. **Wine marketing.** A 2001 Danish study published in the *Archives of Internal Medicine* casts significant doubt on suggestions that adults who drink wine have higher levels of "good" cholesterol and fewer heart attacks. These researchers followed a group of individuals born at a Copenhagen hospital between 1959 and 1961 for 40 years. Their study found that in this group the adults who drank wine were richer and better educated than those who did not.

a) What kind of study was this?

b) It is generally true that people with high levels of education and high socioeconomic status are healthier than others. How does this call into question the supposed health benefits of wine?

c) Can studies such as these prove causation (that wine helps prevent heart attacks, that drinking wine makes one richer, that being rich helps prevent heart attacks, etc.)? Explain. **LO ❶, ❷**

25. SAT prep courses. Can special study courses actually help raise SAT scores? One organization says that the 30 students it tutored achieved an average gain of 60 points when they retook the test.

a) Explain why this does not necessarily prove that the special course caused the scores to go up.

b) Propose a design for an experiment that could test the effectiveness of the tutorial course.

c) Suppose you suspect that the tutorial course might be more helpful for students whose initial scores were particularly low. How would this affect your proposed design? **LO ❷**

26. Safety switch. An industrial machine requires an emergency shutoff switch that must be designed so that it can be easily operated with either hand. Design an experiment to find out whether workers will be able to deactivate the machine as quickly with their left hand as with their right hand. Be sure to explain the role of randomization in your design. **LO ❷**

27. Vancouver flights. An airline monitors the number of seats sold in Executive class on flights from Calgary to Vancouver on weekday mornings, afternoons, and evenings, and obtains the boxplots shown below.

a) What are the null and alternative hypotheses? Talk about passengers and flights, not symbols.

b) Do the conditions for ANOVA appear to be met? State your reasons clearly. **LO ❸**

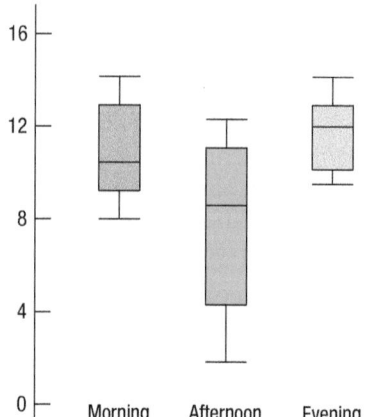

28. Wine production. The boxplots below display case prices (in dollars) of wine produced by wineries in Ontario.

a) What are the null and alternative hypotheses? Talk about prices and location, not symbols.

b) Do the conditions for ANOVA seem to be met here? Why or why not? **LO ❸**

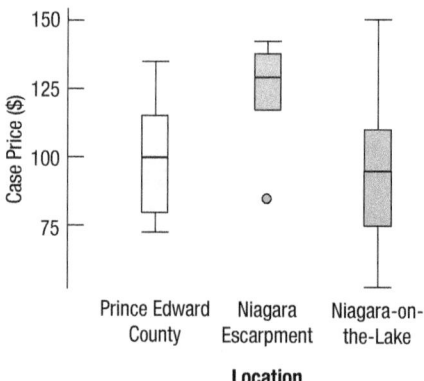

29. Cell phone adoption. Cell phone adoption rates are available for various countries in the United Nations Database (unstats.un.org). Countries were randomly selected from three regions (Africa, Asia, and Europe), and cell phone adoption (per 100 inhabitants) rates retrieved. The boxplots display the data:

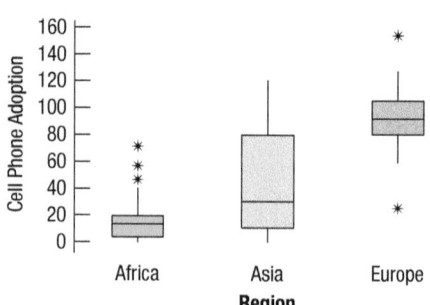

a) What are the null and alternative hypotheses (in words, not symbols)?

b) Are the conditions for ANOVA met? Why or why not? **LO ❸**

30. Canadian managers' salaries. A sample of companies was selected randomly from each of three regions in Canada, and annual salaries for marketing managers were graphed as boxplots:

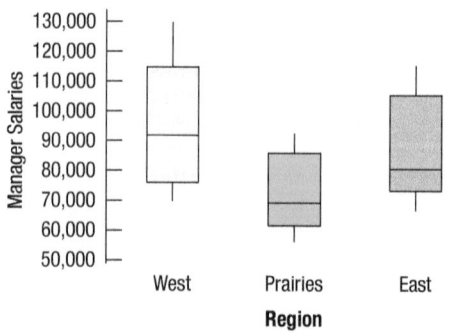

a) What are the null and alternative hypotheses (in words, not symbols)?
b) Are the conditions for ANOVA met? Why or why not? **LO ❸**

31. **Bank tellers.** A bank is studying the average time that it takes six of its tellers to serve a customer. Customers line up in the queue and are served by the next available teller. Here is a boxplot of the times it took to serve the last 140 customers:

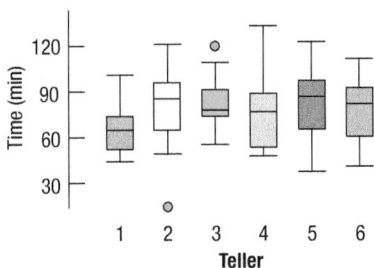

Source	df	Sum of Squares	Mean Square	F-ratio	P-value
Teller	5	3,315.32	663.064	1.508	0.1914
Error	134	58,919.1	439.695		
Total	139	62,234.4			

a) What are the null and alternative hypotheses?
b) What do you conclude? **LO ❸**

32. **Product development.** Vendors of hearing aids test them by having patients listen to lists of words and repeat what they hear. The word lists are supposed to be equally difficult to hear accurately. But the challenge of hearing aids is perception when there is background noise. A researcher investigated four different word lists used in hearing assessment. She wanted to know whether the lists were equally difficult to understand in the presence of a noisy background. To find out, she tested 24 subjects with normal hearing and measured the number of words perceived correctly in the presence of background noise. Here are the boxplots of the four lists:

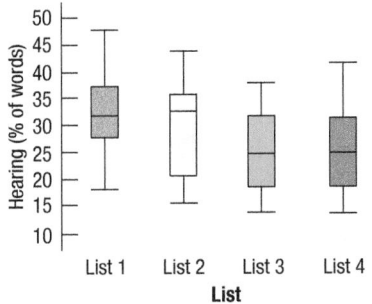

Source	df	Sum of Squares	Mean Square	F-ratio	P-value
List	3	920.4583	306.819	4.9192	0.0033
Error	92	5738.1667	62.371		
Total	95	6658.6250			

a) What are the null and alternative hypotheses?
b) What do you conclude? **LO ❸**

33. **Online security.** A report released by the Pew Internet & American Life Project entitled *The Internet & Consumer Choice* focused on current online issues (www.pewinternet. org/data.asp). Respondents were asked to indicate their level of agreement (1 = Strongly Agree to 4 = Strongly Disagree) with a variety of statements, including "I don't like giving my credit card number or personal information online." A part of the data set was used to determine whether the type of community in which the individual resided (urban, suburban, or rural) affected responses. Here are the results in the form of a partially completed analysis of variance table:

Source	df	Sum of Squares	Mean Square	F-ratio	P-value
Community	2	6.615			
Error	183	96.998			
Total	185	103.613			

a) Is this an experimental or observational study? Explain.
b) Is this a prospective or retrospective study? Explain.
c) State the null and alternative hypotheses.
d) Calculate the *F*-statistic.
e) The P-value for this statistic turns out to be 0.002. State the conclusion. Can a causal link be established? Explain. (*Source*: Norean Sharpe, Richard D De Veaux, Paul Velleman, David Wright, Business Statistics, Third Canadian Edition, 3e, © 2018, Pearson Education, Inc.) **LO ❶, ❸**

34. **Six Sigma training.** A large financial institution is interested in training its university-educated workforce in Six Sigma principles and methods. One part of the training involves basic statistical concepts and tools. Management is considering three approaches: *online*, *traditional classroom*, and *hybrid* (a mix of both). Prior to launching the program throughout the entire organization, the company decided to pilot test the three approaches. Because it believed that educational background may affect the results, it selected three employees from each of 10 different university major programs of study (*liberal arts, accounting, economics, management, marketing, finance information systems, computer science, operations, other*), and randomly assigned each to one of the three approaches.

At the end of training, each participant took an exam. The results are shown here:

Source	Degrees of Freedom	Sum of Squares	Mean Square	F-ratio	P-value
Major	9	2239.47	248.830	21.69	<0.001
Training	2	171.47	85.735	7.47	0.004
Error	18	206.53	11.474		
Total	29	2617.47			

a) Was this an observational study or an experiment?
b) What was the purpose of using *Major* as a blocking factor?
c) Given the results, was it necessary to use *Major* as a blocking factor? Explain.
d) State the conclusion from this analysis. LO❶, ❸

35. Online trust. Online retailers want customers to trust their websites and want to alleviate any concerns potential customers may have about privacy and security. In a study investigating the factors that affect online trust, participants were randomly assigned to carry out online transactions on fictitious retailers' websites. The sites were configured in one of three ways: (1) *with a third-party assurance seal (e.g., BBBOnLine) displayed*, (2) *a self-proclaimed assurance displayed*, or (3) *no assurance*. In addition, participants made a transaction involving one of three products (*book, camera,* or *insurance*). These products represent varying degrees of risk. After completing the transaction, they rated how "trustworthy" the website was on a scale of 1 (not at all) to 10 (extremely trustworthy).

a) Is this an experiment or an observational study? Explain.
b) What is the response variable?
c) How many factors are involved?
d) How many treatments are involved?
e) State the hypotheses (in words, not symbols). LO❶

36. Injection moulding. In order to improve the quality of moulded parts, companies often test different levels of parameter settings in order to find the best combinations. Injection moulding machines typically have many adjustable parameters. One company used three different mould temperatures (25, 35, and 45 degrees Celsius) and four different cooling times (10, 15, 20, and 25 minutes) to examine how they affect the tensile strength of the resulting moulded parts. Five parts were randomly sampled and measured from each treatment combination.

a) Is this an experiment or an observational study? Explain.
b) What is the response variable?
c) What are the factors?

d) How many treatments are involved?
e) State the hypotheses (in words, not symbols). LO❶

37. Stock patterns. Some people believe that the stock market shows patterns according to the day of the week or the month of the year ("Sell in May and walk away"). We have the closing price of the Dow Jones Industrial Average for every day from January 2009 through February 2013. Here is the ANOVA:

Source	df	Sum of Squares	Mean Square	F-ratio	P-value
day	4	415,903	103,976	0.03514	0.9976
month	11	78,391,675	7,126,516	2.4082	0.0059
day*month	44	12,814,707	291,243	0.09842	1.0000
Error	975	2,885,283,286	2,959,265		
Total	1034	2,976,872,229			

a) Is this an experiment or an observational study?
b) State the hypotheses.
c) What do you conclude about the average value of the DJIA on different days of the week? Explain.
d) What do you conclude about the average value of the DJIA in different months? Explain.
e) What does the interaction term test and what do you conclude about that? LO❶, ❸

38. Company bonuses. After complaints about gender discrimination in bonus incentive pay, a large multinational firm collected data on bonuses awarded during the previous year (percentage of base pay). Human Resources (HR) randomly sampled male and female managers from three different levels: *senior, middle,* and *supervisory.* The two-way ANOVA results are presented here:

Source	df	Sum of Squares	Mean Square	F-ratio	P-value
Gender	1	32.033	32.033	9.76	0.005
Level	2	466.200	233.100	70.99	0.000
Interaction	2	20.467	10.233	3.12	0.063
Error	24	78.800	3.283		
Total	29	597.500			

a) Is this an experiment or an observational study?
b) State the hypotheses.
c) Given the small P-value associated with gender and that the mean annual bonus percent for females is 12.5% compared with 14.5% for males, HR concludes that gender discrimination exists. Do you agree? Explain. LO❶, ❸

39. Managers' hourly wages. What affects marketing managers' hourly wages? In order to find out, hourly wages were obtained from a survey for two managerial occupations in marketing (*sales managers, advertising managers*) for a random sample of companies from three regions. Here are boxplots showing hourly wages for the two marketing occupations and the three regions as well as the results for a two-way ANOVA:

Source	df	Sum of Squares	Mean Square	F-ratio	P-value
Manager Type	1	1325.93	1325.93	31.84	0.000
Region	2	153.55	76.78	1.84	0.176
Interaction	2	32.74	16.37	0.39	0.678
Error	30	1249.32	41.64		
Total	35	2761.55			

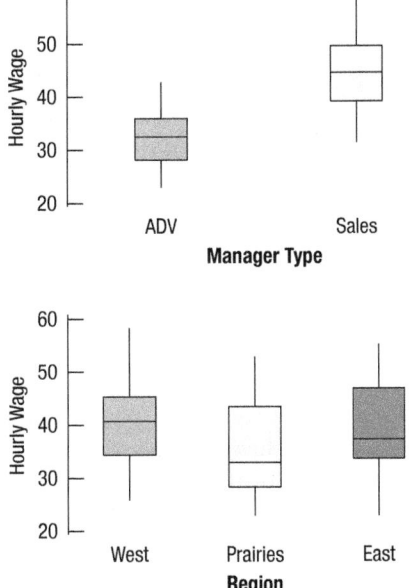

a) Is this an experiment or an observational study? Explain.
b) Are the conditions for two-way ANOVA met?
c) If so, perform the hypothesis tests and state your conclusions in terms of hourly wages, occupational type, and region.
d) Is it appropriate to interpret the main effects in this case? Explain. **LO ❶, ❸**

40. Concrete testing. A company that specializes in developing concrete for construction strives to continually improve the properties of its materials. In order to increase the compressive strength of one of its new formulations, it varied the amount of alkali content (*low, medium, high*). Since the type of sand used may also affect the strength of concrete, it used three different types of sand (*Types I, II, III*). Four samples were randomly selected from each treatment combination to be tested. The boxplots show the test results on compressive strength (in pounds per square inch (psi)) for the three levels of alkali content and three types of sand. Two-way ANOVA results are also given.

Square	df	Sum of Squares	Mean Source	F-ratio	P-value
Alkali Content	2	4,016,600	2,008,300	46.38	0.000
Sand Type	2	1,547,817	773,908	17.87	0.000
Interaction	4	177,533	44,383	1.02	0.412
Error	27	1,169,250	43,306		
Total	35	6,911,200			

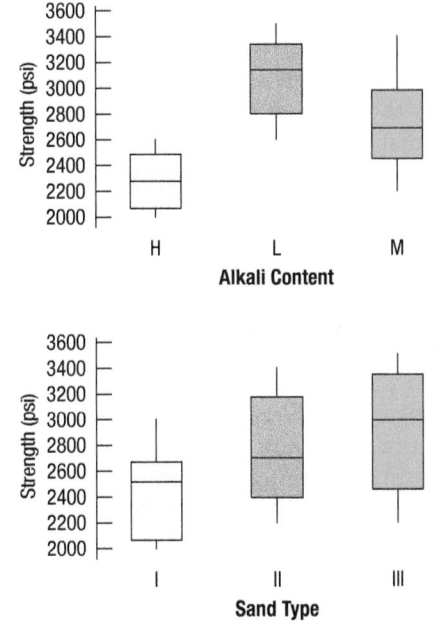

a) Is this an experiment or an observational study? Explain.
b) Are the conditions for two-way ANOVA met?
c) If so, perform the hypothesis tests and state your conclusions in terms of compressive strength, alkali content, and sand type.
d) Is it appropriate to interpret the main effects in this case? Explain. **LO ❶, ❸**

❶ 41. Production problems. A manufacturing company that makes dental drills was experiencing problems with a specific part on the production line. Management suspected a machining problem was causing the length of the part to vary outside of target specifications. Two factors were examined: the machine setting (at three levels) and the shift (*morning, afternoon,* and *night*). New hires were typically scheduled for night shift, and management believed that their relative inexperience might also be contributing to the variation. Three parts were randomly selected and measured from each treatment combination. The deviation from specified size was measured in microns. The two-way ANOVA results are as follows:

Square	df	Sum of Squares	Mean Source	F-ratio	P-value
MachSet	2	17.1119	8.55593	7.3971	0.0045
Shift	2	24.9607	12.4804	10.790	0.0008
Interaction	4	1.4970	0.374259	0.32357	0.8585
Error	18	20.8200	1.15667		
Total	26	64.3896			

a) Is this an experiment or an observational study? Explain.
b) What is the response variable?
c) How many treatments are involved?
d) Based on the two-way ANOVA results, management concluded that shift has a significant impact on the length of the part and that consequently operator inexperience is the root cause of the part problems. Do you agree with this conclusion? Explain. **LO❶, ❸**

❶ 42. Process improvements. One way to improve a process is to eliminate non–value-added activities (e.g., extra movements) and wasted effort (e.g., looking for materials). A consultant was hired to improve the efficiency in a large shop floor operation. She tested three different workspace designs and two different storage/retrieval systems. She measured process flow time for three randomly selected operations through each of the combinations of workspace design and storage/retrieval systems. The two-way ANOVA results are as follows:

Square	df	Sum of Squares	Mean Source	F-ratio	P-value
Workspace Design	2	0.30867	0.15433	1.56	0.230
Storage System	1	0.07500	0.07500	0.76	0.392
Interaction	2	4.87800	2.43900	24.72	<0.001
Error	24	2.36800	0.09867		
Total	29	7.62967			

a) Is this an experiment or observational study? Explain.
b) What is the response variable?
c) How many treatments are involved?
d) Based on the two-way ANOVA results, management concludes that neither the workspace design nor the storage/retrieval system impacts process flow time (and that

the consultant wasn't worth the money). Do you agree with this conclusion? Explain. **LO❶, ❸**

43. Yogurt research. An experiment to determine the effect of several methods of preparing cultures for use in commercial yogurt was conducted by a food science research group. Three batches of yogurt were prepared using each of three methods: traditional, ultrafiltration, and reverse osmosis. A trained expert then tasted each of the nine samples, presented in random order, and judged them on a scale from 1 to 10. A partially complete analysis of variance table of the data follows:

Source	Sum of Squares	Degrees of Freedom	Mean Square	F-ratio
Treatment	17.300			
Residual	0.460			
Total	17.769			

a) Calculate the mean square of the treatments and the mean square of the error.
b) Form the F-statistic by dividing the two mean squares.
c) The P-value of this F-statistic turns out to be 0.000017. What does this say about the null hypothesis of equal means?
d) What assumptions have you made in order to answer (c)?
e) What would you like to see in order to justify the conclusions of the F-test?
f) What is the average size of the error standard deviation in the judge's assessment? **LO❸**

44. Smokestack scrubbers. Particulate matter is a serious form of air pollution often arising from industrial production. One way to reduce the pollution is to put a filter, or scrubber, at the end of the smokestack to trap the particulates. An experiment to determine which smokestack scrubber design is best was run by placing four scrubbers of different designs on an industrial stack in random order. Each scrubber was tested five times. For each run, the same material was produced, and the particulate emissions coming out of the scrubber were measured (in parts per billion). A partially complete analysis of variance table of the data is shown here:

Square	Sum of Squares	Degrees of Freedom	Mean Source	F-ratio
Treatment	81.2			
Residual	30.8			
Total	112.0			

a) Calculate the mean square of the treatments and the mean square of the error.

b) Form the *F*-statistic by dividing the two mean squares.

c) The P-value of this *F*-statistic turns out to be 0.00000949. What does this say about the null hypothesis of equal means?

d) What assumptions have you made in order to answer (c)?

e) What would you like to see in order to justify the conclusions of the *F*-test?

f) What is the average size of the error standard deviation in particulate emissions? **LO ❸**

45. Cereal shelf placement, part 1. Supermarkets often place similar types of cereal on the same supermarket shelf. The shelf placement for 77 cereals was recorded as well as their sugar content. Does sugar content vary by shelf? Here's a boxplot and an ANOVA table:

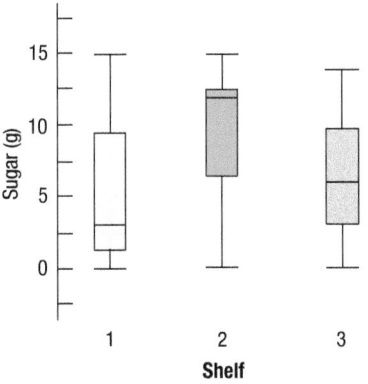

Source	df	Sum of Squares	Mean Square	*F*-ratio	P-value
Shelf	2	248.4079	124.204	7.3345	0.0012
Error	74	1253.1246	16.934		
Total	76	1501.5325			

Level	*n*	Mean	StdDev
1	20	4.80000	4.57223
2	21	9.61905	4.12888
3	36	6.52778	3.83582

a) What kind of design or study is this?

b) What are the null and alternative hypotheses?

c) What does the ANOVA table say about the null hypothesis? (Be sure to report this in terms of sugar content and shelf placement.)

d) Can we conclude that cereals on shelf 2 have a different mean sugar content than cereals on shelf 3? Can we conclude that cereals on shelf 2 have a different mean sugar content than cereals on shelf 1? What can we conclude? **LO ❶, ❸**

46. Cereal shelf placement, part 2. We also have data on the protein content of the 77 cereals in Exercise 45. Does protein content vary by shelf? Here's a boxplot and an ANOVA table:

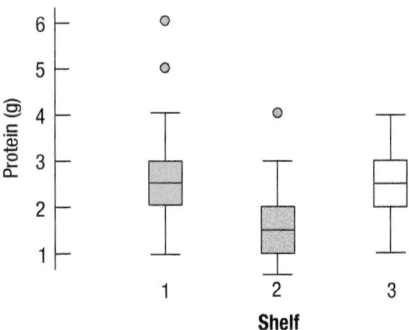

Source	df	Sum of Squares	Mean Square	*F*-ratio	P-value
Shelf	2	12.4258	6.2129	5.8445	0.0044
Error	74	78.6650	1.0630		
Total	76	91.0909			

Level	*n*	Mean	StdDev
1	20	2.65000	1.46089
2	21	1.90476	0.99523
3	36	2.86111	0.72320

a) What kind of design or study is this?

b) What are the null and alternative hypotheses?

c) What does the ANOVA table say about the null hypothesis? (Be sure to report this in terms of protein content and shelf placement.)

d) Can we conclude that cereals on shelf 2 have a lower mean protein content than cereals on shelf 3? Can we conclude that cereals on shelf 2 have a lower mean protein content than cereals on shelf 1? What can we conclude? **LO ❶, ❸**

47. Automotive safety. Automobiles are crashed into a wall at 55 kilometres per hour with dummies in both the passenger's and the driver's seats. The THOR Alpha crash dummy is capable of recording 134 channels of data on the impact of the crash at various sites on the dummy. The response variable is a measure of head injury. Researchers want to know whether the seat the dummy is sitting in affects head-injury severity, as well as whether the type of car affects severity. Here are boxplots for the two different *Seats* (*driver, passenger*) and the six different *Size* classifications (*compact, light, medium, mini, pickup, van*):

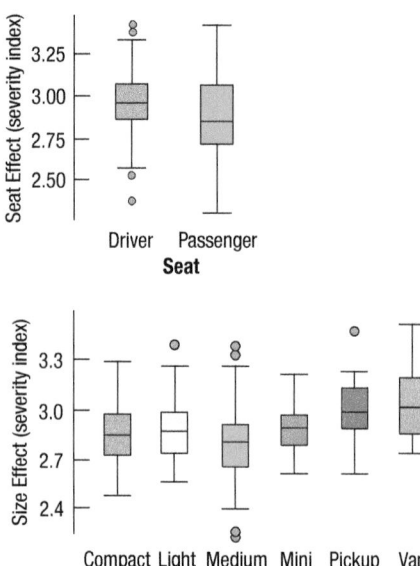

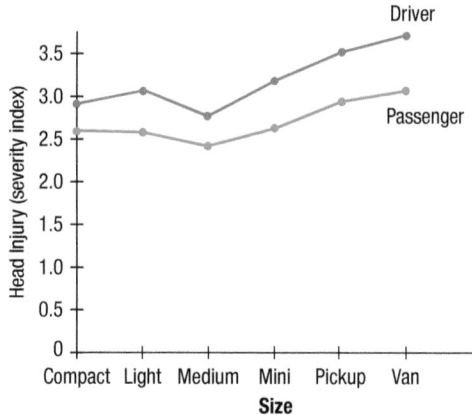

An interaction plot shows:

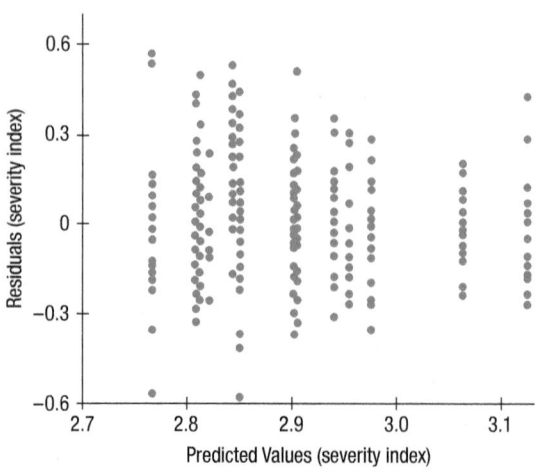

A scatterplot of residuals vs. predicted values shows:

The ANOVA table follows:

Source	df	Sum of Squares	Mean Square	*F*-ratio	P-value
Seat	1	0.88713	0.88713	25.501	<0.0001
Size	5	1.49253	0.29851	8.581	<0.0001
Seat × Size	5	0.07224	0.01445	0.415	0.838
Error	282	9.8101	0.03479		
Total	293	12.3853			

a) State the null hypothesis about the main effects (in words, not symbols).
b) Are the conditions for two-way ANOVA met?
c) If so, perform the hypothesis tests and state your conclusion. Be sure to state it in terms of head injury severity, seats, and vehicle types. **LO ❸**

48. **Gas additives.** An experiment to test a new gasoline additive, *Gasplus*, was performed on three different cars: a sports car, a minivan, and a hybrid. Each car was tested with both *Gasplus* and regular gas on 10 different occasions, and its gas mileage was recorded. Here are the boxplots:

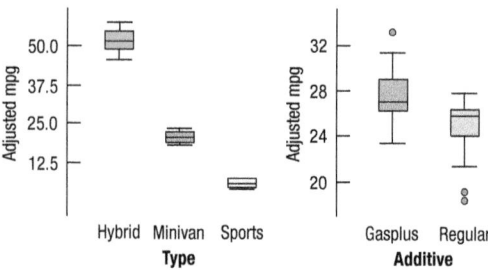

A two-way ANOVA with interaction model was run, and the following ANOVA table resulted:

Source	df	Sum of Squares	Mean Square	*F*-ratio	P-value
Type	2	23,175.4	11,587.7	2712.2	<0.0001
Additive	1	92.1568	92.1568	21.57	<0.0001
Interaction	2	51.8976	25.9488	6.0736	0.0042
Error	54	230.711	4.27242		
Total	59	23,550.2			

A plot of the residuals vs. predicted values showed:

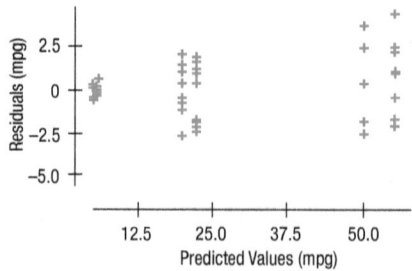

What conclusions about the additive and car types do you draw? Do you see any potential problems with the analysis? **LO ❸**

T 49. Canadian canola. Canola (CANada Oil Low Acid) was bred naturally at the University of Manitoba and today farms in the prairies produce about 20 million metric tonnes per year, higher than any other country in the world. The Canola Council of Canada organizes trials of new varieties of canola at multiple sites in Alberta, Saskatchewan, and Manitoba. A trial could test new varieties at multiple sites to get an estimate of whether there is any difference among them in terms of overall yield. Simplified data on the yield in bushels/acre from such a trial might look like this:

	Variety			
Site	A	B	C	D
1	25.2	27.6	30.2	26.8
2	32.4	34.7	35.4	33.9
3	27.1	30.1	30.2	26.1

a) Is this an observational study or a statistical experiment? What information is missing from the above description that would ensure that it is statistically well designed?

b) Assuming the trial is statistically well designed, analyze the effect of variety and site on yield with $\alpha = 0.05$. State the type of analysis you are performing.

c) Write a three-sentence report on your analysis for the Canola Council of Canada. **LO ❶, ❷, ❸**

T 50. Ottawa experimental farm. The experimental farm in Ottawa performs research on a wide range of crops including grains and oil seeds for farms across the country. About 30 million tonnes of wheat are produced each year in Canada but yields can be affected by *Fusarium*, a fungus. Antifungal agents can be researched by measuring their impact on wheat yield in bushels per acre. A trial of five different antifungal agents could be conducted on four blocks of land, with each divided into five plots, and one randomly assigned for each agent. Results might look like this:

	Antifungal Agent				
Block	A	B	C	D	E
1	41.1	37.7	34.2	32.2	39.9
2	40.2	35.4	38.2	32.7	40.1
3	39.9	41.1	39.4	38.9	41.2
4	37.2	40.5	37.7	36.8	42.1

a) Is this an observational study or a statistical experiment?

b) Conduct two different ANOVA analyses of this data with $\alpha = 0.05$, and compare their results.

c) Write a three-sentence report on your analysis for the Ottawa experimental farm. **LO ❶, ❷, ❸**

T 51. Morgan Solar of Toronto. Morgan Solar develops optical systems for concentrating sunlight on solar cells and sells the resulting solar systems in Southern California and other locations with intense direct sunlight. They continuously come up with new optical designs that need testing in a range of environmental conditions, from arid deserts to more humid coastal sites. Researchers aim to produce a single design that works well in all conditions. A trial of four designs randomly arranged at four sites could typically produce the following annual amounts of electricity generated, measured in kilowatt-hours per dollar of capital cost:

	Optical Design			
Environment	A	B	C	D
Desert	1.7	1.8	1.8	2.1
Coast	1.6	1.5	1.4	1.7
Urban	1.4	1.5	1.4	1.9
Farmland	1.5	1.9	2.1	2.2

a) What type of experimental design is used here?

b) Conduct the appropriate ANOVA analysis with $\alpha = 0.05$.

c) Write a three-sentence report on your analysis for Morgan Solar. **LO ❶, ❷, ❸**

52. Canadian divorce law and artificial intelligence. The IBM artificial intelligence system, Watson, achieved fame when it beat human champions at the TV trivia game *Jeopardy*. It works by being able to understand English text in a vast database of documents relating to a certain subject area. In the case of *Jeopardy*, the subject area is very broad, but for commercial applications, increased reliability can be obtained by focusing on a narrow subject area such as Canadian divorce law. The database consists of the laws made by governments, rulings of judges that interpret the law, articles in legal journals discussing the law, and any other documents regarded as authoritative in the area of divorce law. Watson is then trained by being given questions about divorce law together with the answers and links to the paragraphs in the database where the answer can be found. It is then given 100 test questions and is rated on a scale of 1 to 10 as to the answers it provides. Test questions are of four different types, provided by different people who are potential users of a commercial system: lawyers, legal assistants, law students, and people without legal training. We decide to use three stages of training. Watson is trained on 1000 questions/answers/links and then tested. It is then trained on an additional 1000 questions/answers/links and re-tested. Finally, it is trained again on an additional 1000 questions/answers/links (making 3000 in all) and re-tested. We are interested in whether there is any difference between the three sets of test results. That is, is Watson getting better with additional training, or is it becoming confused by being provided with additional information, or does it not benefit from being trained beyond a certain level? Our aim is to develop a trained version of Watson that can answer questions about Canadian divorce law from lawyers, legal assistants, law students, and people without legal training.

Design three statistical experiments for this testing using
  (i) completely randomized design
  (ii) randomized block design
  (iii) factorial design
For each experiment, show how the test results would be laid out in a table.
  (iv) Provide a comparison among the three designs from the point of view of their potential accuracy. LO ❶, ❷, ❸

Samoth/Fotolia

16

Inference for Counts: Chi-Square Tests

Sprott Asset Management of Toronto

When *Investment Executive*, Canada's newspaper for financial advisors, was evaluating fund managers in 2007, Eric Sprott came out on top. Sprott's name and expertise are behind many mutual funds and hedge funds on Bay Street, and he founded his first company there in 1981 to serve the many needs of institutional investors. In 2000 he decided to focus on investment management, and today heads up Sprott Private Wealth, advising high-net-worth investors, and Sprott Asset Management LP (SAM), which manages hedge funds and mutual funds. He was named Entrepreneur of the Year for the Ontario region by Ernst & Young in 2006, and his company, Sprott Inc., went public in 2008, raising $200 million in an initial public offering on the Toronto Stock Exchange.

Eric Sprott was named Most Influential Hedge Fund Manager in 2012 by wealth advisors surveyed by Terrapinn Inc.

Hedge funds, like mutual funds and pension funds, pool investors' money in order to make profits. Unlike those other funds, however, hedge funds are subject to various risk factors and should be considered only by people financially able to bear that risk. A minimum of $150,000 as an initial investment applies to most individual investors. Hedge funds use multiple, often complex, strategies to exploit inefficiencies in the market. In 2015, then 70-year-old Sprott passed the management of some of his major funds on to two new hires at SAM.

ROADMAP FOR STATISTICAL INFERENCE					
Number of Variables	Objective	Large Sample or Normal Population		Small Sample and Non-normal Population or Non-numeric Data	
		Chapter	Parametric Method	Chapter	Nonparametric Method
1	Calculate confidence interval for a proportion	11			
1	Compare a proportion with a given value	12	z-test		
1	Calculate a confidence interval for a mean and compare it with a given value	13	t-test	17.2	Wilcoxon Signed-Rank Test
2	Compare two proportions	12.8	z-test		
2	Compare two means for independent samples	14.1–14.5	t-test	17.4, 17.5	Wilcoxon Rank-Sum (Mann-Whitney) Test Tukey's Quick Test
2	Compare two means for paired samples	14.6, 14.7	Paired t-test	17.2	Wilcoxon Signed-Rank Test
≥3	Compare multiple means	15	ANOVA: ANalysis Of VAriance	17.3 17.6	Friedman Test Kruskal-Wallis Test
≥3	Compare multiple counts (proportions)	16	χ^2 test		
2	Investigate the relationship between two variables	18	Correlation Regression	17.7, 17.8	Kendall's tau Spearman's rho
≥3	Investigate the relationship between multiple variables	20	Multiple Regression		

LO❶

In a business as competitive as hedge fund management, information is gold. Being the first to have information and knowing how to act on it can mean the difference between success and failure. Hedge fund managers look for small advantages everywhere, hoping to exploit inefficiencies in the market and to turn those inefficiencies into profit.

Stockbrokers have plenty of "wisdom" about market patterns. For example, investors are advised to watch for "calendar effects," certain times of the year or days of the week that are particularly good or bad: "As goes January, so goes the year" and "Sell in May and go away." Some analysts claim that the "bad period" for holding stocks is from the sixth trading day of June to the fifth-to-last trading day of October. Of course, there is also Mark Twain's advice.

October. This is one of the peculiarly dangerous months to speculate in stocks. The others are July, January, September, April, November, May, March, June, December, August, and February.
—Pudd'nhead Wilson's Calendar

One common claim is that stocks show a weekly pattern. For example, some argue that there's a *weekend effect* in which stock returns on Mondays are often lower than those of the immediately preceding Friday. Are patterns such as this real? We have the data, so we can check. Between October 1, 1928, and February 25, 2013, there were 21,186 trading sessions. Let's first see how many trading days fell on each day of the week. It's not exactly 20% for each day because of holidays. The distribution of days is shown in Table 16.1.

Day of the Week	Count	% of Days
Monday	4090	19.305
Tuesday	4293	20.263
Wednesday	4317	20.377
Thursday	4253	20.075
Friday	4233	19.980

Table 16.1   The distribution of days of the week among the 21,186 trading days from October 1, 1928, to February 25, 2013. We expect about 20% to fall in each day, with minor variations due to holidays and other events.

Of these 21,186 trading sessions, 11,113, or about 52% of the days, saw a gain in the Dow Jones Industrial Average (DJIA). To test for a pattern, we need a model. The model comes from the supposition that any day is as likely to show a gain as any other. In any sample of positive or up days, we should expect to see the same distribution of days as in Table 16.1—in other words, about 19.31% of up days would be Mondays, 20.26% would be Tuesdays, and so on. Table 16.2 gives the distribution of days in one such random sample of 1110 "up" days.

Of course, we expect some variation. We wouldn't expect the proportions of days in the two tables to match exactly. In our sample, the percentage of Mondays in Table 16.2 is slightly lower than in Table 16.1, and the proportion of Fridays is a little higher. Are these deviations enough for us to declare that there's a recognizable pattern?

LO❷   **16.1**

Goodness-of-Fit Tests

To address this question, we use a **goodness-of-fit test** on the table, where *fit* refers to the null model proposed. Here, the null model is that there is no pattern, that the distribution of *up* days should be the same as the distribution of trading days overall. (If there were no holidays or other closings, that would just be 20% for each day of the week.)

Day of the Week	Count	% of Days in the Sample of "Up" Days
Monday	195	17.568
Tuesday	223	20.090
Wednesday	239	21.532
Thursday	223	20.090
Friday	230	20.721

Table 16.2 The distribution of days of the week for a sample of 1110 "up" trading days selected at random from October 1, 1928, to February 25, 2013. If there is no pattern, we would expect the proportions here to match fairly closely the proportions observed among all trading days in Table 16.1.

Assumptions and Conditions

Data for a goodness-of-fit test are organized in tables, and the assumptions and conditions reflect that. Rather than having an observation for each individual, we typically work with summary counts in categories. Here, the individuals are trading days, but rather than list all 1110 trading days in the sample, we have totals for each weekday.

- **Counted Data Condition:** The data must be counts for the categories of a categorical variable. This might seem a silly condition to check, but many kinds of values can be assigned to categories, and it is unfortunately common to find the methods of this chapter applied incorrectly (even by business professionals) to proportions or quantities just because they happen to be organized in a two-way table. So check to make sure that you really have counts.
- **Independence Assumption:** The counts in the cells should be independent of each other. You should think about whether that's reasonable. If the data are a random sample, you can simply check the Randomization Condition.
- **Randomization Condition:** The individuals counted in the table should be a random sample from some population. We need this condition if we want to generalize our conclusions to that population. We took a random sample of 1110 trading days on which the DJIA rose. That lets us assume that the market's performance on any one day is independent of performance on another. If we had selected 1110 consecutive trading days, there would be a risk that market performance on one day could affect performance on the next, or that an external event could affect performance for several consecutive days.
- **Sample Size Assumption:** We must have enough data for the methods to work. We usually just check the following condition.
- **Expected Cell Frequency Condition:** We should expect to see at least five individuals in each cell. The Expected Cell Frequency Condition should remind you of—and is, in fact, quite similar to—the two conditions that np and nq be at least 10 when we test proportions in section 11.4. If you have some categories that occur only rarely, a quick fix is to combine them with other categories so that the expected number in each cell is greater than five. Alternatively, you need to increase your sample size.

Chi-Square Model

We have observed a count in each category (weekday). We can compute the number of up days we'd *expect* to see for each weekday if the null model were true. For the trading days example, the **expected count** comes from the null hypothesis that the up days are distributed among weekdays just as trading days are. Of course, we could imagine almost any kind of model and base a null hypothesis on that model.

To decide whether the null model is plausible, we look at the differences between the expected values from the model and the counts we observe. We wonder: Are these differences so large that they call the model into question, or could they have arisen from natural sampling variability? We denote the *differences* between these observed and expected counts $(Obs - Exp)$. As we did with variance, we square them and use $(Obs - Exp)^2$. That gives us positive values and focuses attention on any cells with large differences, whether those differences are positive or negative. Because the differences between observed and expected counts generally get larger the more data we have, we also need to get an idea of the *relative* sizes of the differences. To do that, we divide each squared difference by the expected count for that cell.

The test statistic, called the chi-square (or chi-squared) statistic, is found by adding up the sum of the squares of the deviations between the observed and expected counts divided by the expected counts:

$$\chi^2 = \sum_{all\ cells} \frac{(Obs - Exp)^2}{Exp}$$

The chi-square statistic is denoted χ^2, where χ is the Greek letter chi (pronounced like "ki" in the word "kite"). The resulting family of sampling distribution models is called the **chi-square models**.

The members of this family of models differ in the number of degrees of freedom. The number of degrees of freedom for a goodness-of-fit test is $k - 1$, where k is the number of cells—in this example, five weekdays.

We will use the chi-square statistic only for testing hypotheses, not for constructing confidence intervals. For our example, the hypotheses are as follows:

H_0: The distribution of "up" days is the same as the distribution of trading days.

H_A: The distribution of "up" days is different from the distribution of trading days.

NOTATION ALERT

We compare the counts *observed* in each cell with the counts we *expect* to find. The usual notation uses *Obs* and *Exp*, as we've used here. The expected counts are found from the null model.

NOTATION ALERT

The only use of the Greek letter χ in Statistics is to represent the chi-square statistic and the associated sampling distribution. This is a violation of the general rule that Greek letters represent population parameters. Here we're using a Greek letter to name a family of distribution models and a statistic.

GUIDED EXAMPLE   Stock Market Patterns

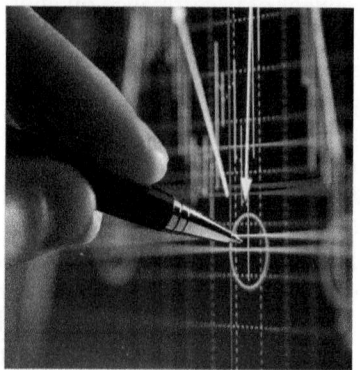

Tischenko Irina/Shutterstock

We have counts of the "up" days for each day of the week. The economic theory we want to investigate is whether there is a pattern in "up" days. So, our null hypothesis is that across all days in which the DJIA rose, the days of the week are distributed as they are across all trading days. (As we saw, the trading days are not quite *evenly* distributed because of holidays, so we use the *trading days* percentages as the null model.) The alternative hypothesis is that the observed percentages are *not* uniform. The test statistic looks at how closely the observed data match this idealized situation.

PLAN

Setup State what you want to know.

Identify the variables and context.

Hypotheses State the null and alternative hypotheses. For χ^2 tests, it's usually easier to state the hypotheses in words than in symbols.

Model Think about the assumptions and check the conditions.

Specify the sampling distribution model.

Name the test you will use.

We want to know whether the distribution for up days differs from the null model (the trading days distribution). We have the number of times each weekday appeared among a random sample of 1110 up days.

H_0: The days of the work week are distributed among the up days as they are among all trading days.

H_A: The trading days model does not fit the up days distribution

✓ **Counted Data Condition.** We have counts of the days of the week for all trading days and for the up days.

✓ **Independence Assumption.** We have no reason to expect that one day's performance will affect another's, but to be safe we've taken a random sample of days. The randomization should make them far enough apart to alleviate any concerns about dependence.

✓ **Randomization Condition.** We have a random sample of 1110 days from the time period.

✓ **Expected Cell Frequency Condition.** All the expected cell frequencies are much larger than five.

The conditions are satisfied, so we'll use a χ^2 model with $5 - 1 = 4$ degrees of freedom and do a chi-square goodness-of-fit test.

DO

Mechanics To find the expected number of days, we take the fraction of each weekday from all days and multiply by the number of up days.

For example, there were 4090 Mondays out of 21,186 trading days.

So, we'd expect there would be $1110 \times 4090 \div 21{,}186$ or 214.2877 Mondays among the 1110 up days.

Each cell contributes a value equal to $\dfrac{(Obs - Exp)^2}{Exp}$ to the chi-square sum.

Add up these components. If you do it by hand, it can be helpful to arrange the calculation in a table or spreadsheet.

The P-value is the probability in the upper tail of the χ^2 model. It can be found using software or a table (see Table X in Appendix B).

Large χ^2 statistic values correspond to small P-values, which would lead us to reject the null hypothesis, but the value here is not particularly large.

The expected values are:

Monday: 214.28774
Tuesday: 224.92353
Wednesday: 226.18097
Thursday: 222.82781
Friday: 221.77995

And we observe:

Monday: 195
Tuesday: 223
Wednesday: 239
Thursday: 223
Friday: 230

$$\chi^2 = \frac{(195 - 214.28774)^2}{214.28774} + \cdots + \frac{(230 - 221.77995)^2}{221.77995} = 2.7838$$

Using Table X in Appendix B, we find that for a significance level of 5% and four degrees of freedom, we'd need a value of 9.488 or more to have a P-value less than 0.05. Our value of 2.7838 is less than that.

Using a computer to generate the P-value, we find:

$P\text{-value} = P(\chi^2_4 > 2.7838) = 0.5946$

(continued)

REPORT

Conclusion Link the P-value to your decision. Be sure to say more than a fact about the distribution of counts. State your conclusion in terms of what the data mean.

MEMO

Re: Stock market patterns

Our investigation of whether there are day-of-the-week patterns in the behaviour of the DJIA in which one day or another is more likely to be an up day found no evidence of such a pattern. Our statistical test indicated that a pattern such as the one found in our sample of trading days would happen by chance about 60% of the time.

We conclude that there is, unfortunately, no evidence of a pattern that could be used to guide investment in the market. We were unable to detect a "weekend" or other day-of-the-week effect in the market.

A small chi-square statistic means that our model fits the data well, so a small value gives us no reason to doubt the null hypothesis. If the observed counts don't match the expected counts, the statistic will be large. If the calculated statistic value is large enough, we'll reject the null hypothesis. So the chi-square test is always one-sided. What could be simpler? Let's see how it works.

FOR EXAMPLE   Goodness-of-fit test for telemarketing

Atara manages eight call centre operators at a telecommunications company. To develop new business, she gives each operator a list of randomly selected phone numbers of rival phone company customers. She also provides the operators with a script that tries to convince the customers to switch providers. Atara notices that some operators have found more than twice as many new customers as others, so she suspects that some of the operators are performing better than others.

The 120 new customer acquisitions are distributed as follows:

Operator	1	2	3	4	5	6	7	8
New customers	11	17	9	12	19	18	13	21

QUESTION   Is there evidence to suggest that some of the operators are more successful than others?

ANSWER   Atara has randomized the potential new customers to the operators, so the Randomization Condition is satisfied. The data are counts, and there are at least five in each cell, so we can apply a chi-square goodness-of-fit test to the null hypothesis that the operator performance is uniform and that each of the operators will convince the same number of customers. Specifically, we expect each operator to have converted one-eighth of the 120 customers who switched providers.

Operator Observed Expected	1 11 15	2 17 15	3 9 15	4 12 15	5 19 15	6 18 15	7 13 15	8 21 15
Observed − Expected	−4	2	−6	−3	4	3	−2	6
$(Obs - Exp)^2$	16	4	36	9	16	9	4	36
$(Obs - Exp)^2 / Exp$	$16/15 = 1.07$	$4/15 = 0.27$	$36/15 = 2.40$	$9/15 = 0.60$	$16/15 = 1.07$	$9/15 = 0.60$	$4/15 = 0.27$	$36/15 = 2.40$

$$\sum \frac{(Obs - Exp)^2}{Exp} = 1.07 + 0.27 + 2.40 + \cdots + 2.40 = 8.68$$

(continued)

The number of degrees of freedom is $k - 1 = 7$.

$$P(\chi_7^2 > 8.68) = 0.2765$$

8.68 is not a surprising value for a chi-square statistic with seven degrees of freedom. So, we fail to reject the null hypothesis that the operators actually find new customers at different rates.

LO❶   16.2   # Interpreting Chi-Square Values

When we calculated χ^2 for the trading days example, we got 2.62. That value wasn't large for four degrees of freedom, so we were unable to reject the null hypothesis. In general, what *is* big for a χ^2 statistic?

Think about how χ^2 is calculated. In every cell, any deviation from the expected count contributes to the sum. Large deviations generally contribute more, but if there are a lot of cells, even small deviations can add up, making the χ^2 value larger. So the more cells there are, the higher the value of χ^2 has to be before it becomes significant. For χ^2, the decision about how big is big depends on the number of degrees of freedom.

Unlike the Normal and t families, χ^2 models are skewed. Curves in the χ^2 family change both shape and centre as the number of degrees of freedom grows. Figure 16.1, for example, shows the χ^2 distributions for five and nine degrees of freedom.

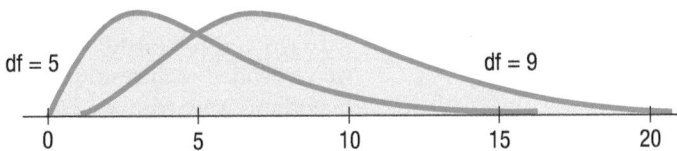

Figure 16.1   The χ^2 distributions for five and nine degrees of freedom.

Notice that the value $\chi^2 = 10$ might seem somewhat extreme when there are five degrees of freedom, but that it appears to be rather ordinary for nine degrees of freedom. Here are two simple facts to help you think about χ^2 models:

- The mode is at $\chi^2 = \text{df} - 2$. (Look at the distributions; their peaks are at three and seven.)
- The expected value (mean) of a χ^2 model is its number of degrees of freedom. That's a bit to the right of the mode—as we would expect for a right-skewed distribution.

Goodness-of-fit tests are often performed by people who have a theory of what the proportions *should* be in each category and who believe their theory to be true. In some cases, unlike our market example, there isn't an obvious null hypothesis against which to test the proposed model. So, unfortunately, in those cases, the only null hypothesis available is that the proposed theory is true. And as we know, the hypothesis testing procedure allows us only to reject the null or fail to reject it. We can never confirm that a theory is in fact true; we can never confirm the null hypothesis.

At best, we can point out that the data are consistent with the proposed theory. But this doesn't prove the theory. The data *could* be consistent with the model even if the theory were wrong. In that case, we fail to reject the null hypothesis but can't conclude anything for sure about whether the theory is true.

LO❶   16.3   Examining the Residuals

The chi-square statistic is always positive, and a large value provides evidence against the null hypothesis (because it shows that the fit to the model is *not* good), while small values provide little evidence that the model doesn't fit. A large statistic doesn't tell us *how* the null model doesn't fit. In our market theory example, if we had rejected the uniform model, we wouldn't have known *how* it failed. Was it because there weren't enough Mondays represented, or was it that all five days showed some deviation from the uniform?

When we reject a null hypothesis in a goodness-of-fit test, we can examine the residuals in each cell to learn more. In fact, whenever we reject a null hypothesis, it's a good idea to examine the residuals. (We don't need to do that when we fail to reject because when the χ^2 value is small, all of its components must have been small.) Because we want to compare residuals for cells that may have very different counts, we standardize the residuals. We know the mean residual is zero,[1] but we need to know each residual's standard deviation. When we tested proportions, we saw a link between the expected proportion and its standard deviation. For counts, there's a similar link: The square root of the expected value is the estimate of the standard deviation. To standardize a cell's residual, we therefore divide by the square root of its expected value:

$$\frac{(Obs - Exp)}{\sqrt{Exp}}$$

Notice that a **standardized residual** is the square root of the chi-square component we calculated for each cell, with the plus (+) or the minus (−) sign indicating whether we observed more or fewer cases than we expected.

The standardized residuals give us a chance to think about the underlying patterns and to consider how the distribution differs from the model. Now that we've divided each residual by its standard deviation, they are z-scores. If the null hypothesis were true, we could even use the 68-95-99.7 Rule to judge how extraordinary the large ones are.

Table 16.3 shows the standardized residuals for the trading days data:

	Standardized Residual = $\dfrac{(Obs - Exp)}{\sqrt{Exp}}$
Monday	−1.3176
Tuesday	−0.1283
Wednesday	0.8524
Thursday	0.0115
Friday	0.5520

Table 16.3   Standardized residuals for the trading days data.

None of these values is remarkable. The largest in absolute value, Monday, at −1.3176, isn't impressive when viewed as a z-score. The deviations are in the direction suggested by the "weekend effect," but they aren't large enough for us to conclude that they're real.

---

[1] Residual = observed − expected. Because the total of the expected values is the same as the observed total, the residuals must sum to zero.

> **FOR EXAMPLE** | **Examining residuals from a chi-square test for telemarketing**
>
> **QUESTION** In the call centre example (see For Example: "Goodness-of-fit test for telemarketing"), examine the residuals to see if any operators stand out as having especially strong or weak performance.
>
> **ANSWER** Because we failed to reject the null hypothesis, we don't expect any of the standardized residuals to be large, but we will examine them nonetheless.
>
> The standardized residuals are the square roots of the components (from the bottom row of the table in For Example: "Goodness-of-fit test for telemarketing").
>
> | Standardized Residuals | −1.03 | 0.52 | −1.55 | −0.77 | 1.03 | 0.77 | −0.52 | 1.55 |
> |---|---|---|---|---|---|---|---|---|
>
> As we expected, none of the residuals is large. Even though Atara notices that some of the operators enrolled more than twice the number of new customers as others did, the variation is typical (within two standard deviations) of what we would expect if all their performances were, in fact, equal.

LO❸ **16.4** The Chi-Square Test of Homogeneity (Independence)

Skin care products are big business. According to the American Academy of Dermatology, "the average adult uses at least seven different products each day," including moisturizers, skin cleansers, and hair cosmetics.[2] Global companies must understand cultural differences in the importance of various skin care products in order to compete effectively.

The GfK Roper Reports Worldwide Survey asked 30,000 randomly selected consumers in 23 countries about their attitudes toward health, beauty, and other personal values. One question that participants were asked was how important "seeking the utmost attractive appearance" was to them. Responses were on a scale with 1 = not at all important and 7 = extremely important. Is agreement with this question the same across the five countries for which we have data (China, France, India, the United Kingdom, and the United States)? Table 16.4 shows the counts.

		Country					
		China	France	India	U.K.	U.S.	Total
	7—Extremely important	197	274	642	210	197	1520
	6	257	405	304	252	203	1421
	5	315	364	196	348	250	1473
Appearance	4—Average importance	480	326	263	486	478	2033
	3	98	82	41	125	100	446
	2	63	46	36	70	58	273
	1—Not at all important	92	38	53	62	29	274
	Total	1502	1535	1535	1553	1315	7440

Table 16.4 Responses to how important "seeking the utmost attractive appearance" is.

[2]From American Academy of Dermatology: Allergies: The Culprit Could Be Hiding In Your Cosmetic Bag. Published by American Academy of Dermatology, © 2000.

We can compare the countries more easily by examining the column percentages (Table 16.5).

		Country					
		China	France	India	U.K.	U.S.	Row%
Appearance	7—Extremely important	13.12%	17.85	41.82	13.52	14.98	20.43%
	6	17.11	26.38	19.80	16.23	15.44	19.10
	5	20.97	23.71	12.77	22.41	19.01	19.80
	4—Average importance	31.96	21.24	17.13	31.29	36.35	27.33
	3	6.52	5.34	2.67	8.05	7.60	5.99
	2	4.19	3.00	2.35	4.51	4.41	3.67
	1—Not at all important	6.13	2.48	3.45	3.99	2.21	3.68
	Total	1502	1535	1535	1553	1315	7440

Table 16.5   Responses as a percentage of respondents by country.

The stacked bar chart of the responses by country (Figure 16.2) shows the patterns more vividly:

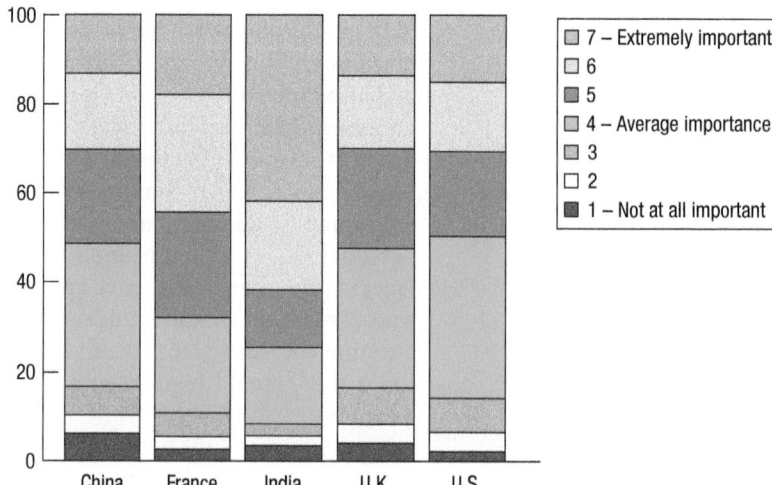

Figure 16.2   Responses to the question of how important "seeking the utmost attractive appearance" is by country. India stands out for the proportion of respondents who said it is important or extremely important.

It seems that India stands out from the other countries. There's a much larger proportion of respondents from India who responded *extremely important*. But are the observed differences in the percentages real or just natural sampling variation? Our null hypothesis is that the proportions choosing each alternative are the same for each country. To test that hypothesis, we use a **chi-square test of homogeneity (independence)**. This is just another chi-square test. It turns out that the mechanics of the test of this hypothesis are nearly identical to the chi-square goodness-of-fit test we just saw in Section 16.1. The difference is that the goodness-of-fit test compared our observed counts with the expected counts from a *given* model. The test of homogeneity, by contrast, has a null hypothesis that the distributions are the same for all the groups. The test examines the differences between the observed counts and what we'd expect under that assumption of homogeneity.

For example, 20.43% (the row %) of *all* 7440 respondents said that looking good was extremely important to them. If the distributions were homogeneous across the five countries (as the null hypothesis asserts), then that proportion should be the same for all five countries. So 20.43% of the 1315 U.S. respondents, or 268.66, would have said that looking good was extremely important (Table 16.6). That's the number we'd *expect* under the null hypothesis.

To find the expected value for row i and column j, we take

$$Exp_{ij} = \frac{Total_{row\ i} \times Total_{Col\ j}}{Table\ Total}.$$

Working in this way, we (or, more likely, the computer) can fill in expected values for each cell. Table 16.6 shows these expected values for each response and each country.

		Country					
		China	France	India	U.K.	U.S.	Row %
Appearance	7—Extremely important	306.86	313.60	313.60	317.28	268.66	20.43%
	6	286.87	293.18	293.18	296.61	251.16	19.10
	5	297.37	303.91	303.91	307.47	260.35	19.80
	4—Average importance	410.43	419.44	419.44	424.36	359.33	27.33
	3	90.04	92.02	92.02	93.10	78.83	5.99
	2	55.11	56.32	56.32	56.99	48.25	3.67
	1—Not at all important	55.32	56.53	56.53	57.19	48.43	3.68
	Total	1502	1535	1535	1553	1315	7440

Table 16.6 Expected values for the responses. Because these are theoretical values, they don't have to be integers.

The term *homogeneity* means that things are the same. Here, we ask whether the distribution of responses about the importance of looking good is the same across the five countries. The chi-square test looks for differences large enough to step beyond what we might expect from random sample-to-sample variation. It can reveal a large deviation in a single category or small but persistent differences over all the categories—or anything in between.

Testing for *homogeneity* is almost the same as testing for *independence*. Homogeneity tests whether appearance is of equal importance in different countries. Independence tests whether appearance and country are dependent on each other, which is essentially the same thing. There are some technical differences, but they are beyond the scope of this book. We will therefore use the terms interchangeably and refer to testing for homogeneity/independence.

Our hypotheses can be phrased in terms of homogeneity or in terms of independence.

In terms of homogeneity:

H_0: The importance of "appearance" is the same across countries.
H_A: The importance of "appearance" is different across countries.

In terms of independence:

H_0: The importance of "appearance" is independent of country.
H_A: The importance of "appearance" is dependent on country.

The assumptions and conditions are the same as for the chi-square test for goodness-of-fit. The Counted Data Condition says that these data must be counts.

You can never perform a chi-square test on a quantitative variable. For example, if Roper had recorded how much respondents spent on skin care products, you wouldn't be able to use a chi-square test to determine whether the mean expenditures in the five countries were the same.[3]

So that we can generalize, we need the counts to be independent of each other. Here, we have a professional survey with random samples, so we *can* assume that the observations are independent and draw a conclusion comparing the populations from which the samples were taken.

We must be sure we have enough data for this method to work. The sample size assumption can be checked with the Expected Cell Frequency Condition, which says that the expected count in each cell must be at least five. Here, our samples are certainly large enough.

Following the pattern of the goodness-of-fit test, we compute the component for each cell of the table:

$$\text{Component} = \frac{(Obs - Exp)^2}{Exp}$$

Summing these components across all cells gives the chi-square value:

$$\chi^2 = \sum_{all\ cells} \frac{(Obs - Exp)^2}{Exp}$$

The degrees of freedom are different from what they were for the goodness-of-fit test. For a test of homogeneity, there are $(R - 1) \times (C - 1)$ degrees of freedom, where R is the number of rows and C is the number of columns.

In our example, we have $6 \times 4 = 24$ degrees of freedom. We'll need the degrees of freedom to find a P-value for the chi-square statistic.

GUIDED EXAMPLE   Attitudes About Appearance

PLAN **Setup** State what you want to know. Identify the variables and context.	We want to know whether the distribution of responses to the importance of "seeking the utmost attractive appearance" is the same for the five countries for which we have data: China, France, India, the United Kingdom, and the United States.
Hypotheses State the null and alternative hypotheses.	H_0: The importance of "appearance" is independent of country. H_A: The importance of "appearance" is dependent on country.
Model Think about the assumptions and check the conditions.	We have counts of the number of respondents in each country who chose each response. ✓ **Counted Data Condition.** The data are counts of the number of people choosing each possible response. ✓ **Randomization Condition.** The data were obtained from a random sample by a professional global marketing company. ✓ **Expected Cell Frequency Condition.** The expected values in each cell are all at least five.
State the sampling distribution model. Name the test you will use.	The conditions seem to be met, so we can use a χ^2 model with $(7 - 1) \times (5 - 1) = 24$ degrees of freedom and use a chi-square test of homogeneity.

---

[3]To do that, you'd use a method called *analysis of variance* (see Chapter 15).

DO | **Mechanics** You could make separate tables for the observed and expected counts or put both counts in each cell.

Use software to calculate χ^2 and the associated P-value.

Here, the calculated value of the χ^2 statistic is extremely high, so the P-value is very small.

The observed and expected counts are in Table 16.4 and Table 16.6.

$$\chi^2 = \frac{(197 - 306.86^2)}{306.86} + \cdots + \frac{(29 - 48.43^2)}{48.43} = 810.65$$

P-value $= P(\chi^2_{24} > 810.65) < 0.001$, so we reject the null hypothesis.

REPORT | **Conclusion** State your conclusion in the context of the data. Discuss whether the distributions for the groups appear to be different. For a small table, examine the residuals.

MEMO

Re: Importance of Appearance

Our analysis of the Roper data shows large differences across countries in the distribution of how important respondents say it is for them to look attractive. Marketers of cosmetics are advised to take note of these differences.

If you find that simply rejecting the hypothesis of homogeneity is a bit unsatisfying, you're in good company. It's hardly a shock that responses to this question differ from country to country. What we'd really like to know is where the differences were and how big they were. The test for homogeneity doesn't answer these interesting questions, but it does provide some evidence that can help us. A look at the standardized residuals can help identify cells that don't match the homogeneity pattern.

FOR EXAMPLE — **Testing for homogeneity (independence) in opinions about inflation**

QUESTION Although annual inflation has been low for several years, many people fear that inflation may return. A Gallup poll recently asked 1020 Canadian adults, "Are you very concerned, somewhat concerned, or not at all concerned that inflation will climb?" Does the distribution of responses appear to be the same for Conservatives as it is for Liberals?

Ideology	Very Concerned	Somewhat Concerned	Not at All Concerned	Total
Conservative	232	83	25	340
Liberal	143	126	71	340
Total	375 (55.15%)	209 (30.74%)	96 (14.12%)	680

ANSWER This is a test of homogeneity, testing whether the distribution of responses is the same for the two ideological groups. The data are counts, the Gallup poll selected adults randomly (stratified by ideology), and all expected cell frequencies are much greater than five (see table below).

There are $(3 - 1) \times (2 - 1)$ or 2 degrees of freedom.

(continued)

If the distributions were the same, we would expect each cell to have expected values that are 55.15%, 30.74%, and 14.12% of the row totals for Very Concerned, Somewhat Concerned, and Not at All Concerned, respectively. These values can be computed explicitly from:

$$Exp_{ij} = \frac{Total_{Row\ i} \times Total_{Col\ j}}{Table\ Total}$$

So, in the first cell (Conservative, Very Concerned):

$$Exp_{11} = \frac{Total_{Row\ 1} \times Total_{Col\ 1}}{Table\ Total} = \frac{340 \times 375}{680} = 187.5.$$

Expected counts for all cells are:

Expected Numbers	Very Concerned	Somewhat Concerned	Not at All Concerned
Conservative	187.5	104.5	48.0
Liberal	187.5	104.5	48.0

The top left $\frac{(Obs - Exp)^2}{Exp}$ is $(232 - 187.5)^2/187.5 = 10.56$. Here is the complete table.

Components	Very Concerned	Somewhat Concerned	Not at All Concerned
Conservative	10.56	4.42	11.02
Liberal	10.56	4.42	11.02

Summing these gives $\chi^2 = 10.56 + 4.42 + \cdots + 11.02 = 52.01$, which, with 2 df, has a P-value of < 0.0001.

We therefore reject the hypothesis that the distribution of responses is the same for Conservatives and Liberals.

JUST CHECKING

Which of the chi-square tests would you use in each of the following situations—goodness-of-fit or homogeneity (independence)?

1 A restaurant manager wonders whether customers who dine on Friday nights have the same preferences among the chef's four special entrees as those who dine on Saturday nights. One weekend he has the wait staff record which entrees were ordered each night. Assuming these customers to be typical of weekend diners throughout the year, he'll compare the distributions of meals chosen Friday and Saturday.

2 Company policy calls for parking spaces to be assigned to everyone at random, but you suspect that may not be so.

There are three lots of equal size: lot A, next to the building; lot B, a bit farther away; and lot C, on the other side of the highway. You gather data about employees at middle-management level and above to see how many were assigned parking in each lot.

3 Is a student's social life affected by where the student lives? A campus survey asked a random sample of students whether they lived in a campus residence, in off-campus housing, or at home, and whether they had been out on a date 0, 1–2, 3–4, or 5 or more times in the past two weeks.

Answers are found in Appendix A.

Chi-Square Tests and Causation

Chi-square tests are common. Tests for homogeneity (independence) are especially widespread. Unfortunately, many people interpret a small P-value as proof of causation. We know better. Just as correlation between quantitative variables doesn't demonstrate causation, a failure of independence between two categorical variables doesn't show a cause-and-effect relationship between them.

(continued)

The chi-square test for independence treats the two variables symmetrically. There is no way to differentiate the direction of any possible causation from one variable to the other.

Of course, there's never any way to eliminate the possibility that a lurking variable is responsible for an observed lack of independence. In some sense, a failure of independence between two categorical variables is less impressive than a strong, consistent, linear association between quantitative variables. Two categorical variables can fail the test of independence in many ways, including ways that show no consistent pattern of failure. Examination of the chi-square standardized residuals can help you think about the underlying patterns.

WHAT CAN GO WRONG?

- **Don't use chi-square methods unless you have counts.** Other kinds of data can be arrayed in two-way tables. Just because numbers are in a two-way table doesn't make them suitable for chi-square analysis. Data reported as proportions or percentages can be suitable for chi-square procedures, *but only after they're converted to counts.* If you try to do the calculations without first finding the counts, your results will be wrong.

- **Don't say that one variable "depends" on the other just because they're not independent.** "Depend" can suggest a model or a pattern, but variables can fail to be independent in many different ways. When variables fail the test for independence, it may be better to say they are "associated."

ETHICS IN ACTION

Deliberately Different specializes in unique accessories for the home, such as hand-painted switch plates and hand-embroidered linens, offered through a catalogue and a website. Its customers tend to be women, generally older, with relatively high household incomes. Although the number of customer visits to the site has remained the same, management noticed that the proportion of customers visiting the site who make a purchase has been declining. Megan Cally, the product manager for Deliberately Different, was in charge of working with the market research firm hired to examine this problem. In her first meeting with Jason Esgro, the firm's consultant, she directed the conversation toward website design. Jason mentioned several reasons for consumers abandoning online purchases, the two most common being concerns about transaction security and unanticipated shipping/handling charges. Because Deliberately Different's shipping charges are reasonable, Megan asked him to look further into the issue of security concerns. They developed a survey that randomly sampled customers who had visited the website. They contacted these customers by email and asked them to respond to a brief survey, offering the chance of winning a prize, which would be awarded at random among the respondents. A total of 2450 responses were received. The analysis of the responses included chi-square tests for independence checking to see if responses on the security question were independent of gender and income category. Both tests were significant, rejecting the null hypothesis of independence. Megan reported to

management that concerns about online transaction security were dependent on gender and income, so Deliberately Different began to explore ways in which it could assure older female customers that transactions on the website are indeed secure. As product manager, Megan was relieved that the decline in purchases wasn't related to product offerings.

Ethical Issue: *The chance of rejecting the null hypothesis in a chi-square test for independence increases with sample size. Here the sample size is very large. In addition, it is misleading to state that concerns about security depend on gender, age, and income. Furthermore, patterns of association were not examined (for instance, with varying age categories). The response rate to the survey is not given, nor is there any analysis of whether the response rate was related to age or income. Finally, as product manager, Megan intentionally steered attention away from examining the product offerings, which could be a factor in declining purchases. Instead she reported to management that they had pinpointed the problem without noting that they hadn't explored other potential factors (related to Items A and H, ASA Ethical Guidelines; see Appendix C, the American Statistical Association's Ethical Guidelines for Statistical Practice, also available online at www.amstat.org/about/ethicalguidelines.cfm).*

Ethical Solution: *Interpret results correctly, cautioning about the large sample size and looking for any patterns of association, realizing that there is no way to estimate the effect size.*

WHAT HAVE WE LEARNED?

Learning Objectives

❶ We've learned how to test hypotheses about categorical variables using counts of data in categories, and all rely on chi-square models, a new family indexed by degrees of freedom.

Although the tests appear to be one-sided, we've learned to examine standardized residuals in order to better understand the patterns in the table.

❷ Goodness-of-fit tests compare the observed distribution of a single categorical variable with an expected distribution based on a theory or model.

❸ Tests of homogeneity (independence) compare the distribution of several groups for the same categorical variable.

Terms

Chi-square models

Chi-square models are skewed to the right. They are parameterized by their degrees of freedom and become less skewed with increasing degrees of freedom.

Chi-square test of homogeneity (independence)

A test comparing the distribution of counts for two or more groups on the same categorical variable. A chi-square test of homogeneity finds

$$\chi^2 = \sum_{all\ cells} \frac{(Obs - Exp)^2}{Exp},$$

where the expected counts are based on the overall frequencies, adjusted for the totals in each group. We find a P-value from a chi-square distribution with $(R - 1) \times (C - 1)$ degrees of freedom, where R gives the number of categories (rows) and C gives the number of groups (columns).

Expected count

$$Exp = \frac{Row\ Total \times Column\ Total}{Table\ Total}$$

Goodness-of-fit test

A test of whether the distribution of counts in one categorical variable matches the distribution predicted by a model. A chi-square test of goodness-of-fit finds

$$\chi^2 = \sum_{all\ cells} \frac{(Obs - Exp)^2}{Exp},$$

where the expected counts come from the predicting model. It finds a P-value from a chi-square model with $n - 1$ degrees of freedom, where n is the number of categories in the categorical variable.

Standardized residual

In each cell of a two-way table, a standardized residual is the square root of the chi-square component for that cell with the sign of the *Observed − Expected* difference:

$$\frac{(Obs - Exp)}{\sqrt{Exp}}$$

When we reject a null hypothesis using a chi-square test, an examination of the standardized residuals can sometimes reveal more about how the data deviate from the null model.

Skills

Plan

- Be able to recognize when a test of goodness-of-fit or a test of homogeneity (independence) would be appropriate for a table of counts.
- Understand that the degrees of freedom for a chi-square test depend on the dimensions of the table and not on the sample size. Understand that this means that increasing the sample size increases the ability of chi-square procedures to reject the null hypothesis.

Do

- Be able to display and interpret counts in a two-way table.
- Know how to use the chi-square tables to perform chi-square tests.
- Know how to perform a chi-square test using statistics software or a calculator.
- Be able to examine the standardized residuals to explain the nature of the deviations from the null hypothesis.

Report

- Know how to communicate the results of chi-square tests, whether goodness-of-fit or homogeneity (independence), in a few sentences.

Carbon Disclosure Project: Canada and International

The Carbon Disclosure Project (CDP) acts on behalf of over 700 institutional investors (pension funds, mutual funds, etc.) with almost $100 trillion of investments to collect and distribute information on corporate greenhouse gas (carbon) emissions. These investors are interested in taking carbon emissions into account in selecting companies in which to invest, and the CDP maintains a database of that information, based on responses to a questionnaire that it sends each year to the largest companies in the world. The annual CDP reports, produced by Pricewaterhouse Coopers, are used not only by investors but also by governments and corporate supply chain managers in choosing suppliers. UN Secretary-General Ban Ki-moon stated, "The Carbon Disclosure Project is harnessing the power of information and investor activism to encourage a more effective corporate response to climate change."[4]

The CDP Supply Chain Report 2014–15[5] asks suppliers in major countries to (i) report their greenhouse gas emissions; (ii) report any emissions reduction targets they have set themselves; and (iii) report any emissions reduction initiatives they are implementing. The percentage of companies complying with these requests is given in the table below, together with the total number of companies surveyed in a random selection of countries as well as the global average over all countries included. The data are also available in the file **ch16_MCSP_CDP**.

	Canada	Brazil	China	France	Germany	United States	Global Average
Reporting emissions	60%	53%	49%	77%	61%	54%	60%
Target setting	32%	26%	59%	64%	54%	37%	48%
Emission reduction initiatives	50%	30%	49%	78%	61%	45%	52%
Number of companies	72	118	167	112	147	1379	2756

Using the appropriate chi-square tests with a 95% significance level, determine: (a) for target setting, (i) whether results are uniform across all the countries, and (ii) whether results for Canada are different from the global average; and (b) for emission reduction initiatives, (i) whether results are uniform across all the countries, and (ii) whether results for Canada are different from the global average. (c) Select a single country and describe how it explains your result for (a). (*Hint:* It's important to organize the data into the appropriate formats for the chi-square tests.)

Photo credits (left): Chiyacat/Shutterstock; Plutonius 3d/Shutterstock

[4]UN Secretary-General Ban Ki-moon. (2009, June 30). Commentary for the Carbon Disclosure Project. Retrieved from http://www.cdproject.net

[5]Supply Chain Sustainability Revealed: A Country Comparison. Retrieved from www.cdp.net

(*continued*)

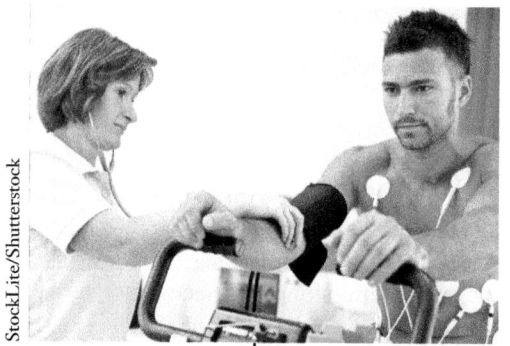

StockLite/Shutterstock

Health Insurance

With the rising costs of U.S. medical insurance and the declining interest and ability of employers to maintain proper medical coverage for their employees, business owners and employees alike are wondering: Who will insure future workers in the United States? The government has spent decades debating different initiatives to expand health insurance coverage.

Just how widespread is the lack of medical coverage? The media claims that the segments of the population most at risk are women, children, and the elderly. The tables give the number of uninsured (in thousands) by sex and by age in 2004.[6] Using the appropriate chi-square test and the statistics software of your choice, investigate the accuracy of the media's statement using these data. Be sure to discuss your assumptions, methods, results, and conclusions.

	Sex		
	Male	**Female**	**Total**
Insured	86,176	93,329	**179,505**
Uninsured	16,026	15,117	**31,143**
Total	**102,202**	**108,446**	**210,648**

	Age Group					
	0–17	**18–24**	**25–44**	**45–64**	**65–80**	**Total**
Insured	57,375	12,755	47,850	41,176	20,349	**179,505**
Uninsured	6,755	5,464	12,105	6,607	212	**31,143**
Total	**64,130**	**18,219**	**59,955**	**47,783**	**20,561**	**210,648**

Loyalty Program

A marketing executive tested two incentives to see what percentage of customers would enrol in a new web-based loyalty program. The customers were asked to log on to their accounts on the web and provide some demographic and spending information. As an incentive, they were offered either nothing (*No Offer*), free flight insurance on their next flight (*Free Insurance*), or a free companion airline ticket (*Free Flight*). The customers were segmented according to their past year's spending patterns as spending primarily in one of five areas: *Travel, Entertainment, Dining, Household,* or *Balanced*. The executive wanted to know whether the incentives resulted in different enrollment rates (*Response*). Specifically, she wanted to know how much higher the enrollment rate for the free flight was compared with the free insurance. She also wanted to see whether *Spending Pattern* was associated with *Response*. Using the data in the file **ch16_MCSP_Loyalty_Program,** write up a report for the marketing executive using appropriate graphics, summary statistics, statistical tests, and confidence intervals.

---

[6]Derived from U.S. Census Bureau. (2005). Current Population Survey: Annual Social and Economic Supplement.

TECHNOLOGY HELP: Chi-Square

Most statistics packages associate chi-square tests with contingency tables. Often chi-square is available as an option only when you make a contingency table. This organization can make it hard to locate the chi-square test and may confuse the different roles that the chi-square test can take. In particular, chi-square tests for goodness-of-fit may be hard to find or missing entirely.

Most statistics packages work with data on individuals rather than with the summary counts. If the only information you have is the table of counts, you may find it more difficult to get a statistics package to compute chi-square. Some packages offer a way to reconstruct the data from the summary counts so that they can then be passed back through the chi-square calculation, finding the cell counts again. Many packages offer chi-square standardized residuals (although they may be called something else).

EXCEL

To perform a chi-square goodness-of-fit test using Excel:

If you have two parallel columns, one holding observed counts and the other expected counts, follow these steps:

- In columns D through F, you can use spreadsheet calculations and built-in functions to calculate $(Obs - Exp)$, $(Obs - Exp)^2$, and $(Obs - Exp)^2/Exp$. Type the following into cells D2, E2, and F2 respectively:
  - =(B2-C2)
  - =D2^2
  - =E2/C2
- Copy the formulas from D2, E2, and F2 and paste into the remainder of the rows in columns D, E, and F.
- Using the =SUM function, add the values contained in the cells in column F to get the χ^2 value.
- The CHISQ.INV.RT and CHISQ.DIST.RT functions can then be used to calculate the critical value and P-value of the chi-square statistic that is calculated. See the image below for commands. Note that the function used to calculate degrees of freedom (=COUNT) should reflect rows containing data.

	A	B	C	D	E	F	G
1	Operator	Observed	Expected	(Obs-Exp)	$(Obs-Exp)^2$	$(Obs-Exp)^2/Exp$	Excel Syntax
2	1	11	15	-4	16	1.0667	
3	2	17	15	2	4	0.2667	
4	3	9	15	-6	36	2.4000	
5	4	12	15	-3	9	0.6000	
6	5	19	15	4	16	1.0667	
7	6	18	15	3	9	0.6000	
8	7	13	15	-2	4	0.2667	
9	8	21	15	6	36	2.4000	
10					Chi-Square=	8.6667	=SUM(F2:F9)
11					Alpha=	0.0500	[enter value]
12					df=	7	=COUNT(A2:A9)-1
13					χ^2 critical=	14.0671	=CHISQ.INV.RT(F11,F12)
14					p-value=	0.2775	=CHISQ.DIST.RT(F10,F12)

To perform a chi-square test of independence using Excel:

- Summarize raw data into a row by column pivot table—this will be the observed table. It should have row and column totals and a grand total.
- In the same spreadsheet, create a row by column table that mirrors the observed table without the rows and columns—this will be the expected table.

- In each corresponding cell in the expected table, calculate the expected value. In the example that follows, the formula in cell B11 is =(D5*B7)/D7; repeat this for all cells in the expected table.
- Create a third row by column table that mirrors the observed table without the rows and columns—this will be the table that holds the chi-square calculation for each cell.

(continued)

- In each corresponding cell in the chi-square table, calculate the chi-square value. In the example shown here, the code for cell B15 is =((POWER((B5-B11),2)/B11)); repeat this for all cells in the expected table.

- Below the table, designate cells to hold the values for alpha and degrees of freedom (recall that degrees of freedom for this statistic are [number of rows] − 1 × [number of columns] − 1), and then type in the code to calculate the chi-square value, critical chi-square value, and P-value.

	A	B	C	D
1				
2				
3	*Pivot Table*	▾		
4		▾ **No AC**	**AC**	**Grand Total**
5	Old	1055	592	1647
6	New	38	43	81
7	**Grand Total**	**1093**	**635**	**1728**
8				
9				
10	*Expected Values*	**No AC**	**AC**	
11	**Old**	1041.765625	605.234375	
12	**New**	51.234375	29.765625	
13				
14	*(O-E)²/E Values*	**No AC**	**AC**	
15	**Old**	0.168126762	0.28938984	
16	**New**	3.418577501	5.88426017	
17				
18			**Excel Syntax**	
19	*Chi-Square=*	9.7604	=SUM(B15,B16,C15,C16)	
20	*Alpha=*	0.0500	[enter value]	
21	*df=*	1	[enter value]	
22	χ^2 *critical=*	3.8415	=CHISQ.INV.RT(B20,B21)	
23	*p-value=*	0.0018	=CHISQ.DIST.RT(B19,B21)	

Comments

Excel offers the function CHISQ.TEST (actual_range, expected_range), which computes a chi-square P-value for independence. However, this command will only provide the P-value and no other values. Both ranges are of the form UpperLeftCell:LowerRightCell, specifying two rectangular tables. The two tables must be of the same size and shape. The function is called CHITEST in Excel versions earlier than 2010.

From the **Start** menu,

- Choose the **Tables** submenu.
- From that menu, choose **Chi Square Test**....
- In the dialogue, identify the columns that make up the table. Minitab will display the table and print the chi-square value and its P-value.

Comments

Alternatively, select the Cross Tabulation ... command to see more options for the table, including expected counts and standardized residuals.

From the **Analyze** menu, choose the **Descriptive Statistics** submenu. From that submenu, choose **Crosstabs** .... In the Crosstabs dialogue, assign the row and column variables from the variable list. Both variables must be categorical. Click the **Cells** button to specify that standardized residuals should be displayed. Click the **Statistics** button to specify a chi-square test.

Comments

SPSS offers only variables that it knows to be categorical in the variable list for the Crosstabs dialogue. If the variables you want are missing, check that they have the right type.

From the **Analyze** menu, select **Fit Y by X**. Choose one variable as the **Y, response** variable, and the other as the **X, factor** variable. Both selected variables must be nominal or ordinal. JMP will make a plot and a contingency table. Below the contingency table, JMP offers a **Tests** panel. In that panel, the chi-square for independence is called a **Pearson ChiSquare**. The table also offers the P-value.

Click on the contingency table title bar to drop down a menu that offers to include a **Deviation** and **cell Chi square** in each cell of the table.

Comments

JMP will choose a chi-square analysis for a **Fit Y by X** if both variables are nominal or ordinal (marked with an N or O), but not otherwise. Be sure the variables have the right type. Deviations are the observed-expected differences in counts. Cell chi-squares are the squares of the standardized residuals. Refer to the deviations for the sign of the difference. Look under **Distributions** in the **Analyze** menu to find a chi-square test for goodness-of-fit.

EXERCISES

SECTION 16.1

1. If there is no seasonal effect on human births, we would expect equal numbers of children to be born in each season (winter, spring, summer, and fall). A student takes a census of her Statistics class and finds that of the 120 students in the class, 25 were born in winter, 35 in spring, 32 in summer, and 28 in fall. She wonders if the excess in the spring is an indication that births are not uniform throughout the year.

a) What is the expected number of births in each season if there is no "seasonal effect" on births?
b) Compute the χ^2 statistic.
c) How many degrees of freedom does the χ^2 statistic have? **LO ❷**

2. At a major credit card company, the percentages of people who historically apply for the Silver, Gold, and Platinum cards are 60%, 30%, and 10%, respectively. In a recent sample of customers responding to a promotion, of 200 customers, 110 applied for Silver, 55 for Gold, and 35 for Platinum. We are interested in whether the percentages for this promotion are different from the historical percentages.

a) What is the expected number of customers applying for each type of card in this sample if the historical proportions are still true?
b) Compute the χ^2 statistic.
c) How many degrees of freedom does the χ^2 statistic have? **LO ❷**

SECTION 16.2

3. For the births in Exercise 1,

a) If there is no seasonal effect, about how big, on average, would you expect the χ^2 statistic to be (what is the mean of the χ^2 distribution)?
b) Does the statistic you computed in Exercise 1 seem large in comparison to this mean? Explain briefly.
c) What does that say about the null hypothesis?
d) Find the $\alpha = 0.05$ critical value for the χ^2 distribution with the appropriate number of df.
e) Using the critical value, what do you conclude about the null hypothesis at $\alpha = 0.05$? **LO ❶**

4. For the customers in Exercise 2,

a) If the customers apply for the three cards according to the historical proportions, about how big, on average, would you expect the χ^2 statistic to be (what is the mean of the χ^2 distribution)?
b) Does the statistic you computed in Exercise 2 seem large in comparison to this mean? Explain briefly.

c) What does that say about the null hypothesis?
d) Find the $\alpha = 0.05$ critical value for the χ^2 distribution with the appropriate number of df.
e) Using the critical value, what do you conclude about the null hypothesis at $\alpha = 0.05$? **LO ❶**

SECTION 16.3

5. For the data in Exercise 1,

a) Compute the standardized residual for each season.
b) Are any of these particularly large? (Compared with what?)
c) Why should you have anticipated the answer to (b)? **LO ❶**

6. For the data in Exercise 2,

a) Compute the standardized residual for each type of card.
b) Are any of these particularly large? (Compared with what?)
c) What does the answer to (b) say about this new group of customers? **LO ❶**

SECTION 16.4

7. An analyst at a local bank wonders if the age distribution of customers coming in for service at his branch in town is the same as at the branch located near the mall. He selects 100 transactions at random from each branch and researches the age information for the associated customer. Here are the data:

	Age			
	Younger Than 30	30–55	56 or Older	Total
In-town Branch	20	40	40	100
Mall Branch	30	50	20	100
Total	50	90	60	200

a) What is the null hypothesis?
b) What type of test is this?
c) What are the expected numbers for each cell if the null hypothesis is true?
d) Find the χ^2 statistic.
e) How many degrees of freedom does it have?
f) Find the critical value at $\alpha = 0.05$.
g) What do you conclude? **LO ❸**

8. A market researcher working for the credit card company in Exercise 2 wants to know if the distribution of applications by card is the same for the past three mailings. She takes a random sample of 200 from each mailing and counts the number applying for Silver, Gold, and Platinum. The data follow:

	Type of Card			
	Silver	**Gold**	**Platinum**	**Total**
Mailing 1	120	50	30	200
Mailing 2	115	50	35	200
Mailing 3	105	55	40	200
Total	340	155	105	600

a) What is the null hypothesis?
b) What type of test is this?
c) What are the expected numbers for each cell if the hypothesis is true?
d) Find the χ^2 statistic.
e) How many degrees of freedom does it have?
f) Find the critical value at $\alpha = 0.05$.
g) What do you conclude? **LO ❹**

CHAPTER EXERCISES

9. Concepts, part 1. For each of the following situations, state whether you'd use a chi-square goodness-of-fit test, chi-square test of homogeneity (independence), or some other statistical test.

a) A brokerage firm wants to see whether the type of account a customer has (Silver, Gold, or Platinum) affects the types of trades that customer makes (in person, by phone, or on the internet). It collects a random sample of trades made for its customers over the past year and performs a test.
b) That brokerage firm also wants to know if the type of account affects the size of the account (in dollars). It performs a test to see if the mean size of the account is the same for the three account types.
c) The academic research office at a large community college wants to see whether the distribution of courses chosen (Humanities, Social Science, or Science) is different for its residential and nonresidential students. It assembles last semester's data and performs a test. **LO ❶**

10. Concepts, part 2. For each of the following situations, state whether you'd use a chi-square goodness-of-fit test, a chi-square test of homogeneity (independence), or some other statistical test.

a) Is the quality of a car affected by what day it was built? A car manufacturer examines a random sample of the warranty claims filed over the past two years to test whether defects are randomly distributed across days of the work week.
b) A researcher for the Booksellers' Association wants to know if retail sales per square metre are related to serving coffee or snacks on the premises. She examines a database of 1000 independently owned bookstores to test whether retail sales (dollars/sq. ft.) are related to whether or not the store has a coffee bar.
c) A researcher wants to find out whether education level (some high school, high school graduate, university graduate, advanced degree) is related to the type of transaction most likely to be conducted using the internet (shopping, banking, travel reservations, auctions). He surveys 500 randomly chosen adults and performs a test. **LO ❶**

11. Dice. After getting trounced by your little brother in a children's game, you suspect that the die he gave you is unfair. To check, you roll it 60 times, recording the number of times each face appears. Do the results in the table cast doubt on the die's fairness?

a) If the die is fair, how many times would you expect each face to show?
b) To see if these results are unusual, will you test goodness-of-fit or homogeneity (independence)?
c) State your hypotheses.
d) Check the conditions.
e) How many degrees of freedom are there?
f) Find χ^2 and the P-value.
g) State your conclusion. **LO ❷**

Face	Count
1	11
2	7
3	9
4	15
5	12
6	6

12. Sales rep travel. A sales representative who is on the road visiting clients thinks that, on average, he drives the same distance each day of the week. He keeps track of his driving distance for several weeks and discovers that he averages 122 kilometres on Mondays, 203 kilometres on Tuesdays, 176 kilometres on Wednesdays, 181 kilometres on Thursdays, and 108 kilometres on Fridays. He wonders if this evidence contradicts his belief in a uniform distribution of kilometres across the days of the week. Is it appropriate to test his hypothesis using the chi-square goodness-of-fit test? Explain. **LO ❶**

13. Lottery. For a lottery to be successful, the public must have confidence in its fairness. An example is a Pick-3 Lottery, wherein three random digits are drawn each day. A fair game depends on every value (0 to 9) being equally likely at each of the three positions. If not, then someone detecting a pattern could take advantage of that and beat the lottery. To investigate the randomness, we'll look at data collected over a recent 32-week period. Although the winning numbers look like three-digit numbers, in fact each digit is a randomly drawn numeral. We have 654 random digits in all. Are each of the digits from 0 to 9 equally likely? Here's a table of the frequencies:

Group	Count	%
0	62	9.480
1	55	8.410
2	66	10.092
3	64	9.786
4	75	11.468
5	57	8.716
6	71	10.856
7	74	11.315
8	69	10.550
9	61	9.327

a) Select the appropriate procedure.
b) Check the assumptions.
c) State the hypotheses.
d) Test an appropriate hypothesis and state your results.
e) Interpret the meaning of the results and state a conclusion. **LO ❷**

14. Employment discrimination? Census data for New York City indicate that 29.2% of the under-18 population is white, 28.2% black, 31.5% Latino, 9.1% Asian, and 2% are of other ethnicities. The New York Civil Liberties Union points out that of 26,181 police officers, 64.8% are white, 14.5% black, 19.1% Hispanic, and 1.4% Asian. Do the police officers reflect the ethnic composition of the city's youth?

a) Select the appropriate procedure.
b) Check the assumptions.
c) State the hypotheses.
d) Test an appropriate hypothesis and state your results.
e) Interpret the meaning of the results and state a conclusion. **LO ❷**

T 15. *Titanic*, part 1. Here is a table showing who survived the sinking of *Titanic* based on whether they were crew members or passengers booked in first-, second-, or third-class staterooms:

	Crew	First	Second	Third	Total
Alive	212	202	118	178	710
Dead	673	123	167	528	1491
Total	885	325	285	706	2201

a) If we draw an individual at random from this table, what's the probability that we'll draw a member of the crew?
b) What's the probability of randomly selecting a third-class passenger who survived?
c) What's the probability of a randomly selected passenger surviving, given that the passenger was in a first-class stateroom?

d) If someone's chances of surviving were the same regardless of his or her status on the ship, how many members of the crew would you expect to have lived?
e) State the null and alternative hypotheses we would test here.
f) Give the degrees of freedom for the test.
g) The chi-square value for the table is 187.8, and the corresponding P-value is barely greater than 0. State your conclusions about the hypotheses. **LO ❸**

T 16. Promotion discrimination? The table shows the rank attained by male and female officers in the New York City Police Department (NYPD). Do these data indicate that men and women are equitably represented at all levels of the department?

		Male	Female
Rank	Officer	21,900	4281
	Detective	4058	806
	Sergeant	3898	415
	Lieutenant	1333	89
	Captain	359	12
	Higher Ranks	218	10

a) What's the probability that a person selected at random from the NYPD is a female?
b) What's the probability that a person selected at random from the NYPD is a detective?
c) Assuming no bias in promotions, how many female detectives would you expect the NYPD to have?
d) To see if there's evidence of differences in ranks attained by males and females, will you test goodness-of-fit or homogeneity (independence)?
e) State the hypotheses.
f) Test the conditions.
g) How many degrees of freedom are there?
h) Find the chi-square value and the associated P-value.
i) State your conclusion.
j) If you concluded that the distributions are not the same, analyze the differences using the standardized residuals of your calculations. **LO ❸**

17. Birth order and choice of major. Students in an Introductory Statistics class at a large university were classified by birth order and by their study major:

		Birth Order (1 = oldest or only child)				
		1	2	3	4 or More	Total
Major	Arts and Sciences	34	14	6	3	57
	Agriculture	52	27	5	9	93
	Social Science	15	17	8	3	43
	Professional	13	11	1	6	31
	Total	114	69	20	21	224

	Expected Values Birth Order (1 = oldest or only child)			
Major	**1**	**2**	**3**	**4 or More**
Arts and Sciences	29.0089	17.5580	5.0893	5.3438
Agriculture	47.3304	28.6473	8.3036	8.7188
Social Science	21.8839	13.2455	3.8393	4.0313
Professional	15.7768	9.5491	2.7679	2.9063

a) What kind of chi-square test is appropriate—goodness-of-fit or homogeneity (independence)?
b) State your hypotheses.
c) State and check the conditions.
d) How many degrees of freedom are there?
e) The calculation yields $\chi^2 = 17.78$, with P $= 0.0378$. State your conclusion.
f) Examine and comment on the standardized residuals below. Do they challenge your conclusion? Explain. **LO ❸**

	Standardized Residuals Birth Order (1 = oldest or only child)			
Major	**1**	**2**	**3**	**4 or More**
Arts and Sciences	0.92667	−0.84913	0.40370	−1.01388
Agriculture	0.67876	−0.30778	−1.14640	0.09525
Social Science	−1.47155	1.03160	2.12350	−0.51362
Professional	−0.69909	0.46952	−1.06261	1.81476

18. Automobile manufacturers. *Consumer Reports* uses surveys given to subscribers of its magazine and website (www.ConsumerReports.org) to measure reliability in automobiles. One annual survey asks about problems that consumers have had with their cars, vans, SUVs, or trucks during the previous 12 months. Each analysis is based on the number of problems per 100 vehicles.

	Origin of Manufacturer			
	Asia	**Europe**	**U.S.**	**Total**
No Problems	88	79	83	250
Problems	12	21	17	50
Total	100	100	100	300

	Expected Values		
	Asia	**Europe**	**U.S.**
No Problems	83.33	83.33	83.33
Problems	16.67	16.67	16.67

a) State your hypotheses.
b) State and check the conditions.
c) How many degrees of freedom are there?

d) The calculation yields $\chi^2 = 2.928$, with P $= 0.231$. State your conclusion.
e) Would you expect that a larger sample might find statistical significance? Explain. **LO ❸**

🖥 19. Cranberry juice. It's common folk wisdom that cranberries can help prevent urinary tract infections in women. A leading producer of cranberry juice would like to use this information in its next ad campaign, so it needs evidence of this claim. The *British Medical Journal* reported the results of a Finnish study in which three groups of 50 women were monitored for these infections over six months. One group drank cranberry juice daily, another group drank a lactobacillus drink, and the third group drank neither of those beverages, serving as a control group. In the control group, 18 women developed at least one infection compared with 20 of those who consumed the lactobacillus drink and only 8 of those who drank cranberry juice. Does this study provide supporting evidence for the value of cranberry juice in warding off urinary tract infections in women?

a) Select the appropriate procedure.
b) Check the assumptions.
c) State the hypotheses.
d) Test an appropriate hypothesis and state your results.
e) Interpret the meaning of the results and state a conclusion.
f) If you concluded that the groups are not the same, analyze the differences using the standardized residuals of your calculations. **LO ❸**

20. Car company. A European manufacturer of automobiles claims that its cars are preferred by the younger generation and would like to target university students in its next ad campaign. Suppose we test the manufacturer's claim with our own survey. A random survey of autos parked in the student lot and the staff lot at a large university classified the brands by country of origin, as seen in the following table. Are there differences in the national origins of cars driven by students and staff?

	Driver	
Origin	**Student**	**Staff**
American	107	105
European	33	12
Asian	55	47

a) Is this a test of homogeneity (independence) or goodness-of-fit?
b) Write appropriate hypotheses.
c) Check the necessary assumptions and conditions.
d) Find the P-value of your test.
e) State your conclusion and analysis. **LO ❸**

🖥 21. Market segmentation, part 1. A female fashion study surveyed customers to determine characteristics of the "frequent" shoppers at different department stores. Suppose you're a marketing manager at one of the department stores. You'd like to know if a customer's shopping frequency and her age are related. Here are the data:

		Age			
Shopping Frequency		18–24	25–44	45–54	55 or Over
	Never/Hardly Ever	32	171	45	24
	1–2 Times/Yr	18	134	40	37
	3–4 Times/Yr	21	109	48	27
	≥5 Times/Yr	39	134	71	50

		Standardized Residuals Age			
Shopping Frequency		18–24	25–44	45–54	55 or Over
	Never/Hardly Ever	0.3803	1.7974	−1.4080	−2.2094
	1–2 Times/Yr	−1.4326	0.7595	−0.9826	0.9602
	3–4 Times/Yr	−0.3264	−0.3151	0.9556	−0.2425
	≥5 Times/Yr	1.1711	−2.1360	1.4235	1.4802

a) Is this a test of homogeneity (independence) or goodness-of-fit?
b) Write an appropriate hypothesis.
c) Are the conditions for inference satisfied?
d) The calculation yields $\chi^2 = 26.084$, P-value = 0.002. State your conclusion.
e) Given the standardized residuals in the table, state a complete conclusion. **LO ❸**

T 22. Seafood company. A large company in New Brunswick that buys fish from local fisheries and distributes them to major companies and restaurants is considering launching a new ad campaign on the health benefits of fish. As evidence, it would like to cite the following study. Medical researchers followed 6272 Swedish men for 30 years to see if there was any association between the amount of fish in their diet and prostate cancer. (*Source:* Inoue, K., Takano, H., & Yoshikawa, T. [2001, June]. Fatty fish consumption and risk of prostate cancer. *Lancet, 358*(9290), 1367.)

		Prostate Cancer	
Fish Consumption		No	Yes
	Never/Seldom	110	105
	Small Part of Diet	2420	201
	Moderate Part	2769	209
	Large Part	507	42

a) Is this a test of homogeneity (independence) or goodness-of-fit?

b) Do you see evidence of an association between the amount of fish in a man's diet and his risk of developing prostate cancer?
c) Does this study prove that eating fish does not prevent prostate cancer? Explain. **LO ❸**

23. Shopping. A survey of 430 randomly chosen adults finds that 47 of 222 men and 37 of 208 women had purchased books online. Is there evidence that the gender of the person and whether he or she buys books online are associated? **LO ❷, ❸**

24. Information technology. A report suggests that chief information officers (CIOs) who report directly to chief financial officers (CFOs) rather than chief executive officers (CEOs) are more likely to have IT agendas that deal with cost cutting and compliance. (*Source:* Based onSearchCIO.com.) In a random sample of 535 companies, it was found that CIOs reported directly to CFOs in 173 out of 335 service firms and in 95 out of 200 manufacturing companies. Is there evidence that type of business (service vs. manufacturing) and whether the CIO reports directly to the CFO are associated? **LO ❷, ❸**

25. Fast food. GfK Roper Consulting gathers information on consumer preferences around the world to help companies monitor attitudes about health, food, and health-care products. It asked people in many different cultures how they felt about the following statement: *I try to avoid eating fast foods.*

In a random sample of 800 respondents, 411 people were 35 years old or younger and, of those, 197 agreed (completely or somewhat) with the statement. Of the 389 people over 35 years old, 246 people agreed with the statement. Is there evidence that the percentage of people avoiding fast food is different in the two age groups? **LO ❷, ❸**

26. Investment options. The economic slowdown in early 2008 and the possibility of future inflation prompted a full-service brokerage firm to gauge the level of interest in inflation-beating investment options among its clients. It surveyed a random sample of 1200 clients, asking them to indicate the likelihood that they would add inflation-linked annuities and bonds to their portfolios within the next year. The table below shows the distribution of responses by the investors' tolerance for risk. Test an appropriate hypothesis for the relationship between risk tolerance and the likelihood of investing in inflation-linked options. **LO ❸**

		Risk Tolerance			
Likelihood of Investing in Inflation-Linked Options		Averse	Neutral	Seeking	Total
	Certain Will Invest	191	93	40	324
	Likely to Invest	82	106	123	311
	Not Likely to Invest	64	110	101	275
	Certain Will Not Invest	63	91	136	290
	Total	400	400	400	1200

27. Market segmentation, part 2. The survey described in Exercise 21 also investigated the customers' marital status. Using the same definitions for *Shopping Frequency* as in that exercise, the calculations yielded the following table. Test an appropriate hypothesis for the relationship between marital status and the frequency of shopping at the same department store as in the other exercise, and state your conclusions. **LO ❸**

	Counts			
	Single	Widowed	Married	Total
Never/Hardly Ever	105	5	162	272
1–2 Times /Yr	53	15	161	229
3–4 Times/Yr	57	8	140	205
≥5 Times/Yr	72	15	207	294
Total	287	43	670	1000

28. Entrepreneurial executives, part 1. A leading CEO mentoring organization offers a program for chief executives, presidents, and business owners with a focus on developing entrepreneurial skills. Women and men executives who recently completed the program rated its value. Are perceptions of the program's value the same for men and women?

		Men	Women
	Excellent	3	9
Perceived Value	Good	11	12
	Average	14	8
	Marginal	9	2
	Poor	3	1

a) Will you test goodness-of-fit or homogeneity (independence)?
b) Write appropriate hypotheses.
c) Find the expected counts for each cell, and explain why the chi-square procedures are not appropriate for this table. **LO ❸**

29. Market segmentation, part 3. The survey described in Exercise 21 also investigated the customers' emphasis on *Quality* by asking them to respond to the statement, "For the same amount of money, I will generally buy one good item rather than several of lower price and quality." Using the same definitions for *Shopping Frequency* as in that exercise, the calculations yielded the following table. Test an appropriate hypothesis for the relationship between a customer's emphasis on *Quality* and the *Shopping Frequency* at this department store.

a) Select the appropriate procedure.
b) Check the assumptions.
c) State the hypotheses.

d) Test an appropriate hypothesis and state your results.
e) Interpret the meaning of the results and state a conclusion. **LO ❸**

	Counts			
	Disagree	Moderately Disagree/Agree	Agree	Total
Never/Hardly Ever	15	97	160	272
1–2 Times/Yr	28	107	94	229
3–5 Times/Yr	30	90	85	205
≥5 Times/Yr	35	140	119	294
Total	108	434	458	1000

30. Small business. The director of a small business development centre located in a mid-sized city is reviewing data about its clients. In particular, she's interested in examining if the distribution of business owners across the various stages of the business life cycle is the same for white-owned and visible-minority–owned businesses. The data are shown in the following table:

		White-Owned	Visible-Minority–Owned
	Planning	11	9
Stage in Business	Starting	14	11
	Managing	20	2
	Getting Out	15	1

a) Will you test goodness-of-fit or homogeneity (independence)?
b) Write the appropriate hypotheses.
c) Find the expected counts for each cell and explain why chi-square procedures are not appropriate for this table.
d) Create a new table by combining categories so that a chi-square procedure can be used.
e) With this change in the table, what has happened to the number of degrees of freedom?
f) Test your hypothesis about the two groups and state an appropriate conclusion. **LO ❸**

31. Entrepreneurial executives, part 2. In some situations where the expected counts are too small, as in Exercise 28, we can complete an analysis anyway. We can often proceed after combining cells in some way that makes sense and also produces a table in which the conditions are satisfied. Here's a new table displaying the same data, but combining "Marginal" and "Poor" into a new category called "Below Average."

		Men	Women
	Excellent	3	9
Perceived Value	Good	11	12
	Average	14	8
	Below Average	12	3

a) Find the expected counts for each cell in this new table, and explain why a chi-square procedure is now appropriate.
b) With this change in the table, what has happened to the number of degrees of freedom?
c) Test your hypothesis about the two groups and state an appropriate conclusion. **LO ❸**

32. *Titanic*, part 2. Newspaper headlines at the time and traditional wisdom in the succeeding decades have held that women and children escaped *Titanic* in greater proportion than men. Here's a table with the relevant data. Do you think survival was independent of whether the person was male or female? Defend your conclusion. **LO ❸**

	Female	Male	Total
Alive	343	367	710
Dead	127	1364	1491
Total	470	1731	2201

33. Industry sector and outsourcing, part 1. Many companies have chosen to outsource segments of their business to external providers in order to cut costs and improve quality and/or efficiencies. Common business segments that are outsourced include information technology (IT) and human resources (HR). The data below show the types of outsourcing decisions made (no outsourcing, IT only, HR only, both IT and HR) by a sample of companies from various industry sectors:

Industry Sector	No Outsourcing	IT Only	HR Only	Both IT and HR
Health Care	810	6429	4725	1127
Financial	263	1598	549	117
Industrial Goods	1031	1269	412	99
Consumer Goods	66	341	305	197

Do these data highlight significant differences in outsourcing by industry sector?

a) Select the appropriate procedure.
b) Check the assumptions.
c) State the hypotheses.
d) Test an appropriate hypothesis and state your results.
e) Interpret the meaning of the results and state a conclusion. **LO ❸**

34. Industry sector and outsourcing, part 2. Consider only the companies that have outsourced their IT and HR business segments. Do these data suggest significant differences between companies in the financial and industrial goods sectors with regard to their outsourcing decisions?

Industry Sector	IT Only	HR Only	Both IT and HR
Financial	1598	549	117
Industrial Goods	1269	412	99

a) Select the appropriate procedure.
b) Check the assumptions.
c) State the hypotheses.
d) Test an appropriate hypothesis and state your results.
e) Interpret the meaning of the results and state the conclusion. **LO ❸**

35. Management styles. Use the survey results in the table below to investigate differences in employee job satisfaction among organizations in the United States with different management styles.

Management Styles	Employee Job Satisfaction			
	Very Satisfied	Satisfied	Somewhat Satisfied	Not Satisfied
Exploitative Authoritarian	27	82	43	48
Benevolent Authoritarian	50	19	56	75
Laissez-Faire	52	88	26	34
Consultative	71	83	20	26
Participative	101	59	20	20

a) Select the appropriate procedure.
b) Check the assumptions.
c) State the hypotheses.
d) Test an appropriate hypothesis and state your results.
e) Interpret the meaning of the results and state a conclusion. **LO ❸**

36. Ranking companies. Every year, *Fortune* magazine lists the 100 best companies to work for, based on criteria such as pay, benefits, turnover rate, and diversity. In 2013, the top three were Google, SAS, and CHG Healthcare. Of the top 30, 11 experienced double-digit job growth (10% or more), 16 had single-digit growth (1% to 10%), 2 had no growth, and Google did not report. Of the bottom 30, only 5 experienced double-digit job growth, 16 had single-digit growth, and 9 had no growth or job loss. Ignoring Google, is job growth in the best of the best places to work different from job growth in the bottom of that elite list?

a) Select the appropriate procedure.
b) Check the assumptions.
c) State the hypotheses.
d) Test an appropriate hypothesis and state your results.
e) Interpret the meaning of the results and state a conclusion. **LO ❷**

37. Businesses and blogs. The Pew Internet & American Life Project routinely conducts surveys to gauge the impact of the internet and technology on daily life. A recent survey asked respondents if they read online journals or blogs, an internet activity of potential interest to many businesses. A subset of the data from this survey (*February–March 2007 Tracking Data Set*) shows responses to this question.

Test whether reading online journals or blogs is independent of generation. **LO ❸**

	Read Online Journal or Blog			
Generation	Yes, Yesterday	Yes, but Not Yesterday	No	Total
Gen Y (18–30)	29	35	62	126
Gen X (31–42)	12	34	137	183
Trailing Boomers (43–52)	15	34	132	181
Leading Boomers (53–61)	7	22	83	112
Matures (62+)	6	21	111	138
Total	69	146	525	740

38. Cybershopping. It has become more common for shoppers to "comparison shop" using the internet. Respondents to a Pew survey in 2013 who owned cell phones were asked whether they had, in the past 30 days, looked up the price of a product while they were in a store to see if they could get a better price somewhere else. Here is a table of their responses by income level:

	< $30K	$30K–$49.9K	$50K–$74.9K	>$75K
Yes	207	115	134	204
No	625	406	260	417

a) Is the frequency of comparison shopping on the internet independent of the income level of the respondent? Perform an appropriate chi-square test and state your conclusion.
b) Calculate and examine the standardized residuals. What pattern (if any) do they show that would be of interest to retailers concerned about cybershopping comparisons? **LO ❸**

39. Information systems. In a recent study of enterprise resource planning (ERP) system effectiveness, researchers asked companies about how they assessed the success of their ERP systems. Out of 335 manufacturing companies surveyed, they found that 201 used return on investment (ROI), 100 used reductions in inventory levels, 28 used improved data quality, and 6 used on-time delivery. In a survey of 200 service firms, 40 used ROI, 40 used inventory levels, 100 used improved data quality, and 20 used on-time delivery. Is there evidence that the measures used to assess ERP system effectiveness differ between service and manufacturing firms? Perform the appropriate test and state your conclusion. **LO ❸**

40. Online dating. According to recent research (www.nas.org), married couples who met their spouse through an online dating service may have a different divorce rate than those who met offline. (*Source:* From *Proceedings of the*

National Academy of Sciences of the United States of America. Copyright 2008 National Academy of Sciences. Reproduced by the permission of National Academy of Sciences.) The survey polled couples who married between 2005 and 2012. The baseline divorce rate (by 2013) for offline marriages in this cohort is 7.73%. The report gives the following divorce statistics according to the online dating service where the couple met:

Service	Couples (*n*)	Divorces/Separation
eHarmony	791	29
Match	775	58
Plenty of Fish	201	20
Yahoo	227	12
Small Sites	777	37

a) If the divorce rate were the same for these couples as for those who met offline, how many divorces would you expect for each group of couples?
b) To test whether these couples are different from offline couples, will you perform a goodness-of-fit test, a test of homogeneity, or a test of independence?
c) State the hypotheses.
d) Check the conditions.
e) Find the standardized residuals and the chi-square components. (*Hint:* Use a spreadsheet to perform the calculations.)
f) State the number of degrees of freedom and find χ^2 and the P-value.
g) State your conclusion.
h) Online dating services are a billion-dollar business in the United States. Does it change your conclusion to know that the study was funded by eHarmony? **LO ❶, ❷**

41. Crime in Canada. How should governments deal with crime? Should they focus on punishing criminals, or should they aim to prevent crime happening in the first place? It's important for government policy to take public opinion into account, so Angus Reid conducted a poll to determine public opinion on this issue. It surveyed 1013 Canadian adults and got the results in the following table in response to the question, "In your view, what should be the main priority for the federal government when it comes to crime?" (Note that "ATL" in the table is all of the Atlantic provinces combined.)

	BC	AB	MB/SK	ON	QC	ATL	Total
Preventing Crime	49%	47%	46%	49%	50%	61%	50%
Punishing Criminals	48%	50%	48%	43%	46%	38%	45%
Not Sure	3%	3%	6%	8%	4%	1%	5%

Assume that the sample surveyed is distributed among the provinces according to the percentage of the Canadian population in each province.

	BC	AB	MB/SK	ON	QC	ATL	Total
% Population	13%	11%	7%	39%	23%	7%	100%

Determine whether there is a significant difference among the provinces on this issue.

42. Large-format retail chains in Canada. A councillor in the Vancouver Island region of Tofino proposed "discouraging the future development and location of large-format retail chains and fast-food chains." Angus Reid Strategies interviewed 1003 adult Canadians to see whether they agreed with this proposal. (Note that "ATL" in the table is all of the Atlantic provinces combined.) The results are as follows:

	BC	AB	MB/SK	ON	QC	ATL	Total
Support	69%	67%	53%	66%	47%	62%	60%
Oppose	24%	15%	25%	14%	19%	11%	17%
Not Sure	7%	18%	22%	20%	34%	27%	23%

Assume that the sample surveyed is distributed among the provinces according to the percentage of the Canadian population in each province.

	BC	AB	MB/SK	ON	QC	ATL
% pop	13%	11%	7%	39%	23%	7%

Determine whether there is a significant difference among the provinces on this issue. LO ❸

43. Gender equality in Canada and internationally. Governments around the world implement measures to promote gender equality, and they need to know whether voters think they're being successful. Angus Reid Strategies conducted a survey in Canada, the United States, and the United Kingdom to provide information on this issue. A key question asked was, "From what you have seen, read, or heard, do you think women and men in [Canada, the United States, the United Kingdom] are paid the same salary when working the same job?" The results are given in the table at the bottom of this page.

a) In Canada, is there a difference between the responses of men and women to this question? Assume the respondents are split 50/50 between men and women.

b) Is there a difference among the three countries for the "total" responses (i.e., men plus women) to this question? LO ❸

44. Canadians and their decks. In a survey of 616 Canadian homeowners who have a wooden deck attached to their homes, Ipsos Reid found a substantial percentage had never inspected their decks for safety, 40% say they never really think about whether their deck is safe, and 11% say their deck "could collapse at any minute." Interest in prefabricated materials for decks that are made of nondegradable, safer, and maintenance-free materials is high. The results for different parts of Canada are given in the table and are of considerable interest to those selling prefabricated decks, since 62% of Canadian homeowners have a deck. (Note that "ATL" in the table is all of the Atlantic provinces combined.)

	BC	AB	MB/SK	ON	QC	ATL
Never inspected	25%	20%	18%	29%	16%	28%
Interested in prefabrication	84%	83%	77%	69%	81%	76%
Percent of population	13%	11%	7%	39%	23%	7%

Is there a difference among the provinces on these issues:

a) For inspection?

b) For prefabrication?

c) If there is a difference significant at the 95% level, identify which province contributes most to that difference and in what way. LO ❶, ❸

❶ **45. Nordion of Ottawa.** Nordion has developed a medical device that inserts a radioisotope inside a patient's liver for the treatment of liver cancer. About half of the world's liver cancer patients are in China, and Nordion is planning to market the technology there, using methods that include making presentations at medical conferences. Suppose that a survey of 344 randomly selected oncologists from three cities at such a conference gave the following responses to the question of usefulness of the device:

	Shanghai	Beijing	Guangzhou	Total
Very useful	89	34	42	165
Acceptable	41	27	41	109
Too costly	31	20	19	70
Total	161	81	102	344

Is there a difference among the cities as to the acceptability of the device at the 95% significance level? LO ❸

	Canada			U.S.			U.K.		
No. of Respondents	1004			1005			2001		
	Total	Male	Female	Total	Male	Female	Total	Male	Female
Yes, They Are	19%	26%	12%	17%	23%	10%	20%	30%	11%
No, They Are Not	71%	66%	76%	69%	61%	76%	65%	55%	74%
Not Sure	10%	8%	11%	14%	16%	14%	15%	15%	15%

Scale of Importance

Not at all	Not very	No Opinion	Some-what	Extremely
1	2	3	4	5
1	2	3	4	5
1	2	3		5
1	2	3		5
1	2	3		5
1	2		4	5
1	2		4	5
1	2		4	5
1	2	3	4	5

Karen Roach/Shutterstock

17

Nonparametric Methods

LEARNING OBJECTIVES

In this chapter we show you how to recognize the circumstances in which nonparametric tests are appropriate and give a number of examples. After reading and studying this chapter, you should be able to:

❶ Recognize which nonparametric tests can be used in given business situations, together with their advantages and disadvantages

❷ Perform nonparametric tests on one, two, or more groups

❸ Perform nonparametric tests to identify the degree of relationship between two variables

Ipsos Canada

Ipsos Canada is a curious company. It is curious about you and me, why we value the brands we purchase, and how we fit into our ever-changing society. It tests our response to advertising, measures our opinions on political and other issues, and hence helps its corporate clients develop long-term relationships with us as customers. And by now you've probably guessed that it uses a lot of surveys and statistical analysis so that its advice to its clients is based on a factual foundation.

Ipsos conducts its own surveys, analyzes the results, and sells the reports. Companies that purchase those reports know that their competitors can also purchase the same information. Ipsos therefore offers its clients the opportunity to add their own proprietary questions to a survey, the results of which will be disclosed only to the company paying for the question. It charges $1000 to $2000 per question. Some companies commission Ipsos to conduct a survey on their behalf so that none of the results will be available to their competitors.

To do all this requires a lot of surveys, with different styles of questions. Some questions elicit a numeric response—for example, "How many times during the past year did you use an indoor tanning bed?" Another group of questions involve a "scale" of responses—for example, "Over the past five years, do you believe the Newfoundland fishing industry has declined significantly, declined moderately, improved moderately, or improved significantly?" The statisticians at Ipsos Canada use different statistical techniques to analyze different types of responses.

ROADMAP FOR STATISTICAL INFERENCE					
Number of Variables	Objective	Large Sample or Normal Population		Small Sample and Non-normal Population or Non-numeric Data	
		Chapter	Parametric Method	Chapter	Nonparametric Method
1	Calculate confidence interval for a proportion	11			
1	Compare a proportion with a given value	12	z-test		
1	Calculate a confidence interval for a mean and compare it with a given value	13	t-test	17.2	Wilcoxon Signed-Rank Test
2	Compare two proportions	12.8	z-test		
2	Compare two means for independent samples	14.1–14.5	t-test	17.4, 17.5	Wilcoxon Rank-Sum (Mann-Whitney) Test Tukey's Quick Test
2	Compare two means for paired samples	14.6, 14.7	Paired t-test	17.2	Wilcoxon Signed-Rank Test
≥3	Compare multiple means	15	ANOVA: ANalysis Of VAriance	17.3 17.6	Friedman Test Kruskal-Wallis Test
≥3	Compare multiple counts (proportions)	16	χ^2 test		
2	Investigate the relationship between two variables	18	Correlation Regression	17.7, 17.8	Kendall's tau Spearman's rho
≥3	Investigate the relationship between multiple variables	20	Multiple Regression		

LO❶ 17.1 Data Types for Nonparametric Tests

Numeric Data

The Canadian Cancer Society commissioned Ipsos Canada to survey Ontario youth about the use of indoor tanning beds. From a sample of 1476 youth aged 12 to 17, it found that, on average, a tanner used a bed 10 times per year. The Cancer Society may well be interested in what this implies about the average usage of tanning beds by youth *throughout* Ontario. For instance, does it imply that the average usage exceeds nine times per year? Ipsos could answer this question using the one-sample *t*-test (see Chapter 13), but one of the conditions for this test is that the sample comes from a Normally distributed population. Suppose, however, that when we draw a histogram of the sample we find that it's very skewed. There may well be a few people who use tanning beds several times a week, while the vast majority of people use them much less than nine times per year. A skewed distribution is particularly troublesome if the sample size is small, for instance if we wanted to focus on just part of our sample, say, people aged 16 or people living in Guelph. In these cases, where the conditions for a *t*-test aren't satisfied, we can use the methods described in this chapter: nonparametric tests.

In summary, the main situation for using **nonparametric methods** for numeric data is when we have a small sample or we suspect that the population isn't Normally distributed.

Ordinal Data

A 2010 online survey of 817 Ontario adults, conducted by Ipsos Canada on behalf of the Responsible Gambling Council, included the question: "Do you agree that 'a lot more is being done today to prevent problem gambling compared to five years ago'?" The responses were as follows:

11%	Agree strongly
51%	Agree somewhat
28%	Disagree somewhat
10%	Disagree strongly

This is an example of a survey question with a "scale" response, in which the respondent chooses one option from an ordered list of options. We're not trying to estimate any quantitative population *parameter* when we ask this question. We therefore use "nonparametric" statistics (the subject of this chapter) to analyze the responses.

You might think of these responses as "grading" how much is being done to prevent problem gambling: 11% of people give an A, 51% give a B, etc. In this example there are only four possible grades, and more could be used if required. A "Likert" scale (named after Rensis Likert, who demonstrated the value of such scales for his Ph.D. in psychology) has typically five or seven categories.

Here's an example of a survey question using a Likert scale: "Thinking about your recent car rental experience, would you say that you were

- very satisfied
- satisfied
- neither satisfied nor dissatisfied
- dissatisfied, or
- very dissatisfied?"

Data recorded on a *Likert scale* such as this can be quite useful, but it has one major disadvantage: It isn't numeric. Specifically, although we can be reasonably sure that a "satisfied" response is more favourable than a "neither" response, we can't tell whether the difference between "very satisfied" and "satisfied" is the same, in any sense, as the difference between "dissatisfied" and "very dissatisfied."

In order to figure out which car rental location provides the most customer satisfaction, we should be very cautious if we want to find a difference in means or compare boxplots.

In fact, we can be reasonably certain that there'll be an occasional customer whose dissatisfaction with his or her experience will be quite extreme and (we hope) some whose joy with their rental experience exceeds all bounds. Our questionnaire can't record such extreme responses. All we really have to go on is an ordering or ranking of customer opinion without a way of measuring numerically the actual level of customer satisfaction.

When to Use Nonparametric Methods

In this chapter, we illustrate nonparametric methods in two situations:

1. We start with numeric data and convert it to ranks in order to perform the test, for example, in the Wilcoxon signed-rank test.
2. We start with ranked data and perform the test using those ranks, for example, in the Wilcoxon rank-sum test.

		Parametric Test	Nonparametric Test
Conditions for Use		Normally distributed data "Large" sample size	Some tests require data to be symmetrically distributed.
Advantages		High power	Wide applicability

Number of Samples	Type of Samples		
1		*t*-test (see Chapter 13)	Wilcoxon Signed-Rank Test
2	Paired	*t*-test (see Chapter 14)	Wilcoxon Signed-Rank Test
3	One block variable	ANOVA (see Chapter 15)	Friedman Test
2	Independent	*t*-test (see Chapter 14)	Wilcoxon Rank-Sum (Mann-Whitney) Test Tukey's Quick Test
3	Independent	ANOVA (see Chapter 15)	Kruskal-Wallis Test

Table 17.1   The situations in which each test should be used.

In the case of numeric data, we could use a parametric test as long as the data are Normally distributed and the sample size is "large." If those conditions don't apply, we use a nonparametric test. Table 17.1 summarizes which test to use in each situation.

LO❷ 17.2 The Wilcoxon Signed-Rank Test

Paired Data

Frank Wilcoxon (1892–1965) was a statistician and chemist who worked primarily in industry. During his career he published more than 70 papers. Perhaps the best known is a paper from 1945 in which he proposed the two tests bearing his name that are discussed in this chapter.

Companies that devise tests for students (e.g., for university applications) and for professional certification have been looking to online testing as a way to increase efficiency, save money, and provide results to test-takers more rapidly. But there's a natural concern about whether someone taking a test at a computer screen will achieve the same result as he or she would taking the test with pencil and paper.

A testing company devised an experiment to investigate the problem. Researchers randomly assigned subjects to take one of two tests (form A or form B) either electronically or with pencil and paper. Subjects then took the *other* test using the other method. The two forms had been designed to be equivalent in difficulty, but nevertheless, that equivalence was checked as part of the experiment. Our concern is whether subjects did equally well with each testing method.

We have two test scores for each subject. Clearly these are paired, given that they're two scores from the same subject. How can we tell whether there's a difference in methods? From Chapter 14, we could use a paired *t*-test, subject to the condition that the histogram of the differences in the scores is approximately Normal. In our case, however, the data in Table 17.2 result in Figure 17.1, which clearly shows that the histogram has multiple modes and is nowhere near Normally distributed. In this case the *t*-test is invalid and we use a nonparametric test instead. The **Wilcoxon signed-rank test** is designed for comparing paired data of this type. It's based on ranks, and hence tests the null hypothesis that the median of the differences is zero.

Subject	Online	Paper	Difference
1	13	14	−1
2	13	10	3
3	8	16	−8
4	14	15	−1
5	11	18	−7
6	11	14	−3
7	12	9	3
8	12	12	0
9	16	16	0
10	14	7	7
11	13	6	7
12	13	11	2
13	17	15	2
14	13	11	2
15	14	6	8
16	9	9	0
17	9	15	−6
18	15	14	1
19	11	18	−7
20	10	10	2

Table 17.2   Test scores for two testing methods.

First find the pairwise difference for each subject. Then set aside any ties (zero differences) and, using the new count of cases, rank the absolute values of the differences. Organize the differences in order of their absolute values. When the absolute values are the same, as in 1, 2 and 3, the rank is calculated as the average of the order: For 1, 2 and 3, the rank is $(1 + 2 + 3)/3 = 2$.

Order	Difference	Rank
1	−1	2
2	−1	2
3	1	2
4	2	5.5
5	2	5.5
6	2	5.5
7	2	5.5
8	3	9
9	−3	9
10	3	9
11	−6	11
12	7	13.5
13	7	13.5
14	−7	13.5
15	−7	13.5
16	8	16.5
17	−8	16.5

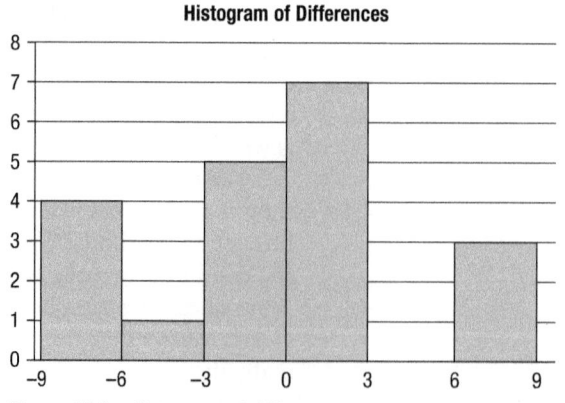

Figure 17.1   Histogram of differences between test scores.

> **Wilcoxon signed-rank test**
>
> When the assumptions are satisfied, we can test whether the median M_d of the differences between the two populations (online and paper) is zero.
>
> $H_0: M_d = 0$
> $H_A: M_d \neq 0$ (two-tailed test)
> or
> $H_A: M_d > 0$ (one-tailed test)
> or
> $H_A: M_d < 0$ (one-tailed test)

Under the null hypothesis that the two testing methods are the same, we'd expect these ranks to appear about equally between the two groups of positive and negative differences. We sum up the ranks for all the positive differences (T^+) and for all the negative differences (T^-).

$$T^+ = 2 + 5.5 + 5.5 + 5.5 + 5.5 + 9 + 9 + 13.5 + 13.5 + 16.5 = 85.5$$

$$T^- = 2 + 2 + 9 + 11 + 13.5 + 13.5 + 16.5 = 67.5$$

We concentrate on the smaller of these two totals and call it $T = 67.5$. This is our test statistic. A table of critical values for the statistic will tell us if it's sufficiently small to reject the null hypothesis. Consulting Table W2 in Appendix B, we see that critical values for $n = 17$ are all substantially smaller than 67.5, so we can't reject the null hypothesis.

Assumptions and Conditions

- **Independence Assumption:** As with our previous consideration of paired data in Chapter 14, the primary assumption is that the data are appropriately paired and the subjects are randomly selected. You can't just match up values arbitrarily. There's no condition to check here; you just have to think it through.
- **Symmetry Assumption:** We also need to assume that the distributions of the test scores using the two different methods are symmetric. Histograms indicate that this is approximately true in the example with the test scores.

When to Use the Wilcoxon Signed-Rank Test

We must have paired data for this test to be appropriate, for instance, the results about *the same subjects* under two different conditions, as in the example above.

The test requires numeric data, since we need to calculate differences between the results of the subjects in the two different situations. If we start with non-numeric data, such as results from a Likert scale survey question, then it needs to be converted into a numeric form. For instance, the top level of the Likert scale could be converted to 1, the second level to 2, etc. We can only do this if we have some reason to think that the responses in the Likert scale are equally spaced (e.g., "very satisfied" is the same amount above "satisfied" as "very dissatisfied" is below "dissatisfied").

The test is appropriate when the Normality assumptions of parametric statistics don't apply, and particularly when we have a small sample. Otherwise, a paired t-test will be more powerful than the Wilcoxon signed-rank test.

FOR EXAMPLE   Paired data for flexible work scheduling

An employer experimented with a flexible four-day work week. For a year, the employer recorded the mileage driven by 11 field workers on an ordinary five-day work week. Then it changed to a flexible four-day work week and recorded mileage for another year. The data are in the first 3 columns of the following table:

Name	5-Day Mileage	4-Day Mileage	Difference	Rank of absolute differences
Jeff	2798	2914	−116	2
Betty	7724	6112	1612	8
Roger	7505	6177	1328	7
Tom	838	1102	−264	3
Aimee	4592	3281	1311	6
Greg	8107	4997	3110	11
Larry G.	1228	1695	−467	5
Tad	8718	6606	2112	10
Larry M.	1097	1063	34	1
Leslie	8089	6392	1697	9
Lee	3807	3362	445	4

QUESTION   Do flexible schedules reduce mileage?

ANSWER   These data are clearly paired, and we have no particular reason to assume Normal distributions. We can use a Wilcoxon signed-rank test to compare the mileages.

H_0: Difference in mileage is zero, i.e., $M_d = 0$.

H_A: Difference in mileage is positive, i.e., $M_d > 0$.

The differences and the ranks of their absolute values are included in the above table.

The total of the positive ranks is $1+4+6+7+8+9+10+11 = 56$.

The total of the negative ranks is $2+3+5 = 10$.

For $n = 11$, Table W2 of Appendix B shows that 10 is less than the critical value (11) for a one-tailed test with $\alpha = 0.025$.

We can therefore conclude that the 4-day work week has reduced mileage at this level of significance.

GUIDED EXAMPLE   Do Hormones Boost Profits?

"Hormones may boost profits," read a headline in *The Globe and Mail*. Is this true? To examine the question, Canadian researcher John Coates took saliva samples in the morning, twice a day for eight days, from 17 men working on a midsize London trading floor (trading a wide range of assets, with largest exposure to German interest rate futures), and classified each trader according to whether his testosterone level was high or low on that day (compared with the trader's median over the period). High-testosterone days differed from trader to trader, and high days differed from low days on average by 25% in testosterone level. Coates also recorded the profits or losses (P&L) in pounds sterling of each trader from 11 a.m.–4 p.m. daily. (**Source:** Coates, J. M., & Herbert, J. [2008]. *Proceedings of the National Academy of Sciences, 105*, 6167–6172.)

PLAN **Setup** State the objectives. Check the assumptions and conditions.	We want to perform a test to determine if there's evidence of a testosterone effect on traders' daily profits. For each trader, we've recorded a profit (or loss) average for his high-testosterone days (testosterone level above his own median) during this eight-day period, and another profit average for his low-testosterone days during this eight-day period.
Hypotheses State the null and alternative hypotheses.	H_0: $M_d = 0$, i.e., the median of the differences between profits on the high-testosterone days and the low-testosterone days is zero.
	H_A: $M_d \neq 0$, i.e., the median of the differences between profits on the high-testosterone days and the low-testosterone days is not zero.
Model Think about the assumptions and check any conditions.	The data are paired. The researcher took an average on both high- and low-testosterone days for the same trader, so each trader gives us paired responses.
	It's reasonable to assume that the traders are independent of each other, although this is not a random sample of traders.
	We're assuming that the distributions of profits are symmetric. We have no evidence for or against this assumption, but it seems reasonable.
	Coates provided the following data from his study. We've added the pairwise differences.

Trader	P & L (£) with Low Testosterone	P & L (£) with High Testosterone	Difference
1	127	−63	−190
2	113	725	612
3	−2	−5	−3
4	−292	1780	2072
5	−98	262	360
6	−1308	1401	2709
7	88	2092	2004
8	361	887	526
9	−700	2500	3200
10	143	82	−61
11	1448	1547	99
12	1625	7000	5375
13	−127	38	165
14	−2066	1941	4007
15	183	268	85
16	483	513	30
17	−115	−4	111

Select a method.	The differences include some extraordinarily large values. A nonparametric method would be more appropriate for these data. We'll use a Wilcoxon signed-rank test.

(continued)

DO

Mechanics Compute the difference for each trader (in the previous table). Throw out any zero differences.

List the differences in order of magnitude. Sum the ranks for either the positive or the negative differences. Clearly the latter will be smaller here, so we compute that rank sum.

Determine if T differs significantly from its expectation under the null by using either the table of exact critical values or the Normal approximation (if appropriate).

n is the number of pairs = number of traders = 17

Here are the differences, in order of magnitude, with ranks shown underneath:

−3	30	−61	85	99	111	165	−190	360
1	2	3	4	5	6	7	8	9

526	612	2004	2072	2709	3200	4007	5375
10	11	12	13	14	15	16	17

The sum of the ranks for negative differences is $1 + 3 + 8 = 12$. All the ranks must add up to $n(n + 1)/2$; therefore, a quick way to calculate the sum of the ranks for the positive differences is $17(18)/2 − 12 = 141$. We use the smaller of 12 and 141, which is 12.

According to a table of critical values (Table W2 in Appendix B) for $n = 17$, the value 12 is less than any of the critical values listed.

Since this is a two-tailed test, we can reject the null hypothesis at the 99% level.

REPORT

Conclusion State the conclusion in the context of the problem.

MEMO

Re: Hormones and Trading
We investigated whether testosterone levels have a measurable effect on the success of traders. We found that there was a statistically significant difference: When traders' testosterone levels were higher, their profits were higher.

Single Sample

We can also use the Wilcoxon signed-rank test when we have a single sample of data. For instance, suppose the Canadian Cancer Society wants to know whether the usage of tanning beds by 16-year-olds in Guelph, Ontario, is 10 times per year. Survey results from 16 subjects indicate the usage as follows:

6	6	7	7	7	7	9	10	10	12	13	14	14	15	15	15

We could use a one-sample t-test (as described in Chapter 13), subject to the condition that the population is Normally distributed. The histogram in Figure 17.2

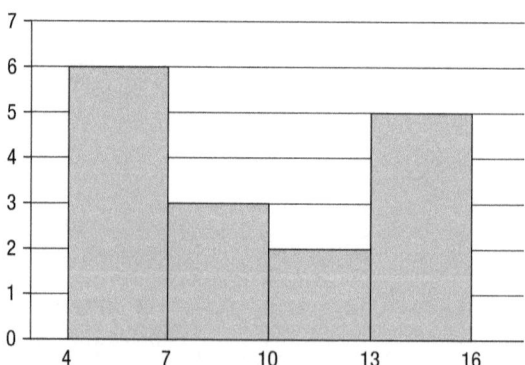

Figure 17.2   Histogram of the annual usage of tanning beds in Guelph by 16-year-olds.

shows that the sample data are very far from Normally distributed, so the t-test cannot be used. Instead, we use the Wilcoxon signed-rank test.

H_0: The median annual usage of tanning beds is 10, i.e., M = 10.
H_A: The median annual usage of tanning beds is not 10, i.e., M ≠ 10.

We subtract 10 from each of our data values to create some values that are negative and others that are positive:

| −4 | −4 | −3 | −3 | −3 | −3 | −1 | 0 | 0 | 2 | 3 | 4 | 4 | 5 | 5 | 5 |

We then apply the signed-rank test to these values:

Order	1	2	3	4	5	6	7	8	9	10	11	12	13	14
Value	−1	2	3	−3	−3	−3	−3	−4	−4	4	4	5	5	5
Rank	1	2	5	5	5	5	5	9.5	9.5	9.5	9.5	13	13	13

$$T^+ = 2 + 5 + 9.5 + 9.5 + 13 + 13 + 13 = 65$$
$$T^- = 1 + 5 + 5 + 5 + 5 + 9.5 + 9.5 = 40$$

The smaller of these two values is 40, and the number of data points is 14. Table W2 in Appendix B indicates that critical values for $n = 14$ are all lower than 40. We can't therefore reject the null hypothesis that the median annual usage of tanning beds is 10.

LO❷ 17.3 Friedman Test for a Randomized Block Design

The Wilcoxon signed-rank test is fine for comparing paired data. But what if we have more groups of data than just two? Enter the Friedman test, which is designed to figure out whether there's any difference among multiple groups. It doesn't tell us which group differs from the others, but it does tell us whether all the groups have the same distribution. If we had a lot of Normally distributed data, we could use analysis of variance (ANOVA, as described in Chapter 15) to do the same job. However, when the conditions for ANOVA aren't satisfied, we use the Friedman test.

Micky Parker, the owner of Mick's Comicks, a store that deals in collector's comic books and memorabilia, wondered what method to use to attract customers into his store. He decided to compare three methods:

- Coupons distributed on the street by a model dressed as a superhero
- A sale announced by a large sign in the window
- Music from movies based on comics played loud enough to be heard in the street

Micky reasons that customer traffic is different in the morning, in the afternoon, and in the evening, so he decides to block on time of day. On three weekdays, he randomly decides which method to use for each time of day. After three days, his customer counts look like this:

Block		Coupons	Sale	Music
	Morning	9	12	2
	Afternoon	5	10	4
	Evening	7	11	1

Treatment spans Coupons, Sale, Music.

The method we'll use for these data is the Friedman test. Again, we need to convert to ranks, but now we *rank separately within each block*, yielding the following ranks (in parentheses):

Friedman Test
When the assumptions are satisfied, we can test whether there's a difference among multiple samples.
H_0: The samples come from the same distribution.
H_A: At least one of the samples comes from a distribution that is shifted up or down relative to one of the others

		Treatment		
		Coupons	**Sale**	**Music**
Block	Morning	9(2)	12(3)	2(1)
	Afternoon	5(2)	10(3)	4(1)
	Evening	7(2)	11(3)	1(1)
	Rank Sums	6	9	3

We wish to test for significant variation among the treatment rank sums. The Friedman statistic is

$$F = \frac{12}{bt(t+1)}\sum_{i=1}^{t} T_i^2 - 3b(t+1),$$

where T_i are the rank sums for the various treatments (6, 9, 3 in our example), b is the number of blocks, and t is the number of treatments.

We reject H_0: All treatments are identical, at the desired significance level if

$$F > \chi^2$$

with degrees of freedom $= t - 1$

This is an approximate result. There are tables of exact critical values available for small sample sizes, but this approximation works well for most cases.

Assumptions and Conditions

There are two basic assumptions required for the application of the Friedman test:

- **Independence Assumption:** The blocks are independent.
- **Interaction Assumption:** There is no interaction between blocks and treatments.

When to Use the Friedman Test

We use the Friedman test if we have more than two groups to compare. The test is based on ranks, so the data don't need to be numeric. If they are numeric, as in the example above, they're first converted to ranks.

Because the test is based on ranks, it is distribution-free, meaning that it can be used when the Normality assumptions of parametric statistics don't apply.

FOR EXAMPLE   **Friedman test: Comparing more than two marketing methods**

QUESTION   Is there a difference among the three methods of attracting customers to Mick's Comics according to the data presented in this section?

ANSWER   We first formulate our hypotheses:

H_0: There is no difference in the distribution of the number of customers attracted by the three methods.

H_A: One of the methods attracts a distribution of customers that is shifted higher or lower than the other methods.

In our case we have three treatments: $t = 3$ and three blocks: $b = 3$.

Therefore $F = \dfrac{12}{3 \times 3 \times 4}(6^2 + 9^2 + 3^2) - 3 \times 3 \times 4 = 6.$

> For a confidence level $\alpha = 0.05$ and df $= 2$, the χ^2 table gives $\chi^2 = 5.991$.
>
> Therefore $F > \chi^2$, and we conclude that we can reject the null hypothesis. In other words, there's a significant difference among the methods used to attract customers.

LO❷ **17.4**

The Wilcoxon Rank-Sum Test (or, the Mann-Whitney Test)

This test goes under two names, "Wilcoxon rank-sum" and "Mann-Whitney," since it was developed near simultaneously by those statisticians. It's used to compare two samples that are independent of each other, whereas the Wilcoxon signed-rank test applies to two paired samples. We'll illustrate it first using ordinal data, with grades we can rank, and then in a Guided Example with numeric data that we convert into ranks in order to use the test. If our numeric data satisfied the conditions for using the *t*-test, that would be a more powerful test to use. If not, or if we have only ordinal data or rankings, then we use the Wilcoxon rank-sum test, also known as the Mann-Whitney test.

Let's first take the example of a car rental company that records customer satisfaction for two rental locations using grades from A+ to D− (see Table 17.3).

We could treat these as categorical data, total up the number of customers at each location that gave each grade, and then use a chi-square test (from Chapter 16). However, categorical data lose the ordering that is implicit in the grades, and we have far too little data for the chi-square test anyway.

We can get a clearer understanding of our customers' opinions if we *rank* these values. To rank values, all we need to do is put them in order. It doesn't really matter whether we assign rank "1" to the lowest value and count up or assign rank "1" to the highest value and count down—but we should make clear which we choose. We can rank any quantitative values. Ranks have the additional advantage that we can assign them even if we have no more than a clear ordering, as we do here (Table 17.4).

WHO	Rental car customers
WHAT	Satisfaction grades
WHEN	2017
WHERE	Airport & Main Street
WHY	Investigation of whether one location gives more satisfaction than the other

Airport	Main Street
C+	B
B−	C
A−	D−
D+	B+
A+	C+
B+	

Table 17.3 Customer grades for two car rental sites.

Airport	Rank	Main Street	Rank
C+	4.5	B	7
B−	6	C	3
A−	10	D−	1
D+	2	B+	8.5
A+	11	C+	4.5
B+	8.5		

Table 17.4 Customer grades with their ranks.

We assign rank 1 to the lowest grade—here a D−. If there are any ties, we simply give all the values that are tied the *average* rank they're at. In this example, there are two C+ grades and two B+ grades, so those get ranks of 4.5 (averaging 4 and 5) and 8.5, respectively.

To assign these ranks, all we did was put all the grades in order (Table 17.5):

D−	D+	C	C+	C+	B−	B	B+	B+	A−	A+
1	2	3	4.5	4.5	6	7	8.5	8.5	10.5	11

Table 17.5 All the grades in order. Red indicates the Main Street location.

Because they're "grades," they have no numeric value, but they do have a clear order. The ranks in Table 17.5 order all the grades from the worst (a D−, assigned rank 1) to the best (an A+, assigned rank 11).

Such a ranking can be used whenever we have data that can be placed in order. Of course, that includes data that have numeric values as well as grades that tell us no more than the order.

Now that we've ranked the data, let's see how we can use the ranking to assess whether satisfaction levels differ between these two locations. In formal terms, the manager of the car rental company wants to test a hypothesis:

H_0: The locations have the same distribution of satisfaction among customers.

vs.

H_A: One location has a distribution of customer satisfaction that is shifted higher or lower than the other location.

How can we perform such a test? The key is that we'll give up an aspect of hypothesis testing that we've maintained for other inference methods, in which a null hypothesis specified a parameter and a null value for that parameter. The parameter was a number that specified something about the distribution of values in a population. Thus, for example, we might hypothesize a value for a mean or for a difference between two means. The parameters would be the underlying population mean or the means of the two populations from which two samples had been drawn.

But with only grades, no parameters are available. That's why we call the methods in this chapter "*non*parametric." Indeed, it might be hard to say just exactly what it would mean for customers to be more satisfied at one location compared with the other. If *all* the grades for one location were better than the grades for the other, we'd be pretty sure which was the better one. That would show up clearly when we ranked the grades together. And if the grades alternated from one location to the other when we put them all in order, we'd probably conclude that there wasn't much difference.

So we need a statistic that measures where the data stand between the extremes of clearly favouring one site and showing no difference between them.

We'll start by computing the sum of the ranks (called the *rank sums*) in each group. In general, we can call them T_1 and T_2, but it helps to name them. In the example, $T_{\text{Airport}} = 42$ and $T_{\text{Main Street}} = 24$.

The sum of all the ranks for 11 customers, 1 to 11, is $1 + 2 + 3 + \cdots + 11 = 66$. There's a formula for this: The sum of the first n integers 1, 2, and up to n is equal to $n(n + 1)/2$. So $T_{\text{Airport}} + T_{\text{Main Street}} = 66$ and, in general, if you know one rank sum, the other is completely determined.

We don't need to compare rank sums with each other. The rank sum for one of the groups tells the whole story. So we can pick one rank sum and ask whether this is unusually big or small. The conventional choice is to pick the rank sum that has the smaller sample. That's the Main Street location in this example.

What do we know about this rank sum? It could be as small as $1 + 2 + 3 + 4 + 5 = 15$ or as big as $11 + 10 + 9 + 8 + 7 = 45$. You might guess that its expectation (under H_0) would be right in the middle of these two values—that is, equal to 30—and you'd be right. Under the null hypothesis that the two groups are drawn from the same population, the rankings in either sample are a random selection from all the rankings, so each sample should, on average, receive its fair share of the ranks. The Main Street sample has 5 of the 11 grades, so its expected rank sum is 5/11 of 66, the sum of all the ranks. That's 30.

So we know that the rank sum of 24, which we have for the Main Street location, is a bit low. But to test the hypothesis we must determine whether it's unusually low. That is, if H_0 were true, how likely would we be to find a rank sum of 24 or less for a comparison like this? That probability would be a P-value because it gives the probability of observing the statistic value we've observed—or something more extreme—if the null hypothesis were true.

When dealing with ranks rather than with numeric values, there are only so many possibilities. In particular, we can consider *all possible* rankings. Under the null hypothesis, each of them is equally likely. So we can calculate what fraction of them would give rank sums less than 24. Fortunately, the "we" here is the computer, which does the work for us. The results are in Table W1 in Appendix B. The "W" comes from the name of this test: the **Wilcoxon rank-sum test**, or sometimes the **Mann-Whitney test**.[1] The table gives critical values for the rank sum of the sample with fewer observations. The rank sum for the smaller sample here is 24. From the table, for samples of sizes five and six, the closest value to 24 is 20.4 and the probability beyond that is 0.05. The manager has chosen a two-sided alternative hypothesis, so we'll double that value and conclude that the probability of a difference this great is more than 0.10. We wouldn't reject the null hypothesis, so we can't conclude that there's a significant difference in customer satisfaction between these two sites.

Using the Central Limit Theorem for Larger Groups

Table W1 in Appendix B only goes as far as groups of 10. What can we do for larger groups? The Central Limit Theorem comes to the rescue. We know from the CLT that means tend to be Normally distributed as the sample size grows, and that this happens more quickly for well-behaved, unimodal population distributions with no skewness or outliers. If a mean has a Normal sampling distribution, then so does the sum of the values before dividing by n. (After all, n is a constant and can't change the distribution.) So when we add up the ranks, that rank sum will tend toward a Normal sampling distribution as the number of ranks in the sum grows. And we know that the ranks can't be badly distributed. After all, under the null hypothesis they're uniformly distributed, so there are no outliers or long tails. A sum of even 10 ranks has a sampling distribution that's close enough to Normal for our purposes. All we need to know is the mean and standard deviation, and we can find those easily:

For groups one and two, with corresponding rank sums, T_1 and T_2,

$$\mathrm{E}(T_i) = n_i(n_1 + n_2 + 1)/2 \text{ and } Var(T_i) = n_1 n_2 (n_1 + n_2 + 1)/12 \; [\, i = 1 \text{ or } 2 \,].$$

So we can find a P-value directly from the Normal tables (or with the 68-95-99.7 Rule).

Assumptions and Conditions

Nonparametric methods require no assumptions about distributions. However, we still have some assumptions about the structure of the data:

- **Independence Assumption:** The sampled observations are independent. Appropriate randomization in data collection is one way to accomplish this.
- **Independent Groups Assumption:** The two groups must be independent of each other.

The hypotheses don't have numerical values in them, since it's a feature of the method that it doesn't test properties of any population parameter. That's what makes it a *nonparametric* method.

Wilcoxon rank-sum test

When the assumptions are satisfied, we can test:

H_0: The two samples are from the same distribution.

vs.

H_A: The two samples are from distributions that are shifted relative to each other.

Calculate T = the rank sum for the smaller sample. Then estimate the P-value using tables of critical values or the Normal approximation, if either sample size is off the table.

---

[1]Frank Wilcoxon first proposed this test to compare equal-size groups. H. B. Mann and D. R. Whitney extended it to work with groups of unequal size.

FOR EXAMPLE **Comparing two groups of commercial properties**

QUESTION A database contains sample data on commercial properties in a large city. One variable available for those properties is a "quality" ranking into one of six categories, with 1 as the "best" and 6 as the "worst." A realtor wanted to know how that quality index related to the "extras" available, such as food service on site, an atrium, or a fitness centre. He grouped the properties into two categories: those that had at least one of these extras and those that had no extras. How can he use a nonparametric method to compare the quality rankings of the two groups?

ANSWER To compare the quality rankings for these two groups, he used the Mann-Whitney or Wilcoxon rank-sum test. The Minitab results are typical of those from a statistics package:

$W \neq 21642.5$

Test of Extras = No Extras vs. Extras not = No Extras is significant at 0.0008.

The realtor concluded that these extras might be an effective quick method of judging the quality of commercial properties in this city.

When to Use the Wilcoxon Rank-Sum Test

The Wilcoxon test applies to situations, such as the customer-provided grades in our example, in which we aren't working with numeric data. Data consisting only of grades or ordered categories are one example. We might also choose to replace numeric values with their ranks because we fear there may be extreme outliers in the data. If the data were numeric and came from approximately Normal distributions, we could alternatively use a two-sample t-test to compare the means between two groups.

The other situation in which this test is useful is where the data are numeric but we have a small sample or we suspect that the Normality assumptions of parametric statistics aren't appropriate. In these cases the Wilcoxon rank-sum test provides a distribution-free alternative to parametric methods like t-tests.

The Wilcoxon test makes no assumptions about the distribution of the data or the errors. That frees us from checking the corresponding assumptions. But what do we pay for these advantages? Statisticians evaluate statistical methods in terms of their *power*: the ability of the test to reject a false null hypothesis. When it's possible to perform both tests (because we have numeric measurements), reducing the data to ranks and using the Wilcoxon test will have about 95% of the power of a corresponding two-sample t-test. And, as we've seen, outliers are often interesting in their own right. An analysis that simply ignores them may miss an important fact or instance.

GUIDED EXAMPLE **Buying from a Friend**

The question of interest is whether there's a difference between what people tend to offer to a friend and what they would offer to a stranger. Subjects were randomly assigned either to imagine purchasing a camera from a friend or to imagine purchasing the same camera from a stranger. They were asked to make a single bid. The table shows their bids. The two groups were separated and were blind to the purpose of the study.

Price Offered for a Used Camera ($)	
Buying from a Friend	**Buying from a Stranger**
275	260
300	250
260	175
300	130
255	200
275	225
290	240
300	

PLAN	**Setup** State the objectives. Check the assumptions and conditions.	We want to test whether people tend to offer a different amount to a friend than they would to a stranger when making a purchase offer.

The subjects in this experiment were randomly assigned individually to imagine dealing either with a friend or with a stranger. That randomization allows us to assume independence both among the subjects and between the two groups. That's the only assumption we'll need to check to perform a nonparametric test.

The null hypothesis is that the two groups are the same—that there's no difference in offering price between those negotiating with a friend and those negotiating with a stranger.

DO	**Mechanics** Choose a method. Rank the data from the two groups together.	Since the original data are numeric (prices offered for cameras), we could perform a t-test to figure out whether there's a difference between the two groups. However, t-tests require more assumptions than nonparametric tests; in particular, the prices offered in each group must be nearly Normally distributed. We choose the Wilcoxon rank-sum test in order to avoid having to make additional assumptions.

We start by ranking all the bids as a single group. We give average ranks to ties:

Data	130	175	200	225	240	250	255	260	260	275	275	190	300	300	300
Rank	1	2	3	4	5	6	7	8.5	8.5	10.5	10.5	12	14	14	14
Group	S	S	S	S	S	S	F	S	F	F	F	F	F	F	F

Now we add up the ranks of the smaller (strangers) group: $1 + 2 + 3 + 4 + 5 + 6 + 8.5 = 29.5$.

From Table W1 in Appendix B, the critical value for a two-sided test at $\alpha = 0.05$ and groups of seven and eight is 39. Our observed rank sum is less than this, so we can reject the null hypothesis and conclude that there is in fact a difference in the two groups.

REPORT	**Conclusion** State the conclusion in the context of the problem.	MEMO

Re: Friendship in Negotiations

We investigated whether friendship has an influence on what negotiators are willing to bid for a mid-priced object—in our experiment, a camera. We analyzed data from a randomized single-blind experiment using a nonparametric Wilcoxon rank-sum test and found that there is a statistically significant difference. Negotiators appear to bid more when buying from a friend than when buying from a stranger.

LO❷ 17.5 Tukey's Quick Test

The famous statistician John Tukey[2] was once challenged to come up with a simpler alternative to the two-sample t-test that, like the 68-95-99.7 Rule, had critical values that could be remembered easily. The test he came up with (immediately,

[2]Originator of the boxplot and stem-and-leaf display, among other accomplishments.

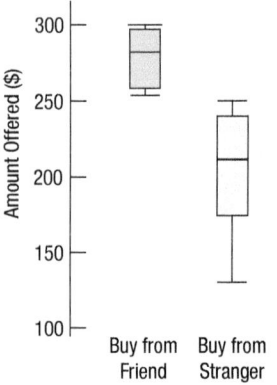

Figure 17.3 Amount offered when buying from a friend or a stranger.

according to the story) asks you only to count and to remember three numbers: 7, 10, and 13.

To test whether two groups differ using Tukey's test, one group must hold the highest value and the other the lowest, as shown in Figure 17.3. Just count how many values in the high group are higher than *all* the values of the lower group. Add to this the number of values in the low group that are lower than *all* the values of the high group. Count ties as 1/2. If your total is seven or more, you can reject the null hypothesis at $\alpha = 0.05$. The "critical values" of 10 and 13 give P-values of 0.01 and 0.001, respectively.

Compare Tukey's test with the Wilcoxon test for the experiment on buying from a friend. The "Friend" group has the highest value ($300) and the "Stranger" group has the lowest ($130). Six of the values in the Friend group (shown in red) are higher than the highest value of the Stranger group ($260) and one is a tie. Six of the Stranger values (shown in green) are lower than the lowest value for Friend ($255). That's a total of 12.5 values. That's more than 10, but less than 13. So the P-value is between 0.01 and 0.001—confirming our result from the Wilcoxon test.

This is a quick and simple test. The only assumption it requires is that the two samples be independent.

Buying from a Friend	Buying from a Stranger
$275	$260
300	250
260	175
300	130
255	200
275	225
290	240
300	

FOR EXAMPLE   Tukey's quick test for negotiating discounts

Men and women sampled at random negotiated different discounts when purchasing cars.

Here are the discounts (in order) received by the men:

130, 158, 303, 340, 353, 390, 415, 423, 536, 566, 588 ... 1606, 1616, 1658, 1763, 1840, 1881, 2030

Here are the discounts received by the women:

503, 526, 574, 579, 603, 630, 794, 831 ... 1727, 1742, 1748, 2142, 2192

QUESTION   Do men and women, in general, negotiate different discounts when purchasing cars? Is Tukey's quick test applicable? If so, find the number of exceedances and report the P-value and conclusion. How does the test compare with the two-sample *t*-test?

ANSWER   Tukey's quick test is applicable because the groups are independent; also, one group (Men) has the smallest value ($130) and the other group (Women) has the largest value ($2192).

There were eight discounts received by men that were smaller than all the women's discounts and two discounts received by women that were larger than all the men's discounts, for a total of 10 exceedances. That corresponds to a P-value of about 0.01 (but larger than 0.001). This gives strong evidence to reject the null hypothesis that the two distributions are the same. The two-sample *t*-test gave a P-value of 0.0028, which is in line with this test.

LO❷ **17.6   Kruskal-Wallis Test**

Suppose that now we have more than two independent groups to compare. We need a generalization of the Wilcoxon test. Suppose the Cancer Society is interested in whether the use of indoor tanning beds varies with age group. Initial focus groups indicate the number of times a respondent used a tanning bed during the last year, as recorded in Table 17.6.

Ages 12–17 Young (Y)	Ages 18–23 Medium (M)	Ages 24–29 Old (O)
4	2	7
4	7	7
6	7	8
6	10	12
12	18	14
28	19	
	20	

Table 17.6   Number of times individual respondents used an indoor tanning bed during the last year.

There's too little data to use ANOVA or the chi-squared test, and the data don't appear to be Normally distributed. We therefore use the Kruskal-Wallis nonparametric test.

H_0: The usage of tanning beds is independent of age group.

H_A: At least one of the age groups uses tanning beds more or less frequently than the others.

First, we rank all the data values together, assigning average ranks to tied values. We then sum up these ranks for each group and calculate

$$H = \frac{12}{N(N + 1)} \sum_{i=1}^{k} \frac{T_i^2}{n_i} - 3(N + 1),$$

where the T_i are the rank sums for each group, n_i is the number of values in the ith group, k is the number of groups, and N is the *total* number of values.

> The test says that we can reject the null hypothesis
>
> H_0: All the samples come from the same distribution
>
> if $H > \chi^2$, with df $= k - 1$,

where χ^2 denotes the chi-square distribution with degrees of freedom equal to the number of groups we are comparing minus one. The chi-square distribution is a large-sample approximation (like the use of Normal for the Wilcoxon rank-sum test). For very small samples, you may want to consult a table of critical values.[3]

First we calculate the ranks for all the age groups combined, based on the usage in Table 17.6. When we have a tie, for example, two usages of 4 in 2nd and 3rd position, we average $(2+3)/2$ to get a rank of 2.5.

> **The Kruskal-Wallis test**
>
> The **Kruskal-Wallis test** extends the Wilcoxon rank-sum (Mann-Whitney) test in order to deal with more than two samples.
>
> H_0: All the samples come from the same distribution.
>
> H_A: At least one of the samples comes from a distribution that is shifted higher or lower than the others.

Order	1	2	3	4	5	6	7	8	9	10	11	12	13	14	15	16	17	18
Usage	2	4	4	6	6	7	7	7	7	8	10	12	12	14	18	19	20	28
Age Group: Y, M, O	M	Y	Y	Y	Y	M	M	O	O	O	M	O	Y	O	M	M	M	Y
Rank	1	2.5	2.5	4.5	4.5	7.5	7.5	7.5	7.5	10	11	12.5	12.5	14	15	16	17	18

---

[3]You can find these on the internet, for example at http://faculty.virginia.edu/kruskal-wallis

For the young (Y) group:

$$T_y = 2.5 + 2.5 + 4.5 + 4.5 + 12.5 + 18 = 44.5$$
$$n_y = 6$$

For the medium (M) group:

$$T_m = 1 + 7.5 + 7.5 + 11 + 15 + 16 + 17 = 75$$
$$n_m = 7$$

For the old (O) group:

$$T_o = 7.5 + 7.5 + 10 + 12.5 + 14 = 51.5$$
$$n_o = 5$$

The total number of respondents is $N = 18$.

Using the formula above:

$$H = \frac{12}{18 \times 19}\left(\frac{44.5^2}{6} + \frac{75^2}{7} + \frac{51.5^2}{5}\right) - 3 \times 19 = 1.39$$

We compare this H value of 1.39 with the chi-square distribution in Appendix B. The number of degrees of freedom is one less than the number of age groups: df = 2. All the critical values in the chi-square table for df = 2 are higher than 1.39, indicating that we can't reject the null hypothesis at any of the significance levels included in the table. The data do not therefore give any reason to think that the usage of indoor tanning beds varies with age group.

Assumptions and Conditions

The assumptions and conditions for the Kruskal-Wallis test are the same as for the Wilcoxon rank-sum (Mann-Whitney) test.

- **Independence Assumption:** The sampled observations within each group are also independent of each other, for example, randomly chosen.
- **Independent Groups Assumption:** All the groups are independent of each other.

When to Use the Kruskal-Wallis Test

There are basically two situations for using the Kruskal-Wallis test:

- Either: The data are non-numeric.
- Or: The Normality assumptions of parametric statistics don't apply. This is particularly important when the sample size is small.

GUIDED EXAMPLE   Rental Car Customer Satisfaction

PLAN **Setup** State the objectives of study.	The objective is to compare customer satisfaction for three car rental sites using the ratings of randomly selected customers given in the following table:

Site 1	Site 2	Site 3
D	C	C
D	D	A
C	B	C
D	B	B
C	C	A
C	D	C
C	C	D
C	C	B
B	B	D
C	C	A

We'll test the following hypothesis:

H_0: All three sites have the same distribution of customer satisfaction.

H_A: At least one of the sites has a different distribution from the others.

We have three groups. It's reasonable to assume that the customers at the three sites are mutually independent and that the customers at each site were selected at random. That's all we need to perform a Kruskal-Wallis test.

DO Rank all the values together assigning average ranks to values that are tied, just as we did before.

Order	1	2	3	4	5	6	7	8	9	10	11	12	13	14	15	16	17	18	19	20	21	22	23	24	25	26	27	28	29	30
Data	A	A	A	B	B	B	B	B	B	C	C	C	C	C	C	C	C	C	C	C	C	C	C	C	C	D	D	D	D	D	D	D
Rank	2.0	2.0	2.0	6.5	6.5	6.5	6.5	6.5	6.5	16.5	16.5	16.5	16.5	16.5	16.5	16.5	16.5	16.5	16.5	16.5	16.5	16.5	16.5	16.5	16.5	27.0	27.0	27.0	27.0	27.0	27.0	27.0

Sum the ranks within each group.

Site 1	Rank	Site 2	Rank	Site 3	Rank
D	27.0	C	16.5	C	16.5
D	27.0	D	27.0	A	2.0
C	16.5	B	6.5	C	16.5
D	27.0	B	6.5	B	6.5
C	16.5	C	16.5	A	2.0
C	16.5	D	27.0	C	16.5
C	16.5	C	16.5	D	27.0
C	16.5	C	16.5	B	6.5
B	6.5	B	6.5	D	27.0
C	16.5	C	16.5	A	2.0
	186.5		156.0		122.5

Calculate the corresponding test statistic H: $H = \dfrac{12}{N(N+1)} \sum \dfrac{T_i^2}{n_i} - 3(N+1)$, where N is the total number of observations from all samples, n_i are the individual sample sizes, and $T_1, T_2,$ and T_3 are the sum of the ranks for sites 1, 2, and 3, respectively.

$$H = \frac{12}{N(N+1)}\left(\frac{T_1^2}{n_1} + \frac{T_2^2}{n_2} + \frac{T_3^2}{n_3}\right) - 3(N+1)$$

$$= \frac{12}{30(30+1)}$$

$$\left(\frac{186.5^2}{10} + \frac{156^2}{10} + \frac{122.5^2}{10}\right) - 3(30+1) = 2.64$$

The Kruskal-Wallis test rejects the null hypothesis when the value of H is large compared with the corresponding χ^2 value.

χ^2 distribution with degrees of freedom equal to the number of sites, three, minus one: df = 2. We use a 95% significance level, corresponding to $\alpha = 0.05$. The χ^2 table (Table X) in Appendix B gives a critical value of 5.991. Since $H = 2.64$ is less than 5.991, we cannot reject the null hypothesis.

REPORT Conclusion State your conclusion in the context of the problem.

MEMO

Re: Customer Satisfaction

An examination of customer ratings from three rental sites did not reveal any significant difference in customer satisfaction.

LO③   17.7   Kendall's Tau

We can use a linear model based on correlation and regression to describe the relationship between two numeric variables. Sometimes, however, we're primarily concerned with the *direction* of the association, but not particularly worried about whether the form of the relationship is linear. In other situations, we may have data measured on a Likert scale or other data that give information only about order and not about numeric value.

A restaurant owner might wonder whether adding more salt really does make fried potatoes taste better. It may be impossible to measure "how much better," but it's certainly possible to ask customers which of several plates of fries they like best and least.

A consistent trend is called *monotone*. Of course, real data are rarely so simple as to line up in a perfect monotone trend. But we can measure how close our data are to overall monotonicity. The statistic we use is **Kendall's tau**.

> **A monotonous relationship?**
> You probably think of monotonous as *boring*. A monotone relationship shares the same root, but it's only the *sameness* that's important. A monotone relationship is one that either increases all the time or decreases all the time; that is, it doesn't oscillate up and down.

Kendall's tau measures monotonicity directly. For each pair of points in a scatterplot, it records only whether the slope of a line between those two points is positive, negative, or zero, as shown in Figure 17.4. (If the points have the same *x*-value, the slope between them is ignored.) In a monotone plot, these pairwise slopes would be either all positive or all negative. In a non-monotone plot, the counts of positive and negative slopes will tend to balance out. Tau (often written with the Greek letter τ) is the difference between the number of positive slopes and the number of negative slopes divided by the total number of slopes between pairs.

Tau can take values between –1.0 and + 1.0. If every pairwise slope is negative, then tau will equal –1.0 and the plot will show a single stream of points trending consistently downward. If every pairwise slope is positive, then tau will equal +1.0 and the plot will show a single stream of points trending consistently upward. In a generally horizontal plot or one that goes up and then down, the counts of positive and negative slopes will balance out and tau will be near zero.

Kendall's tau is easy to understand and is calculated by examining every *pair* of points. We record whether it's *concordant*—that is, with a positive slope between the two points—or *discordant*—having a negative slope. If n_c is the number of concordant points and n_d is the number of discordant points, then

$$\tau = \frac{n_c - n_d}{\frac{1}{2}n(n - 1)}.$$

The denominator, $\frac{1}{2}n(n - 1)$, is the number of pairs to check. We can get a feel for Kendall's tau from a few simple examples.

If half the pairs of points are concordant and the other half are discordant, then $n_c = n_d$ and $\tau = 0$. Kendall's tau is telling us that there is no relationship between our variables.

A positive relationship between our variables would mean that there are more concordant pairs (with a positive slope) than discordant pairs. For example, suppose 80% of our pairs are concordant and 20% are discordant. Then $n_c = 0.8 \ n(n - 1)/2$ and $n_d = 0.2 \ n(n - 1)/2$, giving $\tau = 0.6$, which is telling us that there's a moderate positive relationship between our variables.

If 10% of our pairs are concordant, then $\tau = -0.8$, meaning that there's a strong negative relationship between our variables.

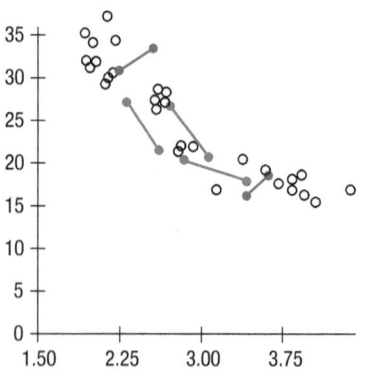

Figure 17.4   For each pair of points, Kendall's tau records whether the slope between them is positive (red), negative (blue), or zero.

Sir Maurice Kendall (1907–1983) was a prominent statistician, writer, and teacher. He made significant contributions to the study of randomness (developing tests for randomness that are still used), the theory of statistics, and rank-based statistics. He also served as director of the World Fertility Study, for which the United Nations awarded him its peace medal.

FOR EXAMPLE   Calculating Kendall's tau for employee and customer satisfaction

A car rental company has six locations in a certain city and is concerned that employee job dissatisfaction is having a bad effect on sales. It surveys employees and customers to come up with an overall ranking of the six locations, by employee satisfaction and by customer satisfaction.

Location	1	2	3	4	5	6
Employee satisfaction ranking	1	3	4	2	6	5
Customer satisfaction ranking	1	2	5	3	4	6

QUESTION   To what extent are customer and employee satisfaction dependent on each other?

ANSWER   For clarity, we can plot the data on a scatterplot, but it's important to note that we're not plotting numeric values; we're plotting rankings.

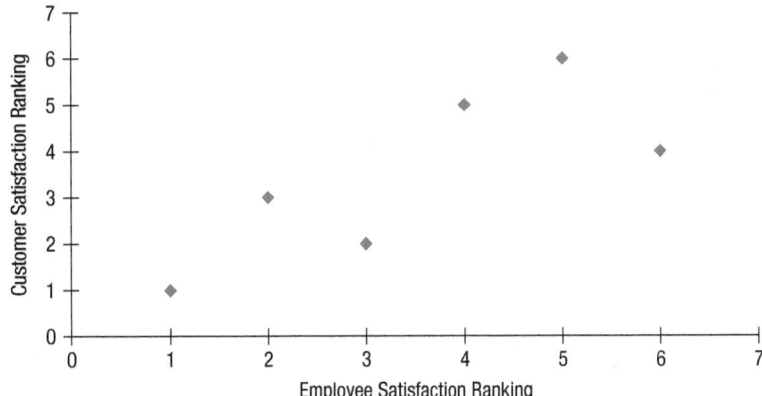

We can now count the number of concordant pairs, i.e., pairs that indicate a positive relationship between the rankings. Starting from the left, if we draw lines from the first point to each of the other five points, the lines all have a positive slope, meaning that all five pairs are concordant. We've already counted the second point's relationship with the first point, so we now look at the slopes of the lines between the second point and the other four points. Three of those pairs are concordant. Proceeding in this way, the total number of concordant pairs is

$$n_c = 5 + 3 + 3 + 1 + 0 = 12.$$

The total number of pairs is $n(n - 1)/2 = 6 \times 5/2 = 15$.
Therefore, $n_d = 15 - 12 = 3$.
$\tau = (12 - 3)/15 = 0.6$, a moderately strong relationship.

So far we've calculated Kendall's tau and commented on the strength of the relationship between the variables. That's different from whether the value of tau is significantly different from zero. A tau derived from a large number of observations is more significant than the same tau derived from only a few observations. If the tau is significantly different from zero, we can conclude that the variables are dependent on each other by using the fact that it's approximately Normally distributed with a zero mean and a standard deviation:

$$\sigma = \sqrt{\frac{2(2n + 5)}{9n(n - 1)}}$$

FOR EXAMPLE   The significance of Kendall's tau for employee and customer satisfaction

QUESTION   Using the data in For Example: "Calculating Kendall's tau for employee and customer satisfaction," is there a significant dependence between customer satisfaction and employee satisfaction?

ANSWER   The database is not available here, but our analysis of it shows that:

H_0: There is no dependence between customer satisfaction and employee satisfaction, i.e., $\tau = 0$.

H_A: There is a dependence, i.e., $\tau \neq 0$

In the previous example, we calculated $\tau = 0.6$.

We now calculate

$$\sigma = \sqrt{\frac{2(2n + 5)}{9n(n - 1)}} = \sqrt{\frac{2(2 \times 6 + 5)}{9 \times 6 \times 5}} = 0.355.$$

$z = 0.6/0.355 = 1.69$, which isn't high enough to be significant at the 95% level.

We therefore conclude that we can't reject the null hypothesis. We don't have enough data to conclude that tau is significantly different from zero.

The above examples have illustrated the numerical calculations involved in calculating Kendall's tau. For larger data sets we would use a computer. However, we need to interpret the results carefully instead of just blindly accepting what the computer tells us, as shown in the following example.

FOR EXAMPLE   Estimating association for diamond price and quality

A database contains data on diamond prices and quality. Parametric methods deal with colour only as a category. But since diamond colours are ordered with D as the best and later letters labelling lower-quality colours, it makes sense to ask whether prices change consistently with colour quality. We can rank the colours, assigning rank 1 to colour D, 2 to colour E, and so on. Of course, these ranks have no measurement units, so a least squares regression would make no sense. But it is appropriate to use Kendall's tau to assess the association between *Price* and *Colour Rank*.

QUESTION   What is Kendall's tau for these data, and what does it mean?

ANSWER   Kendall's tau for these data is 0.175. It seems that lower-quality (later letter; higher rank) colours are associated with *higher* prices!

QUESTION   That doesn't make sense. How can we explain this apparent anomaly?

ANSWER   These diamonds are not all the same *carat weight*. Perhaps larger diamonds of the best colour are harder to find. If we restrict our analysis to diamonds that are 1.0 carat in weight, we find that Kendall's tau for the selected diamonds is –0.463. That indicates a strong association with "better" colours associated with higher prices.

LO❸   17.8   Spearman's Rank Correlation

One of the problems with the regular correlation coefficient between numeric variables is that it's very sensitive to violations of the Linearity Condition. Both outliers and bends in the data make it difficult to interpret. **Spearman's rho** (often denoted by the Greek letter ρ) can deal with both of these problems. Rho

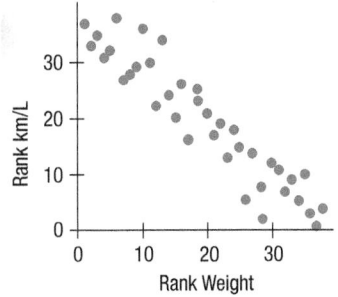

Figure 17.5 Spearman's rho finds the correlation of the ranks of the two variables, the weight and fuel efficiency of passenger vehicles.

Charles Edward Spearman, FRS (1863–1945), was an English psychologist known for his work in statistics, as a pioneer of factor analysis, and for Spearman's rank-correlation coefficient. He also did fundamental work on measures of human intelligence.

replaces the original data values with their ranks within each variable. That is, it replaces the lowest value in x by the number 1, the next lowest value by 2, and so on, until the highest value is assigned the value n. The same ranking method is applied to the y-variable. A scatterplot of the y-ranks against the x-ranks, as shown in Figure 17.5, shows the same general trend as the original data, going up whenever the data went up and down whenever the data went down. If the original scatterplot shows a consistent but bent trend, however, the scatterplot of the ranks is likely to be more nearly linear. And if either variable has an extreme outlying value, the ranking process keeps it from being extreme by simply counting it as the highest or lowest value, ignoring how extreme it really is.

Spearman's rho is the correlation of the two rank variables. Because this is a correlation coefficient, it must be between –1.0 and 1.0. We can also calculate Spearman's rho using the following formula, which is simpler than calculating the correlation coefficient:

$$\rho = 1 - \frac{6\sum D_i^2}{n(n^2 - 1)}$$

where D_i are the differences in the ranks.

FOR EXAMPLE — Calculating Spearman's rho for employee and customer satisfaction

QUESTION Using the data in the example about the car rental company in For Example: "Calculating Kendall's tau for employee and customer satisfaction," calculate Spearman's rho.

ANSWER The differences in the ranks are calculated in the table below:

Location	1	2	3	4	5	6
Employee Satisfaction Ranking	1	3	4	2	6	5
Customer Satisfaction Ranking	1	2	5	3	4	6
Differences in Ranks, D_i	0	1	−1	−1	2	−1
D_i^2	0	1	1	1	4	1

$$\rho = 1 - \frac{6 \times 8}{6(36 - 1)} = 0.771$$

We can calculate whether Spearman's rho is significantly different from zero—that is, whether the two variables are dependent on each other—using a t-test, with

$$t = \rho\sqrt{\frac{n - 2}{1 - \rho^2}}$$

and $n - 2$ degrees of freedom.

FOR EXAMPLE — The significance of Spearman's rho for employee and customer satisfaction

QUESTION Using the results of For Example: "Calculating Spearman's rho for employee and customer satisfaction," are customer satisfaction and employee satisfaction dependent on each other?

(continued)

ANSWER H_0: There is no dependence between customer satisfaction and employee satisfaction, i.e., $\rho = 0$.

H_A: There is a dependence, i.e., $\rho \neq 0$

In the previous example, we calculated $\rho = 0.771$.

Therefore:

$$t = \rho\sqrt{\frac{n-2}{1-\rho^2}} = 0.771\sqrt{\frac{4}{1-0.771^2}} = 2.42, \text{ with 4 degrees of freedom. This is not}$$

significant at the 95% level.

In our examples thus far, we've checked whether the car rental company's employee satisfaction and customer satisfaction are dependent on each other using both Kendall's tau and Spearman's rho. The results are consistent using both approaches: no significant dependence at the 95% level.

Both Kendall's tau and Spearman's rho have advantages over the correlation coefficient r:

- First, they can be used even when we know only the ranks.
- Second, they measure the consistency of the trend between the variables without insisting that the trend be linear.
- Third, they're not much affected by outliers. Spearman's rho limits the outlier to the value of its rank, and Kendall's tau cares only about the sign of each slope between points, not how steep it might be.

Neither tau nor rho is changed at all by re-expressing variables by functions that don't alter the order of values (e.g., by just the sort of functions we might use to straighten a scatterplot, such as taking logarithms or square roots). But, unlike the correlation coefficient, neither statistic can be used as a base for more advanced or complex methods, so they tend to be specialized methods used when we care primarily about consistent trends between two variables.

FOR EXAMPLE   **Estimating association for height and price of commercial properties when there are outliers**

How are the prices of commercial properties related to the number of storeys high they are? A scatterplot for the commercial properties in one city that are built with masonry construction looks like this:

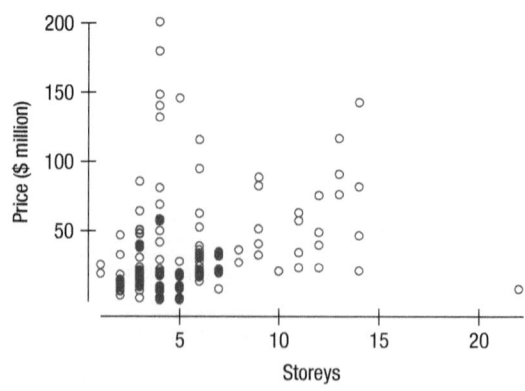

> **QUESTION**   The Linearity Assumption is clearly not satisfied by these data, and there's one building of more than 20 storeys with a low price that's likely to be influential. What's an appropriate way to summarize the relationship between *Price* and *Storeys*?
>
> **ANSWER**   The standard correlation for these data is 0.280, but it wouldn't be right to interpret it. The high-leverage case on the right and the two particularly expensive buildings at the top of the plot are both likely to influence the value of the correlation. Both violate the Linearity Assumption. Spearman's rho is more appropriate because it's based on the ranks, so it doesn't require an assumption of linearity and can deal with outliers in either direction. Spearman's rho for these properties is 0.467. That's probably a better assessment of association.

LO❶ 17.9   When Should You Use Nonparametric Methods?

Nonparametric methods such as those discussed in this chapter (there are others) are particularly valuable when your data contain only information about order. But they can also be valuable for numeric data—especially when the numeric variables violate one or more of our assumptions and conditions by, for example, not being Normally distributed.

We should use the nonparametric methods described in this chapter with *numeric* data when the assumptions of the parametric methods (such as *t*-tests) do not apply. For instance, when we use a *t*-test, we're relying on the Central Limit Theorem (CLT) to base our test on a sampling distribution that's Normally distributed. The CLT says this is approximately true for "large" samples independent of the distribution of the population, but it doesn't tell us how large is "large." In fact, we need a larger sample for populations that are very different from Normal (e.g., skewed) than we do for populations that are approximately Normal. Since we often don't know the population distribution, it's tough to figure out whether our sample size is large enough. If we have a reasonably sized sample, we can always draw a histogram to get an idea of what the population distribution might look like, so our main problem is when we have a small sample. Nonparametric methods deal with small samples when we don't know the distribution of the population, and are therefore also sometimes called **distribution-free methods**.

Translating numeric values to ranks protects us from the influence of outliers (which simply become the "biggest ones" without being extreme), from the effects of two or more modes in the data (because the ranks ignore modes), and from skewed distributions and nonlinear relationships. They "charge" for this service by being a bit less powerful than corresponding parametric methods when the assumptions and conditions of those methods *are* met. But when those assumptions are violated, nonparametric methods can be not only more powerful, but also more appropriate. It's unwise to use methods when their underlying assumptions aren't met.

On the other hand, the choice of nonparametric methods should not be made to ignore or hide features of the data. For example, although nonparametric methods can protect us from the influence of an outlier, we know already that outliers themselves often hold valuable information. You should certainly examine any outliers, even if you elect to then use a nonparametric method. Similarly, nonparametric methods can protect us from the effects of a bimodal variable (where parametric methods assume a nearly Normal distribution). But if the data are bimodal, they may be trying to tell us that we have two fundamentally different subgroups in the data. It would be wise not to ignore that information.

Although nonparametric methods are appropriate for skewed data and non-linear relationships, it may be more effective to re-express one or more variables to improve symmetry and straighten relationships. The resulting models using the re-expressed variables may be simpler, be more useful, and have wider applicability.

WHAT CAN GO WRONG?

- **Don't forget to check independence.** Nonparametric methods are free of many of the assumptions and conditions we check for in other methods, but they're not entirely free of assumptions. The assumption that the cases are independent is especially important when P-values and critical values are determined by probability calculations based on the assumption that all orderings are equally likely.

- **Don't degrade your data unnecessarily.** If you have numeric data that satisfy the assumptions and conditions of statistics methods such as *t*-tests, correlation, regression, and ANOVA, you're generally better off using those methods rather than the corresponding nonparametric methods. Working with the ranks rather than measurements inevitably throws away some information in return for protection from outliers and violations of other assumptions.

ETHICS IN ACTION

Green Edibles, a large manufacturing company specializing in the production of frozen and canned organic vegetables, has successfully implemented Six Sigma practices to increase efficiencies, eliminate waste, and improve its manufacturing processes. Some members of the senior management team are proposing that the company use the same practices to improve quality in its administrative and non-manufacturing processes. Since a sizable investment is required to train employees in quality improvement practices, the team decided to implement a pilot training program that involves only a subset of the company's administrative departments. Patrick Day, vice president of Human Resources (HR), was placed in charge of implementing the pilot program and evaluating its effectiveness. His first task was to select 10 administrative departments to participate in the pilot program; he chose not to include the HR department, as it was currently understaffed. Each of the participating departments identified a process to target for improvement and gathered quality-related data on the process (e.g., number of data entry errors) both before and after its employees were trained in quality improvement practices. Since the sample size was small (only 10 departments), the data were analyzed using the Wilcoxon rank-sum test. The results revealed no significant improvement in administrative processes after training compared with

before; consequently, Patrick reported to the senior management team that there was no evidence to suggest that the pilot program was effective in improving processes in administrative and non-manufacturing departments. When the team subsequently decided not to invest in such a company-wide quality improvement training program, Patrick was somewhat relieved. After all, releasing some of his HR employees to attend training sessions would only make his current staffing situation even worse.

Ethical Issue *Patrick should not have let his concerns about the current staffing situation in his department affect his judgment. He should have selected departments for the pilot program at random, including possibly HR. Also, the data are paired, not independent. Assuming independent groups when the data are paired increases the chances of not rejecting the null hypothesis when it should be rejected (related to Item C, ASA Ethical Guidelines; see Appendix C, the American Statistical Association's Ethical Guidelines for Statistical Practice, also available online at www.amstat.org/about/ethicalguidelines.cfm).*

Ethical Solution *Although nonparametric methods have relatively few assumptions and conditions, it's still important to check the assumptions for each test. The Wilcoxon rank-sum test makes two assumptions: (1) Independence, and (2) Independent Groups. These data are paired, so these assumptions are violated. The Wilcoxon signed-rank test should have been used.*

WHAT HAVE WE LEARNED?

Learning Objectives

❶ Nonparametric methods require fewer assumptions about the data, which can be a major advantage. They can work with data that provide only order information, such as Likert scale data. And they can protect us from outliers, multimodality, and skewness in numeric data.

Nonparametric methods "charge" for these advantages by being less powerful than corresponding parametric methods *when the assumptions and conditions of the parametric methods are satisfied*. But they can be more powerful, or simply more appropriate, when the assumptions are not met.

❷ We've learned how to perform the major nonparametric tests used in business to compare two or more groups: the Wilcoxon rank-sum test; Tukey's quick test; the Kruskal-Wallis test; the Wilcoxon signed-rank test; and the Friedman test.

❸ We've learned how to perform the major nonparametric tests used in business to investigate the degree of relationship between two variables: Kendall's tau test and Spearman's rho test.

We can figure out which test to use from the following diagram:

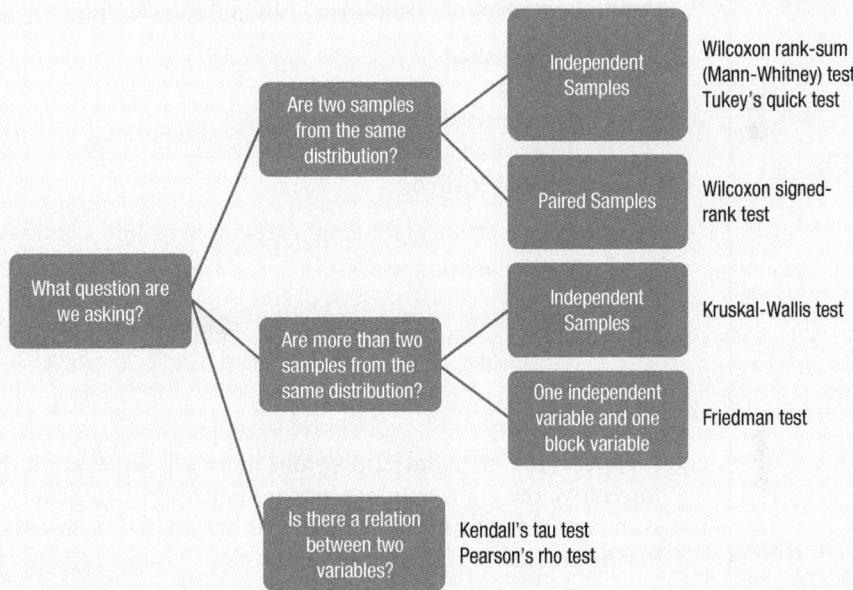

Terms

Distribution-free methods	Statistical tests that are not based on assuming a specific population distribution.
Kendall's tau	A statistic that measures how close the relationship between two variables is to being monotone.
Kruskal-Wallis test	A statistical test that uses the sums of the ranks for the groups being compared.
Mann-Whitney test	See *Wilcoxon rank-sum test*.
Nonparametric methods	Statistical tests that investigate characteristics of populations without using specific parameters; these tests use the sign or the rank of the data rather than the specific numerical value of the variable, and they can also be used with ordinal data (categorical data with a logical order, such as survey results based on a scale).
Spearman's rho	A correlation computed on the ranks of data values rather than their numeric values.
Wilcoxon rank-sum test	A statistical method used to test for the differences between two independent groups.
Wilcoxon signed-rank test	A statistical test used to test the difference between paired measurements in two groups.

Air Canada and Flight Attendants' Schedules

After emerging from bankruptcy protection in 2004, Air Canada worked with its employees at numerous measures to maintain profitability. However, its share price dropped from around $18 at the end of 2006 to around $3.50 at the end of 2010. Then, in 2011, Air Canada experienced labour-relations problems with the union representing flight attendants, involving calls by union members to go on strike in September and October of that year. A major issue was the schedules that the flight attendants worked.

Put yourself in the place of a human resource scheduler at one of Air Canada's competitors. It's clear that operating an airline requires flight attendants to work early mornings, late evenings, weekends, and holidays. However, the individual flight attendants' schedules should be acceptable to employees as well as the employer. You decide to survey a random sample of flight attendants on two different schedules to assess their job satisfaction. Employees rate job satisfaction on a Likert scale:

A: very satisfied
B: satisfied
C: neither satisfied or dissatisfied
D: dissatisfied
E: very dissatisfied

The results from eight employees on Schedule 1 and seven employees on Schedule 2 are as follows:

Survey (A)							
SCHEDULE 1	A	C	C	C	B	E	D	D
SCHEDULE 2	B	B	A	C	C	D	D	

It appears that Schedule 2 provides more job satisfaction than Schedule 1. You therefore move the eight employees from Schedule 1 to Schedule 2. After they've become accustomed to the new schedule, you survey their job satisfaction and obtain the following results:

Survey (B)								
EMPLOYEE #	1	2	3	4	5	6	7	8
SCHEDULE 1, FROM SURVEY (A)	A	C	C	C	B	E	D	D
SCHEDULE 2	B	B	B	A	A	D	C	B

Do the survey results (A) and (B) in fact indicate a significant difference between the two schedules? Suggest an appropriate next step for this project.

Real Estate

Use the data file **Real-Estate** to consider what factors might contribute to the price of a home. Specifically, consider:

- Does the price for homes with a fireplace differ significantly from the price for homes without fireplaces? Select an appropriate nonparametric test to obtain your results.

- Does the price for homes depend on the number of bedrooms? Code the bedrooms as 1, 2, 3, 4, or more. Perform an appropriate nonparametric test and report on your findings.

- Does the price of a home depend on its living area? Select an appropriate nonparametric method, and discuss your conclusions.

EXERCISES

SECTIONS 17.1 AND 17.2

1. Which of the following variables are ranks? For those that are not ranks, give the units.

a) Student ratings of a course on a five-point Likert scale.
b) Students' letter grades in that course.
c) Students' point scores on the final exam. **LO ❶, ❷**

2. Which of the following variables are ranks? For those that are not ranks, give the units.

a) Canadian coins by relative size: dime, penny, nickel, quarter, dollar, two dollar.
b) Canadian coins by value: penny, nickel, dime, quarter, dollar, two dollar.
c) The coins in your pocket by year minted. **LO ❶, ❷**

3. For which one of the following situations would a Wilcoxon signed-rank test be appropriate?

a) Comparing the ratings of a new product on a five-point Likert scale by a panel of consumers with their ratings of a competitor's product on the same scale.
b) Comparing the sweetness of a diet drink (rated from 1 to 10) as judged by a panel of teenaged tasters and a panel of adult tasters.
c) Judging whether the height of the water at high tide at a marina increases more or less consistently as the phase of the moon changes from new to full.
d) Testing whether the distributions of the ratings of a new distance-learning course were the same as rated (on the usual five-point Likert scale) by first-, second-, third-, and fourth-year students who had taken the course.
e) Estimating the association between the value of homes and their age in a community known to have a number of very expensive mansions. **LO ❶, ❷**

4. For which one of the following situations would a Wilcoxon signed-rank test be appropriate?

a) The Mohs scale rates the hardness of minerals. If one mineral can scratch another, it's judged to be harder. (Diamond, the hardest mineral, is a 10.) Is hardness related to the weight of a $1 \times 1 \times 1$ cm cube of the mineral?
b) Each member of a group of professional chefs rates the quality of a basket of organic vegetables on a five-point scale. The same chefs then rate the quality of a basket of nonorganic vegetables on the same scale. Are the organic veggies rated higher?

c) During a smart phone game's initial release, is there an association between the number of downloads and the number of hours since it's been released?
d) The Richter scale measures the damage potential of earthquakes. Some scientists think it's best used for judging the relative size of earthquakes and not their absolute size. Are earthquakes around the Pacific "Ring of Fire" stronger in general than those around the Atlantic? Compare earthquakes over a recent five-year period.
e) A dog's intelligence can be judged roughly by how many times a new command must be repeated until it is learned. A researcher trained several dogs of each of four different breeds, teaching them three new commands. Are the breeds equally "intelligent"? **LO ❶, ❷**

SECTION 17.4

5. For which one of the situations described in Exercise 3 would a Wilcoxon rank-sum (or Mann-Whitney) test be appropriate?

6. For which one of the situations described in Exercise 4 would a Wilcoxon rank-sum (or Mann-Whitney) test be appropriate? **LO ❷**

SECTION 17.5

7. What additional information would you need to know before using Tukey's quick test instead of the Wilcoxon rank-sum (Mann-Whitney) test in Exercise 5? **LO ❷**

8. What additional information would you need to know before using Tukey's quick test instead of the Wilcoxon rank-sum (Mann-Whitney) test in Exercise 6? **LO ❷**

SECTION 17.6

9. For which one of the situations described in Exercise 3 would a Kruskal-Wallis test be appropriate? **LO ❷**

10. For which one of the situations described in Exercise 4 would a Kruskal-Wallis test be appropriate? **LO ❷**

SECTION 17.7

11. For which one of the situations described in Exercise 3 would a Kendall's tau be appropriate? **LO ❸**

12. For which one of the situations described in Exercise 4 would Kendall's tau be appropriate? **LO ❸**

SECTION 17.8

13. For which one of the situations described in Exercise 3 would Spearman's rho be appropriate?

14. For which one of the situations described in Exercise 4 would Spearman's rho be appropriate? **LO ❸**

CHAPTER EXERCISES

Ⓣ 15. **Product testing.** A company is producing and marketing new reading activities for elementary school children that it believes will improve reading comprehension scores. A researcher randomly assigns grade three students to an eight-week program in which some will use these activities and others will experience traditional teaching methods. At the end of the experiment, both groups take a reading comprehension exam. Their scores are shown in the back-to-back stem-and-leaf display.

a) Do these results suggest that the new activities are better with $\alpha = 0.01$? Test an appropriate hypothesis with a Wilcoxon (or Mann-Whitney) rank-sum test and state your conclusion.

b) How would you redesign this study? What nonparametric method would be appropriate then? **LO ❷**

New Activities		Control
	1	07
4	2	068
3	3	377
96333	4	12222238
9876432	5	355
721	6	02
1	7	
	8	5

Ⓣ 16. **Product placement.** The owner of a small organic food store was concerned about her sales of a specialty yogurt manufactured in Greece. As a result of increasing fuel costs, she recently had to increase its price. To help boost sales, she decided to place the product on a different shelf (near eye level for most consumers) and in a location near other popular international products. She kept track of sales (number of containers sold per week) for six months after she made the change. The values are shown below, along with the sales numbers for the six months prior to making the change, in stem-and-leaf displays.

After	Change
3	2
3	9
4	23
4	589
5	0012
5	55558
6	00123
6	67
7	0

Before	Change
2	0
2	899
3	224
3	7789
4	0000223
4	5567
5	0
5	6

Do these results suggest that sales are better after the change in product placement? Test an appropriate hypothesis and state your conclusion. Be sure to check assumptions and conditions. **LO ❶, ❷**

Ⓣ 17. **Cereal sugar.** A food company is concerned about recent criticism of the sugar content of its children's cereals. The data show the sugar content (as a percentage of weight) of several national brands of children's and adults' cereals. Are children's cereals really different from adults' cereals in sugar content?

Children's cereals: 40.3, 55, 45.7, 43.3, 50.3, 45.9, 53.5, 43, 44.2, 44, 47.4, 44, 33.6, 55.1, 48.8, 50.4, 37.8, 60.3, 46.6

Adults' cereals: 20, 30.2, 2.2, 7.5, 4.4, 22.2, 16.6, 14.5, 21.4, 3.3, 6.6, 7.8, 10.6, 16.2, 14.5, 4.1, 15.8, 4.1, 2.4, 3.5, 8.5, 10, 1, 4.4, 1.3, 8.1, 4.7, 18.4

a) Write the null and alternative hypotheses.

b) Check the conditions for a Wilcoxon rank-sum (or Mann-Whitney) test.

c) Complete the test and report your conclusion.

d) Make histograms of each group. Discuss whether you would choose a nonparametric test for these data or a two-sample t-test. **LO ❷**

Ⓣ 18. **Foreclosure rates.** Home foreclosures in the United States were up 47% in March 2008 compared with the previous year (http://realestate.msn.com). The data show home foreclosure rates (as percent change from the previous year) for a sample of cities in two regions, the Northeast and the Southwest.

Northeast: 2.99, −2.36, 3.03, 1.01, 5.77, 9.95, −3.52, 7.16, −3.34, 4.75, 5.25, 6.21, 1.67, −2.45, −0.55, 3.45, 4.50, 1.87, −2.15, −0.75

Southwest: 10.15, 23.05, 18.95, 21.16, 17.45, 12.67, 13.75, 29.42, 11.45, 16.77, 12.67, 13.69, 25.81, 21.16, 19.67, 11.88, 13.67, 18.00, 12.88

a) Write the null and alternative hypotheses.
b) Check the conditions for a Wilcoxon rank-sum (or Mann-Whitney) test.
c) Complete the test and report your conclusion.
d) Make histograms of each group. Discuss whether you would choose a nonparametric test for these data or a two-sample *t*-test. **LO ❷**

T 19. Trophy sizes. The following table gives the names, dates first awarded, and heights (inches) of major trophies and awards in sports and entertainment. The America's Cup, awarded for sailing, claims to be the oldest such award. The first five were created in the 19th century (which ended in 1900, not in 1899). The others were created after a gap of 26 years. When the creation of new awards was begun again, were the trophies the same size? Compare the two groups with an appropriate nonparametric measure. Complete the test at $\alpha = 0.10$. **LO ❷**

Award	Year	Size (in.)
America's Cup	1851	27
Kentucky Derby	1875	22
Wimbledon Men's Singles	1887	18.5
Stanley Cup	1892	35.2
Davis Cup	1900	42
Ryder Cup	1927	17
Oscar	1929	13.5
Jules Rimet Trophy (World Cup Soccer)	1929	14
Heisman Trophy	1935	15
Primetime Emmy	1949	15.5
Vince Lombardi Trophy	1967	22
Commissioner's Trophy (World Series)	1967	24
Larry O'Brien NBA Trophy	1977	24
Webb Ellis Cup (Rugby)	1987	15

T 20. Designated hitter 2012. American League baseball teams play their games with the designated hitter rule, meaning that pitchers do not bat. The league believes that replacing the pitcher, traditionally a weak hitter, with another player in the batting order produces more runs and generates more interest among fans. Below are the average numbers of runs scored per game by American League and National League teams for the 2012 season:

National League		American League	
Team	R/G	Team	R/G
Colorado Rockies	4.68	Los Angeles Angels	4.73
St. Louis Cardinals	4.72	Texas Rangers	4.99
San Francisco Giants	4.43	Detroit Tigers	4.48
Washington Nationals	4.51	Kansas City Royals	4.17
Milwaukee Brewers	4.79	New York Yankees	4.96
Arizona Diamondbacks	4.53	Boston Red Sox	4.53
Philadelphia Phillies	4.22	Minnesota Twins	4.33
Los Angeles Dodgers	3.93	Chicago White Sox	4.62
Cincinnati Reds	4.13	Cleveland Indians	4.12
New York Mets	4.01	Baltimore Orioles	4.40
Atlanta Braves	4.32	Toronto Blue Jays	4.42
San Diego Padres	4.02	Tampa Bay Rays	4.30
Miami Marlins	3.76	Oakland Athletics	4.40
Pittsburgh Pirates	4.02	Seattle Mariners	3.82
Chicago Cubs	3.78		
Houston Astros	3.60		

Use a Mann-Whitney method to test whether there is really a difference in number of runs scored.

T 21. Freshman 15. Cornell Professor of Nutrition David Levitsky recruited students from two large sections of an introductory health course to test the validity of the "Freshman 15" theory that students gain 15 pounds their first year. Although they were volunteers, they appeared to match the rest of the freshman class in terms of demographic variables such as sex and ethnicity. The students were weighed during the first week of the semester, then again 12 weeks later. The data are in the data file.

a) Use a Wilcoxon signed-rank test to test whether these students' weights changed. State your hypotheses, check conditions, and complete the test (with technology).
b) Would you prefer the nonparametric test or the paired *t*-test? Explain. **LO ❷**

22. Job satisfaction. A company institutes an exercise break for its workers to see whether this will improve job satisfaction, as measured by a questionnaire that assesses workers' satisfaction. Scores for 10 randomly selected workers before and after the implementation of the exercise program are shown in the following table:

Worker Number	Job Satisfaction Index	
	Before	After
1	34	33
2	28	36
3	29	50
4	45	41
5	26	37
6	27	41
7	24	39
8	15	21
9	15	20
10	27	37

a) Identify a nonparametric procedure you could use to assess the effectiveness of the exercise program and check to see whether the conditions allow for the use of that procedure.

b) Test an appropriate hypothesis and state your conclusion. **LO❶, ❷**

23. ERP effectiveness. When implementing a packaged enterprise resource planning (ERP) system, many companies report that the module they first install is Financial Accounting. Among the measures used to gauge the effectiveness of their ERP system implementation is acceleration of the financial close process. Below is a sample of eight companies that report their average time (in weeks) to financial close before and after the implementation of their ERP system:

Company	Before	After
1	6.5	4.2
2	7.0	5.9
3	8.0	8.0
4	4.5	4.0
5	5.2	3.8
6	4.9	4.1
7	5.2	6.0
8	6.5	4.2

Use a Wilcoxon signed-rank test to see whether the ERP system seems to be effective with $\alpha = 0.05$. **LO❷**

24. Online insurance. A local insurance agent was concerned that he might lose customers to online discount insurance sites. To investigate, he randomly selected profiles (type of car, coverage, driving record, etc.) for 10 of his clients and checked online price quotes for their policies. The comparisons are shown in the table:

Local	Online	Price Diff
568	391	177
872	602	270
451	488	−37
1229	903	326
605	677	−72
1021	1270	−249
783	703	80
844	789	55
907	1008	−101
712	702	10

Identify an appropriate nonparametric method to compare the two sets of prices and complete the test. **LO❶, ❷**

T 25. Friday the 13th, traffic. The *British Medical Journal* published an article titled "Is Friday the 13th Bad for Your Health?" Researchers in Britain examined how Friday the 13th affects human behaviour (*Source:* Published by The British Medical Journal). One question was whether people tend to stay at home more on Friday the 13th—an issue of great concern, for example, to restaurants and theatres. The data in the table are the number of cars passing Junctions 9 and 10 on the M25 motorway for consecutive Fridays (the 6th and 13th) for five different periods:

Year	Month	6th	13th
1990	July	134,012	132,908
1991	September	133,732	131,843
1991	December	121,139	118,723
1992	March	124,631	120,249
1992	November	117,584	117,263

Identify and use an appropriate nonparametric test to judge whether there's a significant difference in traffic between consecutive Fridays when one is the 13th. **LO❶, ❷**

T 26. Friday the 13th, accidents. The researchers in Exercise 25 also examined the number of people admitted to emergency rooms for vehicular accidents on 12 Friday evenings (6 each on the 6th and 13th):

Year	Month	6th	13th
1989	October	9	13
1990	July	6	12
1991	September	11	14
1991	December	11	10
1992	March	3	4
1992	November	5	12

Is Friday the 13th "unlucky"? Hospital emergency rooms need to plan for any increased "business" if they can. Use an appropriate nonparametric test to decide whether there really is a difference between consecutive Fridays when one of them is a 13th. **LO ❶, ❷**

❶ 27. **Cuckoos and quality control.** Cuckoos lay their eggs in the nests of other (host) birds. The eggs are then adopted and hatched by the host birds. But the potential host birds lay eggs of different sizes. Does the cuckoo change the size of her eggs for different foster species? The numbers in the table are lengths (in millimetres) of cuckoo eggs found in nests of three different species of other birds. The data are drawn from the work of O. M. Latter in 1902 and were used in a fundamental textbook on statistical quality control by L. H. C. Tippett (1902–1985), one of the pioneers in that field.

Cuckoo Egg Length (mm)		
Foster Parent Species		
Sparrow	Robin	Wagtail
20.85	21.05	21.05
21.65	21.85	21.85
22.05	22.05	21.85
22.85	22.05	21.85
23.05	22.05	22.05
23.05	22.25	22.45
23.05	22.45	22.65
23.05	22.45	22.05
23.45	22.65	22.05
23.85	23.05	23.45
23.85	23.05	24.05
24.05	23.05	24.05
25.05	23.05	24.05
	23.25	24.85
	23.85	

Use a Kruskal-Wallis test to decide whether cuckoos really do adjust the size of their eggs. **LO ❷**

28. **Analgesics.** A pharmaceutical company tested three formulations of a pain relief medicine for migraine headache sufferers. For the experiment, 27 volunteers were selected and 9 were randomly assigned to one of three drug formulations. The subjects were instructed to take the drug during their next migraine headache episode and to report their pain on a scale of 1 = no pain to 10 = extreme pain 30 minutes after taking the drug.

Drug	Pain	Drug	Pain	Drug	Pain
A	4	B	6	C	6
A	5	B	8	C	7
A	4	B	4	C	6
A	3	B	5	C	6
A	2	B	4	C	7
A	4	B	6	C	5
A	3	B	5	C	6
A	4	B	8	C	5
A	4	B	6	C	5

a) Use the Kruskal-Wallis test to judge whether there is a difference among the analgesics.
b) What aspect of these data may make the Kruskal-Wallis test more appropriate for these data than the ANOVA methods? **LO ❷**

❶ 29. **Crowdedness.** In a *Chance* magazine article, Danielle Vasilescu and Howard Wainer used data from the United Nations Centre for Human Settlements to investigate aspects of living conditions for several countries. Among the variables they looked at were the countries' per capita gross domestic product (*GDP*, in $) and *Crowdedness*, defined as the average number of persons per room living in homes there. This scatterplot displays these data for 56 countries:

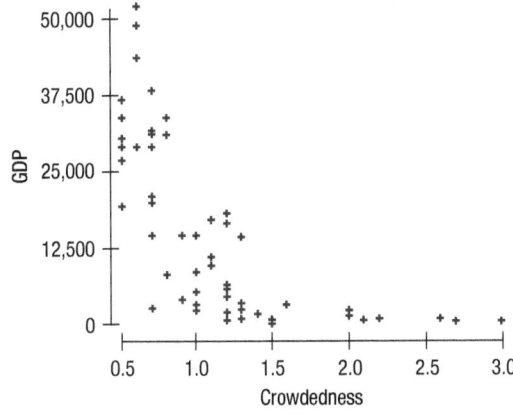

a) The value of Kendall's tau is –0.626. What does this tell us about the association?
b) The value of Spearman's rho is –0.804. What does this tell us about the association?
c) What about these data would make the nonparametric measures appropriate choices? **LO ❸**

❶ 30. **Baseball salaries 2009.** Baseball is big business, and the top salaries have become quite large. The highest salaries (in millions of dollars per season) for some notable players since 1980 are given in the following table:

Player	Year	Salary ($M)
Nolan Ryan	1980	1.0
George Foster	1982	2.0
Kirby Puckett	1990	3.0
Jose Canseco	1990	4.7
Roger Clemens	1991	5.3
Ken Griffey, Jr.	1986	8.5
Albert Belle	1987	11.0
Pedro Martinez	1998	12.5
Mike Piazza	1999	12.5
Mo Vaughn	1999	13.3
Kevin Brown	1999	15.0
Carlos Delgado	2001	17.0
Alex Rodriguez	2001	22.0
Manny Ramirez	2004	22.5
Alex Rodriguez	2005	26.0
Derek Jeter	2006	20.6
Jason Giambi	2007	23.4
Alex Rodriguez	2009	33.0

a) Kendall's tau for these data is 0.887. What does that say about these data?

b) Based on that result, would you predict that salaries will continue to rise? Explain. **LO ❸**

31. The Home Depot. The following scatterplot shows *Sales* at The Home Depot and *Housing Starts* for quarters between 1995 and 2004.

a) Would Kendall's tau be a more appropriate summary than a correlation coefficient? Explain.

b) What could we learn from Kendall's tau that we wouldn't learn from the correlation coefficient? **LO ❶, ❸**

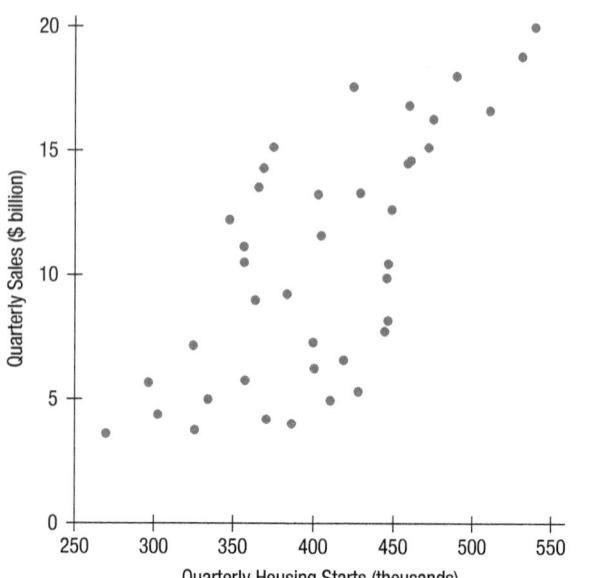

32. Carbon footprint. The scatterplot shows the relationship between the carbon footprint (tonnes of CO_2 per year) and the new Environmental Protection Agency (EPA) highway mileage for 82 family sedans as reported by the U.S. government (www.fueleconomy.gov/feg/byclass.htm). The car with the highest highway miles per gallon (mpg) and lowest carbon footprint is the Toyota Prius.

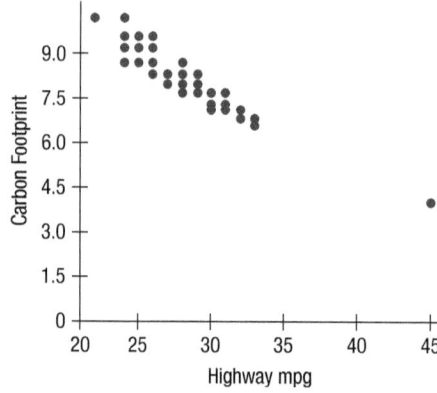

a) Would Spearman's rho be an appropriate summary of the strength of the association shown here?

b) Find rho for the full data and for the relationship with the Prius removed. Comment. **LO ❶, ❸**

33. Income and housing. The Office of Federal Housing Enterprise Oversight (www.ofheo.gov) collects data on various aspects of housing costs around the United States. Here is a scatterplot of the *Housing Cost Index* vs. the *Median Family Income* for each of the 50 states. The correlation is 0.65.

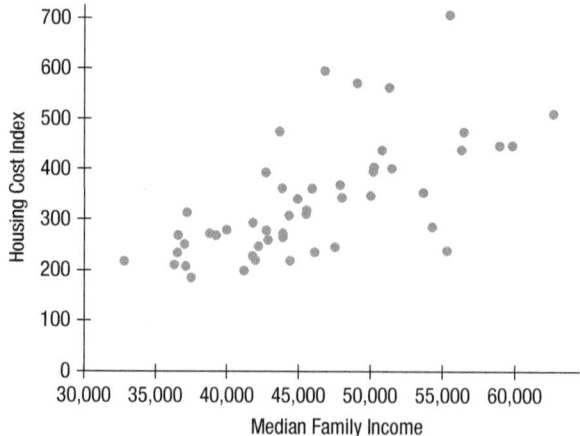

For these data Kendall's tau is 0.51. Does that provide proof that by raising the median income in a state, the *Housing Cost Index* will rise as a result? Explain what Kendall's tau says and does not say. **LO ❸**

34. Interest rates and mortgages. Since 1980, average mortgage interest rates have fluctuated from a low of under 6% to a high of over 14%. Is there a relationship between the amount of money people borrow and the interest rate that's offered? Here is a scatterplot of *Total Mortgages* in the United States (in millions of 2005 U.S. dollars) vs. *Interest Rate* from 1980 to 2005. The correlation is –0.84.

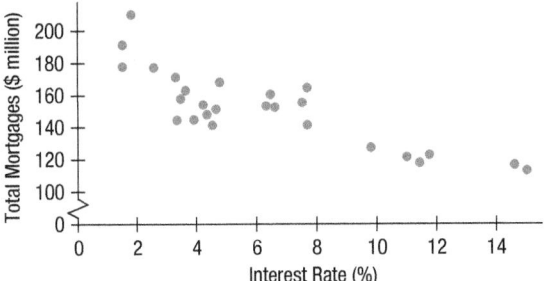

For these data Kendall's tau is –0.61. Does that provide proof that if mortgage rates are lowered, people will take out more mortgages? Explain what Kendall's tau says and does not say. **LO ❸**

35. Canadian taxes. A survey organization obtains the opinions of a random sample of Canadian adults as to how fair the Canadian tax system is on a five-point Likert scale, from "very fair" to "very unfair." Five years later it surveys the same people and asks the same question in order to assess whether opinions have changed. The organization wishes to publish results claiming that opinions haven't changed, and asks its statistician to analyze the results with the aim of producing such a report. The statistician uses Wilcoxon's rank-sum test with a significance level of 95% and reports that opinions haven't changed. According to the ASA Ethical Guidelines in Appendix C, what ethical issues does this raise:

a) For the survey organization?
b) For the statistician?

State your reasons clearly. **LO ❶, ❷**

Congratulations! You have now completed all 10 chapters of Part II of this book, "Understanding Probability Distributions and Statistical Inference." A comprehensive case study is available online in MyStatLab that draws together many of the topics you learned in Part II. Here is a brief summary of that online case study.

Investment Strategy Segmentation

How do people invest? Are there differences between men and women? What about differences in education levels? Do people who are members of a trade union invest differently than those who are not? This case study provides you with a wealth of data to investigate these and similar questions.

Learning Objectives

Chapter	8	9	10	11	12	13	14	15	17
Learning Objective	3	3,4	3	1	1	2	1	1	1

Troy Fleece/The Canadian Press

18

Inference for Regression

LEARNING OBJECTIVES

In this chapter we show you how to make inferences from a regression analysis. After reading and studying this chapter, you should be able to:

❶ Perform a hypothesis test and calculate the confidence interval for the slope of a linear regression

❷ Perform a hypothesis test on a correlation coefficient

❸ Perform a hypothesis test and calculate the confidence interval for predicted values

PotashCorp of Saskatchewan

PotashCorp of Saskatchewan is the world's largest producer of potash (K), a major component of fertilizers. It's also a major producer of nitrogen (N) and phosphate (P), two other major ingredients used in fertilizers. Putting the N, P, and K together, it's not surprising that PotashCorp is also the world's largest producer of fertilizer. PotashCorp, founded in 1975 as a Crown corporation owned by the Government of Saskatchewan, began buying up mines in the province that had been owned by many U.S. companies. This brought the extensive potash reserves of Saskatchewan under Canadian control, but PotashCorp failed to make a profit. The company was sold by the government on the Toronto Stock Exchange in 1989 with an initial public offering price of $18 per share. It continued to expand, buying other mining companies at home and abroad, and now owns assets around the world.

The continuing increase in world population coupled with the growth in global living standards places enormous pressures on the agriculture industry to produce more food, with only limited capability to increase farm area. Therefore, fertilizer plays a major role in feeding the world, and demand has been increasing throughout this century. Can PotashCorp sustain increased levels of production into the future? The answer is a clear Yes! Canada has about 60% of the world's reserves of potash ore, most of it controlled by PotashCorp. A typical example of a PotashCorp mine is near Rocanville in southeast Saskatchewan, which has an operational capacity of 2.7 megatonnes of potassium chloride per year. Plus, there's enough ore still in the ground for PotashCorp's potash mines to continue operation for between 54 and 89 years.

		Large Sample or Normal Population		Small Sample and Non-normal Population or Non-numeric Data	
Number of Variables	**Objective**	Chapter	Parametric Method	Chapter	Nonparametric Method
1	Calculate confidence interval for a proportion	11			
1	Compare a proportion with a given value	12	z-test		
1	Calculate a confidence interval for a mean and compare it with a given value	13	t-test	17.2	Wilcoxon Signed-Rank Test
2	Compare two proportions	12.8	z-test		
2	Compare two means for independent samples	14.1–14.5	t-test	17.4, 17.5	Wilcoxon Rank-Sum (Mann-Whitney) Test Tukey's Quick Test
2	Compare two means for paired samples	14.6, 14.7	Paired t-test	17.2	Wilcoxon Signed-Rank Test
≥3	Compare multiple means	15	ANOVA: ANalysis Of VAriance	17.3 17.6	Friedman Test Kruskal-Wallis Test
≥3	Compare multiple counts (proportions)	16	χ^2 test		
2	Investigate the relationship between two variables	18	Correlation Regression	17.7, 17.8	Kendall's tau Spearman's rho
≥3	Investigate the relationship between multiple variables	20	Multiple Regression		

ROADMAP FOR STATISTICAL INFERENCE

The Rocanville mine of PotashCorp uses some of the latest automated mining equipment to continuously cut into the underground rock face and remove ore on a conveyor system. For efficient operation, a laser guidance system is used to follow the seam of ore. However, the mining operation creates a large amount of dust that may reduce the strength of the laser beam, and powerful fans are used to extract the dust.

In a large mine, the ventilation system circulates several thousand cubic metres of air per minute, drawing fresh air in at one location and venting it at another. In a typical mine, the total power of the fans in one of the underground rooms in which mining takes place is related to the strength of the laser beam used to guide the mining equipment. Let's suppose that we took measurements from 59 Saskatchewan mines, resulting in the graph in Figure 18.1.

In Chapter 7 we modelled relationships like this by fitting a straight line. The equation of the least squares line for these data is

$$\widehat{Strength} = -4.871 + 4.200 \times Power.$$

The slope says that, on average, the laser beam strength increases by 4.2 watts for every extra kilowatt of fan power.

WHO	59 mines
WHAT	Laser strength and fan power
WHEN	2017
WHERE	Saskatchewan
WHY	Estimation of laser strength for a given fan power

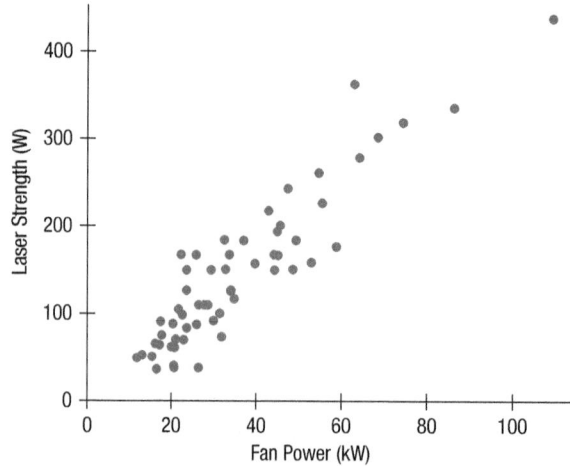

Figure 18.1   A scatterplot of the laser guidance beam strength against the power in kilowatts of the fans in a typical mining operation.

How useful is this model? When we fit linear models before, we used them to describe the relationship between the variables, and we interpreted the slope and intercept as descriptions of the data. Now we'd like to know what the regression model can tell us beyond the sample we used to generate this regression. To do that, we'll want to make confidence intervals and test hypotheses about the slope and intercept of the regression line.

LO❶ 18.1   The Population and the Sample

Our data are one particular sample of 59 measurements. If we take another sample, we hope the regression line will be similar to the one we found here, but we know it won't be exactly the same. Observations vary from sample to sample. But we can imagine a true line that summarizes the relationship between *Strength* and *Power*. Following our usual conventions, we write the idealized line with Greek letters and consider the coefficients (slope and intercept) to be parameters: β_0 is the intercept and β_1 is the slope. Corresponding to our fitted line of $\hat{y} = b_0 + b_1x$, we write $\mu_y = \beta_0 + \beta_1x$. We write μ_y instead of y because the regression line assumes that the *means* of the y values for each value of x fall exactly on the line. We can picture the relationship as in Figure 18.2, which shows that, for instance, at a fan power of 40 kW, there is a distribution of possible laser strengths. The

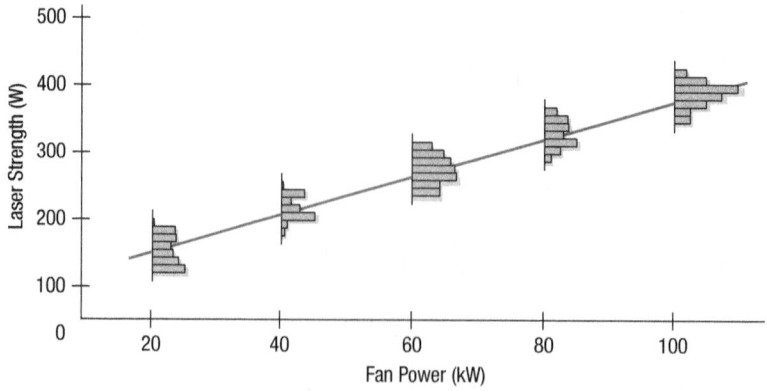

Figure 18.2   There's a distribution of *Strength* for each value of *Fan Power*. The regression model assumes that the means line up perfectly like this.

Naming our Variables

We will avoid the terms **dependent and independent variables** in this chapter to avoid confusion with dependent and independent random events described in Chapter 8. However it is important to know what they mean since they are often used by regression software packages.

means fall exactly on the line (for our idealized model), and the y values at each x are distributed around them.

Now, if only we had all the values in the population, we could find the slope and intercept of this *idealized regression line* explicitly by using least squares.

Of course, not all the individual y's are at these means. In fact, the line will miss most—and usually all—of the plotted points. Some y's lie above the line and some below the line, so, like all models, this one makes errors. If we want to account for each individual value of y in our model, we have to include these errors, which we denote by ε:

$$y = \beta_0 + \beta_1 x + \varepsilon$$

This equation has an ε to soak up the deviation at each point, so the model gives a value of y for each value of x. y is known as the **dependent variable**, **response variable**, or **predicted variable** and is usually plotted on the vertical axis of the graph. x is known as the **independent variable** or **explanatory variable** and is usually plotted on the horizontal axis of the graph.

We estimate the β's by finding a regression line, $\hat{y} = b_0 + b_1 x$, as we did in Chapter 7. The residuals, $e = y - \hat{y}$, are the sample-based versions of the errors, ε. We'll use them to help us assess the regression model.

We know that least squares regression will give us reasonable estimates of the parameters of this model from a random sample of data. We also know that our estimates won't be equal to the parameters in the idealized or "true" model. Our challenge is to account for the uncertainty in our estimates by making confidence intervals, as we've done for means and proportions. For that, we need to make some assumptions about the model and the errors.

FOR EXAMPLE   National survey of food expenditure

A chain store that sells bulk foods is planning a marketing campaign. Using data from a national survey of 905 people, it constructs variables that report for each respondent the weekly amount spent by his or her household on food (both groceries and eating out). A regression of this variable against weekly household income (in $1000) results in the model:

$$\widehat{Food \$/wk} = 101.33 + 0.77 \; HHincome$$

QUESTION Write an interpretation of this model. How should the store managers interpret the relationship between spending on food and weekly household income?

ANSWER The average amount spent by a household on food per week can be estimated as $101.33 plus $0.77 for each $1000 of weekly household income. Managers might use this to target advertising to different communities based on census data about weekly household incomes in those communities.

LO❶   **18.2**   ## Assumptions and Conditions

When we fitted lines to data in Chapter 7, we needed both the Linearity Condition and the Equal Variance Assumption, and we checked the corresponding conditions. Now, when we want to make inferences about the coefficients of the line, we'll have to assume more, so we'll add more conditions.

We need to be careful about the order in which we check conditions. So we number the assumptions and check conditions for each in order: (1) Linearity

Condition, (2) Independence Assumption, (3) Equal Variance Assumption, and (4) Normal Population Assumption.

1. Linearity Condition

If the true relationship of two quantitative variables is far from linear and we use a straight line to fit the data, our entire analysis will be useless, so we always check linearity first (and we check the Quantitative Variable Condition for both variables as well, as in Section 7.2).

The Linearity Condition is satisfied if a scatterplot looks straight. It's generally not a good idea to draw a line through the scatterplot when checking. That can fool your eye into seeing the plot as straighter than it really is. Recall the errors, or residuals, we computed in Chapter 7 for each observation. Sometimes it's easier to see violations of this Linearity Condition by looking at a scatterplot of the residuals against x or against the predicted values, $\hat{y}$. That plot should have no pattern if the condition is satisfied.

If the scatterplot is straight enough, we can go on to some assumptions about the errors. If not, we stop here, or consider transforming the variables to make the scatterplot more linear. We've seen that transforming variables can help us understand relationships in several other contexts in Chapters 6 and 7. Chapter 19 discusses transformations for regressions more thoroughly.

2. Independence Assumption

The errors in the true underlying regression model (the ε's) must be independent of each other. As usual, there's no way to be sure that the Independence Assumption is true.

When we care about inference for the regression parameters, it's often because we think our regression model might apply to a larger population. In such cases, we can check the Randomization Condition that the individuals are a random sample from that population.

We can also check displays of the regression residuals for evidence of patterns, trends, or clumping, any of which would suggest a failure of independence. In the special case when we have a time series, a common violation of the Independence Assumption is for the errors to be correlated with each other (autocorrelated). (The error our model makes today may be similar to the one it made yesterday.) We can check this violation by plotting the residuals against time (usually the x-variable for a time series) and looking for patterns.

3. Equal Variance Assumption

The variability of y should be about the same for all values of x. In Chapter 7 we looked at the standard deviation of the residuals (s_e) to measure the size of the scatter. Now we'll need this standard deviation to build confidence intervals and test hypotheses. The standard deviation of the residuals is the building block for the standard errors of all the regression parameters. But it only makes sense if the scatter of the residuals is the same everywhere. In effect, the standard deviation of the residuals "pools" information across all the individual distributions of y at each x-value, and pooled estimates are appropriate only when they combine information for groups with the same variance.

Equal Spread Condition   A scatterplot of residuals against predicted values can help us see if the spread changes in any way. (You can also plot the residuals against x.)

We always check the Equal Spread Condition by looking at a scatterplot of residuals against x or $\hat{y}$. Make sure the spread around the line is nearly constant.

Be alert for a "fan" shape or other tendency for the variation to grow or shrink in one part of the scatterplot.

If the plot is straight enough, the data are independent, and the spread doesn't change, we can move on to the final assumption and its associated condition.

4. Normal Population Assumption

We assume that the errors around the idealized regression line at each value of x follow a Normal model. We need this assumption so that we can use a Student's t-model for inference.

As in other times when we use Student's t, we'll settle for the residuals satisfying the **Nearly Normal Condition**.[1] The Normality Assumption becomes less important as the sample size grows because the model is about means and the Central Limit Theorem takes over. A histogram of the residuals is one way to check whether they're nearly Normal. Alternatively, we can look at a *Normal probability plot* of the residuals (see Figure 18.3). It finds deviations from the Normal model more efficiently than a histogram would. In Chapter 9 we saw that if the distribution of the data is Normal, the Normal probability plot will look roughly like a diagonal straight line. Deviations from a straight line indicate that the distribution is not Normal. This plot is usually able to show deviations from Normality more clearly than the corresponding histogram, but it's usually easier to understand *how* a distribution fails to be Normal by looking at its histogram. Another common failure of Normality is the presence of an outlier. So we still check the **Outlier Condition** to ensure that no point is exerting too much influence on the fitted model.

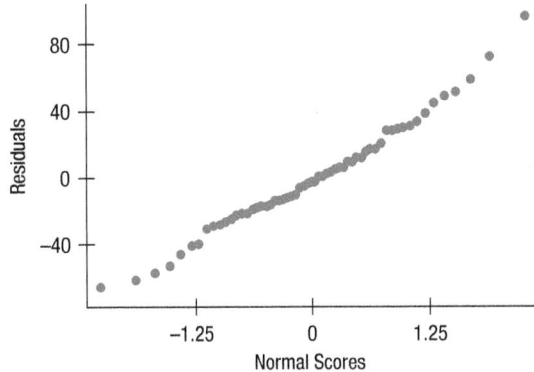

Figure 18.3 A Normal probability plot graphs the actual standardized *Residuals* against those expected (*Normal Scores*) for a sample from a standard Normal containing the same number of observations.

- **How does the Normal probability plot work?** A Normal probability plot compares each value (in our case, each of the 59 residuals) with the value we would have expected to get if we'd just drawn a sample of 59 values from a standard Normal model. The key is to match our numbers in the order of the expected Normal values.

   It helps to think in terms of standardized values. For example, the lowest (most negative) residual in our example has a value of -69.48. Standardizing, we find that it's 2.03 standard deviations below the mean, giving a z-score of

---

[1]*This* is why we check the conditions in order. We check that the residuals are independent and that the variation is the same for all x's before we can lump all the residuals together to check the Normal Condition.

−2.03. We can learn from theory that if we draw a sample of 59 values at random from a standard Normal model, we'd expect the smallest of them to have a value of −2.39. We're drawing from a standard Normal, so that's already a z-score. We can see, then, that our lowest residual isn't quite as far from the mean as we might have expected (had the residuals been perfectly Normal).

We can continue in this way, comparing each observed value with the value we'd expect from a Normal model. The easiest way to make the comparison, of course, is to graph it. If our observed values look like a sample from a Normal model, then the probability plot stretches out in a straight line from lower left to upper right. But if our values deviate from what we'd expect, the plot will bend or have jumps in it.

The values we'd expect from a Normal model are called Normal scores, or sometimes nscores. Statistics programs haven't agreed on whether to plot the Normal scores on the x-axis or the y-axis, so you need to look to be sure. But since you usually just want to check whether the plot is straight or not, it really doesn't matter.

A Normal probability plot is a great way to check whether the distribution is nearly Normal. But when it isn't straight, it's often a good idea to make a histogram of the values as well to get a sense of just how the data are distributed.

The best advice on using a Normal probability plot is to check whether it's straight. If it is, then your data will look like data from a Normal model. If not, make a histogram to understand how they differ from the model.

Summary of Assumptions and Conditions

Truth will emerge more readily from error than from confusion.

—Francis Bacon (1561–1626)

If all four assumptions were true, the idealized regression model would look like Figure 18.4.

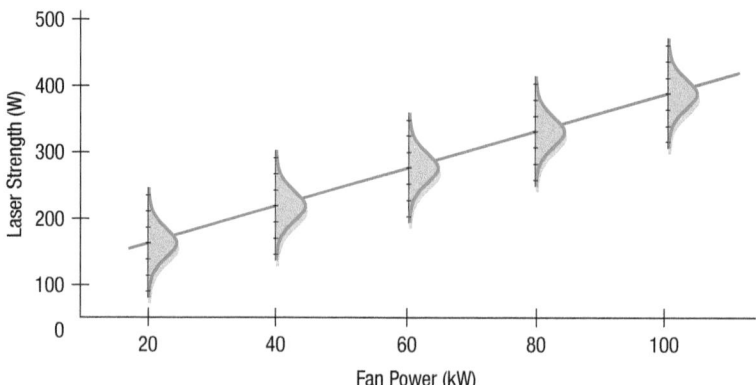

Figure 18.4   The regression model has a distribution of *y*-values for each *x*-value. These distributions follow a Normal model, with means lined up along the line and the same standard deviations.

At each value of *x*, there's a distribution of *y*-values that follows a Normal model, and each of these Normal models is centred on the line and has the same standard deviation. Of course, we don't expect the assumptions to be exactly true. As the statistician George Box said, "All models are wrong." But the linear model is often close enough to be useful.

In regression, there's a little catch. The best way to check many of the conditions is with the residuals, but we get the residuals only *after* we compute the regression. Before we compute the regression, however, we should check at least one of the conditions.

So we work in this order:

1. **Make a scatterplot of the data** to check the **Linearity Condition** (and always check that the variables are quantitative as well).
2. If the data are straight enough, **fit a regression and find the residuals, e, and predicted values, $\hat{y}$.**
3. If you know when the measurements were made, **plot the residuals against time** to check for evidence of patterns that suggest they may not be independent (**Independence Assumption**).
4. **Make a scatterplot of the residuals against x or the predicted values.** This plot should have no pattern. Check in particular for any bend (which would suggest that the data weren't that straight after all), for any thickening (or thinning), and, of course, for any unusual observations, see Chapter 6, Section 1. If you discover any errors, correct them or omit those points, and go back to step 1. Otherwise, consider performing two regressions—one with and one without the unusual observations (**Equal Variance Assumption**).
5. If the scatterplots look okay, then **make a histogram and Normal probability plot of the residuals** to check the **Nearly Normal** and **Outlier Conditions** (**Normal Population Assumption**).

FOR EXAMPLE | **Checking assumptions and conditions for the food expenditure survey**

Here are some displays related to the previous example's regression of the percentage of income spent on food against household income (see For Example: "National survey of food expenditure"). Use them and the other information provided to check the regression assumptions. For each, indicate whether you think it's satisfied and why.

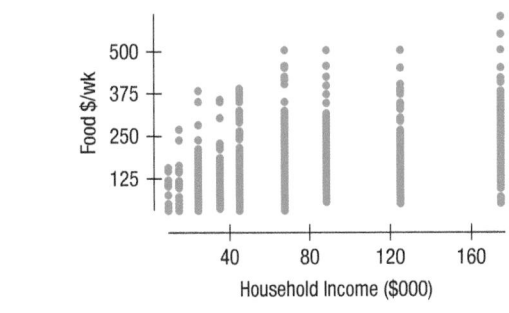

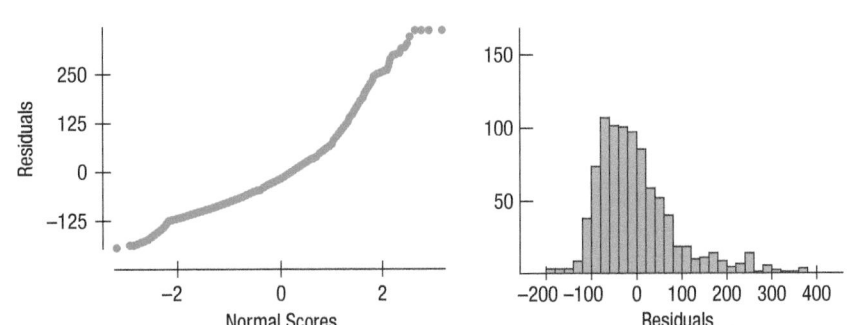

QUESTION Do the assumptions and conditions for regression inference appear to be met?

ANSWER

- **Linearity:** The scatterplot of the data isn't strongly linear, but there's no strong evidence of nonlinearity.

(continued)

- **Independence:** The data are from a national random sample. Respondents are almost surely independent of one another.
- **Equal Variance:** The data may be less variable at the low end (which would be understandable, since households with lower income would be constrained from spending a lot on food).
- **Normal Population:** The Normal probability plot shows some bend and the histogram is unimodal, but it has a longer upper tail. The sample size is large, however, so we probably can proceed with inference.

LO❶   ## 18.3   The Standard Error of the Slope

There's only one regression model for the population. Sample regressions try to estimate the parameters, β_0 and β_1. We expect the estimated slope for any sample, b_1, to be close to—but not actually equal to—the model slope, β_1. If we could see the collection of slopes from many samples (imagined or real), we would see a distribution of values around the true slope. That's the sampling distribution of the slope.

What is the standard deviation of this distribution? In other words, what is the standard error of the slope, $SE(b_1)$? What aspects of the data affect how much the slope varies from sample to sample?

- **Spread around the line.** Figure 18.5 shows samples from two populations. Which underlying population would give rise to the more consistent slopes?

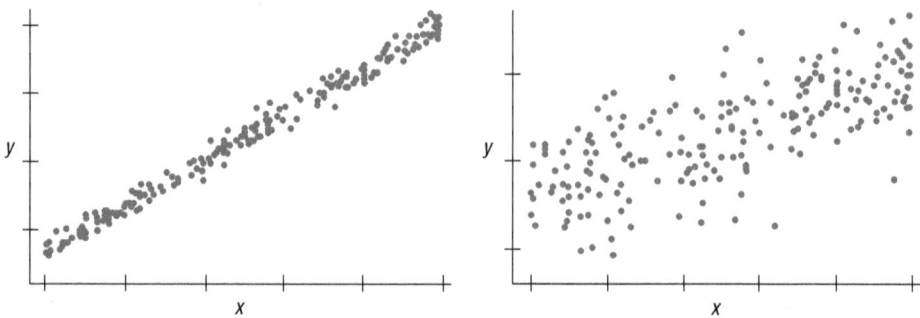

Figure 18.5   Which of these scatterplots would give the more consistent regression slope estimate if we were to sample repeatedly from its underlying population?

Less scatter around the line means the slope will be more consistent from sample to sample. We measure the spread around the line with the **residual standard deviation**:

$$s_e = \sqrt{\frac{\sum(y - \hat{y})^2}{n - 2}}$$

The less scatter around the line, the smaller the residual standard deviation, the lower the $SE(b_1)$, and hence the more accurately we can estimate the regression line.

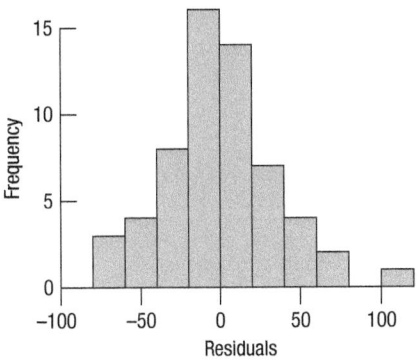

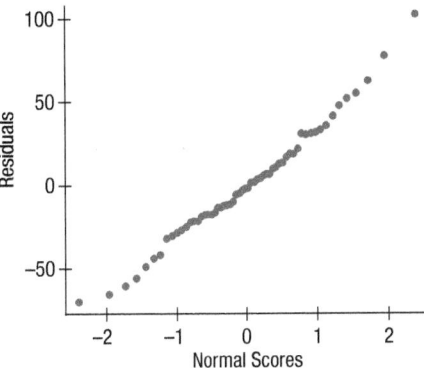

State the sampling distribution model. Choose the method.	Under these conditions, the sampling distribution of the regression slope can be modelled by a Student's t-model with $(n - 2) = 59 - 2 = 57$ degrees of freedom, so we'll proceed with a regression slope t-test.

DO

Mechanics The regression equation can be found from the formulas in Chapter 7, but regressions are almost always found from a computer program or calculator.

Here's the computer output for this regression:

Variable	Cofficient	SE(coeff)	t-ratio	P-value
Intercept	−4.871	9.654	−0.50	0.6159
Power	4.200	0.2385	17.61	<0.0001

From the computer output we can read off the estimates of the regression coefficients, $b_0 = -4.87$, $b_1 = 4.20$, together with their standard errors, 9.65 and 0.2385, respectively. We can read the P-value off the computer output or look it up in Table T in Appendix B.

The P-values given in the regression output table are from the Student's t-distribution on $(n - 2) = 57$ degrees of freedom. They are appropriate for two-sided alternatives.

The P-value <0.0001 means that the association we see in the data is unlikely to have occurred by chance. Therefore, we reject the null hypothesis and conclude that there is strong evidence that the *Laser Strength* is linearly related to the *Fan Power*.

Create a confidence interval for the true slope. To obtain the t-value for 57 degrees of freedom, use Table T in Appendix B. The estimated slope and *SE* for the slope are obtained from the regression output.

A 95% confidence interval for β_1 is
$b_1 \pm t^*_{n-2} \times SE(b_1) = 4.200 \pm 2 \times 0.2385 = (3.722, 4.678)$,
since t^*_{57} for a 95% confidence interval is 2.00.

Since this confidence interval does not contain the value 0, we again conclude that the slope is significant.

(continued)

Interpret the interval.	We are 95% confident that the laser strength increases, on average, between 3.72 and 4.68 watts for each additional kilowatt of fan power. (Technically: We are 95% confident that the interval from 3.72 to 4.68 captures the true rate at which the *Laser Strength* increases with *Fan Power*.)
REPORT **Conclusion** State the conclusion in the proper context.	MEMO: **Re: Mining Operations** We investigated the relationship between fan power and laser strength in 59 different mines. The regression analysis showed that, on average, the laser strength increased by 4.20 watts for every additional kilowatt of fan power. Assuming that these measurements are representative, we are 95% confident that the strength of a guidance laser in a mining operation increases, on average, between 3.72 and 4.68 watts for each additional kilowatt of power of the extraction fans.

FOR EXAMPLE   **Testing the slope for the food expenditure survey**

QUESTIONS

1. Using the computer output from For Example: "Standard error for the food expenditure survey," state and test the standard null hypothesis for the slope. Tell what the hypothesis means in terms of the variables as well as in symbols, and explain what your conclusion means.

2. Construct the corresponding 95% confidence interval for the slope and interpret its meaning.

ANSWERS

1. The null hypothesis is that there is no linear relationship between the amount spent on food and household income:

$$H_0 : \beta_1 = 0$$

$$H_A : \beta_1 \neq 0$$

We now refer to the computer output from For Example: "Standard error for the food expenditure survey." With a P-value less than 0.001, we can be quite confident in rejecting the null hypothesis. We conclude that there is indeed a linear relationship between the amount spent on food and household income.

2. The critical *t*-value for a 95% confidence interval with 57 degrees of freedom is 2.00 from Table T in Appendix B. The confidence interval is therefore:

$$0.769860 - 2.00 \times 0.0608 < \beta_{HHIncome} < 0.769860 + 2.00 \times 0.0608$$

$$0.648 < \beta_{HHIncome} < 0.891$$

We are 95% confident that for every $1000 increase in household income, weekly expenditure on food increases by between $0.65 and $0.89.

LO❷   **18.5   A Hypothesis Test for Correlation**

In the previous section, we tested whether the slope, β_1, was zero. What if we wanted to test whether the *correlation* between x and y is zero? We write ρ for the parameter (true population value) of the correlation, so we're testing $H_0 : \rho = 0$. Remember that the regression slope estimate is $b_1 = r\frac{s_y}{s_x}$. The same is true for the parameter versions of these statistics: $\beta_1 = \rho\frac{\sigma_y}{\sigma_x}$. This means that if the slope is really zero, then the correlation has to be zero, too. So if we test $H_0 : \beta_1 = 0$, that's really the same as testing $H_0 : \rho = 0$. Sometimes, however, a researcher might want to test correlation without fitting a regression, so you'll see the test of correlation as a separate test (it's also slightly more general), but the results are mathematically the same even though the form looks different. The **t-test for the correlation coefficient** can be found in the box on the left.

The t-test for the correlation coefficient

When the conditions are met, we can test the hypothesis $H_0 : \rho = 0$ vs. $H_A : \rho \ne 0$ using the test statistic

$$t = r\sqrt{\frac{n - 2}{1 - r^2}},$$

which follows a Student's t-model with $n-2$ degrees of freedom. We can use the t-model to find the P-value of the test using software or Table T in Appendix B.

FOR EXAMPLE   **Testing correlation between age and electronics spending**

QUESTION   In a national survey of 1000 adults, the correlation between the *Age* of respondents and their *Expenditures on Electronics* is -0.142. The scatter plot indicates a linear relationship. Does this indicate a statistically significant correlation?

ANSWER   To test the hypothesis $H_0 : \rho = 0$ versus $H_A : \rho \ne 0$, we use the test statistic:

$$t = -0.142\sqrt{\frac{1000 - 2}{1-(-0.142)^2}} = -4.53,$$

for which $P < 0.001$. We can reject the null hypothesis that the true correlation, ρ, is zero and conclude that expenditure on electronics is correlated with age.

JUST CHECKING

General economic theory suggests that as unemployment rises and jobs become harder to find, more students will enrol in universities. Researchers analyzed enrollment at the University of New Mexico and unemployment data in New Mexico to determine whether there is any statistical relationship between the two variables. The data were collected by the University of New Mexico over a period of 29 years, starting with 1961 and ending with 1989. The variable *Enrollment* is the number of students and the variable *Unemp* is a percentage. Here is some regression output for these data:

1 What would you like to see before proceeding with inference on this regression? Why?

2 Assuming the assumptions and conditions for regression are met, find the 95% confidence interval for the slope.

3 Clearly state the null and the alternative hypotheses for the slope. Interpret the P-value.

4 Is there a strong relationship between enrollment and unemployment?

5 Interpret the value of R^2 in the output.

6 The correlation between enrollment and unemployment for this sample is 0.391, which gives a t-value of 2.21 with 27 degrees of freedom and a two-sided P-value of 0.036. What does this say about the true correlation between enrollment and unemployment? Does this give you any new information?

Answers are found in Appendix A.

Predictor	Coeff	SE(Coeff)	t-ratio	P-value
Intercept	3957	4000	0.99	0.331
Unemp	1133.8	513.1	2.21	0.036

S = 3049.50 R-Sq = 15.3%

LO❸   18.6   Predicted Values

We've seen how to construct the confidence interval for a slope or intercept, but we're often interested in prediction. We know how to compute predicted values of *y* for any value of *x* from the regression line (we first did this in Chapter 7). This predicted value would be our best estimate, but it's still just an informed guess. Now, however, we have standard errors. We can use those standard errors to construct confidence intervals for the predictions and to report our uncertainty honestly.

From our model of mining data, we can use *Fan Power* to get a reasonable estimate of guidance *Laser Strength*. Suppose we want to predict the *Laser Strength* when we have 40 kilowatts of *Fan Power*. A confidence interval can tell us how precise that prediction is. The precision depends on the question we ask, however, and there are two different things we might ask:

> Do we want to know the mean *Laser Strength* for *all mines* that have 40 kilowatts of *Fan Power*?
>
> *or*
>
> Do we want to estimate the *Laser Strength* for a *particular* mine with 40 kilowatts of *Fan Power*?

What's the difference between the two questions? If we were the manufacturer of the laser guidance system, we might be more naturally interested in the mean *Strength* of the guidance laser averaged over all mines that have a certain amount of *Fan Power*. On the other hand, if we were a mine operator interested in purchasing a laser guidance system, we might be more interested in estimating the *Laser Strength* in our individual mine with its amount of *Fan Power*.

Both questions are important. The predicted *Strength* value is the same for both, but one question leads to a much more precise interval than the other. If your intuition says that it's easier to be more precise about the mean than about the individuals, you're on the right track. Because individual *Laser Strengths* vary much more than *means*, we can predict the *mean Strength* for all mines with a lot more precision than we can predict the *Strength* of a particular mine with the same *Fan Power*.

Let's start by predicting the *Strength* for a new *Power*, one that wasn't necessarily part of the original data set. To emphasize this, we'll call this *x*-value "*x* sub nu," pronounced "new," and write it as x_ν. As an example, we'll take x_ν to be 40 kilowatts. The regression equation predicts *Strength* by $\hat{y}_\nu = b_0 + b_1 x_\nu$. Now that we have the predicted value, we can construct intervals around this number. Both intervals take the form

$$\hat{y}_\nu \pm t^*_{n-2} \times SE.$$

The confidence interval for the predicted mean value

When the conditions are met, we find the **confidence interval for the predicted mean value** μ_ν at a value x_ν as

$$\hat{y}_\nu \pm t^*_{n-2} \times SE(\hat{\mu}_\nu)$$

where the standard error is

$$SE(\hat{\mu}_\nu) = \sqrt{SE^2(b_1) \times (x_\nu - \bar{x})^2 + \frac{s_e^2}{n}}.$$

There are therefore four factors that can contribute to a wide confidence interval: (i) a high standard error of b_1; (ii) x_ν being far away from the mean value of *x*; (iii) the data being spread away from the regression line; and/or (iv) a small sample size.

Even the t^* value is the same for both. It's the critical value (from Table T in Appendix B or software) for $n - 2$ degrees of freedom and the specified confidence level. The difference between the two intervals is in the standard errors.

Figure 18.8 shows the confidence interval for the mean predictions. In this plot, the intervals for all the mean *Strengths* at all values of *Power* are shown together as confidence bands. Notice that the bands get wider as we attempt to predict values that lie farther away from the mean *Fan Power* (35.82 kilowatts). (That's the $(x_\nu - \bar{x})^2$ term in the *SE* formula.) As we move away from the mean *x* value, there is more uncertainty associated with our prediction. A 95% confidence interval for the mean *Laser Strength* when the *Fan Power* is 40 would go from 153.90 to 172.34. The interval is much wider when the *Fan Power* is 100.

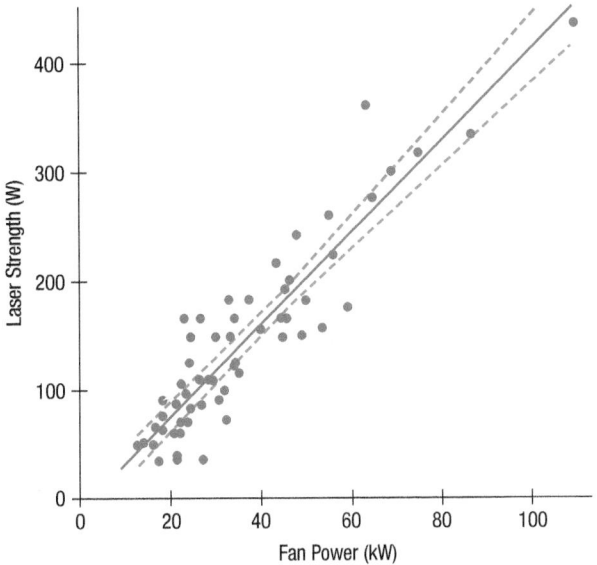

Figure 18.8   The 95% confidence intervals for the mean *Laser Strength* for a given *Fan Power* are shown as the green dashed lines. Near the mean *Fan Power* (35.8 kw), our confidence interval for the mean *Laser Strength* is much narrower than for values far from the mean, such as 100 kilowatts.

Like all confidence intervals, the width of these confidence intervals varies with the sample size. A sample larger than 59 would result in narrower intervals. A regression based on data from 1000 mines would have much narrower bands. The last factor affecting our confidence intervals is the spread of the data around the line. If there's more spread around the line, predictions are less certain, and the confidence interval bands are wider.

From Figure 18.8, it's easy to see that most *points* don't fall within the confidence interval bands—and we shouldn't expect them to. These bands show confidence intervals for the *mean*. An even larger sample would have given even narrower bands. Then we'd expect an even smaller percentage of the points to fall within them.

If we want to capture an individual laser strength, we need to use a wider interval, called a **prediction interval**, shown in Figure 18.9. Prediction intervals are based on the same quantities as the confidence intervals, but they include an extra term for the spread around the line.

The standard errors for prediction depend on the same kinds of things as the coefficients' standard errors. If there's more spread around the line, we'll be less certain when we try to predict the response. Of course, if we're less certain of the

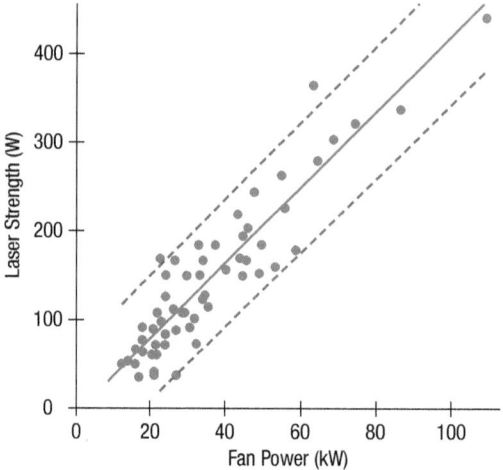

Figure 18.9   95% prediction intervals (in red) estimate the interval that contains 95% of the distribution of the *y* values that might be observed at a given value of *x*. If the assumptions and conditions hold, then there's a 95% chance that a particular *y*-value will be within this interval.

slope, we'll be less certain of our prediction. If we have more data, our estimate will be more precise. And there's one more piece: If we're farther from the centre of our data, our prediction will be less precise. It's a lot easier to predict a data point near the middle of the data set than to extrapolate far from the centre.

The prediction interval for an individual value

When the conditions are met, we can find the prediction interval for all values of y at a value x_v as

$$\hat{y}_v \pm t^*_{n-1} \times SE(\hat{y}_v),$$

where the standard error is

$$SE(\hat{y}_v) = \sqrt{SE^2(b_1) \times (x_v - \bar{x})^2 + \frac{s_e^2}{n} + s_e^2}.$$

This prediction interval is wider than the confidence interval because of the last term under the square root sign.

Remember to maintain the distinction between the two kinds of intervals when looking at computer output. The narrower ones are confidence intervals for the *mean* and the wider ones are prediction intervals for *individual* values.

As an example, let us estimate the mean *Laser Strength* in mines with 25 kilowatts of *Fan Power*. The regression output table provides most of the numbers we need:

Variable	Coefficient	SE(coeff)	*t*-ratio	P-value
Intercept	−4.871	9.654	−0.50	0.6159
Power	4.200	0.2385	17.61	<0.0001

$s_e = 32.54$ R-Sq = 84.5%

The regression model gives a predicted value at $x_v = 25$ kilowatts

$$-4.871 + 4.200 \,(25) = 100.13.$$

Using this, we'll first find the 95% confidence interval for the mean *Laser Strength* for all mines with 25 kilowatts of *Fan Power*. We find the standard error from the formula using the values in the regression output:

$$SE(\hat{\mu}_v) = \sqrt{(SE^2(b_1))(x_v - \bar{x})^2 + \frac{s_e^2}{n}}$$

$$= \sqrt{(0.2385)^2(25 - 35.82)^2 + \frac{32.54^2}{59}} = 4.96$$

The t^* value that excludes 2.5% in either tail with $59 - 2 = 57$ df is (according to the tables) 2.002.

Putting it all together, we find the margin of error as

$$ME = 2.002(4.96) = 9.93.$$

So we are 95% confident that the interval

$$100.13 \pm 9.93 = (90.20, 110.06)$$

includes the true mean *Laser Strength* in mines with 25 kilowatts of *Fan Power*.

Suppose, however, that instead of the mean *Laser Strength*, we want to estimate the *Laser Strength* in our own individual mine, which has 25 kilowatts of *Fan Power*. The confidence interval we just found is too narrow. It may contain the mean *Laser Strength*, but it's unlikely to cover any individual *Laser Strength*. To make a prediction interval for an *individual* mine with a *Fan Power* of 25 kilowatts, we need the larger standard error formula to account for the greater variability. Using the formula

$$SE(\hat{y}_v) = \sqrt{(SE^2(b_1))(x_v - \bar{x})^2 + \frac{s_e^2}{n} + s_e^2} = 32.54$$

we find the ME to be

$$ME = t^* SE(\hat{y}_v) = 2.002 \times 32.92 = 65.14$$

so the prediction interval is

$$\hat{y} \pm ME = 100.13 \pm 65.14 = (34.99, 165.3).$$

Notice how much wider this interval is than the 95% confidence interval for the mean *Laser Strength*. Most of the time we'll use a software package to compute and display these intervals. Most packages generate displays that show the regression line along with both the 95% confidence and prediction intervals (combining what we've

---

FOR EXAMPLE   **Predictions from the food expenditure survey**

Working with the regression model we found in earlier examples (see For Example: "Standard error for the food expenditure survey"), corporate management wants to predict the amount spent on food.

QUESTIONS

1. Construct and interpret a 95% confidence interval for the predicted mean value of the amount spent on food by a household with an annual income of $100,000. You'll need to know also that the mean household income is $81,000.

2. Construct and interpret a 95% prediction interval for the amount spent on food by the Smith household, which has an annual income of $100,000.

(continued)

ANSWERS

1. The predicted value of the mean amount spent on food when income = $100K is
$101.3 + 0.7699 \times 100 = 178.3$.
The standard error for this mean amount is $\sqrt{0.6071^2(100 - 81)^2 + \frac{91.1^2}{905}} = 3.24$.

The sample size is 905, giving 903 degrees of freedom and a critical t-value of 1.96 from Table T in Appendix B. The 95% confidence interval is therefore $178.3 \pm 1.96 \times 3.24 = (172, 185)$. We are 95% confident that the mean weekly amount spent on food by households with an income of $100,000 is between $172 and $185.

2. The standard error for the amount spent on food in a specific household is
$\sqrt{0.6071^2(100 - 81)^2 + \frac{91.1^2}{905} + 91.1^2} = 91.2$.

The 95% confidence interval is therefore $178.3 \pm 1.96 \times 91.2 = (-1, 357)$. We are 95% confident that the weekly amount spent on food by the Smith household is between $0 and $357.

shown in Figures 18.8 and 18.9). This makes it easier to see how much wider the prediction intervals are than the corresponding confidence intervals (see Figure 18.10).

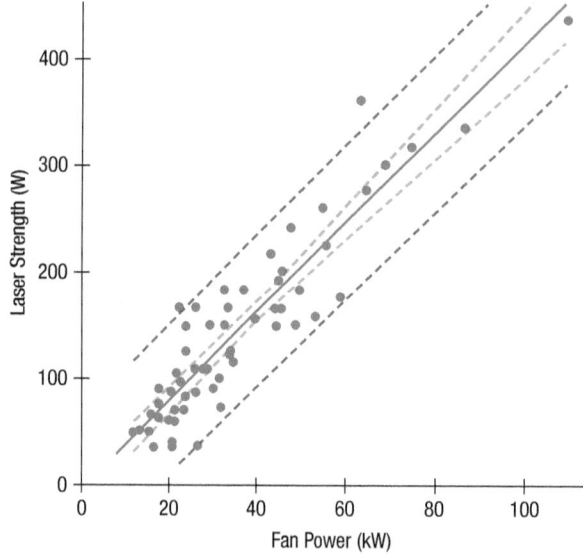

Figure 18.10 A scatterplot of *Laser Strength* against *Fan Power* with a least squares regression line. The inner lines (green) near the regression line show the extent of the 95% confidence intervals, and the outer lines (red) show the prediction intervals. Most of the points are contained within the prediction intervals (as they should be), but not within the confidence interval for the means.

WHAT CAN GO WRONG?

In this chapter we've added inference to the regression explorations that we did in Chapter 7. Everything covered in that chapter that could go wrong with regression can still go wrong.

With inference, we've put confidence intervals on our estimates and predictions, but these numbers are only as good as the model. Here are the main things to watch out for:

- **Don't fit a linear regression to data that aren't straight.** This is the most fundamental assumption. If the relationship between x and y isn't approximately linear, there's no sense in fitting a straight line to it. If part of the data is linear and we are interested in predictions within that range, we could use just that part of the data.

- **Watch out for changing spread.** A common part of confidence and prediction intervals is the estimate of the error standard deviation, or the spread around the line. If it changes with x, the estimate won't make sense.

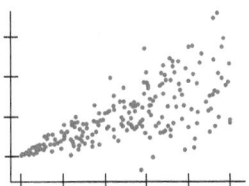

When x is small, we can predict y precisely, but as x gets larger, it's much harder to pin y down. Unfortunately, if the spread changes, the single value of s_e won't pick that up. A re-expression of y (as we'll see in Chapter 19) is often a good fix for changing spread.

- **Watch out for non-Normal errors.** When we make a prediction interval for an individual y-value, the Central Limit Theorem can't come to our rescue. For us to believe the prediction interval, the errors must follow the Normal model. Check the histogram and Normal probability plot of the residuals to see if this assumption looks reasonable.

- **Watch out for extrapolation.** It's tempting to think that because we have prediction *intervals*, they'll take care of all our uncertainty so that we won't have to worry about extrapolating outside the range of our data. Wrong. The interval is only as good as the model. The uncertainty that our intervals predict is only correct if our model is true. There's no way to adjust for wrong models. That's why it's always dangerous to predict for x-values outside the range of the data.

- **Watch out for high-influence points and unusual observations.** We should always be on the lookout for a few points that have undue influence on our estimates, and regression analysis is certainly no exception. There will be more on this in Section 19.3.

- **Watch out for one-tailed tests.** Because tests of hypotheses about regression coefficients are usually two-tailed, software packages report two-tailed P-values. If you're using that type of software and the evidence is in favour of the one-tailed test, you'll need to divide the reported P-value by two.

ETHICS IN ACTION

PotashCorp has installed a video monitoring system in its Rocanville mine in southeast Saskatchewan, which reduces the number of underground personnel required to monitor the operation of the mine. Instead, video displays are mounted at a control centre. Video cameras in the mine monitor for spillage of the ore as it's removed from the rock face and transported by conveyors to the point where it's hauled to the surface. In particular, spillage may occur when the mining equipment loads the ore onto a conveyor, at the point where feeder conveyors transfer ore to the main conveyor, and where the main conveyor dumps ore into skips for hauling to the surface. Conveyors in large mines transport ore at the rate of one tonne per second, so that spillage needs to be dealt with promptly.

(continued)

Felix Choo/Alamy Stock Photo

Karin Duthie/Alamy Stock Photo

Companies that sell video monitoring equipment to mining companies need to demonstrate that there's a reduction in operating costs to offset the capital cost of the video system. One such company provides its salespeople with estimates of how much in operating costs a mine can expect to save for a given capital cost of the system. This is based on a regression analysis of operating cost savings against capital costs for all systems the company has installed to date. The individual data values are confidential to the mines where the equipment is installed, but the regression analysis can be disclosed. It shows that although the R^2 is small, the regression is statistically significant. When a salesperson has estimated the capital cost of a system for a mine, he or she gives the potential client an estimate of the operating costs savings, together with a confidence interval, to assist the client in its purchase decision.

Ethical Issue *The low R^2 means that the predictive capability of the model is questionable. Since the regression is being applied to an individual mine, a prediction interval should be used, not a confidence interval (related to Items A and B, ASA Ethical Guidelines; see Appendix C, the American Statistical Association's Ethical Guidelines for Statistical Practice, also available online at www.amstat.org/about/ethicalguidelines.cfm).*

Ethical Solution *More information should be disclosed to the potential customer. Although the raw data are confidential, the following information should be provided: the regression line, the value of R^2, a graph of the data (so that the customer can see whether the salesperson is extrapolating outside the data range and whether the relationship is linear), and the prediction interval (as opposed to the confidence interval) for a given confidence level.*

WHAT HAVE WE LEARNED?

Learning Objectives

❶ In this chapter we have extended our study of inference methods by applying them to regression models. We've found that the same methods we used for means—Student's *t*-models—work for regression in much the same way. And we've seen that although this makes the mechanics familiar, we need to check new conditions and to be careful when describing the hypotheses we test and the confidence intervals we construct.

- We've learned that under certain assumptions, the sampling distribution for the slope of a regression line can be modelled by a Student's *t*-model with $n - 2$ degrees of freedom.

- We've learned to check four conditions before we proceed with inference. We've learned the importance of checking these conditions in order, and we've seen that most of the checks can be made by graphing the data and the residuals.

- We've learned to use the appropriate *t*-model to test a hypothesis about the slope. If the slope of our regression line is significantly different from zero, we have strong evidence that there's an association between the two variables.

- We've also learned to create and interpret a confidence interval for the true slope.

❷ We've learned how to perform a hypothesis test on a correlation coefficient, and in particular how to test whether the correlation between two variables is significantly different from zero.

❸ We've learned how to perform a hypothesis test and calculate the confidence interval for predicted values, and how to distinguish between predicting a mean value from the population and predicting an individual value.

Terms	
Confidence interval for the predicted mean value	Different samples will give different estimates of the regression model and therefore different predicted values for the same value of x. We find a confidence interval for the mean of these predicted values at a specified x-value, s_ν, as $$\hat{y}_\nu \pm t^*_{n-2} \times SE(\hat{\mu}_\nu),$$ where $$SE(\hat{\mu}_\nu) = \sqrt{SE^2(b_1) \times (x_\nu - \bar{x})^2 + \frac{s_e^2}{n}}.$$ The critical value, t^*_{n-2}, depends on the specified confidence level.
Confidence interval for the regression slope	When the assumptions are satisfied, we can find a confidence interval for the slope parameter from $b_1 \pm t^*_{n-2} \times SE(b_1)$. The critical value, t^*_{n-2}, depends on the confidence level.
Dependent variable	The variable whose value depends on the value of the explanatory variable, usually denoted by y and plotted on the vertical axis of a graph. Also known as the *predicted variable* or *response variable*.
Explanatory variable	The variable used to explain the value of another variable, usually denoted by x and plotted on the horizontal axis of a graph. Also known as the *independent variable*.
Independent variable	See *Explanatory variable*.
Predicted variable	See *Dependent variable*.
Prediction interval for an individual value	Prediction intervals are to observations as confidence intervals are to parameters. They predict the range of individual values, while confidence intervals give the range for a population parameter. The prediction interval takes the form $$\hat{y}_\nu \pm t^*_{n-2} \times SE(\hat{y}_\nu),$$ where $$SE(\hat{y}_\nu) = \sqrt{SE^2(b_1) \times (x_\nu - \bar{x})^2 + \frac{s_e^2}{n} + s_e^2}.$$ The critical value, t^*_{n-2}, depends on the specified confidence level. The extra s_e^2 in $SE(\hat{y}_\nu)$ makes the interval wider than the corresponding confidence interval for the mean.
Residual standard deviation	The measure, denoted s_e, of the spread of the data around the regression line: $$s_e = \sqrt{\frac{\sum (y - \hat{y})^2}{n-2}} = \sqrt{\frac{\sum e^2}{n-2}}$$
Response variable	See *Dependent variable*.
t-test for the correlation coefficient	When the conditions are met, we can test the hypothesis $H_0 : \rho = 0$ *vs.* $H_A: \rho \neq 0$ using the test statistic $$t = r\sqrt{\frac{n-2}{1-r^2}},$$ which follows a Student's t-model with $n-2$ degrees of freedom. We can use the t-model to find the P-value of the test.
t-test for the regression slope	The usual null hypothesis is that the true value of the slope is zero. The alternative is that it is not. A slope of zero indicates a complete lack of linear relationship between y and x. To test $H_0 : \beta_1 = 0$, we find $$t = \frac{b_1 - 0}{SE(b_1)},$$

where $SE(b_1) = \dfrac{s_e}{s_x\sqrt{n-1}}$, $s_e = \sqrt{\dfrac{\sum(y-\hat{y})^2}{n-2}}$, n is the number of cases, and s_x is the standard

deviation of the x-values. We find the P-value from the Student's t-model with $n-2$ degrees of freedom.

Skills

Plan
- Understand that the "true" regression line does not fit the population data perfectly, but rather is an idealized summary of that data.
- Know how to examine your data and a scatterplot of y vs. x for violations of assumptions that would make inference for regression unwise or invalid.
- Know how to examine displays of the residuals from a regression to double-check that the conditions required for regression have been met. In particular, know how to judge linearity and constant variance from a scatterplot of residuals against predicted values. Know how to judge Normality from a histogram and Normal probability plot.
- Remember to be especially careful to check for failures of the Independence Assumption when working with data recorded over time. To search for patterns, examine scatterplots both of x against time and of the residuals against time.

Do
- Know how to test the standard null hypothesis that the true regression slope is zero. Be able to state the null and alternative hypotheses. Know where to find the relevant numbers in standard computer regression output.
- Be able to find a confidence interval for the slope of a regression based on the values reported in a standard regression output table.

Report
- Be able to summarize a regression in words. In particular, be able to state the meaning of the true regression slope, the standard error of the estimated slope, and the standard deviation of the errors.
- Be able to interpret the P-value of the t-statistic for the slope to test whether the slope is zero.
- Be able to interpret a confidence interval for the slope of a regression.

MINI case studies

PotashCorp

The data set in the file **ch18_MCSP_PotashCorp** contains average quarterly share prices for PotashCorp and prices for potash mineral. Investigate the relationship between these variables. (a) Some people think that if the share price of a mining company is high, that is because investors expect high mineral prices for the corresponding quarter. Can the potash price be estimated from the PotashCorp share price? The data includes a period when the price of potash mineral was exceptionally high. If you eliminate the quarters when the price of potash was over CDN\$600/tonne, does that affect your analysis? (b) Other people think that if the price at which a mineral can be sold is high, then the share price of the companies producing that mineral will also be high. Is that the case for PotashCorp? That is, can PotashCorp's share price be estimated from the potash mineral price? If you eliminate the quarters when the price of potash was over CDN\$600/tonne, does that affect your analysis? (c) Compare your answers to (a) and (b) including R-squared, P-value for slope, and the regression lines themselves.

Share Buy-Backs and Special Dividends in Canada

PotashCorp announced a program to buy back up to 5% of its common shares between August 2013 and July 2014.

(*continued*)

When a company has a strong balance sheet with surplus cash, it needs to find a use for that cash consistent with its strategic goals and the current business environment. When economic conditions aren't favourable for spending the cash to pay off debt, acquire another company or expand operations, it can use its cash in two other ways: (1) announcing a special dividend, and (2) buying back shares, otherwise known as stock repurchase agreements. Both of these options return value to shareholders. The difference between them is that share buy-backs can be done gradually over several quarters and the amount of the buy-back can be adjusted to the surplus cash available in future quarters; special dividends, on the other hand, require the company to be pretty certain that a base level of surplus cash will continue to be available in future quarters.

Suppose you're advising the board of directors of a major company that needs to decide between a share buy-back and a special dividend. Surplus cash during the past eight quarters is given in the table. (Quarter 8 is the most recent.)

Quarter	1	2	3	4	5	6	7	8
Surplus Cash ($ billion)	1.2	0.8	1.4	1.3	0.9	1.4	1.3	1.1

The board will issue a special dividend if it can be both 95% certain that surplus cash will exceed $1.15 billion in quarter 9 and 95% certain that it will exceed $1.2 billion in quarter 10. It will announce a share buy-back program if it can be both 90% certain that the total surplus cash from quarter 9 will exceed $1.15 billion and that the surplus cash from quarter 10 will exceed $1.2 billion. Use linear regression to advise the board of directors about its options.

Frozen Pizza

A product manager is interested in learning how sensitive sales are to changes in the unit price of a frozen pizza in Toronto, Montreal, Calgary, and Halifax. Data have been provided in the file on both *Price* and *Sales* volume every 18 weeks over a period of nearly four years for the four cities (**ch18_MCSP_Frozen_Pizza**).

Examine the relationship between *Price* and *Sales* for each city. Be sure to discuss the nature and validity of this relationship. Is it linear? Is it negative? Is it significant? Are the conditions of regression met? Some individuals in the product manager's division suspect that frozen pizza sales are more sensitive to price in some cities than in others. Is there any evidence to suggest that? Write up a short report on what you find. Include 95% confidence intervals for the mean *Sales* if the *Price* is $2.50 and discuss how that interval changes if the *Price* is $3.50.

Global Warming?

Every spring, Nenana, Alaska, hosts a contest in which participants try to guess the exact minute that a wooden tripod placed on the frozen Tanana River will fall through the breaking ice. The contest started in 1917 as a diversion for railroad engineers, with a jackpot of $801 for the closest guess. It has grown into an event in which hundreds of thousands of entrants enter their guesses on the internet and vie for more than $300,000.

Because so much money and interest depends on the time of the ice breakup, it has been recorded to the nearest minute with great accuracy since 1917 (**ch18_MCSP_Global_Warming**). And because a standard measure of breakup has been used throughout this time, the data are consistent. An article in *Science* ([2001, October], Climate change in nontraditional data sets, *Science*, *294*, 811) used the data to investigate global warming. Researchers are interested in the following questions: What is the rate of change in the date of breakup over time (if any)? If the ice is breaking up earlier, what is your conclusion? Does this necessarily suggest global warming? What could be other reasons for this trend? What is the predicted breakup date for the year 2015? (Be sure to include an appropriate prediction or confidence interval.) Write up a short report with your answers.

Technology Help: Regression Analysis

All statistics packages make a table of results for a regression. These tables differ slightly from one package to another, but all are essentially the same. We've seen two examples of such tables already.

All packages offer analyses of the residuals. With some, you must request plots of the residuals as you request the regression. Others let you find the regression first and then analyze the residuals afterward. Either way, your analysis is not complete if you don't check the residuals with a histogram or Normal probability plot and a scatterplot of the residuals against x or the predicted values.

You should, of course, always look at the scatterplot of your two variables before computing a regression.

Regressions are almost always found with a computer or calculator. The calculations are too long to do conveniently by hand for data sets of any reasonable size. No matter how the regression is computed, the results are usually presented in a table that has a standard form. Here's a portion of a typical regression results table, along with annotations showing where the numbers come from.

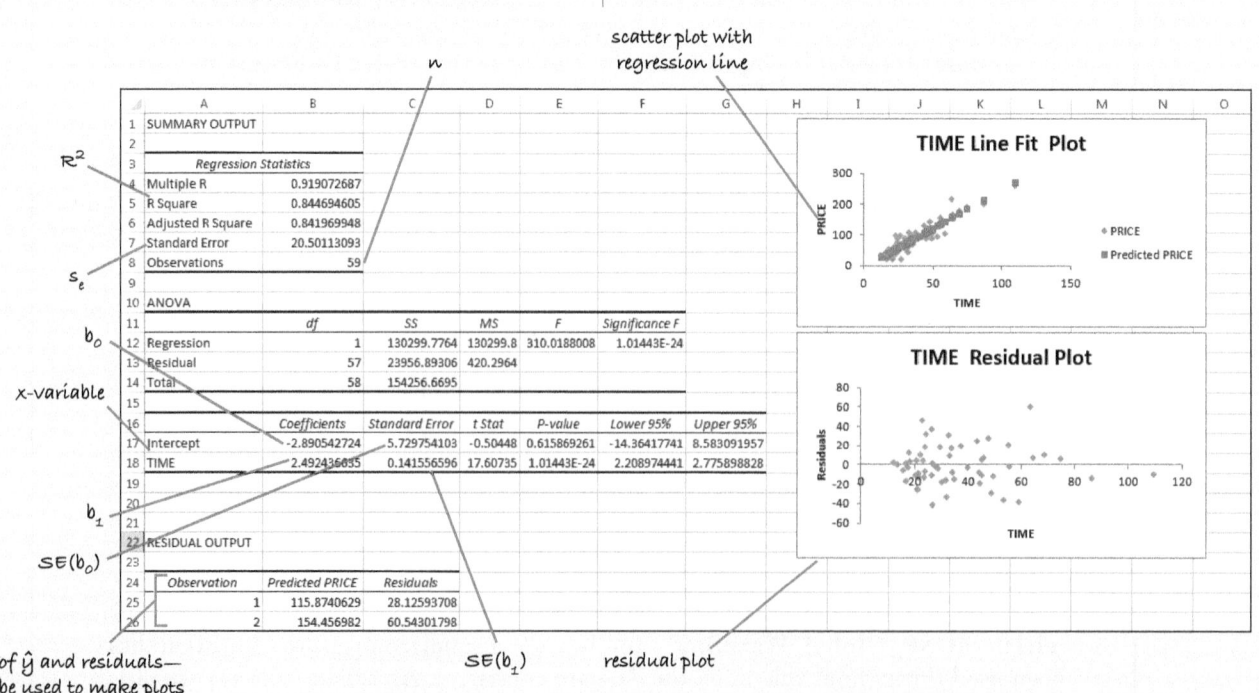

The regression table gives the coefficients (once you find them in the middle of all this other information). This regression (for different items than in the example in the text) predicts *Price* from *Time*. The regression equation is

$$\widehat{Price} = -2.891 + 2.492\ Time$$

and the R^2 for the regression is 84.5%.

The column of *t*-ratios gives the test statistics for the respective null hypotheses that the true values of the coefficients are zero. The corresponding P-values are also usually reported.

EXCEL

To perform a regression analysis in Excel:

- From **Data**, select **Data Analysis** and select **Regression**.
- Enter the data range holding the *y*-variable in the box labelled "Input Y range".
- Enter the range of cells holding the *x*-variable in the box labelled "Input X range".
- Select the **New Worksheet Ply** option to report results in a new worksheet (or identify the output range in the current worksheet or a new workbook) and **Labels** if the first row of the data holds the variable labels.
- Select the **Residuals**, **Residual Plots**, and **Line Fit Plots** options.

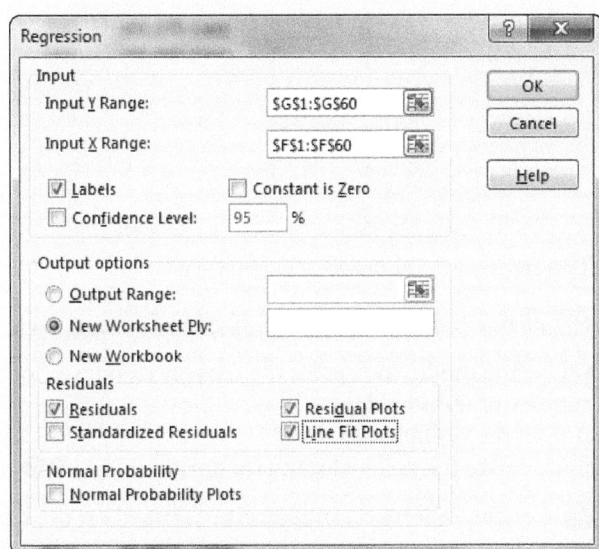

- After the plots are generated, you can delete the predicted values and/or add the least squares line, called a Trendline in Excel, on the Line Fit Plot.
- To obtain a histogram of the residuals, use residuals listed in Excel output to create a histogram using Data + Data Analysis + Histogram.

Comments

The *Y* and *X* ranges do not need to be in the same rows of the spreadsheet, although they must cover the same number of cells. But it is a good idea to arrange your data in parallel columns, as in a data table, to reduce the chance of error. Although the dialogue offers a Normal probability plot of the residuals, the data analysis add-in does not make a correct probability plot, so don't use this option.

MINITAB

- Choose **Regression** from the **Stat** menu.
- Choose **Regression...** from the **Regression** submenu.
- In the Regression dialogue, assign the *y*-variable to the Response box and assign the *x*-variable to the Predictors box.
- Click the **Graphs** button.
- In the Regression-Graphs dialogue, select **Standardized residuals**, and check **Normal plot of residuals, Residuals versus fits**, and **Residuals versus order**.
- Click the **OK** button to return to the Regression dialogue.
- Click the **OK** button to compute the regression.

Comments

You can also start by choosing a Fitted Line plot from the **Regression** submenu to see the scatterplot first—usually good practice.

SPSS

- Choose **Regression** from the **Analyze** menu.
- Choose **Linear** from the **Regression** submenu.
- In the Linear Regression dialogue that appears, select the *y*-variable and move it to the dependent target. Then move the *x*-variable to the independent target.
- Click the **Plots** button.
- In the Linear Regression Plots dialogue, choose to plot the *SRESIDs against the *ZPRED values.
- Click the **Continue** button to return to the Linear Regression dialogue.
- Click the **OK** button to compute the regression.

JMP

- From the **Analyze** menu, select **Fit Y by X**.
- Select variables: a **Y, Response** variable, and an **X, Factor** variable. Both must be continuous (quantitative).
- JMP makes a scatterplot.
- Click on the red triangle beside the heading labelled **Bivariate Fit...** and choose **Fit Line**. JMP draws the least squares regression line on the scatterplot and displays the results of the regression in tables below the plot.
- The portion of the table labelled "Parameter Estimates" gives the coefficients and their standard errors, *t*-ratios, and P-values.

Comments

JMP chooses a regression analysis when both variables are "Continuous." If you get a different analysis, check the variable types.

The Parameter table does not include the residual standard deviation s_e. You can find that as Root Mean Square Error in the Summary of Fit panel of the output.

EXERCISES

SECTION 18.1

1. You're considering opening an Estonian cuisine restaurant and wonder how much people in your target community spend on eating out relative to their household incomes. You commission a telephone survey and build the following regression model for individual respondents:

$$\widehat{EatOut\$/wk} = 17.28 + 0.354\ HHIncome$$

where household income is in \$1000s.
Write an interpretation of this model. **LO ❶**

2. For the model found in Exercise 1, predict how much a person with a household income of \$75,000 would be expected to spend eating out in a week. **LO ❶**

SECTION 18.2

3. A website that rents movies online recorded the age and the number of movies rented during the past month for some of its customers. Here are its data:

Age	Rentals
35	9
40	8
50	4
65	3
40	10
30	12

Make a scatterplot for these data. What does it tell you about the relationship between these two variables? From what you know, which of the following conditions can you check from the scatterplot? Are they satisfied?

a) Linearity
b) Independence
c) Equal Spread
d) Normal Population **LO ❶**

4. Here's a scatterplot of the % of income spent on food vs. household income for respondents to a national survey:

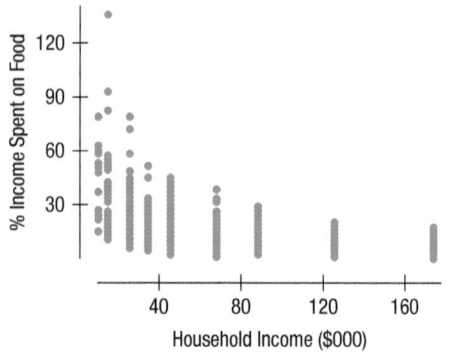

For each of the regression assumptions, state whether it's satisfied, not satisfied, or can't be determined from this plot.

a) Linearity
b) Independence
c) Equal Spread
d) Normal Population **LO ❶**

SECTION 18.3

5. For the data in Exercise 3, the best fitting regression line has $b_0 = 18.9$ and $b_1 = -0.260$.

a) Use the estimated regression equation to predict *Rentals* for all six values of *Age*.
b) Find the residuals, e_i.
c) Calculate the residual standard deviation, s_e. **LO ❶**

6. A training centre, wishing to demonstrate the effectiveness of its methods, tests some of its clients after different numbers of days of training, recording their scores on a sample test. Their data are:

Training Days	Correct Responses
1	4
4	6
8	7
10	9
12	10

The regression model they calculate is

$$\widehat{correct\ responses} = 3.525 + 0.525\ Training\ Days.$$

a) Use the model to predict the correct responses for each number of training days.
b) Find the residuals, e_i.
c) Calculate the residual standard deviation, s_e. **LO ❶**

7. For the regression in Exercise 5, based on the data in Exercise 3, find the standard error of the regression alone. Show all three values that go into the calculation. **LO ❶**

8. For the regression in Exercise 6, find the standard error of the regression slope. Show all three values that go into the calculation. **LO ❶**

SECTION 18.4

9. A data set of five observations for concession *Sales* per person (\$) at a theatre and *Minutes* before the movie begins results in the following estimated regression model:

$$\widehat{Sales} = 4.3 + 0.265\ Minutes$$

The standard error of the regression slope is 0.0454.

a) Compute the value of the t-statistic to test if there's a significant relationship between *Sales* and *Minutes*.
b) What are the degrees of freedom associated with the t-statistic?
c) What is the P-value associated with the t-statistic?
d) At $\alpha = 0.5$, can you reject the standard null hypothesis for the slope? Explain. **LO ❶**

10. A soap manufacturer tested a standard bar of soap to see how long it would last. A test subject showered with the soap each day for 15 days and recorded the *Weight* (in grams) of the soap after the shower. The resulting regression computer output looks, in part, like this:

Dependent variable is: Weight
R squared = 99.5%
S = 2.249

Variable	Coefficient	SE(coeff)	t-ratio	P-value
Intercept	123.141	1.382	89.1	≤0.0001
Day	−5.57476	−0.1068	−52.2	≤0.0001

Find the following facts in this output, or determine them from what you know:

a) The standard deviation of the residuals
b) The slope of the regression line
c) The standard error of b_1
d) The P-value appropriate for testing $H_0 : \beta_1 = 0$ vs. $H_A : \beta_1 \neq 0$
e) Is the null hypothesis rejected at $\alpha = 0.05$? **LO ❶**

SECTION 18.5

11. A study of 98 investment advisors asked them to predict the value of a "penny" stock a week ahead. The correlation between the values predicted and the actual value was 0.20. Was this evidence that they could predict penny stock performance?

a) State the null and alternative hypotheses about the correlation.
b) Calculate the test statistic.
c) Perform the test at $\alpha = 0.05$. **LO ❷**

12. For a physical exam to qualify for company-provided insurance, 14 employees had their blood pressure measured. Their systolic and diastolic BP are given here:

SBP	DBP
140	90
208	114
140	90
164	104
142	88
124	82
120	80
142	72
160	90
142	98
225	125
140	90
220	114
150	85

A regression, found with technology, reports an R^2 of 81.3%.

a) Make a scatterplot of the data. Is it appropriate to interpret correlation?
b) State the null and alternative hypotheses about the correlation.
c) Calculate the test statistic. (*Hint:* Remember the relationship between correlation and R^2.)
d) Perform the test at $\alpha = 0.01$ and state your conclusion. **LO ❷**

SECTION 18.6

13. Here are data from a small bookstore:

Number of Salespeople Working	Sales (in $1000s)
2	10
3	11
7	13
9	14
10	18
10	20
12	20
15	22
16	22
20	26
$\bar{x} = 10.4$	$\bar{y} = 17.6$
$SD(x) = 5.64$	$SD(y) = 5.34$

The regression line is

$$\widehat{Sales} = 8.10 + 0.914 \; Number \; of \; Salespeople \; Working.$$

The assumptions and conditions for regression are met, and from technology we learn that

$$SE(b_1) = 0.0873, \; s_e = 1.477.$$

a) Find the predicted *Sales* on a day with 12 employees working.

b) Find a 95% confidence interval for the mean *Sales* on days that have 12 employees working.
c) Find the 95% prediction interval for *Sales* on a day with 12 employees working. **LO ❸**

14. In Exercise 1 we saw a regression based on a survey of households in a community served by a potential Estonian restaurant that might open. The regression model

$$\widehat{EatOut\$/wk} = 17.28 + 0.354 \ HHIncome$$

related the amount respondents said they spent individually to eat out each week to their household income in $1000s.

a) A 95% prediction interval for a customer with a household income of $80,000 is ($35.60, $55.60). Explain to the restaurant owner how she should interpret this interval.
b) A 95% confidence interval for the mean amount spent weekly to eat out by people with a household income of $80,000 is ($40.60, $50.60). Explain to the restaurant owner how to interpret this interval.
c) Now explain to her why these intervals are different. **LO ❸**

15. In Exercise 9 we saw a regression to predict the sales per person at a movie theatre in terms of the time (in minutes) before the show. The model was

$$\widehat{Sales} = 4.3 + 0.265 \ Minutes.$$

a) A 90% prediction interval for a concessions customer 10 minutes before the movie starts is ($4.60, $9.30). Explain how to interpret this interval.
b) A 90% confidence interval for the mean of sales per person 10 minutes before the movie starts is ($6.65, $7.25). Explain how to interpret this interval.
c) Which interval is of particular interest to the concessions manager? Which one is of particular interest to you, the moviegoer? **LO ❸**

CHAPTER EXERCISES

16. Online shopping. Several studies have found that the frequency with which shoppers browse internet retailers is related to the frequency with which they actually purchase products and/or services online. Here are data showing the age of respondents and their answer to the question "How many minutes do you browse online retailers per week?"

Age	Browsing Time (min./wk.)
22	492
50	186
44	180
32	384
55	120
60	120

38	276
22	480
21	510
45	252
52	126
33	360
19	570
17	588
21	498

a) Make a scatterplot for these data.
b) Do you think a linear model is appropriate? Explain.
c) Find the equation of the regression line.
d) Check the residuals to see if the conditions for inference are met. **LO ❶**

ⓣ 17. El Niño. Concern over the weather associated with El Niño has increased interest in the possibility that the climate on Earth is getting warmer. The most common theory relates an increase in atmospheric levels of carbon dioxide (CO_2), a greenhouse gas, to increases in temperature. Here is part of a regression analysis of the mean annual CO_2 concentration in the atmosphere, measured in parts per thousand (ppt) at the top of Mauna Loa in Hawaii, and the mean annual air temperature over both land and sea across the globe, in degrees Celsius. The scatterplots and residuals plots indicated that the data were appropriate for inference, and the response variable is *Temp*.

Variable	Coeff	SE(Coeff)
Intercept	16.4328	0.0557
CO_2	0.0405	0.0116

R squared = 25.8%
s = 0.0854 with 37 − 2 = 35 degrees of freedom

a) Write the equation of the regression line.
b) Find the value of the correlation and test whether the true correlation is zero. Is there evidence of an association between CO_2 level and global temperature?
c) Find the *t*-value and P-value for the slope. Is there evidence of an association between CO_2 level and global temperature? What do you know from the slope and *t*-test that you might not have known from testing the correlation?
d) Do you think predictions made by this regression will be very accurate? Explain. **LO ❶, ❷**

ⓣ 18. Movie budgets, part 1. How does the production budget of a movie depend on its length? Data on the budgets (millions of dollars) and the running times (minutes) for major-release films in a recent year are summarized in these plots and computer output:

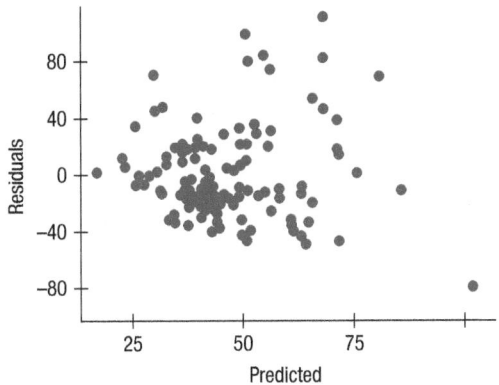

Dependent variable is: Budget ($M)

R squared = 15.4%

s = 32.95 with 120 − 2 = 118 degrees of freedom

Variable	Coefficient	SE(Coeff)	t-ratio	P-value
Intercept	−31.39	17.12	−1.83	0.0693
Run Time	0.71	0.15	4.64	≤0.0001

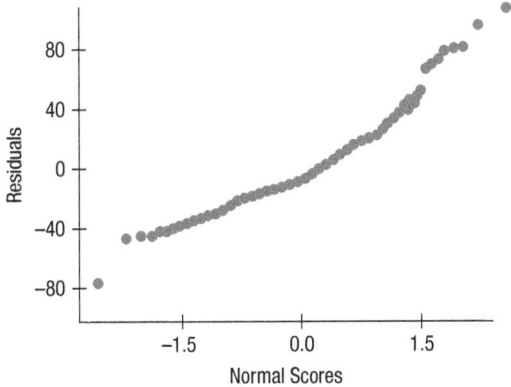

a) Explain in words and numbers what the regression says.
b) The intercept is negative. Discuss its value, taking note of the P-value.
c) The output reports that $s = 32.95$. Explain what that means in this context.

d) What's the value of the standard error of the slope of the regression line?
e) Explain what that means in this context. **LO ❶**

T **19.** **House prices, part 1.** How does the price of a house depend on its size? Data on 1064 randomly selected houses recently sold include data on price ($1000s) and size (1000s m²), producing the following graphs and computer output:

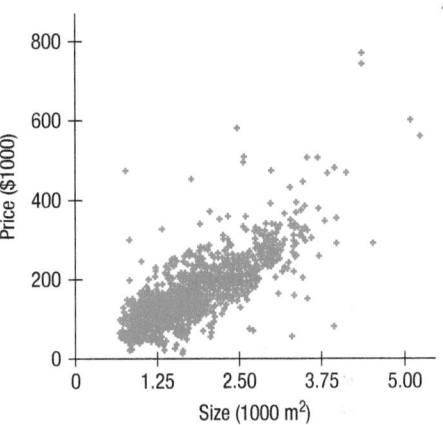

Dependent variable is: Price

R squared = 59.5%

s = 53.79 with 1064 − 2 = 1062 degrees of freedom

Variable	Coefficient	SE(Coeff)	t-ratio	P-value
Intercept	−3.1169	4.688	−0.665	0.5063
Size	94.4539	2.393	39.465	≤0.0001

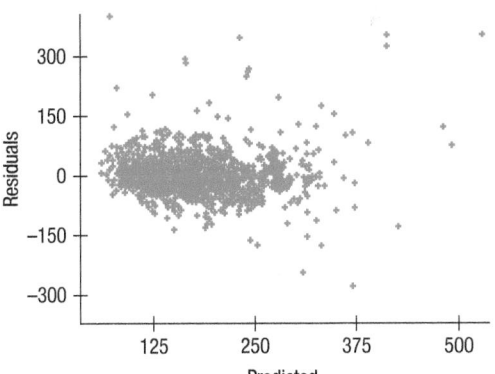

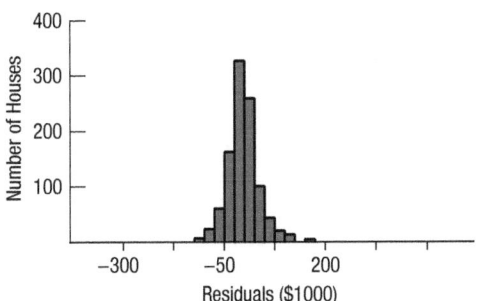

a) Explain in words and numbers what the regression says.
b) The intercept is negative. Discuss its value, taking note of its P-value.
c) The output reports that $s = 53.79$. Explain what that means in this context.
d) What's the value of the standard error of the slope of the regression line?
e) Explain what that means in this context. **LO ❶**

⊤ 20. Movie budgets, part 2. Exercise 18 shows computer output examining the association between the length of a movie and its cost.

a) Check the assumptions and conditions for inference.
b) Find a 95% confidence interval for the slope and interpret it. **LO ❶**

⊤ 21. House prices, part 2. Exercise 19 shows computer output examining the association between the sizes of houses and their sale prices.

a) Check the assumptions and conditions for inference.
b) Find a 95% confidence interval for the slope and interpret it. **LO ❶**

⊤ 22. Water hardness. In an investigation of environmental causes of disease, data were collected on the annual mortality rate (deaths per 100,000) for males in 61 large towns in England and Wales. In addition, the water hardness was recorded as the calcium concentration (parts per million, or ppm) in the drinking water. Here are the scatterplot and regression analysis of the relationship between mortality and calcium concentration, where the response variable is *Mortality*.

Variable	Coeff	SE(Coeff)
Intercept	1676.36	29.30
Calcium	−3.226	0.485

R squared = 42.9%
s = 143.0 with 61 − 2 = 59 degrees of freedom

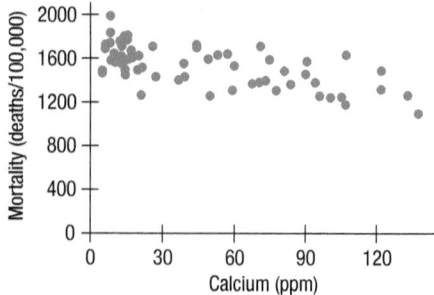

a) Is there an association between the hardness of the water and the mortality rate? Write the appropriate hypothesis.

b) Assuming that the assumptions for regression inference are met, what do you conclude?
c) Create a 95% confidence interval for the slope of the true line relating calcium concentration and mortality.
d) Interpret your interval in context. **LO ❶**

⊤ 23. Male unemployment. Using unemployment data provided by the United Nations, investigate the association between the male unemployment rate in *2007* and *2010* for a sample of 75 countries.

a) Determine a regression model predicting the *2010* rate from the *2007* rate.
b) Examine the residuals to determine if a linear regression is appropriate.
c) Test an appropriate hypothesis to determine if the association is significant.
d) What percentage of the variability in the *2010* rate is accounted for by the *regression model*? **LO ❶**

⊤ 24. Used cars, part 1. Classified ads in a newspaper offered several used Toyota Corollas for sale. Listed below are the ages of the cars and the advertised prices:

Age (yr.)	Prices Advertised ($)
1	13,990
1	13,495
3	12,999
4	9,500
4	10,495
5	8,995
5	9,495
6	6,999
7	6,950
7	7,850
8	6,999
8	5,995
10	4,950
10	4,495
13	2,850

a) Make a scatterplot for these data.
b) Do you think a linear model is appropriate? Explain.
c) Find the equation of the regression line.
d) Check the residuals to see if the conditions for inference are met. **LO ❶**

⊤ 25. Property assessments. The following software outputs provide information about the size (in square feet) of

18 homes and the assessed value of those homes, where the response variable is *AssessedValue*.

Predictor	Coeff	SE(Coeff)	*t*-ratio	P-value
Intercept	37108.85	8664.33	4.28	0.0006
Size	11.90	4.29	2.77	0.0136

s = 4682.10 R-Sq = 32.5%

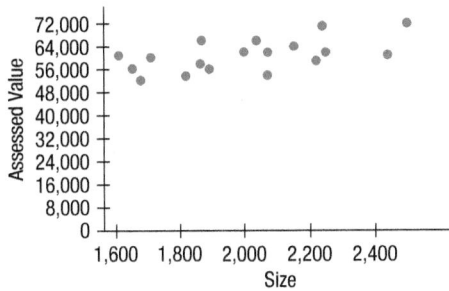

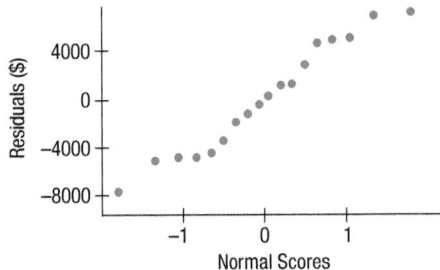

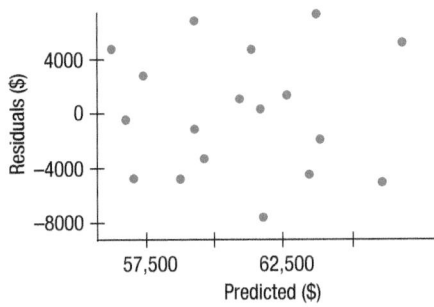

a) Explain why inference for linear regression is appropriate with these data.

b) Is there a significant linear association between the *Size* of a home and its *AssessedValue*? Test an appropriate hypothesis and state your conclusion.

c) What percentage of the variability in assessed value is accounted for by this regression?

d) Give a 90% confidence interval for the slope of the true regression line, and explain its meaning in the proper context.

e) From this analysis, can we conclude that adding a room to your house will increase its assessed value? Why or why not?

f) The owner of a home measuring 2100 square feet files an appeal, claiming that the $70,200 assessed value is too high. Do you agree? Explain your reasoning. **LO ❶, ❸**

26. **Used cars, part 2.** Based on the analysis of used car prices you did for Exercise 24, if appropriate, create a 95% confidence interval for the slope of the regression line and explain what your interval means in context. **LO ❶**

❶ 27. **Assets and sales, part 1.** A business analyst is looking at a company's assets and sales to determine the relationship (if any) between the two measures. She has data (in $ million) from a random sample of 79 Fortune 500 companies, and obtained the linear regression below:

The regression equation is *Assets* = 1867.4 + 0.975 *Sales*				
Predictor	Coeff	SE(Coeff)	*t*-ratio	P-value
Constant	1867.4	804.5	2.32	0.0230
Sales	0.975	0.099	9.84	≤0.0001

S = 6132.59 R-Sq = 55.7% R-Sq(adj) = 55.1%

Use the data provided to find a 95% confidence interval, if appropriate, for the slope of the regression line, and interpret your interval in context. **LO ❶**

❶ 28. **Fuel efficiency, part 1.** A consumer organization has reported test data for 50 car models, which we'll use to examine the association between the weight of the car (in thousands of pounds) and the fuel efficiency (in litres per 100 kilometres). Use the data provided to answer the following questions, where the response variable is *Fuel Efficiency* (L/100 km):

a) Create the scatterplot and obtain the regression equation.

b) Are the assumptions for regression satisfied?

c) Write the appropriate hypotheses for the slope.

d) Test the hypotheses and state your conclusion. **LO ❶**

29. **Consumer Reports.** *Consumer Reports* lists the price (in dollars) and power (in cold cranking amps) of auto batteries. We want to know if more expensive batteries are generally better in terms of starting power. Here are the regression and residual output, where the response variable is *Power*:

Dependent variable is: Power
R squared = 25.2%
s = 116.0 with 33 − 2 = 31 degrees of freedom

Variable	Coefficient	SE(Coeff)	*t*-ratio	P-value
Intercept	384.594	93.55	4.11	0.0003
Cost	4.146	1.282	3.23	0.0029

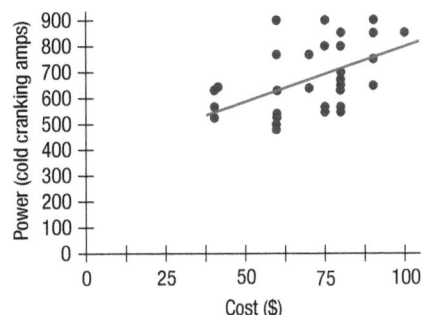

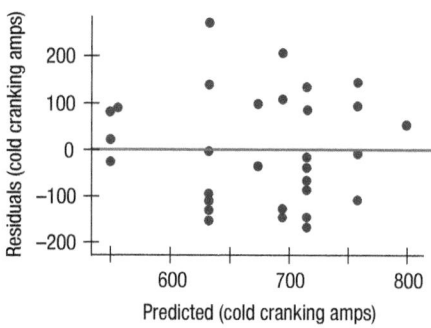

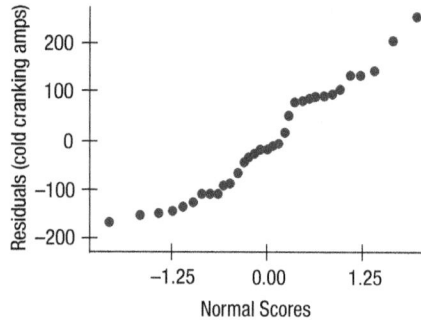

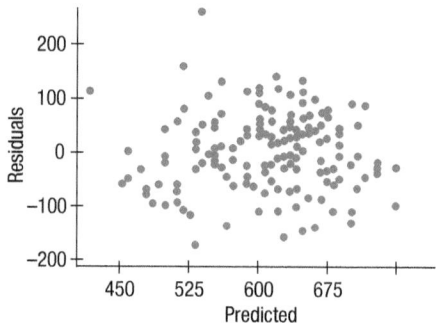

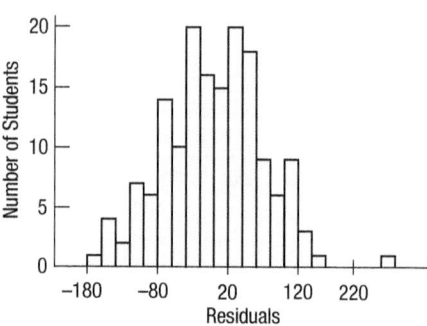

a) How many batteries were tested?

b) Are the conditions for inference satisfied? Explain.

c) Is there evidence of a linear association between the *Cost* and cranking *Power* of auto batteries? Test an appropriate hypothesis and state your conclusion.

d) Is the association strong? Explain.

e) What is the equation of the regression line?

f) Create a 90% confidence interval for the slope of the true line.

g) Interpret your interval in this context. **LO ❶**

❶ 30. **SAT scores, part 1.** How strong was the association between student scores on the Math and Verbal sections of the old SAT? Scores on this exam ranged from 200 to 800 and were widely used by U.S. college admissions offices. Here are summary statistics, a regression analysis, and plots of the scores for a graduating class of 162 students, where the response variable is *Math Score*:

Predictor	Coeff	SE(Coeff)	*t*-ratio	P-value
Intercept	209.55	34.35	6.10	<0.0001
Verbal	0.675	0.057	11.88	<0.0001

s = 71.75 R-Sq = 46.9%

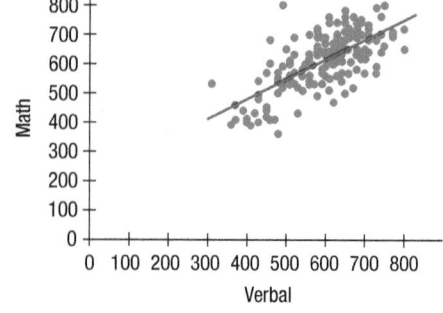

a) Is there evidence of a linear association between *Math* and *Verbal* scores? Write an appropriate hypothesis.

b) Discuss the assumptions for inference.

c) Test your hypothesis and state an appropriate conclusion. **LO ❶**

31. Productivity. How strong is the association between labour productivity and labour costs? Data from the Bureau of Labor Statistics for labour productivity, as measured by *Output per Hour*, and *Unit Labour Costs* across 53 industries, are used to examine this relationship (ftp://ftp.bls.gov; accessed June 2013).

a) From a scatterplot, is there evidence of a linear association between *Labour Productivity* and *Unit Labour Costs*? Plot the reciprocal, *Hours per output (000s)*, against *Unit Labour Costs*. Why did the analysts prefer this measure of productivity?

b) Using the reciprocal measure, *Hours per Output (000s)*, test an appropriate null hypothesis and state an appropriate conclusion (assume that assumptions and conditions are now met). **LO ❶**

❶ 32. **Football salaries.** Football team owners are constantly in competition for good players. The better the winning percentage, the more likely the team will provide good business returns for the owners. Of course, the resources that each of the 32 teams has in the National Football League (NFL) vary. Does the size of the payroll matter? Here are a scatterplot and a regression showing the association between team salaries in the NFL and winning percentage:

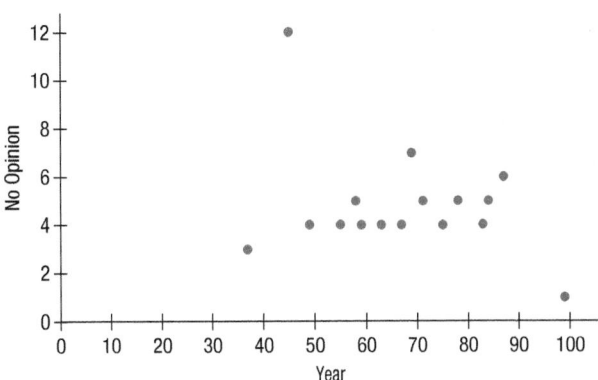

Predictor	Coeff	SE(Coeff)	t-ratio	P-value
Intercept	1.783	3.964	0.45	0.6560
Salary ($M)	0.062	0.039	1.58	0.1244

s = 2.82 R-Sq = 7.7%

a) State the hypotheses about the slope.
b) Perform the hypothesis test and state your conclusion in context. **LO ❶**

Ⓣ 33. Gallup poll. The Gallup organization has, over six decades, periodically asked the following question:

If your party nominated a generally well-qualified person for president who happened to be a woman, would you vote for that person?

We wonder if the proportion of the public who have "no opinion" on this issue has changed over the years. Here's a regression for the proportion of those respondents whose response to this question about voting for a woman president was "no opinion." Assume that the conditions for inference are satisfied and that the response variable is *No Opinion*.

Predictor	Coeff	SE(Coeff)	t-ratio	P-value
Intercept	7.693	2.445	3.15	0.0071
Year	−0.042	0.035	−1.21	0.2460

s = 2.28 R-Sq = 9.5%

a) State the hypotheses about the slope (both numerically and in words) that describe how voters' thoughts have changed about voting for a woman.
b) Assuming that the assumptions for inference are satisfied, perform the hypothesis test and state your conclusion.
c) Examine the scatterplot corresponding to the regression for *No Opinion*. How does it change your opinion of the trend in "no opinion" responses? Do you think the true slope is negative, as shown in the regression output? **LO ❶**

34. Fuel efficiency, part 2. Consider again the data in Exercise 28 about the fuel efficiency and weights of cars.

a) Create a 95% confidence interval for the slope of the regression line.
b) Explain in this context what your confidence interval means. **LO ❶**

35. SAT scores, part 2. Consider the high school SAT scores data from Exercise 30.

a) Find a 90% confidence interval for the slope of the true line describing the association between Math and Verbal scores.
b) Explain in this context what your confidence interval means. **LO ❶**

Ⓣ 36. Cost index 2011, part 1. The *Worldwide Cost of Living Survey* published by *The Economist* provides an index that expresses the cost of living in other cities as a percentage of the New York cost. For example, in 2011, the cost of living index in Tokyo was 161, which means that it was 61% higher than New York. The output shows the regression of the 2011 on the 2010 index for the 10 most expensive cities in 2011, where *Index* is the response variable.

Predictor	Coeff	SE(Coeff)	t-Ratio	P-Value
Intercept	46.73	15.45	3.02	0.0164
Index 2010	0.744	0.115	6.49	0.0002

s = 3.474, R-Sq = 84.0%

a) State the hypotheses about the slope (both numerically and in words).
b) Perform the hypothesis test and state your conclusion in context.
c) Explain what the R-squared in this regression means.
d) Do these results indicate that, in general, cities with a higher index in 2010 had a higher index in 2011? Explain. **LO ❶**

37. Marketing managers. Are wages for various marketing managerial positions related? One way to determine this is to examine the relationship between the mean hourly wages for two managerial occupations in marketing: sales managers and advertising managers. The average hourly wages for both occupations are analyzed. Here are the regression analysis results:

Predictor	Coeff	SE(Coeff)	t-ratio	P-value
Constant	10.317	4.382	2.35	0.0227
Sales Mgr Avg Hourly Wage	0.56349	0.09786	5.76	>0.0001

a) State the null and alternative hypotheses under investigation.
b) Assuming that the assumptions for regression inference are reasonable, test the null hypothesis.
c) State your conclusion. **LO ❶**

T **38.** **Cost index, part 2.** In Exercise 36, we examined the *Worldwide Cost of Living Survey* cost of living index for the 10 most expensive cities, whose 2011 indices range from Singapore's 137 to Tokyo's 161. Let's add the 10 *least* expensive cities to the data. Their 2011 indices range from 46 for Karachi (the least expensive city in 2011) to Dhaka and Manila at 62. Here is the resulting regression:

Dependent variable is: Index
R-squared = 99.3%
s = 4.061 with 20 − 2 = 18 degrees of freedom

Predictor	Coeff	SE(Coeff)	t-Ratio	P-Value
Intercept	−2.6787	2.272	−1.18	0.2537
Index 2010	1.1082	0.022	50.1	<0.0001

a) Sketch what a scatterplot of *Index2011* vs. *Index2010* is likely to look like. You do not need to see the data.
b) Explain why the R^2 of this regression is higher than the R^2 of the regression in Exercise 36. **LO ❷**

39. **Job growth 2012, part 1.** *Fortune* magazine publishes the top 100 companies to work for every year. Among the information listed is the percentage growth in jobs at each company. The period from 2009 to 2011 was a difficult one for job growth in the United States. The output below shows the regression of the 2012 job growth (%) on the 2010 job growth for those companies that appear on both years' lists. (One outlier has been omitted.) *Job Growth 2012* is the response variable (Cable News Network, money.cnn.com/magazines/fortune/bestcompanies/; accessed March 2012).

Dependent variable is: Job Growth 2012
R-squared = 5.7%
s = 0.0738 with 68 − 2 = 6 degrees of freedom

Variable	Coeff	SE(Coeff)	t-Ratio	P-Value
Intercept	0.0628	0.009	7.00	<0.0001
Job Growth 2010	0.2	0.100	2.00	0.0498

a) State the hypotheses about the slope (both numerically and in words).
b) Assuming that the assumptions for inference are satisfied, perform the hypothesis test and state your conclusion in context.
c) Explain what the R-squared in this regression means.
d) Do these results indicate that, in general, companies with a higher job growth in 2010 had a higher job growth in 2012? Explain. **LO ❶, ❷**

T **40.** **All the efficiency money can buy 2013.** A sample of 61 model-2013 cars from an online information service was examined to see how fuel efficiency (as highway miles per gallon (MPG)) relates to the cost (manufacturer's suggested retail price (MSRP) in dollars) of cars. Here are displays and computer output:

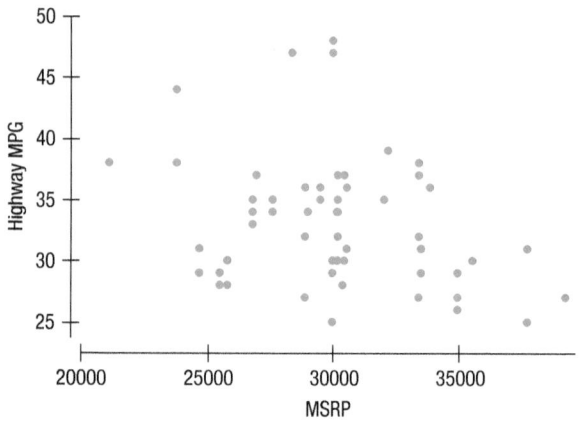

Dependent variable is: Highway MPG
R-squared = 10.36%
s = 4,870 with 61 − 2 = 59 degrees of freedom

Variable	Coeff	SE(Coeff)	t-Ratio	P-Value
Intercept	45.6898 4	4.849	9.42	<0.0001
MSRP	−0.000416	0.000159	−2.61	0.0114

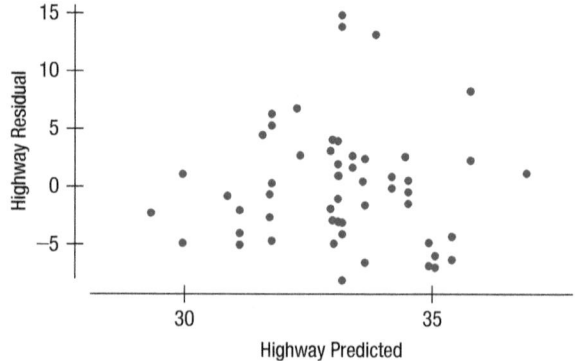

a) State what you want to know, identify the variables, and give the appropriate hypotheses.
b) Check the assumptions and conditions.
c) If the conditions are met, complete the analysis. **LO ❶**

41. Baseball, part 1. Some people claim that video training techniques would improve the performances of Little League pitchers. To test this claim, 20 Little Leaguers threw 50 pitches each, and we recorded the number of strikes. After the players participated in the training program, we repeated the test. The following table shows the number of strikes each player threw before and after the training. A test of paired differences failed to show that this training was effective in improving a player's ability to throw strikes. Is there any evidence that the *Effectiveness (After–Before)* of the training depends on the player's *Initial Ability (Before)* to throw strikes? Test an appropriate hypothesis and state your conclusion. Propose an explanation for what you find. **LO ❶**

Number of Strikes (out of 50)			
Before	After	Before	After
28	35	33	33
29	36	33	35
30	32	34	32
32	28	34	30
32	30	34	33
32	31	35	34
32	32	36	37
32	34	36	33
32	35	37	35
33	36	37	32

42. Fuel efficiency, part 3. Consider again the data in Exercise 28 about the fuel economy and weights of cars.

a) Create a 95% confidence interval for the average fuel efficiency among cars weighing 2500 pounds, and explain what your interval means.
b) Create a 95% prediction interval for the gas mileage you might get driving your new 3450-pound SUV, and explain what that interval means. **LO ❶, ❸**

T 43. Job growth 2012, part 2. In Exercise 39, the company Zappos was omitted. Here is a scatterplot of the data with Zappos plotted as an *x*:

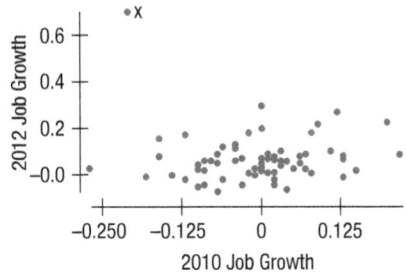

a) In words, what does the outlying point say about Zappos?
b) What effect would this point have on the regression, had it been left with the rest of the data?
c) Using the data supplied, find the regression with and without the outlier. **LO ❶**

T 44. Youth employment. Here is a scatterplot showing the regression line, 95% confidence intervals, and 95% prediction intervals, using youth unemployment data for a sample of 33 nations. The response variable is the Male Rate, and the predictor variable is the Female Rate.

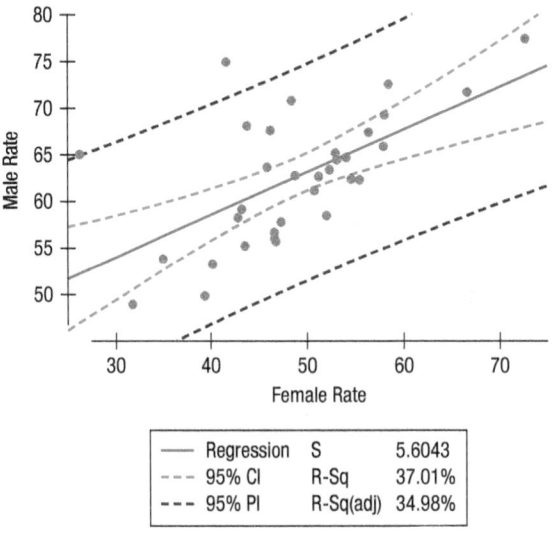

	Regression	S	5.6043
	95% CI	R-Sq	37.01%
	95% PI	R-Sq(adj)	34.98%

a) Explain the meaning of the 95% prediction intervals in this context.
b) Explain the meaning of the 95% confidence intervals in this context.
c) Using a statistics program, identify any unusual observations, and discuss their potential impact on the regression. **LO ❸**

45. Baseball, part 2. Using the data provided, answer the following questions:

a) Find the 95% prediction interval for the effectiveness of the training video on a pitcher with an initial ability of 33 strikes.
b) Do you think predictions made by this regression will be very accurate? Explain. **LO ❸**

T 46. Global reach. The internet has revolutionized business and offers unprecedented opportunities for globalization. However, the ability to access the internet varies greatly among different regions of the world. One of the variables the United Nations collects data on each year is Personal Computers per 100 Population (unstats.un.org/unsd/cdb/cdb_help/cdb_quick_start.asp) for various countries. Below is a scatterplot showing the regression line, 95% confidence intervals, and 95% prediction intervals using 2000 and 2012 computer adoption (personal computers per 100 population) for a sample of 85 countries. The response variable is *PC/100 2012*.

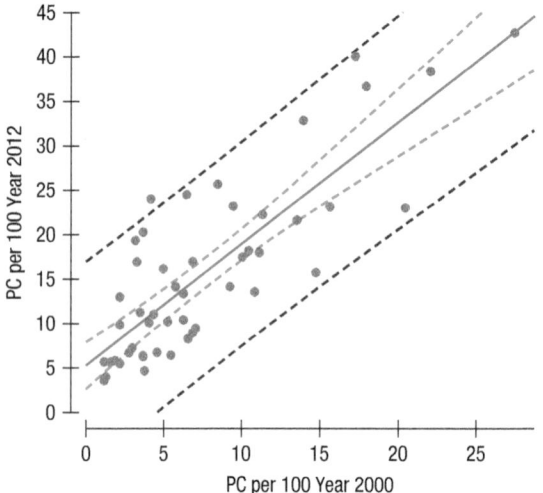

a) Working with the data set with the same name as this exercise, find a regression model showing the relationship between personal computer adoption in 2012, *PC/100 2012* (the response variable), and personal computer adoption in 2000, *PC/100 2000* (the predictor variable).
b) Explain the meaning of the 95% prediction intervals in this context.
c) Explain the meaning of the 95% confidence intervals in this context. **LO ❶, ❸**

47. Assets and sales, part 2. The analyst in exercise 27 further investigated the relationship between assets and sales by taking the logarithm of each variable to achieve a more linear relationship. Economists commonly take the logarithm of these variables to make the relationship more nearly linear, and she did, too. The response variable is *LogSales*. The assumptions for regression inference appeared to be satisfied.

R-squared = 33.9 %; s = 0.4278 with 79 − 2 = 77 degrees of freedom

Variable	Coefficient	SE(Coeff)	t-ratio	P-value
Intercept	1.303	0.3211	4.06	0.0001
LogAssets	0.578	0.0919	6.28	≤0.0001

a) Is there a significant linear association between *LogAssets* and *LogSales*? Test an appropriate hypothesis and state your conclusion in context.
b) Do you think that a company's assets serve as a useful predictor of its sales? **LO ❶**

48. Assets and Sales part 3. Referring to the regression in exercise 47.

a) Interpret the meaning of R squared.
b) Comment on how this meaning is consistent with the significance of the linear regression.

49. Seasonal spending revisited, part 1. Spending on credit cards decreases after the holiday spending season (as measured by amount charged on a credit card in December).

The data set in the file contains the monthly credit card charges of a random sample of 99 cardholders.

a) Build a regression model to predict January spending from December's spending.
b) How much, on average, will cardholders who charged $2000 in December charge in January?
c) Give a 95% confidence interval for the average January charges of cardholders who charged $2000 in December.
d) From part (c), give a 95% confidence interval for the average decrease in the charges of cardholders who charged $2000 in December.
e) What reservations, if any, do you have about the confidence intervals you made in parts (c) and (d)? **LO ❶, ❸**

Ⓣ 50. Seasonal spending revisited, part 2. Financial analysts know that January credit card charges will generally be much lower than those of the month before. What about the difference between January and the next month? Does the trend continue? The data set in the file contains the monthly credit card charges of a random sample of 99 cardholders.

a) Build a regression model to predict February charges from January's charges.
b) How much, on average, will cardholders who charged $2000 in January charge in February?
c) Give a 95% confidence interval for the average February charges of cardholders who charged $2000 in January.
d) From part (c), give a 95% confidence interval for the average decrease in the charges of cardholders who charged $2000 in January.
e) What reservations, if any, do you have about the confidence intervals you made in parts (c) and (d)? **LO ❶, ❸**

Ⓣ 51. Old pitchers. Many factors may affect fans' decisions to go to a ball game. Is it possible that fans prefer teams with an older pitching staff?

a) Examine a scatterplot of *Attend/Game* and *PitchAge*. Check the conditions for regression.
b) Do you think there is a linear association between attendance and pitcher age?
c) Compute and discuss the regression model.

52. Logistics and marketing in Canada. An organic produce company divides Canada into five regions: West, Prairies, Ontario, Quebec, and Atlantic. Each has its own greenhouses for growing organic produce and its own distribution system to retail outlets. The fruits and vegetables are produced without pesticides, thus reducing their shelf life, and for the past two years the company has been facing a problem with spoilage and a short shelf life after delivery to the retailer. Critique (making four separate points) the following discussion between the vice presidents of Logistics and Marketing:

Marketing: "You've got to deliver the product faster to the retailers. We're losing customers because the product has too short a shelf life when they receive it."

Logistics: "Nonsense. The problem is that your salespeople don't get us enough customers. If we had more volume we could make a more efficient delivery system and get the product to the stores earlier."

Marketing: "I think short shelf life is causing reduced sales. You think low sales are causing reduced shelf life. Let's sort this out with actual data. We'll get data on shelf life (at time of delivery) and sales volume for each region for the past 24 months. I'll do a regression of sales against shelf life as the explanatory variable and I bet the slope comes out significantly positive. That will prove that increasing shelf life will increase sales. Also it will tell us how much sales will be if we can increase shelf life beyond what it has been in the past two years."

Logistics: "I don't think the slope in your regression will be significant, but if I regress shelf life against sales as the explanatory variable, I bet my slope will be significantly positive. That will show that if you can increase sales, I will be able to increase shelf life." LO ❶, ❷, ❸

53. Potash mining. In potash mining, large conveyors are used underground to haul ore from the rock face to shafts through which it can be lifted to the surface for processing. A conveyer hauling one tonne per second consumes about 250 kilowatts of electric power. Automatic control of conveyors can reduce electric power consumption by shutting down conveyors when they're not required. A salesperson for such automatic control systems visits PotashCorp of Saskatchewan to offer a system for a new mine that PotashCorp is planning. The system will have a capital cost of $1.3 million, and PotashCorp needs to know (a) how much electric power cost it can expect to save in an average month. The company also wants to be 90% sure of the savings it will get, so management asks the salesperson (b) what level of savings it can be 90% sure of exceeding in any given month.

The salesperson has been provided with a linear regression analysis of *Monthly Power Saving* in $K (MPS) against *System Capital Cost* (SCC) in $M for all installations his company has done to date:

Dependent variable: MPS (average value 11.17)

Explanatory variable: SCC (average value 1.242)

R-squared: 79.1%

s = 3.42

df = 12 − 2 = 10

	Coefficients	Standard Error	t-stat	P-value
Intercept	0.79853	1.953206	0.408831	0.691282
SCC	8.350177	1.357298	6.152057	0.000108

Assuming the conditions for linear regression apply, what answers should the salesperson give to PotashCorp's questions in parts (a) and (b) above? LO ❸

⊤ 54. Provincial bonuses. A company makes parts for small engines. Its monthly sales in the two major Canadian provinces where it operates over the past year are:

British Columbia ($m)	Ontario ($m)
4.61	6.2
4.53	5.69
5.59	6.05
5.04	6.63
3.44	6
3.9	6.94
4.57	6.42
5.7	6.88
5.51	7.28
5.32	7.43
5.89	7.21
5.21	7.09

The vice president of Marketing awards bonuses to the marketing directors of provinces according to their sales growth as measured by the average increase in sales per month from a linear regression of the past year's data. There are two bonuses: (i) for the province with the higher sales growth; and (ii) for the province whose sales growth is more significantly different from zero.

a) Critique this use of linear regression by the vice president as a general methodology to use in any year.

b) Perform the regressions. Does your critique in (a) apply this year? Indicate which provincial marketing director should receive bonus (i) and (ii).

c) The marketing director who does not receive bonus (ii) complains: "Although the other province had a sales growth more significantly different from zero, it is not significantly higher than my sales growth." Confirm how true/false this statement is. LO ❶

55. Investing in Canadian banks. A brokerage company provides advice to investors on which companies to invest in. They specialize in banks and track earnings and share prices of Canadian banks. Two analysts, Allison and Bob, meet at the water cooler.

Allison: "A high share price is brought about by high earnings. The more a bank earns the more it attracts investors, pushing the share price up. I'm going to regress average share price against earnings as the explanatory variable."

Bob: "I think earnings depends on share price. If the share price goes up that's because investors think the bank is doing well and expect higher earnings. I'm going to regress earnings against the average share price as the explanatory variable."

Allison: "Earnings have been low in recent quarters, but my regression will show how much the share price will go up if earnings are twice as high as recently."

Bob: "Good luck, but I'm sure my regression will explain more of the variability than yours."

Critique the above discussion bringing out four clearly separate points. **LO❶, ❷, ❸**

● 56. From Toronto to the Caribbean. A company offers vacations in the Caribbean including charter flights from Toronto's downtown airport at a range of prices per person assuming double occupancy. It plans to offer the same vacations at the same prices next year. Over the past year sales have been as follows:

Selling Price per Vacation ($K)	Sales Revenue ($m)
0.88	16.3
1.078	19.7
1.232	21.5
1.672	24.8
2.156	26.7
2.464	29.1
2.816	28
3.058	19.6
3.388	19.5
3.784	12.4
4.158	13.9
4.378	7.2

The company is negotiating with two new hotels and may be able to offer vacations next year at $1340 and $1750 selling price. These prices would fill gaps in the existing range of selling prices.

a) Use linear regression to estimate the relationship between the number of vacations sold and selling price (explanatory variable). Give the equation for the relationship.

b) How many vacations do you estimate they could sell next year at $1340 and $1750? Give a 95% interval on your estimate.

c) How many vacations do you estimate they could sell on average over several years at $1340 and $1750? Give a 95% interval on your estimate.

d) Comment on the difference between the 95% intervals in parts (b) and (c). **LO❶, ❸**

PR NEWSWIRE/Kellogg Company/ AP Images

19

Understanding Regression Residuals

Kellogg Canada

Kellogg's Corn Flakes were introduced into Canada in 1914, just 17 years after John and Will Kellogg founded the company to manufacture whole grain breakfast cereals. Today Kellogg Canada is a wholly owned subsidiary of Kellogg Company and has manufacturing facilities in London and Belleville, Ontario. The range of Kellogg products available in Canada includes Vector, Eggo, Nutri-Grain, Pop-Tarts, and Froot Loops, which are supported by sales offices in Calgary and Montreal.

At the start of the 20th century, breakfast was typically a large, high-fat meal of eggs and meat for the wealthy and a less nutritious meal of porridge or gruel for the poor. Kellogg brothers Will and John introduced toasted corn flakes as a healthy and affordable alternative. But in 1906 they argued when Will wanted to add sugar to the recipe—an idea that horrified John. Will founded the Battle Creek Toasted Corn Flake Company, which eventually became the Kellogg Company, using its founder's "W. K. Kellogg" signature as a logo—a marketing concept that survives in the "Kellogg's" script on its boxes to this day.

In 1923 Kellogg hired the first dietitian to work in the food industry, and in the 1930s Kellogg was the first company to print nutrition information on its boxes. The W. K. Kellogg Institute for Food and Nutrition Research, a world-class research facility, opened in 1997.

Today, Kellogg Canada supports the communities in which it operates by partnering with Food Banks Canada, United Way, and Breakfast Clubs of Canada.

LO❶   **19.1**   ## Examining Residuals for Groups

WHO   Breakfast cereals

WHAT   Sugar content and calories

WHEN   Recently

WHERE   Canada

WHY   Investigation of a relationship between sugar content and calories

It seems that ever since the Kellogg brothers fought over sugar in breakfast cereals, it's been a concern. Using data from cereals marketed in Canada, we can examine the relationship between the calories in a serving and the amount of sugar (in grams). Figure 19.1 appears to satisfy the conditions for regression; the relationship is linear with no outliers.

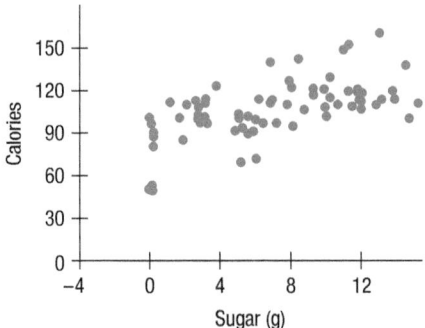

Figure 19.1   *Calories* vs. *Sugar* content (grams) per serving of breakfast cereal.

The least squares regression model

$$\widehat{Calories} = 89.5 + 2.50 \ Sugar$$

has an R^2 of 32%.

The residuals from the fitting of a linear regression hold an incredible amount of information about the model. A residual is the difference between the actual data and the value we predict for it: $e = y - \hat{y}$. Residuals can help tell you how well the model is performing and provide clues for fixing it if it's not working as well as it could. In this chapter, we'll demonstrate a variety of ways in which detecting patterns in the residuals can help you improve the model. Examining residuals can reveal more about the data than was apparent at first, or even second, glance. That's why no regression analysis is ever complete without a display of the residuals and a thorough examination of what they have to say.

Figure 19.2 shows the residuals for our model of calories in breakfast cereal. Note that when we plot residuals, we often plot them against the predicted values, calories, not against the explanatory variable, sugar. The horizontal axes in Figures 19.1 and 19.2 are therefore different. At first glance, the scatterplot in Figure 19.2 seems to have no particular structure, and as you may remember from Chapter 6, that's exactly what we hope to see. But let's check a histogram of the residuals, as shown in Figure 19.3.

How would you describe the shape of this histogram? It looks like there might be small modes on either side of the central body of the data. A few cereals stand out with larger negative residuals—that is, fewer calories than we might have predicted. And a few stand out with larger positive residuals. Of course, the sample size here is not very large. We can't say for sure that there are three modes, but it's worth a closer look.

Let's look more carefully at the residuals. Figure 19.4 repeats the scatterplot of Figure 19.2, but with the points in those modes marked. Now we can see that those two groups stand away from the central pattern in the scatterplot. Doing a little more work and examining the data set, we find that the high-residual cereals (green x's) are Just Right Fruit & Nut; Muesli Raisins, Dates & Almonds and

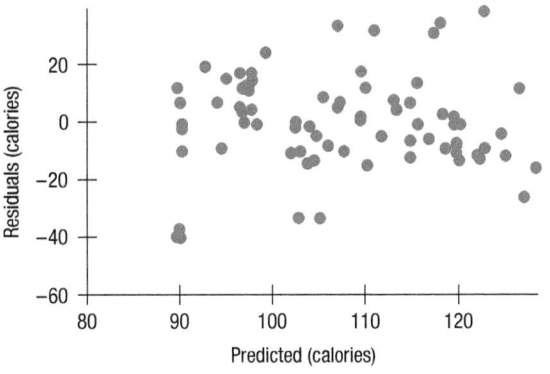
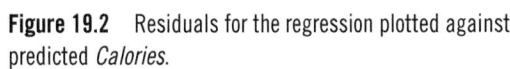
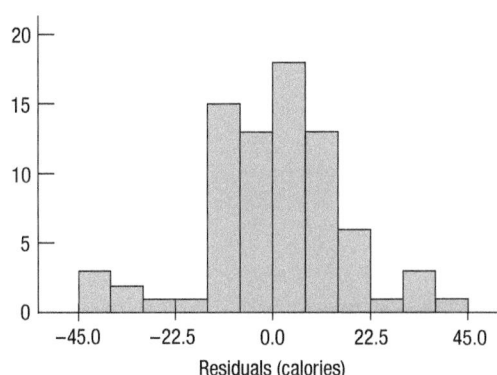

Figure 19.2   Residuals for the regression plotted against predicted *Calories*.

Figure 19.3   The distribution of the regression residuals shows modes above and below the central large mode. These may be worth a second look.

Peaches & Pecans; Mueslix Crispy Blend; and Nutri-Grain Almond Raisin. Do these cereals have something in common? These high-calorie cereals all market themselves as "healthy." This might be surprising, but in fact, "healthy" cereals often contain nuts and oil, which are "natural" and don't necessarily contain sugar, but are higher in fat than grain and sugar. So they may have more calories than we might expect from looking at their sugar content alone.

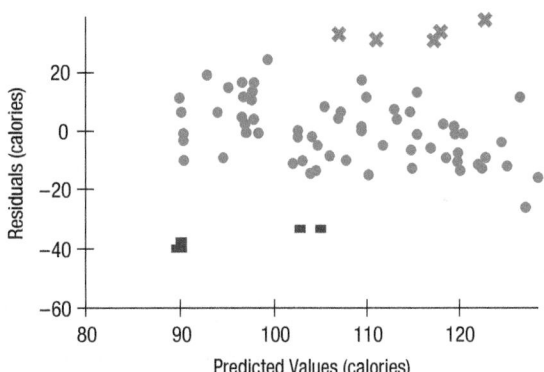

Figure 19.4   A scatterplot of the *Residuals* vs. *Predicted Values* for the cereal regression. The green x's are cereals whose calorie content is higher than the linear model predicts. The red boxes show cereals with fewer calories than the model predicts. Is there something special about these cereals?

The low-residual (red) cereals are Puffed Rice, Puffed Wheat, three bran cereals, and Golden Crisps. These cereals have fewer calories than we would expect based on their sugar content. We might not have grouped these cereals together before. What they have in common is a low calorie count *relative to their sugar content*—even though their sugar contents are quite different. (They're low-calorie because of their shape and structure.)

These observations may not lead us to question the overall linear model, but they do help us understand that other factors may be part of the story. An exploration of residuals often leads us to discover more about individual cases. When we discover groups in our data, we may decide to analyze them separately, using a different model for each group.

Often, more research can help us discover why certain cases tend to behave similarly. Here, certain cereals group together in the residual plot because cereal manufacturers aim cereals at different segments of the market. A common technique used to attract different customers is to place different types of cereals on certain shelves. Cereals for kids tend to be on the "kids' shelf," at their eye level. Toddlers aren't likely to grab a box from this shelf and beg, "Mom, can we please get this All-Bran with Extra Fibre?"

How can we take this extra information into account in our analysis? Figure 19.5 shows a scatterplot of *Calories* and *Sugar*, coloured according to the shelf on which the cereals were found, with a separate regression line fit for each shelf. Now we can see that the top shelf is unlike the bottom two shelves. We might want to report two regressions, one for the top shelf and one for the bottom two shelves.[1]

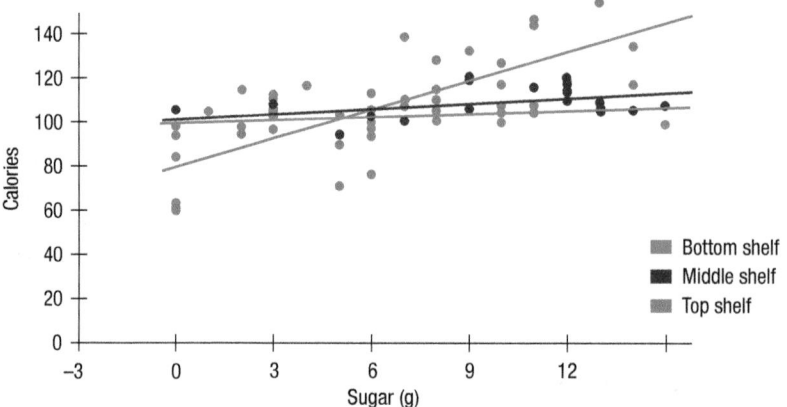

Figure 19.5   *Calories* and *Sugars* coloured according to the shelf on which the cereal was found in a supermarket, with regression lines fit for each shelf individually. Do these data appear homogeneous? That is, do all the cereals seem to be from the same population of cereals? Or are there kinds of cereals that we might want to consider separately?

FOR EXAMPLE   Diamond prices

The price of a jewellery diamond depends on the 4 C's: carat weight, cut, clarity, and colour. Diamond colours are assigned letters from D, for colourless stones, through K, for increasingly more yellow stones. A K-colour stone is only faintly yellow and still considered jewellery quality. We've collected a sample of diamond prices from a website. Here's a scatterplot of *Price* vs. *Carat Weight* with points coloured according to *Colour*:

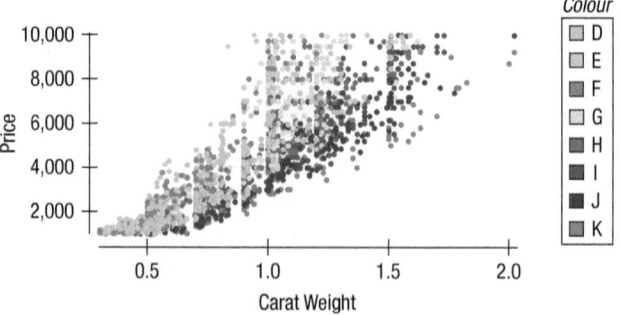

---

[1]Another alternative is to fit a multiple regression model by adding variables (called dummy or indicator variables) that distinguish the groups. This method will be discussed in Chapter 21.

> **QUESTION** How does the relationship of *Price* and *Carat Weight* change with *Colour*?
>
> **ANSWER** For a given *Carat Weight*, diamonds with better (earlier letter) colours are generally worth more. This isn't true for every diamond, but it's generally true. There may be greater variability in the middle of the colour range, with H-colour diamonds showing more variability than either D- or K-colour stones.

LO❶ 19.2 Extrapolation and Prediction

Linear models give a predicted value for each case in the data. Put a new *x*-value into the equation and it gives a predicted value, $\hat{y}$, to go with it. But when the new *x*-value lies far from the data we used to build the regression, how trustworthy is the prediction?

The simple answer is that the farther the new *x*-value is from $\bar{x}$, the centre of the *x*-values, the less trust we should place in the predicted value. Once we venture into new *x* territory, such a prediction is called an **extrapolation**. Extrapolations are dangerous because they require the additional—and questionable—assumption that nothing about the relationship between *x* and *y* changes, even at extreme values of *x* and beyond. Extrapolations can get us into deep trouble, especially if we try to predict far into the future.

As a cautionary example, let's examine oil prices from 1972 to 1981 in constant (2005) dollars.[2] In the mid-1970s, in the midst of an energy crisis, oil prices surged. In 1970, the price of oil was about $3 a barrel. A few years later, it had surged to $15. In 1975, a survey of 15 top econometric forecasting models (built by groups that included Nobel Prize–winning economists) found predictions for 1985 oil prices that ranged from $50 to $200 a barrel (or $181 to $726 [!] dollars a barrel in 2005 dollars). How close were these forecasts? Let's look at Figure 19.6.

The regression model for the *Price* of oil against *Time* (years since 1970) for these data is

$$\widehat{Price} = -0.85 + 7.39 \ Time,$$

Heather A. Craig/Shutterstock

which says that prices increased, on average, $7.39 per year, or nearly $75 in 10 years. If they continued to increase linearly, it would have been easy to predict oil prices. And indeed, many forecasters made that assumption. So how well did they do? Well, in the period from 1982 to 1998, oil prices didn't exactly continue that steady increase. In fact, they went down so much that by 1998, prices (adjusted for inflation) were the lowest they'd been since before World War II (Figure 19.7).

For example, the average price of oil in 1985 turned out to be less than $30 per barrel—not quite the $100 predicted by the model. Extrapolating out beyond the original data by just four years produced some vastly inaccurate forecasts. While the time series plot in Figure 19.7 shows a fairly steady decline, this pattern clearly didn't continue (or oil would be free by now).

In the 1990s, the U.S. government decided to include scenarios in its forecasts. The result was that the Energy Information Administration (EIA) offered

> **When the Data Are Years**
>
> We usually don't enter years as four-digit numbers. Here, we used 0 for 1970, 10 for 1980, and so on. It's common to assign 0 to the date of the first observation in our data set if we're working with a time series. Another option is to enter two digits for the year, using 88 for 1988, for instance. Rescaling years like this often makes calculations easier and equations simpler. But be careful; if 1988 is 88, then 2004 is 104 (not 4).

---

[2]There are special models for fitting data when *x* is time (which we will discuss in Chapter 22), but simple regression models are often used. Even when using more sophisticated methods, the dangers of extrapolation don't disappear.

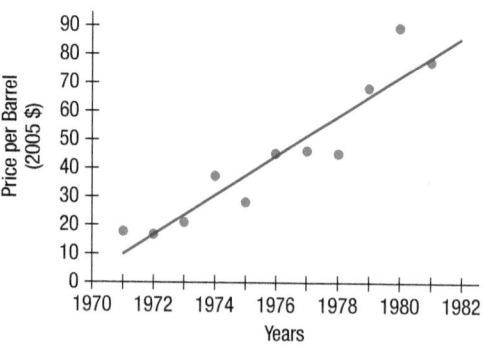

Figure 19.6 The price of oil per barrel in constant (2005) dollars from 1971 to 1982 shows a linear trend increasing at about $7 a year.

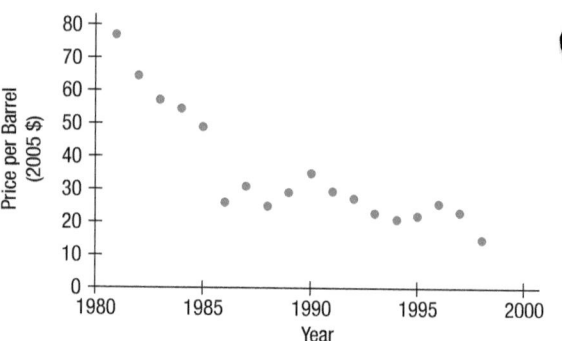

Figure 19.7 This time series plot of the price of oil in constant (2005) dollars shows a fairly constant decrease over time.

two 20-year forecasts for oil prices after 1998 in its Annual Energy Outlook (AEO). Both of these scenarios, however, called for relatively modest increases in oil prices (Figure 19.8).

So how accurate have these forecasts been? Let's compare these predictions to the actual prices in constant (2005) dollars (Figure 19.9).

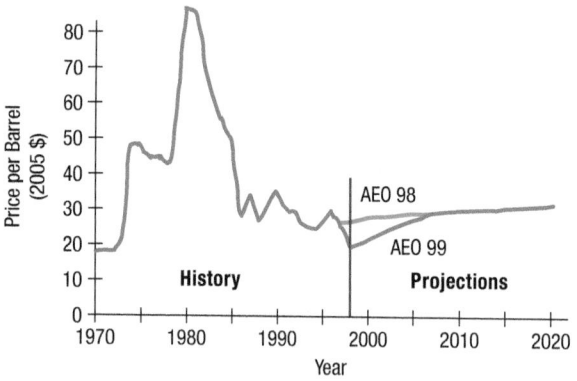

Figure 19.8 This graph, adapted from one by the Energy Information Administration, shows oil prices from 1970 to 1998 with two sets of forecasts for the period 1999 to 2020.

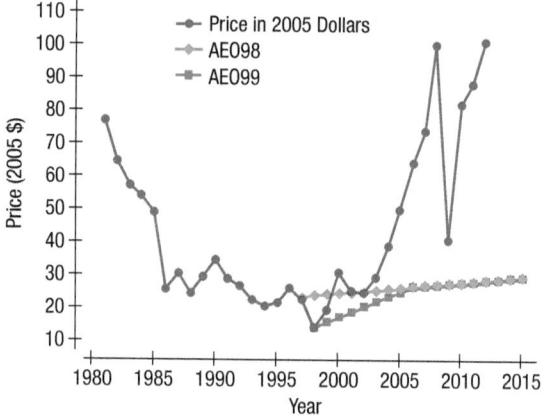

Figure 19.9 Here are the same EIA forecasts as in Figure 16.8, together with the actual prices from 1981 to 2012. Neither forecast predicted the sharp run-up in the first decade of the 21st century.

The experts seem to have missed the sharp run-up in oil prices in the first decade of the 21st century. Where do you think oil prices will go in the *next* decade? Your guess may be as good as anyone's. Clearly, these forecasts did not take into account many of the unforeseen global and economic events that have occurred since 2000. Providing accurate long-term forecasts is extremely difficult.

Extrapolation far from the data is dangerous. Linear models are based on the *x*-values of the data at hand and cannot be trusted beyond that span. Some phenomena do exhibit a kind of inertia that allows us to guess that the currently observed systematic behaviour will continue outside this range. When *x* is time, you should be especially wary. Such regularity can't be counted on in phenomena such as stock prices, sales figures, hurricane tracks, or public opinion.

Extrapolating from current trends is a mistake made not only by regression beginners or the naive. Professional forecasters are prone to the same mistakes, and sometimes the errors are striking. However, because the temptation to predict the future is so strong, our more realistic advice is this:

Prediction is difficult, especially about the future.

—Niels Bohr, danish physicist

If you extrapolate far into the future, be prepared for the actual values to be (possibly quite) different from your predictions.

FOR EXAMPLE   **A big diamond**

GraphicaArtis/Archive Photos/Getty Images

The Cullinan I diamond (the "Star of Africa") owned by the Queen of England is, at 530.20 carats, the largest D-colour cut diamond in the world. It's mounted at the head of the sceptre with the cross in the British crown jewels.

It has an estimated value of about $400 million. When we restrict our analysis of the diamonds we saw in For Example: "Diamond prices" to D-colour diamonds, the regression model of *Price* on *Carat Weight* is

$$\widehat{Price} = -2129.14 + 8081.12 \; CaratWt.$$

QUESTION What does this model predict for the *Price* of the Cullinan I diamond? Is the estimate of $400 million consistent with this model? Do you think this model should be relied on to establish prices for large diamonds?

ANSWER The predicted price from the model is $4,282,482. That's only about 1/100th the price placed on the diamond itself. The rarity of such large diamonds is likely to make them far more valuable than a model based on much smaller stones could predict. Extrapolation that far from the data on which a model is based is not likely to work well.

LO❶   **19.3**   # Unusual and Extraordinary Observations

Each time you use your credit card, the merchant pays the credit card company a percentage of the sale. To encourage you to use your card, the card issuer may offer you an incentive such as airline miles, rebates, or gifts.[3] Of course, this is profitable to the company only if the increased use brings in enough revenue to offset the cost of the incentives. New ideas for offers (referred to as "creatives") are typically tested on a sample of cardholders before they're rolled out to the entire segment or population, a process referred to as a "campaign." Typically, the new offer (the "challenger") is tested against a control group, who may be offered nothing or the current best offer ("the champion").

One campaign offered one of the highest-performing market segments an incentive for three months: one redeemable-any-time air mile for each dollar spent. The company hoped that the cardholders would increase their spending enough to pay for the campaign, but it feared that some cardholders would move spending forward into the incentive period, with a resulting drop in spending afterward.

For this particular segment, the typical cardholder charged about $1700 a month. During the campaign period, the group averaged around $1919.61 a month, a difference that was both statistically and financially significant. But analysts were surprised to see that the increase in spending continued well beyond the offer period. To investigate it, they made a scatterplot like the one shown in Figure 19.10.

---

[3]There are websites dedicated to finding credit card "deals." Search "credit card rewards."

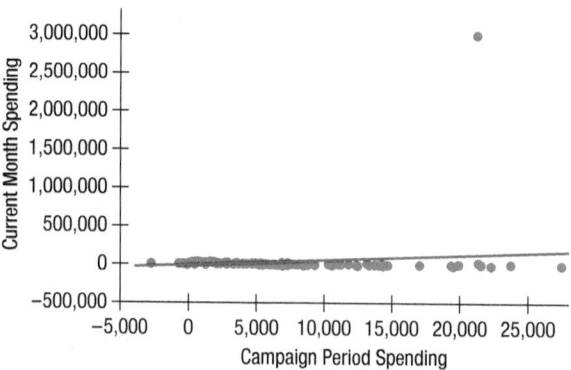

Figure 19.10   Spending after the campaign plotted against spending during the campaign period reveals a surprising value and a positive regression slope.

At first sight the regression line in Figure 19.10 indicates a positive relationship, but the outlying, at the top of the graph, represents a cardholder who charged nearly $3 million in the month after the free miles period ended. Remarkably, the point was verified to be a real purchase! Nevertheless, this cardholder is clearly not typical of the rest of the segment. To answer the company's question, we need to examine the plot without the outlying point (Figure 19.11).

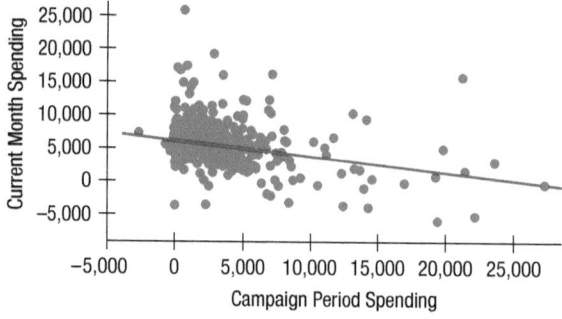

Figure 19.11   A plot of current spending against spending during the campaign period, with the outlier set aside. Now the slope is negative, and significantly so.

The plot does show that those with the largest charges during the campaign spent less in the month after the campaign. Just one outlier was capable of changing the slope's direction from negative to positive. On the basis of this finding, the analysts decided to focus only on those whose spending during *both* periods was less than $10,000 a month, figuring that if people decide to spend more than $10,000 on their credit card, their primary motivation is probably not the airline miles incentive.

Outliers, Leverage, and Influence

By providing a simple description of how data behave, models help us see when and how data values are unusual. In regression, a point can stand out in two ways. A case can have a large residual, as our $3-million spender certainly did. Because it's not like the other cases, a point with a large residual always deserves special attention and is called an **outlier**.

A data point can also be unusual if its *x*-value is far from the mean of the *x*-values. Such a point is said to have high **leverage**. The physical image of a lever is exactly right. The least squares line must pass through $(\bar{x}, \bar{y})$, so you can picture that point

World History Archive/Alamy Stock Photo

Give me a place to stand and I will move the Earth.

—Archimedes (287–211 bce)

> Influence depends on both the leverage and the residual; a case with high leverage whose *y*-value sits right on the line fit to the rest of the data is not influential. A case with low leverage but a very large residual can be influential. The only way to be sure is to fit the regression with and without the potential influential point.

For whoever knows the ways of Nature will more easily notice her deviations; and, on the other hand, whoever knows her deviations will more accurately describe her ways.

—FRANCIS BACON (1561–1626)

as the fulcrum of the lever. Just as sitting farther from the centre of a see-saw gives you more leverage, points with values far from $\bar{x}$ pull more strongly on the regression line.

A point with high leverage has the potential to change the regression line, but it doesn't always use that potential. If the point lines up with the pattern of the other points, it doesn't change our estimate of the line. By sitting so far from $\bar{x}$, though, it may appear to strengthen the relationship, inflating the correlation and R^2.

How can you tell if a high-leverage point changes the model? Just fit the linear model twice, both with and without the point in question. We say that a point has **influence** if omitting it from the analysis gives a very different model (as the high spender did in our example).[4]

Unusual points in a regression often tell us more about the data and the model than any other cases. Whenever you have—or suspect that you have—influential points, you should fit the linear model to the other cases alone and then compare the two regression models to understand how they differ. A model dominated by a single point is unlikely to be useful for understanding the rest of the cases. The best way to understand unusual points is against the background of the model established by the other data values. Don't give in to the temptation to delete points simply because they don't fit the line. That can give a false picture of how well the model fits the data. But often the best way to identify interesting cases and subgroups is to note that they're influential and to find out what makes them special.

Not all points with large influence have large residuals. Sometimes, their influence pulls the regression line so close that it makes the residual deceptively small. Influential points like that can have a shocking effect on the regression. Figure 19.12 shows *IQ* plotted against *Shoe Size* from a fanciful study of intelligence and foot size. The outlier is Bozo the clown, known for his large feet and hailed as a comic genius.

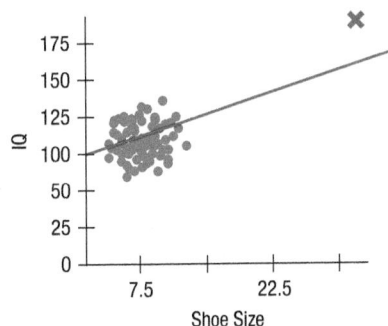

Figure 19.12   Bozo the clown's extraordinarily large shoes give his data point high leverage in the regression of $IQ = 93.3 + 2.08$ *Shoe Size*, even though the R^2 is 25%. Wherever Bozo's IQ happens to be, the regression line will follow.

Although this is a fanciful example, it illustrates an important and common potential problem. Almost all of the variance accounted for ($R^2 = 25\%$) is due to *one* point—namely, Bozo. Without Bozo, there is little correlation between shoe size and IQ. If we run the regression after omitting Bozo, we get an R^2 of only 0.7%—a weak linear relationship (as one might expect). One single point exhibits a great influence on the regression analysis.

---

[4]Some textbooks use the term *influential point* for any observation that influences the slope, intercept, or R^2. We'll reserve the term for points that influence the slope.

JUST CHECKING

Each of these scatterplots shows an unusual point. For each, tell whether the point is a high-leverage point, would have a large residual, and/or is influential.

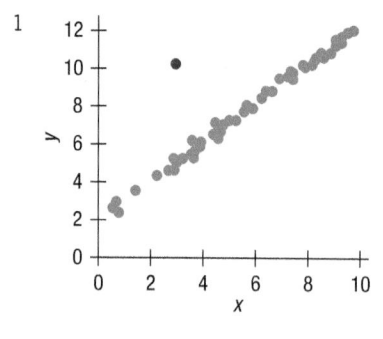
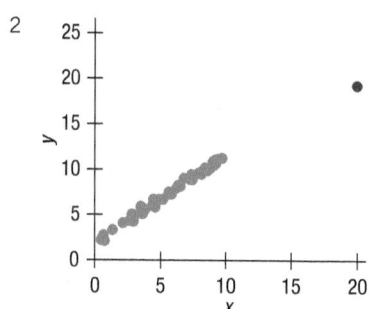
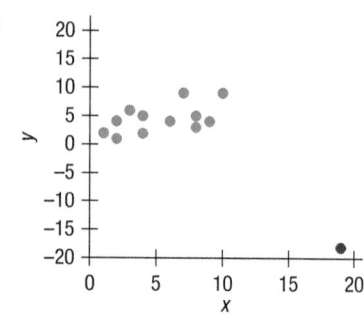

Answers are found in Appendix A.

What should you do with a high-leverage point? Sometimes these values are important (they may be customers with extremely high incomes or employees with unusually long service to the company), and they may say more about the relationship between y and x than any of the other data values. However, at other times, high-leverage points are values that really don't belong with the rest of the data. Such points should probably be omitted, and a linear model should be found without them for comparison. When in doubt, it's usually best to fit regressions both with and without the points and compare the two models.

Warning: Influential points can hide in plots of residuals. Points with high leverage pull the line close to them, so they often have small residuals. You'll see influential points more easily in scatterplots of the original data, and you'll see their effects by finding a regression model with and without the points.

FOR EXAMPLE   Coloured diamonds

Some true diamonds are coloured from inclusions or structural differences. Can the prices of these diamonds be predicted with the models we make for traditional clear diamonds?

One website lists a black diamond that weighs 1.44 carats for $3050. Black diamonds are true diamonds but may have formed from impacts of comets, asteroids, or meteors rather than from geological pressures deep underground. They're probably best compared to the most-coloured K-quality diamonds. Here's a scatterplot of *Price* vs. *Carat Weight* for K-colour diamonds. The black diamond (shown with a red x) has both high leverage and large residual.

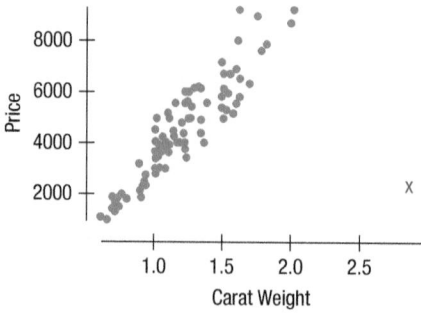

The same site lists a blue diamond that weighs 0.82 carats for $16,500. Blue diamonds are a luxury item, best compared to the best D-colour clear diamonds. Here's a scatterplot of *Price* vs. *Carat Weight* for C-colour diamonds with the blue diamond shown as a red x.

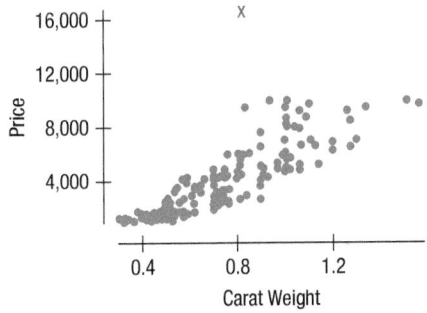

QUESTION What would be the effect of including these exotic diamonds on regression lines fit to each of these scatterplots?

ANSWER The black diamond has high leverage because it's heavier than any of the other diamonds considered. It also has a large negative residual because it's much less expensive than a regression for K-colour diamonds would predict. As a result, it will pull the regression line down, making the slope smaller.

The blue diamond has a large positive residual because it's much more expensive even than the regression on perfect D-colour diamonds would predict. However, because its carat weight is in the middle of the range of weights considered for the regression, it has little leverage. Including this case will increase the intercept slightly, but won't change the slope very much.

LO❶ 19.4 Working with Summary Values

Michael Betts/Digital Vision/Getty Images

Scatterplots of statistics summarized over groups tend to show less variability than we'd see if we measured the same variables on individuals. This is because the summary statistics themselves vary less than the data on the individuals.

Wind power is getting increasing attention as an alternative, carbon-free method of generating electricity. Of course, there must be enough wind to make it cost-effective. In a study to find a site for a wind generator, wind speeds were collected four times a day (at 6:00 A.M., noon, 6:00 P.M., and midnight) for a year at several possible sites. Figure 19.13 plots the wind speeds for two of these sites. The correlation is 0.736.

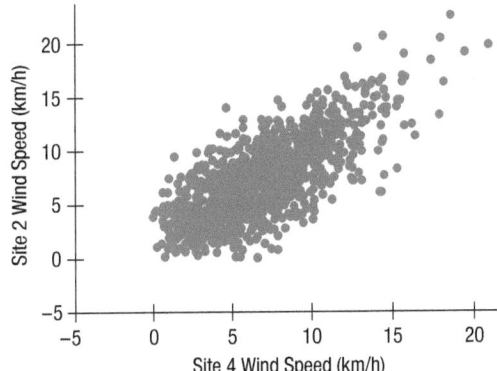

Figure 19.13 The wind speed at sites 2 and 4 are correlated (correlation coefficient = 0.736).

What would happen to the correlation if we used only one measurement per day? If, instead of plotting four data points for each day, we record an average speed for each day, the resulting scatterplot shows less variation, as Figure 19.14 shows. The correlation for these values increases to 0.844.

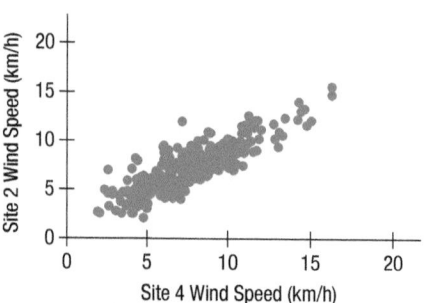

Figure 19.14   Daily average wind speeds show less variation (correlation coefficient = 0.844).

Let's average over an even longer time period. Figure 19.15 shows *monthly* averages for the year (plotted on the same scale). Now the correlation is 0.942.

What these scatterplots show is that summary statistics exhibit less scatter than the data on individuals on which they're based and can give us a false impression of how well a line summarizes the data. There's no simple correction for this phenomenon. If we're given summary data, we usually can't get the original values back. You should be a bit suspicious of conclusions based on regressions of summary data. They may look better than they really are.

Another way to reduce the number of points in a data set is to select or sample points rather than average them. This can be especially important with data, such as the wind speeds, that are measured over time. For example, if instead of finding the *mean* for each day, we select just one of the four daily measurements—say, the one made at noon on each day—we'd have just as many points as in Figure 19.14, but the correlation is 0.730—essentially the same as for the full data. Figure 19.16 shows the relationship.

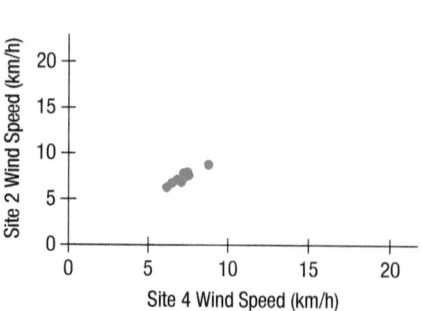

Figure 19.15   Monthly averages are even less variable (correlation coefficient = 0.942).

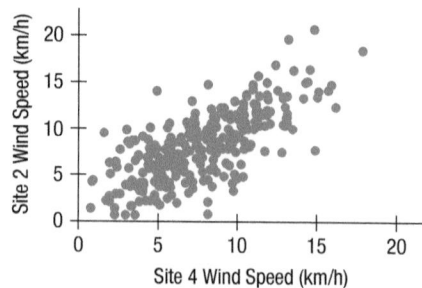

Figure 19.16   Selecting only the noon measurements doesn't reduce the variation. Compare this scatterplot with Figures 19.13 and 19.14 (correlation coefficient = 0.730).

19.5   **Autocorrelation**

Time series data that are collected at regular time points often have the property that points near each other in time will be related. When values at time t are correlated with values at time $t - 1$, we say the values are *autocorrelated* in the first order. If values are correlated with values two time periods back, we say second-order autocorrelation is present, and so on.

A regression model applied to autocorrelated data will have residuals that aren't independent and that violate an assumption for regression. The statistical tests and confidence intervals for the slope depend on independence, and its violation can render these tests and intervals invalid. Fortunately, there's a statistic, called the **Durbin-Watson statistic**, that can detect first-order autocorrelation from the residuals of a regression analysis.

A product manager is interested in learning how sensitive sales are to changes in the unit price of a frozen pizza in downtown Toronto. Here's the regression of *Sales* volume on *Price* for frozen pizza each week for a three-year period:

	Coeff	SE(Coeff)	*t*-value	P-value
Intercept	139547	11302	12.347	<0.0001
Price	−33527	4308	−7.783	<0.0001

A plot of the residuals against predicted values (Figure 19.17) shows nothing particularly unusual.

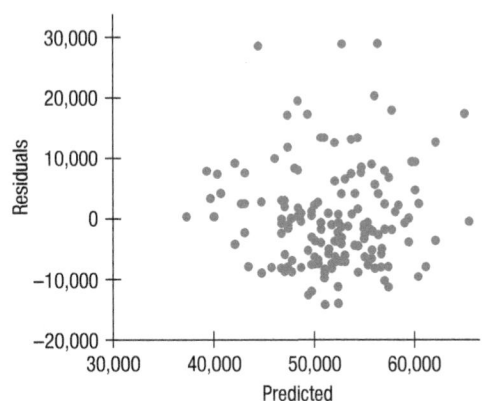

Figure 19.17   A scatterplot of the *Residuals* vs. *Predicted* values for the 156 weeks of pizza sales data reveals no obvious patterns.

But because these data points are consecutive weekly data, we should investigate the residuals vs. time. In Figure 19.18 we've plotted the *Residuals* against *Week* consecutively, from week 1 to week 156.

It may not be obvious that there's a pattern here. Autocorrelation can be difficult to see in residuals. It does seem, however, that there's a tendency in Figure 19.18 for the residuals to be related to nearby points. Notice the overall positive trend. We shouldn't see such a trend in residuals that are independent of each other. The Durbin-Watson statistic allows us to test for autocorrelation. It's calculated by summing the squares of the differences between consecutive residuals and dividing

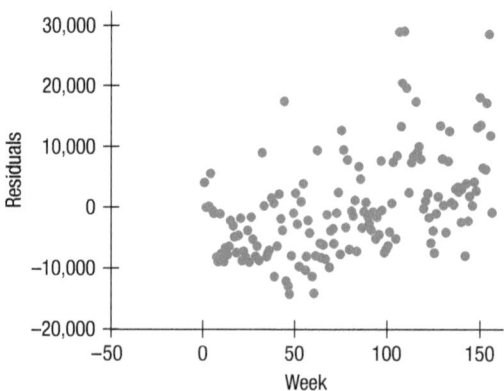

Figure 19.18   A scatterplot of the *Residuals* against *Week* for the 156 weeks of pizza sales data seems to show some trend.

by its expected value under the null hypothesis of no autocorrelation. The Durbin-Watson statistic is computed as follows:

$$D = \frac{\sum\limits_{t=2}^{n}(e_t - e_{t-1})^2}{\sum\limits_{t=1}^{n} e_t^2}$$

Why Is *D* Between Zero and Four?

Notice that if the adjacent residuals are equal (perfectly correlated), then the numerator and the value of *D* equals zero. If, on the other hand, the residuals are equal but have opposite signs (perfectly negatively correlated), then each difference is twice the residual. Then after squaring, the numerator will be 2^2, or four times the denominator.

where e_t is the residual at time *t*. The statistic always falls in the interval from zero to four. When the null hypothesis of no autocorrelation is true, the value of *D* should be two. Values of *D* below two are evidence of positive autocorrelation, while values of *D* above two indicate possible negative autocorrelation. Positive autocorrelation is more common than negative autocorrelation. How far below or above two does *D* need to be to show "strong" or significant autocorrelation? It may be surprising, but the answer to this question depends only on the sample size, *n*, and the number of predictors in the regression model, *k*, which for simple regression is equal to one.

A standard Durbin-Watson table (see Table D in Appendix B) shows the sample size down the left-hand column, so that each row corresponds to a different sample size *n*, with the number of predictors *k* across the top. For each *k* there are two columns: d_L and d_U. (The significance level of the table is also shown at the top of the page.) The test has several possible outcomes:

- If $D < d_L$ (lower critical value), then there is evidence of positive autocorrelation.
- If $d_L < D < d_U$, then the test is inconclusive.
- If $D > d_U$ (upper critical value), then there is no evidence of positive autocorrelation.

To test negative autocorrelation, we use the same values of d_L and d_U, but we subtract them from four:

- If $D > 4 - d_L$ (lower critical value), then there is evidence of negative autocorrelation.
- If $4 - d_L < D < 4 - d_U$, then the test is inconclusive.
- If $D < 4 - d_U$ (upper critical value), then there is no evidence of negative autocorrelation.

We usually rely on technology to compute the statistic. For the pizza example, we have $n = 156$ weeks and one predictor (*Price*), so $k = 1$. The value of *D* is 0.8812. Using the table in Appendix B, we find that the largest value of *n* listed is $n = 100$, and at $\alpha = 0.05$, $d_L = 1.65$. Because our value is less than that, we conclude that there's evidence of positive autocorrelation. (A software package would find the P-value to be < 0.0001.) We conclude that the residuals are *not* independent but that residuals from one week have a positive correlation with the residuals from the preceding week. The standard errors and test for the slope aren't valid since we don't have independence.

Time series methods (see Chapter 22) attempt to deal with the problem of autocorrelation by modelling the errors. Another solution is to find a predictor variable that accounts for some of the autocorrelation and removes the dependence in the residuals (see Chapter 21). A simple solution that often works is to sample from the time series so that the values are more distant in time and thus less likely to be correlated. If, from the pizza data, we take every fourth week of data starting at week four, our regression becomes

	Coeff	SE(Coeff)	*t*-ratio	P-value
Intercept	148350	222668	6.663	8.01e-08
Price	−36762	8583	−4.283	0.000126

Now, $D = 1.617$. With $n = 39$, the upper critical value d_U is 1.54. Since our new value of D is larger than that, we see no evidence of autocorrelation. Output from technology shows the P-value:

Durbin-Watson test

$D = 1.6165$, $P = 0.098740$

We should feel more comfortable basing our confidence and prediction intervals on this model.

Autocorrelation may occur if there is a reason to think that one data point might influence the next one in our data set. This is more likely for time series data than for cross-sectional data. For instance, suppose we want to model the relationship between wages and unemployment last month and we have data for each province in Canada. We do not need to check for autocorrelation since the provinces could have been listed in any order. There is no reason to think that one province's data would influence the next one in the list.

FOR EXAMPLE   Gemstone imports

The U.S. Geological Survey reports facts about a range of mineral and material commodities (minerals.usgs.gov/ds/2005/140/) including gemstones. From their report, we find that imports of gemstones increased between 1990 and 2011:

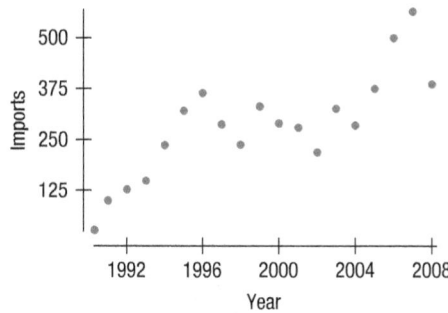

(continued)

A regression gives the following:

Dependent variable is: Imports
R-squared = 36.0% R-squared (adjusted) = 32.8%
s = 83.78 with 22 − 2 = 20 degrees of freedom

Variable	Coefficient	SE(Coeff)	t-ratio	P-value
Intercept	−18615.6	5632	−3.31	0.0035
Year	9.43924	2.815	3.35	0.0032

The Durbin-Watson statistic is $D = 0.92$.

QUESTION Why should we check the Durbin-Watson statistic for this analysis? What does the statistic say about these data?

ANSWER The data are a time series. For time series there is always a possibility of autocorrelation, which we test for with the Durbin-Watson statistic. A value of 0.92 for a regression with $n = 22$ and one predictor is below the lower limit (d_L) for significance, which we can find from Table D in Appendix B to be 1.24. So we conclude that there is evidence of a positive autocorrelation in these data. We should not rely on the standard errors calculated for this regression.

LO❸ 19.6   Linearity

Rising gas prices and concern for the environment have increased our attention to automobile fuel efficiency. In the United States, this is measured in miles per gallon (mpg). The most important factor in fuel efficiency is the weight of the car (Figure 19.19).

The relationship is strong ($R^2 = 81.6\%$), clearly negative, and apparently linear. The regression equation

$$\widehat{Fuel\ Efficiency} = 48.7 - 8.4\ Weight$$

says that fuel efficiency drops by 8.4 mpg per 1000 pounds, starting from a value of 48.7 mpg. We check the Linearity Condition by plotting the residuals vs. either the x variable or the predicted values.

The scatterplot of the *Residuals* against *Weight* (Figure 19.20) holds a surprise. Residuals plots should have no pattern, but this one has a bend. Look back at the original scatterplot. The scatter of points isn't really straight. There's a slight bend to the plot, but the bend is much easier to see in the residuals.

When the relationship isn't straight, we shouldn't fit a regression or summarize the strength of the association with correlation. But often we can make the relationship straighter. All we have to do is re-express (or transform) one or both of the variables with a simple function. In this case, there's a natural function. In the United States, automobile fuel efficiency is measured in miles per gallon. But in Canada, and in many other countries, things are different. Not only do we use metric measures, and thus kilometres and litres, but we measure fuel efficiency in litres per 100 kilometres. That's the *reciprocal* of miles per gallon (times a scale constant). That is, the gas amount (litres or gallons) is **in** the numerator, and the distance (kilometres or miles) is now in the denominator.

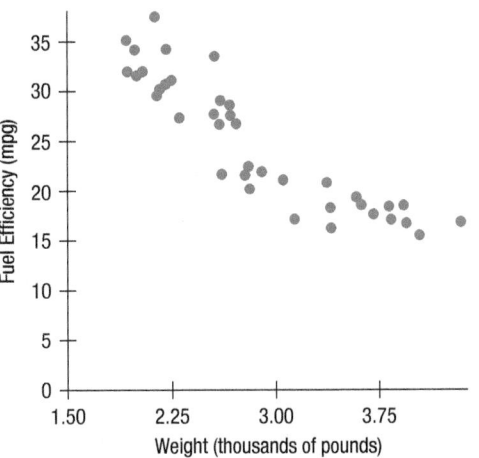

Figure 19.19 *Fuel Efficiency* (mpg) vs. *Weight* (thousands of pounds) shows a strong, apparently linear, negative trend.

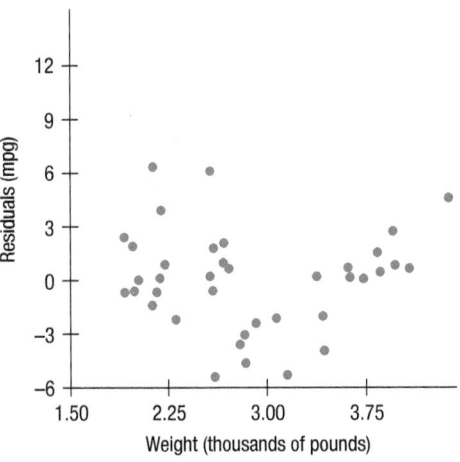

Figure 19.20 Plotting *Residuals* against *Weight* reveals a bend. The bend can be seen if you look carefully at the original scatterplot, but here it's easier to see.

There's no reason to prefer one form or the other, so let's try the (negative) reciprocal form (Figure 19.21). The residuals look better as well (Figure 19.22).

There's a clear improvement using the reciprocal, so we should use the reciprocal as the response in our regression model.

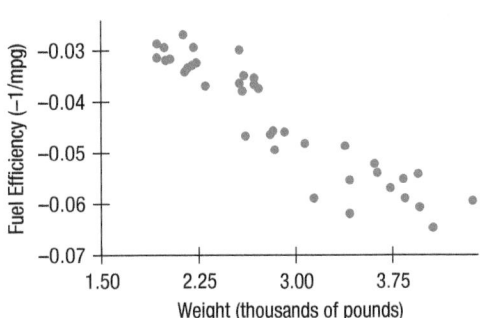

Figure 19.21 The reciprocal of *Fuel Efficiency* vs. *Weight* is straighter.

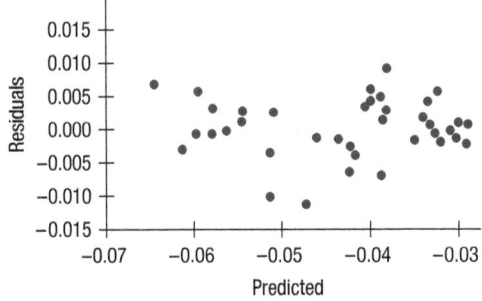

Figure 19.22 Residuals from the regression of *Fuel Efficiency* (−1/mpg) on *Weight* show less bend.

LO③ 19.7 Transforming (Re-expressing) Data

Bryn Lennon/Getty Images

How fast can you go on a bicycle? If you measure your speed, you probably do it in distance per time (miles per hour or kilometres per hour).

If you averaged 12.5 mph (20.1 km/h) for a mile run, would that be fast? Would it be fast for a 100-metre dash? Even if you run the mile often, you probably have to stop and calculate. Although we measure speed of bicycles in distance per time, we don't usually measure running speed that way. Instead, we re-express it as the *reciprocal*—time per distance (minutes per mile, seconds per 100 metres, etc.). Running a mile in under five minutes (12 mph) is fast. A mile at 16 mph approaches the world record (that's a three-minute 45-second mile; the world record is three minutes and 43 seconds).

The point is that there's no single natural way to measure speed. In some cases we use distance travelled per time, and in other cases we use the reciprocal.

Goals of Re-expression

We use **transformation (or re-expression)** on data for several reasons, as we'll see below. But first, note that ease of analysis isn't the only objective; the transformation of the data must also make sense in its context. Taking the reciprocal of speed in miles per hour makes sense, since we often talk about minutes per mile. Likewise, by convention, vehicle fuel efficiency is measured in miles per gallon in the United States and litres per 100 kilometres in Canada. But what about the frequent use of logarithms for dollar values?

Logarithms are useful for this because they have such an enormous range. If, for instance, our data includes both small companies and large multinationals, taking logs makes the data easier to eyeball graphically and easier to analyze with linear regression. But in practice, we must always bear in mind that "log dollars" are not, of course, a natural measure, and that we need to transform these back into dollars to get meaningful results.

Logarithms are also often used when we're modelling a variable that's growing exponentially over time. Many economic variables behave in this way, for example:

- a price, p, that's subject to a percentage inflation from one year to the next: $p(t) \sim p(1+i)^t$
- the value, V, of an investment that grows at a compound growth rate: $V(t) \sim V(1+r)^t$

Taking logs of these variables results not only in a variable that can be regressed as a linear function of time, but also in perhaps other explanatory variables:

$$\text{Log}\,(p(t)) = \text{Log}\,(p) + \text{Log}\,(1+i)\,t + \text{other variables}$$

$$\text{Log}\,(V(t)) = \text{Log}\,(V) + \text{Log}\,(1+r)\,t + \text{other variables}$$

In this case, the regression coefficient of time has a very natural interpretation as the logarithm of one plus the inflation or growth rate: $\text{Log}(1 + i)$ or $\text{Log}(1 + r)$. If we use the regression for prediction, however, we still need to bear in mind that we're estimating the log of the price or the log of the value of the investment.

Each of the goals of re-expression helps make the data more suitable for analysis by our methods. We'll illustrate each goal by looking at data about large companies.

Goal 1 *Make the distribution of a variable (as seen in its histogram, for example) more symmetric.* It's easier to summarize the centre of a symmetric distribution, and for nearly symmetric distributions, we can use the mean and standard deviation. If the distribution is unimodal, then the resulting distribution may be closer to the Normal model, allowing us to use the 68-95-99.7 Rule.

The *Assets* of 77 large companies are shown in Figure 19.23 as a histogram.

The skewed distribution is made much more symmetric by taking logs (Figure 19.24).

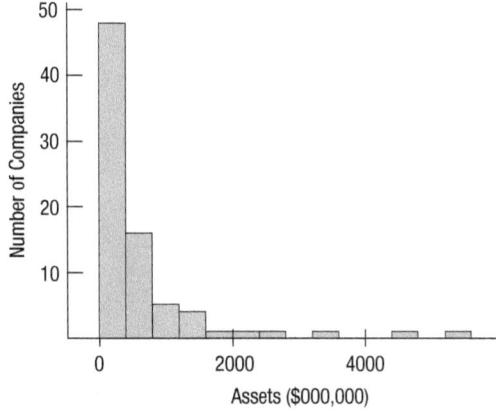

Figure 19.23   The distribution of the *Assets* of large companies is skewed to the right. Data on wealth often look like this.

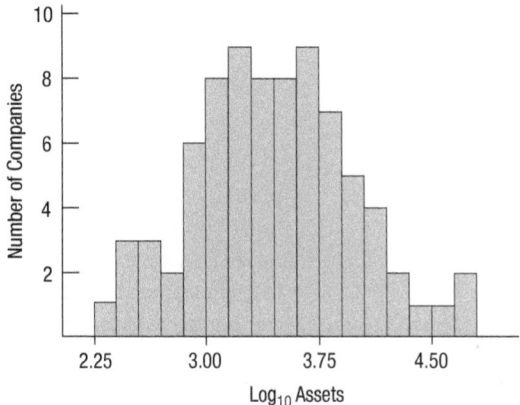

Figure 19.24   Taking logs makes the distribution more symmetric.

Goal 2 *Make the spread of several groups (as seen in side-by-side boxplots) more alike*, even if their centres differ. Groups that share a common spread are easier to compare. We'll see methods later in the book that can be applied only to groups with a common standard deviation. We saw an example of re-expression for comparing groups with boxplots in Chapter 5.

Figure 19.25 shows the *Assets* of these companies by *Market Sector*.

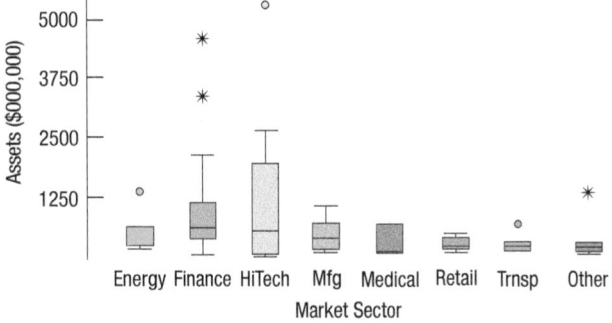

Figure 19.25   *Assets* of large companies by *Market Sector*. It's hard to compare centres of spreads, and there seems to be a number of high outliers.

Taking logs makes the individual boxplots more symmetric and gives them spreads that are more nearly equal (Figure 19.26).

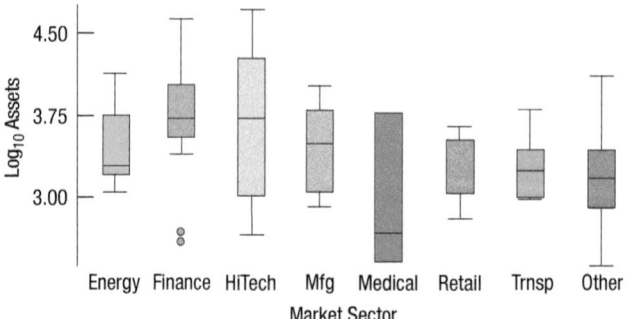

Figure 19.26   After re-expressing using logs, it's much easier to compare across *Market Sectors*. The boxplots are more symmetric, most have similar spreads, and the companies that seemed to be outliers before are no longer extraordinary. Two new outliers have appeared in the finance sector. They're the only companies in that sector that aren't banks.

This makes it easier to compare *Assets* across *Market Sectors*. It can also reveal problems in the data. Some companies that looked like outliers on the high end turned out to be more typical. But two companies in the *Finance* sector now stick out. They're not banks. Unlike the rest of the companies in that sector, they may have been placed in the wrong sector, but we couldn't see that in the original data.

Goal 3 *Make the form of a scatterplot more nearly linear.* Linear scatterplots are easier to describe. The value of re-expressing data to straighten a relationship is that we can fit a linear model once the relationship is straight.

Figure 19.27 shows *Assets* plotted against the logarithm of *Sales* for our 77 large companies.

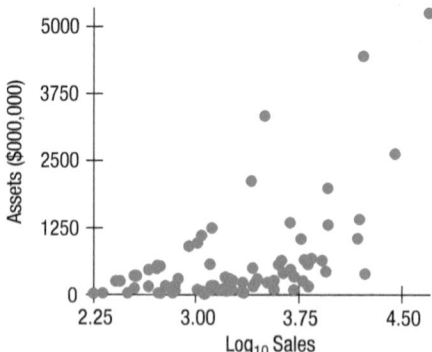

Figure 19.27   *Assets* vs. log *Sales* shows a positive association (bigger *Sales* goes with bigger *Assets*) with a bent shape.

Note that the plot of *Assets* vs. log *Sales* shows that the points go from tightly bunched at the left to widely scattered at the right—a "fan" shape. The plot's shape is bent. Taking logs makes the relationship much more linear (see Figure 19.28).

If we re-express the company *Assets* using logarithms, we get a graph that shows a more linear association. Also note that the fan shape has disappeared and the variability at each value of *x* is about the same.

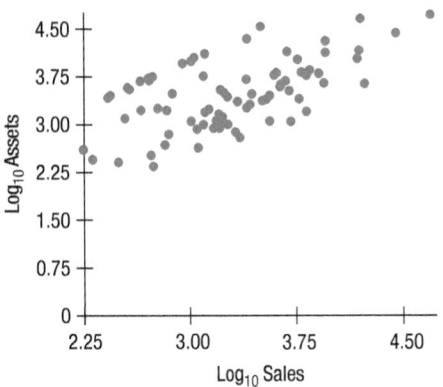

Figure 19.28   Log *Assets* vs. log *Sales* shows a positive linear association.

Goal 4 *Make the scatter in a scatterplot or residual plot spread out evenly rather than following a fan shape.* Having an even scatter is a condition of many methods of Statistics, as we'll see in later chapters. This goal is closely related to Goal 2, but it often comes along with Goal 3. Indeed, a glance back at the scatterplot (Figure 19.27) shows that the plot for *Assets* is much more spread out on the right than on the left, while the plot for log *Assets* (Figure 19.28) has roughly the same variation in log *Assets* for any *x*-value.

FOR EXAMPLE   **Re-expressing diamond prices**

When we first looked at diamond prices (in For Example: "Diamond prices"), we noted that we needed to model prices for different coloured diamonds separately. In other examples, we restricted our attention to either the D- or K-colour diamonds at either end of the colour spectrum. Here's a scatterplot of *Price* vs. *Carat Weight* for the E- and F-colour stones:

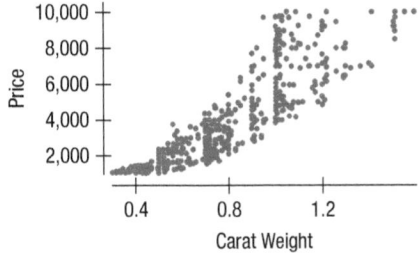

QUESTION   Which assumptions for linear regression are violated in this plot?

ANSWER   The relationship isn't straight. It also spreads out more on the right than on the left in a fan shape.

LO❸   19.8   The Ladder of Powers

We've seen that taking logs or reciprocals can improve an analysis of relationships. Other transformations can be helpful too, but how do we know which re-expression to use? We could use trial and error to choose a re-expression, but there's an easier way. We can choose our re-expressions from a family of simple mathematical expressions that move data toward our goals in a consistent way. This family includes the most common ways to re-express data. More important, the members of the family line up in order, so that the farther you move away from the original data (the "1" position), the greater the effect on the data. This fact lets you search systematically for a transformation that works—stepping a bit farther from "1" or taking a step back toward "1" as you see the results.

Where to start? It turns out that certain kinds of data are more likely to be helped by particular re-expressions. Knowing that gives you a good place to start your search for a mathematical expression. We call this collection of re-expressions the *Ladder of Powers*. The following table shows some of the most useful powers, with each one specified as a single value:

Power	Name	Comment
2	The square of the data values, y^2	Try this for unimodal distributions that are skewed to the left.
1	The raw data—no change at all. This is "home base." The farther you step from here up or down the ladder, the greater the effect.	Data that can take on both positive and negative values with no bounds are less likely to benefit from re-expression.
1/2	The square root of the data values, $\sqrt{y}$	Counts often benefit from a square root re-expression. For counted data, start here.
"0"	Although mathematicians define the "0th" power differently, for us the place is held by the logarithm.	Measurements that cannot be negative, and especially values that grow by percentage increases, such as salaries or populations, often benefit from a log re-expression. When in doubt, start here. If your data have zeros, try adding a small constant to all values before finding the logs.
−1/2	The (negative) reciprocal square root, $-1/\sqrt{y}$	An uncommon re-expression, but sometimes useful. Changing the sign to take the *negative* of the reciprocal square root preserves the direction of relationships, which can be a bit simpler.
−1	The (negative) reciprocal, $-1/y$	Ratios of two quantities (kilometres per hour, for example) often benefit from a reciprocal. (You have about a 50/50 chance that the original ratio was taken in the "wrong" order for simple statistical analysis and would benefit from re-expression.) Often, the reciprocal will have simple units (hours per kilometre). Change the sign if you want to preserve the direction of relationships. If your data have zeros, try adding a small constant to all values before finding the reciprocal.

FOR EXAMPLE — Finding a re-expression for diamond prices

We've seen (in For Example: "Re-expressing diamond prices") that the relationship between *Price* and *Carat Weight* is not linear and spreads out toward the right side of the plot. We can re-express *Price*, hoping to improve these problems. Here are three possible re-expressions of *Price*: square root, $\log_{10}$, and (negative) reciprocal:

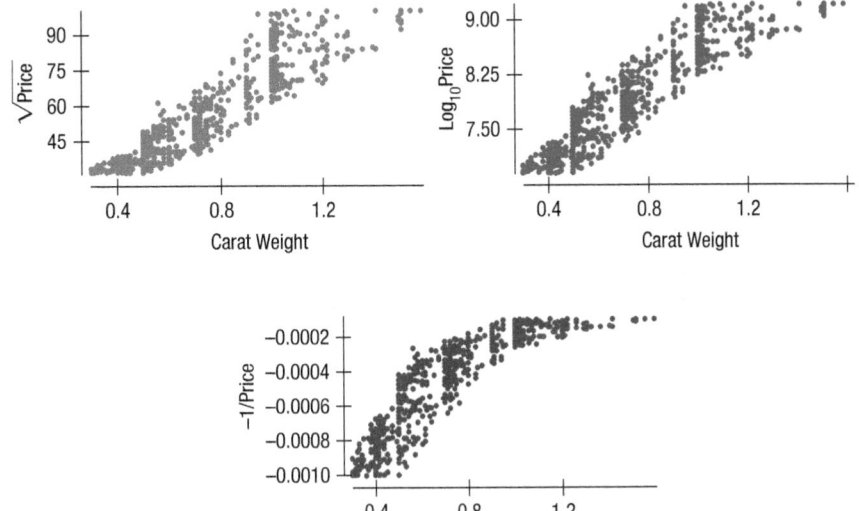

QUESTION Which of these does the best job of making the relationship linear? Does the plot indicate that we've satisfied the regression assumptions?

ANSWER The relationship of $\log_{10}$ *Price* to *Carat Weight* is much more linear and the spread has evened out across the plot. A regression of $\log_{10}$ *Price* on *Carat Weight* would be appropriate as long as we bear in mind that estimates obtained from the regression are logarithms of price.

JUST CHECKING

4 You want to model the relationship between prices for various items in Paris and Hong Kong. The scatterplot of Hong Kong prices vs. Paris prices shows a generally straight pattern with a small amount of scatter. What re-expression (if any) of the Hong Kong prices might you start with?

5 You want to model the population growth of Canada over the past 200 years with a percentage growth that's nearly constant. The scatterplot shows a strong, upwardly curved pattern. What re-expression (if any) of the population might you start with?

Answers are found in Appendix A.

GUIDED EXAMPLE   **Commercial Real Estate**

What determines the value of commercial real estate? In Chapter 7 we used a simple linear relationship with an R^2 of 62.4% to see that living area is a good predictor of the value of a family home. Does the same relationship hold for commercial property?

We have available data on 286 commercial properties in and around a major city.

	Plan State your objective. Identify the quantitative variables you wish to examine. Define each variable. (State the W's.)	Our objective is to investigate the association between the *Price* of a commercial property ($M) and its *Size* (square ft.). We have data for 286 commercial properties in and around a major city. We will build and diagnose a regression model.
	Plot the data.	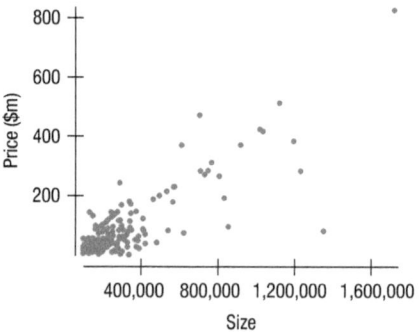
	Check the conditions for regression.	✓ **Quantitative Variable Condition.** Both variables are quantitative. ✓ **Linearity Condition.** The scatterplot is straight enough. ✓ **Outlier Condition.** There are no obvious outliers. ✓ **Equal Spread Condition.** The plot fans out to the right. That makes us suspect skewness, so we'll look at a histogram: 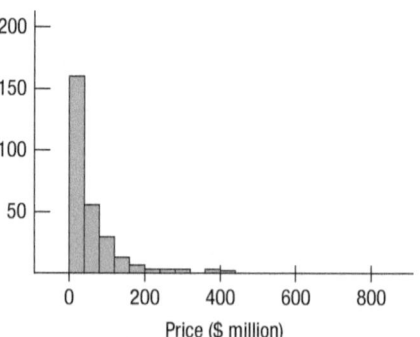
	It isn't surprising to find that *Price* is skewed to the high end. Variables like this that can't get too small but have no real limit on the upper end are often skewed in this way.	The skewness of *Price* suggests a re-expression to make the distribution more nearly symmetric and to even out the spread in the scatterplot.

DO

We will investigate re-expressions of the variables.

A histogram of $\log_{10}$ (*Price*) is much more symmetric:

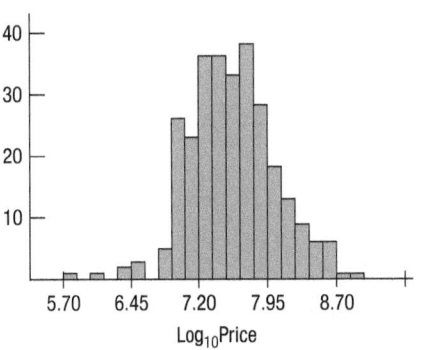

Log₁₀ is easier to interpret than the natural log. The $\log_{10}$ of 1,000,000 is 6. So these prices are mostly between \$1M and \$100M, with some near \$1B ($\log_{10} = 9$).

(Rather than find the log of *Price* in \$M, we used the original *Price* in \$ to aid interpretation.)

The scatterplot of $\log_{10}$ (*Price*) vs. *Size* isn't straight:

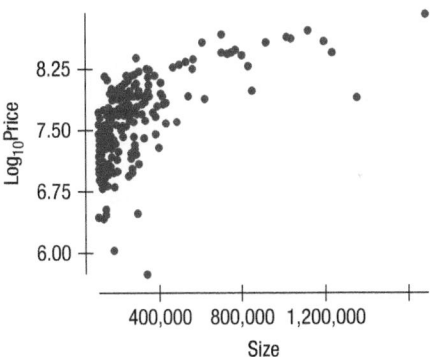

It seems natural to try a square root re-expression for a variable like *Size* that is measured in squared units (ft.²):

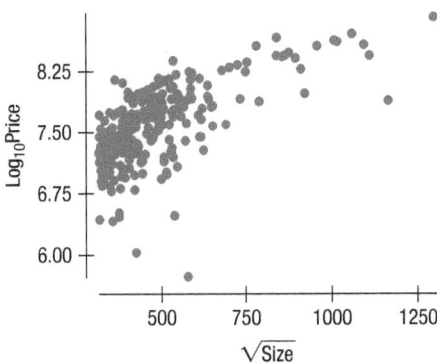

(continued)

This is an improvement, but still not straight. We'll try the next two steps on the Ladder of Powers: log and $-1/\sqrt{y}$:

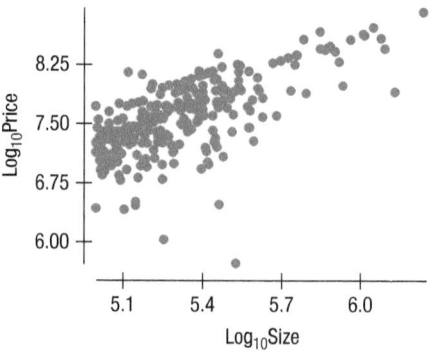

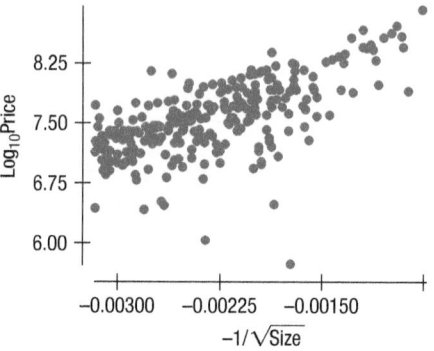

We change the sign when we take the reciprocal to preserve the direction—here a positive relationship.

The log and (negative) reciprocal root look equally good. We could use either one. Let's arbitrarily choose the reciprocal root.

A regression fit to this relationship looks like this:

Dependent variable is: Log_{10} (Price)
$R^2 = 45.7\%$ R^2 (adjusted) $= 45.5\%$
$s = 0.3484$ with $286 - 2 = 284$ df

Variable	Coeff	SE(Coeff)	*t*-ratio	P-value
Intercept	8.842	0.0857	103	≤ 0.0001
-1/Size	561.375	36.34	15.4	≤ 0.0001

As often happens when we re-express data for one reason (in this example, to improve linearity and make the variables more nearly symmetric), we also improve other aspects of the data. Except for these outliers, the residuals have a more symmetric distribution and are more nearly Normal than they would have been for the original variables. When we test coefficients, one condition is that the residuals be nearly Normal, so this can be important.

A plot of the residuals shows some outliers:

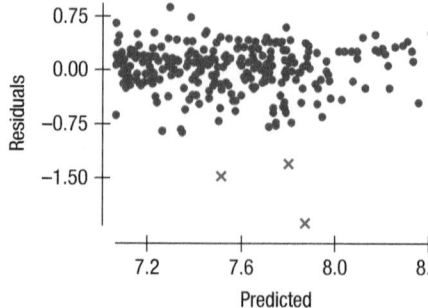

Without knowing more, we can't be sure why these properties appear to be so inexpensive. Perhaps they're an opportunity for a developer.

One suggestive observation is that two of them are among the oldest of the properties in our data, having been built before 1890. But two other properties are still older, and one of our outliers isn't old at all, so that's not a full explanation:

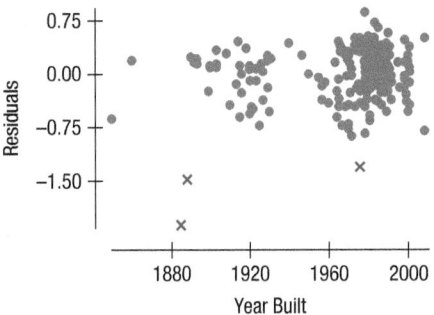

If we set aside the three outliers, the R^2 increases to 59.2%.

REPORT

Conclusion Describe the steps taken and what you learned about the data.

MEMO

Our regression analysis of commercial properties showed that the relationship between price and size was not linear. Re-expressing the variables, we found that the $\log_{10}$ of *Price* can be predicted from $1\sqrt{Size}$ with an R^2 of 59.2%. We also found three outliers, which we set aside for further investigation. They may present investment opportunities because they appear to be unexpectedly inexpensive.

WHAT CAN GO WRONG?

This entire chapter has warned about things that can go wrong in a regression analysis. So let's just recap. When you make a linear model:

- **Make sure the relationship is straight enough to fit a regression model.** Check the Linearity Condition on the scatterplot of *y* against *x* and always examine the residuals for evidence that the Linearity Condition has failed. It's often easier to see deviations from a straight line in the residuals plot than in the scatterplot of the original data. Pay special attention to the most extreme residuals because they may have something to add to the story told by the linear model.

- **Be on guard for different groups.** Check for evidence that the data consist of separate subsets. If you find subsets that behave differently, consider fitting a different linear model to each subset.

- **Beware of extrapolating.** Beware of extrapolation beyond the *x*-values that were used to fit the model. Although it's common to use linear models to extrapolate, be cautious.

- **Beware of extrapolating far into the future.** Be especially cautious about extrapolating far into the future. A model assumes that changes over time will continue forever at the same rate you've observed in the past. Predicting the future is particularly tempting and particularly dangerous.

- **Look for unusual points.** Unusual points always deserve attention and may well reveal more about your data than the rest of the points combined. Always look for them and try to understand why they stand apart. Making a scatterplot of the data is a good way to reveal high-leverage and influential points. A scatterplot of the residuals against the predicted values is a good tool for finding points with large residuals.

- **Beware of high-leverage points, especially of those that are influential.** Influential points can alter the regression model a great deal. The resulting model may say more about one or two points than about the overall relationship.

- **Consider setting aside outliers and re-running the regression.** To see the impact of outliers on a regression, try running two regressions, one with and one without the extraordinary points, and then discuss the differences.

- **Treat unusual points honestly.** If you remove enough carefully selected points, you will eventually get a regression with a high R^2. But it won't get you very far. Some data aren't simple enough for a linear model to fit very well. When that happens, report the failure and stop.

- **Be alert for autocorrelation.** Data measured over time may fail the Independence Assumption. A Durbin-Watson test can check for that.

- **Watch out when dealing with data that are summaries.** Be cautious in working with data values that are themselves summaries, such as means or medians. Such statistics are less variable than the data on which they're based, so they tend to inflate the impression of the strength of a relationship.

- **Watch out for data that need transforming (re-expressing).** When the data don't have the right form for the model you're fitting, your analysis can't be valid. Be alert for opportunities to re-express data to achieve simpler forms.

ETHICS IN ACTION

Monkey Business Images/Shutterstock

The Ontario government's "Second Career" program provides retraining for people laid off from work to the tune of up to $28,000 per person for tuition, living expenses, travel, and caring for dependants. In addition, it provides individual counselling to plan for re-entry into the job market. After the program has been operating for a year, Dan Baker is hired as a consultant for the Ontario government to evaluate Second Career. The government wants to know how much in earnings comes from the investment in retraining. Dan's contact in the government, Jessica Stephens, provides data on 1000 individuals, indicating how much funding they received from Second Career and their weekly income three months after completing the program. Dan performs a regression analysis to estimate weekly earnings from funding. The relationship looks linear on a scatterplot, but it's not very strong and the residuals show several influential outliers. Since the program is ongoing and each week the government is pouring money into it, Jessica wants some results fast, and Dan is under pressure to come up with something. He removes the outliers, hoping to improve the fit, but the R^2 gets worse. He reports the results to Jessica including the outliers.

Ethical Issue *Influential outliers need to be examined further; including them to make a linear relationship appear stronger than it would otherwise be is unethical (related to Item H, ASA Ethical Guidelines; see Appendix C, the American Statistical Association's Ethical Guidelines for Statistical Practice, also available online at www.amstat.org/about/ethicalguidelines.cfm).*

Ethical Solution *The results, even though not as favourable as expected by the funding agency, need to be discussed honestly. Dan must disclose the outliers and their effect on the relationship. Jessica should not put any pressure on the consultant.*

WHAT HAVE WE LEARNED?

Learning Objectives

We've learned that there are many ways in which a data set may be unsuitable for a regression analysis.

❶ Watch out for more than one group hiding in your regression analysis. If you find subsets of the data that behave differently, consider fitting a different regression model to each subset.

There are two ways in which outliers can be important. They can have large residuals or high leverage (or, of course, both). Cases with either kind of extraordinary behaviour can influence the regression model significantly.

❷ Autocorrelated data mean that the observations are not independent of each other, thus rendering our statistical tests and confidence intervals invalid.

❸ The Linearity Condition says that the relationship should be reasonably straight to fit a regression. Paradoxically, it may be easier to see that the relationship isn't straight *after* you fit the regression and examine the residuals.

Terms

Durbin-Watson statistic

Allows us to test for autocorrelation. It's calculated by summing the squares of the differences between consecutive residuals and dividing by its expected value under the null hypothesis of no autocorrelation. Computed as follows:

$$D = \frac{\sum\limits_{t=2}^{n}(e_t - e_{t-1})^2}{\sum\limits_{t=1}^{n}e_t^2}$$

where e_t is the residual at time t. The statistic always falls in the interval from zero to four.

Extrapolation

Although linear models provide an easy way to predict values of y for a given value of x, it's unsafe to predict for values of x far from the ones used to find the linear model equation. This is known as extrapolating.

Influence

If omitting a point from the data changes the regression model substantially, that point is considered influential.

Leverage

Data points whose x-values are far from the mean of x are said to exert leverage on a linear model. High-leverage points pull the line close to them, so they can have a large effect on the line, sometimes completely determining the slope and intercept. Points with high enough leverage can have deceptively small residuals.

Outlier

Any data point that stands away from the regression line by having a large residual.

Transformation (or re-expression)

A function—typically a logarithm, simple power, or root—applied to the values of a quantitative variable to make its distribution more symmetric and/or to simplify its relationship with other variables.

Skills

Plan

- Understand that we can't fit linear models or use linear regression if the underlying relationship between the variables is not itself linear.
- Understand that data used to find a model must be homogeneous. Look for subgroups in data before you find a regression, and analyze each separately.
- Know the danger of extrapolating beyond the range of the x-values used to find the linear model, especially when the extrapolation tries to predict into the future.
- Understand that points can be unusual by having a large residual or by having high leverage.
- Understand that an influential point can change the slope and intercept of the regression line.
- Be able to identify variables that might benefit from a re-expression to make them more symmetric, equalize their spread across groups, or make them more nearly linear when plotted against another variable.

Do

- Know how to look for high-leverage and influential points by examining a scatterplot of the data. Know how to look for points with large residuals by examining a scatterplot of the residuals against the predicted values or against the *x*-variable. Understand how fitting a regression line with and without influential points can add to an understanding of the regression model.
- Know how to look for high-leverage points by examining the distribution of the *x*-values or by recognizing them in a scatterplot of the data, and understand how they can affect a linear model.
- Know how to search for an apt re-expression from the Ladder of Powers, moving up and down the ladder to achieve the best improvement in the form of the variable and its relationship with other variables.

Report

- Include diagnostic information such as plots of residuals and leverages as part of your report of a regression.
- Report any high-leverage points.
- Report any outliers. Consider reporting analyses with and without outliers included to assess their influence on the regression.
- Include appropriate cautions about extrapolation when reporting predictions from a linear model.
- Be able to describe a model that includes re-expressed variables.

MINI case studies

Solar in Southern Ontario

A company based in Kingston, Ontario, has been installing solar modules on residential roofs in Kingston and Ottawa and is planning to expand its operation in the smaller communities along Highway 401 toward Toronto to the southwest of Kingston. One reason for expansion in this direction is that Kingston and the other communities along Highway 401 have less snow than Ottawa and other communities to the north and east of Kingston. Snow often accumulates on solar modules in Ottawa, reducing electricity generation.

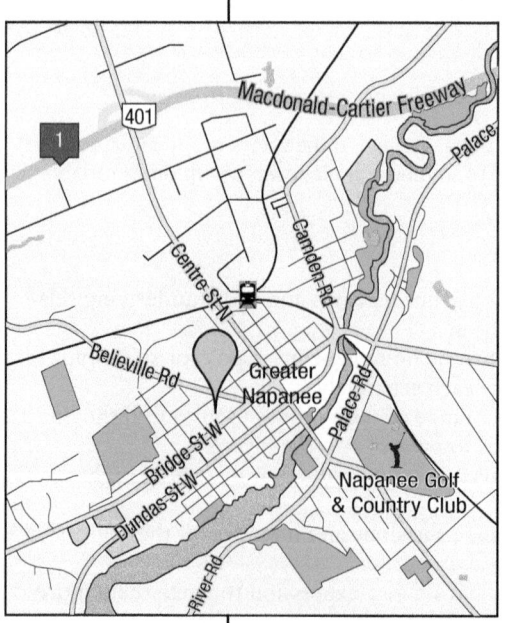

An ideal roof for installing solar modules faces south, thus capturing the greatest amount of solar energy throughout the year. The company has installed modules on roofs facing slightly east and slightly west of south in both Kingston and Ottawa and has monitored the value of the average electricity generated per year (see **ch19_MCSP_solar**). It needs to know how much reduction in value occurs as a result of the orientation of the modules, since the communities along Highway 401 are built on regular grids of roads with the majority of houses facing the same direction (for example, see the map of Napanee, where most houses face 35 degrees east of south or 55 degrees west of south). The company would not want to market its services in a community where the orientation of the roads and houses results in a significant drop in the value of electricity generated.

Model the value of electricity generated as a function of orientation of roof, identifying data groupings, outliers, and influential points. What value of annual electricity generation do you estimate for the following communities?

	Belleville	Napanee	Peterborough	Ottawa	Perth
Orientation east of south (degrees)	−70	35	0	30	40

Wind Power in Canada

In order to plan electric power generation, it is important to identify trends in generation from different sources, including wind. Statistics Canada reports the amount of renewable energy generated (in megawatt-hours) in each province and territory for several renewable sources, including wind power. Monthly data from December 2010 to July 2015 are in the file **ch19_MCSP_Wind_Power** for Ontario, Manitoba, and Alberta. (*Source:* Statistics Canada, Table 1270002—Electric power generation, by class of electricity producer, monthly (megawatt hour). Reproduced and distributed on an "as is" basis with the permission of Statistics Canada.). If possible, find models for the relationships between wind power and month for each of these three provinces individually. Discuss your residual analysis including outliers, influential points, and autocorrelation. You do not need to try to remove any significant autocorrelation present.

During this period, Ontario was the only Canadian province to have a "feed-in" tariff—that is, a price that the Ontario Power Authority guaranteed for wind power from organizations that generated it. The price was higher than what most residential consumers paid for electric power, and it was guaranteed for 20 years in order to stimulate investment in wind turbines. From your analysis of the data, discuss whether Ontario's feed-in tariff resulted in a different pattern of generation of wind power in Ontario compared to Manitoba and Alberta.

MyStatLab   Students! Save time, improve your grades with MyStatLab. Questions marked in ▩ can be found on MyStatLab. You can practise them as often as you want, and most feature step-by-step guided solutions to help you find the right answer. You'll find a personalized study plan available to you too!

Technology Help: Regression Residuals

Most statistics technology offers simple ways to check whether your data satisfy the conditions for regression and to re-express the data when that's called for. We've already seen that these programs can make a simple scatterplot. They can also help us check the conditions by plotting residuals. Most statistics packages offer a way to re-express and compute with variables. Some packages permit you to specify the power of a re-expression with a slider or other movable control, possibly while watching the consequences of the re-expression on a plot or analysis. This is an effective way to find a good re-expression.

EXCEL

To save regression residuals in Excel:

- From **Data**, select **Data Analysis** and select **Regression**. Enter the data ranges and specify a location for the output.

- Select **Residuals**, **Residual Plots**, and **Line Fit Plots**.
- Click **OK**.

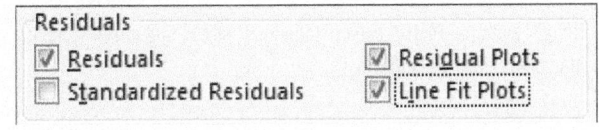

At the end of the output, find the list of observations, predicted values, and residuals. They can be copied to a new worksheet to analyze residuals.

(continued)

To create transformed variables in Excel:

- In a new column, use Excel's built-in functions to transform existing data.

◢	A	B	C	D	I
1	Weight	MPG	MPG^2		
2	3252	22	=power(b2,2)		
3	3219	20	POWER(number, power)		
4					

- Fill down to re-express the entire variable.

XLSTAT

To save residuals using XLSTAT:

- Choose the **Modeling data** menu, and then select **Linear regression**.
- On the **Charts** tab select **residuals**.

To create transformed variables using XLSTAT:

- Choose the **Preparing data** menu, and then select **Variables transformation**.
- Select variable name and location.
- Select **Other** under transformation, and select desired transformation from the **Transformations tab**.
- Transformed variables can also be created using Excel's built-in functions.

MINITAB

To save residuals in Minitab:

- From the **Stat** menu, choose **Regression**.
- From the Regression submenu, select **Regression**.
- In the Regression dialogue, enter the response variable name in the "Response" box and the predictor variable name in the "Predictor" box.
- To specify saved results, in the Regression dialogue, click **Storage**.
- Check "Residuals." Click **OK**.
- To specify displays, in the Regression dialogue, click **Graphs**.
- Under "Residual Plots," select "Individual plots" and check "Residuals versus fits." Click **OK**.

- Now back in the Regression dialogue, click **OK**. Minitab computes the regression and the requested saved values and graphs.

To re-express a variable in Minitab:

- Choose **Calculator** from the **Calc** menu.
- In the Calculator dialogue, specify a name for the new re-expressed variable.
- Use the **Functions List**, the calculator buttons, and the **Variables list** box to build the expression. Click **OK**.

SPSS

From the **Analyze** menu, choose **Regression**. From the Regression submenu, choose **Linear**. After assigning variables to their roles in the regression, click the **Plots ...** button.

In the Plots dialogue, you can specify a Normal probability plot of residuals and scatterplots of various versions of standardized residuals and predicted values.

To re-express a variable in SPSS, choose **Compute** from the **Transform** menu. Enter a name in the Target Variable field. Use the calculator and Function List to build the expression.

Move a variable to be re-expressed from the source list to the Numeric Expression field. Click the **OK** button.

Comments

A plot of *ZRESID against *PRED will look most like the residual plots we've discussed. SPSS standardizes the residuals by dividing by their standard deviation. (There's no need to subtract their mean; it must be zero.) The standardization doesn't affect the scatterplot.

JMP

From the **Analyze** menu, choose **Fit Y by X**. Select **Fit Line**. Under Linear Fit, select **Plot Residuals**. You can also choose to **Save Residuals**.

Subsequently, from the **Distribution** menu, choose **Normal quantile plot** or **histogram** for the residuals.

To re-express a variable in JMP, double-click to the right of the last column of data to create a new column. Name the new column and select it. Choose **Formula** from the **Cols** menu. In the Formula dialogue, choose the transformation and variable that you wish to assign to the new column. Click the **OK** button.

JMP places the re-expressed data in the new column.

Comments

The log and square root re-expressions are found in the **Transcendental** menu of functions in the formula dialogue.

EXERCISES

SECTION 19.1

1. An analysis of spending by a sample of credit card holders shows that spending by cardholders in January (*Jan*) is related to their spending in December (*Dec*):

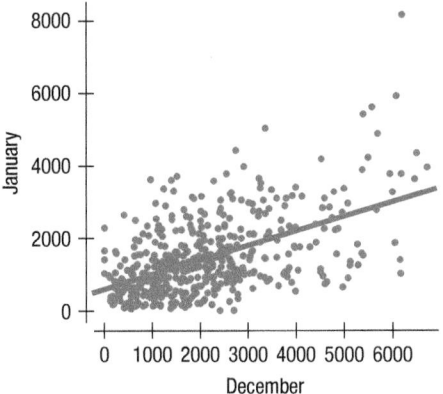

The assumptions and conditions of the linear regression seemed to be satisfied, and an analyst was about to predict January spending using the model shown above:

$$\widehat{Jan} = \$612.07 + 0.403 \ Dec$$

Another analyst worried that different types of cardholders might behave differently. She examined the spending patterns of the cardholders and placed them into five market segments. When she plotted the data using different colours and symbols for the five different segments, she found the following:

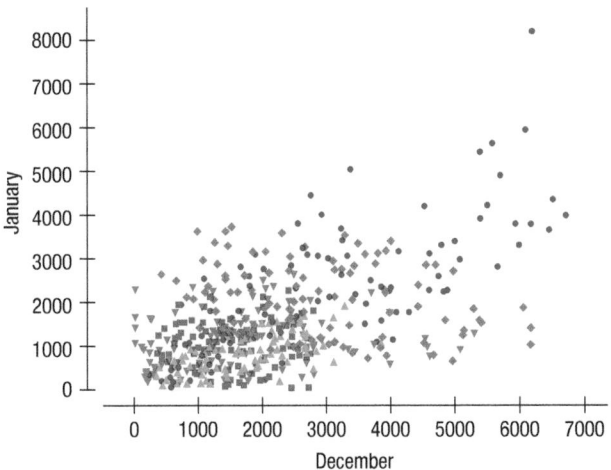

Look at this plot carefully, and discuss why she might be worried about the predictions from the model $\widehat{Jan} = \$612.07 + 0.403 \ Dec$. **LO ❶**

2. A concert production company examined its records. The manager made the following scatterplot. The company places concerts in two venues: a smaller, more intimate theatre (plotted with blue circles) and a larger, auditorium-style venue.

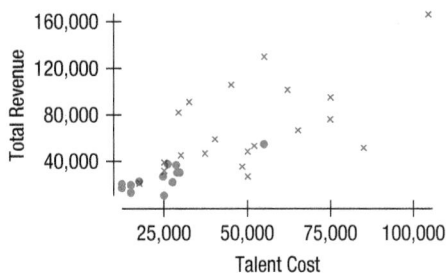

a) Describe the relationship between *Talent Cost* and *Total Revenue*. (Remember: direction, form, strength, outliers.)
b) How are the results for the two venues similar?
c) How are they different? **LO ❶**

3. The analyst in Exercise 1 tried fitting the regression line to each market segment separately and found the following:

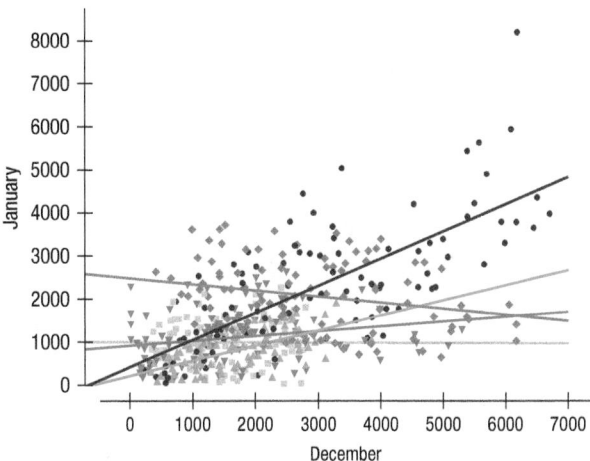

What does this say about her concern in Exercise 1? Was she justified in worrying that the overall model $\widehat{Jan} = \$612.07 + 0.403 \ Dec$ might not accurately summarize the relationship? Explain briefly. **LO ❶**

4. The concert production company of Exercise 2 made a second scatterplot, this time relating *Total Revenue* to *Ticket Sales*:

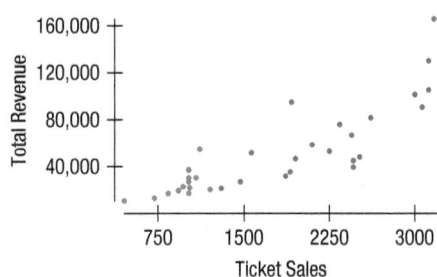

a) Describe the relationship between *Ticket Sales* and *Total Revenue*.

b) How are the results for the two venues similar?
c) How are they different? **LO ❶**

SECTION 19.2

5. Here are data from a small bookstore:

Number of Salespeople Working	Sales (in $1000)
2	10
3	11
7	13
9	14
10	18
10	20
12	20
15	22
16	22
20	26
$\bar{x} = 10.4$	$\bar{y} = 17.6$
$SD(x) = 5.64$	$SD(y) = 5.34$

The regression line is:

$$\widehat{Sales} = 8.10 + 0.913 \ Number \ of \ Salespeople \ Working$$

and we can assume that the assumptions and conditions for regression are met. Calculations with technology find that

$$s_e = 1.477.$$

a) Find the predicted sales on a day with 500 employees working.
b) Is this prediction likely to be useful? Explain. **LO ❶**

6. Here are some prices for external disk drives:

Capacity (in TB)	Price (in $)
0.15	35.00
0.25	39.95
0.32	49.95
1.0	75.00
2.0	110.00
3.0	140.00
4.0	325.00
$\bar{x} = 1.53$	$\bar{y} = 110.7$
$SD(x) = 1.515$	$SD(y) = 102.049$

The least squares line is $\widehat{Price} = 15.11 + 62.417 \ Capacity$.

The assumptions and conditions for regression are met.

$$SE(b_1) = 11.33 \ \text{and} \ s_e = 42.04$$

a) Disk drives keep growing in capacity. Some tech experts now talk about *petabyte* (1 PB = 1000 TB = 1,000,000 GB) drives. What does this model predict that a petabyte-capacity drive will cost?
b) Is this prediction likely to be useful? Explain. **LO ❶**

7. A regression of *Total Revenue* on *Ticket Sales* by the concert production company of Exercises 2 and 4 finds the model

$$\widehat{Revenue} = -14,228 + 36.87 \ Ticket \ Sales.$$

a) Management is considering adding a stadium-style venue that would seat 10,000. What does this model predict revenue would be if the new venue were to sell out?
b) Why would it be a poor business decision to assume that this model accurately predicts revenue for this situation? **LO ❶**

8. The production company of Exercise 7 offers advance sales to "Frequent Buyers" through its website. Here's a relevant scatterplot:

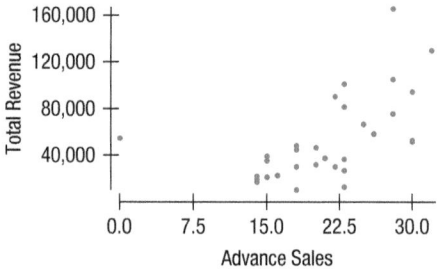

One performer refused to permit advance sales. What effect has that point had on the regression to model *Total Revenue* from *Advance Sales*? **LO ❶**

SECTION 19.3

9. The bookstore in Exercise 5 decides to have a gala event in an attempt to drum up business. It hires 100 employees for the day and brings in a total of $42,000.

a) Find the regression line predicting *Sales* from *Number of Salespeople Working* with the new point added.
b) What has changed from the original regression equation?
c) Is the new point a high-leverage point or an influential point?
d) Does the new point have a large residual? Explain. **LO ❶**

10. The data for hard drives in Exercise 6 omitted a 200 GB drive that sold for $299.00.

a) Find the regression line predicting *Price* from *Capacity* with this hard drive added.
b) What has changed from the original regression equation?

c) Is the new point a high-leverage point or an influential point?
d) Does the new point have a large residual? Explain. **LO ❶**

SECTIONS 19.4 AND 19.5

11. A beverage company specializing in sales of champagne reports four years of quarterly sales as follows (in millions of $):

Quarter	Sales ($M)
1	12
2	41
3	15
4	48
5	25
6	55
7	23
8	69
9	51
10	80
11	54
12	87
13	64
14	94
15	62
16	108

The regression equation is *Predicted Sales* = 14.15 + 4.87 *Quarter*.

a) Find the residuals.
b) Plot the residuals against *Quarter*. Comment.
c) Compute the Durbin-Watson statistic.
d) At $\alpha = 0.05$, what are the values of d_L and d_U?
e) Is there evidence of positive autocorrelation? Explain.
f) Is there evidence of negative autocorrelation? Explain.
LO ❷

12. A company fits a regression to predict monthly *Orders* over a period of 48 months. The Durbin-Watson statistic on the residuals is 0.875.

a) At $\alpha = 0.01$, what are values of d_L and d_U?
b) Is there evidence of positive autocorrelation? Explain.
c) Is there evidence of negative autocorrelation? Explain.
LO ❷

13. The manager of the concert production company considered in earlier exercises considers the regression of *Total Revenue* on *Ticket Sales* (see Exercise 4) and computes the Durbin-Watson statistic, obtaining a value of 0.51.

a) Consult Table D in Appendix B using $k = 1$ and $n = 45$ and complete the test at $\alpha = 0.05$.

b) Specify what this statistic tests and what the test says about these data. **LO ❷**

14. The regression of *Total Revenue* on *Total Expenses* for the concerts of Exercise 13 gives the following model:

Dependent variable is: Total Revenue
R-squared = 56.4% R-squared (adjusted) = 55.0%
$s = 24269$ with $34 - 2 = 32$ degrees of freedom

Variable	Coefficient	SE(Coeff)	t-ratio	P-value
Intercept	−3688.54	9453	−0.390	0.6990
Total Expenses	0.731250	0.1137	6.43	<0.0001

a) The Durbin-Watson statistic for this analysis is 0.73. Consult Table D in Appendix B and complete the test at $\alpha = 0.05$.
b) What do you conclude from this test? **LO ❷**

SECTIONS 19.6 AND 19.7

15. A scatterplot of *Salary* against *Years Experience* for some employees and the scatterplot of residuals against predicted *Salary* from the regression line are shown in the figures. On the basis of these plots, would you recommend a re-expression of either *Salary* or *Years Experience*? **LO ❸**

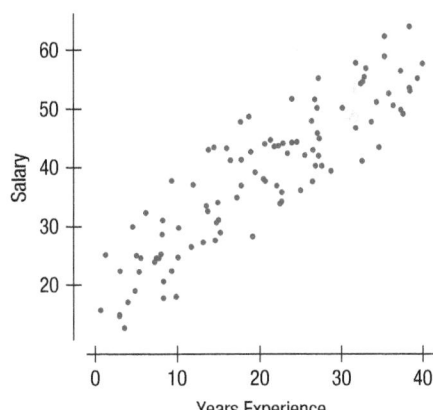

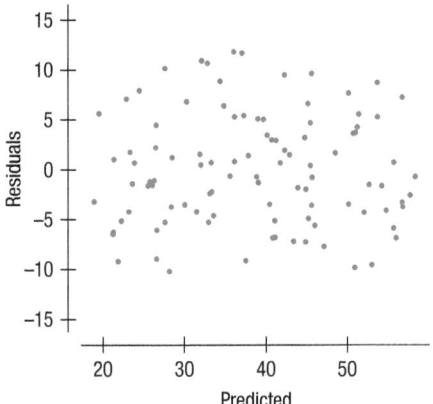

16. A study of homes that looked at the relationship between *Age* of a home and *Price* produced the following scatterplot. A regression was fit to the data, as shown:

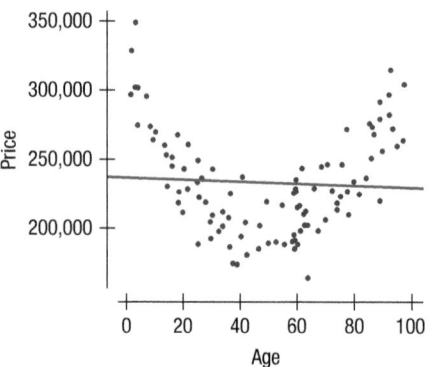

On the basis of this plot, would you advise using this regression? Explain. **LO ❸**

17. A small company has developed an improved process for making solar panels. The company needs to set its prices and wants those prices to reflect the efficiencies of producing larger batches. The data show the following:

#Units	Cost per Unit
10	7.389
20	6.049
30	4.953
40	4.055
50	3.320
60	2.718
70	2.459
80	2.225
90	2.013
100	1.822
120	1.648
140	1.491
160	1.349
180	1.221
200	1.105

A scatterplot of *Cost per Unit* vs. *#Units* looks like this:

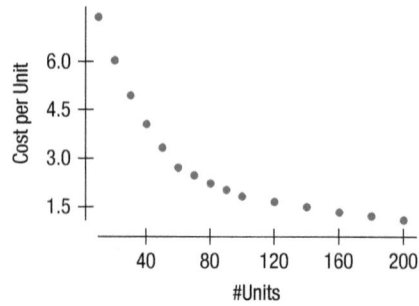

What should be done to make the relationship more nearly linear? **LO ❸**

18. One possible model for the manufacturing process of Exercise 17 is the following:

Dependent variable is: Log (Cost per unit)
R-squared = 90.1% R-squared (adjusted) = 89.3%
s = 0.0841 with 15 − 2 = 13 degrees of freedom

Variable	Coefficient	SE(Coeff)	t-ratio	P-value
Intercept	0.7618	0.0405	18.8	<0.0001
#Units	−0.0041	0.0004	−10.9	<0.0001

Using this model, predict the cost per unit in a batch of 300. **LO ❸**

SECTION 19.8

19. A quickly growing company shows the following scatterplot of customers vs. time (in months).

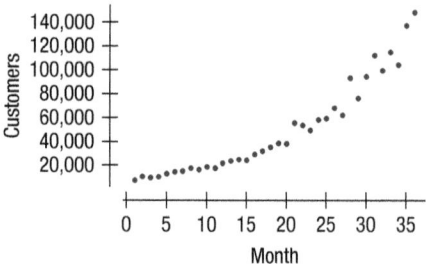

a) What re-expression might you suggest for the number of customers?
b) What power in the Ladder of Powers does that correspond to? **LO ❸**

20. For the regression in Exercise 19:

A student tries taking the reciprocal of customers and produces the plot shown below:

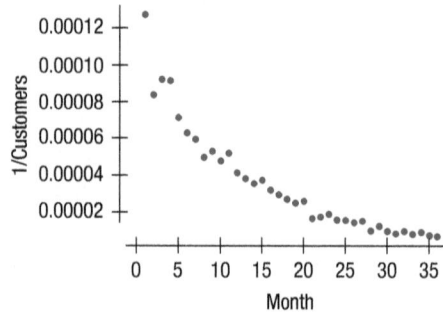

a) Would you recommend this transformation? Why or why not?
b) What would you suggest? **LO ❸**

CHAPTER EXERCISES

21. Canadian earnings. You probably hope your earnings will increase if you spend time studying, but by how much? Statistics Canada answers this question in the research paper from which we have reprinted the following graph. (*Source:* Beckstead, D., Brown, W. M., Guo, Y., & Newbold, K. B. [2010, January 25]. Cities and growth: Earnings levels across urban and rural areas: The role of human capital. Catalogue no. 11-622-M, No. 020. Chart 2, p. 20. Uses 2001 census data. © Minister of Industry, 2010.)

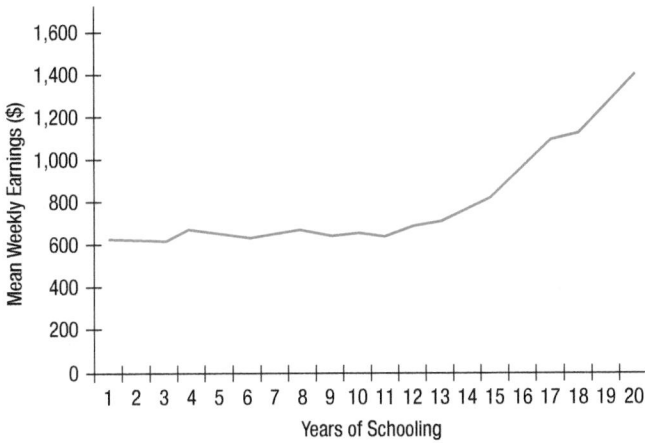

a) Do you think there's a clear pattern? Describe the trend.
b) Is the association strong?
c) Is a linear model appropriate for these data? Explain.
d) If a linear model were used on this entire data set, what pattern would you see if the residuals were plotted on a vertical axis against *Years of Schooling* on a horizontal axis?
e) What transformation could be used before using linear regression on these data? **LO ❶**

22. Human Development Index (HDI) 2012, part 1. The United Nations Development Programme (UNDP) collects data in the developing world to help countries solve global and national development challenges. In the UNDP annual Human Development Report, you can find data on over 100 variables for each of 197 countries worldwide. One summary measure used by the agency is the Human Development Index (HDI), which attempts to summarize in a single number the progress in health, education, and economics of a country. In 2012, the HDI was as high as 0.955 for Norway and as low as 0.304 for the Congo and Niger. The gross domestic product per capita (GDPPC), by contrast, is often used to summarize the *overall* economic strength of a country. Is the HDI related to the GDPPC?

Here is a scatterplot of *HDI* against *GDPPC*:

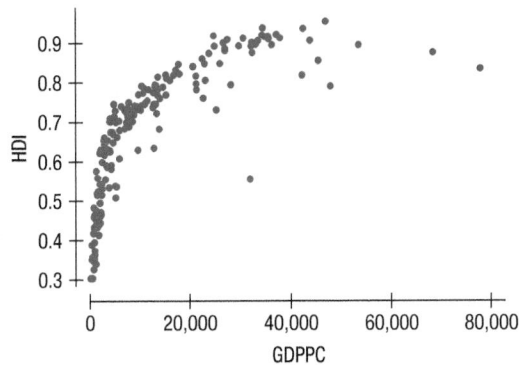

a) Explain why fitting a linear model to these data would be misleading.
b) If you fit a linear model to the data, what do you think a scatterplot of residuals versus predicted HDI will look like?
c) There are two outliers, Qatar and Luxembourg, with very high GDPPC, and Equatorial Guinea with a very low HDI for its GDPPC. Will setting these points aside improve the model substantially? Explain. **LO ❶**

❶ 23. Human Development Index 2012, part 2. The United Nations Development Programme (UNDP) uses the Human Development Index (HDI) in an attempt to summarize in one number the progress in health, education, and economics of a country. The number of internet accounts per 1000 people is positively associated with economic progress in a country. Can that be used to predict the HDI? Here is a scatterplot of HDI against internet subscribers:

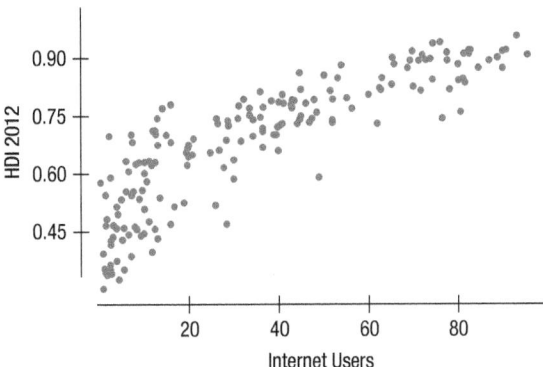

a) Explain why fitting a linear model to these data might be misleading.
b) If you fit a linear model to the data, what do you think a scatterplot of residuals versus predicted HDI will look like? **LO ❶**

24. Good model? In justifying his choice of a model, a consultant says, "I know this is the correct model because $R^2 = 99.4\%$."

a) Is this reasoning correct? Explain.
b) Does this model allow the consultant to make accurate predictions? Explain. **LO ❶**

25. **Bad model?** An intern who has created a linear model is disappointed to find that her R^2 value is a very low 13%.

a) Does this mean that a linear model is not appropriate? Explain.

b) Does this model allow the intern to make accurate predictions? Explain. **LO ❶**

❶ 26. **Movie budgets.** Here's a scatterplot of the production budgets (in millions of dollars) vs. the running time (in minutes) for a collection of major movies. Dramas are plotted in red and all other genres are plotted in blue. A separate least squares regression line has been fitted to each group.

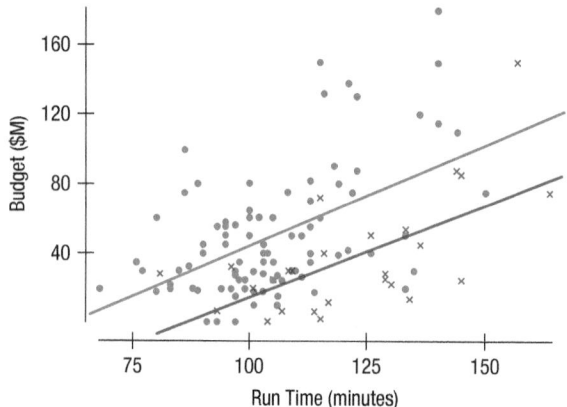

For the following questions, just examine the plot:

a) What are the units for the slopes of these lines?

b) In what way are dramas and other movies similar with respect to this relationship?

c) In what way are dramas different from other genres of movies with respect to this relationship? **LO ❶**

❶ 27. **Movie revenues.** How does what a movie earns relate to its run time? Will audiences pay more for a longer film? Does the relationship depend on the type of film? The scatterplot shows the relationship for the films in Exercise 26 between *U.S. Gross* earnings and *Run Time*. Dramas are plotted with purple dots, comedies with green squares, horror/thriller/action films with blue diamonds, and adventure movies with orange crosses. Regression lines have been drawn for each type of movie.

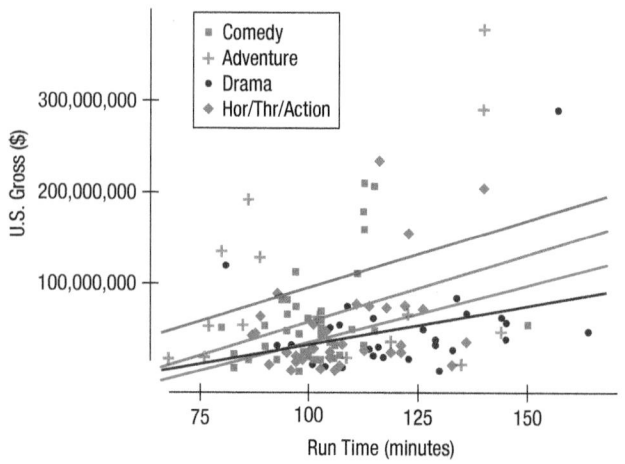

a) In what ways is the relationship between *Run Time* and *U.S. Gross* similar for the four kinds of films?

b) How do the gross receipts of adventure films (the orange line on top) differ from those of comedies (the green line below the orange)? Discuss both the slopes and the intercepts.

c) The film *Harry Potter and the Goblet of Fire* is the purple point in the upper right. If it were omitted from this analysis, how might that change your conclusions about dramas? **LO ❶**

❶ 28. **Canadian airline passengers.** The graph below shows the number of passengers travelling on major Canadian airlines month by month from November 2010 to September 2015. Time is shown as months since October 2010. (*Source:* Statistics Canada Table 4010001—Operating and financial statistics of major Canadian airlines, monthly v11743 Canada; Passengers. Reproduced and distributed on an "as is" basis with the permission of Statistics Canada.)

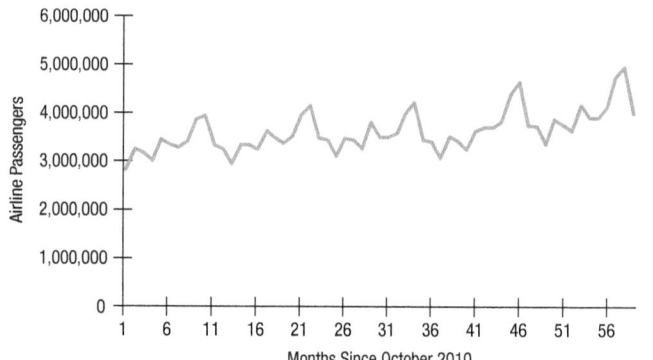

a) Perform a linear regression analysis of this data.

b) Interpret the slope, its P-value, and the R^2.

c) Plot the residuals, calculate the Durbin-Watson statistic, and comment on what these imply for the regression model. **LO ❶, ❷**

❶ 29. **Tracking hurricane 2012.** Like many businesses, The National Hurricane Center also participates in a program to improve the quality of data and predictions by government agencies. It reports its errors in predicting the path of hurricanes. The following scatterplot shows the trend in 48-hour tracking errors since 1970. (www.nhc.noaa.gov/verification/pdfs/1970-present_OFCL_ATL_annual_trk_errors_noTDs.pdf)

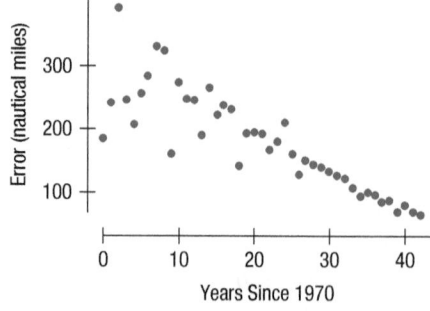

Dependent variable is: Error
R-squared = 75.4% s_e = 39.10

Variable	Coeff
Intercept	294.138
Years – 1970	–5.392

a) Interpret the slope and intercept of the regression model.
b) Interpret s_e in this context.
c) If the Center had a goal of achieving an average tracking error of 50 nautical miles by 2015, will it be achieved? Explain.
d) Use technology to compute the Durbin-Watson statistic and comment.
e) What cautions would you state about your conclusion? **LO ❶, ❷**

30. Unusual points. Each of the four scatterplots that follow shows a cluster of points and one "stray" point. For each, answer questions 1–4:

1) In what way is the point unusual? Does it have high leverage, a large residual, or both?
2) Do you think that point is an influential point?
3) If that point were removed from the data, would the correlation become stronger or weaker? Explain.
4) If that point were removed from the data, would the slope of the regression line increase, decrease, or remain the same? Explain. **LO ❶**

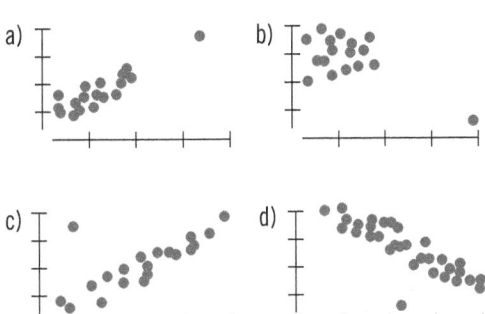

31. More unusual points. Each of the following scatterplots shows a cluster of points and one "stray" point. For each, answer questions 1–4:

1) In what way is the point unusual? Does it have high leverage, a large residual, or both?
2) Do you think that point is an influential point?
3) If that point were removed from the data, would the correlation become stronger or weaker? Explain.
4) If that point were removed from the data, would the slope of the regression line increase, decrease, or remain the same? Explain. **LO ❶**

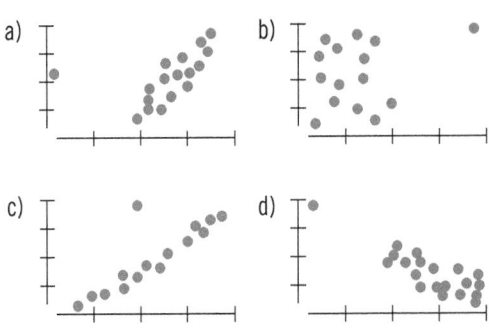

32. The extra point, part 1. The scatterplot shows five blue data points at the left. Not surprisingly, the correlation for these points is $r = 0$. Suppose *one* additional data point is added at one of the five positions suggested below in green. Match each point (a–e) with the correct new correlation from the list given. **LO ❶**

1) –0.90   2) –0.40   3) 0.00   4) 0.05   5) 0.75

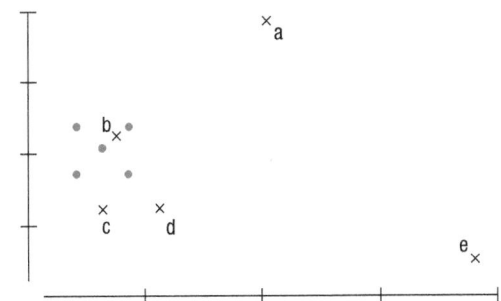

33. The extra point, part 2. The original five points in Exercise 32 produce a regression line with slope zero. Match each of the green points (a–e) with the slope of the line after that one point is added. **LO ❶**

1) –0.45   2) –0.30   3) 0.00   4) 0.04   5) 0.85

34. Heating cost. Small businesses must track every expense. A flower shop owner tracked her costs for heating and related them to the average daily Fahrenheit temperature, finding the model *Cost* = 133 − 2.13 *Temp*. The residuals plot for her data is shown below:

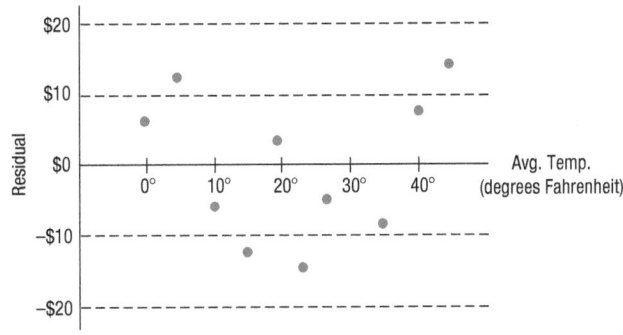

a) Interpret the slope of the line in this context.
b) Interpret the *y*-intercept of the line in this context.

c) During months when the temperature stays around freezing, would you expect cost predictions based on this model to be accurate, too low, or too high? Explain.

d) What heating cost does the model predict for a month that averages 10°?

e) During one of the months on which the model was based, the temperature did average 10°. What were the actual heating costs for that month?

f) Do you think the shop owner should use this model? Explain.

g) Would this model be more successful if the temperature were expressed in degrees Celsius? Explain. **LO ❸**

35. Fuel economy. How does the speed at which a car drives affect fuel economy? Owners of a taxi fleet, watching their bottom line sink as a result of rising fuel costs, hired a research firm to tell them the optimal speed for their taxis to drive. Researchers drove a compact car for 200 miles at speeds ranging from 35 to 75 miles per hour. From their data, they created the model $\widehat{Fuel\ Efficiency} = 32 - 0.1\ Speed$ and created this residual plot:

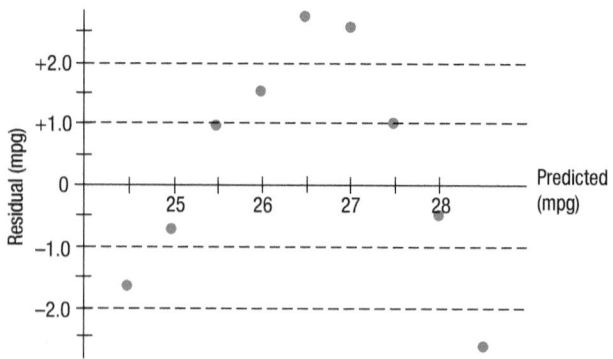

a) Interpret the slope of this line in context.

b) Explain why the y-intercept is meaningless.

c) When this model predicts high *Fuel Efficiency*, what can you say about those predictions?

d) What *Fuel Efficiency* does the model predict when the car is driven at 50 mph?

e) What was the actual *Fuel Efficiency* when the car was driven at 45 mph?

f) Do you think there appears to be a strong association between *Speed* and *Fuel Efficiency*? Explain.

g) Comment on the ethics of the research firm using this model to estimate fuel efficiency in relation to the ASA Ethical Guidelines in Appendix C. **LO ❸**

36. Age at first marriage, part 1. A company selling wedding services needs to take into account the *difference* in age of the two partners when marketing its services. The graph

shows the ages of both men and women at first marriage (www.census.gov):

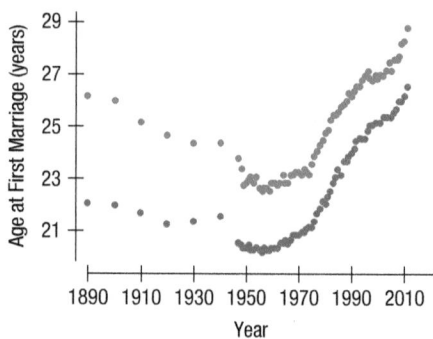

Clearly, the pattern for men is similar to the pattern for women. But are the two lines getting closer together?

Here is a timeplot showing the difference in average age (men's age – women's age) at first marriage, the regression analysis, and the associated residuals plot:

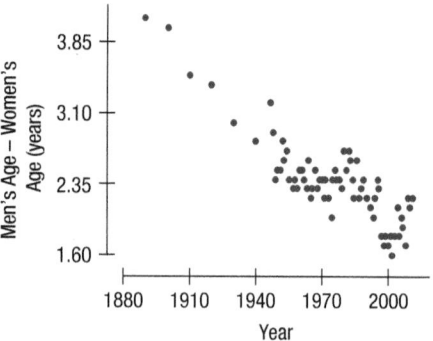

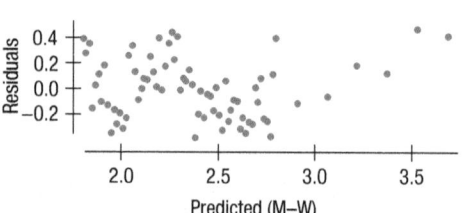

Dependent variable is: Age Difference
R-squared = 74.9% s = 0.2346

Variable	Coeff
Constant	32.9679
Year	−0.01549

a) What is the correlation between *Age Difference* and *Year*?

b) Interpret the slope of this line.

c) Predict the average age difference in 2020.

d) Compute the Durbin-Watson statistic and comment.
e) Describe reasons why you might not place much faith in that prediction. **LO ❶, ❷**

37. **Age at first marriage, part 2.** Has the trend of decreasing difference in age at first marriage seen in Exercise 36 become stronger recently? Here are the scatterplot and residual plot for the data from 1975 through 2011, along with a regression for just those years:

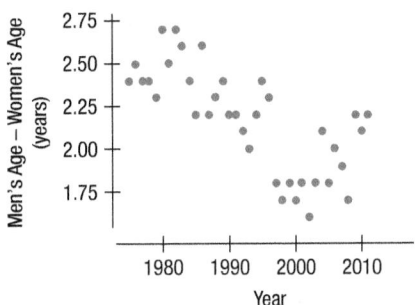

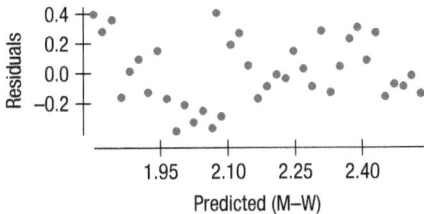

Dependent variable is: Men − Women
R-squared = 51.9% s = 0.2143

Variable	Coeff
Intercept	42.5662
Year	−0.0203

a) Why is R^2 higher for the first model (in Exercise 36)?
b) Is this linear model appropriate for the post-1975 data? Explain.
c) What does the slope say about marriage ages since 1975?
d) Explain why it's not safe to interpret the y-intercept. **LO ❶**

38. **New homes.** A real estate agent collects data to develop a model that will use the *Size* of a new home (in square feet) to predict its *Sale Price* (in thousands of dollars). Which of these is most likely to be the slope of the regression line: 0.008, 0.08, 0.8, or 8? Explain. **LO ❶**

39. **Residuals, part 1.** Suppose you've fit a linear model to some data and now take a look at the residuals. For each

of the following possible residuals plots, tell whether you'd try a re-expression, and if so, why. **LO ❸**

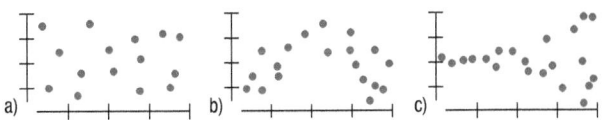

40. **Residuals, part 2.** Suppose you've fit a linear model to some data and now take a look at the residuals. For each of the following possible residuals plots, tell whether you would try a re-expression, and if so, why. **LO ❸**

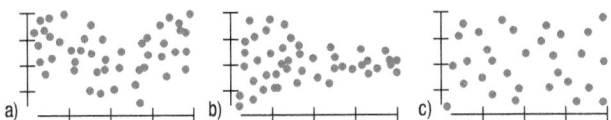

41. **Models, part 1.** For each of the models listed below, predict y when $x = 2$.

a) $\hat{y} = 1.2 + 0.8x$

b) $\ln \hat{y} = 1.2 + 0.8x$

c) $\sqrt{\hat{y}} = 1.2 + 0.8x$

d) $\dfrac{1}{\hat{y}} = 1.2 + 0.8x$

e) $\hat{y} = 1.2x^{0.8}$ **LO ❸**

42. **Models, part 2.** For each of the models listed below, predict y when $x = 2$.

a) $\hat{y} = 1.2 + 0.8 \log x$

b) $\log \hat{y} = 1.2 + 0.8x$

c) $\hat{y} = 1.2 + 0.8\sqrt{x}$

d) $\hat{y} = 1.2(0.8^x)$

e) $\hat{y} = 0.8x^2 + 1.2x + 1$ **LO ❸**

43. **Models, part 3.** Find the predicted value of y, using each model for $x = 10$.

a) $\hat{y} = 2 + 0.8 \ln x$

b) $\log \hat{y} = 5 - 0.23x$

c) $\dfrac{1}{\sqrt{\hat{y}}} = 17.1 - 1.66x$ **LO ❸**

44. **Models, part 4.** Find the predicted value of y, using each model when $x = 4$.

a) $\hat{y} = 10 + \sqrt{x}$

b) $\dfrac{1}{y} = 14.5 - 3.45x$

c) $\sqrt{y} = 3.0 + 0.5x$ **LO ❸**

45. Lobsters, part 1. According to the Maine Department of Marine Resources, in 2012 more than 126,000,000 pounds of lobster were landed in Maine—a catch worth more than $338.9M. The lobster fishing industry is carefully controlled and licensed, and facts about it have been recorded for more than a century, so it is an important industry that we can examine in detail. We'll look at annual data (available at www.maine.gov/dmr) from 1950 through 2012.

The value of the annual lobster catch has grown. Here's a scatterplot of the value in millions of dollars over time:

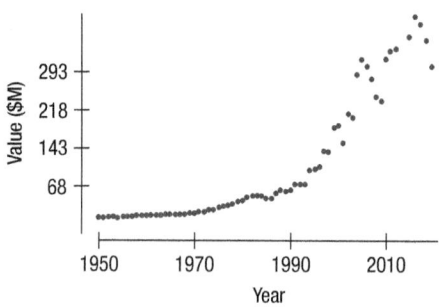

a) Which regression assumptions and conditions appear to be violated according to this plot?

Here's a scatterplot of the *log* of the value:

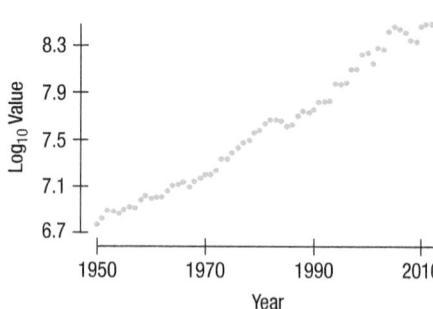

b) Discuss the same assumptions as in (a). Does taking logs make these data suitable for regression?

After performing a regression on the log values, we obtain the following plot of residuals:

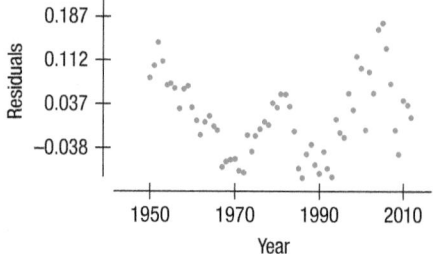

c) Discuss what this plot shows. Would a different transformation be likely to do better than the log? Explain. **LO ❶,❸**

46. Lobsters, part 2. Lobster are caught in traps, which are baited and left in the open ocean. Licences to fish for lobster are limited, there is a small additional fee for each trap in use, and there are limits on the numbers of traps that can be placed in each of seven fishing zones. But those limits have changed over time. Here's a scatterplot of the number of traps per licensed lobster fisher over time:

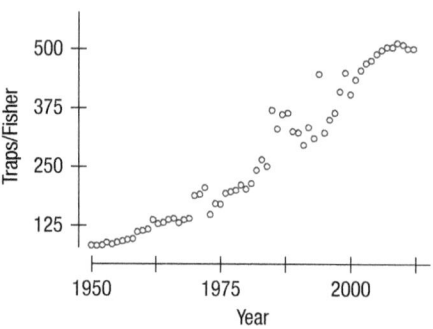

a) Does this plot satisfy the regression assumptions and conditions? Explain.

A regression of *Traps/Fisher* vs. *Year* yields the following plot of residuals:

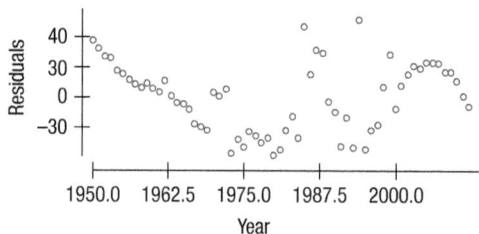

b) What can you see in the plots of residuals that may not have been clear in the original scatterplot of the data? **LO ❶**

47. Lobsters, part 3. Here's a regression model relating the *logValue* of the annual Maine lobster catch to the number of licensed lobster *Fishers* since 1985:

Dependent variable is: LogValue
R-squared = 17.6%
s = 0.2752 with 28 − 2 = 26 degrees of freedom

Variable	Coefficient	SE(Coeff)	*t*-ratio	P-value
Intercept	0.94028	0.5120	13.6	60.0001
Fishers	1.88720e-4	0.0001	2.35	0.0265

a) The number of licensed lobster fishers has fluctuated over the years between roughly 5000 and 10,000. Recently the number has been just over 7000. But licences are in demand (and tightly restricted). What does this model predict the value of the catch would be in a year if there were 10,000 licensed fishers? (Take care to interpret the coefficient correctly and to compute the inverse of the log transformation.)

b) Interpret the slope coefficient. Do more fishers cause a higher valued harvest? Suggest alternative explanations. **LO ❸**

⊤ 48. Lobsters, part 4. Of course, what matters most to the individual entrepreneur—the licensed commercial lobster fisher—is the price of lobster. Here's an analysis relating that price in dollars per pound ($/lb) to the number of traps (millions) since 1950:

Dependent variable is: Price/lb
R-squared = 93.4%
$s = 0.3147$ with $63 - 2 = 61$ degrees of freedom

Variable	Coefficient	SE(Coeff)	t-ratio	P-value
Intercept	−0.251127	0.0844	−2.98	0.0042
Traps(M)	1.22756	0.0417	29.4	60.0001

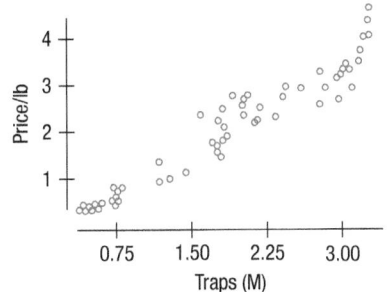

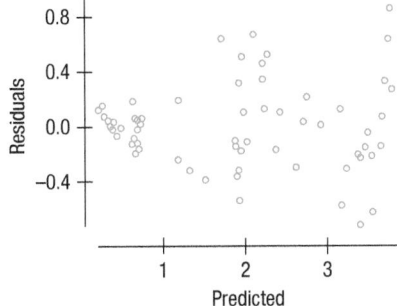

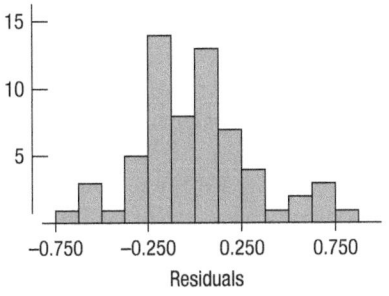

a) Are the assumptions and conditions for regression inference satisfied?

b) What does the coefficient of *Traps* mean in this model? Does it predict that licensing more traps would cause an increase in the price of lobster? Suggest some alternative explanations. **LO ❶**

⊤ 49. Canadian GDP. The data file gives quarterly gross domestic product (GDP) of Canada in billions of dollars for 1Q2000–2Q2015. (*Source:* Based on Statistics Canada. [2015]. CANSIM Table 380-0063: Gross domestic product (GDP), income-based, annual [dollars].)

a) Perform a linear regression analysis of this data.

b) Interpret the slope, its P-value, and the R^2. **LO ❶**

⊤ 50. Better model of Canadian GDP. Probe a little deeper into the analysis in Exercise 49 as follows:

a) Plot the data and the residuals, calculate the Durbin-Watson statistic and comment on what these imply for the regression model.

b) Would a transformation of the data improve the model: (i) for 2000–08; (ii) for 2009–12; (iii) for 2013–15? You are not asked to perform the transformation; if you think a transformation might help, indicate which transformation to use. **LO ❶, ❷, ❸**

51. Logs (not logarithms). Many professions use tables to determine key quantities. The value of a log is based on the number of board feet of lumber the log may contain. (A board foot is the equivalent of a piece of wood 1 inch thick, 12 inches wide, and 1 foot long. For example, a $2'' \times 4''$ piece that's 12 feet long contains 8 board feet.) To estimate the amount of lumber in a log, buyers measure the diameter inside the bark at the smaller end. Then they look in a table based on the Doyle Log Scale. The table below shows the estimates for logs 16 feet long:

Diameter of Log	8"	12"	16"	20"	24"	28"
Board Feet	16	64	114	256	400	576

a) What transformation of *Board Feet* makes this relationship linear?

b) How much lumber would you estimate that a log 10 inches in diameter contains?

c) What does this model suggest about the amount of lumber in logs 36 inches in diameter? **LO ❸**

52. Life expectancy. Life insurance rates are based on life expectancy values compiled for large demographic groups. But with improvements in medical care and nutrition, life expectancies have been changing. Here's a table from the U.S. National Vital Statistics Report that gives the life expectancy for white males in the United States every decade during the past century (1 = 1900 to 1910, 2 = 1911 to 1920, etc.). Consider a linear model to predict future increases in life expectancy. Would re-expressing either variable make a better model? **LO ❸**

Decade	1	2	3	4	5	6	7	8	9	10
Life Exp.	48.6	54.4	59.7	62.1	66.5	67.4	68.0	70.7	72.7	74.9

Ⓣ 53. Human Development Index, part 3. In Exercise 22 we saw that the United Nations Development Programme (UNDP) uses the Human Development Index (HDI) in an attempt to summarize the progress in health, education, and economics of a country with one number. The gross domestic product per capita (GDPPC) attempts to summarize the wealth produced by a country in one number. Here is a plot of *GDPPC* against *HDI*:

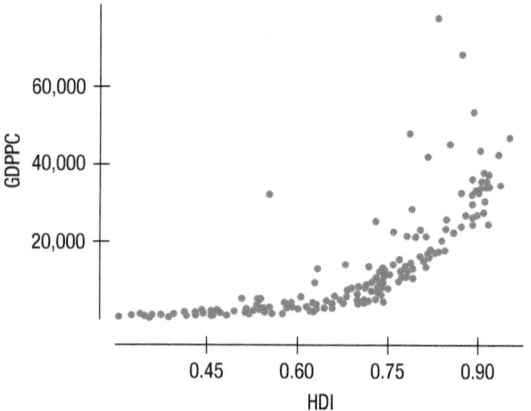

GDPPC is measured in dollars. Incomes and other economic measures tend to be highly right skewed. Taking logs often makes the distribution more unimodal and symmetric. Compare the histogram of *GDPPC* to the histogram of *log(GDPPC)*. **LO ❸**

Ⓣ 54. Human Development Index, part 4. In Exercise 53 we examined the relationship between *log(GDPPC)* and *HDI*. The number of internet users (per 1000 people) is also positively associated with economic progress in a country. Here's a scatterplot of *Internet users* (subscribers per 1000 people) against *HDI*:

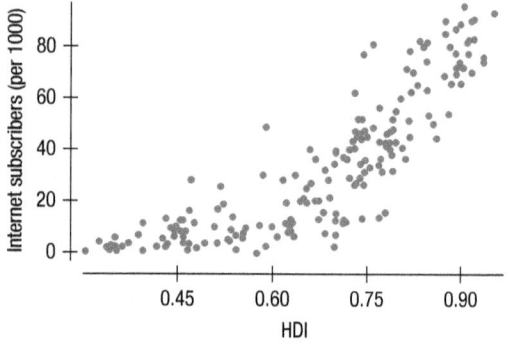

a) *Internet Users* is a count of subscribers (per 1000). What re-expression is often useful for counts? Examine the histogram of *Internet Users* and the histogram of *Internet Users* using the re-expression you suggested. Comment.
b) Use the re-expression in (a) for the scatterplot against *HDI*. Comment.
c) Would you feel confident using this relationship to predict the number of *Internet Users* based on the *HDI*? **LO ❸**

Ⓣ 55. Lobsters, part 5. How has the number of licensed lobster fishers changed? Here's a plot of the number of *Fishers vs. Year*:

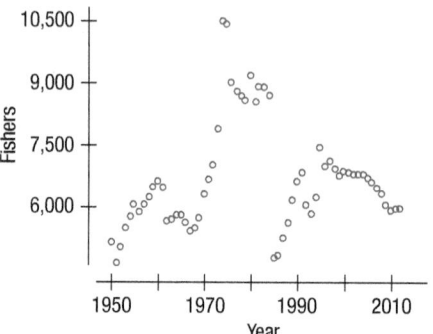

This plot isn't straight. Would a transformation help? If so, which one? If not, why not?

56. Lobster price. How has the price of a lobster changed? Here's a plot tracking the price of lobster per pound in constant year 2000 dollars:

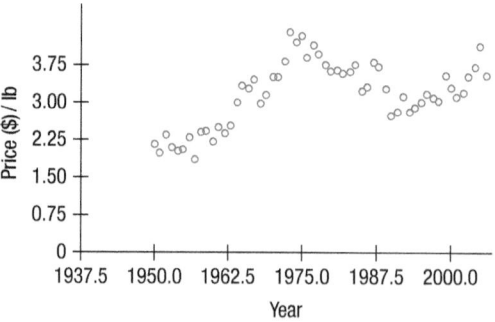

This plot isn't straight. Would a transformation help? If so, which one? If not, why not? **LO ❸**

Ⓣ 57. Canadian building permits. Building permits are a leading indicator of economic growth. But do non-residential permits follow the same pattern as residential permits? Statistics Canada provides us with the requisite data in Table 260-0003, Building Permits, Values by Activity Sector. The graph shows the value of each type of permit in each Canadian province and territory (in $ billion) for the first nine months of 2015:

		ROADMAP FOR STATISTICAL INFERENCE			
Number of Variables	**Objective**	**Large Sample or Normal Population**		**Small Sample and Non-normal Population or Non-numeric Data**	
		Chapter	Parametric Method	Chapter	Nonparametric Method
1	Calculate confidence interval for a proportion	11			
1	Compare a proportion with a given value	12	z-test		
1	Calculate a confidence interval for a mean and compare it with a given value	13	t-test	17.2	Wilcoxon Signed-Rank Test
2	Compare two proportions	12.8	z-test		
2	Compare two means for independent samples	14.1–14.5	t-test	17.4, 17.5	Wilcoxon Rank-Sum (Mann-Whitney) Test Tukey's Quick Test
2	Compare two means for paired samples	14.6, 14.7	Paired t-test	17.2	Wilcoxon Signed-Rank Test
≥3	Compare multiple means	15	ANOVA: ANalysis Of VAriance	17.3 17.6	Friedman Test Kruskal-Wallis Test
≥3	Compare multiple counts (proportions)	16	χ^2 test		
2	Investigate the relationship between two variables	18	Correlation Regression	17.7, 17.8	Kendall's tau Spearman's rho
≥3	Investigate the relationship between multiple variables	20	Multiple Regression		

ow exactly does PURVIEW determine the worth of a house? Not surprisingly, Teranet doesn't publish the details of its model, but does tell us that it uses statistics. Real estate valuation models first appeared in the 1990s and produce a statistically derived estimate of value based on analysis of public record data, property location, market conditions, and real estate characteristics at a specific point in time. It's very likely that PURVIEW uses regression, and if it does, then simple regression with just one explanatory variable isn't going to do a good job. With so many factors determining house prices, multiple regression is needed so that all these explanatory variables can be taken into account. Multiple regression is probably the most powerful and widely used statistical tool today.

Let's demonstrate the dramatic effect of including multiple variables in a regression model using a sample of 1057 home sales. We'll start with a single explanatory variable and see the improvement we get when we add more variables. The first thing often mentioned in describing a house for sale is the number of bedrooms. Let's start with just one predictor variable. Can we use *Bedrooms* to predict home *Price*?

The number of *Bedrooms* is a quantitative variable, but it holds only a few values (from 1 to 5 in this data set). So a scatterplot may not be the best way to examine the relationship between *Bedrooms* and *Price*. In fact, at each value for *Bedrooms* there's a whole distribution of prices. Side-by-side boxplots of *Price* against

Bedrooms (Figure 20.1) show a general increase in price with more bedrooms, and an approximately linear growth.

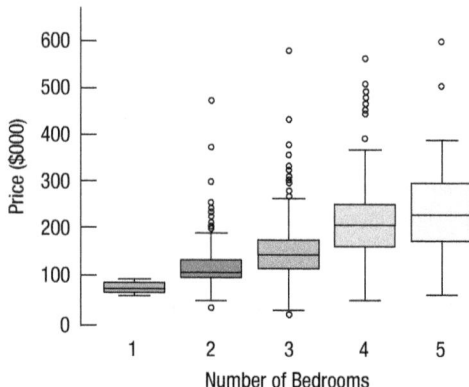

Figure 20.1   Side-by-side boxplots of *Price* against *Bedrooms* show that price increases, on average, with more bedrooms.

Figure 20.1 also shows a clearly increasing spread from left to right, violating the Equal Spread Condition, and that's a possible sign of trouble. For now, we'll proceed cautiously. We'll fit the regression model, but we'll be cautious about using inference methods for the model. Later we'll add more variables to increase the power and usefulness of the model.

The output from a linear regression model of *Price* on *Bedrooms* (Table 20.1) shows:

Response variable: Price
$R^2 = 21.4\%$
$s = 68432.21$ with $1057 - 2 = 1055$ degrees of freedom

Variable	Coeff	SE(Coeff)	t-ratio	P-value
Intercept	14349.48	9297.69	1.5	0.1230
Bedrooms	48218.91	2843.88	16.96	≤0.0001

Table 20.1   Linear regression of *Price* on *Bedrooms*.

The model tells us that, on average, we'd expect the price to increase by almost $50,000 for each additional bedroom in the house, as we can see from the slope value of $48,218.91:

$$\widehat{Price} = 14349.48 + 48218.91 \times Bedrooms$$

Even though the model does tell us something, notice that the R^2 for this regression is only 21.4%. The variation in the number of bedrooms accounts for only 21.4% of the variation in house prices. The standard deviation of the residuals is $s = 68,432$, which tells us that the model only does a modestly good job of accounting for the price of a home. Approximating with the 68-95-99.7 Rule, only about 68% of home prices predicted by this model would be within $68,432 of the actual price. That's not likely to be close enough to be useful for a home buyer. Perhaps some of the other facts about these houses can account for portions of the remaining variation.

20.1 The Linear Multiple Regression Model

For simple regression, we wrote the predicted values in terms of one predictor variable:

$$\hat{y} = b_0 + b_1 x$$

To include more predictors in the model, we just write the regression model with more predictor variables. The resulting **multiple regression** looks like this:

$$\hat{y} = b_0 + b_1 x_1 + b_2 x_2 + \ldots + b_k x_k,$$

where b_0 is still the intercept and each b_k is the estimated coefficient of its corresponding predictor x_k. Although the model doesn't look much more complicated than a simple regression, it isn't practical to determine a multiple regression by hand. This is a job for a statistics program on a computer. Remember that for simple regression, we found the coefficients for the model using the **least squares** solution, the one whose coefficients made the sum of the squared residuals as small as possible. For multiple regression, a statistics package does the same thing and can find the coefficients of the least squares model easily.

If you know how to find the regression of *Price* on *Bedrooms* using a statistics package, you can probably just add another variable to the list of predictors in your program to compute a multiple regression. A multiple regression of *Price* on the two variables *Bedrooms* and *Living Area* generates a multiple regression table like this one (Table 20.2):

Response variable: Price

$R^2 = 57.8\%$

$s = 50142.4$ with $1057 - 3 = 1054$ degrees of freedom

Variable	Coeff	SE(Coeff)	t-ratio	P-value
Intercept	20986.09	6816.3	3.08	0.0021
Bedrooms	−7483.10	2783.5	−2.69	0.0073
Living area	93.84	3.11	30.18	≤0.0001

Table 20.2 Multiple regression output for the linear model predicting *Price* from *Bedrooms* and *Living Area*.

You should recognize most of the numbers in this table, and most of them mean what you expect them to. The value of R^2 for a regression on two variables gives the fraction of the variability of *Price* accounted for by both predictor variables together. With *Bedrooms* alone predicting *Price*, the R^2 value was 21.4%, but this model accounts for 57.8% of the variability in *Price*. We shouldn't be surprised that the variability explained by the model has gone up. It was for this reason—the hope of accounting for some of that leftover variability—that we tried a second predictor. We also shouldn't be surprised that the size of the house, as measured by *Living Area*, also contributes to a good prediction of house prices. Collecting the coefficients of the multiple regression of *Price* on *Bedrooms* and *Living Area* from Table 20.2, we can write the estimated regression as

$$\widehat{Price} = 20,986.09 - 7483.10 Bedrooms + 93.84 Living\ Area.$$

As before, we define the residuals as

$$e = y - \hat{y}.$$

The standard deviation of the residuals is still denoted as s (or also sometimes as s_e as in simple regression, for the same reason—to distinguish it from the standard deviation, s_y, of y). The degrees of freedom calculation comes right from our definition. The degrees of freedom is the number of observations ($n = 1057$) minus one for each coefficient estimated:

$$df = n - k - 1,$$

where k is the number of predictor variables and n is the number of cases. For this model, we subtract three (the two coefficients and the intercept). To find the standard deviation of the residuals, we use that number of degrees of freedom in the denominator:

$$s_e = \sqrt{\frac{\sum(y - \hat{y})^2}{n - k - 1}}$$

For each predictor, the regression output shows a coefficient, its standard error, a **t-ratio for the coefficient**, and the corresponding P-value. As with simple regression, the t-ratio measures how many standard errors the coefficient is away from zero. Using a Student's t-model, we can use its P-value to test the null hypothesis that the true value of the coefficient is zero.

What's different? With so much of the multiple regression looking just like simple regression, why devote an entire chapter to the subject?

There are several answers to this question. First, and most important, is that the meaning of the coefficients in the regression model has changed in a subtle but important way. Because that change isn't obvious, multiple regression coefficients are often misinterpreted. We'll show some examples to explain this change in meaning.

Second, multiple regression is an extraordinarily versatile model, underlying many widely used statistics methods. A sound understanding of the multiple regression model will help you understand these other applications as well.

Third, multiple regression offers you a first glimpse into statistical models that use more than two quantitative variables. The real world is complex. Simple models with only one variable are a great start, but they're not detailed enough to be useful for understanding, predicting, and making business decisions in many real-world situations. Models that use several variables can be a big step toward realistic and useful modelling of complex phenomena and relationships.

FOR EXAMPLE   The multiple regression model for customer response to marketing

A large clothing store has recently sent out a special catalogue of fall clothes, and Leiram, its marketing analyst, wants to find out which customers responded to it and which ones bought the most. She plans to conduct an RFM (Recency, Frequency, Monetary) analysis. The RFM method is based on the principle that 80% of your business comes from the best 20% of your customers and states that the following attributes will be useful predictors of who the best customers will be:

- how *recently* the customer has purchased (Recency)
- how *frequently* the customer shops (Frequency)
- how *much* the customer spends (Monetary)

For each customer, Leiram has information for the past five years on *Date of Last Purchase*, *Number of Purchases*, and *Total Amount Spent*. In addition, she has demographic information, including *Age, Marital Status, Sex, Income,* and *Number of Children.* She chooses a random sample of 149 customers who bought something from the catalogue and who have purchased at least three times in the past five years (*Number of Purchases*). She wants to model how much they bought from the new catalogue (*Respond Amount*).

Leiram fits the following multiple regression model to the response variable *Respond Amount:*

Response Variable: Respond Amount
$R^2 = 91.48\%$ Adjusted $R^2 = 91.31\%$
$s = 18.183$ with $149 - 4 = 145$ degrees of freedom

Variable	Coeff	SE(Coeff)	*t*-ratio	P-value
Intercept	111.01	6.459	17.187	<0.0001
Income	0.00091	0.00012	7.643	<0.0001
Total Amount Spent	0.154	0.00852	18.042	<0.0001
Number of Purchases	−14.81	0.716	−20.695	<0.0001

QUESTIONS How much of the variation in *Respond Amount* is explained by this model? What does the term $s = 18.183$ mean? Which variables seem important in the model?

ANSWERS This model has an R^2 of 91.48%, which means that the model has explained 91.48% of the variation in *Respond Amount* using the three predictors: *Income, Total Amount Spent,* and *Number of Purchases.* The term $s = 18.183$ means that the standard deviation of the residuals is about $18.18. Using the 68-95-99.7 Rule, we know that most prediction errors will be no larger than about $36.36. All terms seem important in this model, since all three have very large *t*-ratios and correspondingly small P-values.

Andy Dean Photography/Shutterstock

LO❶ 20.2 Interpreting Multiple Regression Coefficients

It makes sense that both the number of bedrooms and the size of the living area would influence the price of a house. We'd expect both variables to have a positive effect on price—houses with more bedrooms typically sell for more money, as do larger houses. But look at the coefficient for *Bedrooms* in the multiple regression equation. It's negative: −7483.09. How can it be that the coefficient of *Bedrooms* in the multiple regression is negative? And not just slightly negative; its *t*-ratio is large enough for us to be quite confident that the true value really is negative. Yet from Table 20.1, we saw that the coefficient was equally clearly positive when *Bedrooms* was the sole predictor in the model (see Figure 20.2).

The explanation of this paradox is that in a multiple regression, coefficients have a more subtle meaning. Each coefficient takes into account the other predictor(s) in the model.

Think about a group of houses of about the same size. For the *same-size* living area, a house with more bedrooms is likely to have smaller rooms. That might actually make it less valuable. To see this in the data, let's look at a group of similarly sized homes from 2500 to 3000 square feet of living area and examine the relationship between *Bedrooms* and *Price* just for houses in this size range (see Figure 20.3).

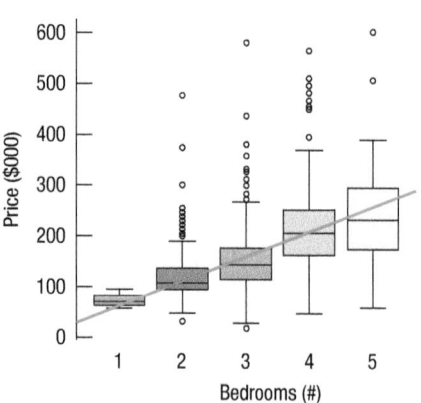

Figure 20.2   The slope of *Bedrooms* is positive. For each additional bedroom, we would predict an additional $48,000 in the price of a house from the simple regression model of Table 20.1.

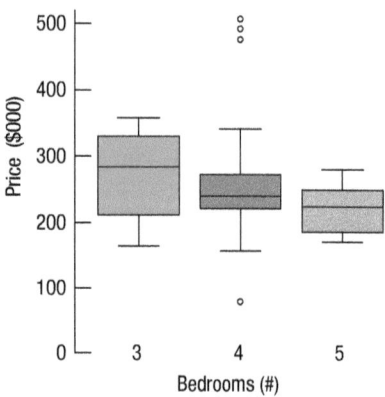

Figure 20.3   For the 96 houses with *Living Area* between 2500 and 3000 square feet, the slope of *Price* on *Bedrooms* is negative. For each additional bedroom, restricting data to homes of this size, we would predict that the house's *Price* was about $17,800 lower.

For houses with between 2500 and 3000 square feet of living area, it appears that those with *fewer* bedrooms have a higher price, on average, than those with more bedrooms. When we think about houses in terms of *both* variables, we can see that this makes sense. A 2500-square-foot house with five bedrooms would have either relatively small, cramped bedrooms or not much common living space. The same-size house with only three bedrooms could have larger, more attractive bedrooms and still have adequate common living space. What the coefficient of *Bedrooms* is saying in the multiple regression is that, after accounting for living area, houses with more bedrooms tend to sell for a *lower* price. In other words, what we saw by restricting our attention to homes of a certain size and seeing that additional bedrooms had a negative impact on price was generally true across all sizes. What seems confusing at first is that without taking *Living Area* into account, *Price* tends to go *up* with more bedrooms. But that's because *Living Area* and *Bedrooms* are also related. Multiple regression coefficients must always be interpreted in terms of the other predictors in the model. That can make their interpretation more subtle, more complex, and more challenging than when we had only one predictor. This is also what makes multiple regression so versatile and effective. The interpretations are more sophisticated and more appropriate.

There's a second common pitfall in interpreting coefficients. Be careful not to interpret the coefficients causally. For example, this analysis can't tell a homeowner how much the price of his home will change if he combines two of his four bedrooms into a new master bedroom. And it can't be used to predict whether adding a 100-square-foot child's bedroom onto the house would increase or decrease its value. The model simply reports the relationship between the number of *Bedrooms* and *Living Area* and *Price* for existing houses. As always with regression, we should be careful not to assume causation between the predictor variables and the response.

FOR EXAMPLE   **Interpreting multiple regression coefficients for customer response to marketing**

QUESTION In the regression model of *Respond Amount* in For Example: "The multiple regression model for customer response to marketing," interpret the intercept and the regression coefficients of the three predictors.

ANSWER The model says that from a base of $111.01 of spending, customers (who have purchased at least three times in the past 12 months), on average, spent $0.91 for every $1000 of *Income* (after accounting for *Number of Purchases* and *Total Amount Spent*), $0.154 for every dollar they've spent in the past five years (after accounting for *Income* and *Number of Purchases*), but $14.81 less for every additional purchase they've made in the past five years (after accounting for *Income* and *Total Amount Spent*). It's important to note especially that the coefficient in *Number of Purchases* is negative, but only after accounting for both *Income* and *Total Amount Spent*.

JUST CHECKING

Body fat percentage is an important health indicator, but it's difficult to measure accurately. One way to do so is to take a magnetic resonance image (MRI), but this is expensive. Insurance companies want to know if body fat percentage can be estimated from easier-to-measure characteristics such as *Height* and *Weight*. A scatterplot of *Percent Body Fat* against *Height* shows no pattern, and the correlation is -0.03 and is not statistically significant. A multiple regression using *Height* (centimetres), *Age* (years), and *Weight* (kilograms) finds the following model:

	Coeff	SE(Coeff)	t-ratio	P-value
Intercept	57.27217	10.39897	5.507	<0.0001
Height	−0.50164	0.05909	−8.064	<0.0001
Weight	0.55805	0.03263	17.110	<0.0001
Age	0.13732	0.02806	4.895	<0.0001

$s = 5.382$ on 246 degrees of freedom
Multiple R-squared: 0.584,
F-statistic: 115.1 on 3 and 246 DF, P-value: <0.0001

1 Interpret the R^2 of this regression model.

2 Interpret the coefficient of *Age* and the coefficient of *Height*. Why is the latter coefficient negative?

3 How can the coefficient of *Height* have such a small P-value in the multiple regression when the correlation between *Height* and *Percent Body Fat* wasn't statistically distinguishable from zero?

Answers are found in Appendix A.

LO❶ **20.3** ## Assumptions and Conditions for the Multiple Regression Model

We can write the multiple regression model like this, numbering the predictors arbitrarily (the order doesn't matter), writing betas for the model coefficients (which we'll estimate from the data), and including the errors in the model:

$$y = \beta_0 + \beta_1 x_1 + \beta_2 x_2 + \ldots + \beta_k x_k + \varepsilon$$

The assumptions and conditions for the multiple regression model are nearly the same as for simple regression, but with more variables in the model, we'll have to make a few changes, as described in the following sections. The conditions are used to test the assumptions.

Linearity Assumption

We are fitting a linear model.[1] For that to be the right kind of model for this analysis, we need to verify an underlying linear relationship. But now we're thinking about several predictors. To confirm that the assumption is reasonable, we'll check the Linearity Condition for *each* of the predictors.

Linearity Condition   Scatterplots of *y* against each of the predictors are reasonably straight. The scatterplots need not show a strong (or any) slope; we just check to make sure that there isn't a bend or other nonlinearity. For the real estate data, the scatterplot is linear in both *Bedrooms* and *Living Area*, as we saw in Chapter 18.

As in simple regression, it's a good idea to check the residual plot for any violations of the Linearity Condition. We can fit the regression and plot the residuals against the predicted values (Figure 20.4), checking to make sure we don't find patterns—especially bends or other nonlinearities.

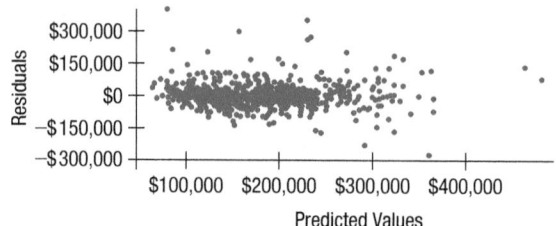

Figure 20.4   A scatterplot of *Residuals* against the *Predicted Values* shows no obvious pattern.

Independence Assumption

As with simple regression, the errors in the true underlying regression model must be independent of each other. As usual, there's no way to be sure that the Independence Assumption is true, but we should think about how the data were collected to see if that assumption is reasonable. We should check the Randomization Condition as well.

Randomization Condition   Ideally, the data should arise from a random sample or randomized experiment. Randomization assures us that the data are representative of some identifiable population. If you can't identify the population, you can interpret the regression model as a description of the data you have, but you can't interpret the hypothesis tests at all because such tests are about a regression model for a specific population. Regression methods are often applied to data that weren't collected with randomization. Regression models fit to such data may still do a good job of modelling the data at hand, but without some reason to believe that the data are representative of a particular population, you should be reluctant to believe that the model generalizes to other situations.

We also check the regression residuals for evidence of patterns, trends, or clumping, any of which would suggest a failure of independence. In the special case when one of the *x*-variables is related to time (or is itself *Time*), make sure that the residuals don't have a pattern when plotted against that variable. In addition to checking the plot of residuals against the predicted values, we recommend that you check the individual plots of the residuals against each of the explanatory, or *x*, variables in the model. These individual plots can yield important information about necessary transformations, or re-expressions, for the predictor variables.

---

[1]By *linear* we mean that each *x* appears simply multiplied by its coefficient and added to the model, and that no *x* appears in an exponent or some other, more complicated function. That ensures that as we move along any *x*-variable, our prediction for *y* will change at a constant rate (given by the coefficient) if nothing else changes.

The real estate data were sampled from a larger set of public records for sales during a limited period of time. The houses weren't related in any way, so we can be fairly confident that their measurements are independent.

Equal Variance Assumption

The variability of the errors should be about the same for all values of each predictor. To see whether this assumption is valid, we look at scatterplots and check the Equal Spread Condition.

Equal Spread Condition   The same scatterplot of residuals against the predicted values (Figure 20.4) is a good check of the consistency of the spread. We saw what appeared to be a violation of the Equal Spread Condition when *Price* was plotted against *Bedrooms* (Figure 20.2). But here in the multiple regression, the problem has dissipated when we look at the residuals. Apparently, much of the tendency of houses with more bedrooms to have greater variability in prices was accounted for in the model when we included *Living Area* as a predictor.

If residual plots show no pattern, if the data are plausibly independent, and if the plots don't thicken, we can feel good about interpreting the regression model. Before we test hypotheses, however, we must check one final assumption: the Normality Assumption.

Normality Assumption

We assume that the errors around the idealized regression model at any specified values of the *x*-variables follow a Normal model. We need this assumption so that we can use a Student's *t*-model for inference. As in other times when we've used Student's *t*, we'll settle for the residuals satisfying the Nearly Normal Condition. As with means, the assumption is less important as the sample size grows. Our inference methods will work well even when the residuals are moderately skewed, if the sample size is large. If the distribution of residuals is unimodal and symmetric, there is little to worry about.[2]

Nearly Normal Condition   Because we have only one set of residuals, this is the same set of conditions we had for simple regression. Look at a histogram or Normal probability plot of the residuals (Figure 20.5).

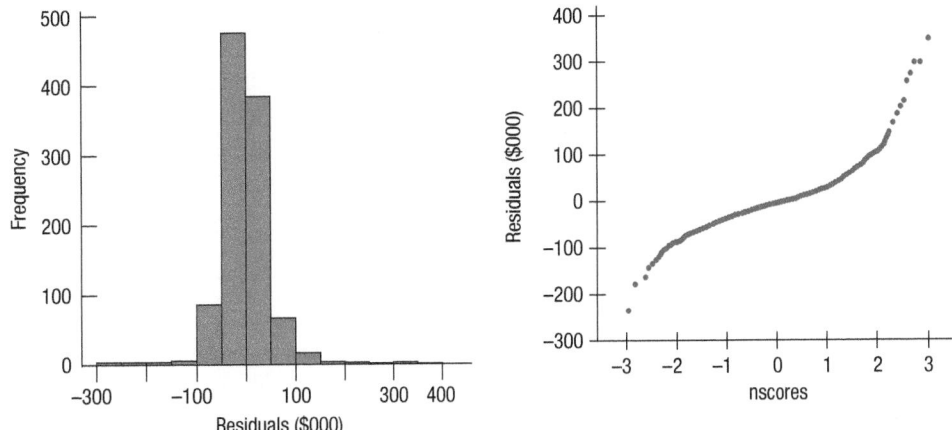

Figure 20.5   A histogram of the residuals shows a unimodal, symmetric distribution, but the tails seem a bit longer than one would expect from a Normal model. The Normal probability plot confirms that.

---

[2]The only procedure that needs strict adherence to Normality of the errors is finding prediction intervals for individuals in multiple regression. Because they're based on Normal probabilities, the errors must closely follow a Normal model.

The histogram of residuals in the real estate example certainly looks unimodal and symmetric. The Normal probability plot has some bend on both sides, which indicates that there are more residuals in the tails than Normally distributed data would have. However, as we've said before, the Normality Assumption becomes less important as the sample size grows, and here we have no skewness and more than 1000 cases. (The Central Limit Theorem will help our confidence intervals and tests based on the t-statistic with large samples.)

Let's summarize all the checks of conditions we've made and the order in which we've made them:

1. Check the Linearity Condition with scatterplots of the y-variable against each x-variable.
2. If the scatterplots are straight enough, fit a multiple regression model to the data. (Otherwise, either stop or consider re-expressing an x-variable or the y-variable.)
3. Find the residuals and predicted values.
4. Make a scatterplot of the residuals against the predicted values (and ideally against each predictor variable separately). These plots should look patternless. Check, in particular, for any bend (which would suggest that the data weren't all that straight after all) and for any thickening. If there's a bend, consider re-expressing the y- and/or the x-variables. If the variation in the plot grows from one side to the other, consider re-expressing the y-variable. If you re-express a variable, start the model fitting over.
5. Think about how the data were collected. Should they be independent? Was suitable randomization used? Are the data representative of some identifiable population? If the data are measured over time, check for evidence of patterns that might suggest they're not independent by plotting the residuals against time to look for patterns.
6. If the conditions check out thus far, feel free to interpret the regression model and use it for prediction.
7. Make a histogram and Normal probability plot of the residuals to check the Nearly Normal Condition. If the sample size is large, the Normality is less important for inference, but always be on the lookout for skewness or outliers.

JUST CHECKING

4 Give two ways that we use histograms to support the construction, inference, and understanding of multiple regression models.

5 Give two ways that we use scatterplots to support the construction, inference, and understanding of multiple regression models.

6 What role does the Normal model play in the construction, inference, and understanding of multiple regression models?

Answers are found in Appendix A.

FOR EXAMPLE   **Assumptions and conditions for customer response to marketing**

Here are plots of *Respond Amount* against the three predictors, a plot of the residuals against the predicted values from the multiple regression, a histogram of the residuals, and a Normal probability plot of the residuals. Recall that the data come from a random sample of customers who both responded to the catalogue and purchased at least three times in the past five years.

QUESTION Do the assumptions and conditions for multiple regression appear to have been met?

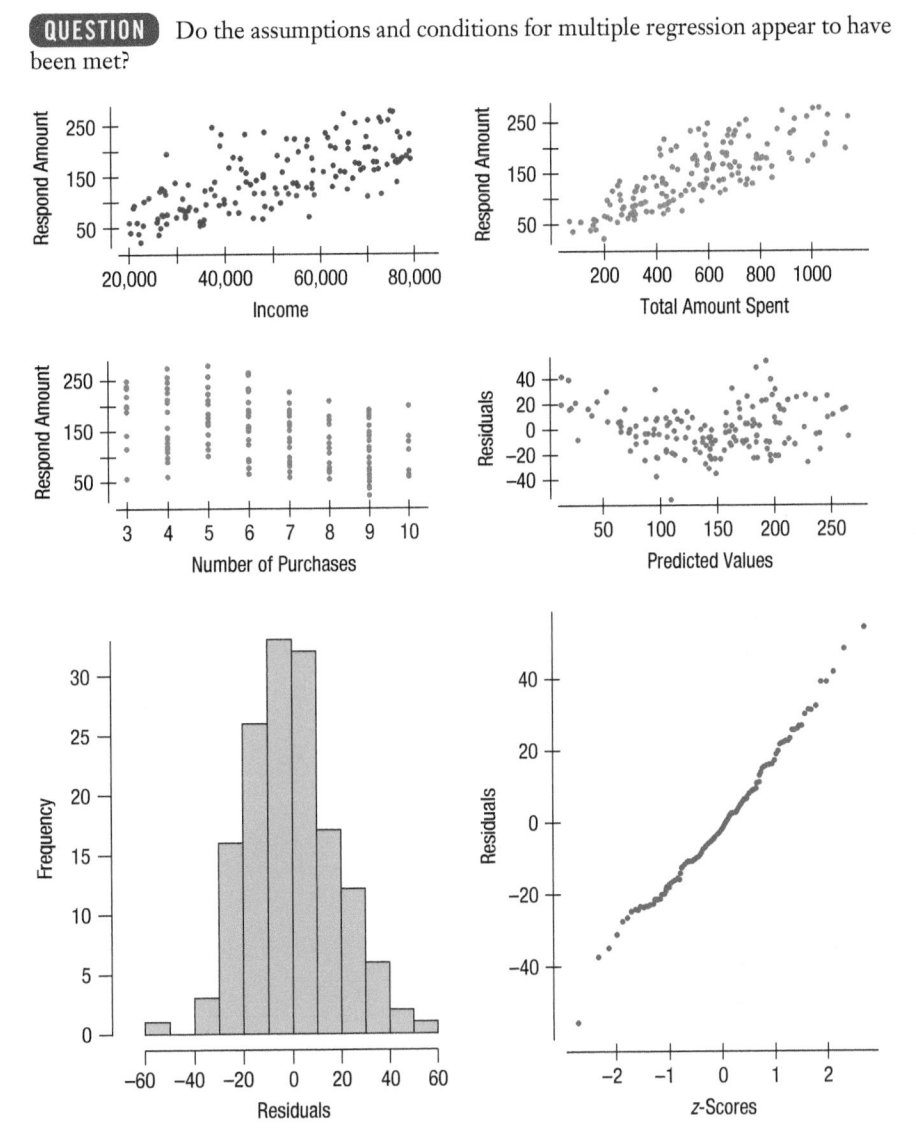

ANSWER Because the sample is random, the randomization condition is satisfied and we assume the responses are independent. The plots of *Respond Amount* against each predictor are reasonably linear, with the possible exception of *Number of Purchases*. There may also be some curvature and increasing spread in the residual plot. The histogram of residuals is unimodal and symmetric with no extreme outliers. The Normal probability plot shows that the distribution is fairly Normally distributed. The conditions aren't completely satisfied and we should proceed somewhat cautiously, especially with regard to *Number of Purchases*.

GUIDED EXAMPLE   Housing Prices

PURVIEW attracts thousands of professionals in the real estate business every month because it provides them with statistical valuations of residential properties. Let's see how well a multiple regression model can do. The variables available include the following:

PRICE	The price of the house as sold in 2002
LIVING AREA	The size of the living area of the house in square feet
BEDROOMS	The number of bedrooms
BATHROOMS	The number of bathrooms (a half bath is a toilet and sink only)
AGE	Age of the house in years
FIREPLACES	Number of fireplaces in the house

(*continued*)

PLAN

Setup State the objective of the study. Identify the variables.

Model Think about the assumptions and check the conditions.

We want to build a model to predict house prices and have data on *Price* ($), *Living Area* (sq. ft.), *Bedrooms* (#), *Bathrooms* (#), *Fireplaces* (#), and *Age* (in years).

✓ **Linearity Condition.** To fit a regression model, we first require linearity. Scatterplots (or side-by-side boxplots) of *Price* against all potential predictor variables are shown below:

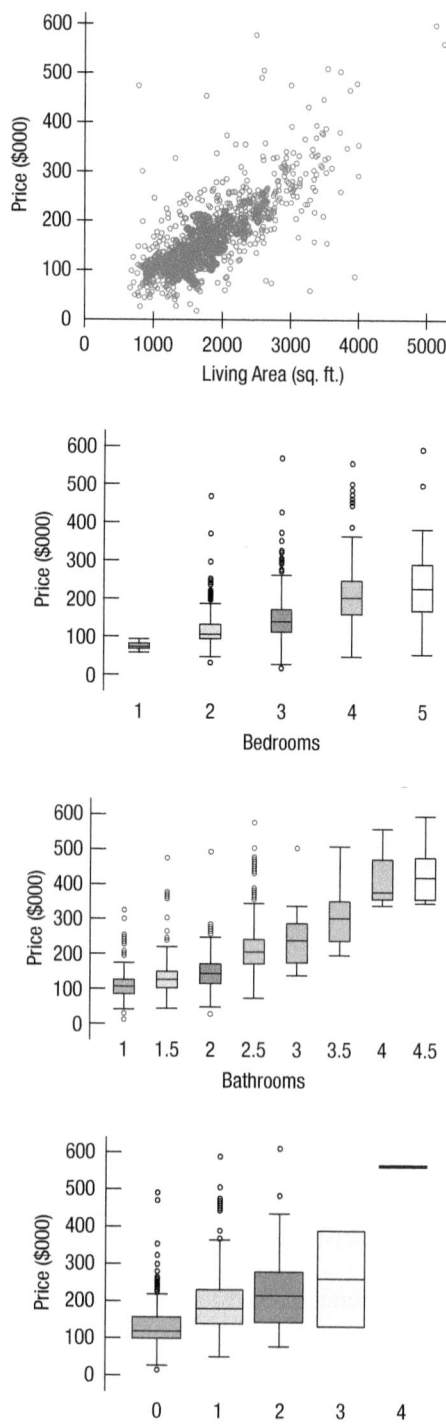

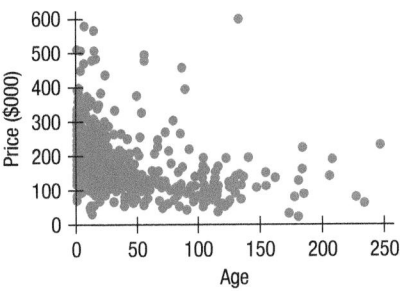

There are a few anomalies in the plots that deserve discussion. The plot of *Price* against *Bathrooms* shows a positive relationship, but it's not quite linear. There seem to be two slopes, one from one to two bathrooms and then a steeper one from two to four. For now, we'll proceed cautiously, realizing that any slope we find will average these two. The plot of *Price* against *Fireplaces* shows an outlier—an expensive home with four fireplaces. We tried setting this home aside and running the regression without it, but its influence on the slopes wasn't great, so we decided to include it in the model. The plot of *Price* against *Age* shows that there may be some curvature. We should be cautious in interpreting the slope, especially for newer homes.

✓ **Independence Assumption.** We can regard the house prices as being independent of one another, since they're from a fairly large geographic area.

✓ **Randomization Condition.** These 1057 houses are a random sample of a much larger set.

✓ **Equal Spread Condition.** A scatterplot of residuals vs. predicted values shows no evidence of changing spread. There is a group of homes whose residuals are larger (both negative and positive) than the vast majority. This is also seen in the long tails of the histogram of residuals.

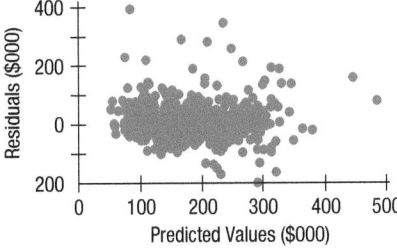

We need the Nearly Normal Condition only if we want to do inference and the sample size isn't large. If the sample size is large, we need the distribution to be Normal only if we plan to produce prediction intervals.

✓ **Nearly Normal Condition, Outlier Condition.** The histogram of residuals is unimodal and symmetric, but long-tailed. The Normal probability plot supports that.

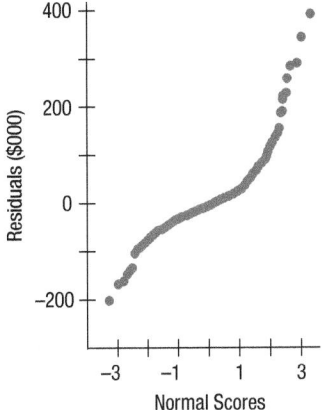

(*continued*)

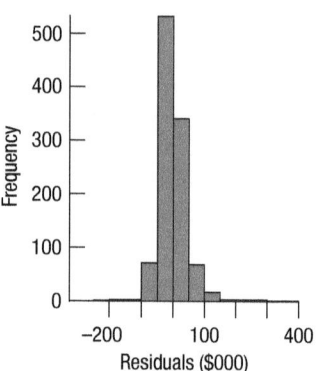

Under these conditions, we can proceed with caution to a multiple regression analysis. We will return to some of our concerns in the discussion.

DO   **Mechanics** We always fit multiple regression models with computer software. An output table like this one isn't exactly what any of the major packages produces, but it's sufficiently like them to look familiar.

Here's the computer output for the multiple regression, using all five predictors:

	Coeff	SE(Coeff)	t-ratio	P-value
Intercept	15712.702	7311.427	2.149	0.03186
Living Area	73.446	4.009	18.321	<0.0001
Bedrooms	−6361.311	2749.503	−2.314	0.02088
Bathrooms	19236.678	3669.080	5.243	<0.0001
Fireplaces	9162.791	3194.233	2.869	0.00421
Age	−142.740	48.276	−2.957	0.00318

Residual standard error: 48615.95 on 1051 degrees of freedom
Multiple R-squared: 0.6049,
F-statistic: 321.8 on 5 and 1051 DF, P-value: <0.0001

The estimated equation is

$$\widehat{Price} = 15{,}712.70 + 73.45 \text{Living Area} - 6361.31 \text{Bedrooms} + 19{,}236.68 \text{Bathrooms} + 3162.79 \text{Fireplaces} - 142.74 \text{Age}$$

All the P-values are small, which indicates that even with five predictors in the model, all are contributing. The R^2 value of 60.49% indicates that more than 60% of the overall variation in house prices has been accounted for by this model. The residual standard error of $48,616 gives us a rough indication that we can predict the price of a home to within about 2 × $48,616 = $97,232. If that's close enough to be useful, then our model is potentially useful as a price guide.

REPORT **Conclusion** Summarize your results and state any limitations of your model in the context of your original objectives.

MEMO

Re: Regression Analysis of Home Price Predictions

A regression model of *Price* on *Living Area, Bedrooms, Bathrooms, Fireplaces,* and *Age* accounts for 60.5% of the variation in the price of homes in our sample. A statistical test of each coefficient shows that each one is almost certainly not zero, so each of these variables appears to be a contributor of the price of a house.

This model reflects the common wisdom in real estate about the importance of various aspects of a home. An important variable not included is the location, which every real estate agent knows is crucial to pricing a house. This is ameliorated by the fact that all these houses are in the same general area. However, knowing more specific information about where they're located would almost certainly help the model. The price found from this model is to be used as a starting point for comparing a home with similar homes in the area.

The model may be improved by re-expressing one or more of the predictors, especially *Age* and *Bathrooms*. We recommend caution in interpreting the slopes across the entire range of these predictors.

LO❷ ## 20.4 Testing the Multiple Regression Model

There are several hypothesis tests in the multiple regression output, but all of them talk about the same thing. Each is concerned with whether the underlying model parameters (the slopes and intercept) are actually zero. The first of these hypotheses is one we skipped over for simple regression (for reasons that will be clear in a minute).

Now that we have more than one predictor, there's an overall test we should perform before we consider inference for the coefficients. We ask the global question: Is this multiple regression model any good at all? If home prices were set randomly or based on other factors than those we have as predictors, then the best estimate would just be the mean price.

To address the overall question, we'll test the null hypothesis that all the slope coefficients are zero:

$$H_0: B_1 = \ldots = \beta_k = 0 \ vs. \ H_A: \text{at least one } \beta \neq 0$$

We can test this hypothesis with an **F-test**. (It's the generalization of the *t*-test to more than one predictor, and the mechanics of the calculation are given in the next section.) The sampling distribution of the statistic is labelled with the letter F (in honour of Sir Ronald Fisher). The F-distribution has two degrees of freedom, k, the number of predictors, and $n - k - 1$. In our Guided Example, we have $k = 5$ predictors and $n = 1057$ homes, which means that the F-value of 321.8 has five, and $1057 - 5 - 1 = 1051$ degrees of freedom. The regression output shows that it has a P-value<0.0001. The null hypothesis is that the regression model predicts no better than the mean. The alternative is that it does. The test is one-sided—bigger F-values mean smaller P-values. If the null hypothesis were true, the F-statistic would be near one. The F-statistic here is quite large, so we can easily reject the null hypothesis and conclude that the

F-Test for Simple Regression?

Should we check the F-test for simple regression, that is, a regression with only one explanatory variable? When you do a simple regression with statistics software, you'll see the F-statistic in the output. But for simple regression, it gives the same information as the t-test for the slope. It tests the null hypothesis that the slope coefficient is zero, and we already test that with the t-statistic for the slope. In fact, the square of that t-statistic is equal to the F-statistic for the simple regression, so it really is the identical test.

multiple regression model for predicting house prices with these five variables is better than just using the mean.[3]

Once we check the F-test and reject its null hypothesis—and, if we're being careful, only if we reject that hypothesis—we can move on to checking the test statistics for the individual coefficients. Those tests look like what we did for the slope of a simple regression in Chapter 18. For each coefficient, we test the null hypothesis that the slope is zero against the (two-sided) alternative that it isn't zero. The regression table gives a standard error for each coefficient and the ratio of the estimated coefficient to its standard error. If the assumptions and conditions are met (and now we need the Nearly Normal Condition or a large sample), these ratios follow a Student's t-distribution:

$$t_{n-k-1} = \frac{b_j - 0}{SE(b_j)}$$

Where did the degrees of freedom $n - k - 1$ come from? We have a guideline that works here. The degrees of freedom value is the number of data values minus the number of estimated parameters (including the intercept). For the house price regression on five predictors, that's $n - 5 - 1$. Almost every regression report includes both the t-statistics and their corresponding P-values.

We can build a confidence interval in the usual way, with an estimate plus or minus a margin of error. As always, the margin of error is the product of the standard error and a critical value. Here the critical value comes from the t-distribution on $n - k - 1$ degrees of freedom, and the standard errors are in the regression table. So a confidence interval for each slope β_j is

$$b_j \pm t^*_{n-k-1} \times SE(b_j).$$

The tricky parts of these tests are that the standard errors of the coefficients now require harder calculations (so we leave it to technology), and the meaning of a coefficient, as we've seen, depends on all the other predictors in the multiple regression model.

That last point is important. If we fail to reject the null hypothesis for a multiple regression coefficient, it doesn't mean that the corresponding predictor variable has no linear relationship to y. It means that the corresponding predictor contributes nothing to modelling y *after allowing for all the other predictors*.

The multiple regression model looks so simple and straightforward. It *looks* like each β_j tells us the effect of its associated predictor, x_j, on the response variable, y. But that's not true. This is, without a doubt, the most common error that people make with multiple regression. In fact:

- The coefficient β_j in a multiple regression can be quite different from zero even when a simple linear regression between y and x_j (with no other explanatory variables) shows no significant relationship.
- It's even possible that the multiple regression slope changes sign when a new variable enters the regression. We saw this for the *Price* on *Bedrooms* real estate example when *Living Area* was added to the regression.

So we'll say it once more: The coefficient of x_j in a multiple regression depends as much on the other predictors as it does on x_j. Failing to interpret coefficients properly is the most common error in working with regression models.

---

[3]There are F tables in the back of the book, and most regression tables include a P-value for the F-statistic.

| FOR EXAMPLE | Testing a multiple regression model for customer response to marketing |

Leiram tries another model, adding the variable *Age* to see if that improves the model:

Response Variable: Respond Amount
$R^2 = 91.50\%$: Adjusted $R^2 = 91.23\%$
$s = 18.179$ with $149 - 5 = 144$ degrees of freedom

Variable	Coeff	SE(Coeff)	t-ratio	P-value
Intercept	114.91	9.244	12.439	<0.0001
Income	0.00091	0.00012	7.619	<0.0001
Total Amount Spent	0.154	0.00855	18.007	>0.0001
Number of purchases	−14,79	0.719	−20.570	<0.0001
Age	−0.1264	0.2144	−0.5898	0.5563

QUESTION   Has the variable *Age* improved the model? Would you leave the term in? Comment.

ANSWER   We'd like to see the residual plots, of course, but given this output it appears that although the R^2 value has increased from 0.9148 to 0.9150, the *t*-ratio for *Age* is only −0.5898 with a P-value of 0.5563. This indicates that there's no evidence to suggest that the slope for *Age* is different from zero. We cannot reject that null hypothesis. There is no reason to leave *Age* in this model.

LO❷   20.5   The *F*-Statistic and ANOVA

In computer output, we often see the *F*-statistic provided in an ANOVA table along with other results that help us understand the regression analysis. ANOVA stands for ANalysis Of VAriance. The key concepts to understand here are the amount of variability that (a) is present in the original data, (b) is explained by the regression, and (c) remains unexplained by the regression. The variability in the original data is measured by the **Sum of Squares, Total (SST)**:

$$\text{SSTotal} = \text{Sum of Squares, Total} = \sum (y - \bar{y})^2$$

The variability that is explained by the regression is measured by the **Sum of Squares, Regression (SSR)**:

$$\text{SSR} = \text{Sum of Squares, Regression} = \sum (\hat{y} - \bar{y})^2$$

The variability that is left unexplained by the regression is measured by the **Sum of Squares, Errors (SSE)** of the residuals left over between the regression, $\hat{y}$, and the data, *y*:

$$\text{SSE} = \text{Sum of Squares, Errors} = \sum (\hat{y} - y)^2$$

Not surprisingly, it can be shown that the total variability is equal to the sum of the explained and unexplained variabilities:

$$\text{SSTotal} = \text{SSR} + \text{SSE}$$

Each of these sums of squares is associated with a number of degrees of freedom, indicated in the ANOVA table:

ANOVA

	Degrees of Freedom (df)	Sum of Squares
Regression (explained variability)	k	SSR
Errors (unexplained variability)	$n - k - 1$	SSE
Total (Sum of Squares, Total)	$n - 1$	SSTotal

When we calculate the variance of some sample data, we divide the total sum of squares by the degrees of freedom $n - 1$, giving the mean sum of squares. We can do the same thing for the other sums of squares in the ANOVA table:

$$\text{Mean square, regression (explained)} = \text{MSR} = \frac{\text{SSR}}{k}$$

$$\text{Mean square, errors (residuals; unexplained)} = \text{MSE} = \frac{\text{SSE}}{(n - k - 1)}. \text{ We}$$
sometimes use a different notation: $s_t^2 = \text{MSE}$.

The F-statistic is then calculated as the ratio of the explained and unexplained mean squares:

$$F = \frac{\text{MSR}}{\text{MSE}} = \frac{\text{(explained)}}{\text{(unexplained)}}$$

When we see a high value for the F-statistic, we know that a lot of the variability in the original data has been explained by the regression. A P-value is also given in the ANOVA table, indicating whether the F-statistic is high enough to imply that the regression is significant overall.

The complete ANOVA table from a regression analysis looks like Table 20.3, with the exact format depending on the software used.

ANOVA

	Degrees of Freedom (df)	Sum of Squares	Mean Square	F-Ratio	P-Value
Regression (explained variability)	k	SSR	$\text{MSR} = \dfrac{\text{SSR}}{k}$	$F = \dfrac{\text{MSR}}{\text{MSE}}$	P
Errors (unexplained variability)	$n - k - 1$	SSE	$\text{MSE} = \dfrac{\text{SSE}}{(n - k - 1)}$		
Total (Sum of Squares, Total)	$n - 1$	SSTotal			

Table 20.3 Typical ANOVA table in multivariate regression analysis. The table indicates the formulas that are used in the software to produce numerical results.

We already know another measure of how much variation in our data is explained by the regression:

$$R^2 = \frac{\text{SSR}}{\text{SSTotal}} = \frac{\text{(explained)}}{\text{(total)}}.$$

In fact, a little algebra shows that:

$$F = \frac{R^2}{(1 - R^2)} \frac{n - k - 1}{k}.$$

In other words, using an F-test to see whether any of the true coefficients is different from zero is equivalent to testing whether the R^2 value is different from zero. A rejection of either hypothesis says that at least one of the predictors accounts for enough variation in y to distinguish it from noise.

LO❷ 20.6 R^2 and Adjusted R^2

Adding new predictor variables will always keep the R^2 value the same or increase it. It can never decrease it. But even if the R^2 value grows, that doesn't mean that the resulting model is a better model or that it has greater predictive ability. If we have a model with k predictors (all of which have statistically significant coefficients at some α level) and want to see if including a new variable, x_{k+1}, is warranted, we could fit the model with all $k + 1$ variables and simply test the slope of the added variable with a t-test of the slope.

The trade-off between a small (parsimonious) model and one that fits the data well is one of the great challenges of any serious model-building effort. Various statistics have been proposed to provide guidance for this search, and one of the most common is called adjusted R^2. **Adjusted R^2** imposes a "penalty" for each new term that's added to the model in an attempt to make models of different sizes (numbers of predictors) comparable. It differs from R^2 because it can shrink when a predictor is added to the regression model or grow when a predictor is removed if the predictor in question doesn't contribute usefully to the model. In fact, it can even be negative.

For a multiple regression with k predictor variables and n cases, it is defined as

$$R^2_{adj} = \left(R^2 - \frac{k}{n - 1} \right)\left(\frac{n - 1}{n - k - 1} \right) = 1 - \frac{\text{SSE}/(n - k - 1)}{\text{SST}/(n - 1)}.$$

In the Guided Example, we saw that the regression of *Price* on *Bedrooms, Bathrooms, Living Area, Fireplaces,* and *Age* resulted in an R^2 of 0.6049. All the coefficients had P-values well below 0.05. The adjusted R^2 value for this model is 0.6030. If we add the variable *Lot Size* to the model, we get the following regression model:

	Coeff	SE(Coeff)	t-Ratio	P-Value
Intercept	15360.011	7334.804	2.094	0.03649
Living Area	73.388	4.043	18.154	<0.00001
Bedrooms	−6096.387	2757.736	−2.211	0.02728
Bathrooms	18824.069	3676.582	5.120	<0.00001
Fireplaces	9226.356	3191.788	2.891	0.00392
Age	−152.615	48.224	−3.165	0.00160
Lot Size	847.764	1989.112	0.426	0.67005

Residual standard error: 48440 on 1041 degrees of freedom
Multiple R-squared: 0.6081, Adjusted R-squared: 0.6059
F-statistic: 269.3 on 6 and 1041 DF, P-value: <0.0001

The most striking feature of this output, as compared with the output in the Guided Example, is that although most of the coefficients have changed very little, the coefficient of *Lot Size* is far from significant, with a P-value of 0.670. Yet the adjusted R^2 value is actually higher than for the previous model. This is why we warn against putting too much faith in this statistic. Especially for large samples, the adjusted R^2 doesn't always adjust downward enough to make sensible model choices. The other problem with comparing these two models is that nine homes had missing values for *Lot Size*, which means that we're not comparing the models on exactly the same data set. When we matched the two models on the smaller data set, the adjusted R^2 value actually did "make the right decision," but just barely—0.6059 vs. 0.6060 for the model without *Lot Size*. One might expect a larger difference, considering we added a variable whose *t*-ratio is much less than one.

The lesson to be learned here is that there is no "correct" set of predictors to use for any real business decision problem, and finding a reasonable model is a process that takes a combination of science, art, business knowledge, and common sense. Look at the adjusted R^2 value for any multiple regression model you fit, but make sure to think about all the other reasons for including or not including any given predictor variable. We'll have much more to say about this important subject in Chapter 21.

FOR EXAMPLE R^2 and adjusted R^2 for customer response to marketing

 QUESTION   In For Example: "The multiple regression model for customer response to marketing," we saw a regression of *Respond Amount* to three explanatory variables. This was extended in For Example: "Testing a multiple regression model for customer response to marketing" to include a fourth explanatory variable, *Age*. Comment on the change in the R^2 and the adjusted R^2 between these two examples.

 ANSWER   When the fourth explanatory variable was introduced, the R^2 increased slightly but the adjusted R^2 decreased slightly. The addition of an extra explanatory variable always results in an increase in the R^2, since the amount of variation explained cannot go down if we introduce a new variable. However, the decrease in the adjusted R^2 is telling us that it may not be worth introducing this extra variable. We usually try to make models with a small number of variables. Adding *Age* increases R^2 but only slightly, at the cost of having an extra variable in our model.

WHAT CAN GO WRONG?

- **Don't claim to "hold everything else constant" for a *single individual*.** It's often meaningless to state that a regression coefficient says what we expect to happen if all variables but one were held constant for an individual and the predictor in question changed. While it's mathematically correct, it often just doesn't make any sense. For example, in a regression of salary on years of experience, years of education, and age, subjects can't gain a year of experience or get another year of education without getting a year older.

- **Don't interpret regression causally.** Regressions are usually applied to observational data. Without deliberately assigned treatments, randomization, and control, we can never be certain that there are no variables lurking in the background, causing everything we've seen. Don't interpret b_1, the coefficient of x_1 in the multiple regression, by saying: "If we were to change x_1 by one unit (holding the other x's constant), it would change y by b_1 units."

- **Be cautious about interpreting a regression model as predictive.** Yes, we do call the x-variables predictors, and you can certainly plug in values for each of the x's and find a corresponding *predicted value*, $\hat{y}$. But the term "prediction" suggests extrapolation into the future or beyond the data, and we know that we can get into trouble when we use models to estimate $\hat{y}$ values for x-variables not in the range of the data. Be careful not to extrapolate very far from the span of your data. In simple regression, it was easy to tell when you extrapolated. With many predictor variables, it's often harder to know when you're outside the bounds of your original data.[4] We usually think of fitting models to the data more as modelling than as prediction, so that's often a more appropriate term.

- **Take care when interpreting the sign of a coefficient.** Sometimes our primary interest in a predictor is whether it has a positive or negative association with y. As we've seen, though, the sign of the coefficient also depends on the other predictors in the model. Don't look at the sign in isolation and conclude that "the direction of the relationship is positive (or negative)." Just like the value of the coefficient, the sign is about the relationship after allowing for the linear effects of the other predictors. The sign of a variable can change depending on which other predictors are in or out of the model. For example, in the regression model for house prices, we saw the coefficient of *Bedrooms* change sign when *Living Area* was added to the model as a predictor. It isn't correct to say either that houses with more bedrooms sell for more on average or that they sell for less. The truth is more subtle and requires that we understand the effect of the other variables in the multiple regression model.

- **If a coefficient's t-statistic isn't significant, don't interpret it at all.** You can't be sure whether the value of the corresponding parameter in the underlying regression model is or isn't really zero.

WHAT ELSE CAN GO WRONG?

- **Don't fit a linear regression to data that aren't straight.** This is the most fundamental regression assumption. If the relationship between the x's and y isn't approximately linear, there's no sense in fitting a linear model to it. What we mean by "linear" is a model of the form we've been writing for the regression. When we have two predictors, this is the equation of a plane, which is linear in the sense of being flat in all directions. With more predictors, the geometry is harder to visualize, but the simple structure of the model is consistent; the predicted values change consistently with equal size changes in any predictor.

---

[4]With several predictors, we can wander beyond the data because of the *combination* of values even when individual values are not extraordinary. For example, houses with one bathroom and houses with five bedrooms can both be found in the real estate records, but a single house with five bedrooms and only one bathroom would be quite unusual. The model we found isn't appropriate for predicting the price of such an extraordinary house.

Usually we're satisfied when plots of y against each of the x's are straight enough. We'll also check a scatterplot of the residuals against the predicted values for signs of nonlinearity.

- **Watch out for the plot thickening.** The estimate of s_e, the error (residual) standard deviation, shows up in all the inference formulas. But that estimate assumes that the error standard deviation is the same throughout the range of the x-variables so that we can combine all the residuals when we estimate it. If s_e changes with any x, these estimates won't make sense. The most common check is a plot of the residuals against the predicted values. If plots of residuals against several of the predictors all show a thickening, and especially if they also show a bend, then consider re-expressing y. If the scatterplot against only one predictor shows thickening, consider re-expressing that predictor.

- **Make sure the errors are nearly Normal.** All our inferences require that the true errors be modelled well by a Normal model. Check the histogram and Normal probability plot of the residuals to see whether this assumption looks reasonable.

- **Watch out for high-influence points and outliers.** We always have to be on the lookout for a few points that have undue influence on our model, and regression is certainly no exception. Chapter 21 discusses this in greater depth.

ETHICS IN ACTION

Alpine Medical Systems Inc. is a large provider of medical equipment and supplies to hospitals, doctors, clinics, and other health-care professionals. Alpine's VP of Marketing and Sales, Kenneth Jadik, asked one of the company's analysts, Nicole Haly, to develop a model that could be used to predict the performance of the company's salesforce. Based on data collected over the past year, as well as records kept by Human Resources, she considered five potential independent variables: (1) gender, (2) starting base salary, (3) years of sales experience, (4) personality test score, and (5) high school grade point average. The dependent variable (sales performance) is measured as the sales dollars generated per quarter. In discussing the results with Nicole, Kenneth asks to see the full regression model with all five independent variables included. Kenneth notes that a t-test for the coefficient of gender shows no significant effect on sales performance and recommends that it be eliminated from the model. Nicole reminds him of the company's history of offering *lower* starting base salaries to women, recently corrected under court order. If starting base salary is instead removed from the model, gender is statistically significant, and its coefficient indicates that women on

the salesforce outperform men (taking into account the other variables). Kenneth argues that because gender isn't significant when all predictors are included, it is the variable that should be omitted.

Ethical Issue *The choice of predictors for the regression model is politically motivated. Because gender and base salary are related, it's impossible to separate their effects on sales performance and inappropriate to conclude that one or the other is irrelevant (related to Item A, ASA Ethical Guidelines; see Appendix C, the American Statistical Association's Ethical Guidelines for Statistical Practice, also available online at www.amstat.org/about/ethicalguidelines.cfm).*

Ethical Solution *The situation is more complex than a single model can explain. Both the model with gender but not base salary and the one with base salary but not gender should be reported. Then the discussion of these models should point out that the two variables are related because of previous company policy and note that the conclusion that those with lower base salary have better sales and the conclusion that women tend to have better sales performance are equivalent as far as these data are concerned.*

WHAT HAVE WE LEARNED?

Learning Objectives

We've learned that there are many points about inference for multiple regression that are the same as for simple regression.

❶ • The assumptions and conditions are the same: linearity (checked now with scatterplots of y against each x), independence (think about it), constant variance (checked with the scatterplot of residuals against predicted values), and nearly Normal residuals (checked with a histogram or probability plot).

❷ • R^2 is still the fraction of the variation in y accounted for by the regression model.

  • s_e is still the standard deviation of the residuals—a good indication of the precision of the model.

  • The degrees of freedom (in the denominator of s_e and for each of the t-tests) follows the same rule: n minus the *number of parameters estimated*.

  • The regression table produced by any statistics package shows a row for each coefficient, giving its estimate, a standard error, a t-statistic, and a P-value.

  • If all the conditions are met, we can test each coefficient against the null hypothesis that its parameter value is zero with a Student's t-test.

And we've learned some new things that are useful, now that we have multiple predictors.

  • We can perform an overall test of whether the multiple regression model provides a better summary for y than its mean by using the F-distribution.

  • We learned that R^2 may not be appropriate for comparing multiple regression models with different numbers of predictors. Adjusted R^2 is one approach to this problem.

We've also learned that multiple regression models extend our ability to model the world to many more situations, but that we must take great care when we interpret their coefficients. To interpret a coefficient of a multiple regression model, remember that it estimates the linear relationship between y and that predictor *after accounting for two things*: (1) the linear effects of all the other predictors on y and (2) the linear relationship between that predictor and all other x's.

Terms

Adjusted R^2

An adjustment to the R^2 statistic that attempts to allow for the number of predictors in the model. It's sometimes used when comparing regression models with different numbers of predictors:

$$R_{adj}^2 = \left(R^2 - \frac{k}{n-1} \right)\left(\frac{n-1}{n-k-1} \right) = 1 - \frac{\text{SSE}/(n-k-1)}{\text{SST}/(n-1)}$$

F-test

The F-test is used to test the null hypothesis that the overall regression is no improvement over just modelling y with its mean:

$$H_0: \beta_1 = \ldots = \beta_k = 0 \text{ vs. } H_A: \text{at least one } \beta \neq 0$$

If this null hypothesis isn't rejected, then you should not proceed to test the individual coefficients.

Least squares

We fit multiple regression models by choosing the coefficients that make the sum of the squared residuals as small as possible. This is called the *method of least squares*.

Multiple regression

A linear regression with two or more predictors whose coefficients are found by least squares. When the distinction is needed, a least squares linear regression with a single predictor is called a *simple regression*. The multiple regression model is

$$y = \beta_0 + \beta_1 x_1 + \ldots + \beta_k x_k + \varepsilon.$$

Sum of Squares, Errors (SSE)

A measure of the variation in the errors—that is, the residuals. $\text{SSE} = \sum (y - \hat{y})^2$.

Sum of Squares, Regression (SSR)	A measure of the total variation in the response variable due to the model.

$$SSR = \sum(\hat{y} - \bar{y})^2.$$

Sum of Squares, Total (SST) — A measure of the variation in the response variable. $SST = \sum(y - \bar{y})^2$. Note that $\dfrac{SST}{n-1} = Var(y)$.

t-ratio for the coefficient — The *t*-ratio for the coefficient can be used to test the null hypothesis that the true value of each coefficient is zero against the alternative that it is not. The *t*-distribution is also used in the construction of confidence intervals for each slope coefficient.

Skills

Plan
- Understand that the "true" regression model is an idealized summary of the data.
- Know how to examine scatterplots of *y* vs. each *x* for violations of assumptions that would make inference for regression unwise or invalid.
- Know how to examine displays of the residuals from a multiple regression to check that the conditions have been satisfied. In particular, know how to judge linearity and constant variance from a scatterplot of residuals against predicted values. Know how to judge Normality from a histogram and Normal probability plot.
- Remember to be especially careful to check for failures of the Independence Assumption when working with data recorded over time. Examine scatterplots of the residuals against time and look for patterns.

Do
- Be able to use a statistics package to perform the calculations and make the displays for multiple regression, including a scatterplot of the response against each predictor, a scatterplot of residuals against predicted values, and a histogram and Normal probability plot of the residuals.
- Know how to use the *F*-test to check that the overall regression model is better than just using the mean of *y*.
- Know how to test the standard hypothesis that each regression coefficient is really zero. Be able to state the null and alternative hypotheses. Know where to find the relevant numbers in standard computer regression output.

Report
- Be able to summarize a regression in words. In particular, be able to state the meaning of the regression coefficients, taking full account of the effects of the other predictors in the model.
- Be able to interpret the *F*-statistic and R^2 for the overall regression.
- Be able to interpret the P-value of the *t*-statistics for the coefficients to test the standard null hypotheses.

MINI case studies

Aeroplan and AIMIA

Aeroplan, the loyalty program of Air Canada, has been in operation since 1984. Travellers on Air Canada flights receive Aeroplan miles, which can be redeemed for free travel, vacations, or merchandise. Aeroplan was originally owned by Air Canada, and was spun off as a separate company in 2002. Its initial public offering in 2005 created the first publicly traded loyalty company worldwide. In 2011 it changed its name to AIMIA, derived from the word "aim," i.e., targeting the right customers. Today, AIMIA manages loyalty programs and provides loyalty analytics for many companies in a broad range of industries.

AIMIA donates Aeroplan miles to international organizations, such as Engineers Without Borders and War Child Canada. Some of the miles donated come from AIMIA itself, matching donations by Aeroplan members.

To encourage members to make donations, loyalty programs track certain information about those people who do make donations. If this information is related to the number of miles donated, then the loyalty program could target advertising to members who are expected to donate a large number of miles. In the case of frequent flyer miles, the following information would probably be available:

D = Number of miles donated during the past five years
I = Average household income of the member's postal code
N = Number of loyalty miles earned during the past five years
S = Percentage of flights taken during the past five years on which a special meal was ordered (limited to those flights on which special meals were available)

Suppose the file **ch20_MCSP_Loyalty** contains data from a random sample of frequent flyers who donated loyalty miles. Obtain a regression in which D is estimated as a function of I, N, and S, using the principles described in this chapter.

Golf Success

Professional sports, like many other professions, require a variety of skills for success. That makes it difficult to evaluate and predict success. Fortunately, sports provides examples we can use to learn about modelling success because of the vast amount of data that are available. Here's an example: What makes a golfer successful? The game of golf requires many skills. Putting well or hitting long drives will not, by itself, lead to success. Success in golf requires a combination of skills. That makes multiple regression a good candidate for modelling golf achievement. A number of internet sites post statistics for the current PGA players. We have data for 204 top players of 2006 in the file **ch20_MCSP_Golfers**.

These players all earned money on the tour, but they didn't all play the same number of events. And the distribution of earnings is quite skewed. (Tiger Woods earned $662,000 per event. In second place, Jim Furyk earned only $300,000 per event. Median earnings per event were $36,600.) So it's a good idea to take logs of *Earnings/Event* as the response variable.

The variables in the data file include:

Log$/E — The logarithm of earnings per event.
GIR — Greens in regulation. Percentage of holes played in which the ball is on the green with two or more strokes left for par.
Putts — Average number of putts per hole in which the green was reached in regulation.
Save% — Each time a golfer hits a bunker by the side of a green but needs only one or two additional shots to reach the hole, he's credited with a save. This is the percentage of opportunities for saves that are realized.
DDist — Average drive distance (yards). Measured as averages over pairs of drives in opposite directions (to account for wind).
DAcc — Drive accuracy. Percentage of drives landing on the fairway.

Investigate these data. Find a regression model to predict golfers' success (measured in log earnings per event). Write a report presenting your model, including an assessment of its limitations.

Note: Although you may consider several intermediate models, a good report is about the model you think best, not necessarily about all the models you tried along the way while searching for it.

Mauro Rodrigues/Fotolia

Nyvlt-art/Shutterstock

Technology Help: Regression Analysis

All statistics packages make a table of results for a regression. The table for multiple regression looks very similar to the table for simple regression. You'll want to look at the analysis of variance (ANOVA) table and information for each of the coefficients.

Most packages offer to plot residuals against predicted values. Some will also plot residuals against the x's. With some packages, you must request plots of the residuals when you request the regression. Others let you find the regression first and then analyze the residuals afterward. Either way, your analysis is not complete if you don't check the residuals with a histogram or Normal probability plot and a scatterplot of the residuals against the x's or the predicted values.

One good way to check assumptions before embarking on a multiple regression analysis is with a scatterplot matrix. This is sometimes abbreviated SPLOM (or Matrix Plot) in commands.

Multiple regressions are always found with a computer or programmable calculator.

EXCEL

- Select **Data Analysis** from the **Analysis Group** on the Data tab.
- Select **Regression** from the **Analysis Tools** list.
- Click the **OK** button.
- Enter the data range holding the y-variable in the box labelled "Y-range."
- Enter the range of cells holding the x-variables in the box labelled "X-range."
- Select **Residuals** options. Click the **OK** button.

Comments

The Y and X ranges don't need to be in the same rows of the spreadsheet, although they must cover the same number of cells. But it's a good idea to arrange your data in parallel columns, as in a data table. The x-variables must be in adjacent columns. No cells in the data range may hold non-numeric values or be left blank.

Although the dialogue offers a Normal probability plot of the residuals, the data analysis add-in doesn't make a correct probability plot, so don't use this option.

XLSTAT

- In the **Modeling Data** menu, choose **Linear Regression**.
- Enter y-variable and x-variable cell ranges.
- Specify desired statistics in the Outputs and Charts tabs, respectively.

Comments

For both Excel and XLStat, the Y and X cell ranges do not need to be in the same rows of the spreadsheet, although they must cover the same

number of cells. It is a good idea to arrange your data in parallel columns, as in a data table. The x-variables must be in adjacent columns. No cells in the data range may hold non-numeric values or be left blank.

MINITAB

- Choose **Regression** from the **Stat** menu.
- Choose **Regression** from the Regression submenu.
- In the **Regression** dialogue, assign the y-variable to the Response box and assign the x-variables to the Predictors box.
- Click the **Graphs** button.
- In the Regression-Graphs dialogue, select **Standardized** residuals, and check **Normal plot of residuals** and **Residuals versus fits**.
- Click the **OK** button to return to the Regression dialogue.
- Click the **OK** button to compute the regression.

SPSS

- Choose **Regression** from the **Analyze** menu.
- Choose **Linear** from the **Regression** submenu.
- When the Linear Regression dialogue appears, select the y-variable and move it to the dependent target. Then move the x-variables to the independent target.
- Click the **Plots** button.
- In the Linear Regression Plots dialogue, choose to plot the *SRESIDs against the *ZPRED values.
- Click the **Continue** button to return to the Linear Regression dialogue.
- Click the **OK** button to compute the regression.

JMP

- From the **Analyze** menu, select **Fit Model**.
- Specify the response, Y. Assign the predictors, X, in the **Construct Model Effects** dialogue box.
- Click on **Run Model**.

Comments

JMP chooses a regression analysis when the response variable is "Continuous." The predictors can be any combination of quantitative or categorical. If you get a different analysis, check the variable types.

EXERCISES

SECTION 20.1

1. A house in the area from which the chapter data was drawn has two bedrooms and 1000 square feet of living area. Using the multiple regression model found in the chapter,

$$\widehat{Price} = 20{,}986.09 - 7483.10 Bedrooms + 93.84 Living\ Area.$$

a) Find the price that this model estimates.
b) The house just sold for $135,000. Find the residual corresponding to this house.
c) What does that residual say about this transaction? **LO ❶**

2. A candy maker surveyed chocolate bars available in a local supermarket and found the following least squares regression model:

$$\widehat{Calories} = 28.4 + 11.37 Fat(g) + 2.91 Sugar(g)$$

a) The hand-crafted chocolate she makes has 15 grams of fat and 20 grams of sugar. How many calories does the model predict for a serving?
b) In fact, a laboratory test shows that her candy has 227 calories per serving. Find the residual corresponding to this candy. (Be sure to include the units.)
c) What does that residual say about her candy? **LO ❶**

SECTION 20.2

❶ 3. What can predict how much a motion picture will make? We have data on a number of recent releases that includes the *USGross* (in $), the *Budget* ($), the *Run Time* (minutes), and the average number of *Stars* awarded by reviewers. The first several entries in the data table look like this:

Movie	US Gross ($M)	Budget ($M)	Run Time (minutes)	Stars
White Noise	56.094360	30	101	2
Coach Carter	67.264877	45	136	3
Elektra	24.409722	65	100	2
Racing Stripes	49.772522	30	110	3
Assault on Precinct 13	20.040895	30	109	3
Are We There Yet?	82.674398	20	94	2
Alone in the Dark	5.178569	20	96	1.5
Indigo	51.100486	25	105	3.5

We want a regression model to predict *USGross*. Parts of the regression output computed in Excel look like this:

Dependent variable is: USGross ($)
R-squared = 47.4% R-squared (adjusted) = 46.0%
s = 46.41 with 120 − 4 = 116 degrees of freedom

Variable	Coefficient	SE(Coeff)	t-ratio	P-value
Intercept	−22.9898	25.70	−0.895	0.3729
Budget ($)	1.13442	0.1297	8.75	≤0.0001
Stars	24.9724	5.884	4.24	≤0.0001
Run Time	−0.403296	0.2513	−1.60	0.1113

a) Write the multiple regression equation.
b) What is the interpretation of the coefficient of *Budget* in this regression model? **LO ❶**

4. A middle manager at an entertainment company, upon seeing this analysis, concludes that the longer you make a movie, the less money it will make. He argues that his company's films should all be cut by 30 minutes to improve their gross. Explain the flaw in his interpretation of this model. **LO ❶**

SECTION 20.3

❶ 5. For the movies examined in Exercise 3, here is a scatterplot of *USGross* vs. *Budget*:

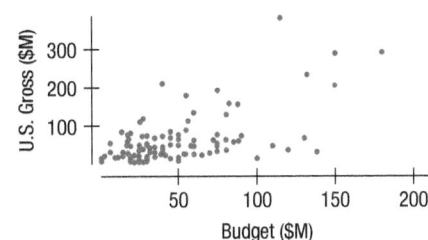

What (if anything) does this scatterplot tell us about the following assumptions and conditions for the regression?

a) Linearity Condition
b) Equal Spread Condition
c) Normality Assumption **LO ❶**

6. For the movies regression, here is a histogram of the residuals. What does it tell us about these assumptions and conditions?

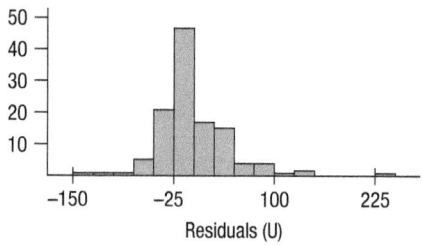

a) Linearity Condition
b) Nearly Normal Condition
c) Equal Spread Condition **LO ❶**

SECTION 20.4

7. Regression output for the movies again.

a) What is the null hypothesis tested for the coefficient of *Stars* in this table?
b) What is the *t*-statistic corresponding to this test?
c) What is the P-value corresponding to this *t*-statistic?
d) Complete the hypothesis test. Do you reject the null hypothesis? **LO ❷**

8. More regression output for movies.

a) What is the null hypothesis tested for the coefficient of *Run Time* in the regression of Exercise 3?
b) What is the *t*-statistic corresponding to this test?
c) What is the P-value corresponding to this *t*-statistic?
d) Complete the hypothesis test. Do you reject the null hypothesis? **LO ❷**

SECTIONS 20.5 AND 20.6

9. In the regression model of Exercise 3,

a) What is the R^2 for this regression? What does it mean?
b) Why is the "Adjusted R-Square" in the table different from the "R-Square"? **LO ❷**

10. Here is another part of the regression output for the movies in Exercise 3:

Source	Sum of Squares	df	Mean Square	F-ratio
Regression	224995	3	74998.4	34.8
Residual	249799	116	2153.44	

a) Using the values from the table above, show how the value of R^2 is computed.
b) What is the *F*-statistic value for this regression?

c) What null hypothesis can you test with it?
d) Would you reject that null hypothesis? **LO ❷**

CHAPTER EXERCISES

The first 12 chapter exercises (11–22) consist of two sets of six (one even-numbered, one odd-numbered). Each set guides you through a multiple regression analysis. We suggest that you do all six exercises in a set. Remember that the answers to the odd-numbered exercises can be found in Appendix A.

11. Police salaries, part 1. Is the amount of violent crime related to what police officers are paid? The U.S. Bureau of Labor Statistics publishes data on occupational employment and wage estimates (www.bls.gov/oes/) for each of the 50 states. Here are data released from 2011 to 2013. The variables are:

Violent Crime (crimes per 100,000 population)
Police Officer Wage (mean $/hr)
Graduation Rate (%)

One natural question to ask of these data is how police officer wages are related to violent crime across these states.
First, here are plots and background information:

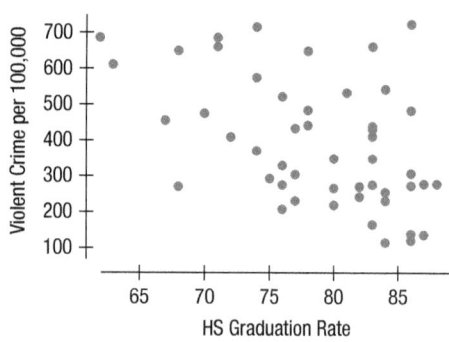

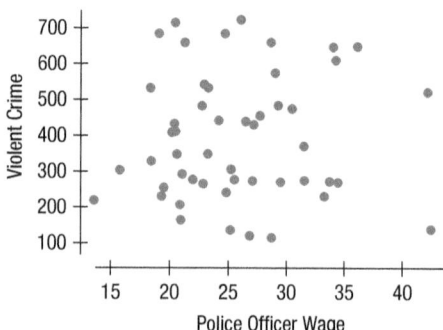

	Correlations		
	Violent Crime	Graduation Rate	Police Officer Wage
Violent Crime	1.000		
Graduation Rate	−0.473	1.000	
Police Officer Wage	0.051	−0.473	1.000

a) Name and check (to the extent possible) the regression assumptions and their corresponding conditions.

b) If we found a regression to predict *Violent Crime* just from *Police Officer Wage*, what would the R^2 of that regression be? **LO ❶**

ⓣ 12. Ticket prices, part 1. On a typical night in New York, about 25,000 people attend a Broadway show, paying an average price of more than $75 per ticket. *Variety* (www.variety.com), a news weekly that reports on the entertainment industry, publishes statistics about the Broadway show business. The data file holds data about shows on Broadway for most weeks of 2006–2008. (A few weeks are missing data.) The following variables are available for each week:

Receipts ($ million)
Paid Attendance (thousands)
No. of Shows
Average Ticket Price ($)

Viewing this as a business, we'd like to model *Receipts* in terms of the other variables.

First, here are plots and background information:

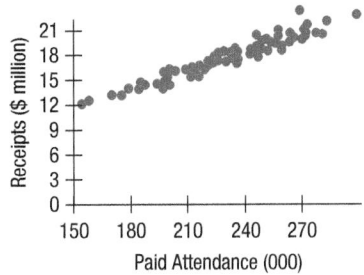

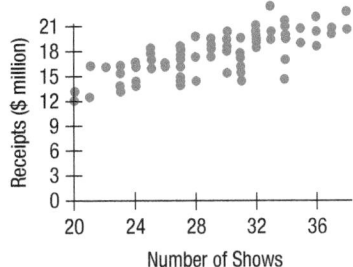

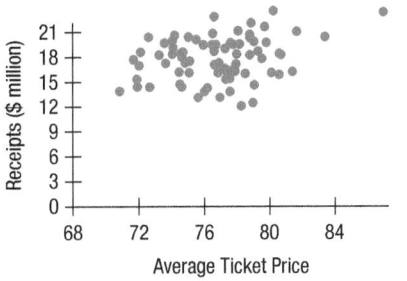

	Correlations			
	Receipts	Paid Attendance	No. of Shows	Average Ticket Price
Receipts ($M)	1.000			
Paid Attendance	0.961	1.000		
No. of Shows	0.745	0.640	1.000	
Average Ticket Price	0.253	0.331	−0.160	1.000

a) Name and check (to the extent possible) the regression assumptions and their corresponding conditions.

b) If we found a regression to predict *Receipts* only from *Paid Attendance*, what would the R^2 of that regression be? **LO❶**

ⓣ 13. Police salaries, part 2. Here's a multiple regression model for the variables considered in Exercise 11:

Dependent variable is: Violent Crime
R-squared = 22.41% R-squared (adjusted) = 19.10%
s = 156.9 with 47 degrees of freedom

Source	Sum of Squares	df	Mean Square	F-ratio
Regression	334246	2	167123	6.786
Residual	1157508	47	24628	

Variable	Coeff	SE(Coeff)	t-ratio	P-value
Intercept	1370.22	292.180	4.690	<0.0001
Police Officer Wage	0.7947	3.598	0.221	0.8262
Graduation Rate	−12.641	3.451	−3.663	0.00063

a) Write the regression model.

b) What does the coefficient of *Police Officer Wage* mean in the context of this regression model?

c) In a state in which the average police officer wage is $20/hour and the high school graduation rate is 70%, what does this model estimate the violent crime rate would be? **LO ❶**

14. Ticket prices, part 2. Here's a multiple regression model for the variables considered in Exercise 12:[5]

---

[5]Some values are rounded to simplify the exercises. If you recompute the analysis with your statistics software, you may see slightly different numbers.

Dependent variable is: Receipts($M)
R-squared = 99.9% R-squared (adjusted) = 99.9%
s = 0.0931 with 74 degrees of freedom

Source	Sum of Squares	df	Mean Square	F-ratio
Regression	484.789	3	161.596	18634
Residual	0.641736	74	0.008672	

Variable	Coeff	SE(Coeff)	t-ratio	P-value
Intercept	−18.320	0.3127	−58.6	<0.0001
Paid Attendance	0.076	0.0006	126.7	<0.0001
No. of Shows	0.0070	0.0044	1.59	0.116
Average Ticket Price	0.24	0.0039	61.5	<0.0001

a) Write the regression model.
b) What does the coefficient of *Paid Attendance* mean in this regression? Does that make sense?
c) In a week in which the paid attendance was 200,000 customers attending 30 shows at an average ticket price of $70, what would you estimate the receipts would be? **LO ❶**

T 15. Police salaries, part 3. Using the regression table in Exercise 13, answer the following questions:

a) How was the t-ratio of 0.221 found for *Police Officer Wage*? (Show what is computed using numbers from the table.)
b) How many states are used in this model? How do you know?
c) The t-ratio for *Graduation Rate* is negative. What does that mean? **LO ❷**

16. Ticket prices, part 3. Using the regression table in Exercise 14, answer the following questions:

a) How was the t-ratio of 126.7 found for *Paid Attendance*? (Show what is computed using numbers found in the table.)
b) How many weeks are included in this regression? How can you tell?
c) The t-ratio for the intercept is negative. What does that mean? **LO ❷**

T 17. Police salaries, part 4. Consider the coefficient of *Police Officer Wage* in the regression table of Exercise 13.

a) State the standard null and alternative hypotheses for the true coefficient of *Police Officer Wage*.

b) Test the null hypothesis (at α = 0.05) and state your conclusion. **LO ❷**

18. Ticket prices, part 4. Consider the coefficient of *No. of Shows*.

a) State the standard null and alternative hypotheses for the true coefficient of *No. of Shows*.
b) Test the null hypothesis (at α = 0.05) and state your conclusion.
c) A Broadway investor challenges your analysis. He points out that the scatterplot of *Receipts* vs. *No. of Shows* in Exercise 12 shows a strong linear relationship and claims that your result in (b) can't be correct. Explain to him why this is not a contradiction. **LO ❷**

T 19. Police salaries, part 5. A Senate aide accepts your analysis in Exercise 17 but claims that it demonstrates that if the state pays police more, it will actually *increase* the rate of violent crime. Explain why this interpretation is not a valid use of this regression model. Offer some alternative explanations. **LO ❶**

20. Ticket prices, part 5. The investor in Exercise 18 now accepts your analysis but claims that it demonstrates that it doesn't matter how many shows are playing on Broadway; receipts will be essentially the same. Explain why this interpretation is not a valid use of this regression model. Be specific. **LO ❶**

T 21. Police salaries, part 6. Here are some plots of residuals for the regression of Exercise 13:

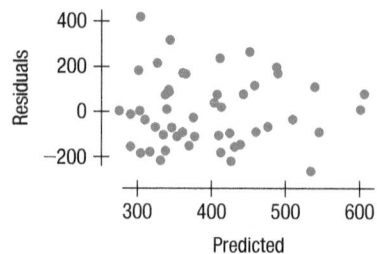

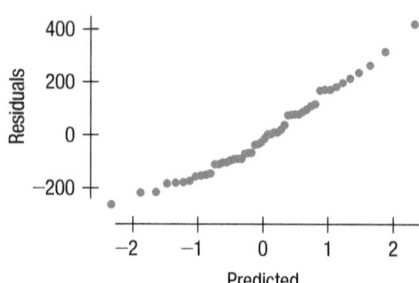

Which of the regression conditions can you check with these plots? Do you find that those conditions are met? **LO ❶**

22. Ticket prices, part 6. Here are some plots of residuals for the regression of Exercise 14:

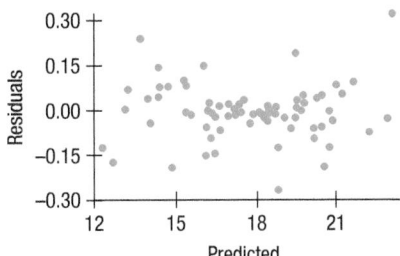

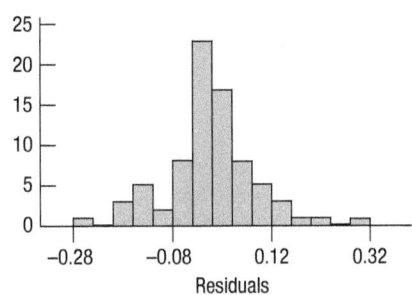

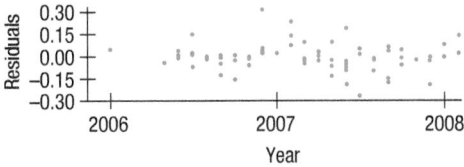

Which of the regression conditions can you check with these plots? Do you find that those conditions are met? LO ❶

23. Real estate prices. A regression was performed to predict the selling price of houses based on *Price* in dollars, *Area* in square feet, *Lotsize* in square feet, and *Age* in years. The R^2 is 92%. The equation from this regression is given here:

$$Price = 169,328 + 35.3 \ Area + 0.718Lotsize - 6543Age$$

One of the following interpretations is correct. Which is it? Explain what's wrong with the others.

a) Each year a house ages, it's worth $6543 less.
b) Every extra square foot of area is associated with an additional $35.30 in average price for houses with a given lot size and age.
c) Every additional dollar in price means lot size increases 0.718 square feet.
d) This model fits 92% of the data points exactly. LO ❶

24. Wine prices, part 1. Many factors affect the price of wine, including such qualitative characteristics as the variety of grape, location of winery, and label. Researchers developed a regression model by considering two quantitative variables: the tasting score of the wine and the age of the wine (in years) when released to market. They found the following regression equation, with an R^2 of 65%, to predict the price (in dollars) of a bottle of wine:

$$Price = 6.25 + 1.22 \ Tasting \ Score + 0.55Age$$

One of the following interpretations is correct. Which is it? Explain what's wrong with the others.

a) Each year a bottle of wine ages, its price increases about $0.55.
b) This model fits 65% of the points exactly.
c) For a unit increase in tasting score, the price of a bottle of wine increases about $1.22.
d) After allowing for the age of a bottle of wine, a wine with a one unit higher tasting score can be expected to cost about $1.22 more. LO ❶

25. Appliance sales. A household appliance manufacturer wants to analyze the relationship between total sales and the company's three primary means of advertising (television, magazines, and radio). All values were in millions of dollars. The company found the following regression equation:

$$Sales = 250 + 6.75TV + 3.5Radio + 2.3Magazine$$

One of the following interpretations is correct. Which is it? Explain what's wrong with the others.

a) If the company did no advertising, its income would be $250 million.
b) Every million dollars spent on radio makes sales increase $3.5 million, all other things being equal.
c) Every million dollars spent on magazines increases TV spending $2.3 million.
d) Sales increase on average about $6.75 million for each million spent on TV, after allowing for the effects of the other kinds of advertising. LO ❶

26. Wine prices, part 2. Here are some more interpretations of the regression model to predict the price of wine developed in Exercise 24. One of these interpretations is correct. Which is it? Explain what is wrong with the others.

a) The minimum price for a bottle of wine that has not aged is $6.25.
b) The price for a bottle of wine increases on average about $0.55 for each year it ages, after allowing for the effects of tasting score.
c) Each year a bottle of wine ages, its tasting score increases by 1.22.
d) Each dollar increase in the price of wine increases its tasting score by 1.22. LO ❶

27. Canadian executives' stock options. A study of the impact of the salary and stock options paid to executives of 77 Canadian companies on the company rating for corporate social responsibility (CSR) came up with the following regression equation:

$$CSR \ Rating = -0.163 \times Salary + 0.320 \times Options + Several \ Other \ Factors$$

All variables are standardized to have a mean of zero and a standard deviation of one. The *t*-statistic and P-value for the *Salary* coefficient are −1.196 and 0.235. The *t*-statistic and P-value for the *Options* coefficient are 2.921 and 0.0046. The *F*-ratio is 4.811, which is significant at the 99% level. (*Source:* Mahoney, L. S., & Thorn, L. [2006]. An examination of the structure of executive compensation and corporate social responsibility: A Canadian investigation. *Journal of Business Ethics, 69,* 149–162, Table VI.)

a) From the information given above, is this regression a good model of how *Salary* and *Options* impact *CSR Rating*?
b) What other factors would be relevant to check in order to determine whether this is a good model?
c) Interpret the *t*-statistics for the two coefficients given.
d) Interpret the meaning of the negative coefficient for *Salary*.
e) The board of directors of one company is thinking of increasing executive options by 0.25 standard deviations. What effect can they expect on their CSR rating? **LO ❷**

28. **OECD economic regulations.** A study by the U.S. Small Business Administration modelled the GDP per capita of 24 of the countries in the Organisation for Economic Co-operation and Development (OECD) (*Source:* Data from Crain, M. W. *The Impact of Regulatory Costs on Small Firms*). One analysis estimated the effect on GDP of economic regulations using an index of the degree of OECD economic regulation and other variables. The study found the following regression model:

$$\widehat{GDP/Capita(1998-2002)} = 10487 - 1343\ OECD$$
Economic Regulation Index + 1.078 *GDP/Capita(1988)* − 69.99 *Ethnolinguistic Diversity Index* + 44.71 *Trade as share of GDP* (1998–2002) − 58.4 *Primary Education*
(*%Eligible Population*)

All *t*-statistics on the individual coefficients have P-values <0.05, except the coefficient of *Primary Education*.

a) Does the coefficient of the OECD *Economic Regulation Index* indicate that more regulation leads to lower GDP? Explain.
b) The *F*-statistic for this model is 129.61 (5, 17 df). What do you conclude about the model?
c) If *GDP/Capita(1988)* is removed as a predictor, then the *F*-statistic drops to 0.694 and none of the *t*-statistics is significant (all P-values > 0.22). Reconsider your interpretation in part (a). **LO ❷**

29. **Home prices, part 1.** Many variables have an impact on determining the price of a house. A few of these are size of the house (square feet), lot size, and number of bathrooms. Information for a random sample of homes for sale in a single housing market was obtained from the internet. Regression output modelling the asking price with square-footage and number of bathrooms gave the following result:

Dependent Variable is: Asking Price
s = 67013 R-Sq = 71.1% R-Sq(adj) = 64.6%

Predictor	Coeff	SE(Coeff)	*t*-ratio	P-value
Intercept	−152037	85619	−1.78	0.110
Baths	9530	40826	0.23	0.821
Area	139.87	46.67	3.00	0.015

Analysis of Variance

Source	DF	SS	MS	F	P-value
Regression	2	99303550067	49651775033	11.06	0.004
Residual	9	40416679100	4490742122		
Total	11	1.39720E + 11			

a) Write the regression equation.
b) How much of the variation in home asking prices is accounted for by the model?
c) Explain in context what the coefficient of *Area* means.
d) A home-renovation contractor, upon seeing this model, objects because the model says that the number of bathrooms has no effect on the price of the home. Is it true that the number of bathrooms is unrelated to house price? **LO ❶**

30. **Home prices, part 2.** Here are some diagnostic plots for the home prices data from Exercise 29. These were generated by a computer package and may look different from the plots generated by the packages you use. (In particular note that the axes of the Normal probability plot are swapped relative to the plots we've made in the text. We only care about the pattern of this plot, so it shouldn't affect your interpretation.) Examine these plots and discuss ethical issues that would arise if this regression was used in practice. (See Appendix C for Ethical Guidelines.) **LO ❶**

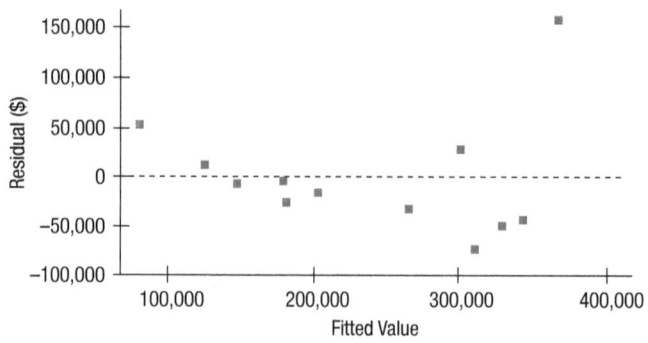

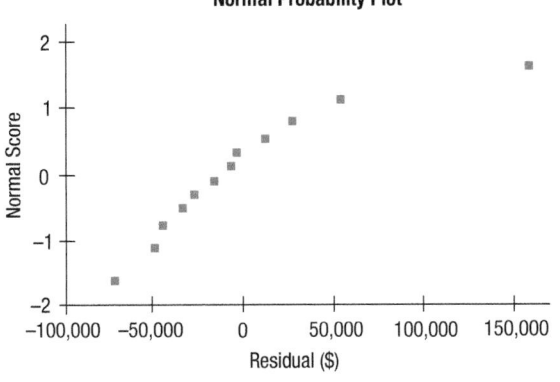

Normal Probability Plot

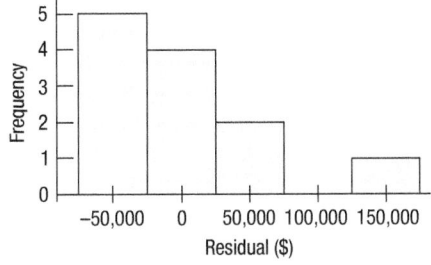

c) Test whether the coefficient for wpm of typing speed (X4) is significantly different from zero at $\alpha = 0.05$.
d) How might this model be improved?
e) A correlation of age with salary finds $r = -0.682$, and the scatterplot shows a moderately strong positive linear association. However, if X6 = Age is added to the multiple regression, the estimated coefficient of age turns out to be $b_6 = -0.154$. Explain some possible causes for this apparent change of direction in the relationship between age and salary. **LO ❷**

32. Canadian food industry. EthicScan Canada monitors the social, labour, and environmental performance of 1500 companies in Canada, and makes comparisons between companies in the same industry sector. In the food industry, six companies are compared by giving a score for nine factors, including environmental performance (EP), management practices and consumer relations (M&C), and progressive staff policy (PSP). (*Source: EthicScan Canada. Investor Report, George Weston Limited.*) A regression analysis to estimate EP from M&C and PSP produced the following results:

Dependent Variable: EP

R-squared	0.033115
Adjusted R-squared	−0.61148
Standard error	18.23166
Observations	6

ANOVA

	df	SS	MS	F	Significance F
Regression	2	34.15256	17.07628	0.051374	0.950741081
Residual	3	997.1808	332.3936		
Total	5	1031.33			

	Coefficients	Standard Error	t-Stat	P-value
Intercept	22.89615385	27.5338532	0.831564	0.466657
M&C	0.47	1.740251398	0.270076	0.804615
PSP	−0.3992307	1.290274746	−0.30942	0.777251

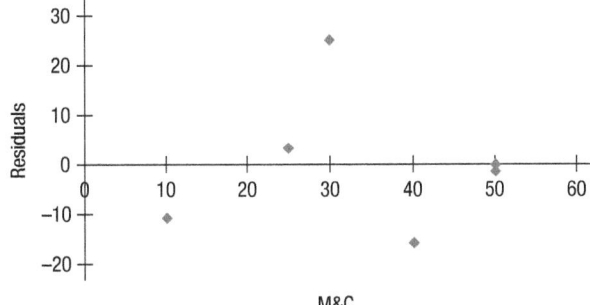

31. Secretary performance. The AFL-CIO has undertaken a study of 30 secretaries' yearly salaries (in thousands of dollars). The organization wants to predict salaries from several other variables. The variables to be considered as potential predictors of salary are:

X1 = Months of service
X2 = Years of education
X3 = Score on standardized test
X4 = Words per minute (wpm) typing speed
X5 = Ability to take dictation in words per minute

A multiple regression model with all five variables was run on a computer package, resulting in the following output:

Variable	Coeff	Std. Error	t-value
Intercept	9.788	0.377	25.960
X1	0.110	0.019	5.178
X2	0.053	0.038	1.369
X3	0.071	0.064	1.119
X4	0.004	0.0307	0.013
X5	0.065	0.038	1.734

$s = 0.430$ R-sq $= 0.863$

Assume that the residual plots show no violations of the conditions for using a linear regression model.
a) What is the regression equation?
b) From this model, what is the predicted salary (in thousands of dollars) of a secretary with 10 years (120 months) of experience, Grade 9 education (9 years of education), a score of 50 on the standardized test, 60 words per minute (wpm) typing speed, and the ability to take 30 wpm dictation?

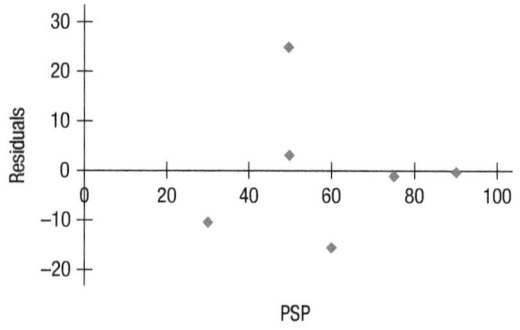

a) Comment on the fact that the adjusted R^2 is much lower than 1.0.
b) Comment on the fact that the adjusted R^2 is negative.
c) Is the regression significant at the 95% level overall?
d) Interpret the regression coefficient for PSP, if appropriate.
e) If appropriate, write the regression equation.
f) Comment on the residual plots.
g) How might this regression be improved?
h) An environmental organization claims that progressive staff policies are very important in achieving high environmental performance, since staff are more motivated to contribute to the environmental goals of the company. What ethical issues would be involved in using this regression to confirm this statement? (See Appendix C for Ethical Guidelines.) **LO ❷**

ⓣ **33.** **Gross domestic product.** The gross domestic product (GDP) is an important measure of the overall economic strength of a country. GDP per capita makes comparisons between different size countries more meaningful. A researcher looking at GDP fit the following model based on an educational variable, *Primary School Completion Rate (%)*, and finds:

Dependent variable is: GDP per Capita
R-squared = 3.44%
s = 15945.46 with 96 − 1 = 95 df

Term	Estimate	Std Error	t-Ratio	P-value
Intercept	1935.5693	5987.938	0.320	0.7472
Primary Completion Rate	122.3288	66.8131	1.830	0.0703

a) Explain to the researcher why, on the basis of the regression summary, she might want to consider other predictor variables in the model.
b) Explain why you are not surprised that the sign of the slope is positive.

The researcher adds two variables to the regression and finds:

Dependent variable is: GDP per Capita
R-squared = 80.00%
s = 7327.65 with 96 − 4 = 92 df

Term	Estimate	SE(Coeff)	t-Ratio	P-value
Intercept	2775.98251	2803.32606	0.99	0.3247
Cell phones/100 people	92.84968	37.38697	2.48	0.0148
Internet users per 100 people (2004)	480.49061	54.04020	8.89	<0.0001
Primary completion rate	−63.28454	32.25614	−1.96	0.0528

c) Explain how the slope of *Primary completion rate* can now be negative. **LO ❷**

ⓣ **34.** **HDI.** In 1990, the United Nations created a single statistic, the Human Development Index, or HDI, to summarize the health, education, and economic status of countries. Using data from 96 countries, here is a multiple regression model trying to predict HDI.

Dependent variable is: HDI
R-squared = 98.23%
s = 0.024 with 96 − 8 = 88 df

Term	Estimate	Std Error	t-Ratio	P-value
Intercept	0.09010	0.04208	2.14	0.0351
Expected years of schooling (yrs)	0.01376	0.00176	7.79	<0.0001
Life expectancy at birth (years)	0.00333	0.00063	5.32	<0.0001
Maternal mortality ratio (deaths per 100,000 live births)	−0.000120	0.0000254	−4.74	<0.0001
Mean years of schooling of adults (years)	0.01686	0.00166	10.19	<0.0001
Population urban (%)	0.000745	0.000181	4.13	<0.0001
GDP per capita	0.000000802	0.000000263	3.05	0.003
Cell phones/100 people	0.000460	0.000141	3.26	0.0016

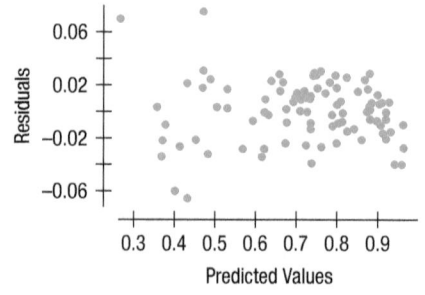

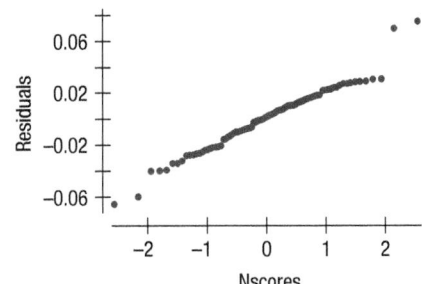

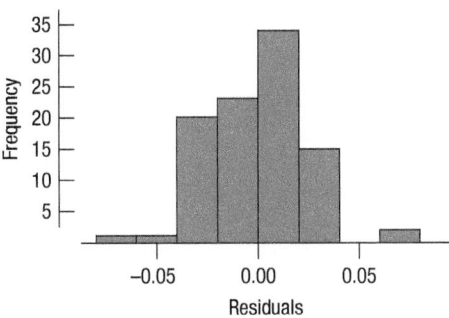

a) Write the regression model.
b) Are the assumptions and conditions met?
c) State and test the standard null hypothesis for the coefficient of *Expected Years of Schooling*. Use the standard level of $\alpha = 0.05$ and state your conclusion.
d) What effects do your observation in response to (b) have on your test in (c)? **LO ❶**

Ⓣ 35. Walmart revenue, part 1. Walmart is the second-largest retailer in the world. The data file holds monthly data on Walmart's revenue, along with several possibly related economic variables.

a) Using computer software, find the regression equation predicting Walmart revenues from the *Retail Index*, the Consumer Price Index (*CPI*), and *Personal Consumption*.
b) Does it seem that Walmart's revenue is closely related to the general state of the economy? **LO ❶**

Ⓣ 36. Walmart revenue, part 2. Consider the model you fit in Exercise 35 to predict Walmart's revenue from the *Retail Index*, *CPI*, and *Personal Consumption*.

a) Plot the residuals against the predicted values and comment on what you see.
b) Identify and remove the four cases corresponding to December revenue and find the regression with December results removed.
c) Does it seem that Walmart's revenue is closely related to the general state of the economy?

37. Clinical trials. An important challenge in clinical trials is patients who drop out before the trial is completed. This can cost pharmaceutical companies millions of dollars because patients who have received a tested treatment for months must be combined with those who received it for a much shorter time. Can we predict who will drop out of a study

early? We have data for 428 patients from a clinical trial of depression. We have data on their *Age* and their *Hamilton Rating Depression Scale* (*HRDS*) and whether or not they completed the study (*Drop 1 = Yes; 0 = No. Completed the study*).

Here is the output from a logistic regression model (see online section 20.7) of *Drop* on *HRDS* and *Age*:

Term	Estimate	Std Error	z	P-Value
Intercept	0.441972938	0.488270354	0.9055	0.3654
Age	0.037904831	0.011511729	3.292	0.001
HRDS	−0.046817607	0.015903137	2.944	0.0032

a) Write out the estimated regression equation.
b) What is the predicted log odds (logit) of the probability that a 30-year-old patient with an HDRS score of 30 will drop out of the study?
c) What is the predicted dropout probability of that patient?
d) What is the predicted log odds (logit) of the probability that a 60-year-old patient with an HDRS score of 8 will drop out of the study?
e) What is the associated predicted probability? **LO ❸**

38. Cost of higher education. Are there fundamental differences between liberal arts colleges and universities? In this case, we have information on the top 25 liberal arts colleges and the top 25 universities in the United States. We'll consider the type of school as our response variable and will use the percentage of students who were in the top 10% of their high school class and the amount of money spent per student by the college or university as our explanatory variables. The output from this logistic regression is given here:

Logistic Regression Table

Predictor	Coeff	SE(Coeff)	z	P
Intercept	−13.1461	3.98629	−3.30	0.001
Top 10%	0.0845469	0.0396345	2.13	0.033
$/Student	0.0002594	0.0000860	3.02	0.003

a) Write out the estimated regression equation.
b) Is the percentage of students in the top 10% of their high school class statistically significant in predicting whether or not the school is a university? Explain.
c) Is the amount of money spent per student statistically significant in predicting whether the school is a university? Explain. **LO ❸**

Ⓣ 39. Motorcycles, part 1. More than a million motorcycles are sold annually (www.webbikeworld.com). Off-road motorcycles (often called "dirt bikes") are a market segment (about 18%) that is highly specialized and offers great variation in features. This makes it a good segment to study to learn about which features account for the manufacturer's suggested retail price (MSRP) of a dirt bike. Researchers collected data on 2005 model dirt bikes (http://lib.stat.cmu.edu/datasets/dirtbike_aug.csv). Their original goal was to study market differentiation among brands (*Source:* See Lu, J., Kadane, J. B., & Boatwright, P. *The Dirt on Bikes: An Illustration of CART Models for Brand Differentiation.* Retrieved from server1.tepper.cmu.edu/gsiadoc/WP/2006-E57.pdf), but we can use these to predict MSRP from other variables.

Here are scatterplots of three potential predictors, *Wheelbase* (in.), *Displacement* (cu. in.), and *Bore* (in.):

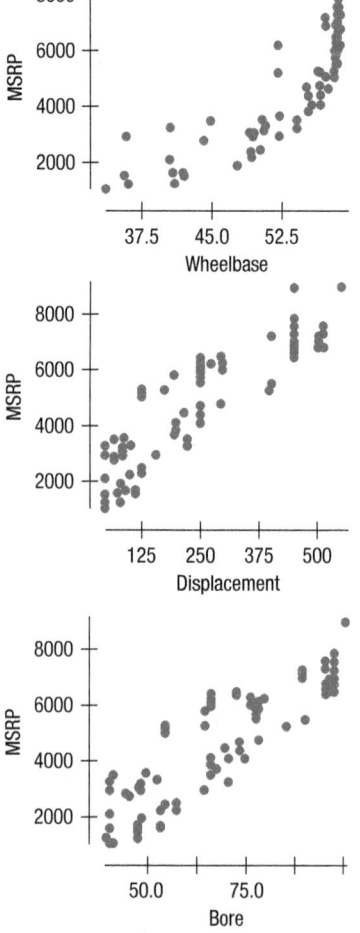

Which of these variables would you choose first as a predictor in a regression to model MSRP? Explain. **LO ❶**

40. **Motorcycles, part 2.** In Exercise 39 we saw data on off-road motorcycles and examined scatterplots. Review those scatterplots. Here's a regression of *MSRP* on both *Displacement* and *Bore*. Both of the predictors are measures of the size of the engine. The displacement is the total volume of air and fuel mixture that an engine can draw in during one cycle. The bore is the diameter of the cylinders.

Dependent variable is: MSRP
R-squared = 77.0% R-squared (adjusted) = 76.5%
s = 979.8 with 98 − 3 = 95 degrees of freedom

Variable	Coeff	SE(Coeff)	t-ratio	P-value
Intercept	318.352	1002	0.318	0.7515
Bore	41.1650	25.37	1.62	0.1080
Displacement	6.57069	3.232	2.03	0.0449

a) State and test the standard null hypothesis for the coefficient of *Bore*.
b) Both of these predictors seem to be linearly related to *MSRP*. Explain what your result in (a) means. **LO ❷**

41. **Motorcycles, part 3.** Here's another model for the *MSRP* of off-road motorcycles:

Dependent variable is: MSRP
R-squared = 90.9% R-squared (adjusted) = 90.6%
s = 617.8 with 95 − 4 = 91 degrees of freedom

Source	Sum of Squares	df	Mean Square	F-ratio
Regression	346795061	3	115598354	303
Residual	34733372	91	381685	

Variable	Coeff	SE(Coeff)	t-ratio	P-value
Intercept	−2682.38	371.9	−7.21	<0.0001
Bore	86.5217	5.450	15.9	<0.0001
Clearance	237.731	30.94	7.68	<0.0001
Engine strokes	−455.897	89.88	−5.07	<0.0001

a) Is this a good model of the price of off-road motorcycles? Explain.
b) The Suzuki DR650SE had an *MSRP* of $4999 and a four-stroke engine, with a bore of 100 inches. Can you use this model to estimate its *Clearance*? Explain. **LO ❶**

42. **Canadian earnings levels, part 1.** You've probably heard that earnings are generally higher in urban areas than in rural areas. But why is this so? Perhaps it's because urban areas attract a cluster of employers, producing many employment opportunities. To test this possibility, Statistics Canada used census data to run a multivariate regression of weekly earnings (*w*) in a given location against employment in the same location (EL) and employment in the same location and the same industry (ELI). Preliminary data analysis had shown that these variables are nonlinearly related, so natural logarithms (ln) were taken before running the regression. The result was

$$\ln(w) = 5.85 + 0.035 \times \ln(\text{EL}) + 0.009 \times \ln(\text{ELI}).$$

The P-values associated with the intercept and the two coefficients in the above equation are <0.001, <0.001, and

0.117. The *F*-ratio has a P-value 0.001. (*Source:* Data from Statistics Canada. Beckstead, D., Brown, W. M., Guo, Y., & Newbold, K. B. [2010, January]. Cities and growth: Earnings levels across urban and rural areas: The role of human capital. Catalogue No. 11-622-M, No. 020. Table 4.)

a) Is the regression model significant overall?
b) Which variable(s) is (are) significantly related to weekly earnings at the 95% level? What form does this relation take, linear or other (specify)?
c) Suppose there was a 3% increase in EL in Oshawa, Ontario, but ELI remained constant. By what percentage would you expect weekly earnings to increase in Oshawa?
d) Does this regression show that education level is not linearly related to weekly earnings? **LO❶, ❷**

43. Canadian earnings levels, part 2. Exercise 42 analyzes whether weekly earnings are related to employment opportunities in Canada. Other factors that might impact people's weekly earnings are their number of years of education (ED) and their number of years of work experience (EX). To investigate how important these factors are, Statistics Canada added them to its multivariate regression given in Exercise 42. Preliminary data analysis had shown a nonlinear relationship between weekly earnings and years of experience, which analysts took into account with a term in EX^2. The resulting multivariate regression analysis is

$$\ln(w) = 4.322 + 0.023 \times \ln(EL) + 0.007 \times \ln(ELI) + 0.055 \times EX - 0.001 \times EX^2 \; 0.055 + 0.078 \times ED.$$

The P-values associated with the intercept and the five coefficients in the above equation are <0.001, <0.001, 0.140, <0.001, <0.001, and <0.001. The *F*-ratio has a P-value <0.001. (*Source:* Data from Statistics Canada. Beckstead, D., Brown, W. M., Guo, Y., & Newbold, K. B. [2010, January]. Cities and growth: Earnings levels across urban and rural areas: The role of human capital. Catalogue No. 11-622-M, No. 020. Table 4.)

a) Is the regression model significant overall?
b) Which variable(s) is (are) significantly linearly related to weekly earnings at the 95% level?
c) Does this regression show that employment in the same location is related to weekly earnings at the 95% level? What form does this relation take, linear or other (specify)?

d) Statistics Canada states, "The advantage of cities lies as much in their capacity to educate, attract and retain highly educated workers, as in their innate ability to facilitate the interaction of workers and firms." Which parts of the regression results lead to this conclusion?
e) What other factors might contribute to weekly earnings other than those in this regression equation? **LO❷**

❶ 44. Burger King nutrition. Like many fast-food restaurant chains, Burger King (BK) provides data on the nutrition content of its menu items on its website. Here's a multiple regression predicting calories for Burger King foods from *Protein* content (g), *Total Fat* (g), *Carbohydrate* (g), and *Sodium* (mg) per serving:

Dependent variable is: Calories
R-squared = 100.0% R-squared [adjusted] = 100.0%
s = 3.140 with 31 − 5 = 26 degrees of freedom

Source	Sum of Squares	df	Mean Square	F-ratio
Regression	1419311	4	354828	35994
Residual	256.307	26	9.85796	

Variable	Coeff	SE(Coeff)	t-ratio	P-value
Intercept	6.53412	2.425	2.69	0.0122
Protein	3.83855	0.0859	44.7	<0.0001
Total fat	9.14121	0.0779	117	<0.0001
Carbs	3.94033	0.0338	117	<0.0001
Na/Serv.	−0.69155	0.2970	−2.33	0.0279

a) Is this a good model of *Calories*? Why or why not?
b) The mean of *Calories* is 455.5 with a standard deviation of 217.5. Discuss what the value of *s* in the regression means about how well the model fits the data.
c) Does the R^2 value of 100.0% mean that the residuals are all actually equal to zero? **LO❷**

21

Building Multiple Regression Models

In this chapter we show you how to build regression models from several explanatory variables. After reading and studying this chapter, you should be able to:

❶ Include explanatory variables appropriately (e.g., as indicator variables or using re-expression)

❷ Deal with exceptional data points

❸ Choose which explanatory variables to include in the model

Canada's Wonderland

Although Walt Disney considered building a theme park in the Greater Toronto Area, in the end he decided to expand in Florida instead, as he thought the climate in Toronto would mean too short an operating season. But Ontarians wanted to have fun and so did their premier, William Davis, who detonated the first explosion to start construction of Canada's Wonderland north of Toronto in 1979. It took two years to build. Taft Broadcasting Company opened Canada's first major theme park to the public in 1981, with Wayne Gretzky hoisting the Canadian flag, thousands of helium balloons rising into the sky, and parachutists gliding to earth. Today Canada's Wonderland is owned by Cedar Fair, a company that owns and operates over a dozen amusement and water parks across North America.

Roller coasters are a major attraction at theme parks, and Canada's Wonderland has 16 of them, including Behemoth. Built in 2008 at an estimated cost of $26 million, it has a height of 70 metres and maximum speed of 123 km/h.

Theme and amusement parks are big business, and in Canada there are 30 parks. Theme parks are capital-intensive and rely on a continuous stream of visitors to offset capital costs. A major attraction is roller coasters, and fans will search the web for the "biggest and best" before deciding which theme park to visit.

But what is it about a roller coaster that attracts riders? Some people think the main factor is speed. But the duration of the ride is also important, and some people like to be flipped upside down (inversions). Table 21.1 lists data on the coasters at Canada's Wonderland and elsewhere.[1]

WHO	Roller coasters
WHAT	See Table 21.1 for the variables and their units
WHERE	Worldwide
WHEN	All were in operation in 2009
WHY	To understand characteristics that affect speed and duration

- *Type* indicates what kind of track the roller coaster has. The possible values are "wooden" and "steel." (The frame is usually of the same construction as the track, but it doesn't have to be.)
- *Duration* is the duration of the ride in seconds.
- *Speed* is the top speed in miles per hour.
- *Height* is the maximum height above ground level in feet.
- *Drop* is the greatest drop in feet.
- *Length* is the total length of the track in feet.
- *Inversions* reports whether riders are turned upside down during the ride. It has the values "yes" or "no."

Name	Park	Country	Type	Duration (sec.)	Speed (mph)	Height (ft.)	Drop (ft.)	Length (ft.)	Inversion?
Mighty Canadian Minebuster	Canada's Wonderland	Canada	Wooden	122	56	90	87	3828	No
Behemoth	Canada's Wonderland	Canada	Steel	190	77	230	230	5318	No
Wild Beast	Canada's Wonderland	Canada	Wooden	122	56	82	78	3150	No
New Mexico Rattler	Cliff's Amusement Park	United States	Wooden	75	47	80	75	2750	No
Fujiyama	Fuji-Q Highlands	Japan	Steel	216	80.8	259.2	229.7	6708.67	No
Goliath	Six Flags Magic Mountain	United States	Steel	180	85	235	255	4500	No
Great American Scream Machine	Six Flags Great Adventure	United States	Steel	140	68	173	155	3800	Yes
Hangman	Wild Adventures	United States	Steel	125	55	115	95	2170	Yes
Hayabusa	Tokyo SummerLand	Japan	Steel	108	60.3	137.8	124.67	2559.1	No
Hercules	Dorney Park	United States	Wooden	135	65	95	151	4000	No
Hurricane	Myrtle Beach Pavilion	United States	Wooden	120	55	101.5	100	3800	No

Table 21.1   Facts about some roller coasters.

Source: Based on data from The Roller Coaster Database. Retrieved from www.rcdb.com

Customers not only want the ride to be fast; they also want it to last. It makes sense that the longer the track is, the longer the ride will be. Let's have a look at *Duration* and *Length* to see what the relationship is.

As the scatterplots of the variables (Figure 21.1) and residuals (Figure 21.2) show, the regression conditions seem to be met, and the regression makes sense (Table 21.2). We'd expect longer tracks to give longer rides. Starting from the intercept at about 53.9 seconds, the duration of the ride increases, on average, by 0.0231 seconds per foot of track—or 23.1 seconds more for each 1000 additional feet of track.

---

[1]Data from Ultimate Rollercoaster http://www.ultimaterollercoaster.com/

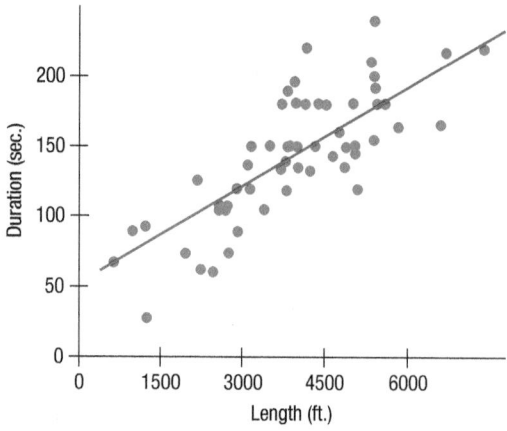

Figure 21.1   The relationship between *Duration* and *Length* looks strong and positive. On average, *Duration* increases linearly with *Length*.

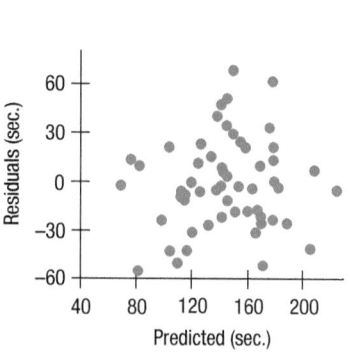

Figure 21.2   Residuals for *Duration*.

Dependent variable is: Duration
R-squared = 62.0% R-squared (adjusted) = 61.4%
$s = 27.23$ with $63 - 2 = 61$ degrees of freedom

Source	Sum of Squares	DF	Mean Square	F-ratio
Regression	73901.7	1	73901.7	99.6
Residual	45243.7	61	741.700	

Variable	Coefficient	SE(Coeff)	*t*-ratio	P-value
Intercept	53.9348	9.488	5.68	<0.0001
Length	0.0231	0.0023	9.98	<0.0001

Table 21.2   The regression of *Duration* on *Length* looks strong, and the conditions seem to be met.

LO❶   21.1   Indicator (or Dummy) Variables

Of course, there's more to these data. One interesting variable might not be one you'd naturally think of. Many modern coasters have "inversions," whereby riders get turned upside down with loops, corkscrews, or other devices. These inversions add excitement, but they must be carefully engineered, and they enforce speed limits on that portion of the ride. Riders like speed, but they also like inversions, which affect the duration of the ride. We'd like to add the information of whether the roller coaster has an inversion to our model. Until now, all our predictor variables have been quantitative. Whether or not a roller coaster has an inversion is a categorical variable ("yes" or "no"). Let's see how to introduce the categorical variable *Inversions* as a predictor in our regression model. Figure 21.3 shows the same scatterplot of *Duration* against *Length*, but now with the roller coasters that have inversions shown as red *x*'s and those without shown as blue dots. There's a separate regression line for each type of roller coaster.

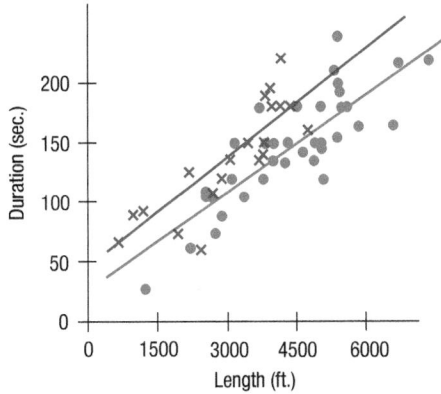

Figure 21.3 The two lines fit to coasters with (red *x*'s) and without (blue dots) inversions are roughly parallel.

It's easy to see that, for a given length, the roller coasters with inversions take a bit longer, and that for each type of roller coaster the slopes of the relationship between duration and length are not quite equal but are similar. If we split the data into two groups—coasters without inversions and those with inversions—and compute the regression for each group (Table 21.3), the output looks like this:

Dependent variable is: Duration
Cases selected according to: No inversions
R-squared = 69.4% R-squared (adjusted) = 68.5%
$s = 25.12$ with $38 - 2 = 36$ degrees of freedom

Variable	Coefficient	SE(Coeff)	t-ratio	P-value
Intercept	25.9961	14.10	1.84	0.0734
Length	0.0274	0.003	9.03	<0.0001

Dependent variable is: Duration
Cases selected according to: Inversions
R-squared = 70.5% R-squared (adjusted) = 69.2%
$s = 23.20$ with $25 - 2 = 23$ degrees of freedom

Variable	Coefficient	SE(Coeff)	t-ratio	P-value
Intercept	47.6454	12.50	3.81	0.0009
Length	0.0299	0.004	7.41	<0.0001

Table 21.3 The regressions computed separately for the two types of roller coasters show similar slopes but different intercepts.

As the scatterplot showed, the slopes are very similar, but the intercepts are different. When we have a situation like this with roughly parallel regressions for the groups,[2] there's an easy way to add the group information to a single regression

---

[2]The fact that the individual regression lines are nearly parallel is part of the Linearity Condition. You should check that the lines are nearly parallel before using this method or read on to see what to do if they're not parallel enough.

model. We create a new variable that *indicates* what type of roller coaster we have, giving it the value 1 for roller coasters that have inversions and the value 0 for those that don't. (We could have reversed the coding; it's an arbitrary choice.[3]) Such a variable is called an **indicator variable**, or *indicator*, because it indicates which category each case is in. It is also often called a **dummy variable**. When we add our new indicator, *Inversions*, to the regression model as a second variable, the multiple regression model looks like this (Table 21.4):

Inversions = 1 if a coaster has inversions
Inversions = 0 if not

Dependent variable is: Duration
R-squared = 70.4% R-squared (adjusted) = 69.4%
$s = 24.24$ with $63 - 3 = 60$ degrees of freedom

Variable	Coefficient	SE(Coeff)	t-ratio	P-value
Intercept	22.3909	11.39	1.97	0.0539
Length	0.0282	0.0024	11.7	<0.0001
Inversions	30.0824	7.290	4.13	<0.0001

Table 21.4　The regression model with a dummy, or indicator, variable for *Inversions*.

This looks like a better model than the simple regression for all the data. The R^2 is larger, the *t*-ratios of both coefficients are large, and now we can understand the effect of inversions with a single model without having to compare two regressions. (The residuals look reasonable as well.) But what does the coefficient for *Inversions* mean? Let's see how an indicator variable works when we calculate predicted values for two of the roller coasters listed in Table 21.1.

Name	Park	Country	Type	Duration	Speed	Height	Drop	Length	Inversion?
Hangman	Wild Adventures	United States	Steel	125	55	115	95	2170	Yes
Hayabusa	Tokyo SummerLand	Japan	Steel	108	60.3	137.8	124.67	2559.1	No

Ignoring the variable *Inversions* for the moment, the model (in Table 21.4) says that for all coasters, the predicted *Duration* is

$$22.39 + 0.0282 \; Length + 30.08 \; Inversions.$$

Now remember that for this indicator variable, the value 1 means that a coaster has an inversion, while a 0 means it doesn't. For Hayabusa, with no inversion, the value of *Inversions* is 0, so the coefficient of *Inversions* doesn't affect the prediction at all. With a length of 2259.1 feet, we predict its duration as[4]

$$22.39 + 0.0282 \; (2559.1) + 30.08 \times 0 = 94.56 \; \text{seconds,}$$

which is close to its actual duration of 108 seconds. The Hangman (with a length of 2170 feet) has an inversion, and so the model predicts an "additional" 30.0824 seconds for its duration:

$$22.39 + 0.0282 \; (2170.0) + 30.08 \times 1 = 113.66 \; \text{seconds}$$

That compares well with the actual duration of 125 seconds.

---

[3]Some implementations of indicator variables use 1 and −1 for the levels of the categories.

[4]We round coefficient values when we write the model but calculate with the full precision, rounding at the end of the calculation.

Notice how the indicator works in the model. When there's an inversion (as in Hangman), the value 1 for the indicator causes the amount of the indicator's coefficient, 30.08, to be *added* to the prediction. When there's no inversion (as in Hayabusa), the indicator is 0, so nothing is added. Looking back at the scatterplot, we can see that this is exactly what we need. The difference between the two lines is a vertical shift of about 30 seconds. This may seem a bit confusing at first because we usually think of the coefficients in a multiple regression as slopes. For indicator variables, however, they act differently. They're vertical shifts that keep the slopes for the other variables apart.

An indicator variable that is 0 or 1 can only shift the line up and down. It can't change the slope, so it works only when we have lines with the same slope and different intercepts.

Indicators for Three or More Categories

It's easy to construct indicators for a variable with two categories; we just assign 0 to one level and 1 to the other. But business and economic variables such as *Month* or *Socioeconomic Class* may have several levels. You can construct indicators for a categorical variable with several levels by constructing a separate indicator for each of these levels. There's just one thing to keep in mind. If a variable has k levels, you can create only $k - 1$ indicators. You have to choose one of the k categories as a "baseline" and leave out its indicator. Then the coefficients of the other indicators can be interpreted as the amount by which their categories differ from the baseline, after allowing for the linear effects of the other variables in the model.

For the two-category variable *Inversions*, we used "no inversion" as the baseline, and coasters with an inversion got a 1. We needed only one variable for two levels. If we wished to represent *Month* with indicators, we would need 11 of them. We might, for example, define *January* as the baseline and make indicators for *February, March . . . November*, and *December*. Each of these indicators would be 0 for all cases except for the ones that had that value for the variable *Month*.

Why couldn't we use a single variable with "1" for *January*, "2" for *February*, and so on? That would require the pretty strict assumption that the responses to the months are linear and equally spaced—that is, that the change in our response variable from January to February is the same in both direction and amount as the change from July to August. That's a pretty severe restriction and usually isn't true. Using 11 indicators releases the model from that restriction even though it adds complexity to the model.

For real estate data, we might want to introduce a variable for the *Fuel Type* used to heat the house. That variable is reported with values: 1 = None; 2 = Gas; 3 = Electric; 4 = Oil; 5 = Wood; 6 = Solar; 7 = Unknown/Other.

Because there are seven levels, we need six indicator variables. We'll use 1 = None as the *baseline*. *Fuel2* would have the value 1 for gas and 0 for all other types, *Fuel3* would have value 1 for electric and 0 for all other types, etc. However, we may find that although there are seven possible levels, very few houses have values other than 2, 3, and 4. So we could work with only two indicators, *Fuel2* and *Fuel3*, indicating gas and electric, respectively, and leaving oil as the baseline. We set aside houses that use other fuels.

Once you've created multiple indicator variables (up to $k - 1$) for a categorical variable with k levels, it often helps to combine levels that have similar characteristics and relationships with the response. This can help keep the number of variables in a multiple regression from exploding.

FOR EXAMPLE   Indicator variables for diamond colour

In Chapter 19 we looked at data on the prices of diamonds (For Example: "Diamond prices"). Although higher carat weight of diamonds generally means higher cost, *Carat Weight* isn't the only factor that determines a diamond's price. A typical diamond is pale yellow. The less colour a diamond has, the higher its colour grade and—generally—its price. We want to build a model that incorporates both *Carat Weight* and *Colour* to predict a diamond's price. The data here are a collection of 749 diamonds: *Weight* is between 0.3 and 1.4 carats; colour grades are D (highest possible), G (medium), and K (fairly low). We'll use Log_{10} *Price* as the response to make the relationship more linear. Here are scatterplots of *Price* and Log_{10} *Price* vs. *Carat Weight* for these diamonds:

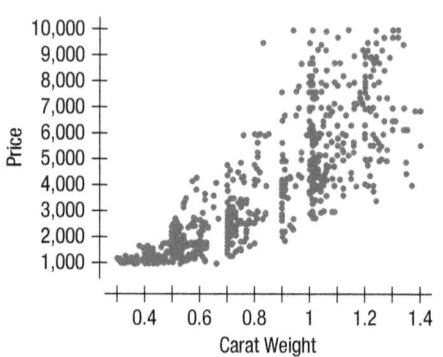 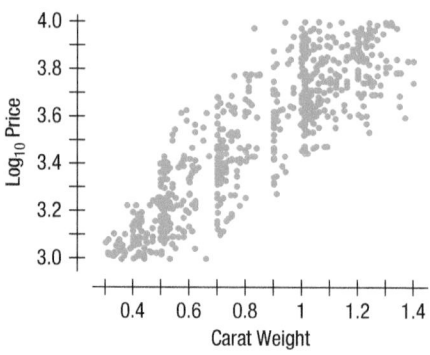

A linear model for Log_{10} *Price* on *Carat Weight* alone finds:
Response Variable: Log_{10}Price
$R^2 = 77.39\%$ Adjusted $R^2 = 77.36\%$
$s = 0.1364$ with $749 - 2 = 747$ degrees of freedom

Variable	Coeff	SE(Coeff)	*t*-ratio	P-value
Intercept	2.76325	0.01532	180.42	<0.0001
Carat.Weight	0.90020	0.01780	50.56	<0.0001

Here is a scatterplot of Log_{10} *Price* vs. *Carat Weight* showing the three different colour grades (D, G, and K):

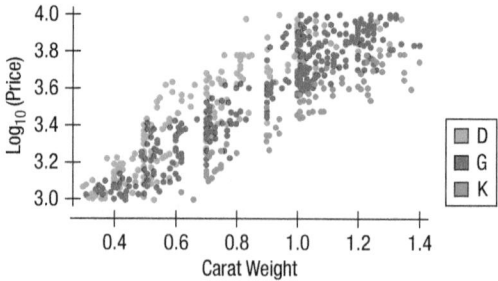

To account for the differences, two indicator variables were created:

$Colour\ D = 1$ if *Colour* = D and 0 otherwise
$Colour\ G = 1$ if *Colour* = G and 0 otherwise

A multiple regression of Log_{10} *Price* was run with three predictors: *Carat Weight*, *Colour D*, and *Colour G*.

Here is the output:

Response Variable: Log_{10} Price
$R^2 = 85.66\%$ Adjusted $R^2 = 85.61$
$s = 0.1088$ with $749 - 4 = 745$ degrees of freedom

Variable	Coeff	SE(Coeff)	t-ratio	P-value
Intercept	2.43978	0.01981	123.14	<0.0001
Carat.Weight	1.02865	0.01589	64.75	<0.0001
ColourD	0.29405	0.01424	20.65	<0.0001
ColourG	0.21883	0.01278	17.12	<0.0001

QUESTIONS   For the three colours of diamonds, what are the models that predict $Log_{10}Price$? Does the addition of the indicator variables for the colours seem like a good idea? Why are there only two indicator variables?

ANSWERS   The indicator variable adds amounts to the intercept value for the two colour levels, D and G. Since diamonds of colour K have both dummy variables set to 0, the equation for diamonds with *Colour K* is simply:

$$\widehat{Log_{10}\ Price} = 2.440 + 1.029\ Carat\ Weight$$

For diamonds with *Colour G*, we add 0.219 to the intercept, so:

$$\widehat{Log_{10}\ Price} = (2.440 + 0.219) + 1.029\ Carat\ Weight = 2.659 + 1.029\ Carat\ Weight$$

Similarly for diamonds with *Colour D*, we add 0.294 to the intercept, so:

$$\widehat{Log_{10}\ Price} = (2.440 + 0.294) + 1.029\ Carat\ Weight = 2.734 + 1.029\ Carat\ Weight$$

Both indicator variables are highly significant, which means that the differences in intercept are large enough to justify the addition of the variables.

With three levels of colour, we need only two indicator variables. (In general, k levels require $k - 1$ indicators.)

LO❶   **21.2   Adjusting for Different Slopes—Interaction Terms**

Even consumers of fast food are increasingly concerned with nutrition. So, like many restaurant chains, Burger King publishes the nutrition details of its menu items on its website (www.bk.com/Nutrition). Many customers count calories or carbohydrates. Of course, these are likely to be related to each other. We can examine that relationship in Burger King foods by looking at the scatterplot in Figure 21.4.

It's not surprising to see that an increase in *Carbs* is associated with more *Calories*, but the plot seems to thicken as we move from left to right. Could there be something else going on?

We divide Burger King foods into two groups, colouring those with meat (including chicken and fish) in orange and those without meat in blue. Looking at the regressions for each group, we see a different picture (Figure 21.5).

Clearly, meat-based items contribute more calories from their carbohydrate content than do other Burger King foods. But unlike Figure 21.2, where the lines were parallel, we can't account for the kind of difference we see here by just including a dummy variable in a regression. It isn't just the heights of the lines that are different; they have entirely different slopes.

Joao Virissimo/Shutterstock

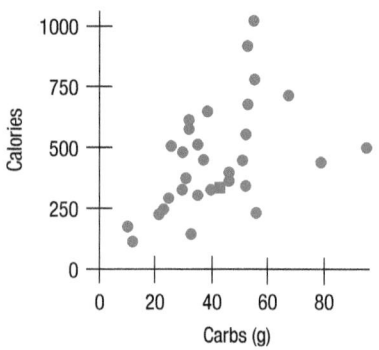

Figure 21.4 *Calories* of Burger King foods plotted against *Carbs* seems to fan out.

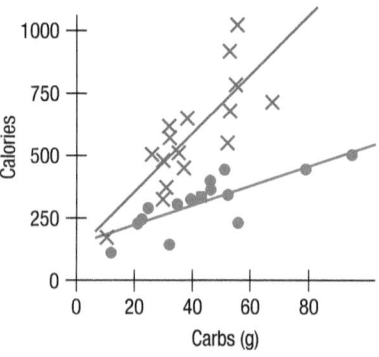

Figure 21.5 Plotting the meat-based (orange x's) and non-meat (blue dots) items separately, we see two distinct linear patterns.

> **Burger King**
>
> James McLamore and David Edgerton, graduates of the Cornell University School of Hotel Administration, opened their first Burger King (BK) restaurant in 1954 in the Miami area and then expanded using a franchising system. After a number of ownership transfers, BK was purchased by private investors and taken public. The initial public offering (IPO) in 2006 generated US$425 million—the largest IPO of a U.S.-based restaurant chain on record.

We'll start, as before, by constructing the indicator for the two groups, *Meat*, which is 1 for foods that contain meat and 0 for the others. The variable *Meat* can adjust the intercepts of the two lines. To adjust the slopes, we have to construct another variable—the *product* of the variables *Meat* and *Carbs*. The coefficient of this **interaction term** in a multiple regression gives an adjustment to the slope for the cases in the indicated group. The resulting variable *Carbs* × *Meat* has the value of *Carbs* for foods containing meat (those coded 1 in the *Meat* indicator) and the value 0 for the others. By including this interaction variable in the model, we can adjust the slope of the line fit to the meat-containing foods. Table 21.5 shows the resulting analysis:

Dependent variable is: Calories
R-squared = 78.1% R-squared (adjusted) = 75.7%
s = 106.0 with 32 − 4 = 28 degrees of freedom

Source	Sum of Squares	DF	Mean Square	F-ratio
Regression	1119979	3	373326	33.2
Residual	314843	28	11244.4	

Variable	Coefficient	SE(Coeff)	t-ratio	P-value
Intercept	137.395	58.72	2.34	0.0267
Carbs(g)	3.93317	1.113	3.53	0.0014
Meat	−26.1567	98.48	−0.266	0.7925
Carbs × Meat	7.87530	2.179	3.61	0.0012

Table 21.5   The regression model with both an indicator variable and an interaction term.

What does the coefficient for the indicator *Meat* do? It provides a different intercept to separate the meat and non-meat items at the origin (where *Carbs* = 0). Each group has its own slope, but the two lines nearly meet at the origin, so there seems to be no need for an additional intercept adjustment. The difference of 26.16 calories is small. That's why the coefficient for the indicator variable *Meat* has a small *t*-statistic (−0.266).

By contrast, the coefficient of the interaction term, *Carbs* × *Meat*, says that the slope relating calories to carbohydrates is steeper by 7.88 calories per carbohydrate gram for meat-containing foods than for meat-free foods. Its small P-value suggests that this difference is real. Overall, the regression model predicts calories to be:

$$137.40 + 3.93 \ Carbs - 26.16 \ Meat + 7.88 \ Carbs \times Meat$$

Let's see how these adjustments work. A BK Whopper has 53 grams of carbohydrates and is a meat dish. The model predicts its *Calories* as

$$137.40 + 3.93 \times 53 - 26.16 \times 1 + 7.88 \times 53 \times 1 = 737.2 \text{ calories,}$$

not far from the measured calorie count of 680. By contrast, the Veggie Burger, with 43 grams of carbohydrates, has value 0 for *Meat* and so has a value of 0 for *Carbs* × *Meat* as well. Those indicators contribute nothing to its predicted calories:

$$137.40 + 3.93 \times 43 - 26.16 \times 0 + 7.88 \times 0 \times 43 = 306.4 \text{ calories}$$

This is close to the 330 measured officially.

FOR EXAMPLE — Adding interaction terms for diamond colour

After adding the indicator variables for *Colour*, which showed different intercepts for the three different colour levels, an analyst wonders if the slopes for the three colour levels might be different as well, so she adds two more predictors, *ColourD*Carat Weight* and *ColourG*Carat Weight*, to the model (see For Example: "Indicator variables for diamond colour"). The regression output shows:

Response Variable: $Log_{10}Price$
$R^2 = 85.77\%$ Adjusted $R^2 = 85.67\%$
$s = 0.1085$ with $749 - 6 = 743$ degrees of freedom

Variable	Coeff	SE(Coeff)	t-ratio	P-value
Intercept	2.54151	0.06000	42.361	<0.0001
Carat.Weight	0.92968	0.05734	16.212	<0.0001
ColourD	0.16466	0.06302	2.613	0.00916
ColourG	0.12656	0.06287	2.013	0.04448
Carat.Weight*ColourD	0.14076	0.06356	2.215	0.02709
Carat.Weight*ColourG	0.08809	0.06095	1.445	0.14877

QUESTION   Based on this, what model might you use to predict $Log_{10}Price$? What other factors should be taken into account?

ANSWER   The only significant interaction term is the one for *Colour D* by *Carat Weight*, so we probably don't need different slopes for levels *G* and *K*. We should refit the regression without the interaction term *ColourG*Carat Weight*. When we do, we find that the term for *Carat Weight*ColourD* is marginally significant. The decision whether to include it is a judgment call. To make a final decision, we should also consider residual analysis and diagnostics. For the sake of simplicity we'll proceed with the simpler model, with only the indicator variables and not the interaction (the model fit in the previous example).

JUST CHECKING

A researcher in the Human Resource department wants to study the relationships among *Salary*, *Years Experience*, *Education*, and *Gender*. For *Education*, there are three levels: high school or some college (*HS*), college grad (*BA*), and post graduate (*PG*).

1 If she wants to account for differences in the relationship between *Salary* and *Years Experience* for men and women, what terms should she enter in the regression?

2 If she wants to study the differences in the relationship between *Salary* and *Years Experience* for different *Education* levels, how many indicator variables will she need for *Education*?

Answers are found in Appendix A.

LO❷   21.3   Multiple Regression Diagnostics

We often use regression analyses to make important business decisions. By working with the data and creating models, we can learn a great deal about the relationships among variables. As we saw with simple regression, sometimes we can learn as much from the cases that *don't* fit the model as from the bulk of cases that do. Extraordinary cases often tell us more just by the ways in which they fail to conform and the reasons we can discover for those deviations. If a case doesn't conform to the others, we should identify it and, if possible, understand why it's different. In simple regression, a case can be extraordinary by standing away from the model in the *y* direction or by having unusual values in an *x*-variable. In multiple regression, it can also be extraordinary by having an unusual *combination* of values in the *x*-variables. Just as in simple regression, large deviations in the *y* direction show up in the residuals as outliers. Deviations in the *x*'s show up as *leverage*.

Leverage

In a regression of a *single* predictor and a response, it's easy to see if a value has high leverage, because it's far from the mean of the *x*-values in a scatterplot. In a *multiple* regression with *k* predictor variables, things are more complicated. A point might actually not be far from any of the *x* means and yet still exert large leverage because it has an unusual *combination* of predictor values. Even a graphics program designed to display points in high-dimensional spaces may not make it obvious. Fortunately, there are values of leverage that can be calculated and are standard for most multiple regression programs.

We calculate *leverage* in a pretty intuitive way. The **leverage** is defined as follows. For any case, add one to its *y*-value. Recompute the regression, and see how much the *predicted* value of the case changes. The amount of the change is the leverage. It can never be greater than one or less than zero. A point with zero leverage has no effect at all on the regression slope, although it does participate in the calculations of R^2, s, and the F- and t-statistics. The leverage of the ith point in a data set is often denoted by h_i.

A point with high leverage may not actually influence the regression coefficients if it follows the pattern of the model set by the other points, but it's worth examining simply because of its *potential* to do so. Looking at leverage values can be an effective way to discover cases that are extraordinary on a combination of *x*-variables. In business, such cases often deserve special attention.

There are no tests for whether the leverage of a case is too large. The average leverage value among all cases in a regression is $1/n$, but that doesn't give us much of a guide. Some packages use rules of thumb to indicate high leverage values,[5] but another common approach is to just make a histogram of the leverages. Any case whose leverage stands out in a histogram of leverages probably deserves special attention. You may decide to leave the case in the regression or to see how the regression model changes when you delete the case, but you should be aware of its potential to influence the regression.

We've already seen that the *Duration* of a roller coaster ride depends linearly on its *Length*. But even more than a long ride, roller coaster customers like speed. So, rather than predict the duration of a roller coaster ride, let's build a model for how fast it travels. A multiple regression in two variables (Table 21.6) shows that both the total *Height* and the *Drop* (the maximum distance from the top to the bottom of the largest drop in the ride) are important factors.

The regression certainly seems reasonable. The R^2 value is high, and the residual plot looks patternless (Figure 21.6). A histogram of the leverage values (Figure 21.7), however, shows something interesting.

---

[5]One common rule for determining when a leverage is large is to indicate any leverage value greater than $3(k + 1)/n$, where *k* is the number of predictors.

Variable	Coeff	SE(Coeff)	t-ratio	P-Value
Intercept	37.01333	1.47723	25.056	<0.0001
Height	0.06581	0.01911	3.444	0.000953
Drop	0.12540	0.01888	6.643	<0.0001

Multiple R-squared: 0.855 Adjusted R-squared: 0.851
F-statistic: 215.2 on 2 and 73 DF, P-value <0.0001

Table 21.6 Regression of *Speed* on *Height* and *Drop* shows both predictor variables to be highly significant.

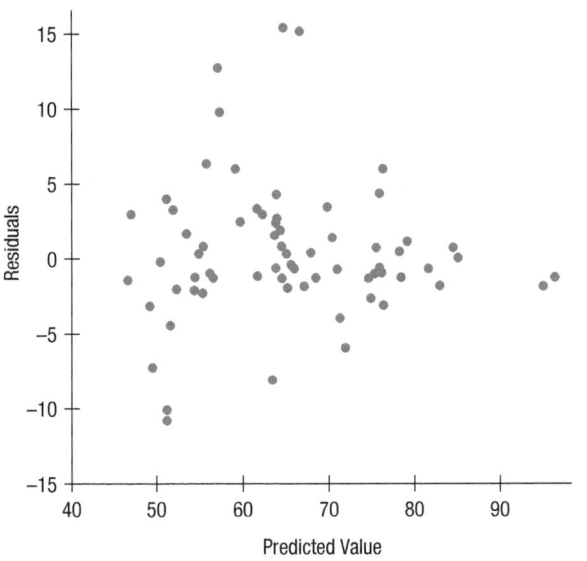

Figure 21.6 The scatterplot of residuals against predicted values shows nothing unusual for the regression of *Speed* on *Height* and *Drop*.

Figure 21.7 The distribution of leverage values shows a few high values and one extraordinarily high-leverage point.

The case with very high leverage is a coaster called Oblivion, a steel roller coaster in England that opened as the world's first "vertical drop coaster" in 1998. What's unusual about Oblivion is that its *Height* is only about 65 feet above ground (placing it below the median), and yet it drops 180 feet to achieve a top speed of 68 mph. The unique feature of Oblivion is that it plunges *underground* nearly 120 feet.

Leverage points can affect not only the coefficients of the model, but also our choice of whether to include a predictor in a regression model as well. The more complex the regression model, the more important it is to look at high-leverage values and their effects.

Residuals and Standardized Residuals

Residuals are not all alike. Consider a point with leverage 1.0. That's the highest a leverage can be, and it means that the line follows the point perfectly. So a point like that must have a zero residual. And since we know the residual exactly, that residual has zero standard deviation. This tendency is true in general: The larger the leverage of a data point, the smaller the standard deviation of its residual. When we want to compare values that have differing standard deviations, it's a good idea to standardize them. We can do that with the regression residuals, dividing each one by an estimate of its own standard deviation. When we do that, the resulting values follow a Student's *t*-distribution. In fact, such a standardized residual is called a **Studentized residual**.[6] It's a good idea to examine the Studentized residuals (rather than the simple residuals) to check the Nearly Normal Condition and the Equal Spread Condition. Any Studentized residual that stands out from the others deserves your attention.

It may occur to you that we've always plotted the *unstandardized* residuals when we made regression models. We treated them as if they all had the same standard deviation when we checked the Nearly Normal Condition. It turns out that this was a simplification. It didn't matter much for simple regression, but for multiple regression models, it's a better idea to use the Studentized residuals when checking the Nearly Normal Condition and when making scatterplots of residuals against predicted values.

Influence Measures

A case that has *both* high leverage and a large Studentized residual is likely to have changed the regression model substantially all by itself. Such a case is said to be *influential*. An **influential case** cries out for special attention because removing it is likely to give a very different regression model. The surest way to tell whether a case is influential is to try leaving it out[7] and see how much the regression model changes. You should call a case "influential" if omitting it changes the regression model by enough to matter for *your* purposes.

To identify possibly influential cases, check the leverage and Studentized residuals. Two statistics that combine leverage and Studentized residuals into a single measure of influence, **Cook's Distance** (Cook's D) and **DFFITS**,[8] are offered by many statistics programs. If either of these measures is unusually large for a case, that case should be checked as a possible influential point. Cook's D for the ith data point is found from its leverage, h_i, its residual, e_i, the number of predictors, k, and the residual standard error, s_e:

$$D_i = \frac{e_i^2}{ks_e^2}\left[\frac{h_i}{(1 - h_i)^2}\right]$$

A histogram of the Cook's Distances from the model in Table 21.6 shows a few influential values (Table 21.7):

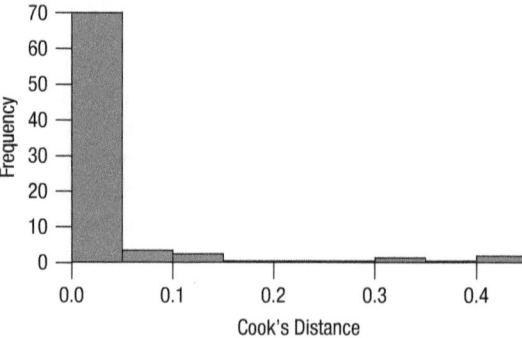

---

[6]There's more than one way to Studentize residuals according to how you estimate *s*. You may find statistics packages referring to *externally Studentized residuals* and *internally Studentized residuals*. It's the *externally Studentized* version that follows a *t*-distribution, so those are the ones we recommend.

[7]Or, equivalently, include an indicator variable that selects only for that case. See the discussion in the next section.

[8]DFFITS is a measure of how much the predicted value of a point changes if that point is left out of the regression.

Here are coasters with the four highest values of Cook's D:

Name	Type	Duration	Speed	Height	Drop	Length	Inversions	Cook's D
HyperSonic XLC	Steel	NA	80	165	133	1560	0	0.1037782
Oblivion	Steel	NA	68	65	180	1222	0	0.1124114
Volcano, The Blast Coaster	Steel	NA	70	155	80	2757	1	0.3080218
Xcelerator	Steel	62	82	205	130	2202	0	0.4319336

Table 21.7   Coasters with high Cook's D.

David C. Rehner/Shutterstock

In addition to the Oblivion, Cook's Distance singles out three other coasters: HyperSonic XLC; Volcano, The Blast Coaster; and Xcelerator. A little research finds that these three coasters *are* different as well. Our model found that *Height* and *Drop* significantly influence a coaster's *Speed*. But these three coasters have something extra—a hydraulic catapult that accelerates the coasters more than gravity alone could do. In fact, the Xcelerator reaches 82 mph in 2.3 seconds, using only 157 feet of track to launch it. Removing these three accelerator coasters from the model has a striking effect (Table 21.8).

Variable	Coeff	SE(Coeff)	t-ratio	P-Value
Intercept	36.47453	1.06456	34.262	<0.0001
Drop	0.17519	0.01493	11.731	<0.0001
Height	0.01600	0.01507	1.062	0.292

Residual standard error: 3.307 on 70 degrees of freedom
Multiple R-squared: 0.9246 Adjusted R-squared: 0.9225
F-statistic: 429.5 on 2 and 70 DF, P-value: < 0.0001

Table 21.8   Removing the three blast coasters has made *Height* no longer important to the model. A simple regression model, such as in Table 21.9, may be a more effective summary than the model with two predictor variables.

The *Height* of the coaster is no longer a statistically significant predictor, so we might choose to omit that variable.

Variable	Coeff	SE(Coeff)	t-ratio	P-Value
Intercept	36.743925	1.034798	35.51	<0.0001
Drop	0.189474	0.006475	29.26	<0.0001

Residual standard error: 3.31 on 71 degrees of freedom
Multiple R-squared: 0.9234 Adjusted R-squared: 0.9224
F-statistic: 856.3 on 1 and 71 DF, P-value: <0.0001

Table 21.9   A simple linear regression model without the three blast coasters and with *Height* deleted.

Indicators for Influence

One good way to examine the effect of an extraordinary case on a regression is to construct a special indicator variable that is zero for all cases *except* the one we want to isolate. Including such an indicator in the regression model has the same effect as removing the case from the data, but it has two special advantages. First, it makes it clear to anyone looking at the regression model that we've treated that case specially. Second, the *t*-statistic for the indicator variable's coefficient can be used as a test of whether the case is influential. If the P-value is small, then that case really didn't fit well with the rest of the data. Typically, we name such an indicator with the identifier of the case we want to remove. Here's the last roller coaster model (Table 21.10), in which we've removed the influence of the three blast coasters by constructing indicators for them instead of by removing them from the data. Notice that the coefficient for *Drop* is just the same as the ones we found by omitting the cases.

Dependent variable is: Speed
R-squared $= 92.7\%$ R-squared (adjusted) $= 92.3\%$
$s = 3.310$ with $76 - 5 = 71$ degrees of freedom

Variable	Coeff	SE(Coeff)	t-ratio	P-Value
Intercept	36.7439	1.035	35.5	<0.0001
Drop	0.189474	0.0065	29.3	<0.0001
Xcelerator	20.6244	3.334	6.19	<0.0001
HyperSonic	18.0560	3.334	5.42	<0.0001
Volcano	18.0981	3.361	5.38	<0.0001

Table 21.10   The P-values for the three indicator variables confirm that each of these roller coasters doesn't fit with the others.

Diagnosis Wrapup

What have we learned from diagnosing the regression? We've discovered four roller coasters that may be strongly influencing the model. And for each of them, we've been able to understand why and how it differed from the others. The oddness of Oblivion plunging into a hole in the ground may cause us to value *Drop* as a predictor of *Speed* more than *Height*. The three influential cases with high Cook's D values turned out to be different from the other roller coasters because they're "blast coasters" that don't rely only on gravity for their acceleration. Although we can't count on always discovering why influential cases are special, diagnosing influential cases raises the question of what about them might be different and can help us understand our model better.

When a regression analysis has cases that have both high leverage and large Studentized residuals, it would be irresponsible to report only the regression on all the data. You should also compute and discuss the regression found with such cases removed, and discuss the extraordinary cases individually if they offer additional insight. If your interest is to understand the world, the extraordinary cases may tell you more than the rest of the model. If your only interest is in the model (e.g., because you hope to use it for prediction), then you'll want to be certain that the model wasn't overly affected by only a few influential cases, but instead was built on the broader base of the body of your data.

FOR EXAMPLE   Regression diagnostics for diamond prices

Two other measures of quality of a diamond (see For Example: "Indicator variables for diamond colour") are its *Table* size and *Depth*; both are expressed as percentages. *Table* size is the ratio of the flat top part (the table) diameter to the diameter of the stone. *Depth* is the ratio of the distance from table to bottom (culet) to the diameter. The output of the regression of Log_{10} *Price* on *Carat Weight*, *Colour D*, *Colour G*, *Table*, and *Depth* shows:

Response Variable: Log_{10}Price

$R^2 = 85.92\%$ Adjusted $R^2 = 85.82\%$

$s = 0.1080$ with $749 - 6 = 743$ degrees of freedom

Variable	Coeff	SE(Coeff)	t-ratio	P-Value
Intercept	3.464326	0.322336	10.748	<0.0001
Carat.Size	1.031627	0.015799	65.295	<0.0001
ColourD	0.291119	0.014214	20.481	<0.0001
ColourG	0.213842	0.012760	16.759	<0.0001
Table	−0.008497	0.002345	−3.623	0.000311
Depth	−0.008638	0.003765	−2.294	0.022043

Influence measures can be adversely affected by indicator variables, so Studentized residuals, Cook's Distance, and leverage were all calculated on this model without the indicator variables for *Colour*.

Here are the histograms and boxplots for these three measures. Several points have unusually high values on one or more measures.

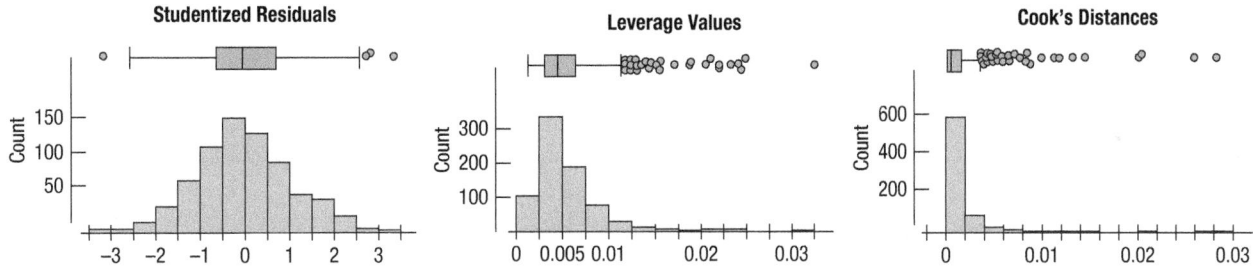

The analyst identified five diamonds that had high leverage (1) or Cook's Distance (4). Two of these also had large Studentized residuals. Indicator variables were created for these five points and a regression was run with these new variables:

Variable	Coeff	SE(Coeff)	t-ratio	P-Value
Intercept	4.5658	0.3972	11.49	<0.0001
Carat Size	0.9125	0.0177	51.54	<0.0001
Depth	−0.0190	0.0047	−4.04	<0.0001
Table	−0.0111	0.0029	−3.84	0.0001
Diamond 1	0.0478	0.1343	0.36	0.7221
Diamond 2	0.0837	0.1344	0.62	0.5336
Diamond 3	−0.1332	0.1361	−0.98	0.3283
Diamond 4	−0.3205	0.1346	−2.38	0.0176
Diamond 5	−0.4284	0.1346	−3.18	0.0015

QUESTION   What would you do next?

ANSWER   The indicator variables indicated that of the five suspected high influence points, only Diamonds 4 and 5 actually influence the regression. Run the regression again without these two points to see what coefficients change. If there's anything identifiably different about these two diamonds, set them aside or create a new variable for the newly identified characteristic (if possible) that distinguishes these diamonds.

LO❸   **21.4   Building Regression Models**

When many possible predictors are available, we will naturally want to select only a few of them for a regression model. But which ones? The first and most important thing to realize is that often there is no such thing as the "best" regression model. In fact, no regression model is "right." Often, several alternative models may be useful or insightful. The "best" for one purpose may not be best for another, and the one with the highest R^2 may not be best for many purposes.

Multiple regressions are subtle. The coefficients often don't mean what they may appear to mean at first. The choice of which predictors to use determines almost everything about the regression. Predictors interact with each other, which complicates interpretation and understanding. So it's usually best to build a parsimonious model, using as few predictors as you can. On the other hand, we don't want to leave out predictors that are theoretically or practically important. Making this trade-off is the heart of the challenge of selecting a good model.[9] The best regression models, in addition to satisfying the assumptions and conditions of multiple regression, have the following attributes:

- Relatively few predictors, to keep the model simple
- A relatively high R^2, indicating that much of the variability in y is accounted for by the regression model
- A relatively small value of s_e, the standard deviation of the residuals, indicating that the magnitude of the errors is small
- Relatively small P-values for the F- and t-statistics, showing that the overall model is better than a simple summary with the mean and that the individual coefficients are reliably different from zero
- No cases with extraordinarily high leverage that might dominate and alter the model
- No cases with extraordinarily large residuals, and Studentized residuals that appear to be nearly Normal; outliers can alter the model and certainly weaken the power of any test statistics, and the Nearly Normal Condition is required for inference
- Predictors that are reliably measured and relatively unrelated to each other

The term "relatively" in this list is meant to suggest that you should favour models with these attributes over others that satisfy them less, but of course there are many trade-offs and no absolute rules. In addition to favouring predictors that can be measured reliably, you may want to favour those that are less expensive to measure, especially if your model is intended for prediction with values not yet measured.

It should be clear from this discussion that the selection of a regression model calls for judgment. This is yet another of those decisions in Statistics that just can't be made automatically. Indeed, it is one that we shouldn't want to make automatically; there are so many aspects of what makes a model useful that human judgment is necessary to make a final choice. Nevertheless, there are tools that can help by identifying potentially interesting models.

Best Subsets and Stepwise Regression

How can we find the best multiple regression model? The list of desirable features we just looked at should make it clear that there is no simple definition of the "best" model. The choice of a multiple regression model always requires judgment

---

[9]This trade-off is sometimes referred to as Occam's Razor, after the medieval philosopher William of Occam.

to choose among potential models. Sometimes it can help to look at models that are "good" in some arbitrary sense to understand some possibilities, but such models should never be accepted blindly.

If we choose a single criterion such as finding a model with the highest adjusted R^2, then for modest size data sets and a modest number of potential predictors, it's actually possible for computers to search through *all* possible models. The method is called a **best subsets regression**. Often the computer reports a collection of "best" models: the best with three predictors, the best with four, and so on.[10] Of course, as you add predictors, the R^2 can never decrease, but the improvement may not justify the added complexity of the additional predictors. One criterion that might help is to use the adjusted R^2. Best subsets regression programs usually offer a choice of criteria, and of course different criteria usually lead to different "best" models.

Although best subsets programs are quite clever about computing far fewer than all the possible alternative models, they do become overwhelmed by more than a few dozen possible predictors or very many cases. So, unfortunately, they aren't useful in many data mining applications. We'll discuss this more in the online Chapter 25.

Another alternative is to have the computer build a regression "stepwise." In a **stepwise regression**, at each step a predictor is either added to or removed from the model. The predictor we choose to add can be selected according to several alternative criteria; for instance, we could choose the one that results in the least P-value for its regression coefficient. Alternatively, we could choose the one that results in the largest value of the adjusted R^2. The criterion used varies from one analyst or software designer to another. Similarly, if we're starting with a model containing a large number of predictors, we could choose to remove one based on the P-value for its regression coefficient or according to the effect on the adjusted R^2 or some other criterion. The hope is that, by following this path, the computer can settle on a good model. The model will gain or lose a predictor only if that change in the model makes a big enough change in the performance measure. The changes stop when no more changes pass the criterion.

Best subsets and stepwise methods offer both a final model and information about the paths they followed. The intermediate stage models can raise interesting questions about the data and suggest relationships you might not have thought about. Some programs offer the chance for you to make choices as the process progresses. By interacting with the process at each decision stage, you can exclude a variable that you judge inappropriate for the model (even if including it would help the statistic being optimized) or include a variable that wasn't the top choice at the next step if you think it's important for your purposes. Don't let a variable that doesn't make sense enter the model just because it has a high correlation, but at the same time, don't exclude a predictor just because you didn't initially think it was important. (That would be a good way to make sure you never learn anything new.) Finding the balance between these two choices underlies the art of successful model building and makes it challenging.

Unlike best subset methods, stepwise methods can work even when the number of potential predictors is large. In such cases, using a stepwise method can help you identify potentially interesting predictors.

Both methods are powerful. But as with many powerful tools, they require care when you use them. You should be aware of what the automated methods *fail* to do: They don't check the assumptions and conditions. Some, such as the independence of the cases, you can check before performing the analyses. Others, such as

Choosing Predictors

Suppose we have 5 possible predictor variables.

Best Subsets: The best combination of 3 predictors out of the 5.

Stepwise Forward: Suppose we have 2 predictors in our model, we select the best one to add from the remaining 3.

Stepwise Backward: Suppose we have 4 predictors in our model, we remove the one of those 4 that causes the least damage.

[10]Best subsets regressions don't actually compute every regression. Instead, they cleverly exclude models they know to be worse than some they've already examined. Even so, there are limits to the size of the data and number of variables they can deal with comfortably.

the Linearity Condition and concerns over outliers and influential cases, must be checked for each model. There's a risk that automated methods will be influenced by nonlinearities, by outliers, by high leverage points, by clusters, and by the need for constructed dummy variables to account for subgroups.[11] And these influences affect not just the coefficients in the final model, but the *selection* of the predictors themselves. If there's a case that's influential for even one possible multiple regression model, a best subsets search is guaranteed to consider that model (because it considers *all* possible models) and have its decision influenced by that one case.

- **Choosing the wrong "best" model.** Here's a simple example of how stepwise and best subsets regressions can go astray. We might want to find a regression to model *Horsepower* in a sample of cars from the cars' engine size (*Displacement*) and *Weight*. The simple correlations are as follows:

	HP	Disp	Wt
Horsepower	1.000		
Displacement	0.872	1.000	
Weight	0.917	0.951	1.000

Because *Weight* has a slightly higher correlation with *Horsepower*, stepwise regression will choose it first. Then, because *Weight* and engine size (*Displacement*) are so highly correlated, once *Weight* is in the model, *Displacement* won't be added to the model. And a best subsets regression will prefer the regression on *Weight* because it has a higher R^2 and adjusted R^2. But *Weight* is, at best, a lurking variable leading to both the need for more horsepower and a larger engine. Don't try to tell an engineer that the best way to increase horsepower is to add weight to the car and that the engine size isn't important! From an engineering standpoint, *Displacement* is a far more appropriate predictor of *Horsepower*, but neither stepwise regression nor best subsets regression can find that model.

Challenges in Building Regression Models

Sometimes we can have a very large number of predictor variables. For instance, the real estate industry records dozens of variables on every house sold, as we saw in the Guided Example of Chapter 20. Part of the challenge in constructing models is simply preparing the data for analysis. A simple scatterplot can often reveal a data value mistakenly coded, but with hundreds of potential variables, the task of checking the data for accuracy, missing values, consistency, and reasonableness can become the major part of the effort. We'll return to this issue in the online Chapter 25.

Another challenge in building large models is Type I error. Although we've warned against using 0.05 as an unquestioned guide to statistical significance, we have to start somewhere, and this critical value is often used to test whether a variable can enter (or leave) a regression model. Of course, using 0.05 means that in about 1 in 20 times, a variable whose contribution to the model may be negligible will appear as significant. Using something more stringent than 0.05 means that potentially valuable variables may be overlooked. Whenever we use automatic methods (stepwise, best subsets, or others), the actual number of different models considered becomes huge, and the probability of a Type I error grows with it. There is no easy remedy for this problem. Building a model that includes

---

[11]This risk grows dramatically with larger and more complex data sets—just the kind of data for which these methods can be most helpful.

predictors that actually contribute to reducing the variation of the response and avoiding predictors that simply add noise to the predictions is the challenge of modern model building. Much current research is devoted to criteria and automatic methods to make this search easier and more reliable, but for the foreseeable future you'll need to use your own judgment and wisdom in addition to your statistical knowledge to build sensible useful regressions.

FOR EXAMPLE   Stepwise regression for diamond prices

In addition to the predictor variables from the last example (For Example: "Regression diagnostics for diamond prices"), we have information on the quality of the *Cut* (four grades: *Good*, *Very Good*, *Excellent*, and *Ideal*) and the quality of the *Clarity* (seven grades: *VVS2, VVS1, VS2, VS1, SI2, SI1*, and *IF*). A model was fit to predict *Log10Price* from all the predictors we have available: *Carat Weight, Colour, Cut, Clarity, Depth,* and *Table* on all 749 diamonds. A stepwise backward removal of predictors was performed, and the following model was selected:

Response Variable: $Log_{10}Price$
$R^2 = 94.46\%$ Adjusted $R^2 = 94.37\%$
$s = 0.06806$ with $749 - 13 = 736$ degrees of freedom

Variable	Coeff	SE(Coeff)	t-ratio	P-Value
Intercept	2.437903	0.014834	164.349	<0.0001
Carat.Weight	1.200301	0.011365	105.611	<0.0001
ColourD	0.342888	0.009107	37.649	<0.0001
ColourG	0.254024	0.008159	31.135	<0.0001
CutGood	−0.028884	0.011133	−2.594	0.00966
CutVeryGood	−0.015374	0.005503	−2.793	0.00535
CutIdeal	0.012127	0.010022	1.210	0.22662
ClaritySI1	−0.237850	0.011736	−20.267	<0.0001
ClaritySI2	−0.312076	0.012454	−25.058	<0.0001
ClarityVS1	−0.130431	0.012118	−10.764	<0.0001
ClarityVS2	−0.178439	0.011684	−15.273	<0.0001
ClarityVVS1	−0.064518	0.012445	−5.184	<0.0001
ClarityVVS2	−0.076747	0.011878	−6.461	<0.0001

QUESTION Compare this model with the model based only on *Carat Weight* and *Colour* from For Example: "Indicator variables for diamond colour" with indicator variables for *Colour*.

ANSWER This new model has several advantages over the simpler model. First, the residual standard error is now 0.068 $\log_{10}$ Price, a decrease from 0.109 $\log_{10}$ Price. (We can transform that back to dollars as $10^{0.068} = \$1.17$—quite a small standard deviation.)

Correspondingly, the R^2 is now 94.46% compared with 85.66%. Nearly all the terms are highly statistically significant. The one exception is the indicator for the *Ideal* level of *Cut*. We could consider omitting this indicator (which would then combine the levels *Excellent* and *Ideal*), but for simplicity we'll leave it as is. Before deploying this model, however, we should look at all the assumptions and conditions, which we'll do in the final example of this chapter.

GUIDED EXAMPLE   Housing Prices

Let's take an example of predicting house prices from 15 other variables. We have data on a random sample of 1734 homes in a single geographic area.

The variables available include:

Price	The price of the house as sold
Lot Size	The size of the land in acres
Waterfront	An indicator variable coded as 1 if the property contains waterfront, 0 otherwise
Age	The age of the house in years
Land Value	The assessed value of the property without the structures
New Construct	An indicator variable coded as 1 if the house is new construction, 0 otherwise
Central Air	An indicator variable coded as 1 if the house has central air conditioning, 0 otherwise
Fuel Type	A categorical variable describing the main type of fuel used to heat the

house: 1 = None; 2 = Gas; 3 = Electric; 4 = Oil; 5 = Wood; 6 = Solar; 7 = Unknown/Other

Heat Type	A categorical variable describing the heating system of the house: 1 = None; 2 = Forced Hot Air; 3 = Hot Water; 4 = Electric
Sewer Type	A categorical variable describing the sewer system of the house: 1 = None/Unknown; 2 = Private (Septic System); 3 = Commercial/ Public
Living Area	The size of the living area of the house in square feet
Pct Univ	The percent of the residents of the same community that attended university
Full Baths	The number of full bathrooms
Half Baths	The number of half bathrooms
Bedrooms	The number of bedrooms
Fireplaces	The number of fireplaces

PLAN   **Setup** State the objective of the study.

Identify the variables.

Model Think about the assumptions and check the conditions. A scatterplot matrix is a good way to examine the relationships for the quantitative variables.

We want to build a model to predict house prices for a certain geographical region. We have data on *Price* ($) and 15 potential predictor variables selected from a much larger list.

✓ **Linearity Condition.** To fit a regression model, we first require linearity. (Scatterplots of *Price* against *Living Area, Age, Bedrooms, Bathrooms,* and *Fireplaces,* similar to the regression of Chapter 20, are found to be linear and are not shown here.)

✓ **Independence Assumption.** We can regard the house prices as being independent of one another since they're from a fairly large geographic area.

✓ **Randomization Condition.** These 1734 houses are a random sample of a much larger set. That supports the idea that these houses are independent.

To check equal variance and Normality, we usually find a regression and examine the residuals. Linearity is all we need for that.

Remarks

Examination of *Fuel Type* showed that there were only six houses that did not have categories 2, 3, or 4.

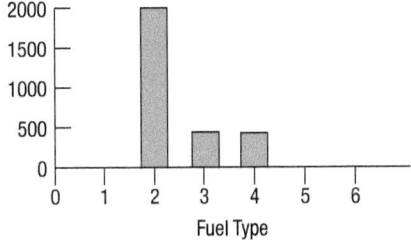

For fuel type and heat type, choose as few variables as possible.

Two of those had unknown Heat Type. We decided to set these six houses aside, leaving three categories. So we can use two dummy variables for each. We combined the two Bathroom variables into a single variable Bathroom equal to the sum of the full baths plus 0.5 x half baths. We now have 17 potential predictor variables.

We started by fitting a model to all of them.

Dependent variable is: Price
R-squared = 65.1% R-squared (adjusted) = 64.8%
s = 584008 with 1728 − 18 = 1710 degrees of freedom

Variable	Coeff	SE(Coeff)	t-Ratio	P-value
Intercept	18794.0	23333	0.805	0.4207
Lot.Size	7774.34	2246	3.46	0.0006
Waterfront	119046	15577	7.64	≤ 0.0001
Age	−131.642	58.54	−2.25	0.0246
Land.Value	0.9258	0.048	19.4	≤ 0.0001
New.Construct	−45234.8	7326	−6.17	≤ 0.0001
Central.Air	9864.30	3487	2.83	0.0047
Fuel Type[2]	4225.35	5027	0.840	0.4008
Fuel Type[3]	−8148.11	12906	−0.631	0.5279
Heat Type[2]	−1185.54	12345	−0.096	0.9235
Heat Type[3]	−11974.4	12866	−0.931	0.3521
Sewer Type[2]	4051.84	17110	0.237	0.8128
Sewer Type[3]	5571.89	17165	0.325	0.7455
Living.Area	75.769	4.24	17.9	<0.0001
Pct.Univ	−112.405	151.9	−0.740	0.4593
Bedrooms	−4963.36	2405	−2.06	0.0392
Fireplaces	768.058	2992	0.257	0.7975
Bathrooms	23077.4	3378	6.83	0.0001

✓ **Equal Spread Condition.** A scatterplot of the Studentized residuals against predicted values shows no thickening or other patterns. There is a group of homes whose residuals are larger (both negative and positive) than the vast majority, whose Studentized residual values are larger than three or four in absolute value. We'll revisit them after we've selected our model.

(continued)

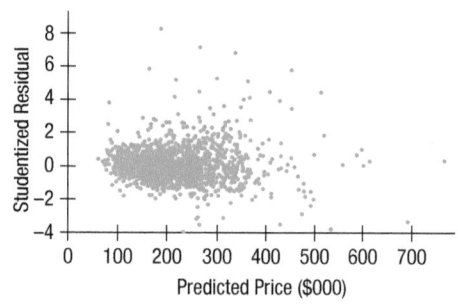

We need the Nearly Normal Condition only if we want to do inference and the sample size is not large. If the sample size is large, we need the distribution to be Normal only if we plan to produce prediction intervals.

✓ **Nearly Normal Condition, Outlier Condition.** The histogram of residuals is unimodal and symmetric, but slightly long-tailed. The Normal probability plot supports that.

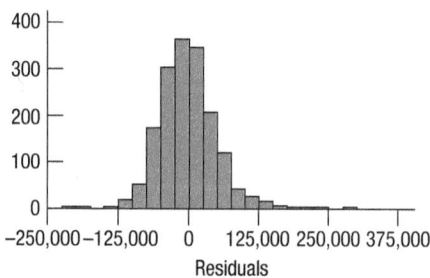

Under these conditions, we can proceed to search for a suitable multiple regression model using a subset of the predictors. We'll return to some of our concerns in the discussion.

DO

Mechanics We first let the step-wise program proceed backward from the full model on all 17 predictors.

Here's the computer output for the multiple regression, starting with all 17 predictor variables and proceeding backward until no more candidates were nominated for exclusion.

Dependent variable is: Price
R-squared = 65.1% R-squared (adjusted) = 64.9%
$s = 58345$ with $1728 - 12 = 1716$ degrees of freedom

Variable	Coeff	SE(Coeff)	t-ratio	P-value
Intercept	9643.14	6546	1.47	0.1409
Lot.Size	7580.42	2049	3.70	0.0002
Waterfront	119372	15365	7.77	≤0.0001
Age	−139.704	57.18	−2.44	0.0147
Land.Value	0.921838	0.0463	19.9	≤0.0001
New.Construct	−44172.8	7159	−6.17	≤0.0001
Central.Air	9501.81	3402	2.79	0.0053
Heat Type[2]	10099.9	4048	2.50	0.0127
Heat Type[3]	−791.243	5215	−0.152	0.8794
Living.Area	75.9000	4.124	18.4	≤0.0001
Bedrooms	−4843.89	2387	−2.03	0.0426
Bathrooms	23041.0	3333	6.91	≤0.0001

The estimated equation is:

$Price = 9643.14 + 7580.42\ LotSize$
$\qquad + 119.372\ Waterfront - 139.70\ Age$
$\qquad + 0.922\ LandValue$
$\qquad - 44{,}172.8\ NewConstruction$
$\qquad + 9501.81\ CentralAir$
$\qquad + 10099.9\ Heat\ Type2$
$\qquad - 791.24\ Heat\ Type3$
$\qquad + 75.90\ Living\ Area$
$\qquad - 4843.89\ Bedrooms$
$\qquad + 23041\ Bathrooms$

Nearly all of the P-values are small, which indicates that even with 11 predictors in the model, most are contributing. The exception is the indicator for *Heat Type 3*, which is *Hot Water*. We could consider dropping this indicator; however, for simplicity we have left the model as the stepwise search found it. The R^2 value of 65.1% indicates that more than 65% of the overall variation in house prices has been accounted for by this model, and the fact that the adjusted R^2 has actually increased suggests that we haven't removed any important predictors from the model. The residual standard error of \$58,345 gives us a rough indication that we can predict the price of a home to within about $2 \times \$58{,}345 = \$116{,}690$. If that's close enough to be useful, then our model is potentially useful as a price guide.

Remarks

We also tried running the stepwise regression program forward and obtained the same model. There are some houses that have large Studentized residual values and some that have somewhat large leverage, but omitting them from the model didn't significantly change the coefficients. We'll use this model as a starting basis for pricing homes in the area.

REPORT

Conclusion Summarize your results and state any limitations of your model in the context of your original objectives.

MEMO

Re: Regression Analysis of Home Price Predictions

A regression model of Price on 11 predictors accounts for about 65% of the variation in the price of homes. Tests of each coefficient show that each of these variables appears to be an aspect of the price of a house.

This model reflects the common wisdom in real estate about the importance of various aspects of a home. An important variable not included is the location, which every real estate agent knows is crucial to pricing a house. This is ameliorated by the fact that all these houses are in the same general area. However, knowing more specific information about where they're located would probably improve the model. The price found from this model can be used as a starting point for comparing a home with comparable homes in the area.

As with all multiple regression coefficients, when we interpret the effect of a predictor, we must take into account all the other predictors and be careful not to suggest a causal relationship between the predictor and the response variable. Here are some interesting features of the model. It appears that among houses with the same values of the other variables,

(continued)

those with waterfront access are worth on average about $119,000 more. Among houses with the same values of the other variables, those with more bedrooms have lower sales prices by, on average, $4843 for each bedroom, while among those with the same values of the other variables, those with more bathrooms have higher prices by, on average, $23,000 per bathroom. Not surprisingly, the value of the land is positively associated with the sale price, accounting for, on average, about $0.92 of the sale price for each $1 of assessed land value among houses that are otherwise alike on the other variables.

This model reflects the prices of 1734 homes in a random sample of homes taken in this area.

LO❸ ## 21.5 Collinearity

Houses with more rooms generally cost more than houses with fewer rooms. A simple regression of *Price* on *Rooms* showed:

Model 1. Price vs. Rooms

Variable	Coeff	SE(Coeff)	t-ratio	P-Value
Intercept	53015.6	6424.3	8.252	<0.0001
Rooms	22572.9	866.7	26.046	<0.0001

An additional room seems to be "worth" about $22,500, on average, to these homes. We also know that the *Living Area* of a house is an important predictor, which associates each extra square foot with an average increase of $113.12:

Model 2. Price vs. Living Area

Variable	Coeff	SE(Coeff)	t-ratio	P-Value
Intercept	13439.394	4992.353	2.692	0.00717
Living Area	113.123	2.682	42.173	<0.0001

Finally, a simple regression on *Bedrooms* also shows increasing price with number of *Bedrooms*, with an additional *Bedroom* associated with an increase, on average, of $48,218:

Model 3. Price vs. Bedrooms

Variable	Coeff	SE(Coeff)	t-ratio	P-Value
Intercept	59863	8657	6.915	<0.0001
Bedrooms	48218	2656	18.151	<0.0001

But when we put more than one of these variables into a regression equation simultaneously, things can change. Here's a regression with both *Living Area* and *Bedrooms:*

Model 4. Price vs. Living Area and Bedrooms

Variable	Coeff	SE(Coeff)	t-ratio	P-Value
Intercept	36667.895	6610.293	5.547	<0.0001
Living Area	125.405	3.527	35.555	<0.0001
Bedrooms	−14196.769	2675.159	−5.307	<0.0001

Now it appears that an extra bedroom is associated with a *lower* sale *Price*.

In Model 4, we see that more bedrooms don't make a house worth more if they just carve up the existing living area. The value of more bedrooms in Model 3 was probably because houses with more bedrooms tend to have more living area as well.

This type of coefficient change often happens in multiple regression and can seem counterintuitive. When two predictor variables are correlated, their coefficients in a multiple regression (with both of them present) can be quite different from their simple regression slopes. In fact, the coefficient can change from being significantly positive to significantly negative with the inclusion of one correlated predictor, as is the case here with *Bedrooms* and *Living Area*. The problem arises when one of the predictor variables can be predicted well from the others. This phenomenon is called **collinearity**.[12]

Collinearity in the predictors can have other consequences in a multiple regression. If instead of adding *Bedrooms* to the model we add *Rooms*, we see a different outcome:

Model 5. Price vs. Living Area and Rooms

Variable	Coeff	SE(Coeff)	*t*-ratio	P-Value
Intercept	11691.586	5521.253	2.118	0.0344
Living Area	110.974	3.948	28.109	<0.0001
Rooms	783.579	1056.568	0.742	0.4584

The coefficient for *Living Area* has hardly changed at all compared with Model 2. It still shows an increase of about $111 per square foot, but the coefficient for *Rooms* is indistinguishable from zero. With the addition of *Living Area* to the model, the coefficient for *Rooms* changed from having a *t*-statistic over 25 with a very small P-value (in Model 1), to having a P-value of 0.458. Notice also that the standard errors of the coefficients have increased. The standard error of *Living Area* increased from 2.68 in Model 2 to 3.95 in Model 5. That may not seem like much, but it's an increase of nearly 50%.

This variance inflation of the coefficients is another consequence of collinearity. The stronger the correlation between predictors, the more the variance of their coefficients increases when both are included in the model. Sometimes this effect can change a coefficient from statistically significant to indistinguishable from zero.

Data sets in business often have related predictor variables. General economic variables, such as interest rates, unemployment rates, GDP, and other productivity measures, are highly correlated. The choice of which subsets to include in the model can significantly change the coefficients, their standard errors, and their P-values, making both selecting the models and interpreting them difficult.

How can we detect and deal with collinearity? Let's look at a regression among just the predictor variables. If we regress *Rooms* on *Bedrooms* and *Living Area*, we find:

Model 6. Rooms vs. Bedrooms and Living Area

Variable	Coeff	SE(Coeff)	*t*-ratio	P-Value
Intercept	0.680	0.141	4.821	<0.0001
Bedrooms	0.948	0.057	16.614	<0.0001
Living Area	0.009	0.000	25.543	<0.0001

Residual standard error: 1.462 on 1725 degrees of freedom
Multiple R-squared: 0.602 Adjusted R-squared: 0.6015
F-statistic: 1304 on 2 and 1725 DF, P-value: <0.0001

---

[12]You may also see this problem called "multicollinearity."

Look at the R^2 for that regression. What does it tell us? Since R^2 is the fraction of variability accounted for by the regression, in this case, that's the fraction of the variability in *Rooms* accounted for by the other two predictors.

Now we can be precise about collinearity. If that R^2 were 100%, we'd have perfect collinearity. *Rooms* would then be perfectly predictable from the other two predictors and so could tell us nothing new about *Price* because it didn't vary in any way not already accounted for by the predictors already in the model. In fact, we couldn't even perform the calculation. Its coefficient would be indeterminate, and its standard error would be infinite. (Statistics packages usually print warnings when this happens.[13]) Conversely, if the R^2 were 0%, then *Rooms* would bring entirely new information to the model, and we'd have no collinearity at all.

Clearly, there's a range of possible collinearities for each predictor. The statistic that measures the degree of collinearity of the jth predictor with the others is called the **variance inflation factor (VIF)** and is found as:

$$\text{VIF}_j = \frac{1}{1 - R_j^2}.$$

The R_j^2 here shows how well the jth predictor can be predicted by the other predictors. The $1 - R_j^2$ term measures what that predictor has left to bring to the regression model. If R_j^2 is high, then not only is that predictor superfluous, but it can damage the predictor model. The VIF tells how much the variance of the coefficient has been inflated due to this collinearity. The higher the VIF, the higher the standard error of its coefficient and the less it can contribute to the regression model. Since R_j^2 can't be less than zero, the minimum value of the VIF is 1.0. The VIF takes into account the influence of all the other predictors—and that's important. You can't judge whether you have a collinearity problem simply by looking at the correlations among the predictors because those only consider each "pair" of predictors.

As a final blow, when a predictor is collinear with the other predictors, it's often difficult to figure out what its coefficient means in the multiple regression. We've blithely talked about "removing the effects of the other predictors," but now when we do that, there may not be much left. What is left isn't likely to be about the original predictor, but more about the fractional part of that predictor not associated with the others. In a regression of *Horsepower* on *Weight* and *Engine Size*, once we've removed the effect of *Weight* on *Horsepower*, *Engine Size* doesn't tell us anything more about *Horsepower*. That's certainly not the same as saying that *Engine Size* doesn't tell us anything at all about *Horsepower*. It's just that most cars with big engines also weigh a lot. So *Engine Size* may be telling us mostly about sporty cars that have larger engines than expected for their weight.

To summarize, when a predictor is collinear with the other predictors in the model, two things can happen:

1. Its coefficient can be surprising, taking on an unanticipated sign or being unexpectedly large or small.

2. The standard error of its coefficient can be large, leading to a smaller *t*-statistic and correspondingly large P-value.

One telltale sign of collinearity is the paradoxical situation in which the overall *F*-test for the multiple regression model is significant, showing that at least one of the coefficients is significantly different from zero, and yet most or all of the individual coefficients have small *t*-values, each in effect denying that *it* is the significant one.

---

[13]Excel does not. It gives zero as the estimate of most values and a NUM! warning for the standard error of the coefficient.

What should you do about a collinear regression model? The simplest cure is to remove some of the predictors. That both simplifies the model and generally improves the *t*-statistics. If several predictors give pretty much the same information, removing some of them won't hurt the model. Which should you remove? Keep the predictors that are most reliably measured, least expensive to find, or even those that are politically important. Another alternative that may make sense is to construct a new predictor by combining variables. For example, several different measures of a product's durability (perhaps for different parts of it) could be added together to create a single durability measure. There is, however, a downside to removing predictor variables, as the remaining variables pick up the effect of the variables we removed. We are, in effect, building a model, knowing that there are additional "lurking variables" we've left out.

Facts About Collinearity

- The collinearity of any predictor with the others in the model can be measured with its variance inflation factor.
- High collinearity leads to the coefficient being poorly estimated and having a large standard error (and correspondingly low *t*-statistic). The coefficient may seem to be the wrong size or even the wrong sign.
- Consequently, if a multiple regression model has a high R^2 and large F, but the individual *t*-statistics aren't significant, you should suspect collinearity.
- Collinearity is measured in terms of the R_j^2 between a predictor and *all* the other predictors in the model. It is not measured in terms of the correlation between any two predictors. Of course, if two predictors are highly correlated, then the R_j^2 with even more predictors must be at least that large and will usually be even higher.

JUST CHECKING

3 In a study of *Salary*, a regression on several variables shows high collinearity of *Age* and *Years Experience*. Explain why this might be and what you would do about it.

Answer is found in Appendix A.

"Quadratic Terms," an advanced section, can be found on MyStatLab.

WHAT CAN GO WRONG?

- **Beware missing data.** Values may be missing or unavailable for any case in any variable. In simple regression, when the cases are missing for reasons that are unrelated to the variable we're trying to predict, that's not a problem. We just analyze the cases for which we have data. But when several variables participate in a multiple regression, any case with data missing on any of the variables will be omitted from the analysis. You can unexpectedly find yourself with a much smaller set of data than you started with. Be especially careful, when comparing regression models with different predictors, that the cases participating in the models are the same.
- **Don't forget linearity.** The Linearity Assumption requires linear relationships among the variables in a regression model. As you build and compare

regression models, be sure to plot the data to check that it's straight. Violations of this assumption make everything else about a regression model invalid.

- **Check for parallel regression lines.** When you introduce an indicator variable for a category, check the underlying assumption that the other coefficients in the model are essentially the same for both groups. If not, consider adding an interaction term.

ETHICS IN ACTION

Grape and Wine Tours, located in Niagara-on-the-Lake, Ontario, offers winery tours and culinary experiences for birthdays, anniversaries, bridal parties, and corporate retreats. It offers day trips as well as overnight stays for groups from 8 to 300. The business is seasonal and dependent on personal discretionary income for trips booked by consumers. Corporate bookings also depend on the state of the economy, particularly the ups and downs of the financial markets.

Before the start of the touring season, Grape and Wine Tours needs to estimate what demand is going to be like for the coming year. Suppose you're a consultant hired to provide a statistical estimate and you've decided to use multiple regression analysis to predict demand for wine tours from a variety of explanatory variables. Discussion with the client identifies the appropriate variables as consumer confidence, consumer satisfaction indices for the travel industry, GDP growth rate, and leading economic indicators such as housing starts. Data are available on a monthly basis from the touring seasons in previous years.

You use a stepwise regression procedure to bring the best variables into your model, and the model you end up with has variables for consumer confidence and satisfaction, but no economic variables. Grape and Wine Tours's CEO is surprised, but she decides this means that it's more important to plan an advertising campaign for consumers than for corporate clients.

Ethical Issue *Although using an automatic stepwise procedure is useful in narrowing down the number of independent variables to consider for the model, more thoughtful analysis is usually required. In this case, many of the potential independent variables are highly correlated with each other. It turns out that the consumer satisfaction indices are correlated with leading economic indicators and GDP growth rate. Their presence in the model would preclude the entry of GDP growth and housing starts, but saying that economic factors don't affect the dependent variable is misleading. Further, these data are time-dependent. No variables capturing trend or potential seasonality are considered (related to Item A, ASA Ethical Guidelines; see Appendix C, the American Statistical Association's Ethical Guidelines for Statistical Practice, also available online at www.amstat.org/about/ethicalguidelines.cfm).*

Ethical Solution *The interrelationships between the independent variables need to be examined. More expertise is required on the part of the model builder; residuals need to be examined to determine if there are any time-dependent patterns (e.g., seasonality).*

WHAT HAVE WE LEARNED?

Learning Objectives

❶ Use indicator (dummy) variables and re-expression intelligently.

- An indicator variable that's 1 for a group and 0 for others is appropriate when the slope for that group is the same as for the others, but the intercept may be different.
- If the slope for the indicated group is different, then it may be appropriate to include an interaction term in the regression model.
- When there are three or more categories, use a separate indicator variable for each, but leave one out to avoid collinearity.

- Consider fitting quadratic terms in your regression model when the residuals show a bend. Re-expressing y is another option, unless the bent relationship between y and the x's is not monotonic.

❷ Diagnose multiple regressions to expose any undue influence of individual cases.

- Leverage measures how far a case is from the mean of all cases when measured on the x-variables.
- The leverage of a case tells how much the predicted value of that case would change if the y-value of the case were changed by adding 1 and nothing else in the regression changed.
- Studentized residuals are residuals divided by their individual standard errors. Externally Studentized residuals follow a t-distribution when the regression assumptions are satisfied.
- A case is influential if it has both sufficient leverage and a large enough residual. Removing an influential case from the data will change the model in ways that matter to your interpretation or intended use. Measures such as *Cook's D* and *DFFITS* combine leverage and Studentized residuals into a single measure of influence.
- By assigning an indicator variable to a single influential case, we can remove its influence from the model and test (using the P-value of its coefficient) whether it is in fact influential.

❸ Build multiple regression models when many predictors are available.

- Seek models with few predictors, a relatively high R^2, a relatively small residual standard deviation, relatively small P-values for the coefficients, no cases that are unduly influential, and predictors that are reliably measured and relatively unrelated to each other.
- Automated methods for seeking regression models include best subsets and stepwise regression. Neither one should be used without carefully diagnosing the resulting model.
- Recognize collinearity and deal with it to improve your regression model. Collinearity occurs when one predictor can be well predicted from the others.

  - The R^2 of the regression of one predictor on the others is a suitable measure. Alternatively, the *variance inflation factor*, which is based on this R^2, is often reported by statistics programs.
  - Collinearity can have the effect of making the P-values for the coefficients large (not significant), even though the overall regression fits the data well.
  - Removing some predictors from the model or making combinations of those that are collinear can reduce this problem.

- Recognize why a particular regression model is fit.

  - We may want to understand some of the individual coefficients.
  - We may simply be interested in prediction and not be concerned about the coefficients themselves.

Terms

Best subsets regression A regression method that checks all possible combinations of the available predictors to identify the combination that optimizes an arbitrary measure of regression success.

Collinearity When one (or more) of the predictors can be fit closely by a regression on the other predictors, we have collinearity. When collinear predictors are in a regression model, they may have unexpected coefficients and will often have inflated standard errors (and correspondingly small t-statistics).

Cook's Distance A measure of the influence of a single case on the coefficients in a multiple regression.

DFFITS A measure of how much the estimate of a single case changes if that case is omitted from the regression.

Dummy variable	An indicator variable.
Indicator variable	A variable constructed to indicate for each case whether it's in a designated group or not. Usually the values are 0 and 1, where 1 indicates group membership.
Influential case	A case is *influential* on a multiple regression model if, when it is omitted, the model changes by enough to matter for your purposes. (There is no specific amount of change defined to declare a case influential.) Cases with high leverage and a large Studentized residual are likely to be influential.
Interaction term	A variable constructed by multiplying a predictor variable by an indicator variable. An interaction term adjusts the slope of that predictor for the cases identified by the indicator.
Leverage	A measure of the amount of influence an individual case has on the regression. Moving a case in the *y* direction by one unit (while changing nothing else) will move its predicted value by the leverage, denoted *h*.
Stepwise regression	An automated method of building regression models in which predictors are added to or removed from the model one at a time in an attempt to optimize a measure of the success of the regression. Stepwise methods rarely find the best model and are easily affected by influential cases, but they can be valuable in winnowing down a large collection of candidate predictors.
Studentized residual	When a residual is divided by an independent estimate of its standard deviation, the result is a Studentized residual. The type of Studentized residual that has a *t*-distribution is an *externally Studentized residual*.
Variance inflation factor (VIF)	A measure of the degree to which a predictor in a multiple regression model is collinear with other predictors. It is based on the R^2 of the regression of that predictor on all the other predictors in the model:

$$VIF_j = \frac{1}{1 - R_j^2}.$$

Skills

Plan
- Understand how individual cases can influence a regression model.
- Know how to define and use indicator variables to introduce categorical variables as predictors in a multiple regression model.
- Know how to examine histograms of leverages and of Studentized residuals to identify extraordinary cases that deserve special attention.
- Know how to recognize when a regression model may suffer from collinearity.

Do
- Know how to check for high-leverage cases by identifying cases whose leverage stands apart from the others.
- Know how to check for cases with large Studentized residuals.
- Be able to use a statistics package to diagnose a multiple regression model.
- Know how to build a multiple regression model, selecting predictors from a larger collection of potential predictors.

Report
- Be able to interpret the coefficients found for indicator variables in a multiple regression.
- Be able to discuss the influence that a case with high leverage or a large Studentized residual may have in a regression.
- Be able to recognize when collinearity among the predictors may be present. Be able to check for it and discuss its consequences.
- Be careful in interpreting regression coefficients when the predictors are collinear. Avoid the pitfalls of interpreting the sign of the coefficient as if it were special. If you can't interpret the first digit of the coefficient, you probably can't interpret the sign either.

MINI case studies

Canadian Snow Birds

Each winter, many Canadians travel to the Caribbean for a winter vacation. Some people call them "snow birds," including Jeff Mohammed who heads up a company offering all-inclusive packages. He has deals with a number of hotels and airlines and offers prices that depend on the quality of the hotel (four or five stars) and the month of the year. The file **ch21_MCSP_snow_birds** contains data on the number of bookings he obtained during January to March last year for three-night stays. This year, he wants to estimate the number of bookings he will obtain based on last year's data. Develop a multiple regression model for Jeff taking into account (i) indicator variables, (ii) interaction terms, and (iii) nonlinearity.

First Quantum Minerals of Vancouver

First Quantum Minerals Ltd., a mining and metals company based in Vancouver, produces copper, gold, and nickel. It's listed on the Toronto and London stock exchanges. The data file **ch21_MCSP_Quantum** contains monthly commodity prices for copper, gold, and nickel together with the share price of First Quantum. Use multiple regression to investigate the relationship between the share price and the commodity prices of these three metals. (a) Regress share price against the three metals' prices in a multiple regression model. Plot residuals against predicted share price and identify an outlying data point. (b) Calculate the leverage of this outlying point. (c) Comment on the effect of removing this point from the analysis, but keep it in for the rest of the analysis. (d) If you were to remove an explanatory variable based on the P-value of its regression coefficient, which variable would you choose? (e) First Quantum's major production is copper and nickel. Investigate the effect of removing the gold price from the analysis. (f) Comment on how your answer to (d) compares with your answer to (e). (g) Should the price of either copper or nickel also be removed from the regression in (e)? (h) What regression model do you recommend for share price as a function of metal price(s)?

Paralyzed Veterans

The Paralyzed Veterans of America (PVA) is a philanthropic organization sanctioned by the U.S. government to represent the interests of veterans who are disabled. To generate donations, the PVA sends out greeting cards and mailing address labels periodically with its requests for donations. To increase its efficiency, the organization would like to be able to model the amount of donations based on past giving and demographic variables of donors. The data set **ch21_MCSP_pva** contains data on 3648 donors who gave to a recent solicitation. There are 26 predictor variables and 1 response variable. The response variable (GIFTAMNT) is the amount of money contributed by the donor to the last solicitation. Find a model from the

(*continued*)

26 predictor variables using any model selection procedure you like to predict this amount. The variables include:

Variables Based on the Donor's Zip Code

> MALEVET (% male veterans)
> VIETVETS (% Vietnam veterans)
> WWIIVETS (% WWII veterans)
> LOCALGOV (% employed by local government)
> STATEGOV (% employed by state government)
> FEDGOV (% employed by federal government)

Variables Specific to the Individual Donor

> CARDPROM (number of card promotions received lifetime)
> MAXADATE (date of most recent promotion received in YYMM year month format)
> NUMPROM (number of promotions received lifetime)
> CARDPRM12 (number of card promotions received in last 12 months)
> NUMPRM12 (number of promotions received in last 12 months)
> NGIFTALL (number of gifts given lifetime to date)
> CARDGIFT (number of gifts to card promotions given lifetime to date)
> MINRAMNT (amount of smallest gift to date in $)
> MINRDATE (date associated with the smallest gift to date—YYMM format)
> MAXRAMNT (amount of largest gift to date in $)
> MAXRDATE (date associated with the largest gift to date—YYMM format)
> LASTGIFT (amount of most recent gift in $)
> AVGGIFT (average amount of gifts to date in $)
> CONTROLN (control number—unique record identifier)
> HPHONE_D (indicator variable for presence of a published home phone number: 1 = Yes; 0 = No)
> CLUSTER2 (classic cluster code—nominal field)
> CHILDREN (number of children living at home)

Response Variable

> GIFTAMNT (response variable—amount of last gift in $)

Be sure to include exploratory data analysis, and evaluate the relationship among these variables using graphical and correlation analysis to guide you in building your regression models. Write a report summarizing your analysis.

MyStatLab Students! Save time, improve your grades with MyStatLab. Questions marked in ▦ can be found on MyStatLab. You can practise them as often as you want, and most feature step-by-step guided solutions to help you find the right answer. You'll find a personalized study plan available to you too!

Technology Help: Multiple Regression Analysis

Statistics packages differ in how much information they provide to diagnose a multiple regression. Most packages provide leverage values. Many provide far more, including statistics we haven't discussed. But for all, the principle is the same. We hope to discover any cases that don't behave like the others in the context of the regression model and then to understand why they're special.

Many of the ideas in this chapter rely on the concept of examining a regression model and then finding a new one based on your growing understanding of the model and the data. Regression diagnosis is meant to provide steps along that road. A thorough regression analysis may involve finding and diagnosing several models.

Statistics software will omit from a regression analysis any case that is missing a value on any variable in the model. As a result, when variables are added to or removed from a model, the cases in that model may change in subtle ways.

EXCEL

Excel does not offer diagnostic statistics with its regression function.

Comments

Although the dialogue offers a Normal probability plot of the residuals, the data analysis add-in doesn't make a correct probability plot, so don't use this option. The "standardized residuals" are just the residuals divided by their standard deviation (with the wrong df), so they too should be ignored.

XLSTAT

XLStat can handle both qualitative (indicator) and quantitative explanatory variables. To use stepwise regression:

- Choose **Modeling data**.
- Select all desired explanatory variables in the dialogue box for **Linear regression**.
- On the **Options** tab, XLStat gives you options for building a Best model using various criteria, or building a model based on significance in a stepwise or forward or backward direction.

MINITAB

- Choose **Regression** from the **Stat** menu.
- Choose **Regression. . .** from the **Regression** submenu.
- In the Regression dialogue, assign the y-variable to the Response box and assign the x-variables to the Predictors box.
- Click on the **Options** button to obtain the VIF in the regression output.
- In the Regression **Storage** dialogue, you can select a variety of diagnostic statistics. They will be stored in the columns of your worksheet.
- Click the **OK** button to return to the Regression dialogue.
- To specify displays, click **Graphs**, and check the displays you want.
- Click the **OK** button to return to the Regression dialogue.
- Click the **OK** button to compute the regression.

Comments

You'll probably want to make displays of the stored diagnostic statistics. Use the usual Minitab methods for creating displays.

Minitab also offers both stepwise and best subsets regression from the **Regression** dialogue. Indicate the response variable, the predictors eligible for inclusion, and any predictors that you wish to force into the model.

SPSS

- Choose **Regression** from the **Analyze** menu.
- Choose **Linear** from the **Regression** submenu.
- When the Linear Regression dialogue appears, select the y-variable and move it to the dependent target. Then move the x-variables to the independent target.
- Click the **Save** button.
- In the Linear Regression Save dialogue, choose diagnostic statistics. These will be saved in your worksheet along with your data.
- Click the **Continue** button to return to the Linear Regression dialogue.
- Click the **OK** button to compute the regression.

Comments

SPSS offers stepwise methods (use the **Method** drop-down menu), but not best subsets (in the student version). Click on the **Statistics** button to find collinearity diagnostics and on the **Save** button for influential point diagnostics. (The residuals SPSS calls "Studentized deleted" are the externally Studentized residuals we've recommended in this chapter.) You may want to plot the saved diagnostics using SPSS's standard graphics methods.

JMP

- From the **Analyze** menu, select **Fit Model**.
- Specify the response, Y. Assign the predictors, X, in the **Construct Model Effects** dialogue box.
- Click on **Run Model**.
- Click on the red triangle in the title of the Model output to find a variety of plots and diagnostics available.

Comments

JMP chooses a regression analysis when the response variable is "Continuous."

In JMP, stepwise regression is a *personality* of the Model Fitting platform; it's one of the selections in the Fitting Personality popup menu on the Model Specification dialogue. Stepwise provides best subsets with an **All Possible Models** command, accessible from the red-triangle drop-down menu on the stepwise control panel after you've computed a stepwise regression analysis.

EXERCISES

SECTION 21.1

1. For each of the following, show how you would code dummy (or indicator) variables to include in a regression model.

a) Company unionization status (Unionized, No Union)
b) Gender (Female, Male)
c) Account Status (Paid on Time, Past Due)
d) Political party affiliation (Liberal, Conservative, NDP, Other) **LO ❶**

2. A marketing manager has developed a regression model to predict quarterly sales of his company's down jackets based on price and amount spent on advertising. An intern suggests that he include an indicator (dummy) variable for the fall quarter.

a) How would you code such a variable? (What values would it have for each quarter?)
b) Why does the intern's suggestion make sense?
c) Do you think a regression with the indicator variable for fall would model down jacket sales better than one without that predictor? **LO ❶**

3. Do movies of different types have different rates of return on their budgets? Here's a scatterplot of *US Gross* ($M) vs. *Budget* ($M) for recent movies whose *MPAA Rating* is either PG (blue) or R (red):

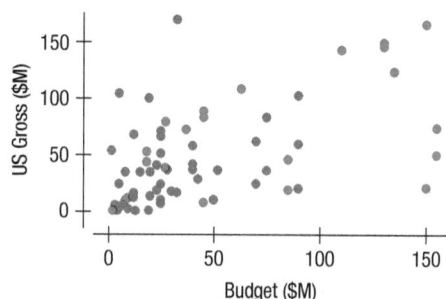

a) Why might a researcher want to use an indicator variable for the *MPAA Rating*?
b) What would the data values in such an indicator variable be? **LO ❶**

4. Here is the regression for Exercise 3 with an indicator variable:

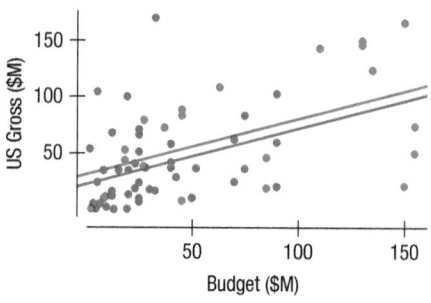

Dependent variable is: USGross ($M)
R-squared = 0.193, Adjusted R-squared: 0.166
$s = 37.01$ with $62 - 3 = 59$ degrees of freedom

Variable	Coefficient	SE(Coeff)	t-ratio	P-value
Intercept	49.2642	12.5736	3.918	0.000235
Budget	0.3292	0.1264	2.605	0.011612
R Rating	-12.4871	11.2145	-1.113	0.270018

a) Write out the regression model.
b) In this regression, the variable *R Rating* is an indicator variable that is 1 for movies that have an R rating. How would you interpret the coefficient of *R Rating*?
c) What null hypothesis can we test with the *t*-ratio for *R Rating*?
d) Can you reject the null hypothesis of (c)? Explain. **LO ❶**

5. For each of the following, show how you would code dummy (indicator) variables to include in a regression model.

a) Type of residence (Apartment, Condominium, Townhouse, Single Family Home)
b) Employment status (Full-time, Part-time, Unemployed) **LO ❶**

6. A marketing manager has developed a regression model to predict quarterly sales of his company's midweight microfibre jackets based on price and amount spent on advertising. An intern suggests that he include indicator (dummy) variables for each quarter.

a) How would you code the variables? (How many dummy variables do you need? What values would they have?)
b) Why does the intern's suggestion make sense?
c) Do you think a regression with the indicator variables would model jacket sales better than one without those predictors? **LO ❶**

SECTION 21.2

7. Are R rated movies as profitable as those rated PG-13? Here's scatterplot of *USGross* ($M) vs. *Budget* ($M) for PG-13 (green) and R (purple) rated movies:

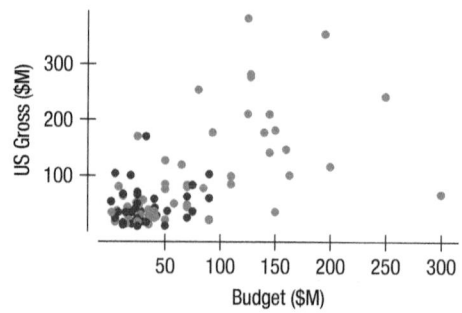

a) How would you code the indicator variable? (Use PG-13 as the base level.)

b) How would you construct the interaction term variable? **LO ❶**

8. Here is the scatterplot of the variables in Exercise 7 with regression lines added for each kind of movie:

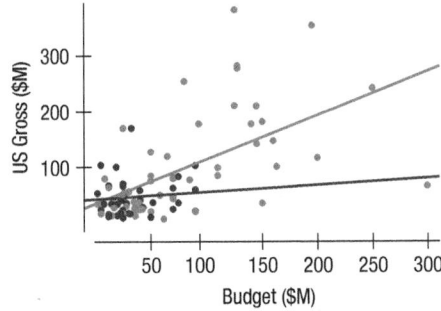

The regression model is:

Dependent variable is: USGross ($M)
R-squared = 0.3674, Adjusted R-squared: 0.3491
s = 58.24 with 107 − 3 = 104 degrees of freedom

Variable	Coefficient	SE(Coeff)	t-ratio	P-value
Intercept	34.0262	10.6595	3.192	0.00187
Budget	0.7902	0.1143	6.912	<0.0001
R Rating	9.9217	18.8666	0.526	0.60009
Budget*R Rating	−0.6679	0.3798	−1.758	0.08163

a) Write out the regression model.

b) In this regression, the variable *Budget*R Rating* is an interaction term. How would you interpret its coefficient?

c) What null hypothesis can we test with the *t*-ratio for *Budget*R Rating*?

d) Would you reject that hypothesis at 0.05? What do you conclude? **LO ❶**

SECTION 21.3

9. For the regression model in Exercise 8, the leverage values look like this:

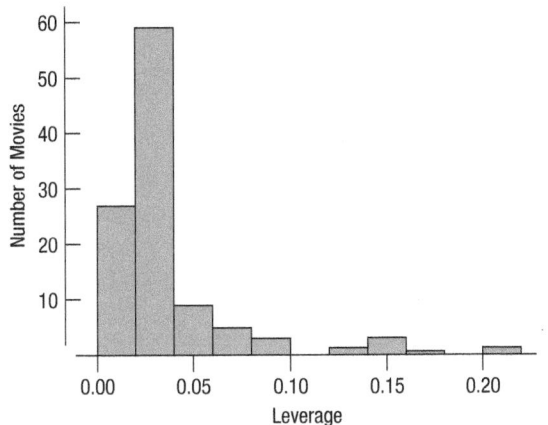

The movie with the highest leverage of 0.219 is Walt Disney's *John Carter*, which grossed $66M but had a budget of $300M. If the budget for *John Carter* had been $1M higher than it was (and everything else remained the same), how much would the model's prediction of *John Carter*'s U.S. gross revenue change? **LO ❷**

10. For the same regression as in Exercise 9, the Cook's Distances look like this:

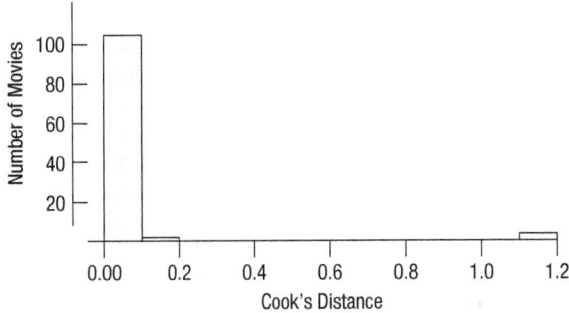

The outlier, once again, is *John Carter*, whose budget was more than $200M more than its gross revenue in the United States Setting this movie aside and rerunning the regression from Exercise 8, we find:

Dependent variable is: USGross ($M)
R-squared = 0.4635, Adjusted R-squared: 0.4478
s = 53.89 with 106 − 3 = 103 degrees of freedom

Variable	Coefficient	SE(Coeff)	t-ratio	P-value
Intercept	21.6562	10.2755	2.108	0.0375
Budget	1.0224	0.1188	8.607	60.0001
R Rating	22.2916	17.6941	1.260	0.2106
Budget*R Rating	−0.9001	0.3556	−2.531	0.0129

a) What are the main differences between this model with *John Carter* removed and the model from Exercise 7 with it included?

b) Which model do you prefer? Explain briefly. **LO ❷**

SECTION 21.4

11. An analyst wants to build a regression model to predict spending from the following four predictor variables: *Past Spending, Income, Net Worth,* and *Age*. A correlation matrix of the four predictors shows the following:

	Income	Net Worth	Age
Past Spending	0.442	0.433	0.446
Income		0.968	0.992
Net Worth			0.976

Why might a stepwise regression search not find the same model as an "all subsets" regression? **LO ❸**

12. The analyst in Exercise 11 fits the model with the four predictor variables. The regression output shows the following:

Response Variable: Spending
$R^2 = 84.92\%$ Adjusted $R^2 = 84.85\%$
$s = 48.45$ with $908 - 5 = 903$ degrees of freedom

Variable	Coeff	SE(Coeff)	t-ratio	P-Value
Intercept Past	$-3.738e+00$	$1.564e+01$	-0.239	0.811
Spending	$1.063e-01$	$4.203e-03$	25.292	<0.0001
Income	$1.902e-03$	$3.392e-04$	5.606	<0.0001
Networth	$2.900e-05$	$3.815e-05$	0.760	0.447
Age	$6.065e-01$	$7.631e-01$	0.795	0.427

a) How many observations were used in the regression?
b) What might you do next?
c) Is it clear that *Income* is more important for predicting *Spending* than *Networth*? Explain. **LO ❸**

SECTION 21.5

13. The analyst from Exercise 11, worried about collinearity, regresses *Age* against *Past Spending, Income,* and *Networth.* The output shows the following:

Response Variable: Age
$R^2 = 98.75\%$ Adjusted $R^2 = 98.74$
$s = 2.112$ with $908 - 4 = 904$ degrees of freedom

Variable	Coeff	SE(Coeff)	t-ratio	P-value
(Intercept)	$2.000e+01$	$1.490e-01$	134.234	<0.0001
Past.Spending	$3.339e-04$	$1.828e-04$	1.826	0.0681
Income	$3.811e-04$	$7.610e-06$	50.079	<0.0001
Networth	$2.420e-05$	$1.455e-06$	16.628	<0.0001

What is the VIF for *Age*? **LO ❸**

14. If the VIF for *Networth* in the regression of Exercise 11 was 20.83, what would the R^2 be from the regression of *Networth* on *Age, Income,* and *Past Spending*? **LO ❸**

CHAPTER EXERCISES

ⓣ 15. Pizza ratings, part 1. Manufacturers of frozen foods often reformulate their products to maintain and increase customer satisfaction and sales. So they pay particular attention to evaluations of their products compared with those of their competitors. Frozen pizzas are a major sector of the frozen food market, accounting for $2.84 billion in sales in 2007 (www.aibonline.org/resources/statistics/2007pizza.htm). The prestigious Consumers Union rated frozen pizzas for flavour and quality, assigning an overall score to each brand tested. A regression model to predict the Consumers Union score from *Calories, Type* (1 = cheese, 0 = pepperoni), and *Fat Content* gives the following result:

Dependent variable is: Score
R-squared = 28.7% R-squared (adjusted) = 20.2%
$s = 19.79$ with $29 - 4 = 25$ degrees of freedom

Source	Sum of Squares	df	Mean Square	F-ratio
Regression	3947.34	3	1315.78	3.36
Residual	9791.35	25	391.654	

Variable	Coeff	SE(Coeff)	t-ratio	P-value
Intercept	-148.817	77.99	-1.91	0.0679
Calories	0.743023	0.3066	2.42	0.0229
Type	15.6344	8.103	1.93	0.0651
Fat	-3.89135	2.138	-1.82	0.0807

a) What is the interpretation of the coefficient of *Type* in this regression? According to these results, what type would you expect to sell better—cheese or pepperoni?
b) What displays would you like to see to check assumptions and conditions for this model? **LO ❶**

ⓣ 16. Roller coasters at Canada's Wonderland, part 1. Data on roller coasters at Canada's Wonderland are available in the data file and include *Speed, Height,* and *Number of Inversions* (*Source:* Data from Coaster Enthusiasts of Canada website. Retrieved from http://cec.chebucto.org/Co-Stats.html). We performed a regression to investigate whether *Speed* is related to *Height,* and then added indicator variables to take into account the number of inversions: none, one, or more than one. Here are the results:

Independent variable is *Speed.*
ANOVA

	df	SS	MS	F	Significance F
Regression	3	4693.345	1564.448	13.38293	0.002761
Residual	7	818.2916	116.8988		
Total	10	5511.636			

Standard	Coefficients	Error	t-Stat	P-Value
Intercept	38.58237	7.063941	5.461876	0.000944
Height	1.198282	0.250517	4.783233	0.002005
More than one	7.690357	8.895165	0.864555	0.415924
One	6.667451	11.65581	0.572028	0.585196

a) What does the coefficient for the indicator variable for "one" mean?
b) Why is there no indicator variable for "none"?

c) Does the information about the *Number of Inversions* contribute to estimating the *Speed*? LO ❶

17. Pizza ratings, part 2. Here's a scatterplot of the residuals against predicted values for the regression model found in Exercise 15:

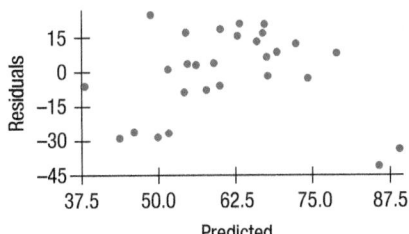

a) The two extraordinary points in the lower right are *Reggio's* and *Michelina's*, two gourmet brands. Interpret these points.
b) Do you think these two pizzas are likely to be influential in the regression? Would setting them aside be likely to change the coefficients? What other statistics might help you decide? LO ❷

18. Roller coasters at Canada's Wonderland, part 2. Here is a scatterplot of the residuals from the regression in Exercise 16:

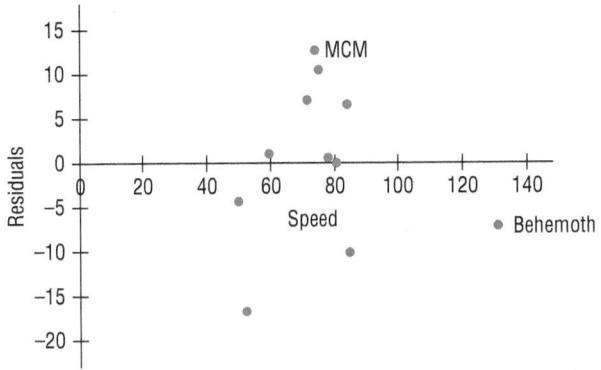

a) For Behemoth, the data value for *Speed* is 123, and the predicted value is 130.15. If we change the data value to 124 and recompute the regression, the predicted value becomes 130.89. What is the leverage for Behemoth?
b) For MCM the data value for *Speed* is 86 and the predicted value is 73.33. Change the data value for MCM to 87, recompute the regression, and calculate the leverage for MCM.
c) Does Behemoth have a high influence on the regression?
d) Does MCM have a high influence on the regression? LO ❷

19. Walmart revenue. Each week about 100 million customers—nearly one-third of the U.S. population—visit one of Walmart's U.S. stores. How does Walmart's revenue relate to the state of the economy in general? Here's a regression table predicting Walmart's monthly revenue ($ billion) from the end of 2003 through the start of 2007 from the consumer price index (CPI), and a scatterplot of the relationship:

Dependent variable is: WM_Revenue
R-squared = 11.4% R-squared (adjusted) = 9.0%
s = 3.689 with 39 − 2 = 37 degrees of freedom

Variable	Coeff	SE(Coeff)	*t*-ratio	P-value
Intercept	−24.4085	19.25	−1.27	0.2127
CPI	0.071792	0.0330	2.18	0.0358

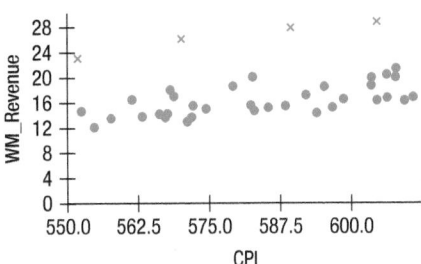

a) The points plotted with "x" are the four December values. We can construct a variable that is "1" for those four values and "0" otherwise. What is such a variable called?

Here's the resulting regression:

Dependent variable is: WM_Rev
R-squared = 80.3% R-squared (adjusted) = 79.2%
s = 1.762 with 39 − 3 = 36 degrees of freedom

Variable	Coeff	SE(Coeff)	*t*-ratio	P-Value
Intercept	−34.7755	9.238	−3.76	0.0006
CPI	0.087707	0.0158	5.55	<0.0001
December	10.4905	0.9337	11.2	<0.0001

b) What is the interpretation of the coefficient of the constructed variable *December*?
c) What additional assumption is required to include the variable *December* in this model? Is there reason to believe that it's satisfied? LO ❶

20. Baseball attendance. Pedro Martinez, who retired from Major League Baseball in 2012, had a stellar career, helping the Boston Red Sox to their first World Series title in 86 years in 2004. The next year he became a free agent and the New York Mets picked him up for $53 million for four years. Even after the move to New York, Martinez had his own fans. Possibly, he attracted more fans to the ballpark when he pitched at home, helping to justify his multimillion dollar contract. Was there really a "Pedro effect" in attendance? We have data for the Mets' home games of the 2005 season. The regression has the following predictors:

Weekend   1 if game was on Saturday or Sunday, 0 otherwise

Yankees   1 if game was against the Yankees (a hometown rivalry), 0 otherwise

Rain Delay   1 if the game was delayed by rain (which might have depressed attendance), 0 otherwise

Opening Day 1 for opening day, 0 for the others

Pedro Start 1 if Pedro was the starting pitcher, 0 otherwise

Here's the regression:

Dependent variable is: Attendance
R-squared = 53.9% R-squared (adjusted) = 50.8%
$s = 6998$ with $80 - 6 = 74$ degrees of freedom

Variable	Coeff	SE(Coeff)	t-ratio	P-Value
Intercept	28896.9	1161	24.9	≤0.0001
Weekend	9960.50	1620	6.15	≤0.0001
Yankees	15164.3	4218	3.59	0.0006
Rain Delay	−17427.9	7277	−2.39	0.0192
Opening Day	24766.1	7093	3.49	0.0008
Pedro Start	5428.02	2017	2.69	0.0088

a) All of these predictors are of a special kind. What are they called?
b) What is the interpretation of the coefficient for *Pedro Start*?
c) If we're primarily interested in Pedro's effect on attendance, why is it important to have the other variables in the model?
d) Could Pedro's agent claim, based on this regression, that his man attracts more fans to the ballpark? What statistics should he cite? **LO ❶**

21. **Pizza ratings, part 3.** In Exercise 17, we raised questions about two gourmet pizzas. After removing them, the resulting regression looks like this:

Dependent variable is: Score
R-squared = 64.4% R-squared (adjusted) = 59.8%
$s = 14.41$ with $27 - 4 = 23$ degrees of freedom

Source	Sum of Squares	df	Mean Square	F-ratio
Regression	8649.29	3	2883.10	13.9
Residual	4774.56	23	207.590	

Variable	Coeff	SE(Coeff)	t-ratio	P-Value
Intercept	−363.109	72.15	−5.03	≤0.0001
Calories	1.56772	0.2824	5.55	≤0.0001
Type	25.1540	6.214	4.05	0.0005
Fat	−8.82748	1.887	−4.68	0.0001

A plot of the residuals against the predicted values for this regression looks like this. It has been coloured according to the *Type* of pizza.

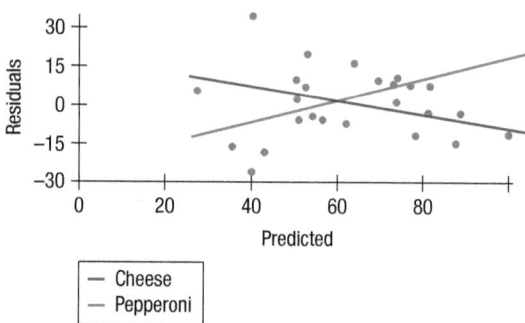

— Cheese
— Pepperoni

a) What does this plot say about how the regression model deals with these two types of pizza?

We constructed another variable consisting of the indicator variable *Type* multiplied by *Calories*. Here's the resulting regression:

Dependent variable is: Score
R-squared = 73.1% R-squared (adjusted) = 68.2%
$s = 12.82$ with $27 - 5 = 22$ degrees of freedom

Source	Sum of Squares	df	Mean Square	F-ratio
Regression	9806.53	4	2451.63	14.9
Residual	3617.32	22	164.424	

Variable	Coeff	SE(Coeff)	t-ratio	P-Value
Intercept	−464.498	74.73	−6.22	≤0.0001
Calories	1.92005	0.2842	6.76	≤0.0001
Type	183.634	59.99	3.06	0.0057
Fat	−10.3847	1.779	−5.84	≤0.0001
Type*Cals	−0.461496	0.1740	−2.65	0.0145

b) Interpret the coefficient of *Type*Cals* in this regression model.
c) Is this a better regression model than the one in Exercise 15 and Exercise 17? **LO ❶**

22. **Roller coasters at Canada's Wonderland, part 3.** Here are plots of two regression analyses of roller coaster *Speed* against *Height*. The first is for roller coasters that don't have inversions and the second is for roller coasters that do.

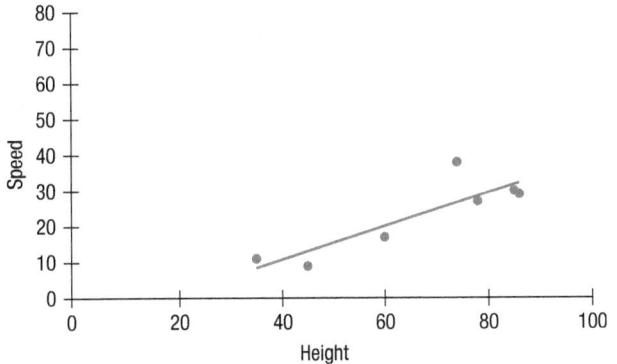

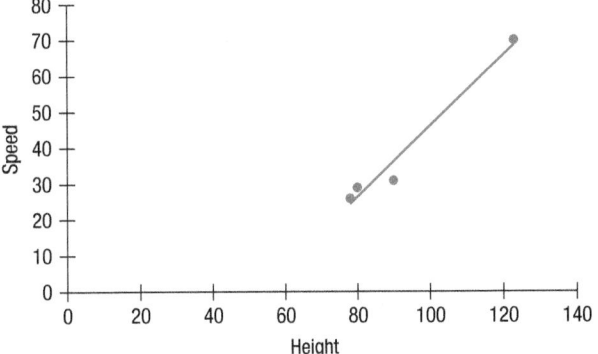

a) Would a *single* indicator variable for *Inversions* added to the regression equation enable us to obtain one regression equation for both sets of data? Explain.

b) Choose an appropriate set of explanatory variables, using an indicator variable (Inv = 1 for no inversions and 0 for some inversions) as necessary, and perform the regression analysis for the combined data set. Write the regression equation. Interpret the meaning of each coefficient and indicate whether the coefficient is significant at the 90% level. **LO ❶**

❶ 23. Insurance (life expectancy). Insurance companies base their premiums on many factors, but basically all the factors are variables that predict life expectancy. Life expectancy varies from place to place. Here's a regression that models *Life Expectancy* in terms of other demographic variables. The *Murder* rate is per 100,000, *High School Graduation* rate is in percent, *Income* is per capita income in dollars, *Illiteracy* rate is per 1000, and *Life Expectancy* is in years.

Dependent variable is: Life exp
R-squared = 67.0% R-squared (adjusted) = 64.0%
$s = 0.8049$ with $50 - 5 = 45$ degrees of freedom

Source	Sum of Squares	df	Mean Square	F-ratio
Regression	59.1430	4	14.7858	22.8
Residual	29.1560	45	0.647910	

Variable	Coeff	SE(Coeff)	t-ratio	P-Value
Intercept	69.4833	1.325	52.4	≤0.0001
Murder	−0.261940	0.0445	−5.89	≤0.0001
HSGrad	0.046144	0.0218	2.11	0.0403
Income	1.24948e-4	0.0002	0.516	0.6084
Illiteracy	0.276077	0.3105	0.889	0.3787

a) The state with the highest leverage and largest Cook's Distance is Alaska. It's plotted with an "*x*" in the residuals plot. What evidence do you have from these diagnostic plots that Alaska might be an influential point?

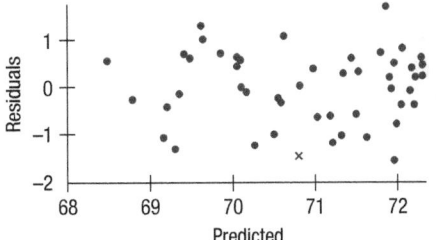

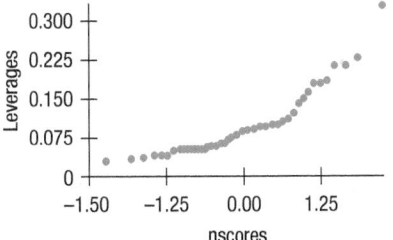

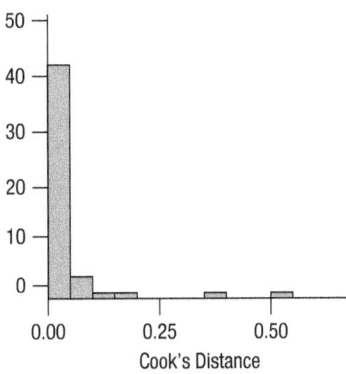

Here's another regression with a dummy variable for Alaska added to the regression model:

Dependent variable is: Life exp
R-squared = 70.8% R-squared (adjusted) = 67.4%
$s = 0.7660$ with $50 - 6 = 44$ degrees of freedom

Source	Sum of Squares	df	Mean Square	F-ratio
Regression	62.4797	5	12.4959	21.3
Residual	25.8193	44	0.586802	

Variable	Coeff	SE(Coeff)	t-ratio	P-Value
Intercept	67.6377	1.480	−45.7	≤0.0001
Murder	−0.250395	0.0426	5.88	≤0.0001
HSGrad	0.055792	0.0212	2.63	0.0116
Illiteracy	0.458607	0.3053	1.50	0.1401
Income	3.68218e − 4	0.0003	1.46	0.1511
Alaska	−2.23284	0.9364	−2.38	0.0215

b) What does the coefficient for the dummy variable for Alaska mean? Is there evidence that Alaska is an outlier in this model?

c) Which model would you prefer for understanding or predicting *Life Expectancy*? Explain. **LO❶, ❷**

🌐 **24. Cereal nutrition.** Breakfast cereal manufacturers publish nutrition information on each box of their product. There is a long history of cereals being associated with nutrition. Here's a regression to predict the number of *Calories* in breakfast cereals from their *Sodium, Potassium,* and *Sugar* content, and some diagnostic plots:

Dependent variable is: Calories
R-squared = 38.4% R-squared (adjusted) = 35.9%
s = 15.60 with 77 − 4 = 73 degrees of freedom

Variable	Coeff	SE(Coeff)	t-ratio	P-Value
Intercept	83.0469	5.198	16.0	≤0.0001
Sodium	0.057211	0.0215	2.67	0.0094
Potassium	−0.019328	0.0251	−0.769	0.4441
Sugar	2.38757	0.4066	5.87	≤0.0001

The shaded part of the histogram corresponds to the two cereals plotted with *x*'s in the Normal probability plot of the leverages. These are *All-Bran with Extra Fibre* and *All-Bran.*

a) What do the displays say about the influence of these two cereals on this regression? (The histogram is of the Studentized residuals.)

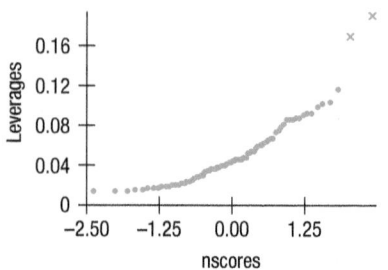

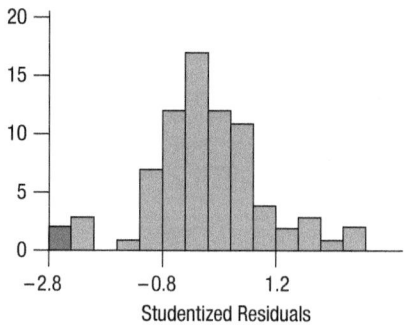

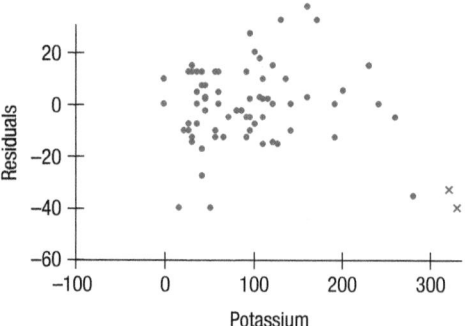

Here's another regression with dummy variables defined for each of the two bran cereals:

Dependent variable is: Calories
R-squared = 50.7% R-squared (adjusted) = 47.3%
s = 14.15 with 77 − 6 = 71 degrees of freedom

Variable	Coeff	SE(Coeff)	t-ratio	P-Value
Intercept	79.0874	4.839	16.3	≤0.0001
Sodium	0.068341	0.0198	3.46	0.0009
Potassium	0.043063	0.0272	1.58	0.1177
Sugar	2.03202	0.3795	5.35	≤0.0001
All-Bran	−50.7963	15.84	−3.21	0.0020
All-Bran Extra	−52.8659	16.03	−3.30	0.0015

b) Explain what the coefficients of the bran cereal dummy variables mean.

c) Which regression would you select for understanding the interplay of these nutrition components? Explain. (*Note:* Both are defensible.)

d) As you can see from the scatterplot, there's another cereal with high potassium. Not too surprisingly, it is *100% Bran*, but its leverage isn't as high as the other two bran cereals. Do you think it should be treated like them (i.e., removed from the model, fit with its own dummy, or left in the model with no special attention, depending on your answer to (c))? Explain. **LO❶, ❷**

🌐 **25. Canadian exchange rate, part 1.** A major sector in the Canadian economy is minerals. Growth in that sector is associated with an increase in the value of the Canadian dollar. The data set contains monthly data for the Canadian exchange rate and stock indices for various sectors of the economy on the Toronto Stock Exchange. (*Sources:* Statistics Canada. [2016]. CANSIM Table 176-0047: Exchange rates, interest rates, money supply, and stock prices; and Bank of Canada, Monthly Average Foreign exchange rates in Canadian dollars, Copyright © 2016. Reproduced and distributed on an "as is" basis with the permission of Statistics Canada.) Investigate how the exchange rate depends on the indices for metals and mining, gold, and energy.

a) Calculate a regression using the exchange rate as the dependent variable and the three indices for metals and mining (M&M), gold, and energy as the independent variables for 2008–2009. Without checking the conditions and assumptions, simply write the regression equation and indicate any regression coefficients that are not significant. How much of the variation in exchange rate does your model explain and what is the standard error?

b) The peak exchange rate during this period (1.0463) occurred in July 2011. What is the predicted value for July 2011 and its associated error?

c) Increase the data value for July 2011 by one and recompute the regression. What is the predicted value for July 2011? What is the leverage of July 2011?

d) Calculate the Cook's Distance for July 2011. **LO ❷**

26. **Lobster price diagnosed.** The price ($/lb) of lobster harvested in the Maine lobster fishing industry is an important factor in the profitability of the industry. Here is a regression model to predict the *Price* from the number of *Traps* (millions), the number of *Fishers*, and the *Catch/Trap* (tonnes):

Dependent variable is: Price/lb
R-squared = 94.4% R-squared (adjusted) = 94.1%
$s = 0.2462$ with $53 - 4 = 49$ degrees of freedom

Variable	Coeff	SE(Coeff)	*t*-ratio	P-Value
Intercept	0.845123	0.3557	2.38	0.0215
Traps (M)	1.20094	0.0619	19.4	≤0.0001
Fishers	−1.21820e − 4	0.0000	−3.30	0.0018
Catch/Trap	−22.0207	10.96	−2.01	0.0500

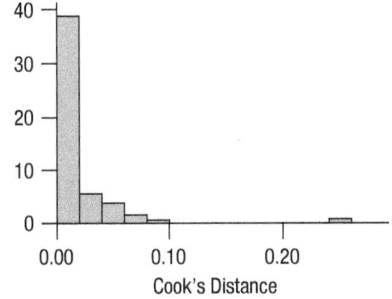

Cook's Distance

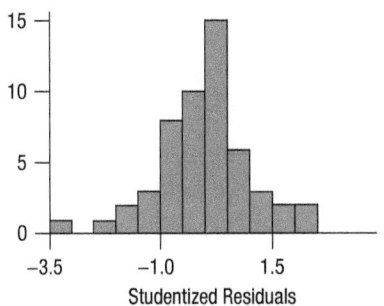

Studentized Residuals

Above is a histogram of the Cook's Distances for this model. The case with the large Cook's Distance is 1994, which was also the year with the lowest Studentized residual. What does this suggest about this model? What would you recommend? **LO ❷**

Ⓣ 27. **Economic regulation model building, part 1.** A study by the U.S. Small Business Administration modelled the GDP per capita of 24 of the countries in the Organisation for Economic Co-operation and Development (OECD) (*Source:* Crain, M. W. The impact of regulatory costs on small firms. Small Business Administration, Office of Advocacy, United States Government. No. 264.) One analysis estimated the effect on GDP of economic regulations using an index of the degree of OECD economic regulation and other variables. The analyst found the following regression model:

Dependent variable is: GDP/Capita
R-squared = 97.4% R-squared (adjusted) = 96.6%
$s = 2084$ with $24 - 6 = 18$ degrees of freedom

Source	Sum of Squares	df	Mean Square	*F*-ratio
Regression	2895078376	5	579015675	133
Residual	78158955	18	4342164	

Variable	Coeff	SE(Coeff)	*t*-ratio	P-Value
Intercept	10487.3	9431	1.11	0.2808
OECD Reg Index	−1343.28	626.4	−2.14	0.0459
Ethnolinguistic Diversity	−69.9875	23.26	−3.01	0.0075
Int'l Trade/GDP	44.7096	14.00	3.19	0.0050
Primary Education(%)	−58.4084	86.11	−0.678	0.5062
1988 GDP/Capita	1.07767	0.0448	24.1	≤0.0001

a) If we remove *Primary Education* from the model, the R^2 decreases to 97.3%, but the adjusted R^2 *increases* to 96.7%. How can that happen? What does it mean? Would you include *Primary Education* in this model?

Here's a part of that regression:

Dependent variable is: GDP/Capita
R-squared = 97.3% R-squared (adjusted) = 96.7%
$s = 2054$ with $24\$ - \$5 = 19$ degrees of freedom

Variable	Coeff	SE(Coeff)	*t*-ratio	P-Value
Intercept OECD	4243.21	2022	2.10	0.0495
Reg Index	−1244.20	600.4	−2.07	0.0521
Ethnolinguistic Diversity	−64.4200	21.45	−3.00	0.0073
Int'l Trade/GDP	40.3905	12.29	3.29	0.0039
1988 GDP/Capita	1.08492	0.0429	25.3	≤0.0001

b) Consider the *t*-statistic for *OECD Regulation* in the reduced model. That was the predictor of interest to this author. Do you agree with his conclusion that OECD regulation reduced GDP/Capita in these countries? Why do you think he chose to include *Primary Education* as a predictor? Explain. **LO ❸**

🕐 **28.** Dirt bikes, part 1. Off-road motorcycles (often called "dirt bikes") are a segment (about 18%) of the growing motorcycle market. Because dirt bikes offer great variation in features, they're a good market segment to study in order to learn about which features account for the cost (manufacturer's suggested retail price, MSRP) of a bike. Researchers collected data on 2005-model dirt bikes (http://lib.stat.cmu.edu/datasets/dirtbike_aug.csv). Their original goal was to study market differentiation among brands (*Source:* Lu, J., Kadane, J. B., & Boatwright, P. [2006]. *The Dirt on Bikes: An Illustration of CART Models for Brand Differentiation.* Retrieved from server1.tepper.cmu.edu/gsiadoc/WP/2006-E57.pdf).

Here's a regression model and some associated graphs:

Dependent variable is: MSRP
R-squared = 91.0% R-squared (adjusted) = 90.5%
s = 606.4 with 100 − 6 = 94 degrees of freedom

Source	Sum of Squares	df	Mean Square	*F*-ratio
Regression	349911096	5	69982219	190
Residual	34566886	94	367733	

Variable	Coeff	SE(Coeff)	*t*-ratio	P-Value
Intercept	−5514.66	826.2	−6.67	≤0.0001
Bore	83.7950	6.145	13.6	≤0.0001
Clearance	152.617	52.02	2.93	0.0042
Engine Strokes	−315.812	89.83	−3.52	0.0007
Total Weight	−13.8502	3.017	−4.59	≤0.0001
Wheelbase	119.138	34.26	3.48	0.0008

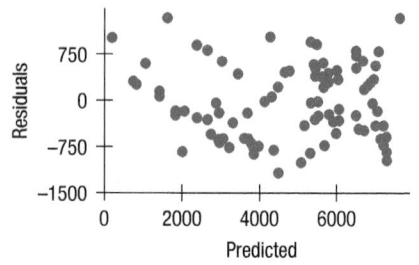

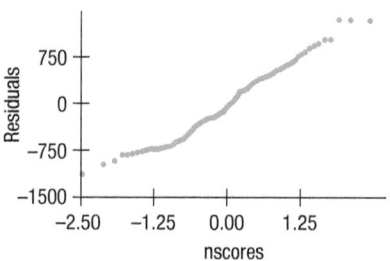

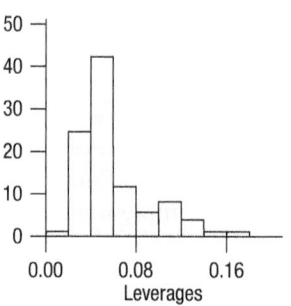

a) List aspects of this regression model that lead to the conclusion that it's likely to be a useful model.
b) What aspects of the displays indicate that the model is a good one? **LO ❶**

29. Airlines on time. Airlines strive to be on time, in part because customers can refer to government-published statistics to select flights that are most often on time. We have data for 19 airlines for March 2006 reporting the following variables:

On Time	(number of on-time arrivals)
Cancelled	(number of cancelled flights)
Diverted	(number of diverted flights)
Carrier	(number of delays due to the carrier)
Weather	(number of delays due to weather)
NAS Delay	(delays due to the National Airspace System [traffic control])
Late Arrival	(number of delays due to late arrival of equipment or crew)

Here's a regression model:

Dependent variable is: On Time
R-squared = 93.9% R-squared (adjusted) = 90.8%
s = 5176 with 19 − 7 = 12 degrees of freedom

Source	Sum of Squares	df	Mean Square	F-ratio
Regression	4947151273	6	824525212	30.8
Residual	321546284	12	26795524	

Variable	Coeff	SE(Coeff)	t-ratio	P-Value
Intercept	1357.10	2316	0.586	0.5687
Cancelled	−18.5514	6.352	−2.92	0.0128
Diverted	39.5623	95.59	0.414	0.6863
Carrier	10.9620	3.104	3.53	0.0041
Weather	10.4637	9.462	1.11	0.2905
NAS Delay	2.46727	1.091	2.26	0.0431
Late Arrival	4.64874	1.445	3.22	0.0074

a) Interpret the coefficient of *Diverted*. (*Hint:* This is a trick question.)

Here's a scatterplot of *On Time* vs. *Diverted* and another regression. Note that *Diverted* is the response variable in this second regression.

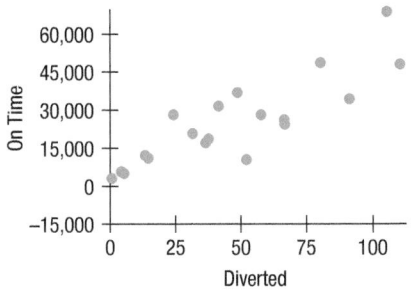

Dependent variable is: Diverted
R-squared = 85.6% R-squared (adjusted) = 80.0%
s = 15.02 with 19 − 6 = 13 degrees of freedom

Variable	Coeff	SE(Coeff)	t-ratio	P-Value
Intercept	−1.65088	6.703	−0.246	0.8093
Cancelled	−0.016896	0.0178	−0.948	0.3604
Carrier	0.013823	0.0081	1.70	0.1136
Weather	0.050714	0.0236	2.15	0.0509
Late Arrival	6.33917e − 3	0.0038	1.67	0.1196
NAS Delay	7.09830e − 3	0.0025	2.86	0.0133

b) It seems from the scatterplot that *Diverted* would be a good predictor of *On Time*, but that seems not to be the case. Why do you think the coefficient of *Diverted* isn't significant in the first regression?
c) How does the second regression explain this apparent contradiction?
d) Find the value of the variance inflation factor statistic for *Diverted* in the first regression. **LO ❶, ❷, ❸**

30. Dirt bikes, part 2. The model in Exercise 28 is missing one predictor that we might have expected to see. *Engine Displacement* is highly correlated ($r = 0.783$) with *MSRP*, but that variable hasn't entered the model (and, indeed, would have a P-value of 0.54 if it were added).

Here's some evidence to explain why that may be. (*Hint:* Notice that *Displacement* is the response variable in this regression.)

Dependent variable is: Displacement
R-squared = 95.9% R-squared (adjusted) = 95.7%
s = 35.54 with 100 − 6 = 94 degrees of freedom

Variable	Coeff	SE(Coeff)	t-ratio	P-Value
Intercept	−8.05901	48.42	−0.166	0.8682
Bore	9.10890	0.3601	25.3	≤0.0001
Clearance	3.55912	3.048	1.17	0.2460
Engine Stroke	−27.3943	5.264	−5.20	≤0.0001
Total Weight	1.03749	0.1768	5.87	≤0.0001
Wheelbase	−10.0612	2.008	−5.01	≤0.0001

a) What term describes the reason why *Displacement* doesn't contribute to the regression model for *MSRP*?
b) Find the value of the variance inflation factor for *Displacement* in the regression on *MSRP*. **LO ❸**

T 31. **Show business diagnosed.** The following regression is based on weekly receipts from shows on Broadway in New York City:

Dependent variable is: Receipts($M)
R-squared = 93.3% R-squared (adjusted) = 93.1%
s = 0.9589 with 92 = 88 degrees of freedom

Source	Sum of Squares	df	Mean Square	F-ratio
Regression	1130.43	3	376.811	410
Residual	80.9067	88	0.919395	

Variable	Coeff	SE(Coeff)	t-ratio	P-Value
Intercept	−22.1715	2.221	−9.98	≤0.0001
Paid Attendance	0.087031	0.0046	19.0	≤0.0001
Number of Shows	−0.024934	0.0338	−0.737	0.4632
Average Ticket Price	0.265756	0.0286	9.29	≤0.0001

Here are some diagnostic plots:

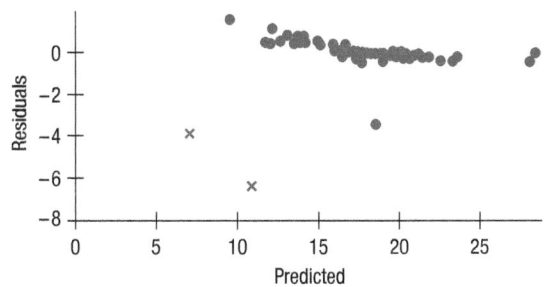

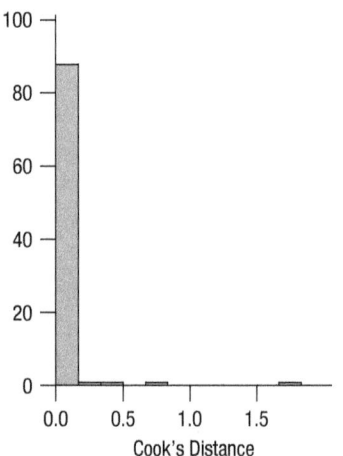

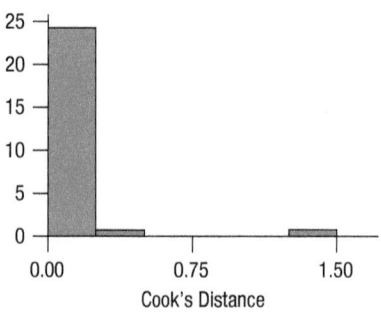

a) The two points plotted with "x" in the residuals vs. predicted plot are the two with the highest Cook's Distances. What does this information say about how those points might be affecting the analysis?

In fact, those points are reports published the last week of November and the first week of December in 2007—a time when the Stagehands Union Local One was on strike, closing down most Broadway shows. It seems that these are not representative weeks for business on Broadway. Removing them results in the following regression:

Dependent variable is: Receipts($M)
R-squared = 98.5% R-squared (adjusted) = 98.5%
s = 0.3755 with 90 − 4 = 86 degrees of freedom

Source	Sum of Squares	df	Mean Square	F-ratio
Regression	809.793	3	269.931	1915
Residual	12.1250	86	0.140988	

Variable	Coeff	SE(Coeff)	t-ratio	P-Value
Intercept	−21.3165	0.8984	−23.7	≤0.0001
Paid Attendance	0.071955	0.0019	37.4	≤0.0001
Number of Shows	0.045793	0.0137	3.35	0.0012
Average Ticket Price	0.274503	0.0115	23.8	≤0.0001

b) What changes in these estimated models support the conclusion that those two weeks were influential points? (*Hint:* The increase in adjusted R^2 isn't one of the reasons.)
c) What ethical issue would be involved in estimating receipts using the first model, i.e., the one including all the data points? (See Appendix C for Ethical Guidelines.)
LO ❷, ❸

32. Economic regulation model building, part 2. Exercise 27 raised some questions about the regression model built to understand the effect of OECD regulation on GDP/Capita in 24 OECD countries. Let's look more deeply. Here's a histogram of the Cook's Distances for that model:

The country with high Cook's Distance is Ireland.
a) What does the Cook's Distance value suggest about Ireland in this model?

Of the predictors available for this model, by far the best (highest R^2 predictor) is *1988 GDP/Capita*. In a scatterplot of *GDP/Capita* vs. *1988 GDP/Capita*, Ireland stands away from the overall linear trend:

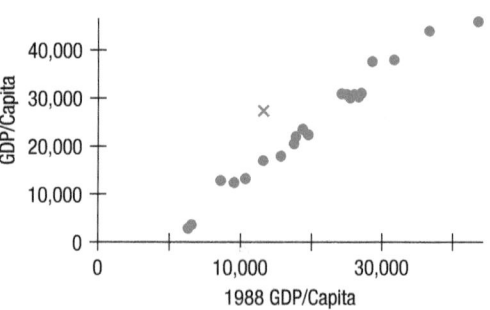

We can define a dummy variable that is "1" for Ireland and "0" for all other countries. The resulting model looks like this:

Dependent variable is: GDP/Capita
R-squared = 98.3% R-squared (adjusted) = 97.7%
s = 1713 with 24 − 7 = 17 degrees of freedom

Variable	Coeff	SE(Coeff)	t-ratio	P-Value
Intercept	13609.0	7818	1.74	0.0998
1988 GDP/Capita	1.10397	0.0378	29.2	≤0.0001
OECD Reg Index	−520.181	579.2	−0.898	0.3816
Int'l Trade/GDP	21.0171	13.81	1.52	0.1463
Ethnolinguistic Diversity	−49.8210	20.19	−2.47	0.0245
Primary Education	−99.3369	72.00	−1.38	0.1856
Ireland	8146.64	2624	3.10	0.0064

b) Explain what the dummy variable for Ireland accomplishes in this model.
c) What ethical issue arises if we were to publish this model and use it to support a claim that OECD regulation

reduces GDP per capita? (See Appendix C for Ethical Guidelines.) **LO ❶, ❸**

33. **HDI diagnostics.** The data file contains data on *HDI* (the UN's Human Development Index) and seven explanatory socioeconomic variables for 96 countries. Using software that provides regression diagnostics (leverage values, Cook's Distance, Studentized residuals), find two countries that have potentially large influence and discuss briefly what is unusual about these countries. **LO ❶, ❷**

34. HDI, model comparison. In Exercise 33 you identified two countries that had potentially large influence on the regression model of *HDI* against seven explanatory socioeconomic variables. Set those countries aside and rerun the model. Write up a few sentences on the impact that leaving these countries out has on the regression and give your recommendation on which model you would prefer. **LO ❶, ❷**

35. Canadian exchange rate, part 2. The Canadian exchange rate may be related to the TSX indices of performance of various sectors of the Canadian economy. The data file used in Exercise 25 contains monthly TSX indices for various sectors of the Canadian economy together with the exchange rate between Canadian and U.S. dollars for the period 2010–2015. Perform a stepwise regression as follows:

a) *Step 1.* Conduct three simple (single-variable) regressions of the exchange rate against the indices for (i) energy, (ii) gold, and (iii) metals and mining (M&M). Without checking the conditions and assumptions, give the equation for each regression and the corresponding value of R^2. Which index explains most of the variability in exchange rate?

b) *Step 2.* Now perform two more regressions. On the basis of the index you chose with the highest R^2 in (a), add each of the other two indices one at a time. Give the equation for each regression and the corresponding value of the adjusted R^2. Just on the basis of the analysis you have done

(Exercise 36 will address other factors), do you recommend adding a second index to combine with the one you chose in Step 1 in order to explain the variability in the exchange rate? If so, which index? **LO ❸**

36. Canadian exchange rate, part 3. In Exercise 25, we regressed the Canadian exchange rate against TSX indices for metals and mining (M&M), gold, and energy, since these are sectors in which the Canadian economy is strong, and they could therefore influence the exchange rate. Investigate the effectiveness of these indices at predicting the exchange rate as follows:

a) Perform a simple (single-variable) regression of exchange rate as the dependent variable against the metals and mining index. Give the results of the regression, including the R^2, the standard errors, and the P-values for each coefficient.

b) Now add the gold index to the regression you did in (a). Give the results of the regression, including the R^2, the standard errors, and the P-values for each coefficient.

c) By what percentage has the coefficient of the M&M index increased between (a) and (b)?

d) In order to see how much additional information the gold index is bringing to our regression over and above what we already had from the M&M index, we now regress the gold index as the dependent variable against the M&M index as the explanatory variable. Give the results of the regression, including the R^2, the standard errors, and the P-values for each coefficient.

e) What is the variance inflation factor (VIF) for the gold index?

f) Using the results of (a) to (e) above, give reasons for including the gold index in the exchange rate regression in addition to the M&M index.

g) Using the results of (a) to (e) above, give reasons against including the gold index in the exchange rate regression in addition to the M&M index. **LO ❷, ❸**

Congratulations, you have now completed all four chapters of Part 3 of this book on "Exploring Relationships Among Variables." A comprehensive case study is available online in MyStatLab that draws together many of the topics you have learned in Part 3. Here is a brief synopsis:

Health Care Costs

Heart disease is a leading cause of death for both men and women, and its costs for the health care system are enormous. To estimate future health care expenditures for heart disease we must analyze how these costs are related to age, gender, diagnosis, and length of stay in hospital. You are provided with data on 12,844 patients and asked to build models for estimating costs.

(*Source:* Centers for Disease Control and Prevention, U.S. Department of Health & Human Services.)

Learning Objectives

Chapter	18	19	20	21
Learning Objective	1, 3	1, 3	1, 2	1, 2, 3

22

Time Series Analysis

LEARNING OBJECTIVES

In this chapter we show you how to make forecasts using past time series data. After reading and studying this chapter, you should be able to:

❶ Recognize when data constitute a time series and how they can be converted into index numbers

❷ Identify four components of a time series: trend, seasonal, cyclic, and irregular

❸ Analyze time series and make forecasts using moving averages, exponential smoothing, and autoregressive models

❹ Measure error in forecasts

❺ Analyze time series and make forecasts using multiple regression models

Whole Foods Market

Whole Foods Market is a natural and organic product retailer that has recently entered the Canadian market. As of 2016, there were five Whole Foods Market stores in British Columbia and five in Ontario. Whole Foods Market has been ranked as one of the "100 Best Companies to Work For" in America by *Fortune* magazine for 19 consecutive years. It was the first major retailer to offset 100% of its energy use with wind energy credits, and it currently maintains a list of ingredients that it won't allow in products sold in its stores, including antibiotics and supplemental growth hormones in meat.

In 1978, 25-year-old John Mackey and 21-year-old Renee Lawson Hardy borrowed $45,000 from family and friends to open the doors of a small natural foods store they named SaferWay in Austin, Texas. Two years later, they joined forces with Clarksville Natural Grocery to open the first Whole Foods Market. With 975 square metres of floor space and a staff of 19, their store was large in comparison to other health food stores of the time. During the next 15 years Whole Foods grew rapidly, in part due to several mergers and acquisitions. Since 2000, Whole Foods has expanded outside of North America with the purchase of seven Fresh & Wild stores in the United Kingdom. In 2007, a major merger with Wild Oats brought 53 more stores to Whole Foods, including two Canadian ones.

Today, Whole Foods Market, Inc. has 91,000 employees and more than 430 stores. The firm has continued to grow, both by opening new stores and by acquiring related firms.[1]

WHAT	Quarterly sales
UNITS	Millions of U.S. dollars
WHEN	1995–2013
WHERE	United States, Canada, and United Kingdom
WHY	To forecast sales for Whole Foods Market

The decade of the 1990s was a period of growth for most companies, but unlike firms in many other industries, Whole Foods Market continued to grow into the next decade. The time series plot in Figure 22.1 shows the quarterly *Sales* ($M) plotted by quarter since 1995. If you were asked to summarize the trend in *Sales* over this decade, what would you say?

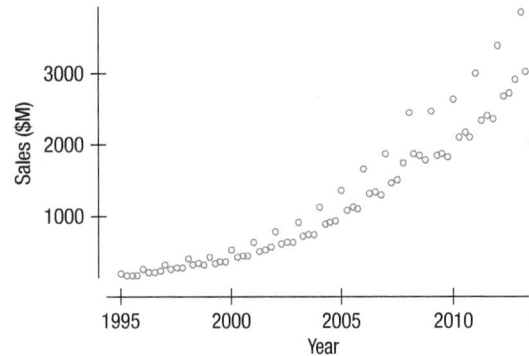

Figure 22.1   Quarterly sales (in $M) for Whole Foods from 1995 to 2013.

Clearly, sales at Whole Foods Market, Inc. grew between 1995 and 2013, starting at below $250 million and reaching nearly $2 billion per quarter. But we'd like to be able to say something more than that, and ultimately we'd like to *model* the growth. Time series models are primarily built for predicting into the near future. Some also offer interpretable coefficients.

Corporations often look at time series plots to examine prior patterns in the data and to forecast future values. The executives at Whole Foods Market, Inc. might be interested in understanding patterns in sales to

- Plan inventory and distribution of goods
- Schedule hiring and staffing
- Understand the impact of seasons, or time of the year, on sales
- Develop advertising campaigns
- Forecast profits and plan corporate strategy

Suppose you're an analyst at Whole Foods Market, Inc. and you've been asked to forecast sales for the next four quarters. How can you analyze the time series to produce accurate forecasts of sales? How can you measure accuracy and compare your different forecasting models?

---

[1]See Whole Foods Market website, www.wholefoodsmarket.com; http://fortune.com/best-companies/whole-foods-market-75/

LO❶   **22.1**   **Time Series and Index Numbers**

Whole Foods, sales are recorded each financial quarter, and we're interested in the growth of sales over time. Whenever we have data recorded sequentially over time, and we consider time to be an important aspect of the data, we have a **time series**.[2] Most time series are equally spaced at roughly regular intervals, such as monthly, quarterly, or annually.[3] The Whole Foods, sales data in Figure 22.1 are a time series measured quarterly. The fiscal year at Whole Foods Market, Inc. starts on or near September 30, so, unlike many companies, the first fiscal quarter reports sales for the end of the calendar year.

Index Numbers

When we want to compare time series with one another, it's often useful to transform the raw data into **index numbers**.

Copper and nickel are important metals for Canadian mining companies; since they often occur together, their ores are often produced by the same mine. However, because prices depend on demand as much as on supply, the price of copper doesn't necessarily mirror the price of nickel. Figures 22.2 and 22.3 show the world prices for copper and nickel during the 49 months from September 2007 to September 2011. To what extent do they mirror each other? It's tough to say. The vertical scales on the graphs are quite different. The shape of the graphs look somewhat similar, but a mining company would be more interested in knowing whether one is trending higher than the other. We can get a better feel for *relative* price trends by scaling each metal price to a common value of 100 in September 2007 and scaling the prices to that base using index numbers.

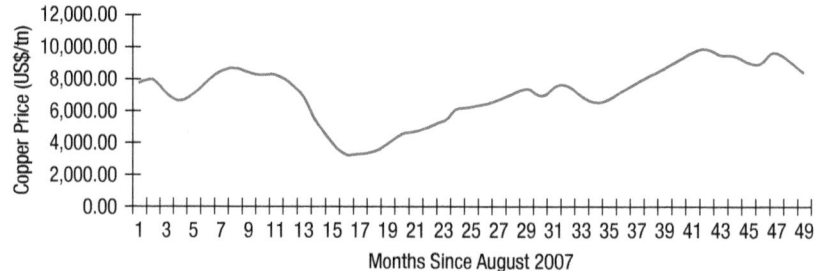

Figure 22.2   World copper price, from September 2007 to September 2011.

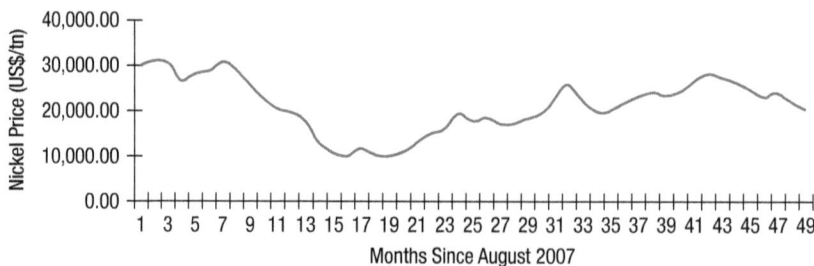

Figure 22.3   World nickel price, from September 2007 to September 2011.

---

[2]Actually, the methods of this chapter will work for any values that are ordered.

[3]Some series, such as those recording values for trading days or on the first day of each month, aren't exactly equally spaced. If there are actual gaps in a time series, researchers use a variety of methods to fill in the missing observations before analyzing the data.

$$\text{Index number for month } k = \text{metal price in month } k * \frac{100}{metal\ price\ in\ September\ 2007}$$

Figure 22.4 shows the result. We can see that the variability in the two prices have similar trends, but that, in general, the price index of nickel is lower than that of copper *relative to September 2007.*

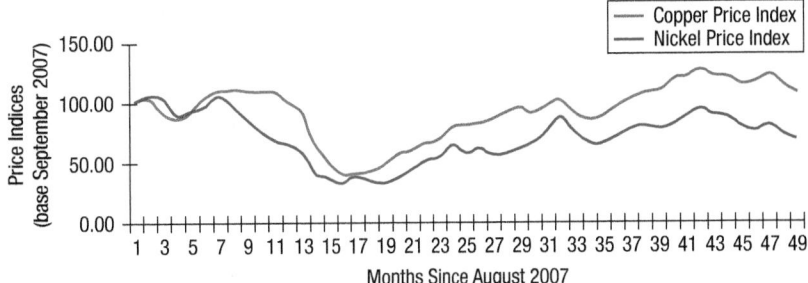

Figure 22.4   Copper and nickel price indices from September 2007 to September 2011, with a base of September 2007.

When making any statement about whether one metal price index is higher or lower than another, we must always state the base month we're using. If we choose June 2008 as our base year, the graph of index numbers looks quite different, as shown in Figure 22.5. Here the price indices of the two metals are more similar than when we used the base month of September 2007. People selling mutual funds often select a base month which shows that their fund has had a better performance than a competitor's; using a different base month could lead to exactly the opposite conclusion.

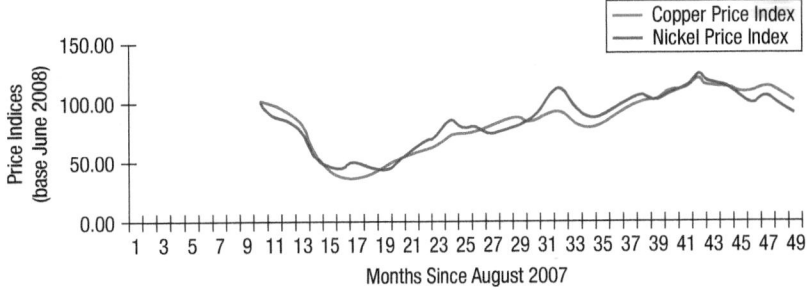

Figure 22.5   Copper and nickel price indices from September 2007 to September 2011, with a base of June 2008.

Above, we calculated the metal price indices from the raw data of metal prices. Sometimes we're given the index itself, as in the case of the Consumer Price Index (CPI). Statistics Canada calculates the CPI based on the prices of a "basket" of consumer goods, weighted in proportion to their importance in consumer purchasing patterns. Many government and business decisions are based on CPI, and it's therefore useful to leave it to Statistics Canada to calculate the index so that everyone uses the same figures. The only thing we need to bear in mind is that Statistics Canada actually provides us with several CPIs. There are CPIs for individual items such as food, shelter, and transportation, a CPI for "all items," and CPIs for "all items excluding food" and "all items excluding energy." Figure 22.6 gives a comparison. Food and energy prices are more volatile than other prices, which is why they're sometimes excluded from the CPI. On the other hand, most consumers purchase food and energy, which of course are important items in their total expenditures. When we include all items, the CPI tends to be higher than when we exclude selected items, like food and energy. We therefore need to be careful about which CPI we're using.

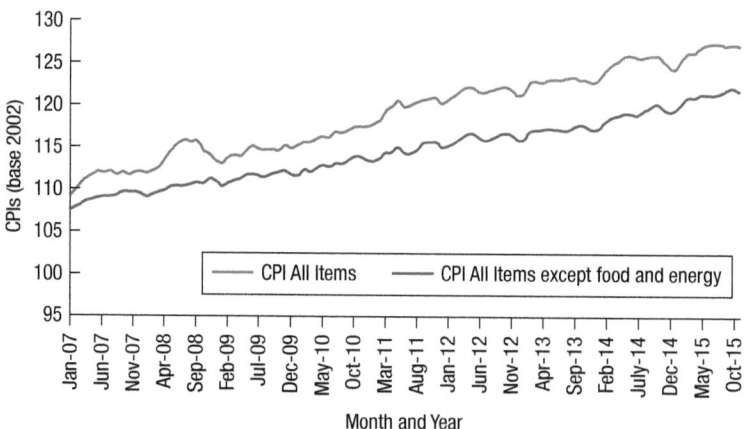

Figure 22.6   Consumer Price Indices in Canada for all items compared with consumer prices excluding food and energy.

Time Series and Forecasting

Because a time series is likely to be revealed to us sequentially and only up to the present, most time series methods use prior values of a series to predict future values. Some methods describe the overall pattern in the series and predict that it will continue, at least for a short while. Other methods estimate *time series models* that identify structured components like trends and seasonal fluctuation in the series and model those. Some introduce external variables to help predict the response, as in regression, while others simply look at the prior values in the series to try to discern patterns.[4] The objective of most time series analyses is to provide a **forecast** of future values of the time series. Of course, predicting the future is valuable to business decision makers, so time series methods are widely used.

LO❷   22.2   ## Components of a Time Series

When we examined the distribution of a single variable, we looked at its shape, centre, and spread. When we looked at scatterplots of two variables, we asked about the direction, form, and strength. For a time series, we look for the trend, seasonal patterns, and long-term cycles. Some time series exhibit some of these components, some show all of them, and others have no particular large-scale structure at all.

The Trend Component

Look at the time series plot of the Whole Foods, sales data in Figure 22.1. What overall pattern are they following? Not only have sales at Whole Foods Market been increasing, they seem to be accelerating. Of course, there are fluctuations around this pattern, but viewed over more than a decade the overall trend is clear. We'd describe the direction as positive, and the shape as curving upward. This

---

[4]Advanced models such as dynamic regression models or distributed lag models are outside the scope of this text.

overall pattern is the **trend component** of the time series. This is often the most interesting aspect of a time series. For example, it's what an investor would want to know about.

Most series have an increasing or decreasing trend with other fluctuations around the trend. Some, however, just fluctuate randomly, much like residual plots from a successful regression. If a series shows no particular trend over time and has a relatively consistent mean, it is said to be **stationary in the mean**.

If the trend grows roughly linearly, we can use the linear regression methods of Chapter 18 to estimate the linear component. We'll do that later in this chapter. (You may wonder if we can use regression for data in which successive values aren't likely to be independent. But if we don't plan to test the coefficients against the standard regression null hypothesis, we don't need any regression assumptions other than linearity.)

The Seasonal Component

Many time series fluctuate regularly. Sales of skis, for example, are always higher in the fall and lower in the spring. Sales of bikinis peak in the summer. The **seasonal component** of a time series is the part of the variation in a time series that fluctuates in a way that is roughly stable over time with respect to timing, direction, and magnitude. In Figure 22.1, you can easily find that kind of consistent pattern around the general trend. In particular, the first quarter of every year records more sales than the adjacent quarters, but these fluctuations are relatively small compared with the overall trend. Because seasonal components are usually related to external patterns, they're generally stable and predictable. For example, a retail outlet can forecast sales for the next holiday season from information about the previous holiday season and the overall trend. Even though the retail environment may change, the outlet knows that this year's holiday season will look more like last year's holiday season than like last April's sales. Typically, seasonal components repeat annually, but patterns that repeat more frequently (e.g., hourly energy use by a company during a 24-hour period) are still called seasonal components and are modelled with the same methods. A **deseasonalized**, or seasonally adjusted, series is one from which the seasonal component has been removed.

The time between peaks of a seasonal component is referred to as the **period**. The period is independent of the actual timing of peaks and valleys. For example, many retail companies' sales spike during the holiday season in December, and sales of water skis peak in early summer, but both have a seasonal period of one year.

Cyclical Component

Regular cycles in the data with periods longer than one year are referred to as **cyclical components**. Economic and business cycles can sometimes be modelled, but often we do little more than describe them. When a cyclical component can be related to a predictable phenomenon, then it can be modelled—by basing it on some regular behaviour or by introducing a variable that represents that predictable phenomenon—and added to whatever model we're building for the time series.

Irregular Component

We will see a number of ways to model time series. Just as we did with linear models and regression in Chapter 7, we'll find that the residuals—the part of the data *not* fit by the model—can be informative. In time series modelling, these residuals are called the **irregular component**. As with regression residuals, it's a good idea to plot the irregular component to look for extraordinary cases or other unexpected patterns. Often our interest in the irregular component is in how variable it is, whether that variability changes over time, and whether there are any outliers or spikes that may deserve special attention. A time series that has a relatively constant variance is said to be **stationary in the variance**.

To summarize, we identify four *components* of a time series:

1. Trend component (T)
2. Seasonal component (S)
3. Cyclical component (C)
4. Irregular component (I)

Table 22.1 provides a summary of the components as applied to the Whole Foods, sales data.

Component	Description	Rationale	Period Length
Trend	Positive and nonlinear	Overall increase in sales, with a change in the rate of increase of sales in the past seven years	
Seasonal	Peaks every first quarter in 1995 through 2013	Larger sales in first quarter; reason unknown at present	Four quarters—yearly
Cyclical	Insufficient data to observe	Could be due to economic cycles and factors, such as inflation, interest rates, and employment, that might impact consumer spending	No expected period length
Irregular	Random fluctuations in data	Due to irregular or unpredictable events, such as mergers and acquisitions of other companies, fluctuating consumer behaviour, or natural disasters such as floods	No regular repeating pattern; no period

Table 22.1   Time series components terms applied to the series *Sales for Whole Foods Market, Inc.* from 1995 to 2013.

Even though some time series exhibit only one or two of these components, an understanding of them can help us structure our understanding of a time series. Just as we look at the direction, form, and strength of a scatterplot, remembering to think about the trend, seasonal, cyclical, and irregular parts of a time series can clarify our view of a time series.

Modelling Time Series

Methods for forecasting a time series fall into two general classes. Smoothing methods work from the bottom up. They try to "smooth out" the irregular component so that any underlying patterns will be easier to see. They have the advantage of not assuming that there's a trend or seasonal component—and indeed, they'll work even when no seasonal component is present and the trend is complex. For example, we can use smoothing methods on a time series that has only a general cyclical component but no clear trend or seasonal fluctuations to model. The disadvantage of smoothing methods is that they can forecast only the immediate future. Lacking a model of behaviours that can be trusted to continue (such as a seasonal component based on calendar shopping patterns or temperature variation over the year), they don't have a basis for long-term forecasting. Instead, they rely on the assumption that most time series show patterns that vary more slowly than each successive observation, so the next value in the future will resemble the most recent ones.

> **Long- vs. Short-Term Forecasting**
>
> Smoothing methods can't be used for long-term forecasts because they lack structural components. While short-term forecasts can be useful, it's often wise to look farther into the future, and that requires behaviours that can be trusted to continue. During the financial crisis of 2008, Denis Lockhart of the U.S. Federal Reserve Board criticized the credit rating agencies because they hadn't used long-term models to predict risk. Agency models "weren't long-term in terms of data," Lockhart was quoted as saying in *The Wall Street Journal Online* (October 20, 2008). "History has proved that they were wrong."

When we can discern a trend or both a trend and a seasonal component, we'll often prefer regression-based modelling methods. These use the methods of multiple regression we learned in Chapters 20 and 21 to estimate each component's contribution to the time series and to build a model for the time series. As with any regression-based model, models of this kind can be used to forecast for any value of *Time* and thus can generate forecasts farther into the future than one time period. However, as always, we'll need to be cautious with such extrapolations.

The next sections discuss several kinds of smoothing methods, followed by a discussion of regression-based models. Although the smoothing methods don't explicitly use the time series components, it's a good idea to keep them in mind. The regression models explicitly estimate the components as a basis for building the models.

FOR EXAMPLE   **Truck border crossings between Canada and Alaska**

Commercial traffic between Canada and Alaska can be of great interest to businesses that ship to and from Alaska and to economists and investors concerned with those businesses. Here are the border crossings by trucks between Canada and Alaska, recorded each month from 1999 through 2009:

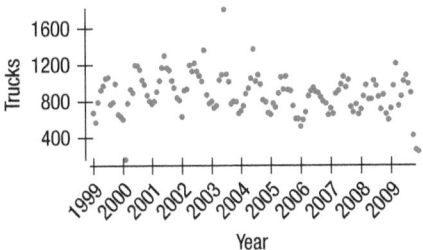

QUESTION   Describe the components of this time series.

ANSWER   Trend: Generally constant; there may be some slight downward trend from 2002 onward. Seasonal: Strong seasonal component each 12 months, possibly reflecting the difficulty of driving in the winter.

Cyclic: Not enough data to see any long-term cycles; trucking should reflect business cycles to some extent.

Irregular: There is clearly some random fluctuation around the seasonal and trend patterns. There are also a few outlying points that may be worth investigating.

LO❸ **22.3** ## Smoothing Methods

Most time series contain some random fluctuations that vary up and down rapidly—often for consecutive observations. But, precisely because they're random, these fluctuations provide no help in forecasting. Even if we believe that a time series will continue to fluctuate randomly, we can't predict *how* it will do so. The only aspects of a time series that we have any hope of predicting are those that vary either regularly or slowly. One way to identify these aspects is to smooth away the rapid random fluctuations.[5] To forecast the value of a time series in the future, we want to identify the underlying, consistent behaviour of the series. In many time series, these slower changes have a kind of inertia. They change and fluctuate, but recent behaviour is often a good indication of behaviour in the near future. Smoothing methods damp down random fluctuations and try to reveal the underlying behaviour so that we can use it to forecast values in the immediate future.

The time series for the daily Intel stock price in 2002 (Figure 22.7) shows no regular repeating patterns and no evidence of a regular seasonal effect. But it does show rapid fluctuations and some evidence of longer-term movements.

> **Intel Corporation**
>
> Intel Corporation, located in Santa Clara, California, was founded by three engineers in 1968 to develop technology for silicon-based electronic chips; the company is currently listed on the NASDAQ as INTC.

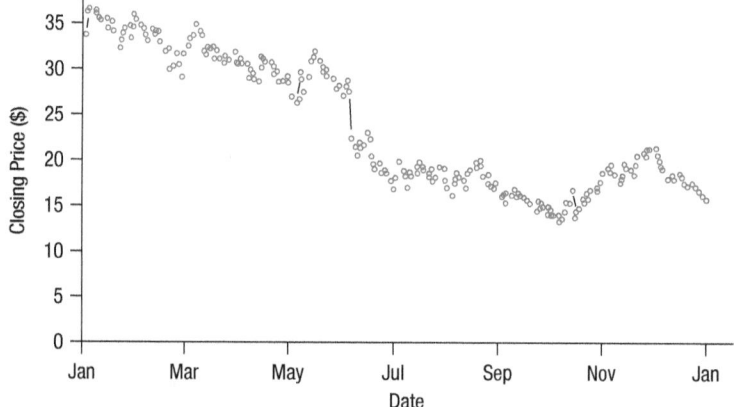

Figure 22.7 Daily closing prices for Intel stock in 2002 show no seasonal or other regular patterns.

Methods for smoothing out the apparently random fluctuations generally work by averaging adjacent values in the series. We know from Chapter 13 that means vary less than the underlying data. We can use that principle to find values that are typical of the local value of the series while varying less than the original data.

Simple Moving Average Methods

The most commonly used smoothing method is the method of moving averages. A **moving average** is an average of recent values. The number of values we use to construct the average is called the *length* of the moving average (L). Almost every stock tracking service on the internet offers a variety of moving averages (often with 50-, 100-, and 200-day lengths) to help track stock movements.

A moving average simply uses the mean of the previous L values as the fitted value at each time. Because it focuses on only the recent values, a moving average with a short length can respond to rapid changes in a time series. A moving average

---

[5]To an engineer, this would be separating the signal from the rapidly varying noise.

with a longer length will respond more slowly. The general form of a moving average is

$$\tilde{y}_t = \frac{\sum\limits_{i=t-L+1}^{t} y_i}{L}$$

The length, L, of a moving average is a subjective choice, but it must be specified when discussing a moving average. We write MA-L for a moving average of length L and use the tilde symbol (~) to denote a moving average calculated from a sequence of data values.

Let's begin by using a moving average of a length of five on the Intel stock series to illustrate the calculation. The data are in Table 22.2, and the formulas to calculate the smoothed stock price for the fifth and sixth day in the series are

$$\widetilde{\text{Price}}_5 = \frac{\sum\limits_{1}^{5} \text{Price}_t}{5} = \frac{33.00 + 35.52 + 35.79 + 35.27 + 35.58}{5} = 35.03 \text{ and}$$

$$\widetilde{\text{Price}}_6 = \frac{\sum\limits_{2}^{6} \text{Price}_t}{5} = \frac{35.52 + 35.79 + 35.27 + 35.58 + 35.36}{5} = 35.50.$$

The MA-5 smoothed stock price for each day in the series in 2002 is computed from that day's closing price and the preceding four daily closing prices using similar formulas. If we instead select $L = 15$ for our moving averages, then the calculations will average the 15 previous closing prices (including today's price). Table 22.2 shows the computed values for the two moving averages using $L = 5$ and $L = 15$

Date	Price	MA-5	MA-15
2-Jan-02	$33.00	*	*
3-Jan-02	$35.52	*	*
4-Jan-02	$35.79	*	*
7-Jan-02	$35.27	*	*
8-Jan-02	$35.58	$35.03	*
9-Jan-02	$35.36	$35.50	*
10-Jan-02	$34.65	$35.33	*
11-Jan-02	$34.55	$35.08	*
14-Jan-02	$34.84	$35.00	*
15-Jan-02	$33.68	$34.82	*
16-Jan-02	$33.71	$34.49	*
17-Jan-02	$34.53	$34.46	*
18-Jan-02	$33.48	$34.25	*
22-Jan-02	$31.70	$33.62	*
23-Jan-02	$32.45	$33.17	$34.34
24-Jan-02	$33.20	$33.07	$34.35
25-Jan-02	$33.68	$32.90	$34.23
28-Jan-02	$33.92	$32.99	$34.11
29-Jan-02	$32.68	$33.19	$33.93

(continued)

30-Jan-02	$35.86	$33.47	$33.82
31-Jan-02	$35.04	$33.84	$33.80
1-Feb-02	$34.67	$34.03	$33.80
4-Feb-02	$33.98	$34.05	$33.76
5-Feb-02	$33.80	$34.27	$33.69
6-Feb-02	$32.92	$34.08	$33.57
7-Feb-02	$32.31	$33.54	$33.48
8-Feb-02	$32.52	$33.11	$33.35
11-Feb-02	$33.57	$33.02	$33.35
12-Feb-02	$32.97	$32.86	$33.44
13-Feb-02	$33.38	$32.95	$33.50

Table 22.2   *Moving Averages L = 5, or MA-5, and L = 15, or MA-15,* for the closing price for Intel stock during the first 30 trading days of 2002.

Smoothed Values and Forecast Values

To model the smooth pattern that we think might underlie a time series, it makes sense to include the observed value at time t in calculating the smooth value we'll plot at that time point. There's little sense in ignoring information we have.

When we forecast the next value, that most recent smoothed value is a good choice, since it's recent and incorporates information from several recent time periods, damping out the short-term fluctuations.

We use a tilde to denote the smoothed values. We follow the convention from regression of using a hat to denote a predicted value.

---

and the actual closing price of Intel daily stock for the first 30 days when the market was open in 2002.

There are no moving averages for the first $(L - 1)$ days in the series for each moving average model. What happens to the moving average as the length, L, increases? The two smoothed series produced by computing moving averages for the daily Intel stock price using $L = 5$ and $L = 15$ in Figure 22.8 show that the

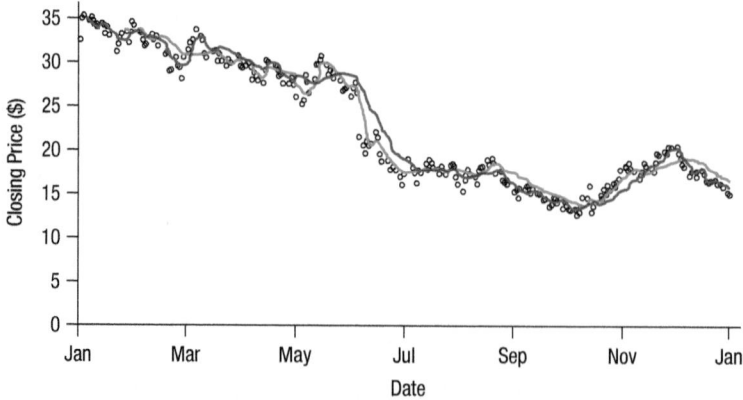

Figure 22.8   A time series plot of the daily Intel stock closing prices in 2002 with MA-5 (in red) and MA-15 (in blue) forecasts superimposed. The moving average with the smaller length, $L = 5$, follows the data more closely while the moving average with the longer length is smoother.

moving average series with the greater length is smoother. That should be what you expected. Of course, a smoother series isn't necessarily a better model for the data, because it has a hard time following the series when it changes rapidly. Look, for example, at the two series during June of that year. The stock price fell rapidly, but the MA-15 changed too slowly, running above the data for several weeks before it "caught up."

To obtain a forecast for a new time point, analysts use the last average in the series:

$$\hat{y}_{t+1} = \tilde{y}_t$$

This is the *simple moving average forecast*. Of course, this method can forecast only one time period into the future, for *Time* $= t + 1$. (You can repeat that value as a forecast beyond period $t + 1$, but unless the time series is essentially unstructured and horizontal, it won't be a very good forecast.) If the length of the moving average is one ($L = 1$), then the forecast is simply that the next value will be the same as the previous one, $\hat{y}_{t+1} = y_t$. As the simplest forecast, this is called the **naive forecast**.

Often, moving averages are used primarily as summaries of how a time series is changing. The length selected depends on the purpose of the analysis. If the focus is on long-term behaviour, a longer moving average is appropriate. But an analyst interested in shorter-term changes would choose a shorter length. Sometimes (as you can see in the box below) analysts compare a shorter-length moving average and one with a longer length, hoping to learn something from how they compare.

One potential problem with a moving average is that, as we know from Chapter 5, means can be affected by outliers. An outlier in a time series would be a spike in the series far from the adjacent values. Such a spike will influence all the averages in which it participates, spreading its influence over a number of values.

Investors and Moving Averages

Moving averages can help investors identify short- and long-term trends for a particular stock or mutual fund. Many analysts will consider it a bull market when the 50-day moving average is above the 200-day moving average, and a bear market if the opposite is true. When the 50-day moving average crosses above the 200-day average, this indicates that recent values have increased above the level established by the longer-term average and is taken as a signal for investors to buy. It's referred to as a "golden cross." When the 50-day moving average moves below the 200-day average, then this is a "sell" signal and is called a "death cross."

—*Fidelity Outlook*, August 2002, p. 6

FOR EXAMPLE   The value of the euro

The euro is the second-most traded currency (after the U.S. dollar), so its value relative to other currencies is of great interest. One euro was equal to one U.S. dollar when the new European currency was launched on January 1, 1999. Since that time the value has fluctuated. On October 26, 2000, one euro cost $0.8252. But on July 15, 2008, it was as high as $1.5990. As the time series plot of 50 weekly euro/dollar values between July 1, 2012, and June 9, 2013, shows, recent fluctuations show little pattern, so smoothing methods may be the best approach to short-term prediction of euro values.

(continued)

Here are some of those euro values in dollars for the weeks of July and August 2012:

Date	Value ($)
Jul 2, 2012–Jul 8, 2012	1.2508
Jul 9, 2012–Jul 15, 2012	1.2257
Jul 16, 2012–Jul 22, 2012	1.2243
Jul 23, 2012–Jul 29, 2012	1.2186
Jul 30, 2012–Aug 5, 2012	1.2291
Aug 6, 2012–Aug 12, 2012	1.2353
Aug 13, 2012–Aug 19, 2012	1.232
Aug 20, 2012–Aug 26, 2012	1.245
Aug 27, 2012–Sep 2, 2012	1.2536

QUESTION Find a three-term moving average for these data and predict the value for the next week.

ANSWER

Date	Value ($)	MA-3
Jul 2, 2012–Jul 8, 2012	1.2508	
Jul 9, 2012–Jul 15, 2012	1.2257	
Jul 16, 2012–Jul 22, 2012	1.2243	1.2336
Jul 23, 2012–Jul 29, 2012	1.2186	1.2229
Jul 30, 2012–Aug 5, 2012	1.2291	1.2240
Aug 6, 2012–Aug 12, 2012	1.2353	1.2277
Aug 13, 2012–Aug 19, 2012	1.232	1.2321
Aug 20, 2012–Aug 26, 2012	1.245	1.2374
Aug 27, 2012–Sep 2, 2012	1.2536	1.2435

The prediction is $1.2435.

Weighted Moving Averages

In a simple moving average, we just average the most recent L values. But we can benefit from a more sophisticated averaging scheme. We can assign a *weight* to each value according to how far it is before the current value. The result is a *weighted* average. In a weighted average, each value is multiplied by a *weight* before it's added up, and the total is divided by the sum of the weights:

$$\tilde{y}_t = \frac{\sum w_i y_{t-i}}{\sum w_i}$$

The weights might be specified, or they might be found as part of the smoothing process.

Weighted moving averages form a very general class of smoothers.[6] We will consider two types of weighted moving average smoothers that are commonly used on time series data: exponential smoothers and autoregressive models.

Exponential Smoothing Methods

Smoothing methods summarize each value of a time series with an average of recent values. In many time series, recent values of the series are more relevant for modelling than older ones. So a weighted moving average that weights the more recent values more heavily than the older ones makes sense. Exponential smoothing does just that. **Exponential smoothing** is a weighted moving average with weights that decline exponentially into the past. The most recent data are weighted the most, and the most distant data are weighted the least. This model is the **single-exponential smoothing (SES) model**:

$$\tilde{y}_t = \alpha y_t + (1 - \alpha)\,\tilde{y}_{t-1}$$

The choice of the weight α is up to the data analyst, although it's usually restricted to $0 < \alpha < 1$. When $\alpha = 0.50$, the current data point and the entire set of historical data (all points before the current one) are weighted equally. If $\alpha = 0.75$, then historical data are weighted only 25%, and the current value has more weight at 75%. If the objective is to produce forecasts that are stable and smoother, then choose a smoothing coefficient closer to zero. If, however, the objective is to react to volatile events rapidly, then choose a smoothing coefficient close to one.[7]

Unlike a simple moving average, exponential smoothing uses *all* previous values, although distant ones typically get very small weights. If we expand the calculation, we can see that the smoothed value at time t is a *weighted* average of the current value and all the previous values, with the weights depending on a smoothing coefficient, α:

$$\tilde{y}_t = \alpha y_t + \alpha(1 - \alpha)y_{t-1} + \alpha(\alpha - 1)^2 y_{t-2} + \alpha(1 - \alpha)^3 y_{t-3} + \cdots$$

As with the moving average model, we use $\tilde{y}_t$ as our prediction for time $t + 1$.

Figure 22.9 shows the Intel stock prices again, this time with exponentially smoothed values using $\alpha = 0.75$ and $\alpha = 0.10$. You can see that the curve

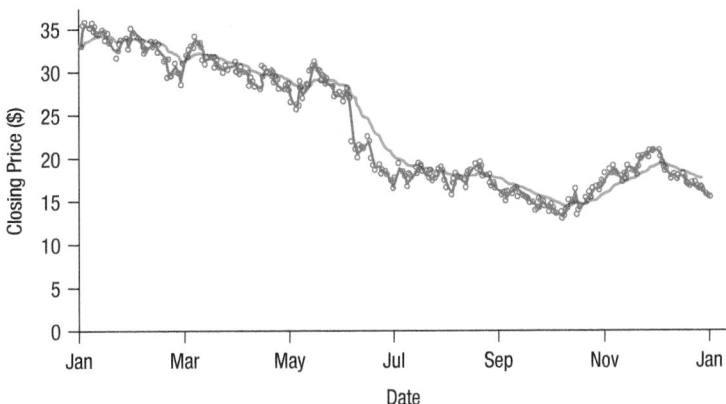

Figure 22.9 The Intel stock prices along with exponential smoothing models ($\alpha = \hat{p}$ 0.75 in orange, $a = \hat{p}$ 0.10 in green). The model with the larger alpha follows the data more closely, and the model with the smaller alpha is smoother.

---

[6]In this general form, these smoothers are known as *linear smoothers*. They're important in engineering and finance.

[7]The initial smoothed value to get the algorithm started is either the initial observed value ($\tilde{y}_1 = y_1$) or the average of some of the initial values. In Minitab, for example, the initial smoothed value is equal to the average of the first six observations.

computed using the larger α follows the original series closely. By contrast, the curve computed using the smaller α is smoother, but doesn't follow rapid changes in the series such as the sharp price drop in June.

LO④   22.4   Summarizing Forecast Error

Whenever we model a time series, it's natural to ask how closely the model fits the series. A closely related question is how well the model *forecasts* the series. For smoothing models, we use the most recent model value as the forecast for the next time period. When we make a plot of the data and the smoothed series, we usually plot the smoothed value $\tilde{y}_t$ at time t. But if we're interested in the error the model makes when trying to forecast each value, we must compare the data value $\tilde{y}_t$ not to the smoothed value $\tilde{y}_t$, but rather to the forecast $\tilde{y}_t$, which is actually equal to $\tilde{y}_{t-1}$. We can find a **forecast error** for each time in the series for which we have such a forecast:

$$e_t = (y_t - \hat{y}_t)$$

When there's a particular forecast of interest, it makes sense to look at the forecast error, e_t. More often, we ask about the overall success of a model at forecasting for a time series. That calls for a summary of the forecast errors and, as often happens in statistics, we have several summaries to choose from.

In Chapter 20, we used the **mean squared error (MSE)** to summarize the magnitude of the errors. We can do the same with the forecast errors:

$$MSE = \frac{1}{n}\sum (y_t - \hat{y}_t)^2$$

The MSE penalizes large forecast errors because the errors are squared. It also has the problem that it's not in the same units as the data, but rather in the square of those units. We can address both of these problems by summing the *absolute values* of the errors. That gives the **mean absolute deviation (MAD)**:

$$MAD = \frac{1}{n}\sum | y_t - \hat{y}_t|$$

The most common approach to measuring forecast error compares the absolute errors with the magnitude of the estimated quantities to sum the *proportions* of the values that are in error. Multiplying the proportions by 100 gives the **absolute percentage error (APE)**. If we average the APE for all the forecasts, we have the **mean absolute percentage error (MAPE)**:

$$MAPE = 100 \times \frac{1}{n}\sum \frac{|y_t - \hat{y}_t|}{| y_t|}$$

The MAPE is expressed in percent, so it's independent of the units of the y variable. If you choose to rescale y, both the MSE and MAD will change, but the MAPE will remain the same.

In summary, MSE resembles the error measures we've used for regression models, but it isn't in the same units as the data. MAD is in the same units as the data, but that means it will be rescaled if the measurements are rescaled. MAPE is a percentage relating the size of the errors to the magnitudes of the data values.

Table 22.3 shows forecast error for two different single exponential smoothing (SES) models over the final 30 days of the Intel stock series, along with the MAD, MSE, and MAPE computed for the entire time series. The smoothing model that uses a larger smoothing coefficient ($\alpha = 0.75$) more accurately forecasts the daily stock price over this time period.

Date	SES $\alpha=75$	Forecast Error	SES $\alpha=00.10$	Forecast Error	Price
31-Oct-02	17.19	0.11	15.74	1.56	$17.30
1-Nov-02	18.02	0.28	16.00	2.30	$18.30
4-Nov-2	18.58	0.19	16.27	2.50	$18.77
5-Nov-02	18.41	−0.06	16.48	1.87	$18.35
6-Nov-02	18.96	0.19	16.75	2.40	$19.15
7-Nov-02	18.57	−0.13	16.92	1.52	$18.44
8-Nov-02	18.26	−0.11	17.04	1.11	$18.15
11-Nov-02	17.57	−0.23	17.07	0.27	$17.34
12-Nov-02	17.73	0.06	17.14	0.65	$17.79
13-Nov-02	18.02	0.10	17.24	0.88	$18.12
14-Nov-02	18.91	0.30	17.44	1.77	$19.21
15-Nov-02	18.83	−0.03	17.57	1.23	$18.80
18-Nov-02	18.62	−0.07	17.67	0.88	$18.55
19-Nov-02	18.27	−0.12	17.72	0.43	$18.15
20-Nov-02	18.93	0.22	17.86	1.29	$19.15
21-Nov-02	19.79	0.32	18.10	2.11	$20.21
22-Nov-02	20.01	0.04	18.29	1.76	$20.05
25-Nov-02	20.36	0.12	18.51	1.97	$20.48
26-Nov-02	20.24	−0.04	18.68	1.52	$20.20
27-Nov-02	20.74	0.16	18.90	2.00	$20.90
29-Nov-02	20.84	0.04	19.10	1.78	$20.88
2-Dec-02	21.00	0.05	19.29	1.76	$21.05
3-Dec-02	20.48	−0.17	19.40	0.91	$20.31
4-Dec-02	19.87	−0.20	19.42	0.25	$19.67
5-Dec-02	19.19	−0.23	19.38	−0.42	$18.96
6-Dec-02	18.83	−0.12	19.31	−0.60	$18.71
9-Dec-02	17.79	−0.29	19.15	−1.47	$17.68
10-Dec-02	18.09	0.04	19.05	−0.92	$18.13
11-Dec-02	18.14	0.02	18.96	−0.80	$18.16
12-Dec-02	18.18	0.01	18.88	−0.69	$18.19
MAD		$0.135		$1.321	
MES		0.026		2.162	
MAPE		0.714%		6.91%	

Table 22.3   The Intel stock prices along with smoothed values reported as forecasts one period ahead for two models. For this series, the single exponential smoothing (SES) model with the larger coefficient ($\alpha = 0.75$) has a lower forecast error.

FOR EXAMPLE   Forecast errors and the euro

QUESTION   For the euro values in For Example: "The value of the euro," find the forecasts, the errors, and the measures of forecast error.

ANSWER

Date	Value ($)	MA(3)	Forecast	Error
2010-05-27	1.2265	*	*	*
2010-05-28	1.2301	*	*	*
2010-05-29	1.2344	1.2303333	*	*
2010-05-30	1.2278	1.2307667	1.2303333	−0.00253333
2010-05-31	1.2276	1.2299333	1.2307667	−0.00316667
2010-06-01	1.2303	1.2285667	1.2299333	0.00036667
2010-06-02	1.2228	1.2269000	1.2285667	−0.0057667

MSE = 0.00001246

MAD = 0.00295835

MAPE = 0.241%

LO❸   22.5   Autoregressive Models

Simple moving averages and exponential smoothing methods are good choices for time series with no regular patterns. But if some patterns are present—even if they don't rise to the level of a well-structured seasonal fluctuation—we may want to choose weights that facilitate modelling that structure—something that exponential smoothing can find difficult to do. Such weights might even be negative. (Imagine a series with values that alternated up and down for successive times. A good weighted average would give a negative weight to the most recent value and a positive weight to the one before that.)

But how could we find appropriate weights and how could we choose among the huge number of possible weights? It turns out that we can use the methods of multiple regression we saw in Chapters 20 and 21, along with the fact that the data come to us in time sequence order, to discover weights for a weighted moving average smoother. We shift the data by a time period or a few time periods. This shift is known as *lagging*, and the resulting variables are called *lagged variables*. For example, Table 22.4 shows the first 15 values of the daily Intel stock prices in 2002 along with the lagged values for lags of one, two, three, and four days.

Date	Price	Price$_{lag1}$	Price$_{lag2}$	Price$_{lag3}$	Price$_{lag4}$
2-Jan-02	$33.00	*	*	*	*
3-Jan-02	$35.52	$33.00	*	*	*
4-Jan-02	$35.79	$35.52	$33.00	*	*
7-Jan-02	$35.27	$35.79	$35.52	$33.00	*
8-Jan-02	$35.58	$35.27	$35.79	$35.52	$33.00
9-Jan-02	$35.36	$35.58	$35.27	$35.79	$35.52
10-Jan-02	$34.65	$35.36	$35.58	$35.27	$35.79
11-Jan-02	$34.55	$34.65	$35.36	$35.58	$35.27
14-Jan-02	$34.84	$34.55	$34.65	$35.36	$35.58
15-Jan-02	$34.68	$34.84	$34.55	$34.65	$35.36
16-Jan-02	$33.71	$34.68	$34.84	$34.55	$34.65

17-Jan-02	$34.53	$33.71	$34.68	$34.84	$34.55
18-Jan-02	$33.48	$34.58	$33.71	$34.68	$34.84
22-Jan-02	$31.70	$33.48	$34.53	$33.71	$34.68
23-Jan-02	$32.45	$31.70	$33.48	$34.53	$33.71

Table 22.4 The lagged values for the first 15 days in the Intel daily stock time series for one, two, three, and four days.

If we fit a regression to predict a time series from its lag1 and lag2 versions

$$\hat{y} = b_0 + b_1 y_{\text{lag1}} + b_2 y_{\text{lag2}},$$

each predicted value, $\hat{y}_1$, is just a sum of the two previous values, $\hat{y}_{\text{log1}}$ and $\hat{y}_{\text{log2}}$ (plus a constant) weighted by the fitted coefficients b_1 and b_2. That's just a weighted moving average with weights found by the regression.

But wait. Regression methods assume that the data values are mutually independent. And this method works only if the data values are *not* independent—that is, if recent values can help predict current ones. Isn't this a violation of the regression model? Well, yes and no. The Independence Assumption is certainly required for inference on the coefficients, for example, to test the standard null hypothesis that the true coefficient is zero. But we're not doing inference here; we're just building a model. And for that purpose, the failure of independence is really more an opportunity than a problem.

In fact, we can specifically account for the association of cases with previous ones. The correlation between a series and a (lagged) version of the same series that is offset by a fixed number of time periods is called **autocorrelation**. Recall that we evaluated the presence of lag-1 autocorrelation using the Durbin-Watson statistic in Chapter 19. Table 22.5 shows some autocorrelations for the Intel series.

	Price	Lag1	Lag2	Lag3	Lag4
Price	1.000				
Lag1	0.992	1.000			
Lag2	0.984	0.992	1.000		
Lag3	0.978	0.984	0.992	1.000	
Lag4	0.973	0.977	0.984	0.992	1.000

Table 22.5 Autocorrelations of the daily Intel closing stock price for the entire year 2002 for lags 1, 2, and 3.

A regression model that's based on an average of prior values in the series weighted according to a regression on lagged versions of the series is called an **autoregressive model**. A model based on only the first lagged variable is called a first-order autoregressive model, often abbreviated as AR(1).

A pth-order autoregressive model AR(p) has the form

$$\hat{y} = b_0 + b_1 y_{\text{lag1}} + \cdots + b_p y_{\text{lag}p}.$$

For the Intel stock price series, we find the coefficients for a fourth-order autoregressive model from a multiple regression of the series on its first four lagged values, as shown in Table 22.6.

The resulting fourth-order autoregressive model is

$$\hat{y}_t = 0.126434 + 0.963981 y_{lag1} - 0.046396 y_{lag2} - 0.056936 y_{lag3} + 0.134714 y_{lag4}.$$

Dependent variable is: Price
R-squared = 98.4% R-squared (adjusted) = 98.4%
s = 0.8793 with 236 − 5 = 231 degrees of freedom

Variable	Coefficient	SE(Coeff)	t-ratio	P-value
Intercept	0.126434	0.2032	0.622	0.5344
Lag1	0.963981	0.0655	14.7	≤0.0001
Lag2	−0.046396	0.0911	−0.509	0.6110
Lag3	−0.056936	0.0905	−0.629	0.5300
Lag4	0.134714	0.0641	2.10	0.0368

Table 22.6   A fourth-order autoregressive model for the Intel stock prices. Note that there are 240 values in the series, but, because lagged variables have missing values at the beginning of the series, there are only 236 complete cases.

Looking at the coefficients in Table 22.6, we can see that the model puts most of its weight on the data value just preceding the one we're estimating (the lag1 value), some on the lag4, and relatively little on the other two lags.

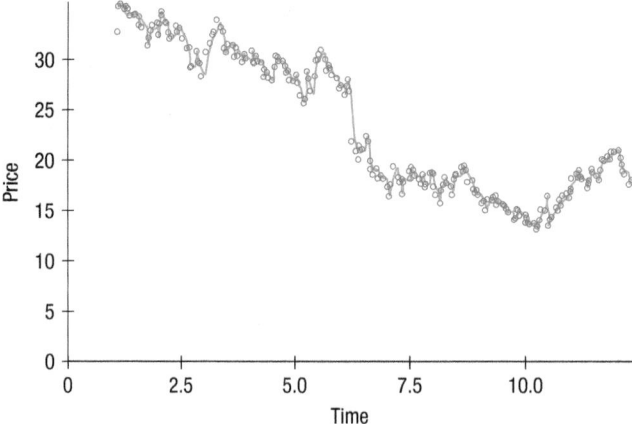

Figure 22.10   The Intel stock price series with an AR(4) model.

We can use an autoregressive model to predict the latest value in the Intel stock price series from previous values and then compare our forecast with the true value. The forecasts, forecast errors, and APE produced by the two moving average models, the exponential smoothing models ($\alpha = 0.10$) and ($\alpha = 0.75$), and the fourth-order autoregressive model, or AR(4), are shown in Table 22.7.

Model	Forecast ($\hat{y}_t$)	Actual Price (y_t)	Forecast Error ($y_t - \hat{y}_t$)	Absolute Percent Error $100 \times |y_t - \hat{y}_t| / |y_t|$
MA-5	$17.95	$17.58	−$0.37	2.10%
MA-15	$19.40	$17.58	−$1.82	10.35%
SES ($\alpha = 0.10$)	$18.75	$17.58	−$1.17	6.66%
SES ($\alpha = 0.75$)	$17.45	$17.58	$0.13	0.74%
AR(4)	$18.17	$17.58	−$0.59	3.36%

Table 22.7   The forecasts and forecast error for each of the moving average and autoregressive models for the Intel daily stock price on December 13, 2002.

FOR EXAMPLE   An autoregressive model for the euro

QUESTION Find and interpret an autoregressive model for the euro prices.

ANSWER

Dependent variable is: Value($)
50 total cases of which 2 are missing
R-squared = 90.3% R-squared (adjusted) = 89.9%
s = 0.0104 with 48 − 3 = 45 degrees of freedom

Variable	Coefficient	SE(Coeff)	t-ratio	P-value
Intercept	0.106611	0.0595	0.1429	0.1429
Lag1	1.25427	0.1429	0.1429	<0.0001
Lag2	−0.336069	0.1429	0.1429	0.0215

Both the lag1 and lag2 terms are significant, suggesting that changes in the value of the euro show short-term serial correlation; today's value is much like yesterday's.

Unlike simple moving average models and single exponential smoothing models, AR models can follow time series that have seasonal fluctuations. The AR method will assign a larger weight to lags that correspond to the period of the fluctuation. For example, AR models will tend to predict quarterly sales that show a seasonal cycle by assigning a large weight to the lag4 version of the series, so sales in the same quarter of the previous year are counted heavily.

JUST CHECKING

J. Crew is a clothing company known for its preppy fashions, including jeans, khakis, and other basic items sold to youngprofessionals through its catalogues, websites, and some 260 retail and outlet stores in the United States. (Michelle Obama shops there.) We have their reported quarterly revenue from Q1 2003 through 2007. Here's a time series plot:

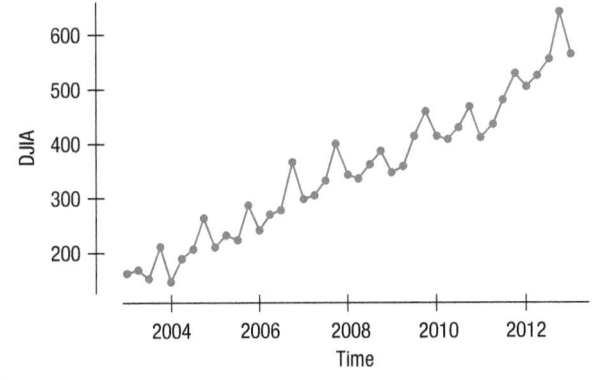

1 Which time series components do you see in this plot?

2 The final four values for 2012 are

Q1 2012 503.5

Q2 2012 525.5

Q3 2012 555.8

Q4 2012 642.9

Given these four values, where on the graph would the final value of a four-point simple moving average be? Do you think it would be a good prediction for Q1 of 2013?

3 If the exponential smooth value for Q3 of 2012 is 550, what is the exponential smooth value of Q4 when an α of 0.5 is used?

4 If you wished to fit an autoregressive model, how many terms should you include? Why?

Answers are found in Appendix A.

Random Walks

If each new value can be thought of as a random step away from the previous value, the time series is sometimes called a **random walk**. A series with no other structure can be described as just adding a random kick to the previous value:

$$y_{t+1} = y_t + e_t$$

where the "*e*" are independent random values with some distribution. The "*e*" are sometimes referred to as "white noise." This kind of time series is called a *random walk* because each new value can be thought of as a random step away from the previous value.

Time series that are modelled by a random walk can have rapid and sudden changes in direction, but they also may have long periods of runs up or down that can be mistaken for cycles.[8] Random walks include series such as the assets of a gambler over time and stock prices.[9]

Random walks have no trend, seasonality, or cycles that can be modelled, and the forecast we get from them is therefore called "naive," as we've mentioned. Since we don't know where the data are going to jump to next, we simply forecast that they will stay where they are:

$$\hat{y}_{t+1} = y_t$$

GUIDED EXAMPLE   Comparing Time Series Methods

Shutterstock

The Home Depot chain of home improvement stores grew in the 1980s and 1990s faster than any other retailer in history. By 2005, it was the second largest retailer in the United States. But its extraordinary record of growth was slowed by the financial crisis of 2008. How do different methods of modelling time series compare for understanding these data?

PLAN	**Setup** State your objective. Identify the quantitative variables you wish to examine. Report the time frame over which the data have been collected and define each variable.	We want to build time series models for quarterly sales at The Home Depot from 1995 through 2012. We have quarterly sales ($billion):

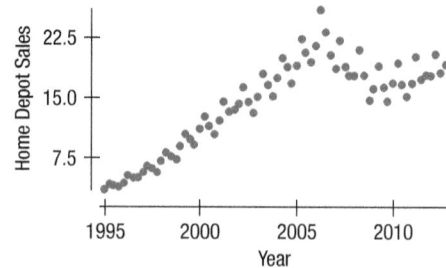

Plot Plot the time series and clearly label the axes to identify the scale and units.

Model Think about the assumptions and check the conditions.

These are quantitative data measured over time at consistent intervals. So it is appropriate to use time series methods.

There was a consistent increasing trend until the end of 2006. After that, sales fell sharply. They appear to have been recovering. Throughout this period, however, there are fluctuations around the trend that appear to be seasonal because they repeat every four quarters. Some smoothing methods may have difficulty with the seasonal fluctuations, but they are likely to be successful at following the sudden change in fortunes following 2006.

(continued)

---

[8]This is one reason why we recommended that the identification of cycles be based on theory, on established patterns, or on other variables.

[9]Princeton economist Burton Malkiel made the random walk theory of the stock market famous in his book *A Random Walk Down Wall Street: The Time-Tested Strategy for Successful Investing*, first published in 1973. The theory originated in the 1950s with Maurice Kendall, a British statistician.

DO

Mechanics, Part 1 Try a moving average. For data with a strong seasonal component, such as these, a moving average length that is a multiple of the period is a good idea. But series with a strong trend, such as this one, won't be fit well by an uncentred moving average.

Here is a simple moving average of length 4:

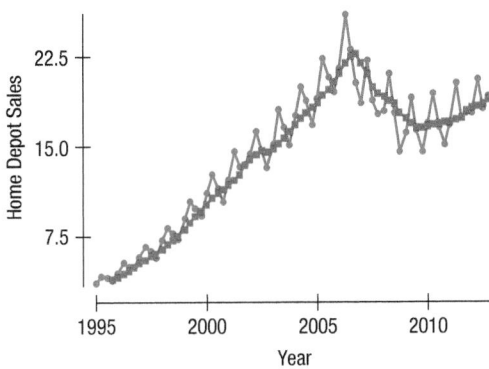

Evaluate how well this method fits the series.

We can also calculate

MAD = 1.134

MSE = 2.209

MAPE = 7.756

Make a forecast for Q1 2013.

The program offers a forecast of 18.908 $B for the first quarter of 2013.

Mechanics, Part 2 Exponential smoothing can be a good compromise between a simple moving average smoother and a fit with a seasonal component. In series with a strong trend, such as this one, exponential smooths will inevitably lag behind the data.

Let's try an exponential smooth. Now we have to choose a smoothing weight.

We'll use $\alpha = 0.5$, which weights the current data value equally with all the rest in the past. Here's the result from a computer-generated smooth:

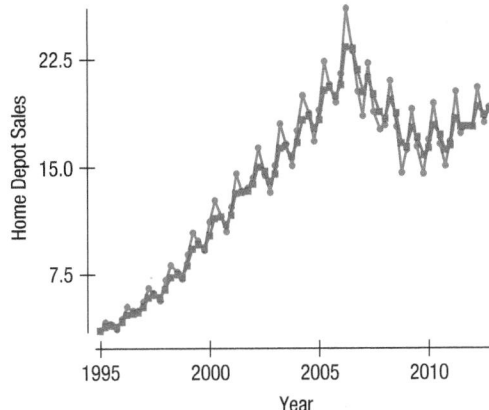

MAD = 0.7277

MSE = 0.8677

MAPE = 5.043

Evaluate how well this model fits.

The smoother generates a prediction of $18.8928 billion for the first quarter of 2013.

Forecast sales for Q1 2013.

Now let's fit an autoregressive model. Because we know that the seasonal pattern is four quarters long, we'll fit four terms, using multiple regression to find the smoothing weights:

Mechanics, Part 3 An autoregressive model is a multiple regression on the series itself lagged, or offset, by one, two, or more time periods. When we know that there is a seasonal component, it is important to include the corresponding lag—here lag4. This model has terms for each lag.

Dependent variable is: HDSales
72 total cases of which 4 are missing
R-squared = 94.2% R-squared (adjusted) = 93.8%
$s = 1.319$ with $68 - 5 = 63$ degrees of freedom

Variable	Coefficient	SE(Coeff)	t-ratio	P-value
Intercept	1.69432	0.4721	3.59	0.006
Lag1	0.469540	0.1124	4.18	<0.0001
Lag2	−0.255134	0.1245	−2.05	0.0446
Lag3	0.223335	0.1284	1.74	0.0869
Lag4	0.487104	0.1123	4.34	<0.0001

The AR(4) model is

$$\hat{y}_t = 1.694 + 0.4695y_{t-1} - 0.255y_{t-2} + 0.223y_{t-3} + 0.487y_{t-4}$$

Plot the fit.

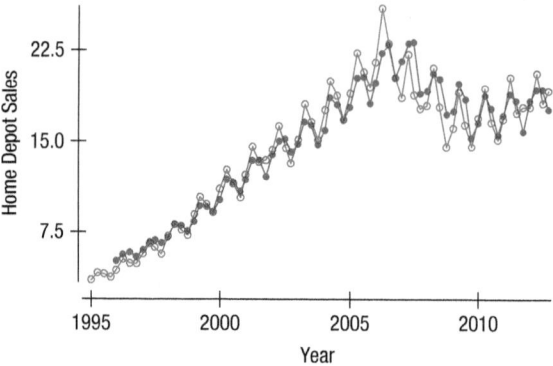

Plot the residuals.

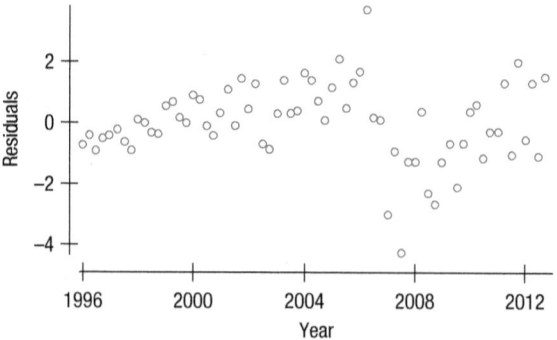

The forecast errors show some disturbance around the time of the financial crisis. Because sales at that time stopped resembling previous behaviour with respect to growth, lagged versions of the series were less successful predictors.

Calculate fit measures and a prediction.

MAD = 0.952

MSE = 1.1612

MAPE = 6.517

A predicted value for the first quarter of 2013 is:

$$1.694 + 0.4695 \times 17.61$$
$$- 0.225 \times 19.226 + 0.2233$$
$$\times 19.237 + 0.487 \times 18.348 = 19.317$$

REPORT

Conclusion Compare the advantages and disadvantages of the time series methods. Be sure to state your interpretations in the proper context.

MEMO

Re: Time series analyses of The Home Depot's quarterly sales

We compared several time series methods to fit quarterly data on sales at The Home Depot for the period from 1995 through 2012. The actual sales in Q1 of 2013 were $19.124 billion.

The different methods had differing strengths and weaknesses. The moving average method smooths out most of the seasonal effects, but because it lags behind the series, it has trouble modelling the sudden change in 2007, but it provides a good description of the trend.

The exponential smoothing method follows the seasonal pattern more closely and has the best average error.

The autoregressive method seems to have the greatest difficulty following the sudden adjustment in 2007. It appears to be getting back on track as growth resumed in the most recent years.

Each of these methods is within about 1% in its prediction for the first quarter of 2013.

LO⑤ **22.6 Multiple Regression–Based Models**

We noted earlier that some time series have identifiable components: a trend, a seasonal component, and possibly a cyclical component. Simple moving average models work best on time series that lack any consistent structures like these. Exponential smoothing models don't usually follow a seasonal component well either. Autoregressive models can follow all of these components, provided the length of the lag is at least as long as the period of the seasonal or cyclical component.

When some or all of these components are present, we can gain a distinct advantage by modelling them directly, since we may be able to understand the components and reach a deeper understanding of the time series itself.

Modelling the Trend Component

When a time series has a linear trend, the natural thing to do is to model it with a regression. If the trend is linear, a linear regression of y_t on *Time* can model the trend. The residuals would then be a *detrended* version of the time series.

During its period of record growth until about 2006, The Home Depot's sales seem to have a roughly linear trend. We can't fit a linear model to the entire series, but we can model that period of initial growth. The regression to estimate the trend for 1995 to the end of 2005 is in Table 22.8.

Dependent variable is: HDSales
R-squared = 95.5% R-squared (adjusted) = 95.4%
s = 1.044 with 40 − 2 = 38 degrees of freedom

Variable	Coeff	SE(Coeff)	t-ratio	P-value
Intercept	2.67102	0.3241	8.24	≤0.0001
Time	0.405707	0.0143	28.4	≤0.0001

Table 22.8 Estimating the trend component in Home Depot sales data by regression.

One attractive feature of a regression-based model is that the coefficient of *Time* can be interpreted directly as the change in *y* (here, Home Depot sales) *per* time unit (here, quarters). The trend in Home Depot sales was that they increased by $0.406 billion per quarter.

By contrast, we saw in Figure 22.1 that the Whole Foods, sales data *don't* have a linear trend. However, as we learned in Chapter 19, we can often improve the linearity of a relationship with a re-expression. The re-expression that most often works for time series is the logarithm. That's because many time series grow or shrink exponentially. Typically, the bigger you are, the larger the absolute increment in your profits. Growth by a consistent percentage is *exponential growth*. For example, if sales each year are 5% higher than the previous year, then the overall growth will be exponential. And the logarithm makes exponential growth linear. Figure 22.11 shows the result of taking logs in the Whole Foods, data.

Which log?

Financial models that talk about exponential growth usually describe them using the constant *e* = 2.71828, and its corresponding inverse function is the *natural* logarithm, written *ln*. When we re-express data to improve linearity, we usually prefer the base-10 logarithm, written *log* or *log10*, because it's a bit easier to interpret. Which should you use? In fact, it doesn't matter at all. For all values, ln (*y*) = log (*y*) × ln(10), so the two functions differ only by a scale factor—a constant that doesn't affect our analyses. For consistency with our earlier analyses, we'll use base 10 logarithm here.

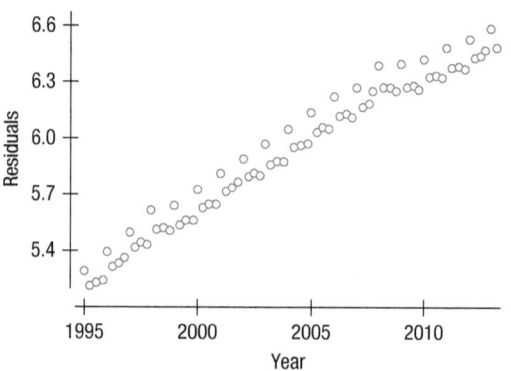

Figure 22.11 The logarithm of Whole Foods, quarterly sales is approximately linear over time.

The corresponding model for the trend is

Dependent variable is: LogSales
R-squared = 96.9% R-squared (adjusted) = 96.9%
s = 0.0687 with 74 − 2 = 72 degrees of freedom

Variable	Coefficient	SE(Coeff)	t-ratio	P-value
Intercept	−139.924	2.999	−46.7	<0.0001
Year	0.071282	0.0015	47.6	<0.0001

Table 22.9 A regression model for the trend in LogSales of Whole Foods. Taking logs has made the relationship more nearly linear.

Now the interpretation of the trend coefficient is different. Adding 0.071282 to the logarithm of sales each year is the same as multiplying sales by $10^{0.071282} \approx 1.18$. And that's an increase of 18 percent. So we can say that Whole Foods Market's sales were increasing by 18 percent per year.

Re-expressing the Whole Foods, quarterly sales data by logarithms reveals a second advantage of the re-expression. The seasonal fluctuations evident in Figure 22.1 grew in magnitude as the sales themselves grew. But in Figure 22.11, those fluctuations are nearly constant in size. That will make them much easier to model. And, although it is visible in Figure 22.1, the "adjustment" in sales growth due to the financial crisis of 2008 is much easier to see in Figure 22.11. It appears that after the crisis, sales growth has been slower than it had been before 2008.

Recording *Time*

Whole Foods Market sales are reported quarterly, but the time variable here is *Year*. The time variable in a time series is often just a count of the number of time periods (weeks, months, quarters, etc.) since the series began. So, the periods are often recorded as 1, 2, 3, ... as we did for the Home Depot sales data. If we want to use the actual date as the predictor variable and we have quarterly data, we need to express each time period as a fractional year, such as 1995.0, 1995.25, 1995.5, ... The only difference this will make is in interpreting the coefficients. Moving average methods take no note of how time is recorded, but when you use a regression-based model, you must interpret the *Time* coefficient correctly.

For example, if we'd used a *Time* variable that counted 1, 2, 3, ... in the regression instead of fractional year, the slope coefficient would have been one-quarter of the one we found $(0.07865/4 = 0.01966)$ and it would have estimated the *quarterly* growth in log sales rather than the annual growth.

Modelling the Seasonal Component

Figure 22.11 shows that the Whole Foods, data have a strong seasonal component. Every fourth quarter there's a spike. That's not unusual in time series related to retail sales. The simplest version of a seasonal component is one that adds a different value to the series (in addition to the trend) for each season. We can see that this is a good description of the Whole Foods, data; the first quarter is above the overall trend by roughly the same amount each year. Figure 22.12 shows the pattern.

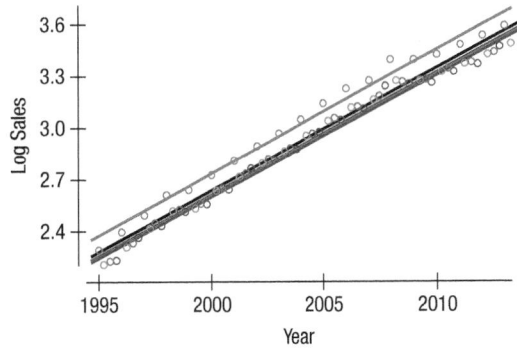

Figure 22.12 The logarithm of Whole Foods, quarterly sales. Each quarter is displayed in its own colour and has a regression line fit to it. The lines differ almost exclusively by a shift up or down.

As we learned in Chapter 21, a pattern such as the one shown in Figure 22.12 can be modelled by introducing an indicator or dummy variable for each season. For example, we can define our dummy variables to be

$Q_1 = 1$ in quarter 1, and 0 otherwise
$Q_2 = 1$ in quarter 2, and 0 otherwise, and
$Q_3 = 1$ in quarter 3, and 0 otherwise.

For a categorical variable with k levels to enter a regression model, we use $k - 1$ dummy variables. We can't use all k because that would create a collinearity. So we leave out one of them. It doesn't really matter which one we choose to leave out. The intercept coefficient will estimate a level for the period "left out," and the coefficient of each dummy variable estimates the shift up or down in the series relative to that base level. With four quarters, we use three dummy variables. For this example, we'll arbitrarily choose to leave out the dummy for Q_4. Then cases in Q_4 will have the value zero for all three of our dummy variables (Q_1, Q_2, and Q_3) and the mean adjustment relative to the trend will be estimated by the intercept (b_0). In any other quarter, the adjustment relative to Q_4 will be the coefficient for that quarter's dummy variable.

FOR EXAMPLE   A regression model for truck border crossings

QUESTION   Find and interpret a multiple regression model for the Canada–Alaska truck border crossing data from For Example: "Truck border crossings between Canada and Alaska." (The data are in the file **Trucks**.)

ANSWER   The model is:

Dependent variable is: Trucks
R-squared = 54.2%   R-squared (adjusted) = 49.6%
$s = 156.7$ with $132 - 13 = 119$ degrees of freedom

Variable	Coefficient	SE(Coeff)	t-ratio	P-value
Intercept	27539.6	8719	3.16	0.0020
Decimal Year	−13.3027	4.350	−3.06	0.0028
Jan	−187.342	46.93	−3.99	0.0001
Feb	−160.325	46.93	−3.42	0.0009
Mar	−2.03334	46.93	−0.043	0.9655
May	129.728	46.94	2.76	0.0066
Jun	311.474	46.95	6.63	≤0.0001
Jul	195.491	46.97	4.16	≤0.0001
Aug	125.531	50.71	2.48	0.0147
Sep	23.3453	47.00	0.497	0.6203
Oct	−4.27389	47.03	−0.091	0.9277
Nov	−139.893	47.05	−2.97	0.0036
Dec	−209.693	47.08	−4.45	≤0.0001

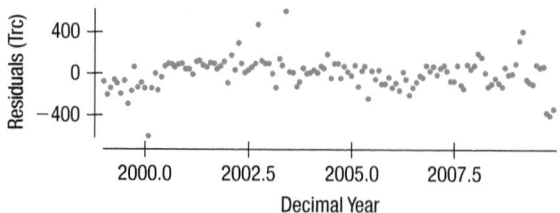

The model finds that the trend is declining over time, but only by about 13 trucks per month per year. (The units of the series are "Trucks per month.") The coefficient of the trend indicates that 13 fewer trucks cross the border each month than in the previous year, after allowing for the (very substantial) seasonal pattern. The model estimates a strong seasonal pattern, with crossings low in winter months (November to February) and high in the summer (May to August)—not a surprising pattern for Alaska.

LO❷   22.7   Additive and Multiplicative Models

Adding dummy variables to the regression of a time series on *Time* turns what was a simple one-predictor regression, such as we dealt with in Chapter 7, into a multiple regression, such as those we learned about in Chapter 20. That, combined with the question of whether to work with the original time series or the logarithm of the series, raises a new question. If we model the original values, we have added the seasonal component, S (in the form of dummy variables), to the trend component, T (in the form of an intercept coefficient and a regression with the *Time* variable as a predictor). We can write

$$\hat{y}_t = T + S.$$

This is an **additive model** because the components are added up in the model. For example, we've seen that sales from The Home Depot seem to grow linearly with a seasonal pattern. Table 22.10 shows the regression that models those sales in terms of a trend component and three quarterly dummy variables.

Dependent variable is: HDSales
R-squared = 98.7% R-squared (adjusted) = 98.5%
$s = 0.5915$ with $40 - 5 = 35$ degrees of freedom

Variable	Coeff	SE(Coeff)	t-ratio	P-value
Intercept	1.38314	0.2534	5.46	≤0.0001
Time	0.410336	0.0081	50.4	≤0.0001
Q1	1.22191	0.2657	4.60	≤0.0001
Q2	2.41907	0.2650	9.13	≤0.0001
Q3	1.14944	0.2647	4.34	0.0001

Table 22.10   A regression to model Home Depot sales with a trend component and three dummy variables representing a seasonal component in an additive model.

The model contains a trend component that predicts growth at about $0.41 billion per quarter with adjustments for each quarter that are consistent over the entire time period. For example, because Q4 is the quarter without a dummy variable, sales in Q4 are predicted to be, on average, $1.38 + 0.41\,Time$ billion dollars. The seasonal dummy variable coefficients adjust the predictions for each quarter by adding the value of their coefficients to the intercept. For example, sales in Q1 are predicted to be $1.38 + 0.41\ Time + 1.22 = \$2.60B + 0.41\ Time$. But you can see from Figure 22.13 that the seasonal fluctuations in the data are small early in the series and grow larger later in the series—a pattern this model doesn't fit.

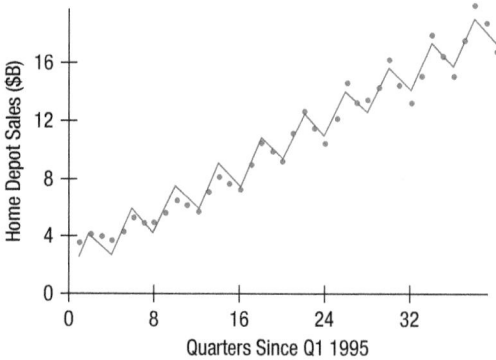

Figure 22.13   Sales at The Home Depot with predictions from the additive model. The model predicts a consistent seasonal component, although the seasonal component of the data varies.

When we examined the Whole Foods, sales data, we saw that we could straighten the trend and make the seasonal fluctuations more nearly the same size by finding the *logarithm*. We can still find a multiple regression, but now the response variable is re-expressed by logarithms. The model is in Table 22.11.

Dependent variable is: Log WFSales
R-squared = 99.6% R-squared (adjusted) = 99.6%
$s = 0.0188$ with $52 - 5 = 47$ degrees of freedom

Variable	Coefficient	SE(Coeff)	*t*-ratio	P-value
Intercept	147.856	2.239	−66.0	<0.0001
Year	0.075217	0.0011	67.4	<0.0001
Q1	0.156682	0.0153	10.3	<0.0001
Q2	0.040523	0.0152	2.67	0.0094
Q3	0.035156	0.0156	2.25	0.0276

Table 22.11   A regression model for the logarithm of the Whole Foods, quarterly sales data with trend and seasonal components.

Now, however, there's a difference in the model. Because we're modelling the logarithm of sales, when we think in terms of the sales themselves, the model components are multiplied rather than added, so we have a **multiplicative model**

$$\hat{y} = T \times S.$$

Although we acknowledge that the terms in a multiplicative model are multiplied, we always fit the multiplicative model by taking logs, changing the form to an additive model that can be fit by multiple regression.

As we observed earlier, seasonal fluctuations are often proportional to the overall level of the values in the series, so the Q1 lift in sales in a multiplicative model is a *proportion* of overall sales, not a fixed additive increment. Specifically, it's $10^{0.1325} \approx 1.36$—about 36% higher than the sales at that time. Because the sales themselves were growing (at 20% per year), this 36% lift grew as well, in dollar terms. But after taking logs, it's a constant lift, and easier to model.

Look back at the Whole Foods, sales in Figure 22.1. You can see this growth in the size of the seasonal component in the plot as well as in the trend. Taking logs not only turns exponential growth into linear growth, but it also tends to stabilize the size of the seasonal fluctuations.

LO❷   22.8   Cyclical and Irregular Components

Many time series are more complex than the trend and seasonal components can model. The Intel stock price data of Figure 22.7 is one example. Models of time series components are usually said to include two additional components: a cyclical component and an irregular component. Consistent with their form for the trend and seasonal components, we write for additive models

$$\hat{y}_t = T + S + C + I,$$

and for multiplicative models

$$\hat{y}_t = T \times S \times C \times I.$$

The Cyclical Component

Long-term business cycles may influence economic and financial time series. Other time series may be influenced by other long-term fluctuations. Whenever there's a business, economic, or physical cycle whose cause is understood and can be relied on, we should look for an external or **exogenous** variable to model the cycle. The regression models we've been considering can accommodate such additional predictors naturally.

Just calling a long-term fluctuation in the data that isn't fit by the trend or seasonal component a "cyclical component" doesn't add much to our understanding. Cyclical patterns may not be immediately evident in the data, so it's wise to compute and plot the residuals, known for time series models as the irregular component.

Irregular Components

The irregular components are the residuals—what's left over after we fit all the other components. We should examine them to check any assumptions and also to see if there might be other patterns apparent in the residuals that we might model. For multiple regression, most statistics programs plot the residuals against the predicted values, but for time series models, it's essential to plot them against *Time*. Figure 22.14 shows the residuals of the Whole Foods, data plotted against year. Two quarters stand out. Both extraordinary quarters are fourth quarters of their years, which suggests that our seasonal model may need to be improved.[10] We also see a possible cyclical pattern with a period of about four years. This might be something worth investigating to see if we can add a component to our model.

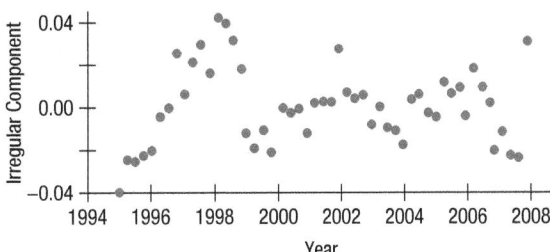

Figure 22.14   The irregular component, or residuals, of the multiplicative model for the Whole Foods, sales. In the beginning years, growth was apparently faster than after 1999 or so. There are also a couple of quarters that deserve attention: Q4 of 2001 and Q4 of 2007, which were underestimated.

---

[10]It's possible to include a dummy variable to model a specific event in time. Doing so is known as intervention analysis.

> **FOR EXAMPLE**   Additive and multiplicative models for truck border crossings
>
> **QUESTION** Is the model for Alaska truck border crossings in For Example: "A regression model for truck border crossings" an additive or a multiplicative model? Describe the components. Which month was left out? Why?
>
> **ANSWER** This is an additive model. There is an overall negative trend of -13.3 truck crossings per month per year. There is a strong seasonal pattern, fit by the indicator variables for month. April was left out. One month had to be left out to avoid collinearity among the indicator variables.[11] There are generally fewer border crossings between October and March and more between April and September—probably due to the difficulty of driving in the winter in Alaska.
>
> The residuals show no cyclic pattern. The irregular component shown in the residuals has a few outlying months that may deserve looking into. (For example, January of 2000 was a month with particularly heavy snows in Alaska.)

JUST CHECKING

Continuing our analysis of the J. Crew revenue data, here is a regression fitting a linear model to predict *Revenue* ($M):

Dependent variable is: Revenue
R-squared = 97.2% R-squared (adjusted) = 96.9%
$s = 21.75$ with $40 - 5 = 35$ degrees of freedom

Variable	Coefficient	SE(Coeff)	*t*-ratio	P-value
Intercept	191.904	9.316	20.6	<0.0001
Q#since 2003	10.0017	0.2993	33.4	0.0001
Q1	−65.1649	9.766	−6.67	0.0001
Q2	−59.5866	9.744	−6.12	0.0001
Q3	−48.8483	9.730	−5.02	0.0001

5 Locate and interpret the trend coefficient.

6 Why is there no term for Q4?

7 Is the average value for Q4 higher or lower than the other three quarters? Why?

Answers are found in Appendix A.

LO❺   22.9   **Forecasting with Regression-Based Models**

Regression models are easy to use for forecasting because they give us a formula. It's easy to substitute future values for *Time*, for the appropriate dummy variables, and for any exogenous variables and calculate a predicted value. But any kind of forecast is uncertain, and the uncertainty grows the further we extrapolate, so it's wise to limit forecasts to the near term. The forecast error measures we discussed in Section 22.4 apply equally well to regression models and are computed from the residuals (or irregular component).

The most reliable part of a regression time series model is the seasonal component, because it's probably driven by fairly regular economic or environmental phenomena. We can reasonably expect those patterns to continue into the future, so we can feel comfortable basing longer-term forecasts on them. A company that has seen large fourth-quarter holiday season sales in the past can probably count on higher fourth-quarter sales even several years into the future.

---

[11]April was selected by technology because it was alphabetically first. That's not a particularly good reason. You should be alert for arbitrary decisions by technology like this one.

Using a **linear trend model** is less reliable. As much as we might like to think that a growing company will continue to grow, it should be clear that no company can grow forever. Exponential growth is even harder to maintain. Changes in the trend can be quite sudden. The business news is filled with stories of companies whose growth "suddenly" stopped or slowed, of products whose sales unexpectedly shot up and then just as unexpectedly fell back, and of economic predictions by experts who, in retrospect, look ill-informed. While government forecasts can be found for such reliable indicators as the gross domestic product (GDP) and disposable income (DI), long-term forecasts should be made with great care. Changes in the economy or the market cannot be anticipated by the trend component and can change a company's business quite suddenly.

The reliability of cyclical components for forecasting is something you must simply judge for yourself based on your knowledge and understanding of the underlying economic cycles. An empirical cycle that is not understood makes a risky basis for prediction. A cycle that is understood and is due to underlying phenomena that are stable over time would be a more reliable component of a forecast.

GUIDED EXAMPLE   Comparing Time Series Methods, Part 2

Alan Novelli/Alamy Stock Photo

In 2010, the People's Republic of China became the world's second largest economy. China is the largest foreign holder of U.S. public debt. Trade between the two largest economies of the world is an important factor in the global economy. Forecasting U.S. imports from China is important because these are a key factor in the health of the U.S. economy. We have quarterly data starting in 1995. Let's try the regression models to see how well they do.

PLAN

Setup State your objective. Identify the quantitative variables you wish to examine. Report the time frame over which the data have been collected and define each variable.

Plot Plot the time series and clearly label the axes to identify the scale and units.

We want to build regression-based time series models for the logarithm of U.S. imports from China. Because we have already concluded that the exponential growth in imports calls for taking logarithms, we will fit a multiplicative model.

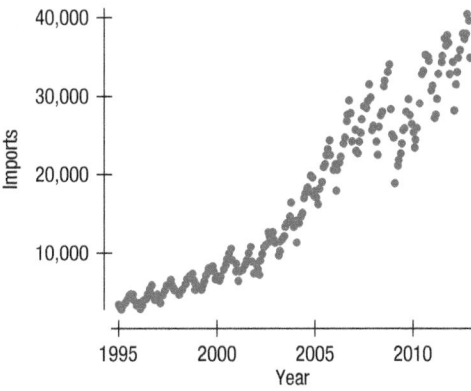

(continued)

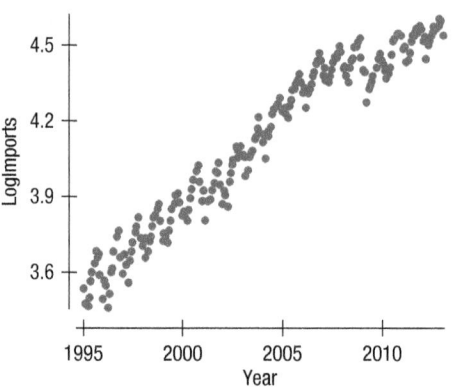

Model Think about the assumptions and check the conditions.

This is a time series recording quantitative values. There is a consistent, increasing trend and fluctuations around it that may be seasonal. However, it is clearly growing exponentially. The logarithm is much more nearly linear. So we should take logs and fit a multiplicative model.

DO **Mechanics** Fit a multiplicative model with trend and seasonal terms.

Dependent variable is: LogImports
R-squared = 96.6% R-squared (adjusted) = 96.4%
$s = 0.0625$ with $216 - 13 = 203$ degrees of freedom

Variable	Coefficient	SE(Coeff)	t-ratio	P-value
Intercept	−118.340	1.641	−72.1	<0.0001
Year	0.061102	0.0008	74.6	<0.0001
Feb	−0.061534	0.0208	−2.96	0.0035
March	−0.062441	0.0208	−3.00	0.0030
April	−0.025918	0.0208	−1.24	0.2146
May	6.30778e-4	0.0208	0.030	0.9759
June	0.026409	0.0208	1.27	0.2061
July	0.049512	0.0208	2.38	0.0183
Aug	0.069299	0.0208	3.33	0.0010
Sep	0.072621	0.0208	3.49	0.0006
Oct	0.085385	0.0208	4.10	<0.0001
Nov	0.037045	0.0208	1.78	0.0768
Dec	−0.022210	0.0208	−1.07	0.2877

Plot the fit vs. the data (here on the log scale) and the residuals.

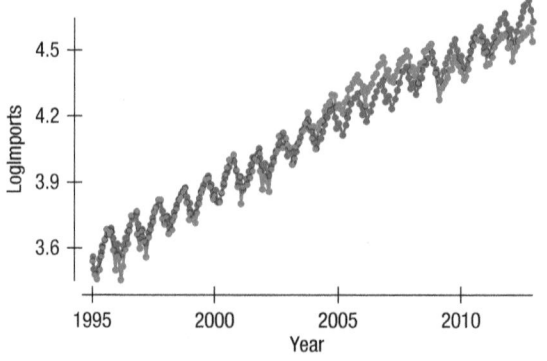

The data are the blue series and the model is the more regular orange pattern.

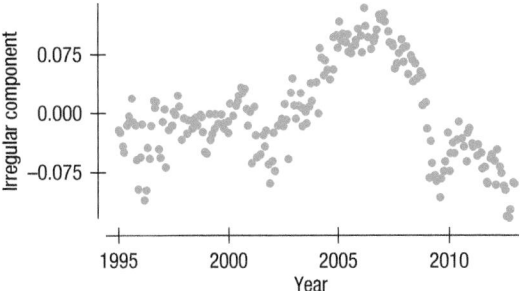

To make a prediction with a multiplicative model, we use the inverse function of the logarithm.

The irregular component shows that the growth in imports slowed during the financial crisis of 2008.

MAD = 0.049

MSE = 0.0391

MAPE = 1.1614

Forecast for January 2013 is easy to find because January is the indicator that was left out. We calculate $2013 \times 0.061102 - 118.340 + 46,583$ corresponding to $10^{4.6583} = \$45,553M$.

REPORT **Conclusion** Compare the advantages and disadvantages of the time series models. Be sure to state your interpretations in the proper context.

MEMO

Re: Time series analyses of U.S. imports from China

A multiplicative regression model fit to the monthly data on U.S. imports from China for the period from 1995 through 2012 provides a reasonable fit. However, its greatest value is to highlight the fact that the nature of the series changed with the financial crisis of 2008. Models that expect a consistent pattern, such as the regression models, can't follow sudden changes as well as smoothers.

The actual imports in January 2013 were $37,172M.

To obtain a better prediction, it might be better to model only the years since 2011; however, such a short series might not have sufficient data for reliable model-fitting.

LO❸,❺   22.10   Choosing a Time Series Forecasting Method

We've considered several methods for modelling and forecasting time series. How can you choose among them the ones that fit your needs? Your choice depends both on the nature of your data and on what you hope to learn from the data.

Simple moving averages demand the least of the data. You can apply them to almost any time series. However:

- They can forecast well only for the next time period. Longer forecasts just repeat the single forecast value.
- They're sensitive to spikes or outliers in the series and can smear the shock of a spike across several adjacent time periods.
- They don't do well on series that have a strong trend, tending to lag behind the trend.

Exponential smoothing methods also make few assumptions about the data. They have the advantage of controlling the importance of recent values relative to older ones and do a good job of following the movement of a time series. However:

- They can forecast well only for the next time period. Longer forecasts just repeat the single forecast value.
- They're sensitive to spikes or outliers in the series.
- They don't do well on series that have a strong trend, tending to lag behind the trend.

Autoregressive models use automatically determined weights to allow them to follow time series in which there is correlation between each data point and the neighbouring points. However:

- They can forecast for only a limited span, depending on the parameters of the model.
- They're sensitive to spikes or outliers in two different ways. Those outliers will influence the regression that determines the smoothing weights. And then again, when the forecasting is done, the effect of spikes in the series can be spread out, contaminating several points.

Regression-based models estimate the trend and seasonal components by regression against *Time* and the use of dummy variables to represent the seasonal period. They can incorporate exogenous variables to help model business cycles and other phenomena. And, unlike moving average and exponential smoothing models, they can forecast farther into the future. However:

- You must decide whether to fit an additive model to the time series (if the trend is linear and the seasonal fluctuations have a consistent size) or to re-express the series by logarithms and fit the resulting multiplicative model.
- Because they're based on regression, these models are sensitive to outliers and failures of linearity. Because they use dummy variables to estimate the seasonal effects, those effects must be consistent in magnitude during the time covered by the data.
- Forecasts depend on the continuation of the trend and seasonal patterns. Although seasonal patterns may be reliable, trends are difficult to forecast and hazardous to assume beyond the near future. Cycles are best forecast when they're based on some identifiable (and predictable) phenomenon.

LO❸, ❺ 22.11 Interpreting Time Series Models: The Whole Foods, Data Revisited

When you use a time series model based on smoothing methods, you can (and should) summarize the patterns seen in the series and any patterns noticed in the residuals around the smooth trend. But time series models based on regression encourage us to interpret the coefficients.

Many time series of retail sales have a strong seasonal component. We've seen two in this chapter. But one of those, the quarterly sales at Whole Foods, is problematic. No, there's no problem with the models we've fit. But there is a problem if we interpret them without thinking.

Why should there be a seasonal spike in Whole Foods sales? Food isn't a seasonal item. To be honest, it took the authors a while before we asked these questions. But that sent us back to the data. It turns out that Whole Foods Market divides its financial year into three quarters of 12 weeks and one of 16 weeks. The spike is entirely due to this bookkeeping anomaly. You can check for yourself; the

Rachel L. Sellers/Shutterstock

seasonal peaks are $16/12 = 1.33$ times as big as the other quarters—almost exactly what the multiplicative model estimated them to be.

That doesn't invalidate any of our models. We'd still have to allow for the seasonal peak to model Whole Foods, sales. But it is a cautionary tale that warns us not to jump to conclusions when interpreting our models.

WHAT CAN GO WRONG?

- **Don't use a linear trend model to describe a nonlinear trend.** Be sure to examine the scatter of the observations around the linear trend line to determine if there's a pattern. A curved pattern may indicate a need to transform the series. Plot the residuals. Variation in the residuals that increases when the central value is higher is a sign of a need to take logarithms. Series that grow or shrink by a constant percentage each time period are exponential and should be transformed before fitting a model.

- **Don't use a trend model for short-term forecasting.** Trend models are most effective for long-term forecasting and are rarely the best models to forecast one or two time periods ahead. Be aware that forecast errors are greater for long-term forecasting.

- **Don't use a moving average, an exponential smoothing, or an autoregressive model for long-term forecasting.** Smoothing models are most effective for short-term forecasting. However, it's less important to transform an exponentially trending series for these models because they base their predictions on recent values.

- **Don't ignore autocorrelation if it's present.** Look at correlations among the lagged versions of the time series. If present, then try using lagged variables to model the time series.

ETHICS IN ACTION

Kevin Crammer, a broker for a large financial services firm, is getting ready to meet with a new client, Sally Martinez. Sally just inherited a rather large sum of money and is looking to invest it long-term. She is not an experienced investor, and even though Kevin sent her information about various financial investment options, she's confused and still wants to meet with him to get his advice. Kevin's company has several of its own mutual fund products it likes its brokers to push. Kevin selected one of these funds and, based on historical returns, prepared a graph showing how an initial amount of $10,000 invested for 20 years would have grown over time. While some cyclical fluctuations tied to economic conditions were noticeable, the underlying trend was upward. Kevin decided to fit a linear trend line to the graph. Checking out the residuals, he did notice a pattern indicating a curvature. Transforming the data by logs yielded a better model. Upon closer examination, he was able to see that a straight line didn't fit as well

to the raw data as to the transformed data. Although past pattern is no indication of future behaviour, he did use both models to project future values for an initial investment of the size Sally was considering. The linear trend line on the transformed data provided higher values. As he prepared for his meeting with Sally, he thought it would be a good idea to keep the linear trend analysis on the transformed data handy when discussing this investment option.

Ethical Issue *In this case, the linear trend on the transformed data produced forecasts that suited Kevin's purpose, so he ignored the observed cyclical variation in the data (related to Item B, ASA Ethical Guidelines; see Appendix C, the American Statistical Association's Ethical Guidelines for Statistical Practice, also available online at www.amstat.org/about/ethicalguidelines.cfm).*

Ethical Solution *Present all relevant models. Caution about forecasting future values based on past patterns.*

WHAT HAVE WE LEARNED?

Learning Objectives

① Be able to recognize when data are in a time series.

- A *time series* consists of data recorded sequentially over time, usually at equally spaced intervals.
- Time series analyses often attempt to provide forecasts of future values of the series.
- Be able to convert a time series into index numbers.

② Recognize the four components of a time series.

- The trend component measures the overall tendency of the series to increase or decrease. It's ordinarily estimated as the slope of a regression against *Time*.
- The seasonal component measures regular, repeating fluctuations. Often these are due to seasons of the year, but the term applies to any such regular fluctuation. Seasonal components are often estimated by introducing indicator (dummy) variables in a regression model.
- The cyclic component accounts for such things as long-term business cycles.
- The irregular component is the random fluctuation around the time series model. It corresponds to the residuals from a time series model.

③ Use smoothing methods to see past random fluctuations (noise) in a time series to detect an underlying smoother pattern (signal).

- Simple moving average methods average a relatively small number of adjacent values to obtain a smooth value for each time period.
- Weighted moving average methods introduce weights. Because the weights can determine the behaviour of the smoother, these are a very general class of time series methods.
- Exponential smoothing methods are weighted moving averages with weights that decline exponentially into the past.
- Autoregressive models use regression methods, predicting the time series from versions of the same series offset, or *lagged*, in time. The result is a weighted moving average method in which the weights are estimated from the data.

④ Estimate and report forecast error with statistics such as MSE, MAD, and MAPE.

⑤ Use multiple regression methods to model a structured time series, using *Time*, indicator variables for the seasonal component, and exogenous variables that might account for the cyclic component.

- Multiple regression models have the advantage that they can provide forecasts further into the future.

- Additive models estimate the components using multiple regression methods to find a model in which the estimates are added to yield the predicted values.

- Multiplicative models for a time series model the series as a product of its components.

- Multiplicative models are ordinarily estimated by taking the logarithm of the time series values and then using multiple regression as for additive models.

Terms

Absolute percentage error (APE)

A measure of the error of a forecast:

$$APE = \frac{|y_t - \hat{y}_t|}{|y_t|}$$

Additive model

A model for a time series that models the time series with a sum of all or some of the following terms: a trend, a seasonal pattern, and a cyclical pattern.

Autocorrelation

The correlation between a data sequence, such as a time series, and that same sequence offset (or lagged) by one or more positions. Autocorrelation is one measure of lack of independence of the individual cases.

Autoregressive model	A pth-order autoregressive model has the form $$\hat{y} = b_0 + b_1 y_{lag1} + \ldots + b_p y_{lagp}.$$
Cyclical components	Parts of a model for a time series that describe regular repeating fluctuations with a period of several years.
Deseasonalized	A time series that has had a seasonal component estimated and subtracted.
Exogenous	Variables that are not part of a time series but nevertheless might be helpful in modelling it.
Exponential smoothing, single exponential smoothing (SES) model	An exponential smoother has the form $$\tilde{y} = \alpha y_t + (1 - \alpha)\tilde{y}_{t-1}$$ or equivalently $$\tilde{y}_t = \alpha y_t + \alpha(1 - \alpha)y_{t-1} + \alpha(1 - \alpha)^2 y_{t-2} + \alpha(1 - \alpha)^3 y_{t-3}\ldots$$ The parameter α determines how the smoother behaves. Larger values of α give more weight to recent values of the series. Smaller values give more weight to more distant values.
Forecast	Many analyses of time series attempt to forecast future values. We denote a forecast value $\hat{y}_t$.
Forecast error	The difference between the observed value and the forecasted value for a particular time in a time series: $$e_t = y_t - \hat{y}_t$$
Index numbers	The value of a time series relative to its value in a base year.
Irregular component	The part of a time series model that describes random, or unpredictable, behaviour; the residuals.
Linear trend model	A time series model that assumes a constant rate of increase (or decrease) over time: $$\hat{y} = b_0 + b_1 t$$
Mean absolute deviation (MAD)	A measure of forecast error of the form $$\text{MAD} = \frac{1}{n}\sum |y_t - \hat{y}_t|.$$
Mean absolute percentage error (MAPE)	A measure of forecast error of the form $$\text{MAPE} = 100 \times \frac{1}{n}\sum \frac{|y_t - \hat{y}_t|}{|y_t|}.$$
Mean squared error (MSE)	A measure of forecast error of the form $$\text{MSE} = \frac{1}{n}\sum (y_t - \hat{y}_t)^2.$$
Moving average	An estimate that uses the arithmetic average of the prior L values in a time series: $$\tilde{y}_t = \frac{\sum_{i=t-L+1}^{t} yi}{L}$$
Multiplicative model	A classical time series model consisting of four components, $$\hat{y} = T \times S \times C \times I,$$ where T is the trend component, S is the seasonal component, C is the cyclic component, and I is the irregular component.
Naive forecast	Forecasting that the next value in a time series will be equal to the current one: $$\hat{y}_{t+1} = y_t$$

Period	The time between peaks of a seasonal component in a time series.
Random walk	A time series that exhibits random periods of upturns and downturns and is best modelled using a naive forecast.
Seasonal component	The part of a model for a time series that fits a regular pattern that has a period of less than or equal to 12 months.
Single exponential smoothing (SES) model	(See *Exponential smoothing*.)
Stationary in the mean	A time series that has a relatively constant mean value over the time frame of the series is said to be stationary in the mean.
Stationary in the variance	A time series that has a relatively constant variance is said to be stationary in the variance.
Time series	A time series is data recorded sequentially over time.
Trend component	The part of a model for a time series that fits long-term changes in the mean of the series.

Skills

Plan

- Be able to recognize when data are a time series.
- Know how to identify whether a linear or nonlinear trend model is appropriate.
- Be able to judge whether a time series is stationary in the mean and/or variance.
- Be able to recognize when a seasonal or cyclical component is present in a time series.
- Understand the impact of changing lengths on a moving average model.
- Understand the impact of changing smoothing coefficients on a single exponential smoothing model.

Do

- Know how to develop linear and nonlinear trend models.
- Be able to compute moving averages of different lengths to obtain forecasts.
- Be able to compute a single exponential smoothing model using different coefficients.
- Know how to calculate forecast error, including MAD, MSE, and MAPE.
- Know how to determine if autocorrelation is present.
- Be able to develop autoregressive models for seasonal and nonseasonal models.
- Know how and when to use dummy variables to develop seasonal models.

Report

- Know how to use forecast error to compare alternative time series models.
- Know how to determine which lagged variables are significant in an autoregressive model.
- Know how to identify different advantages for alternative time series models depending on the objective.

MINI case studies

Canadian Fruit Production

Blueberries are the most important fruit in Canada. Not only do they taste good, but they also occupy over half of the land area devoted to fruit production, with blueberry exports valued at several hundred million dollars per year. There are two main varieties of blueberries: small, wild berries that grow on low bushes and larger, juicer berries that grow on high bushes. British Columbia is famous for the high-bush variety and is the third-largest producing region in the world. Peaches, another delicious fruit, are grown in B.C.'s Okanagan Valley and in larger numbers in Ontario's Niagara Peninsula, where the industry began in the early 1800s. By 1900 it had expanded to about 200,000 trees, and today Ontario boasts over a million peach trees.

JoannaTkaczuk/Fotolia

Growers are supported by organizations such as the BC Blueberry Council and Foodland Ontario, a program of the Ontario Ministry of Agriculture. These organizations need to keep track of trends in the fruit-growing industry and determine whether those trends can be expected to continue into the future.

The data file **ch22_MCSP_Fruit** contains the acreage planted in blueberries and peaches in British Columbia and Ontario, respectively, during the period 1996 to 2011. Forecast the acreage for one year and five years ahead for each of these crops in each of these provinces. Use linear regression first, and then correct your forecasts using exponential smoothing (with parameter $\alpha = 0.2$ and 0.8) on the residuals from the regression. Comment on the validity of each regression, and explain the role of exponential smoothing in addressing any problems in the regressions. Then comment on which of these methods is/are appropriate for each series, and give a final forecast using the method you consider appropriate for each forecast of each crop.

Tiffany & Co.

Tiffany was founded in 1837 when Charles Lewis Tiffany opened his first store in downtown Manhattan. Tiffany retails and distributes a selection of Tiffany & Co. brand jewellery at a range of prices. Today, more than 150 Tiffany & Co. stores sell to customers in the U.S. and international markets. In addition to jewellery, it sells Tiffany & Co. brand merchandise in the following categories: timepieces and clocks; sterling silver merchandise; stainless steel flatware; crystal, glassware, china, and other tableware; custom engraved stationery; writing instruments; and fashion accessories. Fragrance products are sold under the trademarks Tiffany, Pure Tiffany, and Tiffany for Men. Tiffany also sells other brands of timepieces and tableware in its U.S. stores. Tiffany's quarterly sales from 2005 to the start of 2013 are in the file Tiffany 2013. They are shown here:

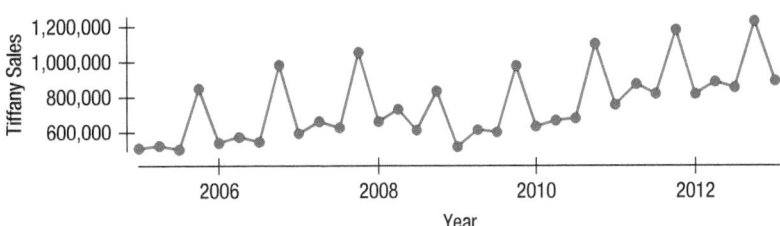

Build alternative time series models for Tiffany's sales, and forecast future sales. In addition, develop multiple regression models to forecast Tiffany's sales by using economic data, such as gross domestic product (GDP), Consumer Price Index (CPI), disposable income, unemployment, and interest rates over this same time period. These economic data are also provided in the data file. Given that Tiffany is known for its high-end quality and price, it was of interest for the corporate executives to see how sensitive Tiffany's sales were to economic indicators. Develop a hypothesis before developing your models. Compare your models and recommend a model for the executives at Tiffany to use for forecasting their quarterly sales.

Technology Help: Time Series Analysis

EXCEL

Excel offers some, but not all, time series methods in this chapter.

Exponential Smoothing

Data >Data Analysis >Exponential Smoothing and enter the input and output range as well as the smoothing coefficient ("damping factor" in Excel).

Moving Averages

Data >Data Analysis >Moving Average and enter the input and output range as well as the length ("interval" in Excel).

XLSTAT

To construct an autoregressive moving average (ARMA(p,q)) model:

- Select **Modeling data**, then select **ARMA**.
- Enter the cell range of the data under **Time series**.
- Note that you can centre the data by selecting the appropriate box.
- XLStat requires input of parameters of the model such that $p + q > 0$.

MINITAB

The time series commands are in the **Time Series** submenu of the **Stat** menu. They are generally self-explanatory. Most commands open a dialogue in which you specify the series to analyze, specify parameters (e.g., for smoothers), and request predictions.

SPSS

SPSS 20 and higher offers an add-on Forecasting Module, which can be purchased as an addition to the SPSS Statistics Core System. All Forecasting analyses discussed in this chapter can be done using this module.

JMP

- From the **Analyze** menu choose **Modeling >Time Series.**
- Put the data series in **Y.** The data must be in time order and equally spaced.
- JMP will display a time series plot and report the autocorrelation.
- Commands for analyzing the series are under the red triangle.

MyStatLab Students! Save time, improve your grades with MyStatLab. Questions marked in # can be found on MyStatLab. You can practise them as often as you want, and most feature step-by-step guided solutions to help you find the right answer. You'll find a personalized study plan available to you too!

EXERCISES

SECTION 22.1

1. Are the following data time series? If not, explain why.

a) Quarterly earnings of Microsoft Corp.
b) Unemployment in August 2010 by education level.
c) Time spent in training by workers in NewCo.
d) Numbers of emails sent by employees of SynCo each hour in a single day. **LO ❶**

2. Are the following data time series? If not, explain why.

a) The Statistics Canada Labour Force Survey showing the number of Canadian adults who are employed full-time in each major sector of the economy.
b) The quarterly gross domestic product (GDP) of France from 1980 to the present.
c) The dates on which a particular employee was absent from work due to illness over the past two years.
d) The number of cases of flu reported by the CDC each week during a flu season. **LO ❶**

SECTION 22.2

Here is a table of values from the U.S. Bureau of Labor Statistics (file **BLS_Output**):

Year	Output/Hr Labour (2005 = 100)	Output/Unit Capital (2005 = 100)
1993	73.407	86.944
1994	74.049	90.416
1995	74.086	92.913
1996	76.248	94.391
1997	77.577	97.576
1998	79.879	99.502
1999	82.692	101.488
2000	85.553	102.534
2001	88.146	100.316
2002	92.081	97.905
2003	95.623	97.247

2004	98.279	98.417
2005	100	100
2006	100.945	102.071
2007	102.407	102.617
2008	103.111	100.573
2009	106.251	93.383
2010	109.484	93.309
2011	109.852	95.200
2012	110.554	97.273

T 3. For the series of output per hour of labour:

a) Make a time series plot.
b) Describe the trend component. (Remember: direction, form, and strength)
c) Is there evidence of a seasonal component? **LO ❷**

T 4. For the series of output per unit of capital:

a) Make a time series plot.
b) Describe the trend component.
c) Is there evidence of a seasonal component?
d) Is there evidence of a cyclic component? **LO ❷**

SECTION 22.3

Here are data on the monthly price of Delicious apples and gas, which are both components of the U.S. Consumer Price Index.[12] The timeplot shows the years 2006–2009 for apples; the data table shows just 2006 for both apples and gas.

Month	Apples	Gas
Jan	0.963	2.359
Feb	0.977	2.354
Mar	0.935	2.444
Apr	0.958	2.801
May	1.021	2.993
Jun	1.053	2.963
Jul	1.146	3.046
Aug	1.235	3.033

---

[12]The Consumer Price Index (CPI) represents changes in prices of all goods and services purchased for consumption by urban households. User fees (such as water and sewer service) and sales and excise taxes paid by the consumer are also included. Income taxes and investment items (such as stocks, bonds, and life insurance) are not included. Most of the specific CPI indices have a 1982–1984 reference base. That is, the average index level (representing the average price level) is set with the 36-month period covering the years 1982, 1983, and 1984 equal to 100 and then measures changes in relation to that figure. An index of 110, for example, means that there's been a 10% increase in price since the reference period. See www.bls.gov/cpi for more information.

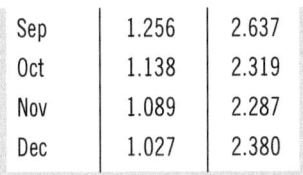

Sep	1.256	2.637
Oct	1.138	2.319
Nov	1.089	2.287
Dec	1.027	2.380

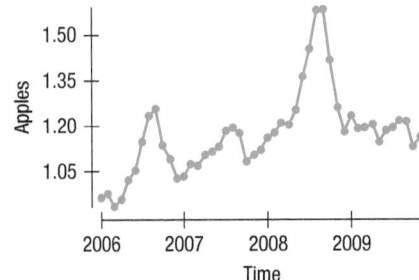

T 5. For the apple prices:

a) Find a two-point moving average of the first year (2006).
b) Use it to predict the value for January 2007. **LO ❸**

T 6. For the gas prices:

a) Find a two-point moving average of the first year.
b) Use it to predict the value for January 2007. **LO ❸**

SECTION 22.4

T 7. For the apple prices smoothed in Exercise 5, the actual value for January 2007 was 1.034. Find the absolute percentage error of your forecast. **LO ❹**

T 8. For the gas prices of Exercise 6, the actual value for January 2007 was 2.321. Find the absolute percentage error of your forecast. **LO ❹**

SECTION 22.5

T 9. For the apple prices of Exercise 5, find the lag1 version of the prices. **LO ❸**

T 10. For the gas prices of Exercise 6, find the lag2 version of the prices. **LO ❸**

T 11. A second-order autoregressive model for the apple prices (for all four years of data) is

Dependent variable is: Apples
R-squared = 78.1% R-squared (adjusted) = 71.9%
$s = 0.0574$ with $10 - 3 = 7$ degrees of freedom

Variable	Coefficient	SE(Coeff)	t-ratio	P-value
Intercept	0.327717	0.1881	1.74	0.1250
Lag1<Apples>	1.32814	0.3114	4.27	0.0037
Lag2<Apples>	−0.634127	0.2959	−2.14	0.0693

Using the values from the table, what is the predicted value for January 2007 (the value just past those given in the table in exercise 5)? **LO ❸**

① 12. A second-order autoregressive model for the gas prices is:

Dependent variable is: Gas
R-squared = 82.2% R-squared (adjusted) = 77.1%
$s = 0.1498$ with $10 - 3 = 7$ degrees of freedom

Variable	Coefficient	SE(Coeff)	t-ratio	P-value
Intercept	1.28207	0.4644	2.76	0.0281
Lag1<Gas>	1.31432	0.2383	5.51	0.0009
Lag2<Gas>	−0.788250	0.2457	−3.21	0.0149

Using values from the table, what is the predicted value for January 2007 (the value just past those given in the table in exercise 5)? **LO ❸**

SECTIONS 22.6 TO 22.9

① 13. An additive regression model for the apple prices is:

Dependent variable is: Apples
R-squared = 51.9% R-squared (adjusted) = 34.9%
$s = 0.1108$ with $47 - 13 = 34$ degrees of freedom

Variable	Coefficient	SE(Coeff)	t-ratio	P-value
Intercept	114.825	29.46	3.90	0.0004
Time	0.057746	0.0147	3.94	0.0004
Jan	0.001438	0.0783	0.018	0.9855
Feb	0.007062	0.0783	0.090	0.9287
Mar	0.003626	0.0784	0.046	0.9634
Apr	0.015064	0.0784	0.192	0.8488
May	0.058751	0.0785	0.749	0.4592
Jun	0.115689	0.0786	1.47	0.1501
Jul	0.173627	0.0787	2.21	0.0342
Aug	0.169815	0.0788	2.16	0.0383
Sep	0.049253	0.0789	0.624	0.5368
Oct	0.006191	0.0791	0.078	0.9381
Nov	0.014249	0.0847	0.168	0.8675

a) What is the name for the kind of variable called *Jan* in this model?
b) Why is there no predictor variable for December?
c) Is there evidence of a cyclic component in these data? **LO ❷, ❺**

① 14. An additive model for the gas prices is:

Dependent variable is: Gas
R-squared = 28.6% R-squared (adjusted) = 3.3%
$s = 0.5524$ with $47 - 13 = 34$ degrees of freedom

Variable	Coefficient	SE(Coeff)	t-ratio	P-value
Intercept	66.3101	146.9	0.451	0.6546
Time	0.031816	0.0732	0.435	0.6664
Jan	0.036401	0.3907	0.093	0.9263
Feb	0.162901	0.3907	0.417	0.6793
Mar	0.395053	0.3908	1.01	0.3192
Apr	0.644704	0.3910	1.65	0.1084
May	0.788105	0.3914	2.01	0.0520
Jun	0.774757	0.3918	1.98	0.0562
Jul	0.673908	0.3923	1.72	0.0949
Aug	0.544059	0.3929	1.38	0.1752
Sep	0.333961	0.3937	0.848	0.4022
Oct	0.167112	0.3945	0.424	0.6745
Nov	0.029645	0.4226	0.070	0.9445

a) What is the value predicted by this model for January 2010 (Time = 2010)?
b) Is there evidence of a cyclic component for these data? **LO ❷, ❺**

CHAPTER EXERCISES

15. Concepts, part 1.
a) Which will be smoother, a 50-day or a 200-day moving average?
b) Which will be smoother, a single exponential smoothing (SES) model using $\alpha = 0.10$ or a model using $\alpha = 0.80$?
c) What is the difference in how historical data are used when the smoothing coefficient in a single exponential smoothing (SES) model is raised from 0.10 to 0.80? **LO ❷**

16. Concepts, part 2. We're trying to forecast monthly sales for a company that sells ski equipment and clothing. Assume that the company's sales peak each December and that the monthly sales have been growing at the rate of 1% each month. Answer the following questions:

a) Based on the description of these data, what time series components can you identify?
b) If you identified a seasonal component, what is the period?
c) If you use seasonal dummy variables, specify the dummy variables you would use.
d) After examining the residuals and using the information provided, you decide to transform the sales data. What transformation are you likely to suggest? Why? **LO ❷, ❺**

17. Concepts, part 3. For each of the following time series, suggest an appropriate model:

a) Weekly stock prices that reveal erratic periods of up and down swings.

b) Annual sales that reveal a consistent percentage annual increase.

c) Quarterly sales for a bicycle shop that reveal a sales peak in Q2 of each year. **LO ❸, ❺**

18. Concepts, part 4. For each of the following time series, suggest an appropriate model:

a) Daily stock prices that reveal erratic periods of up and down swings.

b) Monthly sales that reveal a consistent percentage increase from month to month.

c) Quarterly sales for a women's clothing company that reveal an annual peak each fourth quarter.

Ⓣ 19. Liquid assets. The Bank of New York Company was founded by Alexander Hamilton in 1784 and was a major commercial bank until its merger with the Mellon Financial Corporation in 2007. Its year-end financial reports for the final five years of independent operation give the following values for its liquid assets. (*Source:* Data from *The Financial Times.* Bank of New York Company: Liquid assets for 2002–2006.)

Year	Liquid Assets ($M)
2002	18,546
2003	22,364
2004	22,413
2005	19,881
2006	26,670

a) Use a three-year moving average to predict what liquid assets would have been in 2007.

b) Predict the value for 2007 using a single exponential smoothing model with smoothing parameter $\alpha = 0.2$. **LO ❸**

Ⓣ 20. Baking profits. Sara Lee Corp., maker of food, beverage, and household products, is known especially for its baked products, marketed under its corporate name. For the five years ending July 1 of each year from 2002 to 2006, its bakery division reported the following profits:

Fiscal Year	Profits ($M)
2002	97
2003	98
2004	156
2005	−4
2006	−197

a) Use a four-year moving average to predict profits for 2007.

b) Predict the profits for 2007 using a single exponential smoothing model with smoothing parameter $\alpha = 0.5$.

c) Think about the exponential smoother. If the parameter were 0.8, would you expect the prediction to be higher or lower? What if it were 0.2? Explain. **LO ❸**

Ⓣ 21. Banana prices. The price of bananas fluctuates on the world market. Here are the prices ($/tonne) for the years 2000–2004. (*Source:* Data from *Holy See Country Review.* [2008].)

2000	2001	2002	2003	2004
422.27	584.70	527.61	375.19	524.84

a) Find a three-year moving average prediction for the price in 2005.

b) Find a prediction for 2005 with an exponential smoothing model with $\alpha = 0.4$.

c) The actual price of bananas in 2005 was $577/tonne (www.imf.org/external/np/res/commod/table3.pdf). Compute the absolute percentage error for each prediction. **LO ❸, ❹**

Ⓣ 22. Target earnings. Target Corp. operates "big box" stores that sell everyday essentials and fashionable, differentiated merchandise. It also operates an online business. Target's reported gross earnings per share for the years 2003–2006 are given here:

2003	2004	2005	2006
$1.82	2.02	2.17	2.73

a) Find a prediction for 2007 based on a three-year moving average and one for a four-year moving average.

b) Find a prediction for 2007 based on an exponential smoothing model with $\alpha = 0.8$.

c) Earnings per share in 2007 were, in fact, $3.18. Compute the absolute percentage error for each prediction. **LO ❸, ❹**

Ⓣ 23. Toyota stock prices. The following time series graph shows daily closing stock prices for Toyota Motor Manufacturing from April 1, 2008, through June 21, 2013 (Source: Yahoo! Finance).

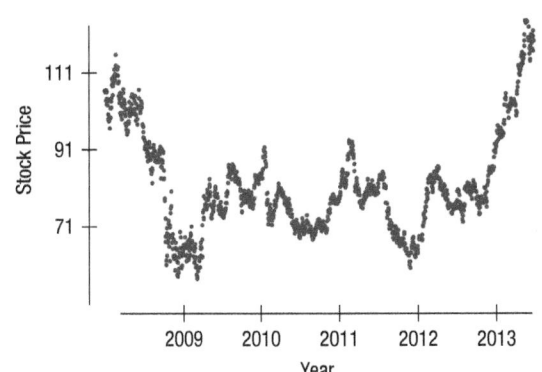

a) Which time series components seem to be present?

The method of moving averages was applied to these data. Here are time series graphs showing moving average results using two different lengths:

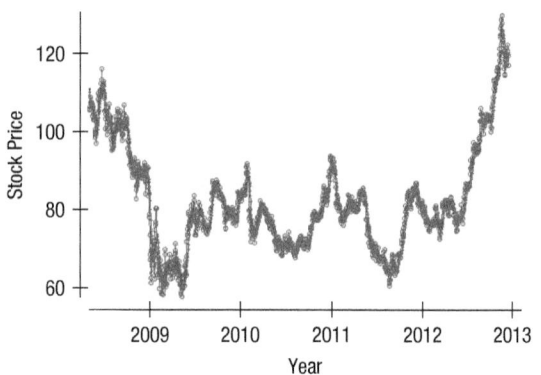

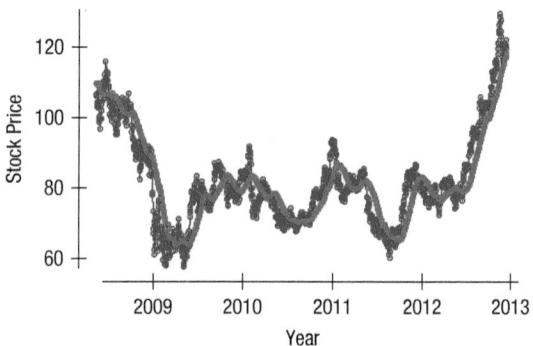

b) In which application is a larger length used? **LO ❷, ❸**

⊤ 24. Google stock price. The following time series graph shows daily closing stock prices (adjusted for splits and dividends) for Google Inc. from January 1, 2008, through June 21, 2013 (Source: Yahoo! Finance).

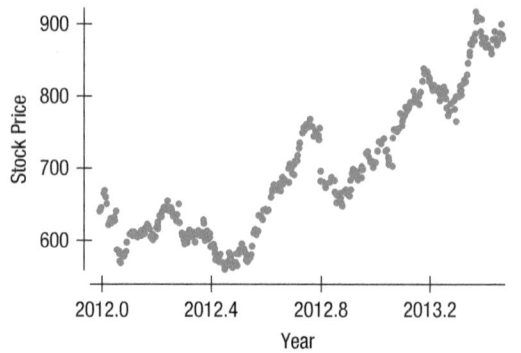

a) Which time series components are evident?

Single exponential smoothing (SES) models were found for these data. Examine the following time series graphs showing two different smoothing coefficients values ($\alpha = 0.2$ and $\alpha = 0.8$).

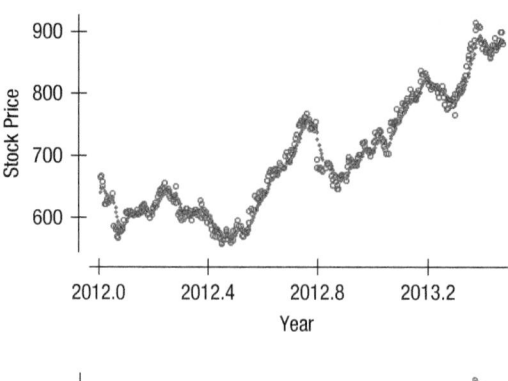

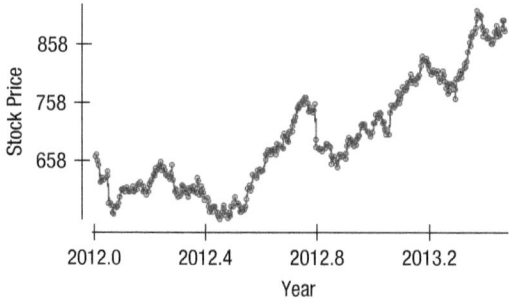

b) In which graph is a larger value of α used? **LO ❷, ❸**

⊤ 25. Canadian wheat exports, part 1. The graph shows Canadian wheat exports in dollars from January 2006 to May 2009 in blue, together with two moving averages. One moving average is averaged over four data points and the other over seven data points. (*Source:* Based on Statistics Canada. [2011]. CANSIM Table 228-0001—Merchandise imports and exports, by major groups and principal trading areas for all countries, monthly [dollars].)

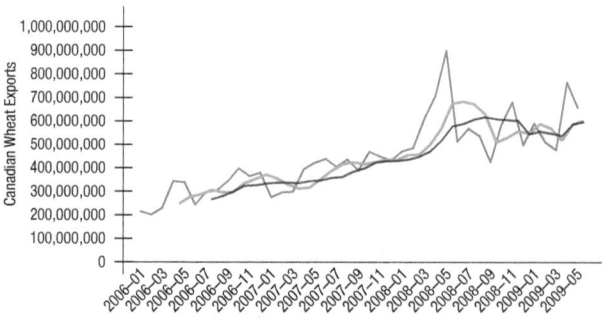

a) Which moving average corresponds to the graph in green?
b) Which moving average corresponds to the graph in purple?
c) Why do the graphs start in different months at the left of the graph? **LO ❸**

⊤ 26. Canadian wheat exports, part 2. The graph shows Canadian wheat exports in dollars, from January 2006 to May 2009, in light blue, together with two exponential smoothings. One exponential smoothing has the smoothing parameter $\alpha = 0.5$, and the other has $\alpha = 0.2$.

(*Source:* Based on Statistics Canada. [2011]. CANSIM Table 228-0001—Merchandise imports and exports, by major groups and principal trading areas for all countries, monthly [dollars].)

a) Which exponential smoothing corresponds to the graph in orange?

b) Which exponential smoothing corresponds to the graph in dark blue?

c) Canadian wheat exports peaked in May 2008. Which exponential smoothing is affected for a longer period of time after this peak? **LO ❸**

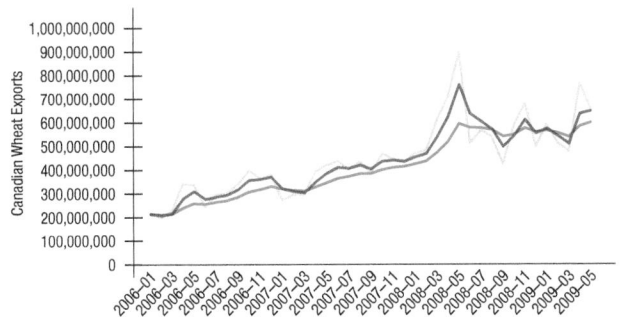

27. **Autoregressive model, part 1.** Suppose an autoregressive model is used for data in which quarterly sales in 2017 were 1.9, 1.7, 2.2, and 2.3 ($ billion).

a) If a first-order autoregressive model is developed with estimated parameters of $b_0 = 0.100$ and $b_1 = 1.12$, compute the forecast for Q1 of 2018.

b) Compare this forecast with the actual value ($2.9 billion) by computing the absolute percentage error (APE). Did you over-forecast or under-forecast?

c) Assuming these quarterly sales have a seasonal component of length four, use the following model to compute a forecast for Q1 of 2018: $y_t = 0.410 + 1.35y_{t-4}$. Compare the APE for this forecast to that in (a). Compare the appropriateness of the different models. **LO ❸, ❹**

28. **Autoregressive model, part 2.** Suppose an autoregressive model is used to model sales for a company that peaks twice per year (in June and December).

a) What lagged variables would you try in a regression to forecast sales? Explain.

b) How would you determine which of your lagged variables should remain in the model? Explain. **LO ❸**

ⓣ 29. **Coffee prices.** Coffee is the world's second largest legal export commodity (after oil) and is the second largest source of foreign exchange for developing nations. The United States consumes about one-fifth of the world's coffee. The International Coffee Organization (ICO) computes a coffee price index using Colombian, Brazilian, and a mixture of other coffee data. Data are provided for the daily ICO price index (in $US) from January 2013 to April 2013.

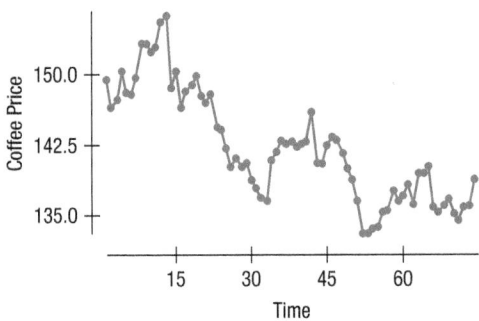

Here's an autoregressive model for the composite prices:

Dependent variable is: Coffee
73 total cases of which 2 are missing
R-squared = 88.7% R-squared (adjusted) = 88.4%
$s = 2.034$ with $71 - 3 = 54$ degrees of freedom

Variable	Coefficient	SE(Coeff)	t-ratio	P-value
Intercept	6.75323	5.922	1.14	0.2581
Lag1	0.838228	0.1194	7.02	<0.0001
Lag2	0.113135	0.1192	0.949	0.3459

a) Here are the last several values of the series: 134.45, 135.85, and 136.10. What price does this model predict for the next value in the series?

b) The next value in the series was, in fact, 138.90. Compute the APE.

c) Find a prediction based on a two-point moving average. How does it compare with the AR model? **LO ❸, ❹**

30. **Canadian wheat exports, part 3.** The graphs in Exercises 25 and 26 show Canadian wheat exports in dollars from January 2006 to May 2009. (*Source:* Based on Statistics Canada. [2011]. CANSIM Table 228-0001—Merchandise imports and exports, by major groups and principal trading areas for all countries, monthly [dollars].) The last four months of data are as follows:

2009–02	511,600,000
2009–03	478,900,000
2009–04	764,500,000
2009–05	658,300,000

An exponential smoothing model, ES, with $\alpha = 0.2$ gives a smoothed value of $585,200,000 for April 2009.

An autoregressive model with one lagged independent variable, AR(1), gives:

	Coefficients	Standard Error	t-stat	P-value
Intercept	119328842.1	52774663	2.261101	0.029722
Y (lag 1)	0.757028401	0.115727	6.541492	1.17E-07

a) Give three values for May 2009 from MA-4, ES, and AR(1).

b) Calculate the absolute percentage error, APE, for May 2009 for each of the three values. **LO ❸, ❹**

31. Gallup poll. The Gallup organization in the United States periodically asks the following question:

If your party nominated a generally well-qualified person for president who happened to be a woman, would you vote for that person?

Here is a time series plot of the percentage answering "yes" vs. the year of the (20th) century. The least squares trend line is given by $\hat{y}_t = 5.58 + 0.999\,Year$, where $Year = 37$, 45, ... 99 to represent the years during which the survey was given.

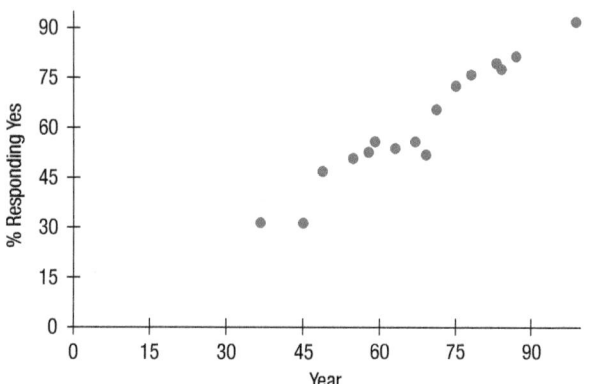

a) The R^2 for this trend line is 94%. A student decided to use this linear model to obtain a forecast for the percentage who will respond "yes" in 2012. What value should the student use for *Year*?
b) Find the predicted value for the year 2012. Is it realistic? **LO ❺**

⊤ 32. Consumer Price Index. The most common use of the CPI is as an economic indicator to forecast inflation and evaluate the effectiveness of government policies. Following is the time series plot for the monthly CPI (not seasonally adjusted) from January 2007 to May 2013. The linear trend line is CPI = 206 + 0.346 t, where $t = 0, 1, \ldots 76$ to represent the months in the series.

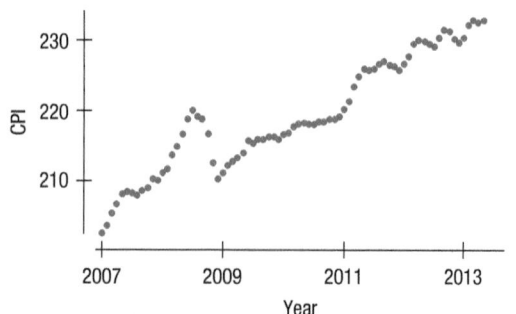

a) What does the intercept 206 represent in this trend line? What does the slope represent?
b) Is this model appropriate for this series? Explain.

c) A regression model fit to the same data from 2009 on has the equation of $201.8 + 0.419t$. Which model would you prefer to use to predict the CPI for June 2013? Explain. **LO ❺**

33. Canadian retail sales, part 1. Canadian retail sales in dollars for September 2006–August 2009 are shown in the graph. The horizontal axis represents the number of months since August 2006. (*Source:* Statistics Canada. [2011]. CANSIM Table 800-014—Retail trade, sales by trade group based on the North American Industry Classification System [NAICS], monthly [total, all trade groups; unadjusted, dollars].)

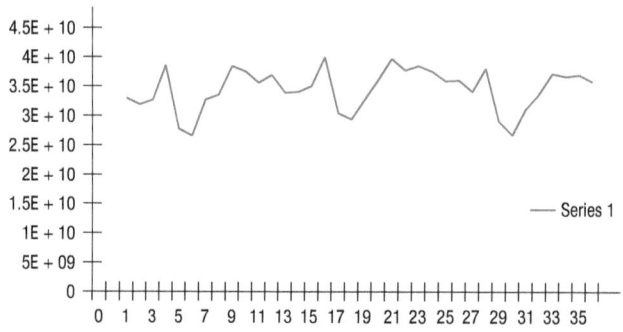

A linear regression analysis gives the following result:

	Coefficients	Standard Error	t-Stat	P-Value
Intercept	33448518381	1.23E+09	27.30383	1.04E-24
Months	55724727.16	57738651	0.96512	0.3413

The residual graph is:

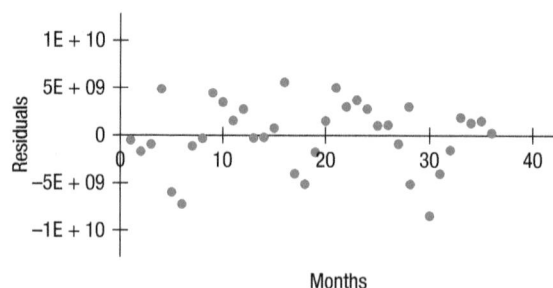

a) What does the intercept represent?
b) What does the coefficient of months represent?
c) What is the forecast of the retail sales for October 2009?
d) What do you notice about the residuals?
e) Do you think the R^2 value for this regression is high or low? **LO ❺**

⊤ 34. Interest rates. Average annual interest rates (banks, prime lending) in the United States from 1980 through 2006 are shown in the following time series graph (*Source:* United Nations Statistics Division, http://unstats.un.org):

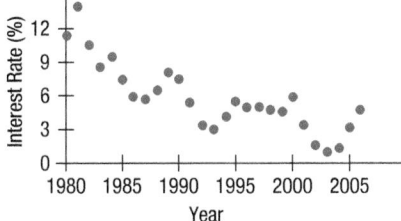

a) What components do you see in this series?

Here's a linear trend model fit to these data:

Dependent variable is: Interest Rate
R-squared = 69.9% R-squared (adjusted) = 68.7%
s = 1.732 with 27 − 2 = 25 degrees of freedom

Variable	Coeff	SE(Coeff)	t-ratio	P-value
Intercept	656.539	85.30	7.70	≤0.0001
Year	−0.326490	0.0428	−7.63	≤0.0001

b) Interpret the trend coefficient mean in this model.
c) Predict the interest rate for 2006. Do you trust the prediction? Why or why not?

Here's a time series plot of the residuals from this model:

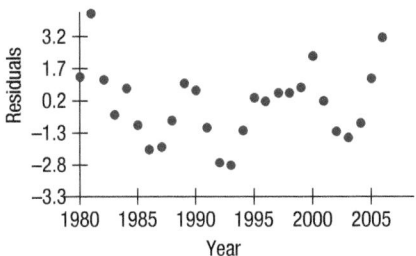

d) Discuss any patterns you see in this plot.
e) Would an exponential transformation likely do better for these data? Explain. **LO❺**

35. Seasonal model, part 1. Use the following model to forecast quarterly sales ($ million) for a company (where time is rescaled to begin at zero [the first quarter has $t = 1$], and Q_2, Q_3, and Q_4 are dummy variables for the indicated quarters), and answer the following questions.

$$\hat{y} = 1.1 + 0.2t − 0.1Q_2 − 0.5Q_3 + 0.5Q_4$$

a) For the first quarter of the time series, what are the sales?
b) What is the quarter that, on average, has the lowest level of sales over the time frame of the series?
c) What is the quarter that, on average, has the highest level of sales over the time frame of the series?
d) Interpret the coefficient of the dummy variable named Q_4. **LO❺**

36. Seasonal model, part 2. Use the following model to forecast quarterly sales ($000) for a startup (where time is rescaled to begin at zero [the first quarter has $t = 1$], and Q_2, Q_3, and Q_4 are dummy variables for the indicated quarters), and answer the following questions.

$$\hat{y} = 15.1 + 10.5t − 5.0Q_2 − 7.2Q_3 + 7.5Q_4$$

a) For the first quarter of the time series, what are the sales?
b) What is the quarter that, on average, has the lowest level of sales over the time frame of the series?
c) What is the quarter that, on average, has the highest level of sales over the time frame of the series?
d) Interpret the coefficient of the dummy variable named Q_4. **LO❺**

❶ 37. Hawaii tourism, pre-crisis, part 1. Much of the public and private industry in Hawaii depends on tourism. The following time series plot shows the number of domestic visitors to Hawaii by air from the rest of the United States per month from January 2002 through December 2006 before the financial crisis of 2008.

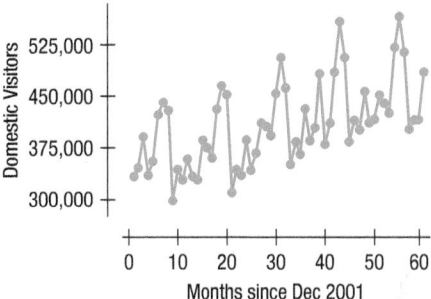

Here is a regression model fit to these data with dummy variables for months and a *Time* variable that starts at 0 and counts months:

Dependent variable is: Domestic Visitors
R-squared = 96.6% R-squared (adjusted) = 95.8%
s = 12870 with 60 − 13 = 47 degrees of freedom

Variable	Coefficient	SE(Coeff)	t-ratio	P-value
Intercept	302,921.34	6256.51	48.417	<0.0001
Time	2,197.59	97.94	22.439	<0.0001
Feb	15,741.81	8142.96	1.9333	0.059251
Mar	66,348.41	8144.73	8.146	<0.0001
Apr	29,403.22	8147.67	3.609	0.000744
May	23,988.62	8151.79	2.943	0.005039
Jun	97,126.83	8157.08	11.907	<0.0001
Jul	138,669.03	8163.55	16.986	<0.0001
Aug	100,621.64	8171.18	12.314	<0.0001
Sep	−24,572.56	8179.98	−3.004	0.004262
Oct	5,725.25	8189.94	0.699	0.487961
Nov	−8,112.14	8201.06	−0.989	0.327651
Dec	44,985.86	8213.33	5.477	<0.0001

a) Interpret the P-value for the trend coefficient.
b) You are planning to visit Hawaii and hope to avoid the crowds. A friend says that September and November have the fewest average visitors. Why might that not be correct?
c) Do you find evidence of a seasonal effect? Explain.
d) How many tourists would you predict for Hawaii in April 2007 (month 63 of this series)? **LO❷, ❺**

⊤ 38. Hawaii tourism, pre-crisis, part 2. In Exercise 37 we examined domestic tourists who visit Hawaii. Now, let's consider international tourism. Here's a time series plot of international visitors for the same time period:

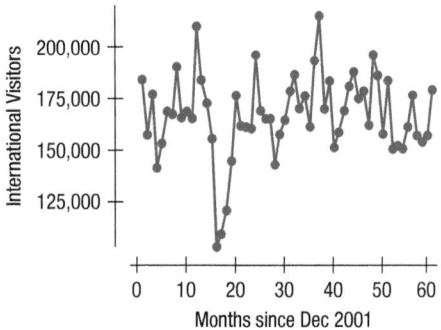

Here's the linear trend model with dummy variables for months:

Dependent variable is: International
R-squared = 59.9% R-squared (adjusted) = 49.7%
$s = 13540$ with $60 - 13 = 47$ degrees of freedom

Variable	Coefficient	SE(Coeff)	t-ratio	P-value
Intercept	175289	6580	26.639	<0.0001
Time	104	103	1.009	0.318049
Feb	−12411	8564	−1.449	0.153943
Mar	−4284	8566	−0.500	0.619369
Apr	−39269	8569	−4.583	<0.0001
May	−32214	8574	−3.757	0.000474
Jun	−23988	8579	−2.796	0.007468
Jul	−11384	8586	−1.326	0.191275
Aug	4737	8594	0.551	0.584075
Sep	−12792	8603	−1.487	0.143706
Oct	−10780	8614	−1.252	0.216944
Nov	−17519	8625	−2.031	0.047919
Dec	14338	8638	1.660	0.103617

a) Interpret the P-value for the *Time* coefficient.
b) The R^2 for this model is lower than for the model fit to domestic visitors in Exercise 37. Does that mean that an exponential trend model would do better?

c) International tourists often visit Hawaii in January. How can you tell that from this model?
d) Even though the R^2 for this model is lower than the corresponding R^2 for the model fit in Exercise 37 to domestic tourist visits, you might feel more comfortable predicting the number of international visitors for April 2007 with this model than you did predicting the number of domestic visitors with the previous model. Explain why. **LO❷, ❺**

⊤ 39. Oakland passengers. The Port of Oakland airport reports the number of passengers passing through each month. At first glance, this is just simple growth, but by recognizing the series as a time series, we may learn more.

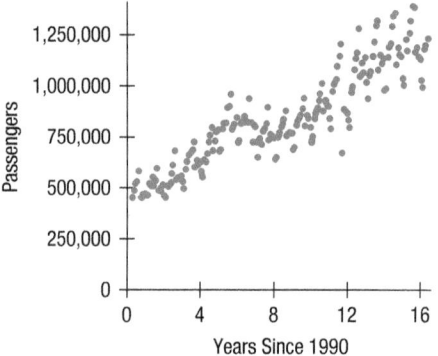

The increasing spread of the data suggests that a multiplicative model may fit better.

Here's an exponential trend model with seasonal (monthly) dummy variables:

Dependent variable is: LogPassengers
R-squared = 92.4% R-squared (adjusted) = 91.9%
$s = 0.0358$ with $194 - 13 = 181$ degrees of freedom

Variable	Coeff	SE(Coeff)	t-ratio	P-value
Intercept	5.64949	0.0101	558	≤0.0001
Years since '90	0.024929	0.0006	45.2	≤0.0001
Feb	−0.013884	0.0127	−1.10	0.2747
Mar	0.048429	0.0127	3.82	0.0002
Apr	0.049028	0.0125	3.93	0.0001
May	0.066227	0.0125	5.30	≤0.0001
Jun	0.082862	0.0127	6.54	≤0.0001
Jul	0.095295	0.0127	7.52	≤0.0001
Aug	0.121779	0.0127	9.61	≤0.0001
Sep	0.029382	0.0127	2.32	0.0216
Oct	0.049596	0.0127	3.91	0.0001
Nov	0.039649	0.0127	3.13	0.0020
Dec	0.043545	0.0127	3.44	0.0007

a) Interpret the slope.
b) Interpret the intercept.
c) Which months have the lowest traffic at Oakland airport? (*Hint:* Consider all 12 months.)

Here's a plot of the residuals from the model fit to the Oakland airport passengers:

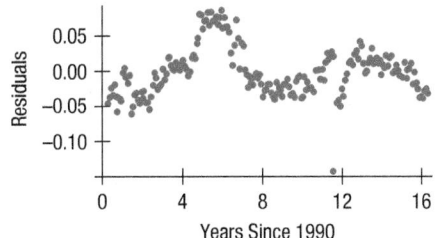

d) What components would you now say are in this series?

40. Canadian retail sales, part 2. Canadian retail sales in dollars for September 2006 to August 2009 are shown in the graph for Exercise 33. An autoregressive model has been fitted with two independent variables at lags of 1 and 12, with the following result:

	Coefficients	Standard Error	*t*-stat	P-value
Intercept	1308797295	4.35E+09	0.301185	0.766236
Y(Lag1)	0.21799026	0.105997	2.056569	0.052365
Y(Lag12)	0.74949759	0.100199	7.480117	2.8E-07

Retail sales from September 2008 to August 2009 were:

Sep-08	35,889,612,000
	36,013,720,000
	34,073,597,000
	38,037,305,000
	29,041,595,000
	26,706,563,000
	31,176,227,000
	33,701,529,000
	37,170,039,000
	36,654,794,000
	36,927,938,000
Aug-09	35,794,721,000

a) What feature in the graph in Exercise 33 leads us to include *Y*(Lag12) in the model?
b) What does the coefficient of *Y*(Lag1) represent?
c) What does the coefficient of *Y*(Lag12) represent?
d) What is the forecast of retail sales for September 2009?
LO❸, ❹

41. Oakland outlier. The plot of residuals in Exercise 39 shows an outlier that wasn't as evident in the data. The outlier is September 2001. Clearly, this wasn't a typical month for air travel. Here are three models fit to this series: a single exponential smooth, a 12-point moving average, and the fitted values from the seasonal regression model of Exercise 39. Discuss how each deals with the outlier. **LO❷, ❸**

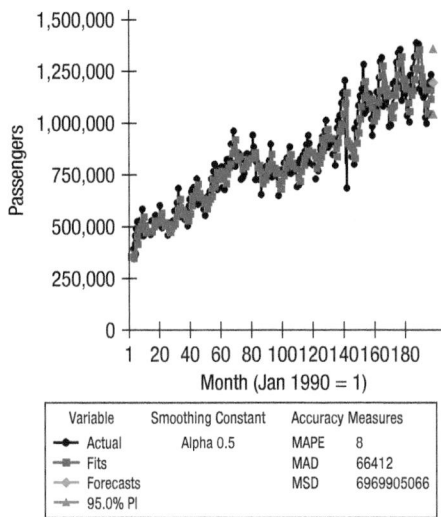

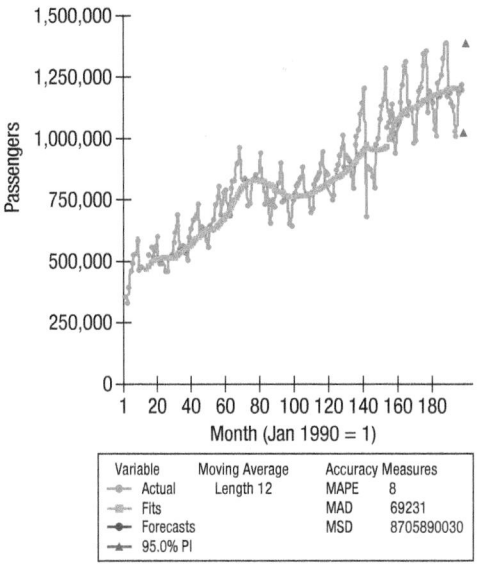

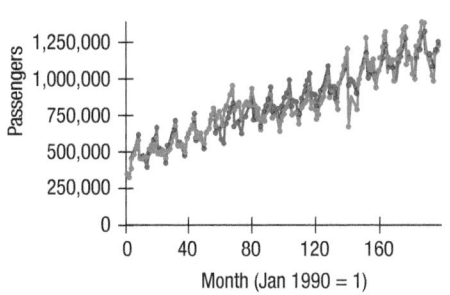

The remaining exercises require the use of statistics software. Statistics packages vary in their capabilities and in the default decisions some make. As a result, depending on which package you choose, your answers may differ from those in Appendix A.

T 42. Ecommerce, part 1. Quarterly ecommerce retail sales (in millions of dollars) in the United States are provided in the data file. (*Source:* US Census Bureau. US Dept of Commerce. Retrieved from www.census.gov.) Use this time series to answer the following questions:

a) Fit a linear trend model to this series, but don't use the last two quarters (Q4 2007 and Q1 2008).

b) Fit an exponential trend model to this series, but don't use the last two quarters.

c) Use both models to forecast the quarterly values for Q4 2007 and Q1 2008. Which model produces better forecasts?

d) What other time series components (besides trend) are likely present in this series? **LO❺**

43. Ecommerce, part 2.

a) Fit a linear trend model with dummy variables for the seasonal effect on the ecommerce data in Exercise 42.

b) Fit an exponential trend (multiplicative) model with dummy variables to these data.

c) Which model fits better? **LO❷, ❺**

T 44. Canadian exports of industrial machinery. Trends in exports of industrial machinery are extremely important to Canada because of overseas competition from countries with lower wage rates. The data file contains monthly Canadian exports of industrial machinery from June 2006 to May 2009 in millions of dollars. (*Source:* Data from Statistics Canada. [2011]. CANSIM Table 228-0001—Merchandise imports and exports, by major groups and principal trading areas for all countries, monthly [dollars].)

a) Fit an AR(2) model to the data. Which range of months do you use to fit the model? Give the regression output plus the equation for the model. What forecast does this model give for June 2009?

b) Calculate a fourth-order moving average, MA-4, of the data. Which is the first month for which the MA-4 can be calculated? What is the value of the MA-4 for May 2008 and for May 2009? What forecast does this model give for June 2009?

c) Perform exponential smoothing on these data using a smoothing parameter of $\alpha = 0.3$. Use the initial condition that the smoothed value for June 2006 is the same as the data value for June 2006. What is the smoothed value for July 2006 and for May 2009? What forecast does this model give for June 2009? **LO❸**

T 45. Canadian exports of natural gas. Natural gas is a major Canadian export and hence a major source of foreign exchange. The data file contains monthly Canadian exports of natural gas from April 2006 to March 2009 in

millions of dollars. (**Source:** Data from Statistics Canada. [2011]. CANSIM Table 228-0001—Merchandise imports and exports, by major groups and principal trading areas for all countries, monthly [dollars].)

a) Fit an AR(2) model to the data. Which range of months do you use to fit the model? Give the regression output plus the equation for the model. What forecast does this model give for April 2009?

b) Calculate a fourth-order moving average, MA-4, of the data. Which is the first month for which the MA-4 can be calculated? What is the value of the MA-4 for March 2008 and for March 2009? What forecast does this model give for April 2009?

c) Perform exponential smoothing on these data using a smoothing parameter of $\alpha = 0.2$. Use the initial condition that the smoothed value for April 2006 is the same as the data value for April 2006. What is the smoothed value for May 2006 and for March 2009? What forecast does this model give for April 2009? **LO❸**

T 46. Oil prices, part 1. A time series plot of monthly crude oil price ($/barrel) from January 2001 to March 2007 is shown here:

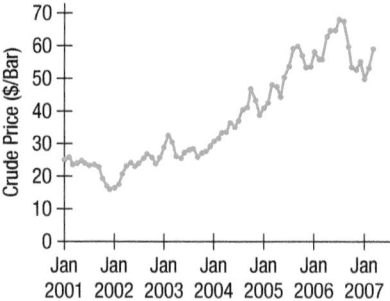

Using these data,

a) Fit an appropriate autoregressive model by testing for the significance of each autoregressive term.

b) Obtain a forecast for March 2007. **LO❸**

T 47. Oil prices, part 2. Return to the oil price data of Exercise 46.

a) Find a linear model for this series.

b) Find an exponential model for this series.

c) Use these methods to forecast the crude oil price for March 2007.

d) The actual price for March 2007 was $58.70. Compute measures of forecast error (e.g., MAD and MAPE) and compare the accuracy of the forecasts for the models of Exercises 46 and 47. **LO❹, ❺**

T 48. Canadian airline passengers. Many businesses are affected by the number of airline passengers, including the airlines themselves, plus hotels, restaurants, and the entertainment industry. It is therefore important to keep track of trends and make forecasts about the number of airline passengers. The data file contains the number of Canadian airline passengers from July 2006 to November 2009. (**Source**: Data from Statistics Canada. [2010]. CANSIM Table 401-0001—Operating and financial statistics of major Canadian airlines, monthly [passengers unless otherwise noted].)

a) Plot the data and identify the seasonal pattern.

b) Fit an autoregressive model to the data, including one term with a single lag and another term with a lag corresponding to the seasonality. What is the first month you can use to fit the model? Give the result of the regression analysis and the model equation. Is the seasonality significant?

c) Forecast the number of Canadian airline passengers in December 2009. **LO ❸**

❶ 49. OPEC production. Using the monthly data for OPEC oil production in thousands of barrels per day, develop and compare the following models.

a) Fit an appropriate autoregressive model by testing for the significance of each autoregressive term.

b) Obtain a forecast for March 2007.

c) Compare your forecast for March to the actual value (by computing APE). Also compare the APE of forecasts made by MA(6), MA(12) and SES with $\alpha = 0.9$.

d) Recommend an appropriate model for forecasting this time series. **LO ❸, ❹**

50. Canadian mutual fund. You're working in the Marketing department of a financial institution and are preparing promotional materials for one of its mutual funds. Your boss has told you to prepare a graph showing how the past performance of the fund compares with the S&P TMX Composite Price Index during 2010 and 2011, and gives you data for the first trading day of each month during those years. "Use index numbers to make the comparison," he says, "and choose a start date that makes our fund look good."

a) What start date would you use?

b) Produce a graph comparing the index numbers.

c) What ethical issue arises in this project? (Refer to the ASA Ethical Guidelines in Appendix C.) **LO ❶**

	S&P/TMX Composite Price Index	Mutual Fund Unit Value ($)
04/01/2010	11866.9	1706
01/02/2010	11317.55	1768
01/03/2010	11728.06	1645
01/04/2010	12151.06	1628
03/05/2010	12196.51	1585
01/06/2010	11571.97	1501
02/07/2010	11196.06	1423
03/08/2010	11782.6	1534
01/09/2010	12003.78	1546
01/10/2010	12363.08	1599
01/11/2010	12664.81	1678
01/12/2010	13148.35	1756
04/01/2011	13402.31	1856
01/02/2011	13712.62	1934
01/03/2011	14122.85	2012
01/04/2011	14130.15	2067
02/05/2011	13934.51	2115
01/06/2011	13527.88	2108
04/07/2011	13386.49	2098
02/08/2011	12752.32	2034
01/09/2011	12700.74	2053
03/10/2011	11251.84	2061
01/11/2011	12115.1	2012
01/12/2011	12113.29	2023

51. Forecasting methods overview. Give examples of forecasting situations in which you would use (i) exponential smoothing, (ii) additive regression, and (iii) multiplicative regression. Describe whether these methods should be used for short- or long-term forecasts and the type of data to which they should be applied. **LO ❷, ❸, ❺**

Andrey Popov/Shutterstock

23

Decision Making and Risk

LEARNING OBJECTIVES

In this chapter we show you how to make decisions in the presence of uncertainty. After reading and studying this chapter, you should be able to:

❶ Assess the costs and benefits of alternative actions, given possible states of nature

❷ Take into account the probabilities of the states of nature in making a decision

Data Description, Inc.

Data Description was founded in 1985 by Paul Velleman to develop, market, and support the Data Desk statistics program. Personal computers were becoming more widely available, and graphical desktop interfaces offered new and exciting opportunities for data analysis and graphics. Data Desk was introduced in 1986 for the newly released Macintosh computer and re-released for the PC in 1997, with expanded capabilities for analysis and the ability to work efficiently with large (several million case) data sets. Data Description then launched ActivStats, a multimedia education product on DVD, which pioneered multimedia teaching in Statistics and led to the development of MediaDX, a development platform that deploys a full array of media, narration, animation, video, sound, and interactive tools for teaching.

Data Description employs both a local staff and programmers who work remotely from other parts of the country by telecommuting. In these ways, the company is typical of many technologically centred small businesses that rely on the internet for development, marketing, and customer support and compete with larger firms by staying fast and flexible.

Company president John Sammis notes that the internet has enabled small businesses such as Data Description to compete with larger international firms, and that decisions about how best to use the internet are key to competing successfully. By its 20th anniversary, Data Description (www.datadesk.com), based in Ithaca, New York, was providing software and services to education and business clients throughout the world.

We make decisions every day, often without knowing how they'll turn out. Most of our daily decisions have no serious consequences. But the decisions a business makes determine the success or failure of the venture. The consequences of business decisions can often be quantified in monetary terms, but the costs and benefits themselves often depend on events beyond the control or foresight of decision makers. Decisions must be made nevertheless. So how can people make intelligent decisions when they don't know for certain what the future holds?

One decision facing Data Description (and many other high-tech companies) is how best to provide technical support for its customers. In the past, Data Description has relied on its thorough documentation, a built-in help system, and free telephone support. But as its user base has grown, telephone-based customer support has become a significant expense. Data Description's president, John Sammis, must decide whether to invest in developing an online FAQ help system as the first line of defence for customer support, to continue free telephone support through the help desk, or to hire and train additional telephone support staff and charge customers for it. For a small business, decisions such as these carry significant costs, but making the right decision can be the difference between keeping customers happy and losing them to larger competitors.

LO❶ 23.1 Actions, States of Nature, and Outcomes

We refer to the alternative choices we can make for a decision as **actions**. Actions are mutually exclusive; if you choose one course of action, you haven't chosen the others. We'll call Data Description's choices

- Online FAQ
- Free help desk
- Pay help desk

The facts about the world that affect the consequences of each action are called **states of nature**, or sometimes just *states*. We often simplify the states to make it easier to understand the decision alternatives. We know, for example, that the economy isn't just "good" or "bad," and that the number of customers can be any value in some reasonable range. But we'll simplify by grouping the states of nature into a few categories and treating them as discrete possibilities.

For Data Description, the *states of nature* concern the type of question coming into the help desk. Management classifies them into two basic types:

- Simple
- Complex

A simple question is one that can be answered with an online FAQ system alone. A complex question requires either human technical support by telephone or backup email support for FAQ users.

Each *action* has consequences that depend on the *state of nature* that actually occurs. These consequences are called the **outcomes** or **payoffs** (because usually in business the consequence can be measured in money).

To make informed decisions, Data Description president John Sammis must estimate the costs and benefits of each action under each state of nature. According to his estimates,

- The FAQ system can answer a simple question for about $3.50. A complex question can't be answered by the FAQ system and needs additional resources. Unfortunately the backup system is slow, and the marketing manager estimates that this would cost about $15 in goodwill and future business. Adding that to the FAQ system cost gives a total cost of $18.50 for a complex question.
- A live telephone support person costs about $10 per question, whether the question is simple or complex.

- Charging the customer $3 for the telephone support could defray some of the cost, but it might upset a customer with only a simple question. That resulting ill will would cost the company an estimated $15 for each simple question. On the other hand, customers with a complex question might be happy to pay for the telephone support, so the net cost for them would be $7.

FOR EXAMPLE   **Actions, states of nature, and outcomes for purchasing airline tickets**

Pat needs to purchase airplane tickets to fly home at the end of the term. The last exam schedule slot is Friday at 3 P.M., but Pat's exams haven't yet been scheduled. Exams are scheduled centrally at Pat's school, and there's no alternative time to take them. Pat simply must be there. A ticket to fly out on Thursday morning costs $750. If the exam is scheduled on Thursday or Friday, Pat would have to sacrifice the ticket and buy a new one for $1200. An advance-purchase ticket for Saturday morning costs $900, but, the end of term being a busy time, Pat doubts this option will be available for many more days.

QUESTIONS

What are the actions in this decision process?
What are the states of nature?
What are the outcomes?

ANSWERS

The actions are purchasing a ticket for Thursday or Saturday.
The states of nature are the exam being scheduled before Thursday or afterward.
The outcomes are $750 for a Thursday ticket and early exam, $900 for a Saturday ticket, and $1950 for a Thursday ticket but late exam.

LO❶   23.2   Payoff Tables and Decision Trees

We can summarize the actions, states of nature, and corresponding payoffs in a **payoff table**. Table 23.1 shows the payoff table for Data Description's decision about customer support. Customer support is an expense, so all the entries in the payoff table are costs, which Data Description hopes to keep to a minimum. The table shows the costs for a single tech support request.

The payoff table is easy to read, but it doesn't display the sequential nature of the decision process. Another way to display this information that shows the dynamics of the decision-making process is with a **decision tree**. The decision tree mimics the actual decision-making process by showing actions followed first by the possible states of nature and then by the outcomes that would result from each combination (Figure 23.1).

		State of Nature	
		Simple Question	Complex Question
Action	FAQ	$ 3.50	$18.50
	Free Help Desk	$10.00	$10.00
	Pay Help Desk	$15.00	$ 7.00

Table 23.1   A payoff table showing costs of actions for two states of nature. Note that these are costs and not profits. As "payoffs" they might be written as negative values, but it's simpler to just remember that we want to minimize costs. Payoff tables of profits look to maximize values.

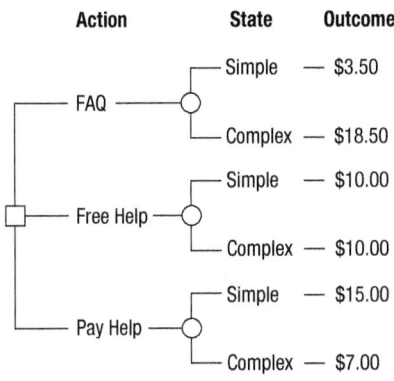

Figure 23.1 A decision tree for the customer support decision.

> The square node, or decision node, indicates that a decision must be made. The circular node, or chance node, indicates a choice made by nature.

The decision process moves from left to right through the decision tree. The decision maker chooses an action (indicated by a square node), determining which branch of the tree to follow. The circle nodes indicate branches due to the state of nature, which lie outside the control of the decision maker. The tree can expand to show decisions with any (reasonable) number of actions and states of nature.

FOR EXAMPLE   Payoff tables for purchasing airline tickets

QUESTION Pat must decide which ticket to purchase (see For Example: "Actions, states of nature, and outcomes for purchasing airline tickets"). What is Pat's payoff table?

ANSWER

		Exam Date	
		Wed. or before	After Wed.
Ticket	Thursday	$750	$1950
	Saturday	$900	$ 900

LO❶ ## 23.3   Minimizing Loss and Maximizing Gain

A conservative approach to decision making would look at the worst possible loss and try to minimize it. Table 23.2 lists the outcomes for each decision and the greatest cost for each.

		State of Nature		
		Simple Question	Complex Question	Greatest Cost
Action	FAQ	$ 3.50	$18.50	$18.50
	Free Help Desk	$10.00	$10.00	$10.00
	Pay Help Desk	$15.00	$ 7.00	$15.00

Table 23.2 The greatest cost for each decision.

The decision to go with an FAQ could cost the company as much as $18.50 when complex calls come in, and the decision for a pay help desk could cost up to $15. The safe choice—the one that minimizes the maximum cost—is the free help desk. This is known as the **minimax choice**.

Of course, one could take the other extreme position and try for the maximum gain (or, equivalently here, the minimum cost). In this table, that would call for committing to an FAQ system (and hoping that the calls are simple). Such a choice is known as the **maximax choice** (when maximizing return) or the **minimin choice** (when minimizing cost).

Choosing actions based on worst- and best-case scenarios rarely leads to the best business decision. Instead, successful small business executives rely on knowing their market so that they can make less absolute decisions. A more realistic modelling approach takes into account how frequently the decision maker expects to experience each of the states of nature and finds the optimum under that model.

FOR EXAMPLE	Minimizing loss and maximizing gain for purchasing airline tickets

QUESTIONS   Recall Pat's payoff table for purchasing an airplane ticket from For Example: "Payoff tables for purchasing airline tickets." What is Pat's minimax choice? What is Pat's minimin choice?

ANSWERS   Pat's minimax choice, minimizing the worst cost, is to purchase a Saturday ticket.

Pat's minimin choice, minimizing the minimum cost, is to purchase a Thursday ticket.

LO❷   23.4   The Expected Value of an Action

How can Data Description choose an action to maximize profit (or minimize loss)? It can be pretty sure that it'll get a mix of both simple and complex questions. Decision makers often estimate the *probability* of a state of nature based on their understanding of their business. Such probabilities can be *subjective* probabilities, or they can be grounded in data like the empirical probabilities we saw in Chapter 8. In either case they express the expert's opinion of and belief in the relative likelihood of the states. We'll write $P(s_j)$ for the probability of the jth state of nature.

As with all probabilities, we need to check that the probabilities are *legitimate*. If there are N states of nature, then we require that

$$P(s_j) \geq 0 \text{ for all } j,$$

$$\sum_{j=1}^{N} P(s_j) = 1.$$

If the probabilities are legitimate, then we can find the **expected value (EV)** of action a_i in essentially the same way as we find the expected value of a discrete random variable:

$$EV(a_i) = \sum_{j=1}^{N} o_{ij} P(s_j),$$

where there are N possible states of nature and o_{ij} is the outcome or payoff of action i when the state of nature is s_j.

At Data Description, about 40% of the questions are simple, so managers assigned a probability of 0.4 that a question will be simple and a probability of 0.6 that it will be complex. To compute the expected value, we start by placing the probabilities on the decision tree in the appropriate place (Figure 23.2). With these values in place, we can find the expected value of each of the actions. The probabilities are associated with each state of nature and are the same regardless of the action. We place these values on the branches associated with each state of nature, repeated for each one of the possible actions (the circle nodes).

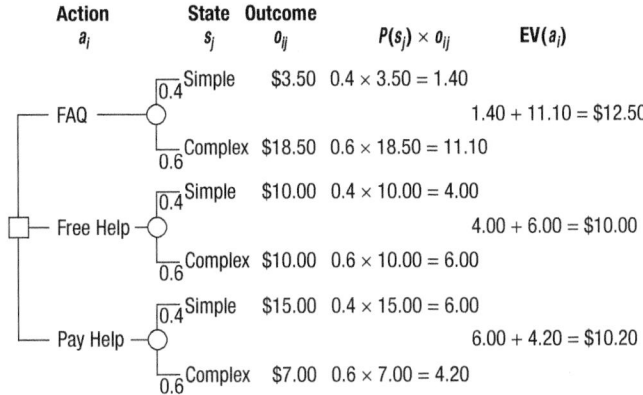

Figure 23.2   Calculating the expected value of each action using a decision tree.

For each combination of outcome and probability, we calculate its contribution to the expected value $P(s_j) \times o_{ij}$. Because only one state of nature can occur for each call, the states of nature are disjoint. We can therefore find the expected value for each action by summing the contributions over all the states of nature, in this case *simple* and *complex*.

From the expected values in Figure 23.2, it appears that expanding free telephone support may be the best action because it costs Data Description the *least*. The expected value of that action is a cost of $10.00.

FOR EXAMPLE   **Expected value of purchasing an airline ticket**

Pat guesses that the course in question has an exam scheduled on the last two days of exam period only about 20% of the time (see For Example: "Minimizing loss and maximizing gain for purchasing airline tickets").

QUESTION   What is the expected value of purchasing a Thursday ticket?

ANSWER $0.8 \times 750 + 0.2 \times 1950 = \$990$

LO❷   **23.5   Expected Value with Perfect Information**

Unfortunately, we can't predict the state of nature with certainty. But it can be informative to consider what it costs us to live with the uncertainty. If we knew the true state of nature—rather than just the probable state of nature—how much might that be worth to us? To help quantify that, let's consider a single customer support question. Knowing whether it was simple or complex would enable us to take the optimal action in each case. For a simple question, we'd offer online FAQ support and the "payoff" would be $3.50. For a complex question, we'd provide paid telephone support, costing the company $7.

Using the probabilities of the two states of nature, we can calculate the expected value of this optimal strategy as

$$0.6 \times \$7 + 0.4 \times \$3.50 = \$5.60.$$

This is called the **expected value with perfect information (EVwPI)**.

By contrast, the expected value of the optimal strategy that we calculated without knowing the state of nature was $10. The absolute value of the difference between these two quantities is called the **expected value of perfect information (EVPI)**.

$$EVPI = |EVwPI - EV|$$

In our example, this difference is $|\$5.60 - \$10| = \$4.40$. (Notice the absolute value in that calculation. Information should increase profit or, as in our example, reduce costs. Either way, the *value* of information is positive.) Our lack of perfect knowledge about the state of nature costs us $4.40 per call. The expected value of information, EVPI, gives the maximum amount the company might be willing to pay for perfect information.

FOR EXAMPLE   EVwPI and EVPI for purchasing airline tickets

QUESTIONS   Recall from For Example: "Expected value of purchasing an airline ticket" that Pat is purchasing an airplane ticket; the payoff table is in For Example: "Payoff tables for purchasing airline tickets." What is Pat's EVwPI? What is the EVPI?

ANSWER   With perfect information, Pat would purchase the early ticket for $750 80% of the time and the late ticket for $900 20% of the time for an EVwPI of
$0.8 \times 750 + 0.2 \times 900 = \$780.$

The EVPI is then $990 - \$780 = \$210$.

LO❷   23.6   **Decisions Made with Sample Information**

Usually the costs and profits—the payoffs—of alternative actions under various states of nature can be estimated fairly well, because they depend on business-related events and actions that are well understood. By contrast, the probabilities assigned to the states of nature may be based only on expert judgment. These probabilities are sometimes called *prior probabilities* because they're determined before obtaining any additional information on the states of nature. A survey of customers or a planned experiment, however, might provide information that could bring the probabilities closer to reality and make for a more informed decision. Revised probabilities are also called *posterior probabilities*. Should the decision maker first gather data to help estimate the probabilities of the states of nature? That's a decision in itself. Surveys and experiments cost money, and the resulting information may not be worth the expense. We can incorporate the decision to gather data into the overall decision process. First, it's worthwhile to ask whether useful information is even possible. If the states of nature in the decision process are about the future health of the economy or the future value of the Dow Jones Industrial Average, it's not likely that we can learn very much new. But market research surveys of customers and trial marketing incentives can often provide useful data.

FOR EXAMPLE	Assessing sensitivity for purchasing airline tickets

Pat is making a decision about whether to purchase a cheaper ticket with a risk of having to purchase another if there's a conflict with the final exam (see For Example: "Estimating variation for purchasing airline tickets").

QUESTION   How sensitive is Pat's decision? Suppose, for instance, that the probability of a late exam were only 0.1. How would that change the expected values?

ANSWER   The EV of the Thursday ticket would now be $870, less than the EV of the Saturday ticket (which would still be $900).

LO②   23.9   Simulation

Another alternative for assessing the sensitivity of a decision model to the choice of probabilities is to simulate the model for a variety of plausible probability values. Rather than specifying single probabilities, you can specify a distribution of plausible values. You can then run a *simulation* in which the computer draws states of nature at random according to your distribution of probabilities and evaluates the consequences. This approach can deal with much more complex decision models than those we've discussed here. The result of the simulation isn't a single decision but rather a distribution of outcomes. Such a distribution may be a more appropriate description for a decision maker than any single expected value.

Programs such as @Risk (www.palisade.com) and Crystal Ball (www.oracle.com) provide ways for you to specify actions, states of nature, and the associated probabilities and outcomes and then use simulation methods to generate distributions of outcomes.

GUIDED EXAMPLE   Insurance Services

InterCon Travel Health is a Toronto-based company that provides services to health insurers of foreign tourists who travel to the United States and Canada.[1] The primary focus of InterCon is to act as an interface between local health providers and the overseas insurance company that insured the tourist should the traveller find him- or herself in need of medical attention. The customer base of sick or injured tourists is potentially profitable because most tourists who fall ill require only minor treatment and rarely come back for expensive follow-up visits. So InterCon can pass savings along to the foreign insurer by facilitating claim management and payment and can collect processing fees from these insurance companies in return.

Currently, InterCon charges a processing fee of 9.5%, collected partly from the medical providers and partly from the foreign insurers. It has experienced an average annual growth of 3%. However, to help with rising costs, it may consider increasing the processing fee from 9.5% to 10.5%. Although this would generate additional revenue, it would also incur the risk of losing contracts with insurers and health-care providers. Table 23.5 gives the company's estimates of the impact of a change in rates on the annual fees, depending on the strength of foreign tourism.

What would be the best choice for the company?

[1]This example is based on the case by Truman, G., Pachamanova, D., & Goldstein, M. (2007, Summer). InterCon travel health case study. *Journal of the Academy of Business Education, 8,* 17–32.

		State of Nature	
		Weak Tourism $P = 0.40$	**Strong Tourism** $P = 0.60$
Action	**9.5% Fee**	$54.07M	$56.23M
	10.5% Fee	$53.67M	$56.73M

Table 23.5 InterCon's estimates of the impact on the annual fees for two different actions (changes in rate) under two possible states of nature (strong or weak tourism).

PLAN	**Setup** State the objective of the study. Identify the variables. **Model** Think about the assumptions and check the conditions.	We want to evaluate the two alternative actions the company is considering. We have estimates of the outcomes and the probabilities of two states of nature: weak or strong tourism. The only condition to check is that the probabilities are legitimate; $0.40 + 0.60 = 1.0$, and 0.4 and 0.6 are both between zero and one.

DO	**Mechanics** The calculations of expected value and standard deviation are straightforward.

Action	**State**	**P**	**Outcome**	$O_{ij}P(s)$	**EV(a_i)**
9.5% fee	Weak	0.4	$54.07M	$21.63M	
					$55.37M
	Strong	0.6	$56.23M	$33.74M	
10.5% fee	Weak	0.4	$53.67M	$21.468M	
					$55.51M
	Strong	0.6	$56.73M	$34.04M	

It can help to diagram the decision process with a tree diagram.

For example,

$$0.4 \times \$54.07M = \$21.63M$$
$$\$21.63M + \$33.74M = \$55.37M.$$

Standard deviations:

For 9.5% fee:

$$(O_{ij} - EV(a_i))$$

$$(O_{ij} - EV(a_i))^2 P(s_j)$$

$$(54.07 - 55.37) = -1.30$$

$$(-1.30)^2 \times 0.4 = 0.676$$

$$(56.23 - 55.37) = 0.86$$

$$(0.86^2) \times 0.6 = 0.444$$

$$SD = \sqrt{0.676 + 0.444}$$

$$= \$1.06M$$

For 10.5% fee:

$$SD = \$1.499M$$

$$RRR\ (9.5\%\ fee) = 55.37/1.06 = 52.24$$

$$RRR\ (10.5\%\ fee) = 55.51/1.499 = 37.03$$

(continued)

Conclusion Summarize your results and state any limitations of your model in the context of your original objectives.

MEMO

Re: Recommendations for Processing Fee Rate

The expected value of the alternative with the lower processing fee rate is slightly lower ($55.37 million compared with $55.51 million), and it's also a less risky decision. The return to risk ratio (RRR) at the higher processing fee rate of 10.5% is 37.03; while at the lower rate it is 52.24.

Because one action has the better expected value but the other seems less risky, the company should determine the impact of risk on its decision.

LO❷ 23.10 **More Complex Decisions**

The methods of this chapter can be extended to decisions that are more complex and that may have second or third stages conditional on the outcomes of the first decisions. For example, customer support questions might be handled best by an initial online FAQ system that then offers customers with complex questions a choice of free email support or paid telephone support. To work out the expected values for these choices, we'd need to estimate the probabilities of a customer with a complex question choosing free email or paid telephone support—something with which the company has no prior experience.

Or the probabilities may be changed by a change in circumstances. When the company releases an upgraded version, technical support calls increase, but there's a higher probability of simple calls. As the customer base learns the new version, their questions generally become more sophisticated.

WHAT CAN GO WRONG?

- **Decision trees don't tell the decision maker the correct decision.** Models can be useful, but they're based on assumptions. Decision trees model the expected outcome and risk for each decision. The best decision depends on the level of risk the decision maker is willing to accept, as well as the state of nature that occurs.

- **The computations of the expected values and standard deviations are sensitive to the probabilities.** The probabilities required by the calculations of expected value and standard deviation may be reliably based on past experience or data, or they may just represent the subjective judgment of the decision maker. Don't trust them blindly. Using a decision model and ignoring the sensitivity of the model to different probabilities can lead to poor decisions and misleading conclusions. One way to address the problem is to solve the model with a range of plausible probabilities to assess how sensitive the conclusions are to the choice of probabilities. Another way is to use software that simulates the results for randomly generated probabilities from an appropriate distribution.

- **Make sure that the probabilities are legitimate and that the action choices are disjoint.** The calculations in this chapter depend on both of these being true. Methods for conditional probabilities exist but are beyond the scope of this chapter.

ETHICS IN ACTION

Nelson Greene develops real estate on Vancouver Island. His next planned project is to build a housing development on a parcel of land not far from Victoria. However, with the recent decline in housing prices, Nelson is reconsidering his decision. He set up a meeting with some key individuals, including Tom Barnick, a representative from the township supervisors. Tom and the township council were positive about the proposed development, since it would provide increased tax revenue. So Tom wanted to influence Nelson to go forward with the development. Tom had some analysis prepared, which he presented at the meeting. Based on several assumptions, including the probabilities associated with different housing market conditions (improving, worsening, or staying the same), the analysis showed a positive expected payoff for going forward with the project. Tom mentioned that the probabilities were obtained from a small group of housing

market experts, although they had difficulty reaching consensus. Nelson noticed that not all the payoffs associated with going forward were positive for each possible market condition, but the positive expected payoff made him view the project more favourably.

Ethical Issue *The expected payoff is a long-run average and not an actual outcome for a decision. Although the expected payoff was positive, there was no mention of the expected payoff for not going forward with the development (related to Item A, ASA Ethical Guidelines; see Appendix C, the American Statistical Association's Ethical Guidelines for Statistical Practice, also available online at www.amstat.org/about/ethicalguidelines.cfm).*

Ethical Solution *If the experts couldn't agree on the probabilities, the sensitivity analysis should be done for a range of probabilities.*

WHAT HAVE WE LEARNED?

Learning Objectives

❶ Assess costs and benefits of various actions given possible states of nature.

- Use judgment or data.

❷ Estimate the likelihood of the possible states of nature.

- Use data, if they're available.
- Confirm that probabilities are legitimate.

Evaluate likely outcomes (costs and benefits) of decisions when faced with uncertainty about the state of nature.

- Make a decision tree and find the expected value of actions.
- Evaluate the relative risk of alternative decisions.

Terms

Actions   Alternative choices that a decision maker can make.

Coefficient of variation   The coefficient of variation (CV) of each action shows the "$ at risk" for each "$ returned":

$$CV(a_i) = SD(a_i)/EV(a_i)$$

Decision tree   A decision tree organizes the actions, states of nature, and outcomes to display the sequence of the elements in a decision.

Dominance   An alternative dominates when it pays off at least as much as (or costs less than) the alternative it dominates.

Expected value (EV)   The expected value of an action under uncertain states of nature is

$$EV(a_i) = \sum_{j=1}^{N} o_{ij} P(s_j),$$

where there are N possible states of nature and o_{ij} is the outcome or payoff of action i when the state of nature is s_j.

Expected value of perfect information (EVPI)	The difference between the expected value with perfect information (EVwPI) and the expected value (without perfect information) (EV): $$EVPI = |EVwPI - EV|$$
Expected value of sample information (EVSI)	The difference between the expected value with sample information (EVwSI) and the expected value (without sample information) (EV): $$EVSI = |EVwSI - EV|$$
Expected value with perfect information (EVwPI)	The expected value of a hypothetical strategy, assuming that the probabilities of the states of nature are known.
Expected value with sample information (EVwSI)	The expected value of a hypothetical strategy, assuming that probabilities of the states of nature are estimated.
Maximax choice	The action that maximizes the maximum possible return across all states of nature in a payoff table.
Minimax choice	The action that minimizes the maximum possible cost across all states of nature in a payoff table.
Minimin choice	The action that minimizes the minimum possible cost across all states of nature in a payoff table.
Outcomes	Consequences of an action combined with a state of nature, usually expressed in monetary units (positive or negative).
Payoffs	See Outcomes.
Payoff table	A table containing the actions, states of nature, and the corresponding payoffs for each combination of the two.
Return to risk ratio (RRR)	The return to risk ratio (RRR) measures the expected return of an action relative to the risk, represented by its standard deviation: $$RRR\,(a_i) = 1/CV = EV(a_i)/SD(a_i)$$
States of nature	The facts about the world that affect the consequences of an action, usually summarized into a few possible values.
Variance and standard deviation of an action	The standard deviation of an action measures the variability of possible outcomes calculated in terms of their estimated probabilities of occurring. The standard deviation is the square root of the variance: $$Var\,(a_i) = \sum_{j=1}^{N} (o_{ij} - EV(a_i))^2\, P(s_j)$$ $$SD(a_i) = \sqrt{Var\,(a_i)}$$

Skills

Plan
- Be able to identify alternative actions and states of nature for a decision process.
- Be able to assign probabilities to states of nature based on judgment or data, and be able to check that these probabilities are legitimate (i.e., that each is between zero and one and that they sum to 1.0).

Do
- Know how to draw the decision tree for a set of alternative actions.

Report
- Be able to find the expected value of an action under uncertain states of nature.
- Know how to find the coefficient of variation and risk to return ratio for an action.
- Know how to evaluate the relative risk of each alternative decision and recommend a decision for decision makers who are risk-averse, risk-neutral, and risk-takers.

Encana Corporation of Calgary

Encana Corporation, whose name is an acronym for ENergy, CANada, and Alberta, is a natural gas company based in Calgary with five major natural gas operations in Canada: Bighorn, Coalbed Methane, Cutbank Ridge, Greater Sierra in western Canada, and Deep Panuke, an offshore project in Nova Scotia.

Encana's revenues fluctuate due to volatile prices for natural gas, the winter temperature in North America, the exchange rate, and the cost and uncertainty of drilling. On top of this, the gas reserves in existing wells are being continuously depleted, so that acquisition of new reserves is essential. Encana owns 4.1 million hectares in western Canada, of which 1.8 million are undeveloped, so it has plenty of scope to explore new sites. Another approach, which we will focus on, is to use improved technology to better exploit existing reserves.

Coalbed methane (CBM) is notoriously difficult to make money on in Alberta, but there's plenty of it there in a region called the Manville. The methane (natural gas) is trapped over 1000 metres below the surface in very narrow coal seams only about 10 metres thick. It's therefore necessary to drill vertically deep under the ground and then turn the drill horizontally to follow a coal seam that often undulates up and down. With a conventional drill, it's tough to be that precise, and only about 60% of the methane can be extracted; moreover, there's a 10% chance that the well will be a total failure and produce nothing at all. Advanced drills have sensors that allow them to transmit data to the operator indicating how close they are to the seam boundary. This technique, known as *logging while drilling* (LWD), allows the operator to follow the seam more accurately, reducing the chance of total failure to 1%. It extracts 90% of the methane but costs $31,000 per day, compared with $21,000 for conventional drilling. LWD is also faster than conventional drilling, taking four instead of five days to complete a CBM well, on average. Additional engineering costs are $120,000 per well for either type of drill.

Budimir Jevtic/Fotolia

Taking a CBM operation with estimated volume of 80 MMcf (million cubic feet) of natural gas and a price of $4/Mcf (thousand cubic feet), would you drill? And, if so, would you use a conventional drill or LWD? The price of natural gas fluctuates widely. Suppose projected price is $3/Mcf with a probability of 0.6, $4/Mcf with a probability of 0.3, and $5/Mcf with a probability of 0.1—does that affect your decision? Estimating the total volume of natural gas in a CBM operation is also uncertain. Suppose the estimated volume is between 50 and 70 Mcf with a probability of 0.3, between 70 and 90 Mcf with a probability of 0.5, and between 90 and 160 Mcf with a probability of 0.2. Combined with the uncertainty in price, does that affect your decision?

Texaco-Pennzoil

"Oil is big business." A classic example of this is the Texaco-Pennzoil court case, which appeared in the book *Making Hard Decisions*[2] and in a subsequent case study by T. Reilly and N. Sharpe (2001). In 1984, a merger was hammered out between two oil giants, Pennzoil and Getty Oil. Before the specifics had been agreed to in a written and binding form, another oil giant—Texaco—offered Getty Oil more money. Ultimately, Getty sold out to Texaco.

Pennzoil immediately sued Texaco for illegal interference, and in late 1985 was awarded $11.1 billion—an enormous award at the time. (A subsequent appeal reduced the award to $10.3 billion.) The CEO of Texaco threatened to fight the judgment further, citing improper negotiations held between Pennzoil and Getty. Concerned about bankruptcy if forced to pay the required sum of money, Texaco offered Pennzoil $2 billion to settle the case. Pennzoil considered the offer, analyzed the alternatives, and decided that a settlement price closer to $5 billion would be more reasonable.

The CEO of Pennzoil had a decision to make. He could make the low-risk decision of accepting the $2 billion offer, or he could decide to make the counteroffer of $5 billion. If Pennzoil countered with $5 billion, what are the possible outcomes? First, Texaco could accept the offer. Second, Texaco could refuse to negotiate and demand settlement in the courts. Assume that the courts could order one of the following:

- Texaco must pay Pennzoil $10.3 billion.
- Texaco must pay Pennzoil's figure of $5 billion.
- Texaco wins and pays Pennzoil nothing.

The award associated with each outcome—whether ordered by the court or agreed upon by the two parties—is what we'll consider to be the "payoff" for Pennzoil. To simplify Pennzoil's decision process, we make a few assumptions. First, we assume that Pennzoil's objective is to maximize the amount of the settlement. Second, the likelihood of each of the outcomes in this high-profile case is based on similar cases. We'll assume that there's an even chance (50%) that Texaco will refuse the counteroffer and go to court. According to a *Fortune* article,[3] the CEO of Pennzoil reportedly believed that should the offer be refused, Texaco had a chance to win the case with appeals, which would leave Pennzoil with high legal fees and no payoff. Based on prior similar court cases and expert opinion, assume that there's also a 50% probability that the court will order a compromise and require Texaco to pay Pennzoil the suggested price of $5 billion. What are the remaining options for the court? Assume that the other two alternatives—Pennzoil receiving the original total award ($10.3 billion) or Pennzoil getting nothing—are almost equal, with the likelihood of the original verdict being upheld slightly greater (30%) than the likelihood of reversing the decision (20%).

Evaluate the expected payoff and risk of each decision for Pennzoil.

InterCon of Toronto

InterCon Travel Health is a Toronto-based company that provides services to health insurers of foreign tourists who travel to the United States and Canada.[4] As described in the Guided Example in this chapter, the primary focus of InterCon is to act as an interface between local health providers and the overseas insurance company that insures

---

[2]Clemen, R. T., & Reilly, T. (2001). *Making Hard Decisions*. New York: Brooks/Cole.

[3]Sherman, S. P. (1987, May 11). The gambler who refused $2 billion. *Fortune*, 50–58.

[4]This example is based on the case by Truman, G., Pachamanova, D., & Goldstein, M. (2007, Summer). InterCon travel health case study. *Journal of the Academy of Business Education, 8*, 17–32.

(continued)

the tourist should the traveller find him- or herself in need of medical attention. The customer base of sick or injured tourists is potentially profitable because most tourists who fall ill require only minor treatment and rarely come back for expensive follow-up visits. Therefore, InterCon can pass savings along to the foreign insurer by facilitating claim management and payment and can collect processing fees from these insurance companies in return.

Currently, this Canadian company charges a processing fee of 9.5% (collected partly from the medical providers and partly from the foreign insurers) and has experienced an average annual growth rate of 3%. However, a backlog of claims and a cyclical pattern to the claims (due to high tourist seasons) has caused a delay in filing claims with the foreign insurers, resulting in a number of noncollectible claims. In addition, while the growing company has been trying to keep costs to a minimum, it's considering adding a new information technology system to help streamline the process. Most of the company's revenue comes from claims for inpatient hospital stays, which average approximately $10,000. These claims represent 20% of InterCon's claims but over 80% of its claim revenue. The remaining claims arise from clinic and emergency room visits.

To help with rising costs, this firm may consider raising the processing fee as high as 11.0%. While this would generate additional revenue, the firm would also incur the risk of losing contracts with insurers and health-care providers. Here are estimates of the impact of a change in rates on the annual fee revenue depending on the strength of foreign tourism:

Foreign Tourism	Probability	Processing Fee Rate at 9.5% Payoff ($)	Processing Fee Rate at 11.0% Payoff ($)
Weak	0.40	54,069,129	53,472,101
Strong	0.60	56,231,894	56,921,006

What is the expected revenue for the respective fee alternatives based on the total income from fees? Should InterCon increase its fees? Suppose the manager gets new information and revises the probabilities for the strength of tourism to be even, at 50/50. What are the new values for expected revenue, CV, and the return to risk ratio? Should the company increase its fees?

MyStatLab   Students! Save time, improve your grades with MyStatLab. Questions marked in ▣ can be found on MyStatLab. You can practise them as often as you want, and most feature step-by-step guided solutions to help you find the right answer. You'll find a personalized study plan available to you too!

EXERCISES

SECTION 23.1

1. Which of the following are actions and which are states of nature?

a) Whether unemployment is above or below 10%.

b) Whether a new product should be brought to market before or after the beginning of the fiscal year.

c) Whether to tell employees to stay home because of a blizzard. **LO ❶**

2. Which of the following are actions and which are states of nature?

a) Whether to invest in solar energy companies.
b) Whether your chief competitor decides to launch a new advertising campaign.
c) Whether the decision you made to outsource manufacturing last year turned out to be the cost-saver you thought it would be. **LO ❶**

SECTION 23.2

3. You're called on to decide how your company should produce its new cell phone screen defroster (for use by skiers and others spending time outdoors in the cold). You develop the following cost matrix ($000s):

		State of Nature (State of the Economy)	
		Recession	Stable	Expansion
Production	Outsource	220	350	300
	In-house	150	240	390

Draw the corresponding decision tree. **LO ❶**

4. Here is a decision tree for the profits (in $000s) you project for your sales of the cell phone screen defroster, depending on the weather this coming winter and your choice of advertising method:

Action	State	Outcome
Point of Sale	Warm	550
	Moderate	600
	Cold	710
Magazine	Warm	410
	Moderate	590
	Cold	800
Internet	Warm	750
	Moderate	710
	Cold	590

Write out the corresponding profit matrix. **LO ❶**

SECTION 23.3

5. For the cost matrix of Exercise 3,
a) What is the minimax choice?
b) What is the minimin choice? **LO ❶**

6. For the decision tree of Exercise 4,
a) What is the maximin choice?
b) What is the maximax choice? **LO ❶**

SECTION 23.4

7. For the cost matrix of Exercise 3,

a) Suppose $P(Recession) = 0.2$, $P(Stable) = 0.2$, and $P(Expansion) = 0.6$. What is the expected value of each action?
b) What is the best choice using the expected-value approach? **LO ❷**

8. For the decision tree of Exercise 4,

a) Suppose $P(Warm) = 0.5$, $P(Moderate) = 0.3$, and $P(Cold) = 0.2$. What is the expected value of each action?
b) What is the best choice using the expected-value approach? **LO ❷**

SECTION 23.7

9. For the probabilities of Exercise 7 and the cost matrix of Exercise 3, using the expected values you found in Exercise 7, compute the standard deviation of values associated with each action and the corresponding coefficient of variation. **LO ❷**

10. For the probabilities of Exercise 8 and the decision tree of Exercise 4, using the expected values found in Exercise 8, compute the standard deviations of the values associated with each action and the corresponding coefficient of variation. **LO ❷**

CHAPTER EXERCISES

11. **Flight decision.** You're planning a trip home at the end of the semester and need to make plane reservations soon. However, you've just had a preliminary interview with a consulting firm that seemed to go very well. There's a chance that it will want you to stay for a few days at the end of the semester for a round of interviews at its offices, which will mean you'll have to change the date of the flight if you make the reservation now. Suppose that you can purchase a changeable fare for $750 or a nonrefundable fare for $650 for which a change costs $150. Construct a payoff table for this set of actions using total cost as the payoff. **LO ❶**

12. **Product introduction.** A small company has the technology to develop a new personal data assistant (PDA), but it worries about sales in the crowded market. It estimates that it will cost $600,000 to develop, launch, and market the product. Analysts have produced revenue estimates for three scenarios: If sales are high, the company will sell $1.2 million worth of the PDAs; if sales are moderate, it will sell $800,000 worth; and if sales are low, it will sell only $300,000 worth. Using net profit as the payoff, construct a payoff table for producing the PDA and for doing nothing. **LO ❶**

13. **Advertising strategies.** After a series of extensive meetings, several of the key decision makers for a small marketing firm have produced the following payoff table (expected profit per customer) for various advertising strategies and two possible states of the economy:

		Consumer Confidence	
		Rising	Falling
Action	Prime-Time Ad	$20	$ 2
	Targeted Web Marketing	$12	$10
	Direct Mail Piece	$10	$15

Construct a decision tree for this payoff table. **LO ❶**

14. **Energy investment.** An investment bank is thinking of investing in a startup alternative energy company. It can become a major investor for $6 million, a moderate investor for $3 million, or a small investor for $1.5 million. The worth of its investment in 12 months will depend on how the price of oil behaves between now and then. A financial analyst produces the following payoff table with the net worth of the bank's investment (predicted worth – initial investment) as the payoff:

		Price of Oil		
		Substantially Higher	About the Same	Substantially Lower
Action	Major Investment	$5,000,000	$3,000,000	−$2,000,000
	Moderate Investment	$2,500,000	$1,500,000	−$1,000,000
	Small Investment	$1,000,000	$ 500,000	−$ 100,000

Construct a decision tree for this payoff table. **LO ❶**

15. **Flight decision tree.** Construct a decision tree for the payoff table in Exercise 11. **LO ❶**

16. **Product introduction tree.** Construct a decision tree for the payoff table in Exercise 12. **LO ❶**

17. **Flight decision expected value.** If you think the probability of being called for an interview is 0.30, calculate the expected value of each action in Exercise 11. Which is the better action in this case? **LO ❶**

18. **Product introduction expected value.** An analyst for the company in Exercise 12 thinks the probabilities of high, moderate, and low sales are 0.2, 0.5, and 0.3, respectively. In this case calculate the expected value of each action. Which is the best? **LO ❷**

19. **Flight decision change.** For the decision of Exercise 11, you've just learned that you're on the short list and now estimate that the chance you'll be called for an interview is 0.70. Does this change your choice of actions? **LO ❷**

20. **Product introduction change.** For the product launch decision of Exercise 12, the economy isn't looking that good. Your very cautious boss says he thinks there's a 60% chance of low sales and a 30% chance of moderate sales. Which course should the company follow? **LO ❷**

21. **Advertising strategies decisions.** For the payoff table in Exercise 13, find the action with the highest expected value.

a) If forecasters think the probability of rising consumer confidence is 0.70, what is its expected value?
b) What action would have the highest expected value if they think the probability of rising consumer confidence is only 0.40? **LO ❷**

22. **Energy investment decisions.**

a) For the payoff table in Exercise 14, find the investment strategy under the assumption that the probability that the price of oil goes substantially higher is 0.4 and that the probability that it goes substantially lower is 0.2.
b) What if those two probabilities are reversed? **LO ❷**

23. **Advertising strategies EVPI.**

a) For the advertising strategies of Exercise 13 and using the probability of 0.70 for rising consumer confidence, what is the expected value of perfect information (EVPI)?
b) What is the EVPI if the probability of rising consumer confidence is only 0.40? **LO ❷**

24. **Energy investment EVPI.** For the energy investment of Exercise 14 and using both of the probabilities considered in that exercise, find the expected value of perfect information. **LO ❷**

25. **Advertising strategies with information.** The company from Exercises 12, 18, and 20 has the option of hiring an economics consulting firm to predict consumer confidence. The company has already considered that the probability of rising consumer confidence could be as high as 0.70 or as low as 0.40. It could ask the consultants for their choice between those two probabilities, or it could just pick a probability in the middle, such as 0.50, and choose a strategy on that basis.

a) Draw the decision tree, including the decision to hire the consultants.
b) Would the consultants' information be useful? Explain.
c) The company thinks there's an equal chance of either of the consulting alternatives being what the consultants report. What's the value to the company (per customer) of the extra information? **LO ❷**

26. **Energy investment with information.** The company in Exercises 14, 22, and 24 could send a team to Saudi Arabia to obtain additional information about the probabilities that oil will increase or decrease in price. It hopes that the fact-finding trip would choose between the two alternatives considered in Exercise 14, or it could just estimate that the probabilities are equal.

a) Make a decision tree for these decisions.
b) Should the company send the fact-finding team? Explain.
c) The company's experts estimate that if they send the fact-finding mission, there's a 70% chance that they'll conclude there's a 0.4 probability of higher oil prices. What would the value of the additional information be to the company? **LO ❷**

27. **Investing in equipment.** KickGrass Lawncare is a service that cares for lawns in a large, affluent community. Akbar Overgrowth, the owner, is considering the purchase of new zero-turn riding lawn tractors, which would allow him to expand his business. The tractors cost $6300 each, and he would purchase two of them. Another alternative is to purchase three additional mowers of the current type to add to his equipment. Those would cost $475 apiece. Or he could face the coming gardening season with his existing equipment. Akbar estimates that in a good growing season, the tractors would allow him to expand his business by $40,000. But if the summer is hot and dry (so lawns don't grow) or cold and wet (ditto), he'd only be able to add about $15,000 in contracts. If he purchases the mowers, he could expand his business by $10,000 in a good year or by just $5000 in a bad one. And if he spends nothing, he won't expand his business. In a bad year, his income would contract by about $1000.

Construct a payoff table and tree diagram for Akbar's decision. Don't forget to include his expenses in the calculations. **LO ❶**

28. **Market segmentation.** Demand and price are related; raising prices typically lowers demand. Many companies understand that if they can *segment* their market and offer different prices to different segments, they can often capture more revenue. Aaron'sAir is a small commuter airline. It typically charges $150 for a one-way flight between a resort island it serves and the mainland. In times of low, medium, and high demand, Aaron (the owner and pilot) estimates that he'll sell 100, 200, or 500 seats per week, respectively. He's considering offering two different fares based on whether his customers stay over a Saturday night on the island. He thinks that business travellers coming to the island for conferences and retreats would typically not stay, but vacationers would. He expects that the low fare will attract additional customers. However, he anticipates that some of his regular customers will also pay less. The two fares would be $90 and $210. Aaron estimates that in times of low demand he'd sell 30 high-fare and 80 low-fare tickets—revenue of $30 \times \$210 + 80 \times \$90 = \$13,500$. In times of medium demand, he estimates 110 high-fare and 250 low-fare tickets, for an estimated revenue of $45,600. And in times of high demand, he expects 500 low-fare customers and 250 high-fare customers, yielding $97,500.

Make a payoff table and decision tree for this decision. **LO ❶**

29. **Investing in equipment, maxes and mins.** Akbar Overgrowth, whom we met in Exercise 27, is an entrepreneur who is optimistic about the growing season. What choice should he make to maximize his return? His assistant, Lance Broadleaf, is very conservative, and argues that KickGrass should minimize its potential downside results. Which alternative decision does he argue for? **LO ❷**

30. **Market segmentation minimax.** Aaron, whom we met in Exercise 28, tends to be optimistic about business conditions. What is his maximax strategy that would maximize his results? **LO ❷**

31. **Whether or not to invest in equipment.** Akbar Overgrowth, from Exercise 27, estimates that the probability of a good growing season is 0.70. On that basis,

a) Find the EV for his actions.
b) Find the standard deviations.
c) Compute the RRRs. Which action is preferred based on the RRRs? **LO ❷**

32. **Market segmentation and chance.** Aaron'sAir (see Exercises 28 and 30) estimates that high-demand periods (which depend on the weather and on bookings for conferences) occur with probability 0.3 and medium-demand periods occur with probability 0.5. The rest are low-demand periods.

a) What's the expected value of each of Aaron's alternative actions?
b) What are the standard deviations for each action?
c) What are the RRRs? Based on the RRRs, what action is best? **LO ❷**

33. **Equipment and data.** Akbar, of Exercises 27, 29, and 31, could obtain long-range predictions of the growing conditions for next summer. He thinks they might show a probability of good growing conditions as low as 50% or as high as 80%. If he doesn't obtain those predictions, he'll make a decision based on his previous estimates (see Exercise 31).

a) Draw the decision tree.
b) If Akbar thinks there's a 60% chance the long-range predictions will predict a 50% chance of good conditions, find the corresponding EVwSI.
c) Should Akbar purchase the long-range predictions? **LO ❷**

34. **Segments and surveys.** Aaron'sAir (see Exercises 28, 30, and 32) could purchase a market survey from a firm that advises the island tourist and conference bureau. He thinks its projections would help him determine whether the probability of high demand might be as high as 0.5

or as low as 0.2, with the corresponding probabilities for medium demand being 0.3 and 0.4. If he doesn't purchase the market survey, he'll make a decision based on his previous best estimates (see Exercise 32).

a) Draw the decision tree.

b) Aaron thinks the market survey is likely to be optimistic. He'd estimate a 65% probability that it would predict the higher (0.5) probability of high demand. What would be the EVwSI?

c) If the consultant's report costs $2000, should Aaron pay for it? **LO ❷**

35. Investment strategy. An investor is considering adding a stock to her portfolio. Assuming she buys 100 shares, here's an estimated payoff table for the alternative stocks if she holds on to them for six months. The value of the stock depends on whether or not an acquisition is approved for one of the companies, since the companies are actually competitors. She estimates the probability of an acquisition to be 0.3.

	Acquisition?	
	Yes (0.3)	**No (0.7)**
Stock A	$5000	−$1000
Stock B	−$500	$3500

a) Compute the EV for each alternative decision.

b) Compute the SD for each decision.

c) Compute the CV and RRR for each decision.

d) Which stock would you choose and why? **LO ❷**

36. Mutual fund investing. An investor is considering how to invest her money. She has two options—either a domestic mutual fund that only invests in blue chip stocks or an international aggressive mutual fund that invests in young technical firms. The payoff (profit) after one year for these investments depends on the state of the economy.

	Economy	
	Improves (0.5)	**Declines (0.5)**
Domestic Mutual Fund	$1500	$1000
International Mutual Fund	$3500	−$1000

a) Compute the EV for each alternative decision.

b) Compute the SD for each decision.

c) Compute the CV and RRR for each decision.

d) Which mutual fund would you invest in and why? **LO ❷**

37. Bicycle sales, part 1. A bicycle shop owner is deciding which products to stock. His distributor will give him a deal if he buys more of one kind of bike. The payoff table shows monthly sales for a high-end bike (selling at $950) or a moderately priced bike (selling at $500). Based on past experience, the shop owner makes the following assumption about the demand for the high-end bike: Demand will be low, moderate, or high with probabilities 0.3, 0.5, and 0.2, respectively. He also assumes that if demand is low for the high-end bike, it will be higher for the moderately priced bike.

	Demand for High-End Bike		
	Low Demand (0.3)	**Moderate Demand (0.5)**	**High Demand (0.2)**
High-End Bike	$1900	$4750	$7600
Moderately Priced Bike	$4000	$2500	$1000

a) Compute the EV for each alternative product (decision).

b) Compute the SD for each decision.

c) Compute the CV and RRR for each decision.

d) Which bike would you stock and why? **LO ❷**

38. Bicycle sales, part 2. The bike shop owner has now done a bit more research and believes that the demand for high-end bikes has shifted, so that now the low demand is 50% likely and the high demand is only 10% likely. How does this change your responses to Exercise 37? Find the new RRR. Does your recommendation to the shop owner change? **LO ❷**

39. Canadian mining company. A small Canadian mining company is issuing an initial public offering (IPO) of shares on the Vancouver Stock Exchange at $17 per share. A limited number of "early" investors were able to purchase these shares at $17 on the IPO date, and the shares were traded on the stock exchange for any member of the public to buy/sell the day after. During the first few weeks of public trading the underwriters may purchase shares if they think the price is dropping too low, and the investors who bought shares the day before at the IPO price of $17 may sell if the price rises above $17 and they want to make a quick profit. You're considering purchasing shares at the start of the first day of public trading and have a target of making a capital gain of 10% in the first year. You ask the advice of a stockbroker about whether you can make a 10% capital gain. "If the underwriters have to buy to prop up the price, that's a bad sign," says the broker. "If a significant number of early investors sell off their shares, that's a bad sign too. In either of those cases you'll have a loss of about 5% in the first year. If both those things happen, you'll have a loss of about 15% in the first year. Looking at similar recent IPOs, the chances of those things happening are about 0.25 and 0.35, respectively. If neither of these happens, you could easily make 30% in the first year." "Okay," you say, "but should I buy?" The stockbroker crunches the numbers for buying:

	Probability	Return	Probability × Return
Underwriters Buy and Early Investors Sell	0.25 × 0.35	−0.15	−0.013
Underwriters Buy and Early Investors Don't Sell	0.25 × 0.65	−0.05	−0.008
Underwriters Don't Buy and Early Investors Sell	0.75 × 0.35	−0.05	−0.013
Underwriters Don't Buy and Early Investors Don't Sell	0.75 × 0.65	0.30	0.146
Expected Return =			0.112

"The expected return from buying is 11.2% and your target was 10%, so you should buy," replies your broker.

Comment on the ethics of the stockbroker's advice in relation to the ASA Ethical Guidelines in Appendix C. **LO ❷**

40. Beaufort Sea exploration. The Beaufort Sea, located to the north of Nunavut and the Northwest Territories, is being explored for oil and natural gas by companies that conduct geological surveys and sell the resulting data to the energy companies that actually do the drilling. Alternatively, the survey company may do the drilling itself. A survey company has spent $1.6 billion on collecting geological data in a certain area of the Beaufort Sea and estimates that drilling will be successful with a probability of 0.6. Drilling costs $0.4 billion with a probability of 0.8 and $0.8 billion with a probability of 0.2, due to the fact that the survey doesn't identify the geological structures precisely. If drilling is successful, the revenue from the sale of oil and gas will be $3.4 billion with a probability of 0.75 and $4.6 billion with a probability of 0.25 due to uncertainty about the future prices at which the company can sell the oil and gas. Alternatively, the company can conduct an auction to sell the geological data; it estimates that the data will sell for $2.1 billion with a probability of 0.65 and $2.8 billion with a probability of 0.35.

a) Based on the expected value of alternative actions, should the company drill or hold the auction?
b) What would the probability of successful drilling need to be in order to reverse your decision (to an accuracy of two significant figures)?
c) What other factors should the company take into account in addition to the expected value of the alternative actions? **LO ❷**

41. Beaufort Sea drilling. Exploration licences for energy companies to drill in the Beaufort Sea are overseen by Indigenous and Northern Affairs Canada. The licences typically grant the right to drill in a certain area of the seabed in return for pledging a sum of money that it plans to spend on drilling. If the company doesn't spend that money on drilling within five years of the licence being issued, it must pay 25% of that sum of money to the government. If it does start drilling, it acquires drilling rights to that area of seabed forever.

An energy company has pledged $1.5 billion for drilling rights in a certain area of the Beaufort Sea on which it plans to drill a maximum of two wells. A survey of the area indicates that drilling will be successful with a probability of 0.3. Drilling a single well costs $0.75 billion and brings in a revenue of $2.1 billion. If the first well is successful, the chance of a second well being successful is increased from 0.3 to 0.9. If the first well is not successful, the chance of a second well being successful is decreased from 0.3 to 0.2.

a) Based on the expected profit (revenue minus cost), should the energy company drill its first well?
b) What would the revenue from a single well need to be (to an accuracy of two significant figures) in order for you to reverse your decision based on expected profit?
c) What other factors should the company take into account in addition to the expected value of the alternative actions? **LO ❷**

42. Niagara tunnel. A treaty between the United States and Canada guarantees that one-third of the water in the Niagara River should flow over the falls. One-third can be removed from the river to generate hydro-electric power by Canada and another third by the United States. Until 2013, Canada had a canal and a tunnel for extracting water upstream of the falls and taking it to two generating stations downstream. A second tunnel was completed in 2013, increasing the water supply to the power stations. Put yourself in the position of a decision maker during the planning for the second tunnel. You have three options: (i) Do nothing, (ii) dig a second tunnel to bring additional water to the two existing power stations, and (iii) dig a second tunnel and construct a third power station. Suppose that the geologists and engineers reach a consensus that the second tunnel will cost $1.4 billion with a probability of 0.7 and $2.3 billion with a probability of 0.3. The engineers estimate that the third power station will cost $0.4 billion with a probability of 0.4 and $0.6 billion with a probability of 0.6. The second tunnel by itself will bring in revenues of $2.1 billion and the second tunnel plus the third generating station will bring in revenues of $2.5 billion.

a) Based on expected profits (revenues minus costs), which of the three options should you take?
b) How much would the revenue from option (iii) need to be (to two significant figures) for you to change your decision?
c) What other factors should be taken into account in addition to expected profits? **LO ❷**

Kimimasa Mayama/EPA/Newscom

24

Quality Control

LEARNING OBJECTIVES

In this chapter we show you how to use statistical control charts to monitor how a process varies over time. After reading and studying this chapter, you should be able to:

❶ Use run charts to track individual measurements

❷ Use $\bar{x}$, R, and s charts to track samples of measurements

❸ Use a p chart to track proportions and a c chart to track the number of defective items

❹ Understand how quality control has been used in industry

❺ Organize possible actions to take to set a process back in control

Sony

In 1945, at the end of World War II, Masaru Ibuka started a radio repair shop in a bombed-out building in Tokyo. The next year Akio Morita joined him, and together they founded a company called Tokyo Tsushin Kogyo K.K. (or Tokyo Communication Engineering Company), which built Japan's first tape recorder. In the early 1950s Ibuka travelled to the United States and convinced Bell Labs to license its transistor technology to his Japanese company, which then released Japan's first commercially produced transistor radio. The next May, the company released a new radio with a slim design and improved sound quality. In 1957 it came out with the TR-63—the smallest transistor radio in commercial production. By all accounts, it was a worldwide commercial success.

With increasing international sales, Ibuka and Morita knew they needed a simpler name for their company. Unfortunately, the name Totsuko didn't work well in English, and their initials, TKK, were already in use by a railroad company, so Ibuka and Morita worked to find a word that didn't exist in any language but would be easy to remember. Finally, they combined the Latin word for sound, *sonus*, with the American word *sonny*, which was a popular word meaning boy or young man in the 1950s. From this the Sony name was born in 1958.

They started their Canadian operation in Winnipeg in 1955 and now have headquarters in Toronto, sales offices in Vancouver and Montreal, and distribution centres in Coquitlam, British

Columbia, and Whitby, Ontario. Sony Canada is a wholly owned subsidiary of Sony Corporation of Tokyo and actively supports Canadian communities through Make-A-Wish Canada, the United Way of Canada, and Earth Day Canada.

Sony is a leader in the collection and recycling of end-of-life products. All of Sony's Canadian retail stores accept Sony products for recycling at no charge, and commercial products can be recycled at a network of collection sites across Canada. The Recycling Council of Ontario has given Sony Canada the Platinum award for waste minimization, including cradle-to-grave product stewardship from product design to recycling.

About 20% of Sony's sales are from networked products such as PCs and gaming consoles; 50% are from TVs, cameras, and audio/video devices; and the rest are from pictures, music, and financial services, making the company one of the world's most recognized brands.

Unfortunately for the young Sony Corporation, in the 1950s the phrase "Made in Japan" was synonymous with cheap and shoddily made goods. Japan's manufacturing capabilities had been destroyed in the latter part of World War II. To rebuild its economy as quickly as possible, Japan started producing and exporting large quantities of inexpensive goods, including electronic products.

The United States sent General Douglas MacArthur to oversee the rebuilding of Japan after the war ended. Realizing the importance of reversing Japan's poor quality image, he recruited two key players, W. Edwards Deming and Joseph Juran, who'd both been active in the field of quality control in the United States. In addition, he enlisted the help of Homer Sarasohn to help rebuild the communication infrastructure of Japan.

One day, Sarasohn made a visit to the Tokyo Communication Engineering Company, a new startup factory that was building radio equipment. The equipment owed to Sarasohn was overdue, and when he arrived at the factory, he found chaos. When the owners (Ibuka and Morita) heard of the surprise inspection, they raced to see Sarasohn in Tokyo, who gave them one more chance to prove they could learn something about quality and apply it to their factory. Luckily Ibuka and Morita learned their lesson, and this young company was the company that eventually changed its name to the Sony Corporation.

These efforts proved enormously fruitful. Over the next 30 years Japan became a world leader in manufacturing, and today Japanese products consistently rank among the world's highest-quality merchandise. The United States has seen its market share in electronics and automobiles shrink in this same time period as a result.

LO❷,❹ 24.1   A Short History of Quality Control

Statistical methods for quality control were pioneered in the 1920s at the Bell Telephone Laboratories in the United States and at roughly the same time at the General Electric Company in the United Kingdom. In this chapter we'll study some tools used in the assessment of the process to investigate whether it has changed, either in its mean or in its variation.

Walter A. Shewhart (1891–1967) was an early pioneer of quality methods. Before his arrival at the Western Electric Company, quality control consisted of inspecting products and removing defective items. Shewhart introduced statistical methods, including the quality control chart that bears his name.

Walter A. Shewhart was a statistician and engineer working at Bell Laboratories in the early part of the 20th century, responsible for improving the quality of manufactured telephones. As early as 1924 he introduced a chart in an internal Bell Labs memo to graphically display variation in a process over time. The kind of chart he used, a time plot of a measure of quality, became known as a **control chart**, or sometimes a **Shewhart chart**, in his honour. In the same memo, he defined the fundamental rule of **statistical process control (SPC)** as follows: "Variation from common-cause systems should be left to chance, but special causes of variation should be identified and eliminated."

Shewhart's insight was that random fluctuations around an average (**common-cause variation**) could be tolerated, as long as those fluctuations stayed within certain specified limits, but special events (**special-cause variation**) should be identified and studied. In that case, a cause for the special-cause variation should be found and corrected. When special-cause variation is present, the process is said to be **out of control**. A more modern view recommends that while common-cause variation may *not* be a cause for alarm, managers should continue to examine common-cause variation in an effort to continually improve the process, using long-term strategies with the objective of reducing variation. Shewhart suggested a system of analysis based on the scientific method to accomplish this.

In 1950, when W. Edwards Deming replaced Sarasohn in Japan, he taught the Shewhart principles and process to Japanese managers. The process became codified into four distinct stages: Plan, Do, Check, and Act—known as the PDCA cycle (see Figure 24.1). In the *plan* stage, the manager identifies and describes the process to be improved and suggests improvements. In the *do* stage, the manager implements on a pilot level the improvement strategies. In the *check* stage, the manager examines variation to see if the improvement strategies have been successful. Finally, in the *act* stage, depending on the results of the *check* stage, the manager implements the improvement strategies on a large scale. These stages are completed continuously and repeatedly, so that they form a cycle, or some say a spiral, of quality improvement.[1]

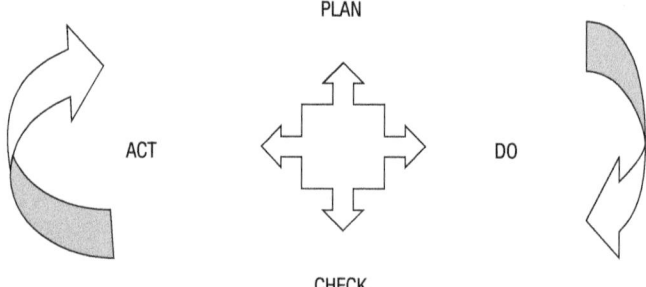

Figure 24.1   The Shewhart PDCA cycle.

Because he helped Japanese industrial leaders to rebuild after World War II and to shed the image of Japanese products as cheap and shoddy, W. Edwards Deming (1900–1993) is known as the father of the Japanese postwar industrial revival. He was also regarded by many as the leading quality guru in the United States until his death in 1993.

Today, quality control is big business. Many companies conduct their own quality control, but some prefer to outsource to third parties. SGS Canada Inc., for example, is a testing company. From minerals to consumer products and from agricultural products to oil and gas, it conducts tests to ensure the quality of Canadian products. These tests are carried out both in production facilities and at the products' point of import into Canada. They cover a range of quality measures; in the case of clothing products, for instance, SGS tests for content, shrinkage, and colour fastness.

---

[1]Some organizations use a modification of this, known as the Define-Measure-Analyze-Improve-Control (DMAIC) cycle.

Control and Specification Limits

Shewhart's idea for monitoring the variability in a process was based on probability theory. He knew that if the common-cause variation in a process was Normally distributed, there would be only a small probability that an individual value could be farther than certain limits from the mean. To monitor the process, Shewhart advocated plotting measurements of the process over time, looking for evidence that the process might change and slip "out of control." He called such a plot a control chart, although they're often referred to as Shewhart charts. Typical examples of measurements for manufactured parts are characteristics such as thickness or size, weight, colour, or electrical properties, just to name a few possibilities. Before starting to monitor the process, however, the process must first be stable, or "in control"—that is, both the mean and the standard deviation must be constant. Then, if an observation deviates far enough from the mean, it could be taken as a signal that either the process mean or the standard deviation has changed.

Figure 24.2 shows a control chart for 15 observations from an automobile manufacturing plant. The measurements are the diameters of bolts used to fasten the car door to the chassis. The desired mean of the bolts' diameters is 23 millimetres.

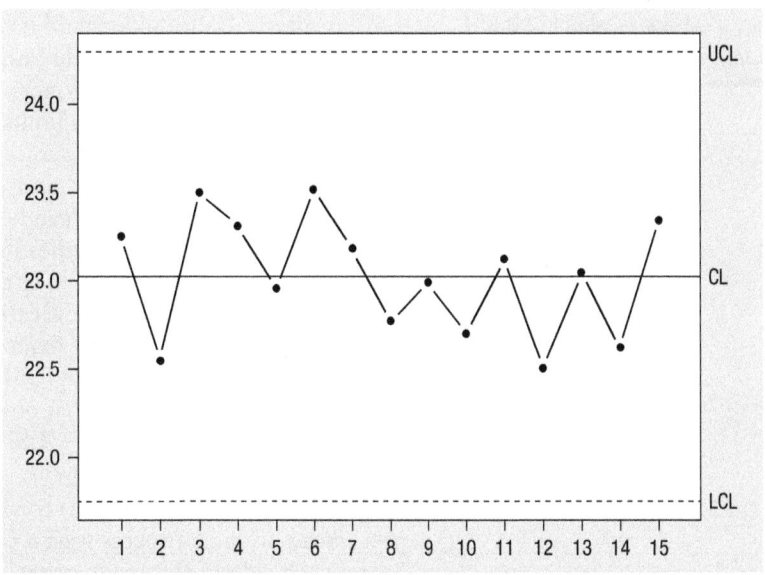

Figure 24.2   A control chart for 15 diameters of bolts with a desired mean of 23 millimetres. The lower (LCL) and upper (UCL) control limits are shown as dotted lines. The centre line (CL) is shown as a solid line.

The main idea of using a control chart to monitor a process is that if the process stays in control, observations will stay within a certain distance of the mean (at least with very high probability). However, if the process mean or standard deviation changes, then the observations will start to drift; by monitoring the process, we'll be able to discover that change. The question then becomes how far the observations must drift before we decide that the process has changed. So, for every process, **control limits** need to be established to decide when to take action. When points fall outside of the control limits, this provides a signal that the process may have changed and some action is needed. We'll discuss how to define the control limits and the various rules for deciding when action is needed in the rest of this chapter.

A Type I error is when a test indicates that the process has changed, when in fact no change has occurred.
A Type II error is when a test indicates that the process has not changed, when in fact a change has occurred.

Using a control chart to monitor a process can be viewed as a graphical hypothesis test. The null hypothesis is that the process hasn't changed (both the mean and variance are constant). Various rules are used to decide when a signal has occurred (e.g., an observation that falls more than three standard deviations from the mean is a common rule). When such a signal occurs, we reject the null hypothesis and conclude that a change has taken place. Of course, like all hypothesis tests, both Type I and Type II errors are always possible. In this context, a Type I error is a **false alarm**, requiring an unnecessary adjustment to the process. A Type II error is a failure to see a change in the process. The trade-off between the two types of errors and their relative costs in particular settings gives rise to the many different rules for deciding when to reject the null hypothesis and declare a change in the process. Of course, rules that make it easier to reject the hypothesis will result in more false alarms and rules that make it harder will allow processes to drift further (on average) before a signal is produced.

Specification limits are imposed on a process by specifying a range of values for a measurement. Upper specification limit (USL) is the highest value we would like the measurement to have. Lower specification limit (LSL) is the lowest value we would like the measurement to have.

Control limits are based on the data themselves, and for that reason it's imperative that the process be in control before starting the monitoring process. Sometimes, however, quality concerns impose *external* limits on the process as well. For example, the diameters of the bolts must fall between certain limits or they just won't work. Limits such as these are called **specification limits** because they're based on external specifications and not on how well the parts are actually produced. These upper and lower specification limits are abbreviated as USL and LSL, respectively. To understand how well the process is behaving compared with the specification limits, a study known as a **process capability study** is undertaken. Quality control practitioners use these studies to understand the relationships between the specification limits and the actual process parameters (mean and variance). Several different *process capability indices* measuring different aspects of the relationship are commonly used.

Process capability studies can be performed only when the process is in control. In other words, these studies involve only the common-cause variation and not special-cause variation. As long as the observations stay between the LSL and USL, the parts will meet specification. Ideally, we'd want the upper and lower specification limits to be as far from the process mean as is economically feasible. That width can be measured by USL – LSL. If the process can be centred at the desired mean, then we know that observations farther than 3σ from the mean will be rare. The ratio $C_p = \dfrac{\text{USL} - \text{LSL}}{6\sigma}$ measures the ratio of the entire specification range (both sides of the mean) to six times the standard deviation of the actual process variation. A process with a C_p value of 1.0 would therefore just satisfy the 3σ on each side of the mean criteria and translates to about one observation in about 370 falling outside the specification limits, which is considered too often for most modern manufacturing and service industries. It's usually recommended that C_p be at least 1.25, and sometimes as high as 2.0, but the actual choice depends on the economics of the situation and the type of industry. The larger this C_p value, the smaller the chance of an observation falling outside the specification limits. A large value of C_p indicates a process with a large potential to produce parts within the specification limits.

Unfortunately, C_p assumes that the mean is perfectly constant. But in any real process, no matter how stable, the mean will drift slightly even when the process is in control. For that reason, C_p tends to overestimate the potential of the process, so a measure known as C_{pk} is often used instead. Here we show the estimated value of C_{pk}, denoted as $\hat{C}_{pk}$: $\hat{C}_{pk} = \min\left[\dfrac{\text{USL} - \hat{\mu}}{3\hat{\sigma}}, \dfrac{\hat{\mu} - \text{LSL}}{3\hat{\sigma}}\right]$, where the hats indicate that the parameters are estimated from the process data. As with C_p, the choice of how large a value of C_{pk} is acceptable or desired depends on the situation and the associated costs. Some industries (such as the automotive manufacturing industry) publish specific guidelines. It's also important to remember that these indices rely heavily on the assumption that all observations are Normally distributed.

FOR EXAMPLE   Capability indices for fudge production

Fudge requires a fairly strict adherence to the sequence of boiling sugar in milk until it reaches a certain consistency and then beating the mixture while it cools so that it acquires a smooth, creamy texture. A small candy company ships fudge worldwide. If its fudge mix has a stable consistency, workers can control the weight of the fudge by simply timing how long they pour the warm fudge into the box prior to shipping. They'd like the labelled 18 oz. box of fudge to contain no more than 18.5 oz. of fudge and no less than 17.9 oz. From the last 100 batches, they estimate the standard deviation of the weights to be 0.1 oz. with a mean of 18.1 oz.

QUESTION Perform a process capability analysis on the candy company and comment on your findings.

ANSWER Our estimate of C_p is $\hat{C}_p = \dfrac{USL - LSL}{6\hat{\sigma}} = \dfrac{18.5 - 17.9}{6(0.1)} = \dfrac{0.6}{0.6} = 1.0$. Our

estimate of $\hat{C}_{pk}$ is $\hat{C}_{pk} = \min\left[\dfrac{USL - \hat{\mu}}{3\hat{\sigma}}, \dfrac{\hat{\mu} - LSL}{3\hat{\sigma}}\right] = \min\left[\dfrac{18.5 - 18.1}{3(0.1)}, \dfrac{18.1 - 17.9}{3(0.1)}\right]$

$= \min\left[\dfrac{0.4}{0.3}, \dfrac{0.2}{0.3}\right] = 0.67$. The C_p value shows that if the weights are Normally

distributed and the mean is centred, about 1 in 370 boxes will exceed the limits. This is a low C_p value, but it may be acceptable in this industry. However, the mean of 18.1 isn't centred between the two limits (17.9, 18.5) and the C_{pk} value of 0.67 is too low. The candy company should work to centre the mean and/or lower the standard deviation of the weights.

LO❶ 24.2 Control Charts for Individual Observations (Run Charts)

The Sony Corporation of the 1950s used transistors and tubes for its electronic equipment, but nearly all its products today rely on computer chips. And almost all computer chips in use today are built on silicon wafers. Silicon is a natural semiconductor—it can be used both as a conductor of electricity and as an insulator to prevent conduction. It's also relatively inexpensive and plentiful. The basic source of silicon is sand, which can be purified to produce chips that are 99.9999% pure silicon. Although there are many different kinds of chips (memory, processors, etc.), they are all built from the basic silicon wafer. Making a wafer involves a number of steps, all of which must be carried out as consistently as possible to ensure that the chip will be able to perform reliably, regardless of its final function. During the manufacturing process a variety of performance characteristics must be checked—physical measurements such as thickness, chemical properties involving purity, and electrical properties such as conductance. All of these have specifications depending on the type of chip being produced. Because billions of chips are manufactured worldwide every year, maintaining quality control on chip manufacturing is big business.

Silicon wafers are produced in varying thicknesses, depending on their diameter. For photovoltaic use in solar panels, a typical wafer is about 100–200 millimetres square with a thickness of 200–300 micrometres (μm). The mean target thickness of the particular wafer whose production is studied here is 300 μm. One way to ensure quality is to keep the thickness as consistent as possible. To establish control limits, we'll use 250 past measurements of the process that have been judged to be in control. Here are the summary statistics and a histogram (Figure 24.3):

maximum	392.423
upper quartile (Q3)	325.067
median	298.521
lower quartile (Q1)	277.030
minimum	221.838
Mean	301.111
Std Dev	32.990

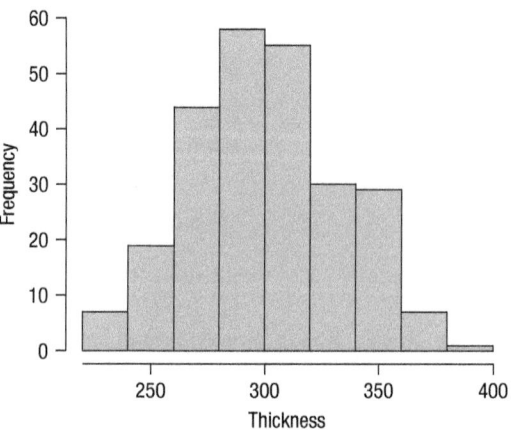

Figure 24.3   A histogram of the thickness shows a nearly Normal distribution centred at 300 μm.

Because the process has been judged to be in control, we can use the statistics from these data to develop control limits. We'll base the mean at 300 μm, the desired thickness. The standard deviation of these measurements is 32.99. Using 33 μm as the standard deviation, (σ), the 68-95-99.7 Rule states that, as long as the process remains stable, only about 0.3% or 3 of 1000 observations will fall outside of 3σ from the mean. Using 3σ, the lower and upper control limits would be

$$\mu - 3\sigma = 300 - 99 = 201 \text{ and } \mu + 3\sigma = 300 + 99 = 399 \ \mu\text{m}.$$

Using these control limits, a control chart can be monitored to see whether the process stays in control.

Figure 24.4 shows a control chart for individual observations (sometimes called a **run chart**), where a measurement is made on every product being produced. As we check each observation we're really performing a graphical hypothesis test, with the null hypothesis that the mean is 300 μm and the (two-sided) alternative that it has changed to something else. The change may be abrupt, caused perhaps by the breakdown of a machine or the introduction of an impurity, in which case it's called a **level shift**. Or the change might be gradual, in which case it's called a **trend**. We'll reject the null hypothesis if any point lies outside the 3σ control limits. The use of 3σ control limits as a standard is fairly widespread in Canada and the United States, while the United Kingdom and

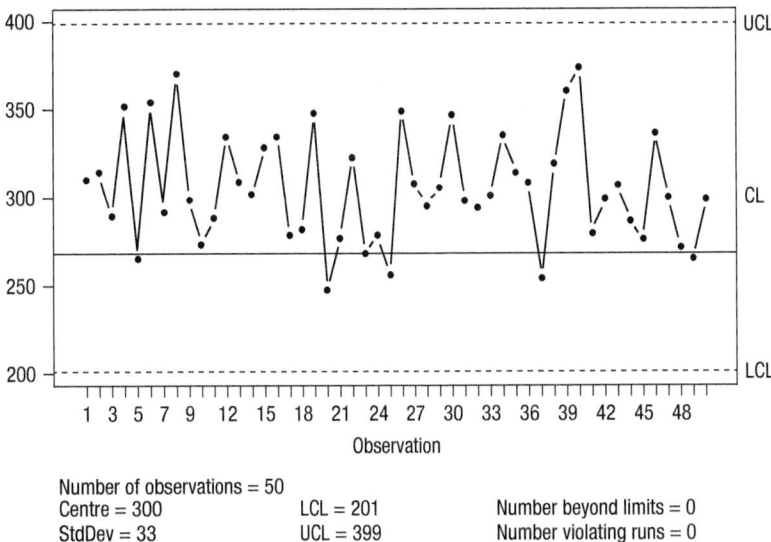

Number of observations = 50
Centre = 300   LCL = 201   Number beyond limits = 0
StdDev = 33   UCL = 399   Number violating runs = 0

Figure 24.4   A control chart of individual observations shows no evidence that the process has slipped out of control. The 3σ lower (LCL) and upper (UCL) control limits are shown as dotted lines. The centre line (CL) is shown as a solid line.

Europe tends to use other multiples of σ that depend on the specified probability of a Type I error, or false alarm signal. Using 3σ control limits will give rise to a false alarm rate of about 0.003 (using $1 - 0.997$ from the 68-95-99.7 Rule), or, more precisely, 0.0027. That's the probability of any *single* observation giving rise to a false alarm. Even a process that is perfectly in control will have observations farther than 3σ from the mean eventually (in fact, about three times in every 1000 observations). The average time between false alarms for a process in control is called the **average run length (ARL)** and can be calculated by taking the reciprocal of the false alarm probability. For 3σ the ARL is

$$\text{ARL} = \frac{1}{p} = \frac{1}{0.0027} = 370.37.$$

On average, we would expect to see a false alarm about every 370 observations for a process that's in control.

If the process mean shifts and we fail to detect it, that is a Type II error. As in any hypothesis testing situation, the probability of the Type II error depends on how long we monitor the process and how large the shift is (the effect size). Balancing Type I and Type II errors is an economic decision and depends on the control limits and the rule for deciding when a process has changed. The ability of any chart to detect shifts can be described by its **operating-characteristic (OC) curve.** We describe the shift in mean in terms of standard deviations. If the process shifts only one standard deviation, the probability of noticing the shift on the next observation will be very small. If the shift were quite large—say, 5σ—we should be surprised if we didn't see it immediately. Figure 24.5 shows an OC curve for the run chart just described.

Even though the probability of detecting a shift of 3σ is only about 0.5 on the *next* observation, the probability of a Type II error on both of the next two observations is about $0.5 \times 0.5 = 0.25$, and the probability of failing to detect the shift after five observations is $(0.5)^5 = 0.031$. More observations, of course, help guard against making errors.

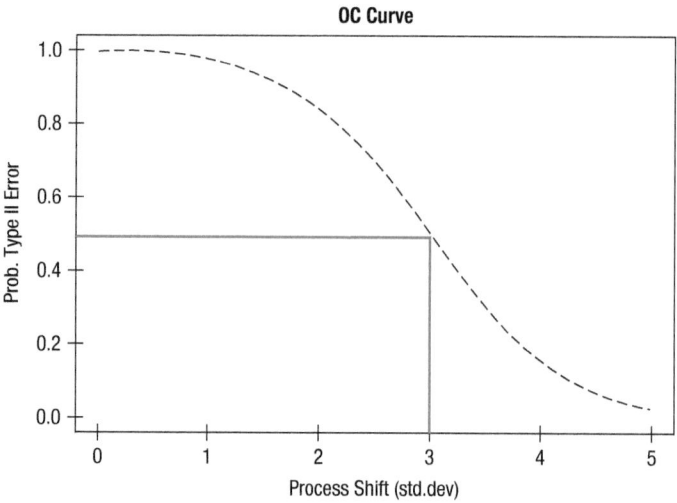

Figure 24.5   The operating-characteristic curve for a run chart. If a process has shifted by 3σ, the probability of not detecting that shift on the next observation is about 0.50.

In addition to the simple 3σ rule, there are many other rules commonly used in industry. The *Western Electric Handbook* (WECO, 1956) suggests several criteria for deciding whether a process is out of control:

1. One point outside of the 3σ control limits on either side
2. Two out of three consecutive points beyond the 2σ "warning limits"
3. Four out of five consecutive points beyond 1σ from the mean
4. Eight points in a row on the same side of the mean
5. Six points in a row increasing (or decreasing)
6. Fourteen points in a row alternatively increasing and decreasing

These rules are commonly used in practice, and some software (notably Excel and Minitab) implement several other rules as well. You may see 8 or even 10 rules used by software to detect a possible shift in the process. However, there are trade-offs. If the simple 3σ rule is the only one used, the ARL before a false alarm, as we've seen, is about 370. If all five additional WECO rules are implemented, the ARL drops to about 92 observations between false alarms. Using more rules only decreases the ARL further. Each user has to decide whether the ability to detect shifts faster is worth the price of more frequent false alarms.

FOR EXAMPLE   Run charts for fudge production

QUESTION   After the report in For Example: "Capability indices for fudge production," the candy company makes some changes to the pouring process and wants the mean now to be 18.15 oz. and the standard deviation to be 0.08 oz. Using these parameter values, construct a run chart for the following weights of recent batches and comment on whether the process is in control.

18.03	18.00	18.12	17.81	18.23
18.11	18.23	18.19	18.00	18.05
18.12	18.05	18.14	18.16	18.11
18.19	18.26	18.11	18.15	18.07
18.04	18.14	18.00	18.21	18.12

ANSWER

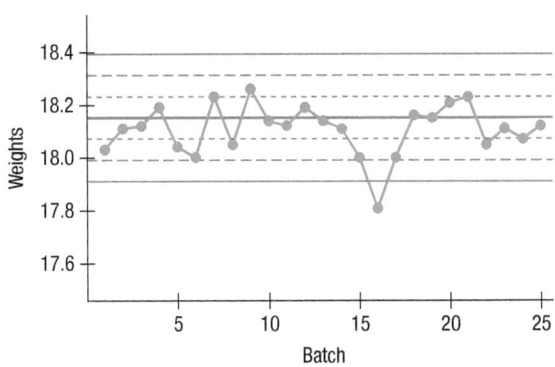

The three pairs of horizontal line indicate one, two and three standard deviations from the mean. It appears that the process is not yet in control. The weight of batch 16 is too low and, in fact, it's outside both 3σ and the lower specification limit of 17.90.

LO❷   24.3   Control Charts for Sample Measurements: x̄, R, and S Charts

Although the run chart of the last section is the easiest to implement and to understand, it's not usually practical to measure *every* item coming down a production line, especially if the testing destroys the product being tested, e.g., crash testing a car. Instead, a sample is taken at periodic intervals and, typically, the *mean* of that sample is plotted. A chart of these sample means is called an $\bar{x}$ **chart** (pronounced "x bar chart" and often written as x-bar or x bar chart).

For detecting a shift in the mean, the $\bar{x}$ chart has several advantages over the run chart. First, a practical advantage is that it tests less frequently. Second, the power for detecting a shift from a sample grows with the sample size. Finally, and most importantly, the averages from a sample of size n are more nearly Normal than individual observations, so that basic assumption of the control chart is more likely to be met. Because the sample sizes are usually small, however, it still relies somewhat on the underlying measurements being approximately Normal. If the data have a very skewed distribution, the Central Limit Theorem (Chapter 10) assures us that the sample means are approximately Normally distributed only if the sample size is large.

When the standard deviation is assumed to be known (perhaps based on a large amount of past data), the implementation of the $\bar{x}$ chart is essentially the same as the individual control chart. Recall that a sample mean has a standard deviation of $\dfrac{\sigma}{\sqrt{n}}$ rather than σ, so the 3σ control limits for the $\bar{x}$ chart become

$$\text{LCL} = \mu - 3\frac{\sigma}{\sqrt{n}}$$

$$\text{UCL} = \mu + 3\frac{\sigma}{\sqrt{n}}.$$

For the silicon wafer data, if we continue to use $\mu = 300$ and $\sigma = 33$, and take a five-item sample at regular intervals, the control limits become

$$\text{LCL} = \mu - 3\frac{\sigma}{\sqrt{n}} = 300 - 3\left(\frac{33}{\sqrt{5}}\right) = 255.7\mu\text{m}$$

$$\text{UCL} = \mu + 3\frac{\sigma}{\sqrt{n}} = 300 + 3\left(\frac{33}{\sqrt{5}}\right) = 344.3\mu\text{m}.$$

Figure 24.6 shows an $\bar{x}$ chart for 25 samples of size five from the wafer production process.

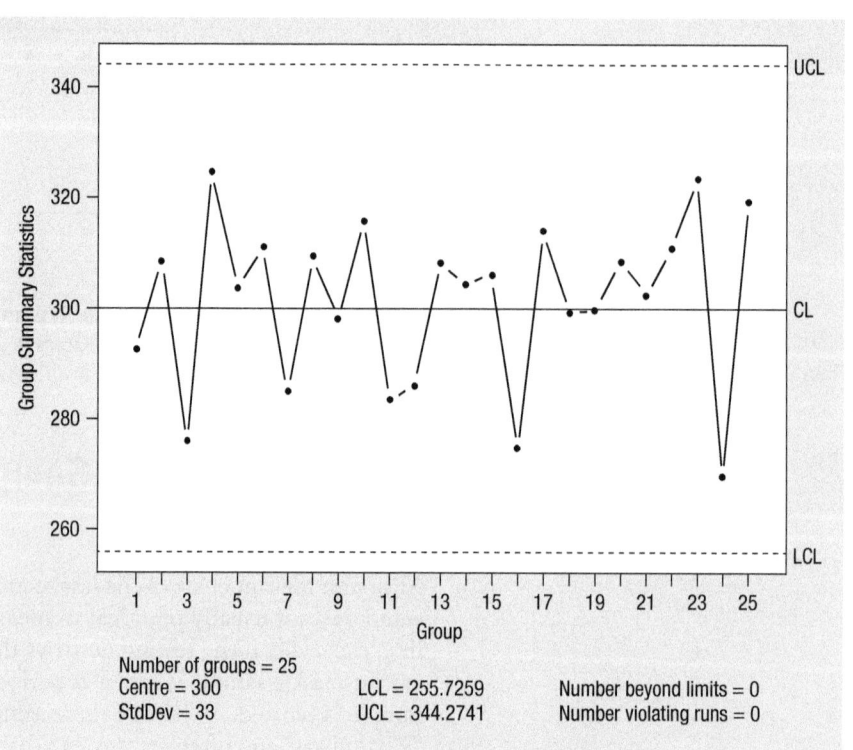

Number of groups = 25
Centre = 300
StdDev = 33

LCL = 255.7259
UCL = 344.2741

Number beyond limits = 0
Number violating runs = 0

Figure 24.6   An $\bar{x}$ chart for 25 samples of size five. The process appears to be in control because all sample means are within the control limits. This particular chart uses two of the Western Electric rules and reports *Number beyond limits* (rule #1 on page 856) and *Number violating runs* (variant of rule #4 on page 856—seven points in a row on same side of mean).

We can also calculate the range, R, which is the difference between the largest and smallest measurements within each sample. This is a measurement of the variability within a sample and is therefore related to the standard deviation. The centre line is $d_2\sigma$.

$$\text{UCL: } d_2\sigma + 3d_3\sigma$$

$$\text{LCL: } d_2\sigma - 3d_3\sigma,$$

where d_2 and d_3 are found in Appendix B, Table R for sample size n.

Up to now we've assumed that the past data are numerous, so the mean and standard deviation of the process are known. In practice, though, we may not have this information, and so we have to estimate both μ and σ. These estimates should be based on as much data as possible—20 to 25 samples at a minimum—and, of course, the process must be in control. If we have k samples of size n, then we can use the average of the averages, called $\bar{\bar{x}}$ ("x double bar"), to get our estimate of μ:

$$\bar{\bar{x}} = \frac{\bar{x}_1 + \cdots + \bar{x}_k}{k}$$

If no external centre were desired, $\bar{\bar{x}}$ would be the centre of our control chart.

> ## Optional Math Box
>
> For Normally distributed data, there's a well-known relationship between the range, R, of a sample and its standard deviation, σ. The mean of the ratio $\dfrac{R}{\sigma}$ is a constant denoted d_2, which depends on the sample size (and is given for various sample sizes in Appendix B, Table R). Using this constant, an estimate of σ is found from $\hat{\sigma} = \dfrac{\overline{R}}{d_2}$, where the average range is given by: $\overline{R} = \dfrac{R_1 + \cdots + R_k}{k}$.
>
> The limits of the control chart then become:
>
> $$\text{LCL} = \bar{\bar{x}} - 3\frac{\hat{\sigma}}{\sqrt{n}} = \bar{\bar{x}} - 3\frac{\overline{R}}{d_2\sqrt{n}} = \bar{\bar{x}} - A_2\overline{R}$$
>
> $$\text{UCL} = \bar{\bar{x}} + 3\frac{\hat{\sigma}}{\sqrt{n}} = \bar{\bar{x}} + 3\frac{\overline{R}}{d_2\sqrt{n}} = \bar{\bar{x}} + A_2\overline{R}$$

To find the control limits, we use the ranges of the samples. Recall that the range of a sample is defined as the maximum minus the minimum:

$$R = \max - \min$$

Here are the upper and lower control limits using a parameter A_2, which depends on the sample size and is given in Appendix B, Table R:

$$\text{LCL} = \bar{\bar{x}} - A_2\overline{R}$$
$$\text{UCL} = \bar{\bar{x}} + A_2\overline{R}$$

Suppose that, instead of the 250 individual measurements we used previously to establish μ and σ, we used the first half of these as a calibration set and then monitored the rest of the samples. In total we have 50 samples of size five. From the first 25 samples of size five we compute their means and ranges and find:

$$\bar{\bar{x}} = 295.27; \ \overline{R} = 81.32$$

To compute the **lower control limit (LCL)** and **upper control limit (UCL)**, we have $n = 5$ and $A_2 = 0.577$ from Appendix B, Table R. Therefore

$$\text{LCL} = 295.27 - 0577 \times 81.32 = 248.36$$
$$\text{UCL} = 295.27 + 0.577 \times 81.32 = 342.18.$$

These aren't very far from the control limits we found by assuming that the mean and standard deviation were known. But control limits often have to be adjusted as new information about the process performance becomes available. Quality control charting involves learning about a process as well as monitoring it.

A more modern approach to process monitoring uses control charts to monitor the *inputs* to the process instead of just the measurements (outputs). In this way of thinking, if the critical inputs to the process are in control, the resulting outputs will be as well.

As we saw with run charts, the power for detecting a shift depends on the size of the process shift. For $\bar{x}$ charts it also depends on the sample size. To choose an appropriate sample size, quality control monitors examine the OC curves, such as the one based on the wafer data shown in Figure 24.7. Both the process shift and the sample size can be used to find the probability of a Type II error for the next sample.

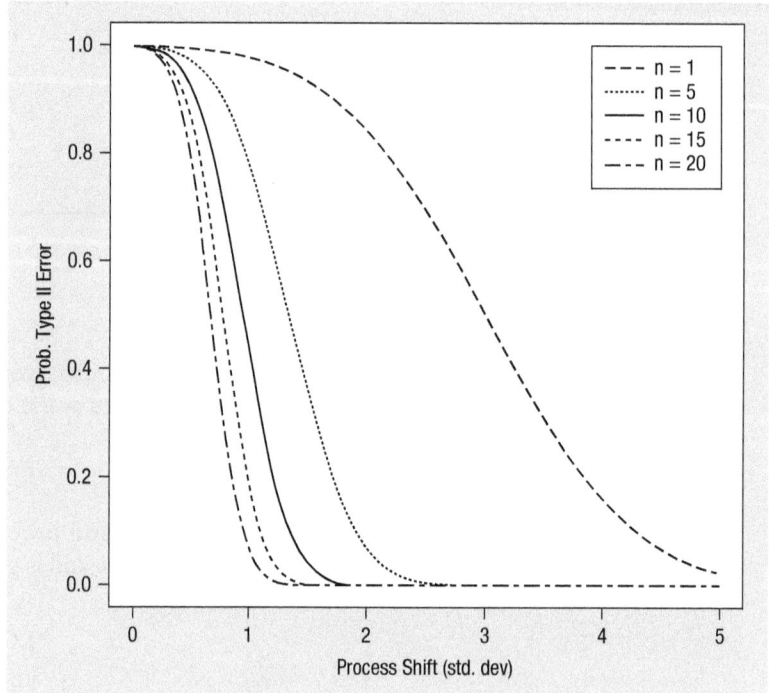

Figure 24.7   Operating-characteristic curves for the wafer data $\bar{x}$ chart. For any proposed value of the process shift (in standard deviations), operators can examine different sample sizes to determine a good sample size with a reasonable probability of a Type II error. For example, for a 1.5σ shift, a sample size of at least 10 would be necessary to produce a probability of a Type II error below 0.10.

In general, we care about both the level of the process and the consistency in variation. For that reason, the ranges themselves are plotted in what's known as an **R chart**. The procedure for setting up the R chart is very similar to the $\bar{x}$ chart.

The upper and lower limits for the R chart are just multiples of $\bar{R}$ (and are found in Appendix B, Table R). For small sample sizes, $D_3 = 0$, which automatically sets the lower range limit to be 0.

$$\text{LCL} = D_3\bar{R}$$

$$\text{UCL} = D_4\bar{R}$$

For $n = 5$, $D_3 = 0$ and $D_4 = 2.114$, so LCL = 0 and UCL = $2.114 \times 81.32 = 171.91$.

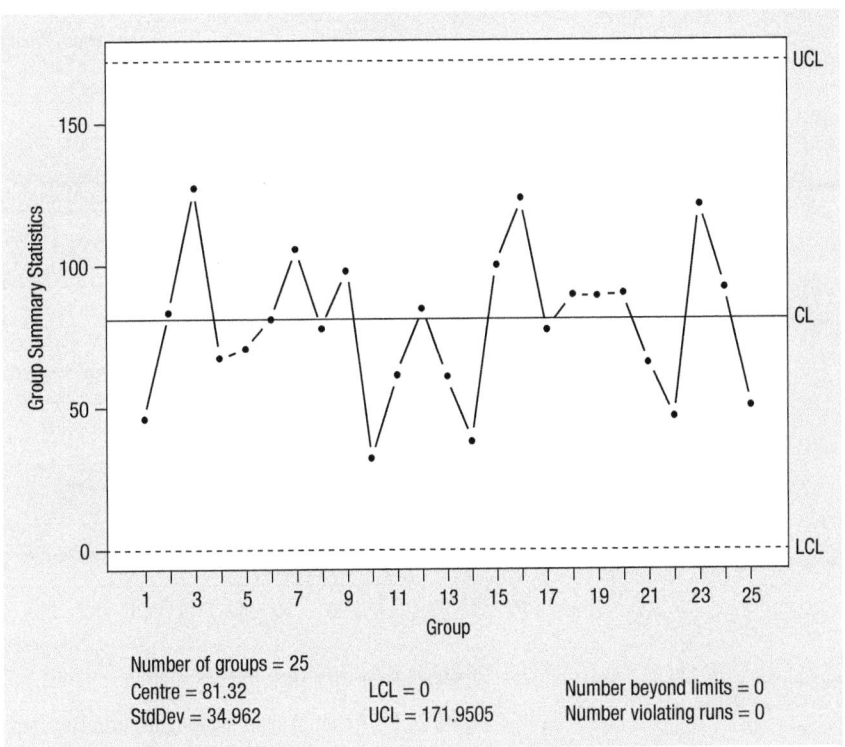

Number of groups = 25
Centre = 81.32   **LCL = 0**   **Number beyond limits = 0**
StdDev = 34.962   **UCL = 171.9505**   **Number violating runs = 0**

Figure 24.8   An R chart for 25 samples of size five. The process appears to be in control in terms of variation because all sample ranges are within the control limit range from 0 to 171.95.

Monitoring the next 25 samples, Figure 24.8 shows that the range stayed in control.

An alternative to the R chart is the **S chart**, which uses the standard deviation, s_i, of each sample rather than its range, R_i. The average of the standard deviations over all k samples is denoted, $\bar{s} = (s_1 + \ldots + s_k)/k$. The most common use of $\bar{x}$ and S charts occurs when the sample sizes are moderately large. The formulas for finding the control limits for $\bar{x}$ are:

$$\text{LCL} = \bar{\bar{x}} + A_3 \times \bar{s}$$

$$\text{UCL} = \bar{\bar{x}} - A_3 \times \bar{s}$$

The control limits for $\bar{s}$ are:

$$\text{LCL} = B_1 \times \bar{s}$$

$$\text{UCL} = B_2 \times \bar{s}$$

In this section we've seen how to establish the most common control limits for $\bar{x}$, S, and R charts. There are, as with run charts, other rules for determining whether a process is out of control. It's also important to note that specification limits (discussed in Section 24.2) are typically for *individual* observations only and cannot, in general, be used on averages or ranges. Because $\bar{x}$, S, and R charts examine different ways that a process may have shifted, it's important that they be used together. It's usually insufficient to monitor only the means or only the ranges or standard deviations.

Finally, it's important to point out that not all process changes are undesirable. In fact, in modern quality control, much emphasis is placed on reducing process variation. A shift indicating that the range or standard deviation has decreased would almost certainly be viewed as beneficial as shown in the example in Figure 24.9.

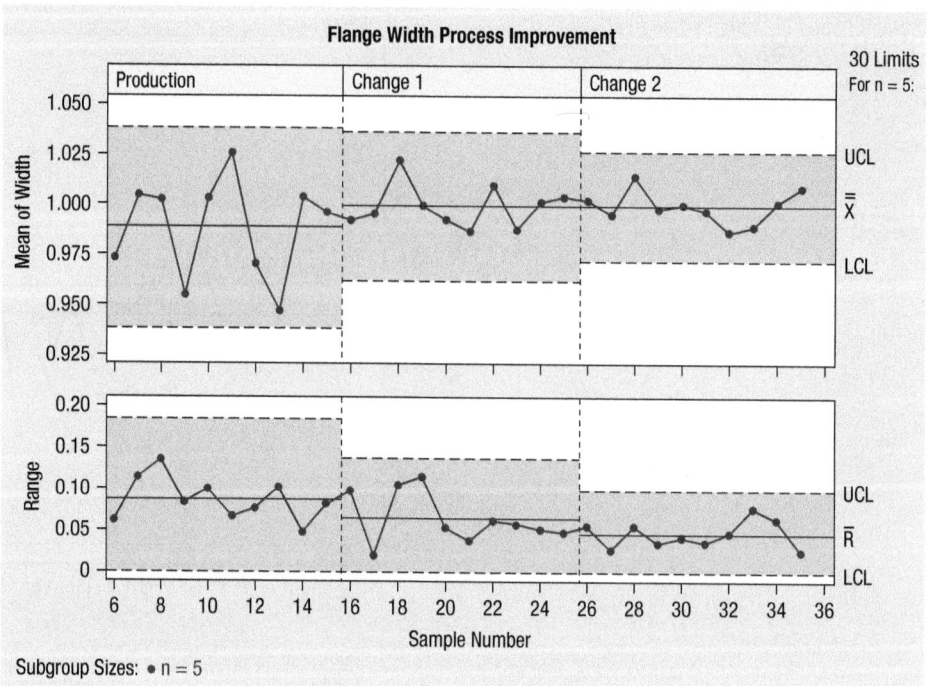

Figure 24.9   A control chart showing reduced standard deviations after changes to improve the production process.

Optional Math Box

For Normally distributed data, the relationship between σ and R is well-known. There is a new parameter d_3, which depends on the sample size, as did d_2. If we assume σ is known, we can find the standard deviation of the range by $\sigma_R = d_3\sigma$. If we need to estimate σ, we can use $\hat{\sigma} = \dfrac{\overline{R}}{d_2}$ as before:

$$\hat{\sigma}_R = d_3\frac{\overline{R}}{d_2}$$

We centre the range chart at $\overline{R}$, so the control limits

$$\text{LCL} = \overline{R} - 3\sigma_R$$

$$\text{UCL} = \overline{R} + 3\sigma_R$$

become

$$\text{LCL} = \overline{R} - 3d_3\frac{\overline{R}}{d_2} = D_3\overline{R}$$

$$UCL = \overline{R} + 3d_3\frac{\overline{R}}{d_2} = D_4\overline{R}.$$

(If we're given both the mean and standard deviation from the process history and wish to establish limits for R, we can alternatively use $R = d_2\sigma$ as the centre line.)

FOR EXAMPLE $\bar{x}$ and R charts for fudge production

The fudge makers (see For Example: "Run charts for fudge production") make more changes to the process and wonder if they've been successful in getting the process under control. They still desire a mean of 18.15 oz. and a process deviation of 0.08 oz. Here are the average weights and ranges of 25 samples of size five:

Batch	Mean	Range	Batch	Mean	Range
1	18.104	0.13	14	18.076	0.20
2	18.014	0.09	15	18.152	0.15
3	18.138	0.14	16	18.114	0.31
4	18.108	0.31	17	18.180	0.36
5	18.118	0.12	18	18.086	0.26
6	18.112	0.18	19	18.104	0.40
7	18.216	0.15	20	18.074	0.20
8	18.332	0.62	21	18.122	0.24
9	18.434	0.19	22	18.146	0.12
10	18.146	0.29	23	18.104	0.36
11	18.032	0.22	24	18.136	0.16
12	18.102	0.39	25	18.104	0.08
13	18.112	0.21			

QUESTIONS Using $\bar{x}$ and R charts with the desired mean of 18.15 oz., and the desired standard deviation of 0.08 oz., does the process seem to be in control now? If not, when did the process seem to slip out of control?

ANSWERS For the $\bar{x}$ chart, we use 18.15 as the centre line and the desired process standard deviation of 0.08. The control limits are found at

$$\mu \pm 3\frac{\sigma}{\sqrt{5}} = 18.15 \pm 3\frac{0.08}{\sqrt{5}} = 18.15 \pm 0.107 = 18.043 \ and \ 18.257.$$

Here is the $\bar{x}$ chart of the 25 batches:

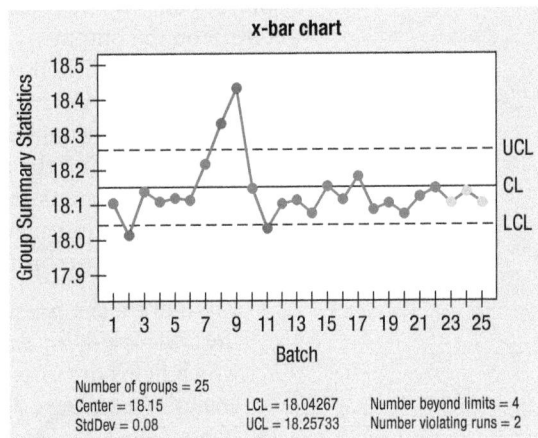

For the ranges, we use the desired process mean and standard deviation as well. So the centre is

$$centre = d_2\sigma = 2.326(0.08) = 0.186$$

$$UCL = centre + 3(d_3\sigma) = 0.186 + 3(0.864 \times 0.08) = 0.393$$

$$LCL = centre - 3(d_3\sigma) = 0.186 - 3(0.864 \times 0.08) = 0.021 \Rightarrow 0.$$

(continued)

Here is the *R* chart:

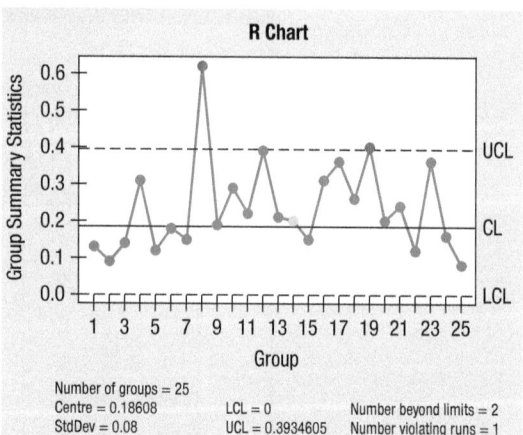

The process is out of control both in mean (x-bar) and in variation (R). In the x-bar chart, samples 2 and 11 were too low, and 8 and 9 were too high. By samples 23, 24, 25 there are more than 6 sample means in a row below the centre line. In the R chart, samples 8 and 19 had ranges too high, and by sample 14, there were six ranges in a row on the same side of the centre line.

LO⑤ 24.4 Actions for Out-of-Control Processes

Once a process has been determined to be "out of control," it doesn't necessarily mean that something is "wrong" with the process. It simply means that a signal has occurred indicating a possible change in the system. An action should be taken to understand the source of the special-cause variation. However, if the change is determined to be detrimental, those in charge of the process must act quickly to resolve the problem. In the case of a detrimental change, an out-of-control signal may necessitate stopping production of the process until the cause has been determined and a correction put into place. This is the "act" part of the Shewhart cycle and a crucial step for process management. If an input to a process is found to be "out of control" then part of our action would be to conduct additional quality control on the outputs.

For an established manufacturing process there may be an **out-of-control action plan (OCAP)** in place based on past experience. An operator seeing an out-of-control signal would consult the OCAP, take the steps outlined in it, and then continue monitoring the process to see if the process regains an in-control state.

If no such plan exists, as would be the case for a new process, an investigation of possible causes is undertaken. The full details of such an investigation are beyond the scope of this text, but the basic steps involve the following:

- Enumerate the possible causes of the shift. A powerful tool in this effort is the *cause-and-effect diagram* (sometimes called an *Ishikawa* or *fishbone diagram*), which helps organize the possible causes and helps prioritize them for further analysis (see Figure 24.10).
- If no simple cause can be determined, it may be necessary to commence a series of experiments using the most probable causes as the factors. There are efficient designs that can accommodate as many as a dozen or more possible factors in the initial investigation of possible causes.
- Once the most likely cause has been identified, and the optimal value for that factor has been determined, the process inputs are changed in an attempt to drive the process back into control.

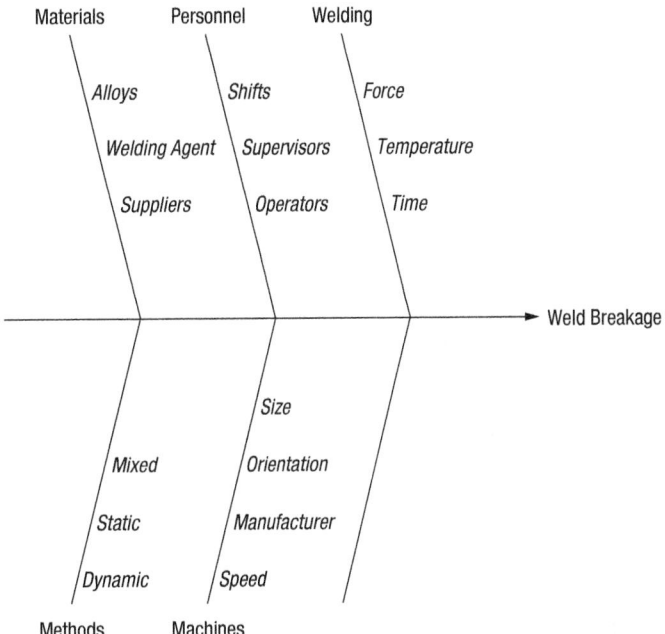

Figure 24.10 Cause-and-effect diagram for a production problem involving faulty welding between a detector and its base in a gas chromatograph. A team was assembled, and together its members listed five potential areas to investigate for process improvement: materials, personnel, welding, welding methods, and the machines involved. For each area, three to four potential factors were listed. From here, the team designed a series of experiments in the factors deemed most likely to affect weld breakage. The factors were manipulated and the resulting weld breakage was measured. Eventually it was determined that the alloy used by one of the suppliers had changed. When the company insisted that the supplier use the alloy that had been historically used for the weld, the problem disappeared.

- The monitoring process is restarted in the hope that the problem has been resolved, and the Shewhart cycle starts again.

  Understanding and controlling processes is a large area of activity in both the manufacturing and service industries, involving the efforts of many people in an organization. The American Society for Quality (www.asq.org) provides a wealth of information on the subject.

FOR EXAMPLE   **Actions for out-of-control process for fudge production**

The fudge company (see For Example: "$\overline{x}$ and R charts for fudge production") wants to bring its process under control and assembles a team of bakers, process engineers, and marketing staff. The team discusses possible factors influencing the weight and groups them into four main categories:

Raw materials (sugar, butter, milk, flavouring)

Oven (oven temperature, pan temperature, time)

Process (timing of stir, amount of stir, pouring of fudge)

Container (pan material, pan size)

QUESTION Organize these possible factors into a fishbone (Ishikawa) diagram to help the team design experiments using these factors.

(continued)

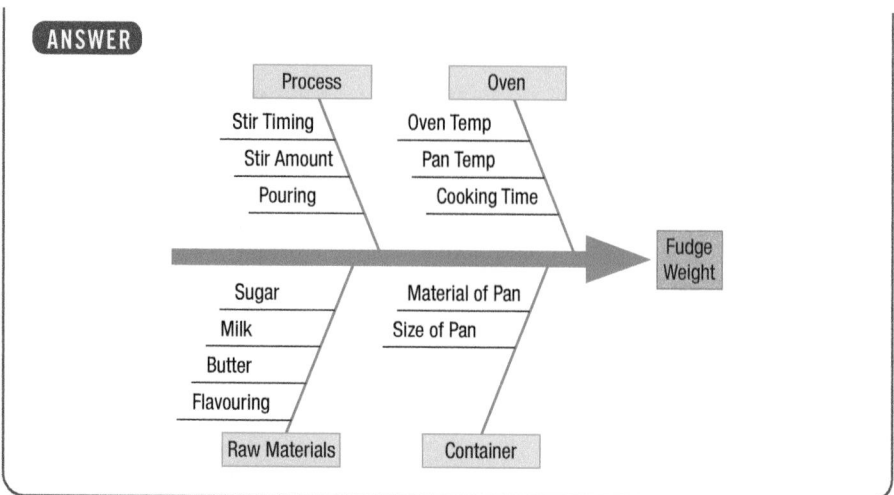

GUIDED EXAMPLE   KomTeK Technologies

KomTeK Technologies, founded in 1984, specializes in the production of nickel- and cobalt-based super alloys—specifically in the production of prosthetic devices. This manufacturing firm sells hip joints to five biomedical companies, and these hips account for 30% to 40% of the firm's annual revenue. This firm uses a cobalt chromium alloy to forge the hips, which are heated in a furnace and then beaten or hammered into shape. Because the prosthetic hips are costly to manufacture, the firm produces the hips only when a customer places an order. The average size of an order is typically between 200 and 600 pieces, and customers require order lead times of less than two weeks.[2]

Each part of the manufacturing process is monitored and controlled, and the corporation has implemented a rigorous program to assist with quality control. Toward the end of the manufacturing process, dimples need to be hammered into each hip to enhance the fit. Occasionally, this hammering process causes the centre line to be off-centre. The tip length of this dimple is a crucial measurement to monitor.

A major customer that accounts for nearly 40% to 50% of the total hip sales at the firm recently placed an order for 1200 prosthetic hips—a larger-than-usual order. Following the manufacturing and shipment of these hips for this customer, the team at the firm responsible for quality control noticed that the overall cost for filling this order was high. The team members realized that the order was larger than usual, but they needed to determine how and why the cost was so high. There was some concern by management that quality control monitoring may not have been in place for the latter part of the order. In particular, there was some suspicion that the last 230 or so hips hadn't been subjected to rigorous quality control.

We want to establish control limits for $\bar{x}$ and R charts for the *Tip Length* and investigate the recent production run to understand why the cost of recent orders has been high.

PLAN	**Setup** State the objectives. Identify the type of data you're examining.	We want to examine the variation in the *Tip Length* of the distal hip for the latter part of a recent large customer order to look for possible quality control issues. To start the monitoring process, we have data from 50 samples of size five from previous orders, when the process was judged to be in control (the calibration period), to use to establish our control limits.

[2]This example is based on a case study written by J. Hunt, E. Landry, and J. Rao as part of the Babson College case series, © Babson College, 1998. The data and setting used in this example are based on the actual case study, but the data have been modified and the conclusions are fictitious.

DO **Mechanics** We can compute the limits using the specs provided by the company.

For the calibration period the overall mean is $\bar{\bar{x}} = 0.250$ cm. A histogram of these 250 observations shows a unimodal and symmetric distribution:

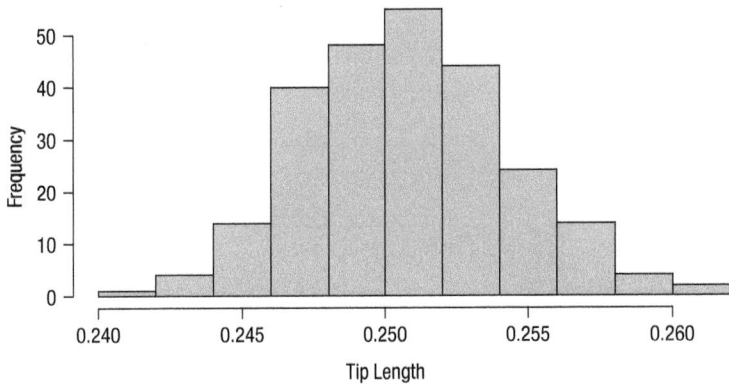

The average range for these 50 samples is $\bar{R} = 0.00847$ cm.

Using Appendix B, Table R, our initial control limits for $\bar{x}$ are therefore

$$LCL = \bar{\bar{x}} - A_2\bar{R} = 0.25 - 0.577 \times 0.00847$$
$$= 0.2452 \text{ cm}$$

$$UCL = \bar{\bar{x}} + A_2\bar{R} = 0.25 + 0.577 \times 0.00847$$
$$= 0.2548 \text{ cm.}$$

We use software to create the $\bar{x}$ control chart.

The $\bar{x}$ chart for the calibration data is shown here for completeness (although, of course, we wouldn't expect to see problems here because these are the data on which the limits are based):

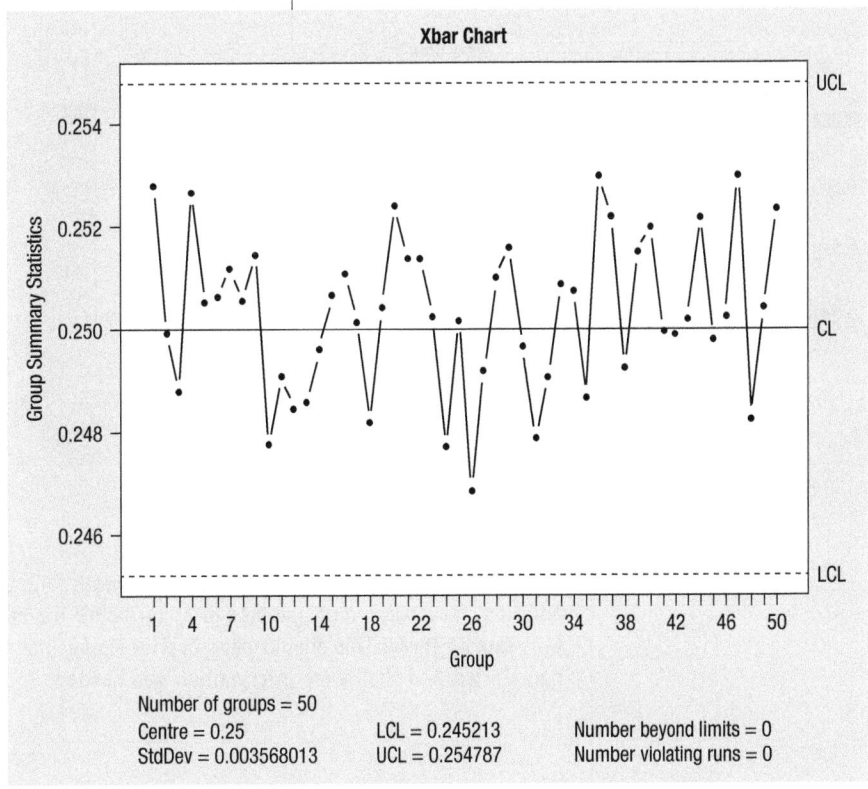

Number of groups = 50
Centre = 0.25
StdDev = 0.003568013

LCL = 0.245213
UCL = 0.254787

Number beyond limits = 0
Number violating runs = 0

(continued)

We use technology to create the R chart on the calibration data.

Similarly, we show the R chart for the calibration period. For this period, $\bar{R} = 0.00841$. To establish control limits for the R chart, we use Appendix B, Table R to obtain

$$LCL = D_3\bar{R} = 0 \times 0.00841 = 0$$

$$UCL = D_4\bar{R} = 2.114 \times 0.00841 = 0.0179$$

as the control limits.

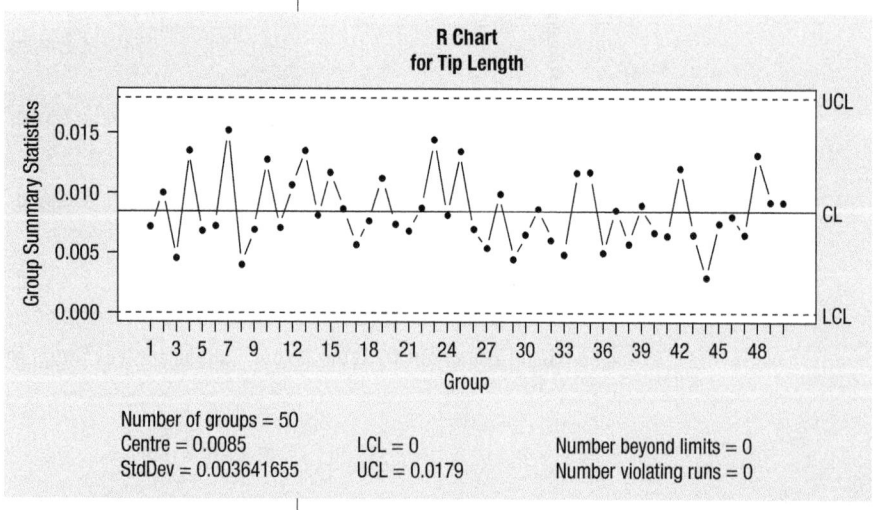

Examine the $\bar{x}$ and R charts for the recent order.

Using these limits, we now create $\bar{x}$ and R charts for 100 hips in the latter part of the recent order, starting with unit 970 (20 samples of size five). The $\bar{x}$ chart shows several problems:

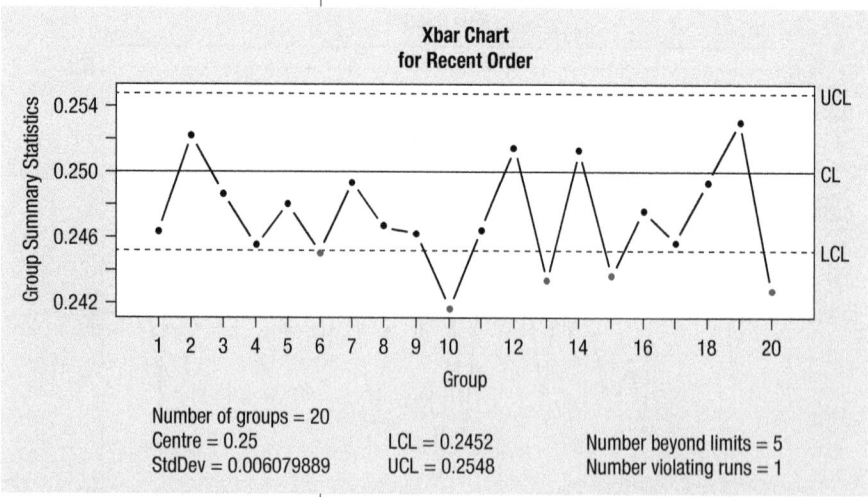

There are five samples whose average *Tip Length* falls below the LCL. In addition, there were nine samples in a row below the centre line starting with sample three. This should have been a signal that the process mean had shifted and that some intervention was needed.

The *R* chart shows similar problems:

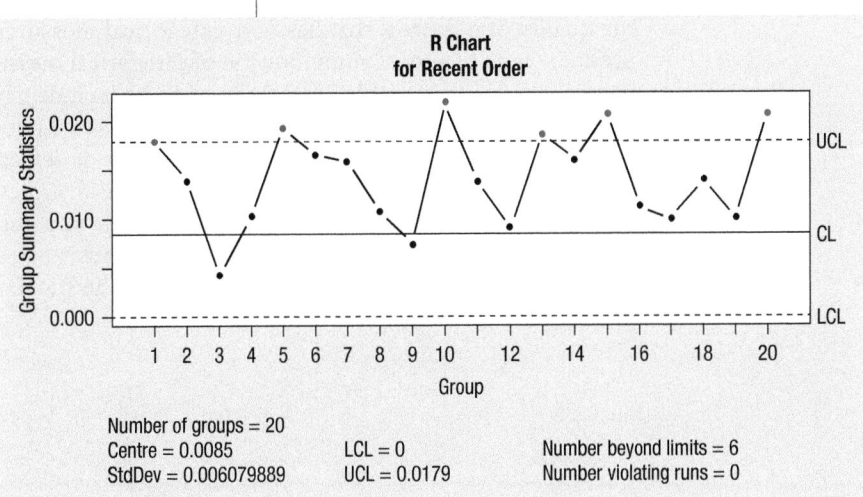

**R Chart
for Recent Order**

Number of groups = 20
Centre = 0.0085
StdDev = 0.006079889

LCL = 0
UCL = 0.0179

Number beyond limits = 6
Number violating runs = 0

There are six samples whose range is too large (outside of the UCL). Starting with the first sample, this should have been a sign that something had changed with the process.

REPORT

Conclusion State the conclusion in the context of the problem.

MEMO

Re: Patterns of Tip Length

We investigated the variation in the length of the distal tip for this unusually large customer order. It's clear that quality control for the latter part of this order was lax. Several samples from units 970 to 1070 had average tip lengths that were too short. In addition, the volatility in the process also seems to have increased. The quality team notes that the length of the distal tip must be monitored using sampling during the process and that the equipment should be checked, recalibrated, and/or changed after every violation of the limits in either the $\bar{x}$ or R charts.

Follow-Up

Following this incident, the team was assembled to try to diagnose the problem. None of the inputs to the machine that produces the part seemed to have changed. However, several possibilities in other settings of the machine were suggested as being most likely to affect the tip length. An experiment in four of these was designed and run. The analysis of the data showed that the tensile strength needed to be increased. A subsequent run of 50 tips showed that the problem had been resolved by this adjustment.

LO❸   **24.5   Control Charts for Attributes:**
***p* Charts and *c* Charts**

We've seen several examples of quantitative measurement that are used to assess quality. For manufacturing processes, these might include physical characteristics such as the thickness or diameter of a silicon wafer. In service industries, we might want to measure the length of time a customer has to wait to talk to a representative at a call centre or how long it's been since a client used one of our branches. Quantitative measurements are common, but we may want to monitor the quality of a process that has only categorical measurements such as colour or product type. The most common type of categorical measurements used in quality control are yes/no variables. Examples of these include whether a part is defective or nondefective and whether the customer has rated a phone call as satisfactory or not. In such cases, we can monitor the *proportion* of defective items in the sample. If it's determined that the proportion of defectives has increased, the special-cause variation will be investigated and the process will be adjusted to reduce variation. The control chart of proportions is called a **p chart**.

If we assume the samples are independent, the standard deviation of a sample proportion $\hat{p}$ (writing q for $(1-p)$) is

$$SD(\hat{p}) = \sqrt{\frac{pq}{n}}.$$

As we did for $\bar{x}$ charts, we start by taking k samples of size n as our calibration data and base our control limits on the results. We'll call the average proportion defective from our k samples $\bar{p} = \dfrac{\hat{p}_1 + \cdots + \hat{p}_k}{k}$.

We estimate the standard deviation and find the control limits by using $\bar{p}$:

$$LCL = \bar{p} - 3\sqrt{\frac{\overline{pq}}{n}}$$

$$UCL = \bar{p} + 3\sqrt{\frac{\overline{pq}}{n}}$$

As with R charts, if the lower limit is negative, we set it to zero.

A point outside of the 3σ rule indicates a process that may be out of control. As with $\bar{x}$ charts, there are a variety of alternative rules. Minitab, for example, uses the following four:

1. One point outside of the 3σ lines
2. Nine points in a row outside of 1σ on the same side
3. Six increasing or decreasing points in a row
4. Fourteen points in a row that alternate up and down

For example, suppose that a wafer is defective if its film thickness is either too thin ($<250\mu$m) or too thick ($>350\mu$m). If we use 25 samples of size 50 as our calibration set, we find $\bar{p} = 0.1544$, and so

$$LCL = \bar{p} - 3\sqrt{\frac{\overline{pq}}{n}} = 0.1544 - 3\sqrt{\frac{0.1544 \times 0.8456}{50}} = 0.001$$

$$UCL = \bar{p} + 3\sqrt{\frac{\overline{pq}}{n}} = 0.1544 + 3\sqrt{\frac{0.1544 \times 0.8456}{50}} = 0.308.$$

The p chart for the next 25 samples (Figure 24.11) shows no evidence of a change in the proportion.

(Some computer programs have the ability to accommodate variable sample sizes for p charts, even though the control limits will vary with the sample size. If

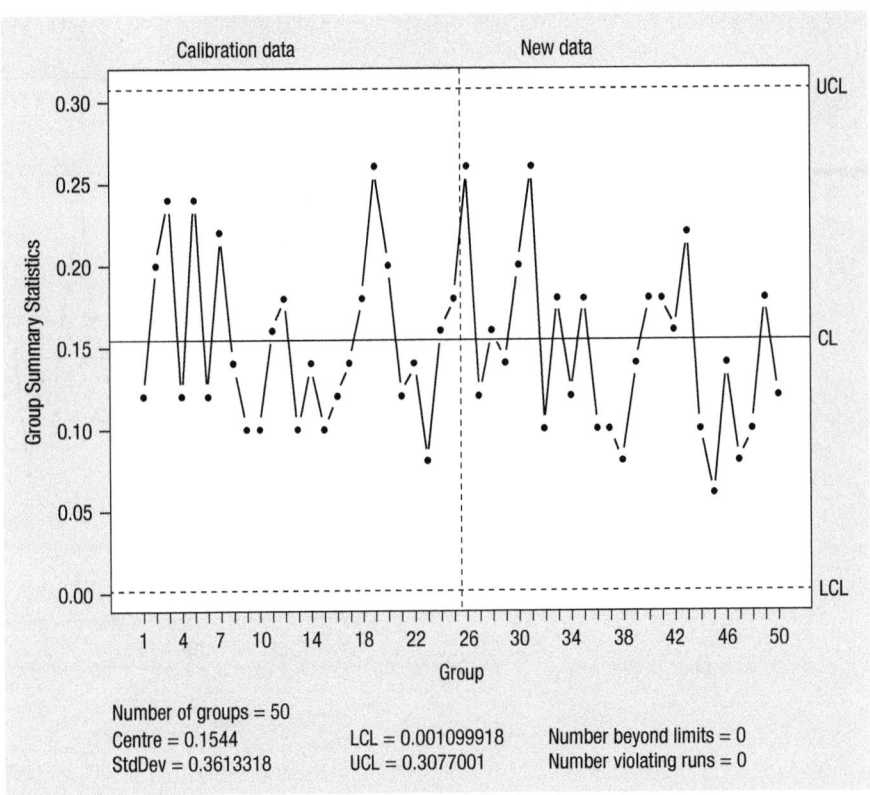

Number of groups = 50
Centre = 0.1544   LCL = 0.001099918   Number beyond limits = 0
StdDev = 0.3613318   UCL = 0.3077001   Number violating runs = 0

Figure 24.11 A p chart based on 25 samples of size 50 with an average proportion defective of 0.1544. The process appears to be in control in terms of variation because all sample proportions for the 25 samples after the initial calibration are within the control limits.

the sample sizes don't vary widely, it's also possible to use the average sample size and keep the control limits constant.)

Another variation on this type of monitoring focuses on the number of defective items in each sample rather than the proportion. This process is tracked in a **c chart**. When the number of defective items is small, the probabilities needed are based on the Poisson model rather than the binomial, which can lead to better ability to detect shifts. Because the standard deviation of a Poisson variable with mean μ is $\sqrt{\mu}$, (see Chapter 9 Section 7), we find the 3σ control limits easily.

We find the average number of defectives, $\bar{c}$, from k samples of size n and use that in the control limits centred at $\bar{c}$:

$$\text{LCL} = \bar{c} - 3\sqrt{\bar{c}}$$
$$\text{UCL} = \bar{c} + 3\sqrt{\bar{c}}$$

In our calibration set of 25 samples of size 50 (Figure 24.12), the average number of defective wafers was 7.72, which results in

$$\text{LCL} = \bar{c} - 3\sqrt{\bar{c}} = 7.72 - 3\sqrt{7.72} = -0.615$$
$$\text{UCL} = \bar{c} + 3\sqrt{\bar{c}} = 7.72 + 3\sqrt{7.72} = 16.055.$$

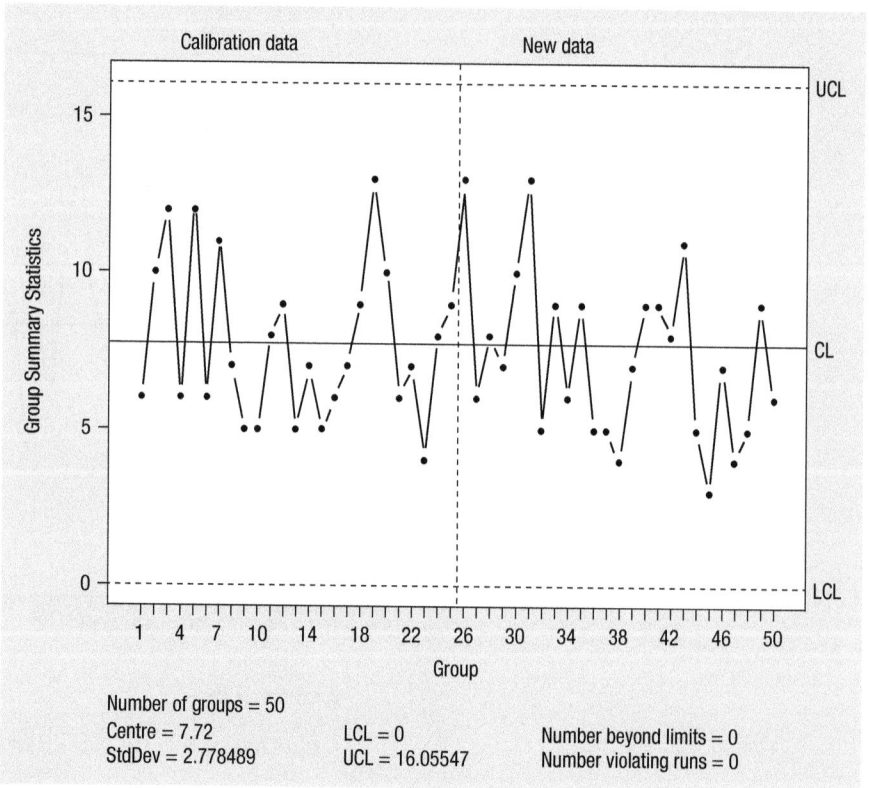

Number of groups = 50
Centre = 7.72
StdDev = 2.778489

LCL = 0
UCL = 16.05547

Number beyond limits = 0
Number violating runs = 0

Figure 24.12   A c chart based on the same 25 samples of size 50 with an average number of defectives of 7.72. The process appears to be in control in terms of variation because all sample counts of defectives for the 25 samples after the initial calibration are within the control limits. Notice that the bottom control limit has been set to zero because three standard deviations below 7.72 was negative.

FOR EXAMPLE   Control charts for attributes for fudge production

The fudge company (see For Example: "Actions for out-of-control process for fudge production") solicits customer feedback by surveys and phone interviews. One of the questions asks how satisfied customers were with the fudge on a scale from 1 to 5, where 1 = Very Dissatisfied; 2 = Dissatisfied; 3 = Neither Satisfied nor Dissatisfied; 4 = Satisfied; 5 = Very Satisfied. Here are the percentages saying "Very Satisfied" from the last 15 surveys of 100 people.

Number responding "5" out of 100: 78 78 88 77 76 79 85 75 81 88 86 74 76 81 78

QUESTION   Is the process "in control"?

ANSWER   The average number responding "5" is 80 out of 100, so $\bar{p} = 0.8$. Using a p chart with centre line $\bar{p} = 0.8$, the control lines are:

$$\text{UCL} = \bar{p} + 3\sqrt{\frac{\bar{p}\bar{q}}{n}} = 0.8 + 3\sqrt{\frac{(0.8)(0.2)}{100}} = 0.92$$

$$\text{LCL} = \bar{p} - 3\sqrt{\frac{\bar{p}\bar{q}}{n}} = 0.8 - 3\sqrt{\frac{(0.8)(0.2)}{100}} = 0.68$$

From the *p* chart, it appears that the process is in control:

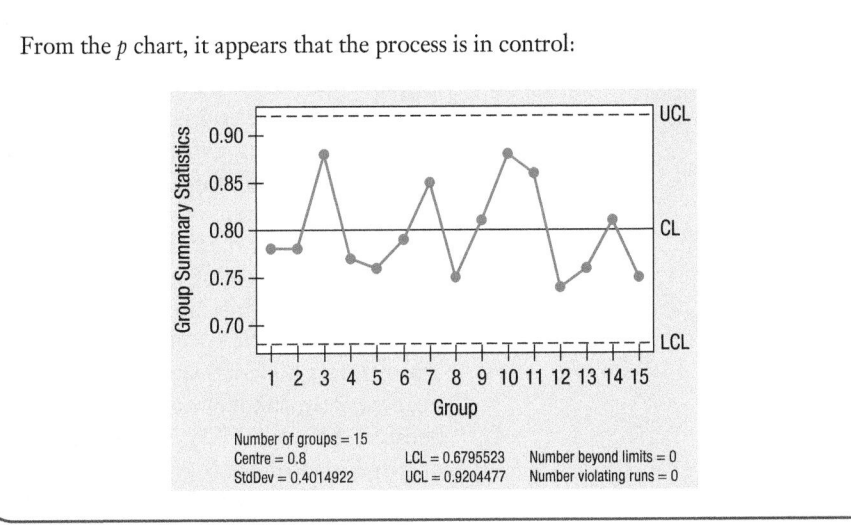

Number of groups = 15
Centre = 0.8
StdDev = 0.4014922

LCL = 0.6795523
UCL = 0.9204477

Number beyond limits = 0
Number violating runs = 0

LO❹ 24.6

Quality Control in Industry

As North American industry saw its global market share slip in the 1970s and 1980s, and worldwide customers began to rely on Japanese and German products for high quality, a renaissance of interest in quality improvement sprang up. During this time, many similar quality approaches, acronyms, and gurus competed for the attention of top management. Most of them share three ideas from statistical thinking, as outlined by the Statistics Division of the American Society for Quality (ASQ):

- All work occurs in a system of interconnected processes.
- Variation exists in all processes.
- Understanding and reducing variation are keys to success.[3]

Although the United States and Britain were the birthplace of modern quality control, the efforts of the quality movement in Japan caught the attention of North American industry in the decades after World War II. Deming is often credited for much of the success of Japan's manufacturing in the latter part of the 20th century.

Deming conveyed the idea that managers need to take responsibility for quality control. He taught the Shewhart cycle and explained the importance of managers "acting" on the analytical information provided by the quality control tools. Deming also explained the importance of viewing the supplier as a partner and of building cooperative relationships so that the supplier, producer, and customer all form a network. Deming's approach can be summarized as **total quality management (TQM)**, although the term wasn't used until 1974 by one of the Deming Prize recipients. TQM extends the theory of quality control in that it encompasses the total organization, uses quality control methods, and focuses the leadership provided by management to ensure long-term success by emphasizing customer satisfaction. It's a broad approach that seeks to improve all areas of the business to better satisfy the customer. TQM plays a central role in the *Criteria for Performance Excellence* and the Baldrige National Quality Program (BNQP), which provides benchmarks for quality for organizations today.

Six Sigma is another business improvement approach that focuses more on the identification and elimination of defects or special-cause variation in business

W. Edwards Deming was decorated by the emperor of Japan with the Second Order Medal of the Sacred Treasure in 1960 for his decade of contributions to Japanese production, and the Japanese created the annual Deming Prize in his honour for recognition of achievements in producing a quality product. Dr. Deming was a member of the international Statistical Institute and was elected to the National Academy of Engineering.

---

[3] *Glossary of Statistical Terms.* (1996). Milwaukee: Quality Press.

processes. Six Sigma was developed at Motorola during the 1980s but was picked up, expanded, and spread to other industries by General Electric and Allied Signal. The core idea of Six Sigma is to reduce variation in the process to the point that inspection is no longer necessary. If the standard deviation can be made small enough so that the specification limits defining what it means for a part to be out of control are 4.5 standard deviations from the mean, then the probability of an out-of-control observation is only about 6 in 1,000,000. In real-life processes, the mean of the process can shift somewhat as well. To account for that, the developers of Six Sigma added an allowance of a 1.5 standard deviation (sigma) shift. In this case, to achieve the 6 in 1,000,000 probability, the standard deviation has to be so small that six standard deviations are still within the control limit. This corresponds to a C_{pk} value of 2.0. At this point, it's no longer necessary (in theory) to monitor the process with control charts for inspection because the probability of being out of control is so small. Although this was the original idea of Six Sigma, it has become a much broader approach to quality, as practised by large firms such as the General Electric Company. There is a hierarchy of certified experts (known as Black Belts) who, after being trained in the Six Sigma approach, act as internal quality consultants on a wide variety of quality issues.

ETHICS IN ACTION

Trax, one of the leading manufacturers of bicycles, is interested in expanding its line to include high-end road bikes. One of the features of high-end bikes, and one that avid cyclists pay top dollar for, is the use of superlight carbon fibre frames. Trax is currently in the process of selecting a supplier for these frames. Potential suppliers were asked to provide reports that included statistical process control (SPC) and capability data on their carbon fibre frame production processes.

Trax had specified the weight for these frames to be between 2 and 3 pounds with a target mean of ± 2.5 pounds. John Dickinson, vice president of Operations, was in charge of summarizing the information contained in these reports to present at an upcoming senior management meeting at which a final decision on a supplier would be made. As he reviewed the reports, he noticed that one supplier, DBS, could provide the frames at a much lower cost than its competitors. Eager to save the company money, he carefully considered this supplier's SPC and process capability data. John was pleased with its x and R charts for weight, which indicated the process was stable (in statistical control). He was also pleased to be able to verify from these charts that DBS's reported process standard deviation was only 0.1 pounds and that the C_p index of 1.67 indicated that it would be able to easily meet Trax's weight requirement. While he did notice that the process mean was a bit off target

(at 2.8 rather than 2.5 pounds), he decided that the significant cost savings that Trax would realize by choosing this supplier outweighed any potential negative consequences of a shifted process mean. John decided to present only cost data and the C_p index for the suppliers under consideration, and to conclude his presentation at the senior management meeting with a recommendation that Trax choose DBS as its supplier of carbon frames. He believed that the team would be quite impressed with his cost-saving recommendation.

Ethical Issue *John is misrepresenting the process capability of DBS. Although the C_p index is greater than one, because the process isn't centred on target John should be reporting the C_{pk} index, which in this case would be 0.67. DBS's process won't be able to meet the upper specification limit, and some of the carbon fibre frames it supplies to Trax will be over 3 pounds (related to Item C, ASA Ethical Guidelines; see Appendix C, the American Statistical Association's Ethical Guidelines for Statistical Practice, also available online at www.amstat.org/about/ethicalguidelines.cfm).*

Ethical Solution *John should report all relevant SPC and process capability data, most importantly the C_{pk} index for any process that isn't centred on target. He shouldn't let his bias toward wanting to save money and impress his colleagues affect his judgment. Carbon fibre frames above the weight limit will adversely affect Trax's bottom line.*

WHAT HAVE WE LEARNED?

Learning Objectives

In this chapter we've learned how to use control charts to examine variation over time in a process. We've focused on six different types of control charts that can be used to identify special-cause and common-cause variation.

❶ • We've learned how to create a run chart for individual measurements.

❷ • We've learned how to create $\bar{x}$, R, and S charts for means and ranges of continuous random variables.

❸ • We've learned how to create a p chart for proportions of either defective or nondefective items.

   • We've learned how to create a c chart for the number of defectives or nondefectives in repeated samples when the samples are the same size.

❹ We've learned the roles that both Shewhart and Deming played in the implementation of control charts and total quality management, starting in Japanese manufacturing and now widely deployed internationally in both manufacturing and service industries.

❺ We've learned how to use fishbone diagrams to organize possible actions to put a process back into control.

Terms

Average run length (ARL)	The average time between false alarms; calculated by taking the reciprocal of the false alarm probability.
c chart	A control chart that displays the counts, or number, of occurrences of defectives (or, if rare, nondefectives) in samples taken from a process over time.
C_p	A process capability index that measures the ratio of the specification limit range to six times the standard deviation of the process without taking into consideration possible drift of the process: $$C_p = \frac{\text{USL} - \text{LSL}}{6\sigma}$$
$\hat{C}_{pk}$	A process capability index that measures what the process is capable of producing, including the possible drift of the process, estimated by: $$\hat{C}_{pk} = \min\left[\frac{\text{USL} - \hat{\mu}}{3\hat{\sigma}}, \frac{\hat{\mu} - \text{LSL}}{3\hat{\sigma}}\right]$$
Common-cause variation	Variation characterized by apparent random fluctuations around an average level within specified limits called control limits.
Control chart	A graph that displays variation by plotting individual measurements or sample statistics taken from a process over time. Sometimes referred to as a *Shewhart chart*.
Control limits	Horizontal lines drawn on a control chart. Various rules are used to determine when a process is out of control depending on the specific control chart.
False alarm	A Type I error indicating that the process is out of control, when in actuality it was due only to common-cause variation.
Level shift	An abrupt shift of a process, caused perhaps by a breakdown of a machine or the introduction of an impurity.
Lower control limit (LCL)	A horizontal line drawn on a control chart three standard deviations below the mean.
Operating-characteristic (OC) curve	A chart that shows the probability of failing to see a process shift (a Type II error) plotted against the size of the shift (in standard deviation units).
Out of control	The presence of special-cause variation in a process.

Out-of-control action plan (OCAP)	A set of instructions to follow for well-established processes indicating what action to take following an out-of-control signal.
p chart	A control chart that displays the proportion of defectives (or nondefectives) in samples taken from a process over time.
Process capability study	A study that compares the variability of the process to the specification limits imposed on the process by external concerns. Two of the most common process capability indices are C_p and C_{pk}.
R chart	A control chart that plots the ranges of samples taken from a process over time.
Run chart	A control chart that displays individual measurements from a process taken over time.
S chart	A control chart that plots the standard deviations of samples taken from a process over time.
Shewhart chart	Another name for a control chart, acknowledging its inventor, Walter Shewhart.
Six Sigma	A quality control philosophy based on reducing variation to the point where inspection sampling is no longer necessary. The philosophy's name comes from the fact that if specification limits (plus possible drift) are six standard deviations from the control centre line, the chances of an out-of-control part are negligible.
Special-cause variation	Observed nonrandom patterns in the variation of a process over time (i.e., trends) or observed values that fall outside of the control limits.
Specification limits	Limits above (and/or below) which a measurement should not lie, imposed by external considerations.
Statistical process control (SPC)	The examination of variation in a process over time to identify sources of variation.
Total quality management (TQM)	Extension of the theory of quality control to include the total organization and the leadership of management.
Trend	The gradual shift of a process mean.
Upper control limit (UCL)	A horizontal line drawn on a control chart three standard deviations above the mean.
x̄ chart	A control chart that displays the averages of samples taken from a process over time; also written as x-bar or x bar chart.

MINI case studies

Trinus of Barrie, Ontario

Trinus Pipes and Tubes, a small company in Barrie, Ontario, produces plastic pipes certified to meet the Canadian Standards Association C448 specification for use in geothermal systems. Trinus provides 50-year warranties on its products against leakage, so the thickness of the pipe wall needs to be controlled carefully.

Suppose you work for a competing company and take four randomly selected samples of one-inch diameter pipes coming off the production line every hour for 10 hours. You measure the thickness of the pipe walls in thousandths of an inch and get the results in the data file **ch24_MCSP_Pipe_Walls**. Past records indicate that the thickness follows a Normal distribution.

Is the process in control? State your reasons clearly. Suppose the thickness of the pipe walls should be 0.100 plus/minus 0.005 inch. Are you meeting that requirement? State your assumptions clearly.

Laptop Touchpad Quality

Consumers always seem to want thinner and lighter electronic products, and computer laptops are no exception. One of the challenges of producing extremely thin and light laptops is the manufacturing of the touch pads. In particular, touch pads are difficult to align. A common complaint is that one corner is higher or lower than another, resulting in what's known as "tilting." Tilting makes navigation difficult, so touch pad manufacturers have strict limits on the amount of tilting they'll allow in a pad.

A company producing touch pads will want to ensure that the pads are flat to within a certain acceptable tolerance. One possible measure is the total deviation from flatness as measured by the maximum difference in height between any two corners (in millimetres). In the data file **ch24_MCSP_Touchpad_calibration** you'll find this flatness measure for 250 touch screens produced during a period that was judged to be in control.

Using the mean and standard deviation from this control period, examine the next 150 samples of five pads (in the data file **ch24_MCSP_Touchpad_production**). Using various quality control rules and appropriate graphs, do you think the process is still in control? Explain.

Instead of samples of size five, suppose they'd used a run chart on the individual pads. Would your answer change? Explain.

Suppose the engineers establish 14 mm as the maximum flatness deviation they'll tolerate and want to use that as an upper specification limit. Does your answer change now? Explain.

A qualitative measure is clarity of the pad. Batches of 100 pads are produced and defects are counted, where "defect" is defined as a pad that doesn't pass the clarity test. From a period that was deemed to be in control, the mean number of defects per 10 was 0.5. Using this mean, determine whether the process stayed in control for the next 50 batches (**ch24_MCSP_Touchpad_clarity_production**).

Ralf Kleemann/Shutterstock

MyStatLab Students! Save time, improve your grades with MyStatLab. Questions marked in ▦ can be found on MyStatLab. You can practise them as often as you want, and most feature step-by-step guided solutions to help you find the right answer. You'll find a personalized study plan available to you too!

Technology Help: Quality Control Charts

EXCEL

Excel does not offer quality control charts. A number of third-party add-ins and templates are available.

XLSTAT

To implement control charts for desired bounds:

- From the XLStat tab, choose the **XLStat-SPC** toolbar.

- Select either **Subgroup charts** (for x-bar and r charts) or **Attribute charts** (for p and c charts).

- Select the desired chart from the **Mode** tab in the dialogue box.

- Under the General tab, type the data range into the **Data** field.

If your data have sampled values in rows for each sample, choose the **Data Format Columns**.

- In the **Options** tab, you can type in your UCL and LCL directly, but if you leave these fields blank, XLStat will compute these for you.

EXERCISES

SECTION 24.1

1. A producer of beverage containers wants to ensure that a liquid at 90°C will lose no more than 4°C after 30 minutes. Containers are selected at random and subjected to testing. Historical data show the standard deviation to be 0.2°C. The quality control team has set 3.5 and 4.5°C as the specification limits. Here are the data from the last 12 containers tested:

Container #	Temperature Loss (°C)	Container #	Temperature Loss (°C)
1	3.89	7	4.22
2	3.71	8	4.02
3	4.14	9	4.48
4	4.12	10	3.93
5	3.74	11	3.87
6	3.99	12	3.94

a) Make a control chart of these data using the specification limits given.
b) Does the process seem to be in control?
c) What is the value of C_p for the process?
d) Given this value of C_p, what recommendations might you make to the quality control team? **LO❶, ❹**

2. A computer screen manufacturing process must produce screens of uniform size. In particular, for a new tablet, the screen should be 10.1 inches long. The engineers have set 10.16 and 10.04 as the upper and lower specifications on screen length. If the actual process standard deviation is 0.01 inches,

a) What is the value of C_p for the process?
b) What might you recommend to the engineers, given this value of C_p? **LO❶, ❹**

SECTION 24.2

3. For the data in Exercise 1, instead of the specification limits,

a) Use the historical standard deviation to set up 1, 2, and 3σ limits and draw the control chart.
b) Are any points outside the 3σ limits on either side?
c) Are two of three consecutive points outside of 2σ on either side?
d) Are four out of five consecutive points outside of lσ on either side?
e) Are there eight points in a row on the same side of the mean?
f) Are any six points in a row increasing (or decreasing)?
g) Are any 14 points in a row alternately increasing and decreasing?
h) Based on your answers to (b) to (g), what do you conclude? **LO❶**

4. For the data in Exercise 1, suppose the historical standard deviation had been 0.1°C instead of 0.2°C. How would that change your answers to the questions in Exercise 3? **LO❶**

SECTION 24.3

5. A process to make dental floss produces spools with a desired mean length of 91.4 m. The historical standard deviation is 1 cm (0.01 m). If samples of size five are taken and measured,

a) What is the standard deviation of the sample mean?
b) How long (or short) would a sample mean have to be to fall outside the 3σ limit?
c) How would the answers to (a) and (b) change if the sample were of size 10? **LO❷**

6. As in Exercise 5, a process to make dental floss produces spools with a desired mean length of 91.4 m. The historical standard deviation is 1 cm (0.01 m). If samples of size five are taken and measured,

a) What is the centre line for the R chart?
b) What is the standard deviation of the sample range?
c) How large (or small) would the sample range have to be to fall outside the 3σ limit? **LO ❷**

SECTION 24.5

7. One of the ways in which the dental floss discussed in Exercise 5 can fail is if it snaps when pulled with a certain tension. Historically, only 2% of the tested floss snaps. Suppose boxes of size 50 are selected at random to be tested.

a) What is the standard deviation for the sample proportion from a box of 50?
b) What are the upper and lower 3σ control limits?
c) How many packages in a box of 50 would have to fail for a process to be declared out of control using the 3σ control limits? **LO ❸**

8. Rather than use the proportion of packages that contain defective floss, another quality control inspector simply counts the number of packages. If historically only 1 package out of 50 is defective,

a) What is the standard deviation of the number of defective packages?
b) What are the upper and lower 3σ control limits on the number of defectives?
c) How does the upper limit compare with the upper limit in Exercise 7(b)? **LO ❸**

CHAPTER EXERCISES

9. **Super Glue.** Cyanoacrylates, the generic name for several compounds with strong adhesive properties, were invented during World War II during experiments to make a special extra-clear plastic suitable for gun sights. They didn't work for gun sights, however, because they stuck to everything. They were first commercialized by the Eastman Kodak company in the 1950s and are now sold under the names Super Glue and Krazy Glue. They're often sold in small quantities, typically 10 gram tubes. The manufacturers want to ensure that the same quantity of glue goes into each tube, so they monitored the process from the past three weeks (when there were no production problems) and calculated the mean and standard deviation weight from 50 tubes. If they use those quantities to calculate future limits for quality control monitoring, are they constructing control or specification limits? Explain. **LO ❹**

10. **MLB.** Major League Baseball (MLB) requires that a ball used in a Major League game weigh between 5 and 5.25 ounces (www.MLB.com). Rawlings is the official supplier of baseballs for MLB. In its production process, does it treat 5 and 5.25 ounces as control or specification limits? Explain. **LO ❹**

11. **Pole vault.** Pole vault technology has evolved considerably since the times of the ancient Greeks, and even more recently, as new materials have found their way into pole manufacturing. There are currently no regulations on the composition of poles, although for safety reasons, there are restrictions on the amount of bend depending on the vaulter's weight. On the other hand, safety considerations have led the U.S. National High School Federation (NHSF) to require that high school vault landing pads be no less than 6.0 metres wide and 6.15 metres long. Should the manufacturers of landing pads treat these as specification or control limits? Explain. **LO ❹**

12. **Milk production.** Whether milk is pasteurized or raw, both the European Economic Council (EEC) and the U.S. Food and Drug Administration (USFDA) require that milk sold to consumers contain no more than 10 coliform bacteria per millilitre of milk (www.cdfa.ca.gov). Should dairies take this as a control or specification limit when applying quality control to milk production? Explain. **LO ❹**

13. **Observatories.** The two Gemini observatories (www.gemini.edu) were built and are operated by a partnership of seven countries, including Canada, the United States, the United Kingdom, Chile, Australia, Brazil, and Argentina. Astronomers in each of these countries are able to apply for time on the telescopes for scientific research. Gemini sets strict technical requirements on many aspects of the filters used on the telescope, including a strict requirement that they be extremely flat—their total deviation from absolute flatness must be no more than 30 nanometres as measured by the root mean square deviation. How should filter manufacturers view this requirement—as a control or specification limit? Explain. **LO ❹**

14. **DVD production.** Plastic covers for DVDs must be manufactured with enough precision so that a DVD can properly fit into the cover. Specifically, the diameter of the central plastic piece over which the DVD is placed must not vary more than a certain amount. A manufacturer has been producing DVD covers for several months and has had no complaints from its customers. It decides to use the past two months of data to estimate the mean and standard deviation of the process. Are the limits for quality monitoring based on these quantities control or specification limits? Explain. **LO ❹**

15. **Roulette.** An observer at the roulette wheel notices that there seems to be no pattern to the numbers that come up during an entire evening. Is this an example of special- or common-cause variation? Explain. **LO ❺**

16. Pennsylvania lottery. In 1980, millions of viewers watched as the number 666 was drawn for the Pick 3 Pennsylvania lottery. Although as likely as any other number, lottery authorities and local bookmakers became suspicious when they noticed that a large number of tickets were purchased for the eight numbers 444, 446, 464, 466, 644, 646, 664, and 666. Soon, a handful of players came forward to claim approximately $1.8 million of the then-record $3.5 million payout. Officials eventually discovered that 8 of the 10 balls were weighted, giving them almost no chance to be selected in the drawing. Is this an example of special- or common-cause variation? Explain. **LO ❺**

17. Out-of-control rules, part 1. Most control charts use three sigmas (standard deviations) to set the upper and lower control limits. For a run chart, what is the probability that an observation would fall beyond 3σ from the mean based on random chance variation alone? What assumptions do you have to make to answer this? **LO ❹**

18. Out-of-control rules, part 2. Instead of one observation outside of 3σ from the mean as in Exercise 17, suppose a quality control engineer decides to use only the run chart rule that the system is out of control if eight observations in a row lie on the same side of the mean. What is the probability that this would happen based on random chance variation alone? What assumptions do you have to make to answer this? **LO ❹**

Ⓣ 19. Basketballs. A company that makes basketballs has the motto "Our basketballs are ready to play." Therefore, it's important to the company that the basketballs be inflated with the proper amount of air when shipped. Most basketballs are inflated to seven to nine pounds per square inch. From a set of calibration data, the following statistics were measured:

$$\bar{x} = 8.05$$

$$\bar{R} = 0.65$$

Recently the company selected a random basketball from its production line at four different time periods over its normal production day. The results were recorded and listed in the table in the next column.

a) Create an $\bar{x}$ chart based on the calibration data statistics for these 30 samples.
b) Create an R chart based on the calibration data statistics for these 30 samples.
c) Assuming that the process was in control during the calibration period, is the company's process for filling its basketballs with the proper amount of air in control? **LO ❷**

	8:00–10:00 A.M.	10:00 A.M.	Noon–2:00 P.M.	2:00–4:00 P.M.
Day 1	8.05	8.49	7.59	7.90
Day 2	8.16	7.62	7.71	7.90
Day 3	8.30	8.07	8.14	8.12
Day 4	7.55	8.82	8.12	8.18
Day 5	8.18	7.76	7.70	7.65
Day 6	7.88	7.90	7.99	7.62
Day 7	8.01	8.02	7.32	8.10
Day 8	8.32	7.89	8.62	7.89
Day 9	7.94	7.75	7.58	7.74
Day 10	7.38	7.47	7.93	7.73
Day 11	7.44	7.84	7.87	8.33
Day 12	8.30	8.04	7.94	8.09
Day 13	8.46	8.20	7.93	7.89
Day 14	8.10	8.38	8.08	7.80
Day 15	7.70	7.68	8.25	8.40
Day 16	8.32	7.98	7.65	8.32
Day 17	8.13	7.96	8.21	8.51
Day 18	7.69	8.07	7.55	8.26
Day 19	7.86	8.55	8.05	7.63
Day 20	7.97	8.08	7.89	7.97
Day 21	8.73	7.84	7.94	8.07
Day 22	8.14	7.56	7.97	7.86
Day 23	7.64	7.89	7.47	7.66
Day 24	8.33	7.87	7.89	7.62
Day 25	8.00	7.61	7.65	7.39
Day 26	7.31	8.66	7.71	7.29
Day 27	7.58	7.95	8.13	8.52
Day 28	7.91	8.53	7.86	7.96
Day 29	8.34	8.10	8.45	8.16
Day 30	8.04	8.25	7.13	8.12

Ⓣ 20. Rulers. A company that traditionally made rulers and yardsticks is setting up a manufacturing process to make metresticks. Obviously, accuracy is important for its new product. The company runs a 24-hour production process. Using a calibration set of data, it found:

$$\bar{x} = 1.000$$

$$\bar{R} = 0.0016$$

It took a sample of three metresticks each hour and recorded the results in the following table:

	Sample 1	Sample 2	Sample 3
Hour 1	0.9983	1.0007	1.0010
Hour 2	1.0005	1.0011	1.0014
Hour 3	1.0002	0.9995	0.9997
Hour 4	1.0004	1.0016	1.0007
Hour 5	1.0014	0.9994	1.0008
Hour 6	0.9990	0.9996	0.9984
Hour 7	1.0014	1.0010	1.0017
Hour 8	1.0017	1.0002	1.0002
Hour 9	1.0003	1.0008	0.9993
Hour 10	0.9998	1.0002	0.9992
Hour 11	0.9985	1.0002	1.0006
Hour 12	1.0003	1.0012	0.9994
Hour 13	0.9998	1.0013	0.9995
Hour 14	1.0000	0.9994	0.9992
Hour 15	1.0005	0.9999	1.0016
Hour 16	1.0019	1.0018	1.0010
Hour 17	0.9993	0.9994	0.9993
Hour 18	1.0020	1.0000	0.9978
Hour 19	1.0007	1.0005	0.9991
Hour 20	1.0009	1.0005	0.9999
Hour 21	1.0002	0.9998	1.0021
Hour 22	1.0019	0.9986	0.9996
Hour 23	1.0011	1.0003	0.9993
Hour 24	0.9993	1.0010	1.0001

a) Create an $\bar{x}$ chart based on the calibration data statistics for these 24 hourly samples.

b) Create an R chart based on the calibration data statistics for these 24 hourly samples.

c) Assuming that the process was in control during the calibration period, is the company's process for making accurate metresticks out of control? **LO ❷**

🌐 **21.** Graphite production, part 1. A graphite manufacturer makes long rolls of flexible graphite to be used to seal components in combustion engines. The specifications state that the mean strength should be 21.2 grams per square metre with a standard deviation of 0.29. Further specifications state that no roll should have a strength less than 20.2 or more than 22.2 grams per square metre. If there's a defect in terms of the strength of the graphite rolls, the seal will not hold. After the roll is created, a beta scanner takes readings of the basis weight in grams per square metre. The data are separated into

three lanes with 20 scans in each lane. A sample consists of one roll from each lane. The results from 20 samples are shown below.

a) Using the given mean and standard deviation, create an $\bar{x}$ chart for these samples.

b) Using the given mean and standard deviation, create an R chart for these samples.

c) Is the company's process for making flexible graphite sheets out of control?

d) Do all the rolls meet the specification limits? **LO ❷**

Sample	Lane 1	Lane 2	Lane 3
1	20.65	21.01	20.76
2	21.27	21.53	21.53
3	21.69	21.53	21.14
4	21.06	20.38	20.62
5	21.18	21.29	20.95
6	21.14	21.01	21.37
7	20.89	20.63	21.24
8	21.73	21.39	20.87
9	21.55	21.34	21.17
10	21.72	21.97	21.84
11	21.26	20.77	21.24
12	21.05	20.70	20.87
13	22.23	22.09	21.62
14	21.27	21.71	21.89
15	21.60	21.03	20.68
16	21.37	21.29	21.13
17	21.19	21.80	21.36
18	21.56	21.64	21.67
19	21.12	20.56	20.57
20	20.88	20.57	20.37

🌐 **22.** Graphite production, part 2. The same graphite manufacturer from Exercise 21 uses an alternative process to make rolls. For this process the data are separated into 10 lanes—a sample consists of one roll from each lane. The results of 25 samples are shown in the table on the next page.

a) Using the same mean and standard deviation as given in Exercise 21, create an $\bar{x}$ chart for these samples.

b) Using the same mean and standard deviation as in Exercise 21, create an R chart for these samples.

c) Is the company's process for making flexible graphite sheets in control?

d) Are all the rolls within the specification limits? **LO ❷**

Sample	Lane 1	Lane 2	Lane 3	Lane 4	Lane 5	Lane 6	Lane 7	Lane 8	Lane 9	Lane 10
1	21.56	21.59	21.26	21.16	21.01	21.10	21.22	20.95	20.78	20.66
2	21.42	21.54	21.43	21.44	20.99	21.10	20.78	21.17	21.21	21.10
3	21.48	21.23	21.19	21.34	21.63	21.47	21.18	21.05	21.21	21.22
4	21.14	21.26	21.57	21.34	21.36	21.37	21.42	21.48	21.14	21.02
5	21.53	21.26	21.43	21.26	20.95	20.86	20.99	20.90	20.69	20.80
6	21.40	21.26	21.19	21.38	21.57	21.30	20.97	20.72	20.78	20.70
7	21.84	21.51	21.71	21.34	21.38	21.32	21.32	21.05	20.57	20.27
8	21.83	21.83	21.56	21.17	20.74	20.83	21.00	21.35	21.54	21.41
9	21.60	21.57	21.44	20.99	20.60	20.83	20.85	20.90	21.14	21.36
10	21.84	21.93	21.99	21.97	21.57	21.56	21.17	20.89	21.20	21.28
11	21.96	21.50	21.48	21.37	21.57	21.68	21.82	21.65	21.20	21.19
12	21.27	21.53	21.31	21.22	21.33	21.31	21.46	21.68	21.69	21.52
13	22.03	21.90	22.02	21.46	21.34	21.35	21.44	21.84	21.55	21.63
14	21.30	21.36	21.28	21.29	21.00	20.82	20.55	20.48	20.46	20.68
15	21.65	21.18	20.77	20.98	20.92	20.99	21.27	21.56	21.72	21.67
16	21.46	21.52	21.47	21.45	21.31	21.76	21.92	21.34	21.11	21.19
17	21.72	21.69	21.77	21.44	21.13	21.12	20.91	20.60	20.69	21.07
18	21.67	22.02	21.78	21.34	21.00	20.80	20.30	20.54	20.59	21.16
19	21.44	21.28	21.15	20.97	20.85	21.17	21.87	21.67	21.59	21.20
20	21.38	21.32	20.91	21.10	21.17	21.58	21.53	21.54	21.12	20.69
21	21.23	21.30	21.57	21.42	21.52	21.42	20.90	20.85	20.60	20.71
22	21.65	21.33	21.44	21.27	21.06	20.80	20.82	20.84	20.98	21.22
23	21.59	21.58	21.13	21.34	21.57	21.47	21.55	21.83	21.56	21.02
24	20.92	20.74	20.30	20.07	20.48	20.39	20.81	20.90	21.18	21.18
25	21.02	21.03	21.00	21.04	21.15	21.10	21.24	21.09	21.25	20.86

① 23. **Computer chip manufacturing.** MediaChip manufactures computer chips. The process uses sophisticated lasers to imprint several hundred chips on a single silicon "wafer." While the process is completely automated and set in a clean room environment, a batch of chips can contain imperfections that render the chips useless. This results in significant cost overruns. MediaChip would like to use a control chart to monitor its manufacturing process. Presently, the production level is set to 250 wafers per day. The average number of defects that can be tolerated is 17. The number of defective wafers was tracked and recorded in the following table:

a) Create a *c* chart.
b) Is MediaChip's manufacturing process in control? **LO ❸**

Day	1	2	3	4	5	6	7	8	9	10	11	12	13	14	15	16	17	18	19	20
Defects	7	13	22	5	20	13	22	28	17	18	30	27	15	15	14	24	6	25	25	8

① 24. **Faulty pixels.** In LCD screens, every attempt is made to make sure that all pixels illuminate when they receive a signal, but it's impossible to ensure that every pixel in a large screen will actually work. A screen is determined to be defective if more than two pixels fail to light. Every week 500 screens are randomly selected and a quality control team member counts the number of defective screens. Out of 500 screens, management would like an average of no more than five defective screens. The results for the past 50 weeks are shown in the following table:

a) Create a *c* chart.
b) Is the number of defective screens out of control? Comment. **LO ❸**

Week	Defective Screens	Week	Defective Screens	Week	Defective Screens
1	5	18	4	35	6
2	6	19	4	36	6
3	4	20	4	37	7
4	5	21	3	38	3
5	1	22	3	39	8
6	7	23	5	40	5
7	1	24	3	41	7
8	4	25	7	42	5
9	3	26	10	43	5
10	4	27	5	44	5
11	4	28	11	45	5
12	6	29	2	46	8
13	4	30	3	47	3
14	3	31	2	48	6
15	4	32	5	49	4
16	1	33	11	50	4
17	4	34	9		

T 25. Patient complaints, part 1. The following data were collected on the number of patient complaints from a small medical service facility over a two-week period. Over the past year, the average number of complaints was 4.57. The management team would like to use that as a baseline for monitoring.

Based on the past year,

a) What is the centre line?
b) Calculate the upper control limit.
c) Calculate the lower control limit.
d) Create a *c* chart for this two-week period.
e) Is this process out of control? **LO ❸**

Day	1	2	3	4	5	6	7	8	9	10	11	12	13	14
Complaints	3	6	1	2	12	5	7	0	4	6	3	5	2	8

T 26. Patient complaints, part 2. The medical facility in Exercise 25 also keeps track of the number of errors found when transcribing information from patient forms. Last year the average number of errors was 1.26 per day, which the facility found acceptable. Here are the past two weeks' data:

Day	1	2	3	4	5	6	7	8	9	10	11	12	13	14
Errors	1	2	1	2	1	2	5	3	3	2	0	3	5	5

Based on last year, using a *c* chart:

a) What is the centre line?
b) Calculate the upper control limit.

c) Calculate the lower control limit.
d) Create the *c* chart for this two-week period.
e) Is this process out of control?

Ⓣ **27.** **Baseball circumferences.** Baseballs used in the Major League in the United States must adhere to strict standards. One such standard is that the circumference must be between 9 and 9.25 inches. One could look at this standard as a target circumference of 9.125 inches with a tolerance of +/−0.125 inches. The data in the table below were taken from a random sample of 50 baseballs from a large production batch. The actual circumference and deviation from the target circumference are listed.

Using the specification limits as the control limits,

a) Create a run chart for the baseballs' circumferences.
b) Is the process for making baseballs, in terms of their circumference, in control?
c) How many baseballs produced were out of spec?
d) When should the quality team have investigated the production process? **LO ❶**

Sample	Circumference	Deviation	Sample	Circumference	Deviation
1	8.998	−0.127	26	9.121	−0.004
2	9.181	0.056	27	9.111	−0.014
3	9.147	0.022	28	9.130	0.005
4	9.182	0.057	29	9.116	−0.009
5	9.087	−0.038	30	9.035	−0.090
6	9.154	0.029	31	9.188	0.063
7	9.108	−0.017	32	9.092	−0.033
8	9.109	−0.016	33	9.078	−0.047
9	9.141	0.016	34	9.101	−0.024
10	9.093	−0.032	35	9.113	−0.012
11	9.142	0.017	36	9.087	−0.038
12	9.140	0.015	37	9.054	−0.071
13	9.125	0.000	38	9.177	0.052
14	9.175	0.050	39	9.058	−0.067
15	8.985	−0.140	40	9.179	0.054
16	9.119	−0.006	41	9.147	0.022
17	9.140	0.015	42	9.123	−0.002
18	9.109	−0.016	43	9.097	−0.028
19	9.190	0.065	44	9.108	−0.017
20	9.087	−0.038	45	9.214	0.089
21	9.046	−0.079	46	9.140	0.015
22	9.108	−0.017	47	9.151	0.026
23	9.188	0.063	48	9.041	−0.084
24	9.125	0.000	49	9.061	−0.064
25	9.114	−0.011	50	9.162	0.037

Ⓣ **28.** **Baseball weights** Baseballs used in the Major League in the United States must adhere to strict standards. One such standard is that the weight must be between 5 and 5.25 ounces. One could look at this standard as a target weight of 5.125 ounces with a tolerance of +/−0.125 ounces. The data in the table on the next page were taken from a random sample of 50 baseballs from a large production batch. The actual weight and deviation from the target weight are listed.

Sample	Weight (oz.)	Deviation	Sample	Weight (oz.)	Deviation
1	5.060	−0.065	26	5.073	−0.052
2	5.014	−0.111	27	5.133	0.008
3	5.118	−0.007	28	5.075	−0.050
4	5.098	−0.027	29	4.971	−0.154
5	5.069	−0.056	30	5.121	−0.004
6	5.159	0.034	31	5.013	−0.112
7	5.099	−0.026	32	5.181	0.056
8	5.031	−0.094	33	5.151	0.026
9	5.067	−0.058	34	5.124	−0.001
10	5.122	−0.003	35	5.044	−0.081
11	5.243	0.118	36	5.054	−0.071
12	5.149	0.024	37	5.020	−0.105
13	5.124	−0.001	38	5.063	−0.062
14	5.077	−0.048	39	5.163	0.038
15	5.178	0.053	40	5.122	−0.003
16	5.165	0.040	41	5.127	0.002
17	5.156	0.031	42	5.016	−0.109
18	5.121	−0.004	43	5.132	0.007
19	5.056	−0.069	44	5.091	−0.034
20	5.127	0.002	45	5.165	0.040
21	5.100	−0.025	46	5.097	−0.028
22	5.057	−0.068	47	5.121	−0.004
23	5.173	0.048	48	5.165	0.040
24	5.160	0.035	49	5.185	0.060
25	5.126	0.001	50	5.173	0.048

Using the specification limits as the control limits,

a) Create a run chart for the baseballs' weights.
b) Is the process for making baseballs in control?
c) How many baseballs produced were out of spec?
d) When should the quality team have investigated the production process? LO ❶

29. Clothing and ethics. A Canadian clothing retailer needs to test whether the content of the fabric, as stated on the label, is within acceptable limits. It outsources this work to a testing company that inspects the fabric at the production facility. Suppose that a line of T-shirts claims to be 50% cotton and that tests of batches coming off a production line indicate the percentages of cotton in the following control chart. A consultant warns that the production process has gone out of control and suggests examining what was happening in the production process during the production of sample 13. Comment on the ethics of the consultant's advice in relation to the ASA Ethical Guidelines in Appendix C. LO ❷

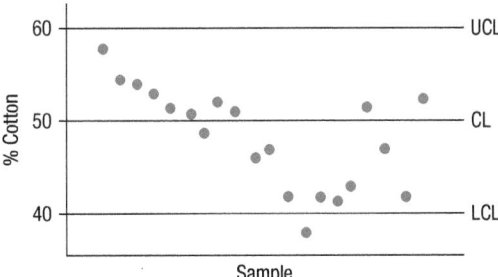

25W

Introduction to Data Mining

MyStatLab   Additional Online Chapter: Chapter 25, Introduction to Data Mining, can be found on MyStatLab.

Answer Key

CHAPTER 2

SECTION EXERCISE ANSWERS

1. a) Each row represents a different house. It is a case.
   b) There are six variables, including the house identifier.

3. a) House_ID is an identifier (categorical, not ordinal).
   Neighbourhood is categorical (nominal).
   ACRES is quantitative (units—acres).
   YR_BUILT is quantitative (units—year).
   FULL_MARKET_VALUE is quantitative (units—dollars).
   SFLA is quantitative (units—square feet).
   b) These data are cross-sectional. All variables were measured at about the same time.

5. It is not clear if the data were obtained from a survey. They are certainly not from an experiment. Most likely they are just a collection of recent sales. We don't know if these sales are representative of all sales, so we should be cautious in drawing conclusions from these data about the housing market in general.

CHAPTER EXERCISE ANSWERS

7. a) Employed.
   b) Unemployed.
   c) Not in labour force.

9. *Who:* years. *What:* domestic credit and GDP. *When:* recent years. *Where:* Canada. *Why:* future trends. *Variables:* domestic credit and GDP, both quantitative and in $billion.

11. *Who:* months at a Canadian company. *What:* $ spent on advertising, and $ sales. *When:* past three years. *Where:* unspecified (Canada?). *Why:* to compare ad $ versus sales $. *How:* unspecified. *Variables:* date, $ spent on ads, $ sales; all quantitative. *Concerns:* none.

13. *Who:* quarterly data. *What:* quarterly sales, unemployment rate, inflation rate. *When:* the past 3 years. *Where:* U.S. *Why:* to determine how sales are affected by the unemployment and inflation rates. *How:* not specified. *Variables:* quarterly sales ($million), unemployment rate (%), and inflation rate (%), which are quantitative. *Concerns:* none.

15. *Who:* MBA applicants. *What:* sex, age, whether or not accepted, whether or not attended, reasons for not attending. *When:* not specified. *Where:* the school. *Why:* to investigate any patterns in female student acceptance and attendance in the MBA program. *How:* admissions office data. *Variables:* sex, whether or not the students accepted, whether or not they attended, reasons for not attending (all categorical); and age in years (quantitative). *Concerns:* none.

17. *Who:* MBA students. *What:* test scores and GPA in MBA program. *When:* the past 5 years. *Where:* London. *Why:* to investigate the association between test scores and performance in the MBA program. *How:* not specified. *Variable:* test scores and GPA, both quantitative. *Concerns:* none.

19. *Who:* experimental participants. *What:* cold remedy or sugar solution, cold severity. *When:* not specified. *Where:* major pharmaceutical firm. *Why:* to test the effectiveness of an herbal compound. *How:* controlled experiment. *Variables:* type of treatment (herbal or sugar solution) is categorical, and severity rating is quantitative. *Concerns:* Severity of a cold might be difficult to quantify. Also, scientists at a pharmaceutical firm could have a predisposed opinion about the herbal solution or may feel pressure to report negative findings about the herbal product.

21. *Who:* cars parked at a large company's lots. *What:* make, country of origin, type of vehicle, age of vehicle. *When:* not specified. *Where:* a large company. *Why:* not specified. *How:* data recorded at parking lots of a large company. *Variables:* make, country of origin, and type of vehicle are categorical variables. Age is a quantitative variable. Whether or not the vehicle is in an executive or staff lot is also a categorical variable. *Concerns:* none.

23. *Who:* streams. *What:* name of stream, substrate of the stream, acidity of the water, temperature, and BCI. *When:* not specified. *Where:* Alberta. *Why:* research conducted for an ecology class. *How:* not specified. *Variables:* name of stream and substrate of the stream (limestone, shale, or mixed) are categorical variables. Acidity of the water (pH), temperature (degrees Celsius), and BCI (a measure of biological diversity—unknown units) are quantitative variables. *Concerns:* none.

25. *Who:* all airline flights in Canada. *What:* type of aircraft, number of passengers, whether departures and arrivals were on schedule, and mechanical problems. *When:* the information is currently recorded. *Where:* Canada. *Why:* information is required by the CTA. *How:* from airline flight information. *Variables:* type of aircraft, whether departures and arrivals were on schedule, and mechanical problems are categorical variables. Number of passengers is a quantitative variable. *Concerns:* none.

27. *Who:* all Canadians. *What:* family type. *When:* every five years. *Where:* Canada. *Why:* to investigate social trends. *Variable:* family type, which is a categorical variable.

29. *Who:* overnight visitors to Canada. *What:* number of nights spent in Canada and money spent in Canada. *When:* each year. *Where:* Canada. *Why:* to provide information for the tourism industry. *Variables:* number of nights and money spent in Canada, which are quantitative variables with no units and units of $, respectively.

31. *Who:* theme park locations. *What:* country of site, estimated cost, potential population size, size of site (hectares), if mass transportation within five minutes of site. *When:* 2017. *Where:* Europe. *Why:* to determine feasibility of various sites. *How:* not specified. *Variables:* country of site and whether or not mass transportation within five minutes of site are both categorical variables. Estimated cost (€), potential population size (counts), and size of site (hectares) are quantitative. *Concerns:* none.

33. *Who:* Kentucky Derby races. *What:* date, winner, winning margin, jockey, winner's payoff, duration of the race, and track conditions. *When:* 1875–2012. *Where:* Churchill Downs. *Why:* examine trends in Kentucky Derby winners. *How:* statistics kept for each race every year. *Variables:* Winner, winning jockey, and track conditions are categorical variables. Date, winning margin (in lengths), winner's payoff ($), and duration of the race (minutes and seconds) are quantitative variables. *Concerns:* none.

35. Each row represents each individual employee. Column headings: Employee ID Number, contract average ($), supervisor's rating (1-10), and years with the company.

37. Each row represents a Broadway show. Column headings: the show name (identifies the row), profit or loss ($), number of investors, and investment total ($).

39. Time series.

41. Cross-section.

43. Answers will vary.

CHAPTER 2 JUST CHECKING ANSWERS

1. *Who*—policies on churches and schools
   What—policy number, years claim-free, net property premium ($), net liability premium ($), total property value ($000), median age in postal code, school, territory, coverage
   How—company records
   When—not given

2. Policy number: identifier (categorical)
   Years claim-free: quantitative
   Net property premium: quantitative ($)
   Net liability premium: quantitative ($)
   Total property value: quantitative ($1000)

Median age in postal code: quantitative
School: categorical (true/false)
Territory: categorical
Coverage: categorical

CHAPTER 3

SECTION EXERCISE ANSWERS

1. a) False. Sampling error cannot be avoided, even with unbiased samples.
   b) True.
   c) True.
   d) False. Randomization will match the characteristics in a way that is unbiased. We can't possibly think of all the characteristics that might be important or match our sample to the population on all of them.

3. a) Professional food preparers in the United States.
   b) *Chef's Collaborative* membership listing.
   c) Proportion who believe that food safety has improved.
   d) Simple random sample.

5. a) No. It would be nearly impossible to get exactly 500 males and 500 females by random chance.
   b) A stratified sample, stratified by whether the respondent is male or female.

7. A systematic sample.

9. a) Population—Human resources directors of Fortune 500 companies.
   b) Parameter—Proportion who don't feel surveys intruded on their work day.
   c) Sampling Frame—List of HR directors at Fortune 500 companies.
   d) Sample—23% who responded.
   e) Method—Questionnaire mailed to all (non-random).
   f) Bias—Hard to generalize because who responds is related to the question itself.

11. a) Professional food preparers in the United States.
    b) The members who attended the recent symposium.
    c) The sampling frame is not necessarily representative of the entire group of food preparers. Those who attended the symposium may have different opinions from those who didn't. His sample isn't random and may be biased toward those most interested in the topic. Finally, the script is biased and may lead to an estimate of a higher proportion who think food safety has improved than is true within the population.

13. a) Answers will vary. Question 1 seems appropriate. Question 2 does not seem appropriate. It is not

clear why it is useful to compare bus passes and internet service.

b) Question 1 is the more neutrally worded. Question 2 is biased in its wording.

15. a) True.
b) True.
c) False. Measurement error refers to inaccurate responses. Sampling error refers to sample-to-sample variability.
d) True.

17. a) This is a multistage design, with a cluster sample at the first stage and a simple random sample for each cluster.
b) If any of the three churches you pick at random is not representative of all churches, then you'll introduce sampling error by the choice of that church.

CHAPTER EXERCISE ANSWERS

19. a) Voluntary response.
b) No confidence in the estimate sampled.

21. a) All adults in the United States aged 18 and older.
b) Adults with telephones.
c) Some people do not have phones, or share a single home phone.

23. a) Population—Researchers.
b) Parameter—Impact of new technologies on fuel efficiency for motor vehicles.
c) Sampling Frame—Established researchers in the automobile industry, the clean tech industry, government research labs, and universities.
d) Sample—Those who respond.
e) Sampling Method—Not stated, probably stratified random sample, so as to get researchers from each of the stated industries with enough famous (high-profile) researchers.
f) Bias—The most knowledgeable researchers may not have time to respond unless they are paid to participate.

25. a) Population—Adults.
b) Parameter—Proportion of sample who believe that global warming is due primarily to human activities.
c) Sampling Frame—Adults aged 18 and over.
d) Sample—1022 randomly selected adults.
e) Sampling Method—Random selection method not specified.
f) Bias—Probably not biased. A large sample of randomly selected participants were interviewed, so it follows that the conclusions could be generalized.

27. a) Population—City voters.
b) Parameter—Not clearly specified; likely, the proportion of voters who think certain issues are important or favour certain issues.
c) Sampling Frame—All city resident voters.
d) Sample—Every city resident voter in one block from each district.
e) Sampling Method—Cluster sampling. This is a convenience sample.
f) Bias—Parameter(s) of interest not clearly specified. Convenience sampling within block clusters is not random and could produce biased results.

29. a) Population—Landlords in a particular area.
b) Parameter—Proportion of landlords illegally denying fair access to rental apartments.
c) Sampling Frame—All advertised apartments.
d) Sample—Apartments actually visited and inquired about.
e) Sampling Method—Not specified how the apartments visited were chosen.
f) Bias—Likely to be a fair study as long as the apartments visited were randomly chosen and not all in one section of town.

31. a) Population—Dairy farms.
b) Parameter—Not clearly specified.
c) Sampling Frame—All dairy farms, although not specifically slated this way.
d) Sample—Not specified.
e) Sampling method—Cluster sampling.
f) Bias—Should be unbiased as long as the farms and the milk samples are randomly selected.

33. The newspaper's faulty prediction is most likely the result of sampling error.

35. a) Volunteer response. Bias is introduced; only those individuals who see the ad and feel strongly about the issue will respond.
b) Volunteer response. Bias is introduced because only those who are strongly motivated to express their opinions will attend the meetings.
c) Cluster sampling. Bias is introduced if there is a large percentage of residents on the selected street who do not participate or if the selected street is unrepresentative of the town as a whole.
d) Systematic sampling. Should be unbiased and fairly representative of the public opinion.

37. a) Systematic sample (every 10th person in line).
b) It is likely to be representative of all of those waiting in line to go on the roller coaster. It would be useful to compare those who have waited and are now at the front with those who are in the back of the line.
c) Persons willing to wait in line for the roller coaster on a particular day within a given time frame.

39. a) Answers will vary. Question 1 is a straightforward question. Question 2 is biased in its wording.
  b) Question 1, since it is a simple, straightforward statement asking for the required response.

41. Only those who think it is worth waiting for the roller coaster ride are likely to still be in line. Those who don't like roller coasters or who don't want to stay in lines are not part of the sampling frame. Therefore, the poll won't get a fair picture of whether park patrons overall would favour more roller coasters.

43. a) Biased because it leads the responder toward yes because of the word "pollute."
  b) Biased because it leads the responder toward no because of the words "enforce" and "strict," which conjure up images that could lead a responder to having a negative reaction.

45. a) Not everyone in the sampling frame has an equal chance of being chosen. People with unlisted phone numbers, without phones, and those at work or away from the home at the designated calling time cannot he contacted.
  b) Generate random numbers and call at random times.
  c) In original plan, families that have one person at home are more likely to be included in the study. With second plan, more people are potentially included.
  d) This change does improve the chance of selected households being included in the study.
  e) Residents not being home at the time of the call and people without phones are still left out of the study.

47. a) Answers will vary.
  b) The parameter being estimated is the true mean amount of cash that you carry daily just before lunch.
  c) Population is now the amount of cash carried by your friends. The average parameter estimates the mean of these amounts.
  d) The 10 measurements in c) are more likely to be representative of your class (peer group with similar needs) but unlikely for larger groups outside of your circle of friends.

49. a) Assign numbers 001 to 120 to represent each order in a day. Use random numbers to select 10 transactions to check for accuracy.
  b) Separate the transactions and sample each type (wholesale and retail) proportionately. This would be a stratified random sample.

51. a) Randomly select three cases and then randomly select one jar from each case.
  b) Select three cases at random, then randomly select one jar from each case.
  c) Cluster sampling.

53. a) It does not specify the method for calling local businesses and whether all or a random sample were called. The mention of signing a petition may bias business owners to respond positively.
  b) If the food court is the only place to get food in the airport, then the results would be fairly representative. However, if there are other restaurants available it would not be representative. If travelers don't like the food available in the food court, they may eat in a restaurant outside the food court.

55. The survey has voluntary response bias and uses stratified sampling based on ranges of BMI. The survey is useful within each stratum, but the individual strata results need to be weighted to get results for the whole population.

CHAPTER 3 JUST CHECKING ANSWERS

1. a) It can be hard to reach all members of a population, and it can take so long that circumstances change, affecting the responses. A well-designed sample is often a better choice.
  b) This sample is probably biased—people who didn't like the food at the restaurant might not choose to eat there.
  c) No, only the sample size matters, not the fraction of the overall population.
  d) Students who frequent this website might be more enthusiastic about statistics than the overall population. A large sample cannot compensate for bias.
  e) It's the population "parameter." "Statistics" describe samples.

2. a) Systematic
  b) Stratified
  c) Simple
  d) Cluster

CHAPTER 4

SECTION EXERCISE ANSWERS

1. a) Frequency table:

None	AA	BA	MA	Ph.D
164	42	225	52	29

  b) Relative frequency table (divide each number by 512 and multiply by 100):

None	AA	BA	MA	Ph.D
32.03%	8.20%	43.95%	10.16%	5.66%

3. a)

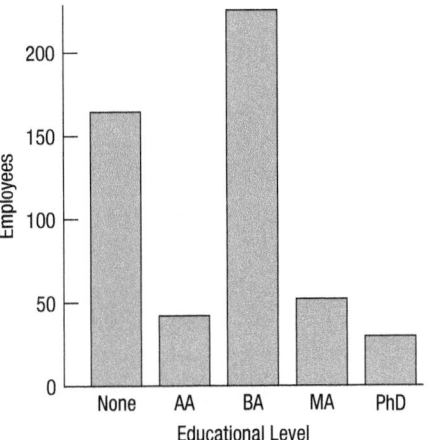

b)

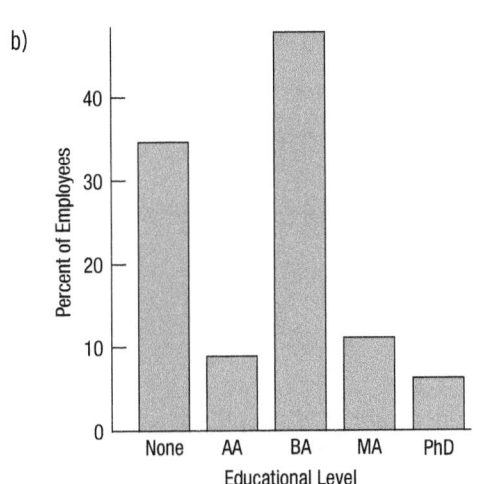

c)

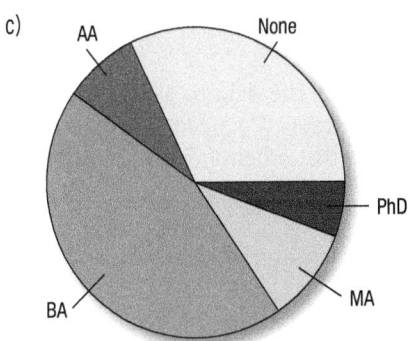

5. a) The vast majority of employees have either no college degree or a bachelor's degree (44% and 32%, respectively). About 10% have master's degrees, 8% have associate's degrees, and nearly 6% have Ph.Ds.

b) I would not be comfortable generalizing this to any other division or company. These data were collected only from my division. Other companies might have vastly different educational distributions.

7. a)

	Totals
<1 year	95
1–5 years	205
More than 5 years	212

b) Yes

None	AA	BA	MA	Ph.D
164	42	225	62	29

9. a)

(%)	None	AA	BA	Ph.D
<1 year	6.1	7.1	38.5	41.4
1–5 years	25.6	21.4	51.9	51.7
More than 5 years	68.3	28	9.6	6.9

b) No. The distributions look quite different. More than two-thirds of those with no college degree have been with the company longer than five years, but almost none of the Ph.Ds (less than 7%) have been there that long.

c)

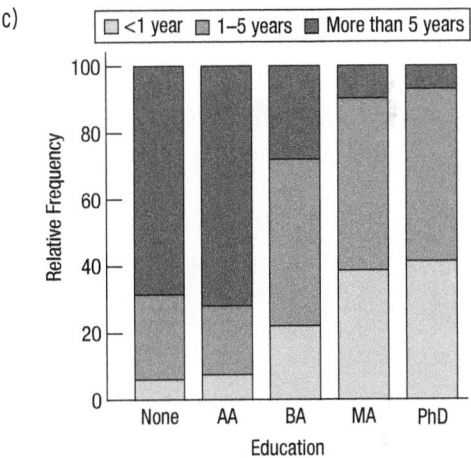

d) It's possible to see it in the table, but the stacked bar chart makes the difference much clearer.

CHAPTER EXERCISE ANSWERS

11. Answers will vary.

13. Answers will vary.

15. a) Yes, the categories divide the whole, and the category "Other" combines the smaller shares.
b) Coca-Cola.

17. a) The pie chart does a better job of comparing portions of the whole.
b) The "Other" category is missing, and without it the results could be misleading.

19. a) Yes.
b) Percentages listed only add up to 73.7%. Hence, other causes must account for 26.3% of deaths.
c) An appropriate display could either be a bar graph or a pie graph, using an "Other" category for the remaining 26.3% of causes of death.

21. Cisco Systems continues to dominate the market for desktop conferencing. Citrix and Microsoft are battling for second place. A pie chart or bar chart would be appropriate.

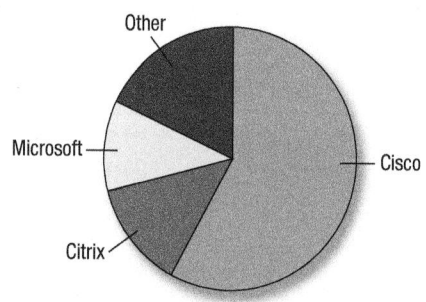

23. a) They don't total 100%. Others must have refused to answer or didn't know.

b)

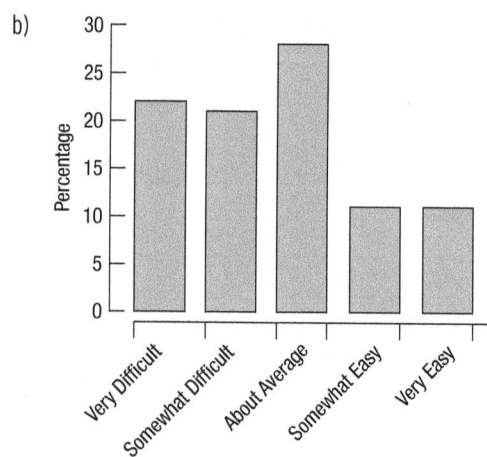

c) Only if the "other" category were added.

d) Answers will vary. Nearly half (43%) of business owners said that it would be somewhat or very difficult to obtain credit. Only 22% said it would be somewhat or very easy. Of the remaining, 28% said it would be about average and 7% didn't answer.

25. a)

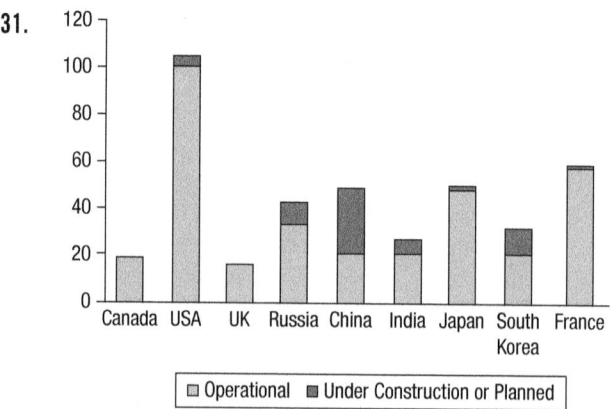

The stacked bar graph is chosen since there are too many causes of spills to compare clearly between pie charts.

b) Collision and grounding are major causes of large spills, whereas equipment failure is the main cause of small spills. More is known about the causes of large spills, whereas over half of small spills are of unknown cause or the cause is not specified: "other."

27. a) India 76.1% – USA 45.3% = 30.8%

b) Looks like India's percentage is about five or six times as big as the U.S. bar, but the actual values are not even twice as big.

c) The display would be improved by starting the vertical axis at 0%, not 40%.

d)

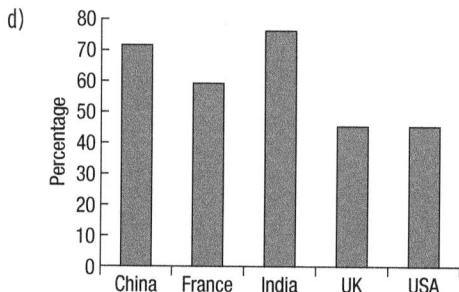

e) The percentage of people who say that wealth is important to them is highest in China and India (over 70%), followed by France (close to 60%), and then the U.S. and U.K., where the percentages were close to 45%.

29. We need to convert the data to a single currency by applying exchange rates. We need a bar chart, since we do not have a total that other figures are a percentage of.

31.

a) A stacked bar graph is chosen since the planned reactors will be added to the operational ones.

b) China is an outlier, since the number of reactors planned is larger than the number operational. The USA is also an outlier since it has more reactors than the other countries.

33.

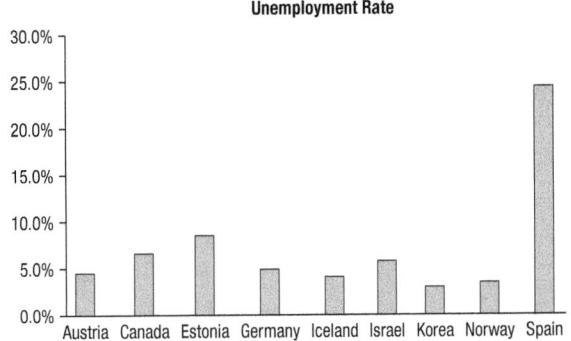

A bar graph is chosen. Although these data are percentages, they are not percentages of a total calculated over all the countries.

35. a) 45.1%
b) 34.9%
c) 5.3%
d) 59.8%
e) 41.3%
f) 65.8%
g) Companies that reported a positive change on October 24 were more likely to report a negative change for the year than companies who reported a negative change on October 24.

37. a) Not possible since we do not have all categories of people (e.g., truck, aircraft occupants)
b) $13/(74 + 13) = 14.9\%$
c) Conflicts with Ethical Guideline A, Professionalism.
d) Conflicts with Ethical Guideline A, Professionalism.
e)

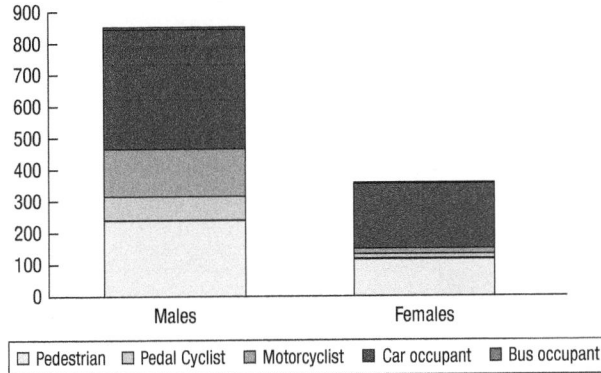

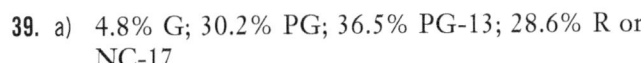

*Other types of injury not included

A stacked bar chart is chosen since different types of injury cumulate.

39. a) 4.8% G; 30.2% PG; 36.5% PG-13; 28.6% R or NC-17
b) 0% G; 2.3% PG; 45.5% PG-13; 52.3% R or NC-17

c)

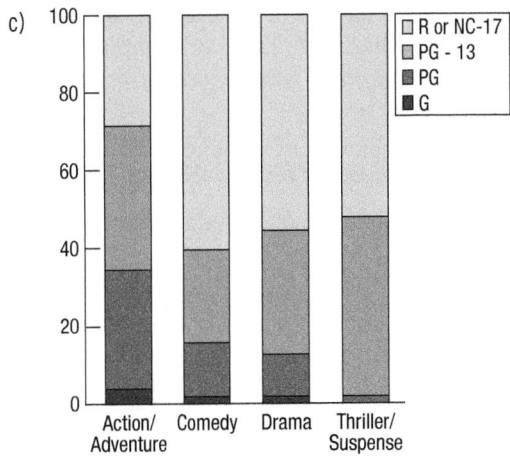

d) Genre and Rating are not independent. Thriller/Suspense movies are nearly all PG-13 or R/NC-17, but 35% of Action/Adventure movies were either G or PG in 2011. Comedy is over 60% R or NC-17 in this year, while Action/Adventure was only 28.6%.

41. a) 32.1% (86/268)
b) 29.3% (48/164)
c) 36.5% (38/104)
d) There seems to be a slightly higher percentage of part-time MBA students who are women. This may be because women have other commitments during the day (such as work, family, etc.) that limit their choices.

43. a) Low 20.0%; Moderate 48.9%; High 31.0%.
b) Under 30: Low 27.6%; Moderate 49.0%; High 23.5% 30–49: Low 20.7%; Moderate 50.8%; High 28.5% Over 50: Low 15.7%; Moderate 47.2%; High 37.1%
c)

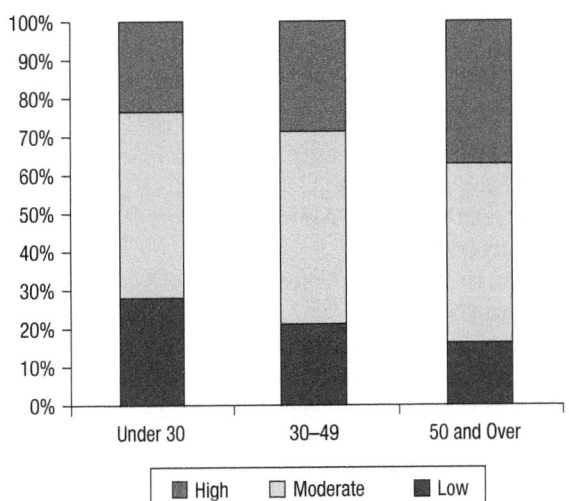

d) As age increases, the percentage of customers reporting a high frequency of shopping increases, and the percentage who report a low frequency of shopping decreases.

e) No. An association between two variables does not imply a cause-and-effect relationship.

45. a) Not appropriate since times do not add to 24 hours

b)

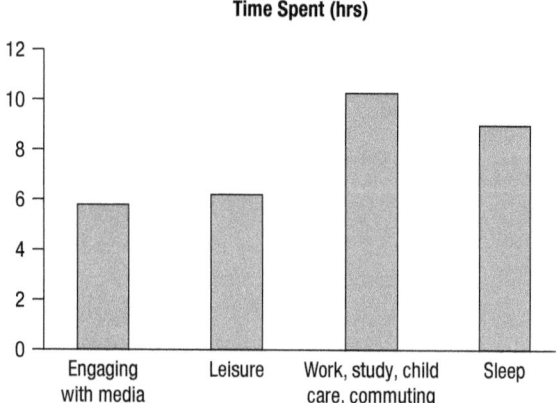

Time Spent (hrs)

c) Canadians are multitasking, since they are spending 31.3 hours on these activities during a 24-hour day.

47. a) The marginal totals have been added to the table:

		Hospital Size		
		Large	Small	Total
Procedure	Major Surgery	120 of 800	10 of 50	**130 of 850**
	Minor Surgery	10 of 200	20 of 250	**30 of 450**
	Total	**130 of 1000**	**30 of 300**	**160 of 1300**

160 of 1300, or about 12.3% of the patients had a delayed discharge.

b) Major surgery patients were delayed 15.3% of the time.
Minor surgery patients were delayed 6.7% of the time.

c) The large hospital had a delay rate of 13%.
The small hospital had a delay rate of 10%.

The small hospital has the lower overall rate of delayed discharge.

d) Large hospital: Major surgery 15% and minor surgery 5%.
Small hospital: Major surgery 20% and minor surgery 8%.
Even though the small hospital had the lower overall rate of delayed discharge, the large hospital had a lower rate of delayed discharge for each type of surgery.

e) Yes. While the overall rate of delayed discharge is lower for the small hospital, the large hospital did better with *both* major surgery and minor surgery.

f) The small hospital performs a higher percentage of minor surgeries than major surgeries. 250 of 300 surgeries at the small hospital were minor (83%). Only 200 of the large hospital's 1000 surgeries were minor (20%). Minor surgery had a lower delay rate than major surgery (6.7% to 15.3%), so the small hospital's overall rate was artificially inflated. The larger hospital is the better hospital when comparing discharge delay rates.

49. a) 1284 applicants were admitted out of a total of 3014 applicants. 1284/3014 = 42.6%

b) 1022 of 2165 (47.2%) of males were admitted. 262 of 849 (30.9%) of females were admitted.

c) Since there are four comparisons to make, the table below organizes the percentages of males and females accepted into each program. Females are accepted at a higher rate in every program.

d) The comparison of acceptance rate within each program is most valid. Women tended to apply to the programs in which gaining acceptance was difficult for everyone.

		Males Accepted (of Applicants)	Females Accepted (of Applicants)	Total
Program	1	511 of 825	89 of 108	600 of 933
	2	352 of 560	17 of 25	369 of 585
	3	137 of 407	132 of 375	269 of 782
	4	22 of 373	24 of 341	46 of 714
	Total	1022 of 2165	262 of 849	1284 of 3014

Program	Males	Females
1	61.9%	82.40%
2	62.9%	68.0%
3	33.7%	35.2%
4	5.9%	7.0%

51. a) A stacked bar chart is used since the successful plus unsuccessful surgeries add to make the total.

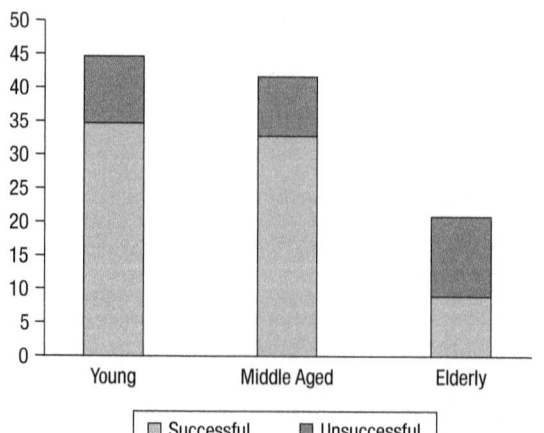

Knee Surgeries Performed by Dr Casio

b)

Successful Knee Surgeries by Dr Almasri

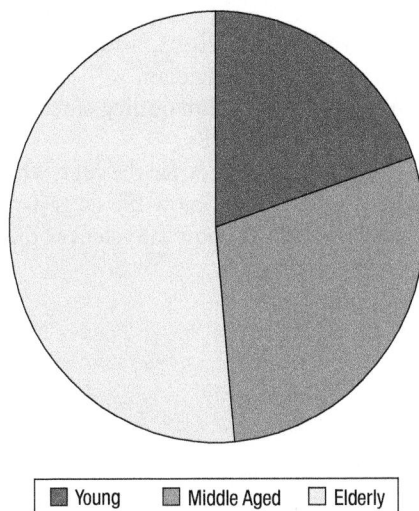

Young   Middle Aged   Elderly

c)

	Young	Middle Aged	Elderly	Total
Dr. Almasri	0.363636	0.467742	0.852459	0.567416
Dr. Casio	0.636364	0.532258	0.147541	0.432584
Total	1	1	1	1

Of the successful surgeries on elderly patients, 85.2% were performed by Dr. Almasri.

d)

	Young	Middle Aged	Elderly	Total
Dr. Almasri	0.162162	0.236486	0.601351	1
Dr. Casio	0.416667	0.388889	0.194444	1
Total	0.269531	0.300781	0.429688	1

60.1% of patients treated by Dr. Almasri were elderly.

e)

	Young	Middle Aged	Elderly	Total
Dr. Almasri	83%	83%	58%	68%
Dr. Casio	78%	79%	43%	71%
Total	80%	81%	55%	70%

This is not a contingency table.
Both tables given in the question are contingency tables.
Both (c) and (d) are contingency tables.

f) Dr. Almasri's response would be to look at the individual age groups. In each age group, Dr. Almasri is more successful than Dr. Casio. Dr. Almasri is right. His overall average is lower than Dr. Casio's because he takes on a lot of elderly patients for whom the success rate is lower than for the younger age groups.

g) (i), (ii), (iii) Dr. Almasri, since his success rate is higher in each age group than Dr. Casio's.

53. Although the percentages add to 100% they are not percentages of a whole, and not all countries are included. We therefore use a bar graph.

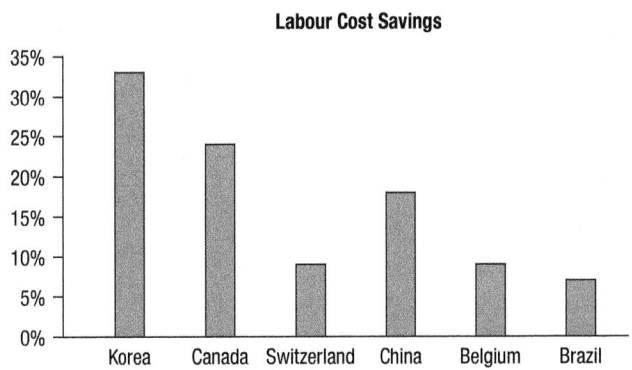

Labour Cost Savings

CHAPTER 4 JUST CHECKING ANSWERS

1. $16/32 = 50\%$

2. $4/10 = 40\%$

3. $16/64 = 25\%$

4. 15.6% nearsighted, 56.3% farsighted, 28.1% need bifocals

5. 18.8% nearsighted, 62.5% farsighted, 18.8% need bifocals

6. 40% of the nearsighted customers are female, while 50% of customers are female.

7. Eye condition and gender appear associated because of reasons such as (i) females are more likely to need bifocals, (ii) males are more likely to be nearsighted.

CHAPTER 5

SECTION EXERCISE ANSWERS

1. a)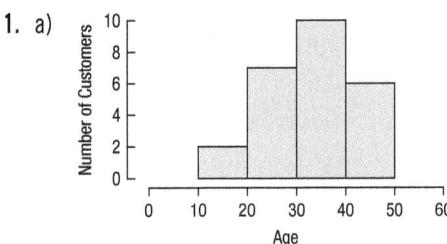

b)

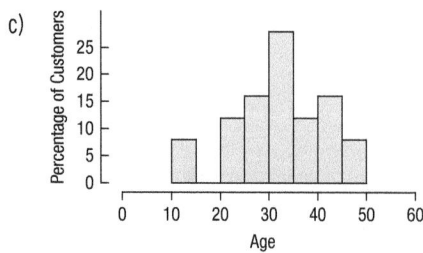

c)

d)
```
1 | 14
2 | 0225699
3 | 0002224558
4 | 244488
```

3. a) Unimodal.
   b) Around 35 years old.
   c) Fairly symmetric.
   d) No outliers.

5. a) About the same. The distribution is fairly symmetric.
   b) 31.84 years.
   c) 32 years.

7. a) Q1 26; Q3 38 (Answers may vary slightly.)
   b) Q1 26; Q3 38
   c) IQR = 12 years
   d) SD = 9.84 years

9. a) The distribution is skewed to the right. There are a few negative values. The range is about $6000.
   b) The mean will be larger because the distribution is right-skewed.
   c) Because of the skewness, the median is a better summary.

11. The mean is $876 + 793 = \$1669$.

    The quartiles and median cannot be calculated.

    The standard deviation is $\sqrt{986^2 + 1298^2} = \$1630$, assuming that spending in the two months is uncorrelated.

13. The average age of males is 39.1.

15. a)

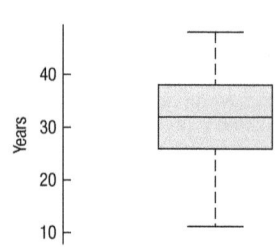

b) No.
c) $32 + 1.5*12 = 50$ years old

17. a) Skewed to the right, since the mean is much greater than the median.
    b) Yes, at least one high outlier, since 250 is far greater than Q3 + 1.5 IQRs.
    c) We don't know how far the high whisker should go because we don't know the largest value inside the fence. We don't know the values of the other outliers.

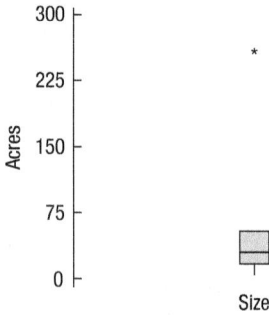

19. $25*10\% = 2.5$. The third data point, 20, is the tenth percentile.
    $25*80\% = 20$. The average of the 20th and 21st data points: $(42 + 44)/2 = 43$ is the 80th percentile.

21. The ages of the women are generally higher than the men by about 10 years. As the boxplot shows, more than three-quarters of the women are older than all the men.

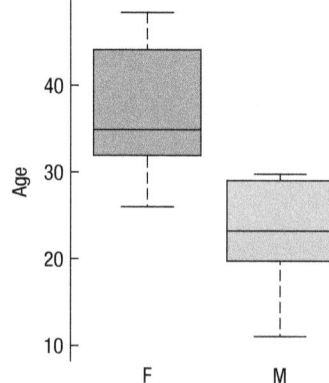

23. The upper outlier limit is
    $123 + 1.5*(123 - 44.9) = 240.15$.
    The lower outlier limit is
    $44.9 - 1.5*(123 - 44.9) = -72.25$.
    Yes, the maximum value is an outlier since it is above the upper outer limit. We should look at a boxplot as the next step to identify any other outliers.

25. Sales at Location #1 were higher than sales at Location #2 in every week except for the high outlier for location #2.

27. a) 11 has a z-score of -2.12; 48 has a z-score of $+1.64$.
    b) The minimum, 11, is more extreme.
    c) 61.3 years old.

29.

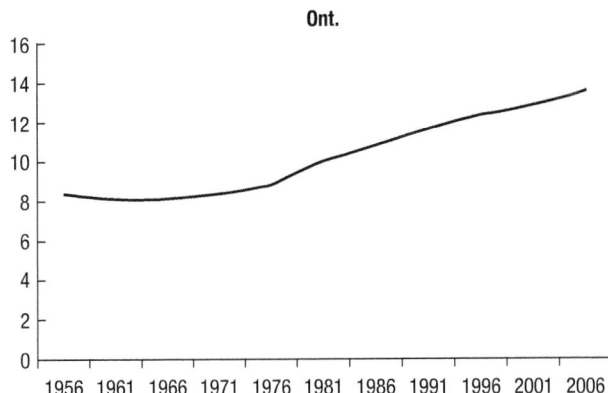

Ont.

Roughly constant between 1956 and 1976. There is a linearly increasing trend thereafter.

31. 16, 16, 36, 49, 49, 64, 100
Skewed to the high end.

CHAPTER EXERCISE ANSWERS

33. Answers will vary.

35. Slightly skewed to the right and unimodal. Centre best represented by the median. Spread determined from the range of data, low to high, or $0.80 − 1.00 =$ approximately $0.20.

37. Distribution is bimodal. Centre of the distribution is the median. Spread is determined from the range of data, high minus low, or approximately $2500 − $100 = $2400 based on the centre points of the bars. There are no outliers or other unusual features.

39. a) Five-number summary (quartile calculations may differ slightly using different software):

Min	1st Qtr	Median	3rd Qtr	Max
$131.00	$831.50	$1327.50	$1668.00	$2520.00

b) Boxplot

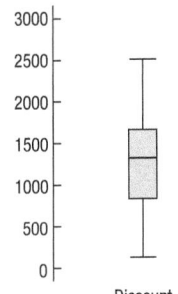

Discount

c) The histogram shows that the distribution is bimodal (two peaks).

41. a)

```
7 | 0
6 | 5
5 | 28
4 | 29
3 | 22399
2 | 29
1 |
0 | 399
```

b) Boxplot

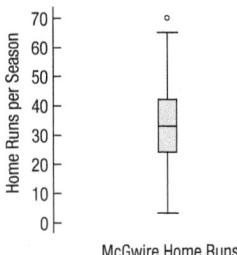

McGwire Home Runs

c) Somewhat skewed to the right with typical season home runs in the 30s. Three seasons when less than 10 home runs were hit. With the exception of those values, the total number of home runs per season was between 22 and 70.

d) The season with 70 home runs is identified as an outlier; however, it is only slightly higher than the season with 65 home runs. The three low values are not officially identified as outliers but can be considered as unusual compared to the other seasons.

43. a) Distribution is somewhat skewed, so the median can be used to represent the centre.

b) The median value is 33.

c) Mean value should be close to the median because the distribution is fairly symmetric. Mean should be slightly higher due to the high outlier.

d) Chart is a time series plot using bars to represent each data point. A histogram would arrange the data into bin intervals rather than displaying the number of games over time.

45. a) Montreal five-number summary (quartile calculations may differ slightly using different software):

Min	1st Qtr	Median	3rd Qtr	Max
$1.55	$2.525	$2.65	$2.74	$3.03

b) Range = max − min = $3.03 − $1.55 = $1.48; IQR = Q3 − Q1 − $2.74 − $2.525 = $0.215

c) Boxplot

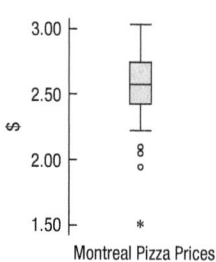

Montreal Pizza Prices

d) Distribution is approximately symmetric with four low outliers identified. Median price is $2.65 and the IQR is $0.22. Due to outliers, the best representation of the centre of the distribution is the median price. The middle half of the prices fell in the range of $2.53 to $2.74.

e) There are four low outliers. All but five of the prices were above $2.20.

47. Median = 124.35
Q1 = 123
Q3 = 126.6
Mean = 124.36
Variance = 10.03
Standard Deviation = 3.17
Coeff of Var = 0.0255

49. a) Range: max − min = 6796 − 5185 = 1611 metres
b) Between Quartile 1 (5586 metres) and Quartile 3 (6131 metres) (quartile calculations may differ slightly using different software).
c) The distribution is approximately symmetric so we use the mean (5893 metres) and the standard deviation (386.6 metres).
d) Shape: roughly symmetric and unimodal. Centre: The mean is 5893 metres. Spread: Spread is represented by the standard deviation of 386.6 metres.
e) We need the 90th percentile of 45 golf courses: $0.9 \times 45 = 40.5$. The 90th percentile is the 41st data value, which we read from the histogram as between 6300 and 6400 metres. We therefore need a length greater than 6400 metres.

51. a) A boxplot is shown. A histogram would also be appropriate.

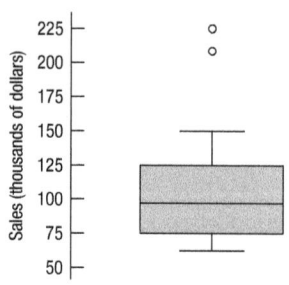

b) Descriptive Statistics: Sales ($) (Different statistics software may yield slightly different results.)

Variable	N	Mean	SE Mean	StDev	Minimum
Sales ($)	18	107845	11069	46962	62006

Q1	Median	Q3	Maximum
73422.5	95975	112330.0	224504

The mean sale is $107,845, and the median is $95,975.
The mean is higher because the outliers pull it up.
c) The median does a better job because the distribution has outliers.
d) The standard deviation of the distribution is $46,962 and the IQR is $38,907.50. (Answers may vary slightly due to different quartile algorithms.)
e) The IQR does a better job because the outliers inflate the standard deviation.
f) The mean would decrease. The standard deviation would decrease. The median and IQR would be less affected.

53. An appropriate graphical display of the distribution is either a histogram or a boxplot. The histogram and boxplot show two high outliers (Greece and Spain). The histogram and the boxplot are skewed to the right, so we use the median instead of the mean to represent a typical country. The median rate for these 34 countries is 7.5%. The highest rate is Spain at 24.6%.

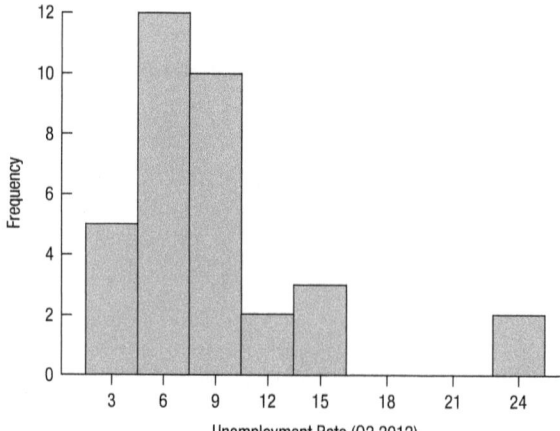

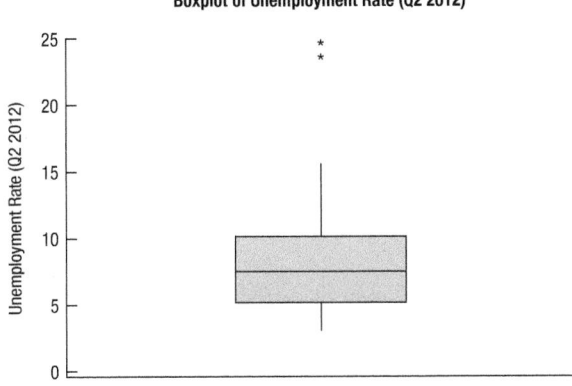

Boxplot of Unemployment Rate (Q2 2012)

Summary of No	
Count	26
Mean	116597.538
Median	112053
Std Dev	51627.346
Variance	2665382807.698
Range	176921
Min	45004
Max	221925
IQR	62319
25th%	79893
75th%	142212

55. An IQR of 0.01 L/100 km would imply that the figure of 3.8 L/100 km hardly changes at all with different drivers and cities; therefore, it is unlikely to be correct. Similarly, an IQR of 5.0 L/100 km implies such a large range that the figure of 3.8 L/100 km is pretty meaningless. 1.0 L/100 km is the best choice. IQR is usually between one and two times the standard deviation for unimodal data. For city driving, our data is almost certainly unimodal. Assuming the IQR is 1.0 L/100 km, the standard deviation is therefore in the range of 0.5 to 1.0 L/100 km, giving a variance in the range of 0.25 to 1.0 1.7 L^2/100 km^2.

Summary of Yes		
Count	34	
Mean	706.1657.735	
Median	136581	
Std Dev	40294275.994	
Variance	1623628677890695	
Range	235022444	
Min	82556	
Max	235105000	
IQR	58064	
25th%	115659	
75th%	173723	

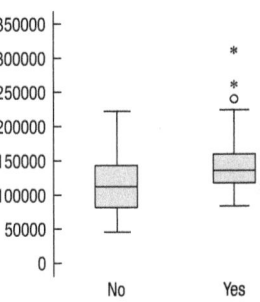

57. a) Both March and April, at approximately 430.

b) February.

c) August.

d) January had median levels slightly lower than June's. June's ozone levels were more consistent, January's ozone range was 300 to 400, while June's range was 310 to 380. June has both low and high outlier values.

e) Generally, ozone levels rose during the winter and were highest in the spring, then fell throughout the summer months and were lowest in the fall. Ozone levels were consistent in the summer and became more variable in the fall and most variable in winter (represented by the expanded distribution). Ozone levels then became more consistent in the spring with levels starting to drop.

59. a) Class 3 has the middle 50% of the data (IQR) nearly above the median of the other two classes.

b) Class 1 has a symmetric distribution and Class 2 has a roughly symmetric distribution. Both are unimodal. Class 3 has a distribution of scores that is skewed to the left and also unimodal.

61. In order to analyze the data, it is appropriate to create summaries separately for the *No Fireplace* and *Fireplace* data sets. In addition, create side-by-side boxplots for comparison of distributions.

Possible error with a high outlier of $235,105,000. This should he investigated to determine the cause and, if erroneous, summary statistics should be recalculated. If the outlier is removed, the side-by-side boxplot shows that the prices for houses with fireplaces are generally higher than for those without. The median price for houses with fireplaces is close to $514,000 compared to a value close to $140,000 for houses without. The spread of sale prices for houses without fireplaces is much greater than for houses with fireplaces. There are only three houses with fireplaces that are more expensive than the most expensive house without a fireplace.

63. Women generally received larger discounts than men. The median discount for women was higher than the third quartile of the men's discounts. The smallest discount received by a woman was larger than the median for males.

▷	Summary of Male	
Count	54
Mean	962.056
Median	870.5
Std Dev	457.741
Variance	209527.261
Range	1859
Min	131
Max	1990
IQR	661
25th%	673
75th%	1334

▷	Summary of Female	
Count	46
Mean	1624.565
Median	1614.5
Std Dev	382.358
Variance	146197.673
Range	1628
Min	892
Max	2520
IQR	476
25th%	1376
75th%	1852

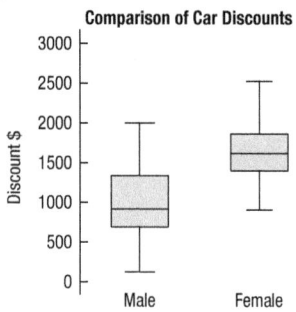

65. a) Histogram

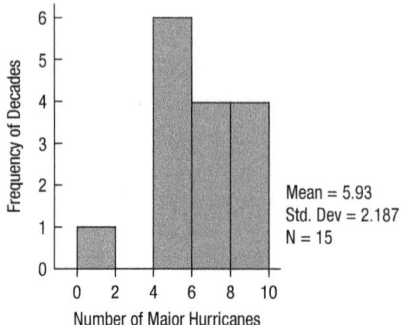

b) Distribution is fairly uniform from 4 to 10 hurricanes, with one outlying decade.

c) Timeplot

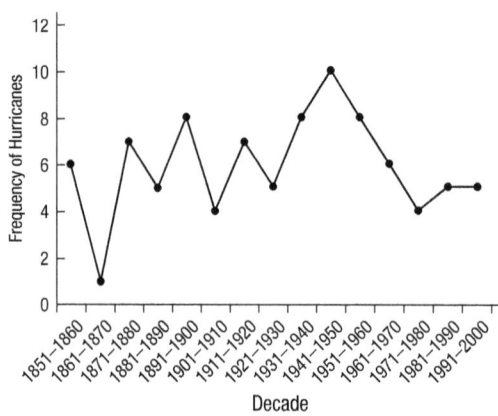

d) No. Most decades have five to eight major hurricanes, with no obvious trend over time.

67. Questions include: What is plotted on the x- and y-axes? What are the units? Since productivity and wages have different units, how does the graph make sense? We are unable to compare the two variables.

69. a) Transformation using logs makes the data more symmetric.

b) The value of 50 corresponds to 50^2, or 2500 ($ million) = $2.5 billion.

71. a) To answer this question, the values have to be standardized and the z-values compared.

z-score	Procedure	Time	Cost
Spain	0.72	0.97	0.07
Guatemala	1.07	−0.10	2.57
Fiji	0.03	0.92	0.86

b) The lowest z-score is for Time in Guatamala. In Guatamala businesses can be set up faster than in the other two countries. The highest z-score is for Cost in Guatamala. The average startup cost as a % of per capita income is higher in Guatamala than in the other two countries.

73. a) The bimodality of the distribution
b) The trend over time
c) The time series plot because it reveals much more of the structure of the data; the rates are not stationary
d) Unemployment decreased from 2004 to 2007 from just over 6% to just under 5%. It then increased steadily until 2010 when it reached nearly 10%. Since then it has decreased to about 8%.

75. 124   9
123
122

```
121
120
119
118    46999
117
116
115
114    79
113    7
112
111
110    111
109    488
108    9
```

The stem and leaf diagram shows that the gas prices are in 3 groups with one outlier, which was not evident from the histogram.

77. a) (16% + 1% + 27%)/3 = 15%
   b) $(1.16*1.01*1.27)^{1/3} = 1.14$. Hence the average return is 14%.

79. Geometric mean = 1.10425. Average rate of increase = 10.4%.

81. Geometric mean = 1.013306. Average rate of increase = 1.33%.

83. a)

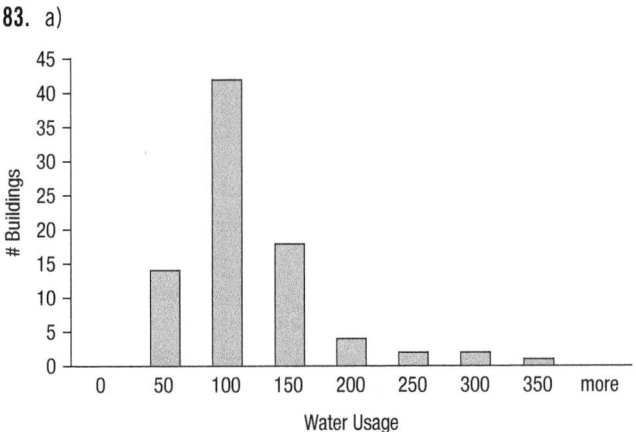

Mode is 50-100 L/ft^2/year.
   b) The fact that the median < mean implies that the distribution is skewed to the right. This is confirmed by the long tail to the right of the histogram.

   c)

Q1	55
Q3	105
IQR	50
Low fence	−20
Hi fence	180

All buildings with water usage > 180 are outliers. From the graph given in the question, this is 5 or 6 buildings.

85. a)

z-scores	Water	Electricity
Mississauga, ON	1.63003317	0.54587154
Burnaby, BC	0.40654975	2.12276019

The Burnaby store uses more electricity than average and the Mississauga store uses more water than average. But the Burnaby store is more exceptional compared to the other stores than is the Mississauga store.
   b) The histograms are both skewed to the right, and are bimodal. The bars should touch each other. The *x*-axis should show values between the bars, not under each bar. The two modes may imply two groups of stores—those selling food (with higher water and electricity usage) and those not selling food. The next step should be to draw separate histograms for stores selling/not selling food.
   c) Selecting stores to the left of the histograms will probably result in selecting stores that do not sell food. The company should let the statisticians do their job and analyze the data in two groups (food/nonfood stores)

87. Answers will vary. This is one possible answer.

   a)

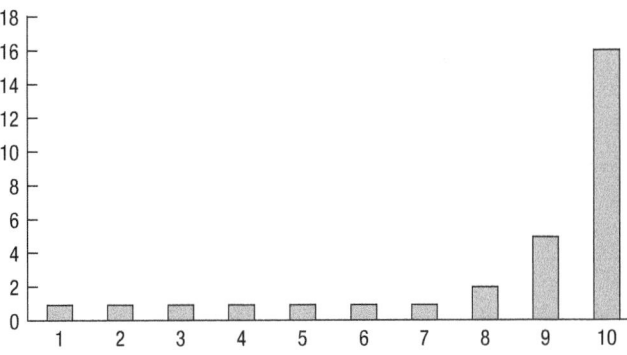

   b) Mean = 8.3; Median = 10; Mode = 10

CHAPTER 5 JUST CHECKING ANSWERS

1. Incomes are skewed to the right, since there are a few high-income families and no family has a negative income, making the median the more appropriate measure of centre. The mean will be influenced by the high end of family incomes and will not reflect the "typical" family income as well as the median would. It will give the impression that the typical income is higher than it is.

2. An IQR of 9 litres per 100 kilometres would mean that only 50% of the cars get fuel efficiency in an interval

9 litres per 100 kilometres wide. Fuel economy doesn't vary that much—2 litres per 100 kilometres is reasonable. It seems plausible that 50% of the cars will be within the range 8–10 litres per 100 kilometres. An IQR of 0.1 litre per 100 kilometres would mean that the fuel efficiency of half the cars varies very little from the estimate. It's unlikely that cars, drivers, and driving conditions are that consistent.

3. We'd prefer a standard deviation of two months. Making a consistent product is important for quality. Customers want to be able to count on the cell phone lasting somewhere close to five years, and a standard deviation of two years would mean that lifespans of the product were highly variable.

CHAPTER 6

SECTION EXERCISE ANSWERS

1. a)

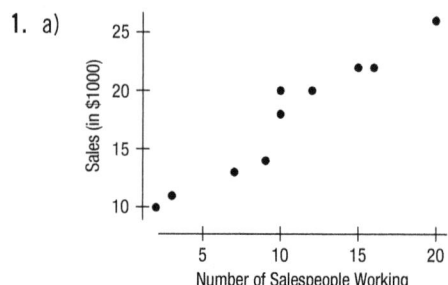

b) Positive.
c) Linear.
d) Strong.
e) No.

3. a) Years of experience.
b) Salary.
c) Salary.

5. a) True.
b) False. It will not change the correlation.
c) False. Correlation has no units.

7. a)

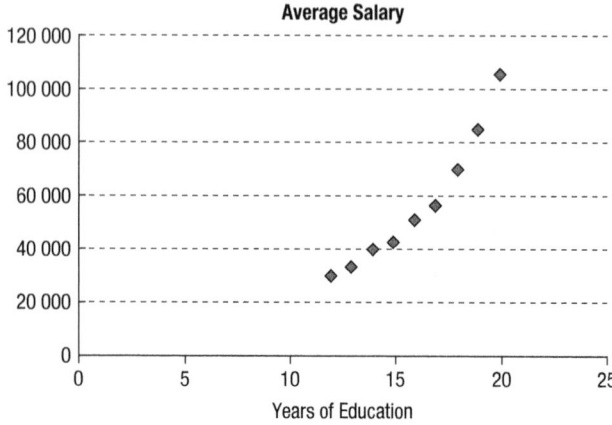

b) The relationship is exponentially increasing, so we take logarithms of the average salary, since that is the variable on the vertical axis.

log avg. salary
4.474
4.52071
4.59881
4.62657
4.70746
4.75003
4.84587
4.92944
5.02416

c)

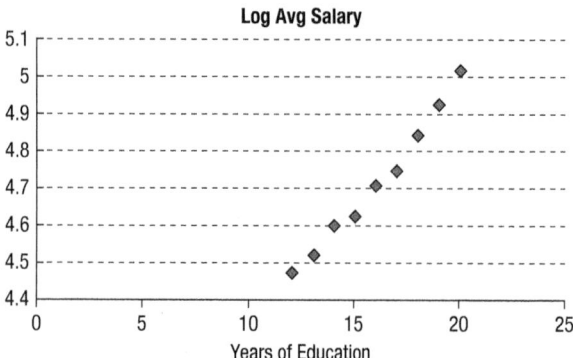

9. Correlation does not demonstrate causation. The analyst's argument is that sales staff cause sales. However, the data may reflect the store hiring more people as sales increase, so any causation would run the other way.

CHAPTER EXERCISE ANSWERS

11. a) Number of text messages—explanatory; cost—response. To predict cost from number of texts. Positive, linear, and moderately strong association.
b) Fuel efficiency—explanatory; sales volume—response. To predict sales from fuel efficiency. We cannot say with certainty what the association is and we have no information about the shape or strength of the relationship.
c) Neither variable is explanatory. Both are responses.
d) Price—explanatory; demand—response. Demand is predicted from price. Association would have a negative direction. Linear shape in a narrow range but curved over a larger range of prices.

13. a) #4 shows little or no association.
b) #3 shows a negative association.
c) #2 and #3 show a straight-line association.
d) #1 and #2 each show a moderately strong association. #1 shows a curved or quadratic association and #2 shows a straight-line association.
e) #3 shows a strong association.

15. a) Histogram:

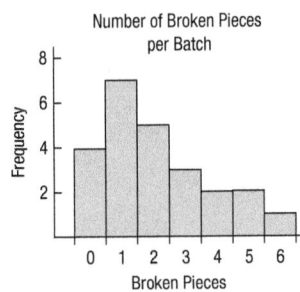

Number of Broken Pieces per Batch

b) Distribution is unimodal and skewed to the right. The skewness is more apparent in the histogram.
c) The positive, somewhat linear relationship between batch number and broken pieces.

17. a) 0.006
b) 0.777
c) −0.923
d) −0.487

19. *Packaging* is a categorical variable. Correlations can be calculated only between quantitative variables.

21. a)

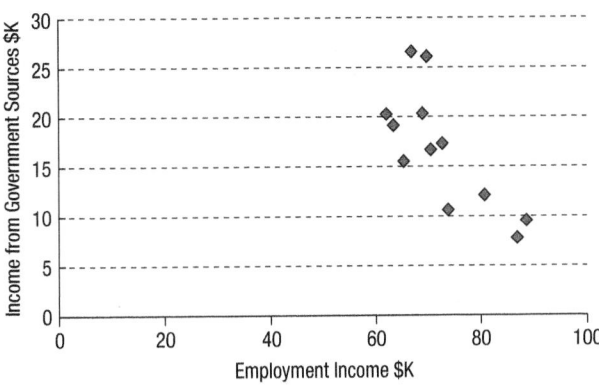

As employment income increases, income from government sources declines.
b) The correlation coefficient is not appropriate as the relationship is not linear.

23.

	Strength	Form	Direction
a) Speed and Time	Strong	Curved then linear	Decreasing
b) Altitude and Time	Strong	Curved	Decreasing
c) Speed and Altitude	Strong	Curved	Increasing

d) Item A is infringed, since the statistician should not have calculated the correlation coefficient for a nonlinear relationship.

25. a) Both variables are quantitative (measured in carats and dollars); the plot is fairly straight and has no outliers. Therefore, the conditions are met.

b) Among diamonds of best colour (D) and very good (VSI) clarity, there is a strong association between the weight of a diamond and its price.

27. a) The two variables are quantitative; however, the scatterplot shows two points that are outside the pattern of data. These outliers make calculating the correlation problematic. In addition, the data points are very scattered and do not show a straight-line relationship.
b) No, except for the two outliers.
c) We can only draw conclusions about this geographic region and not the rest of the world.

29. a) Both are quantitative, but the pattern shown does not appear to be linear, so correlation is not appropriate.
b) For homes between two and six bedrooms, there seems to be a positive association between the number of *Bedrooms* and *Price*. The larger homes do not seem to follow this pattern.

31. *Province* is not a quantitative variable, so the correlation between *Sales* and *Province* is meaningless. The ordering of the provinces' names in alphabetical order is arbitrary. A bar chart might be a better way to display these data.

33. The relationship could be curved, so the correlation would be zero. If there were outliers, the correlation would be affected.

35. a) No, correlation does not imply causation.
b) It is likely that more affluent countries consume more oil and have a greater life expectancy due to improved nutrition, education, and medical care.

37. a) Scatterplot:

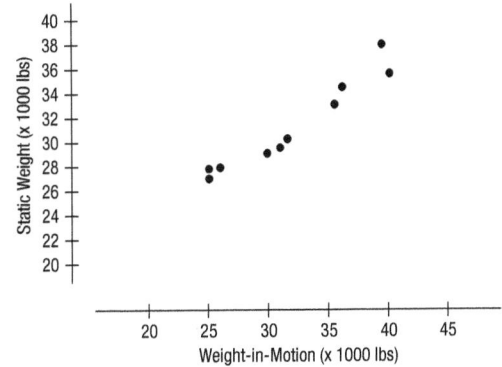

b) Positive, linear, and very strong association.
c) The new scale is able to predict the static weight fairly well, except possibly at the high end. It may be possible to predict the static weight from the new scale accurately enough to be useful. The weight-in-motion measurements seem a bit too high.

d) 0.965

e) Correlation is based on z-scores and is unaffected by changes in units.

f) At the higher end of the scale, there is one point where the weight-in-motion is much higher than the static weight. The new scale may need to he recalibrated.

39. Conclusion is not justified. Both *Marital Status* and *Giving* are categorical variables and not suitable for correlation. A two-way table would be an appropriate way to analyze these data.

41. a) The correlation cannot exceed 1.0.

b) The high correlation does not imply that an increase in one of these variables would cause the other to increase. There may be another variable that affects both of them.

43. Playing computer games could increase aggressiveness. More aggressive children may play more computer games.

The family environment may encourage children to play computer games and become aggressive.

45. a) The correlation coefficient cannot be used because Alzheimer's disease is a categorical variable, not a quantitative one.

b) The correlation coefficient can be used because the Alzheimer Severity Index and the level of aluminum are quantitative variables.

c) We would need to assume that the relationship is approximately linear.

47.

a) Overall correlation is 0.9709. The calculation is statistically sound since both variables are quantitative and the relationship is linear.

b) No grocery correlation –0.8628. The calculation is statistically sound since both variables are quantitative and the relationship is linear.

c) With grocery correlation –0.1326. The calculation is not statistically sound. Both variables are quantitative but the relationship is not linear.

d) The overall correlation is misleading since there are two clusters of data points, not an overall trend. The only realistic correlation is b). The values of the others are meaningless.

CHAPTER 6 JUST CHECKING ANSWERS

1. We know the scores are quantitative. We should check to see if the Linearity Condition and the Outlier Condition are satisfied by looking at a scatterplot of the two scores.

2. If the exchange rate between euros and Canadian dollars had been constant between 1992 and 2014, the correlation would be the same. In fact, the exchange rate varies, resulting in a different correlation.

3. It won't change.

4. They are more likely to do poorly. The positive correlation means that low closing prices for Intel are associated with low closing prices for Cypress.

5. No, the general association is positive, but we can't be sure for every quarter.

CHAPTER 7

SECTION EXERCISE ANSWERS

1. a) False. The line usually touches none of the points. We minimize the sum of the squared errors.

b) True.

c) False. It is the sum of the squares of all the residuals that is minimized.

3. a) $2 \times 0.965 = 1.93$ SDs.

b) $17.6 + 1.93 \times 5.34 = 27.906$ or \$27,906.

c) 0.965 SDs below the mean.

d) \$12,447

5. The winners may be suffering from regression to the mean. Perhaps they weren't really better than other rookie executives, but just happened to have a lucky year.

7. a) Thousands of dollars.

b) 2.77 (the largest residual in magnitude).

c) 0.07 (the smallest residual in magnitude).

9. $R^2 = 93.12\%$. About 93% of the variance in *Sales* can be accounted for by the regression of *Sales* on *Number of Salespeople Working*.

11. 16, 16, 36, 49, 49, 64, 100.

They are skewed to the high end.

CHAPTER EXERCISE ANSWERS

13. a) *Price.*

b) *Sales.*

c) For every extra dollar increase, weekly sales are predicted to decrease by 24,369.49 kilos.

d) The number is not meaningful except as a base or starting value for the line because it is not realistic to set the *Price* at zero dollars.

e) 56,572.32 kg

f) 3,427.68 kg

15. $\widehat{Sales} = 52697 + 10261 \times (-0.547) = 47084$ kg

17. The model is meaningless because the variable *Region* is categorical, not quantitative. Although each *Region* is denoted by a number, the variable is still categorical. The slope makes no sense because *Region* has no units. The boxplot comparisons are informative, but the regression is meaningless.

19. a) The variables are both quantitative (with units % of GDP), the plot is reasonably straight, but there are a couple of outliers that influence the fit (especially 2009). The spread is roughly constant (although the spread is large). We should be cautious in interpreting the model too strictly.

b) About 31.6% of the variation in the growth rates of developing countries is accounted for by the growth rates of developed countries.

21. a) $\widehat{Growth\ (Developing\ Countries)} = 3.38 + 0.468$ *Growth (Developed Countries)*

b) The intercept is the predicted growth of developing countries in years of zero growth in developed countries. Yes, this makes sense.

c) On average, GDP in developed countries is expected to increase by 0.468% for a 1% increase in growth in developed countries.

d) 5.25%

e) More; we would predict 4.62%.

f) 1.47%

23. a) It represents the value for money flowing into mutual funds when mutual fund performance *Return* is zero.

b) For every 1% increase in mutual fund *Return*, the *Flow* into mutual funds is expected to increase by 771 (SM).

c) 9747 (SM)

d) $\widehat{Residual} = -4747$ (SM). This model overestimated the *Flow* value.

25. a) Billions of dollars per thousand *Housing Starts*.

b) 49%

c) 0.70 standard deviations below the mean in *Quarterly Sales*.

27. a) 88.3% of the variation in *Sales* can be accounted for by variation in unemployment *Rate*.

b) 0.94

c) *Sales* decrease by 2.99 ($B).

29. a) The model seems appropriate. Residual plot has an appropriate scatter of points and nothing remarkable.

b) A linear model is not appropriate. The curve indicates a nonlinear relationship.

c) A linear model is not appropriate. The spread increases as x increases.

31. a) For every 1000 increase in *Housing Starts*, the *Sales* is expected to increase by 0.0535 ($B).

b) $15.25B

c) Residual.

33. Two influential outliers give more weight to the linear regression (slope and intercept) and R^2 at 79%. Predictions will not be accurate for this regression. The scatterplot illustrates why. Without these two data points, R^2 drops to about 31%. The analyst should identify these two customers and refit the model.

35. a) Somewhat appropriate. The variables are quantitative, and the relationship is roughly linear with one or two possible outliers. The model may be influenced by at least one of the outliers. R^2 is 56.9%, which makes the value of r close to 0.75, denoting a moderate association. There are only 10 data points and more data for more store locations would provide information that could alter our conclusion.

b) 75%

c) 56.9% of the variability in annual *Sales* can be accounted for by the variability in the *Population* of the town where the store is located.

37. a) R^2 is an indication of the strength of a model but not the appropriateness of the model.

b) The statement should be rephrased as, "The model predicts the quarterly sales will be $10M when $1.5M is spent on advertising."

39. a)

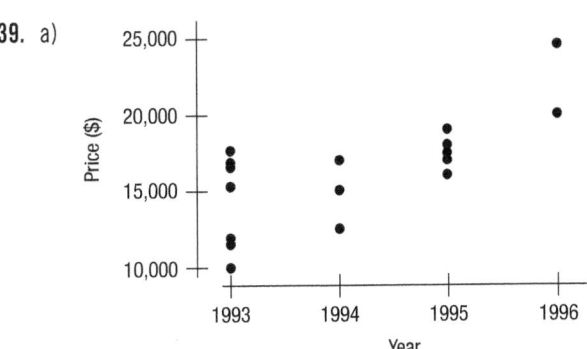

b) There is a strong positive association between *Price* and *Year* of used BMW 850CSi's with some upward curvature.

c) Yes, but with caution because of the curvature.

d) 0.757

e) 57.3% of the variation in *Price* of a used BMW 850 CSi can be accounted for by the *Year* the car was made.

f) The relationship is not perfect. Other factors, such as options, condition, and mileage, may account for some of the variability in price.

41. a) The scatterplot shows a general decreasing trend in *Sales* with *Age*. There is a weak negative association between these variables. There are only 10 data points, with one low outlier and possibly two high ones.

b) Appropriate, but there are only 10 data points with a lot of scatter and three possible outliers—one low value and two high values. Both variables are quantitative and there are no obvious differences in the spread.

c) $\widehat{Sales} = 24.116 - 0.4829 \times Median\ Age.$

d) $8.664M

e) For the same reservations defined in part b), and because the linear model is probably not very accurate. Specifically, in looking at the scatterplot for a *Median Age* of 32, there are no other data than the two high outliers.

43. a) The association between cost of living in 2013 and 2007 is very weak. There are no outliers. The scatterplot indicates that the linear model is appropriate but not likely to reveal much.

b) 7.0% of the variability in cost of living in 2013 can be explained by variability in cost of living in 2007.

c) −0.26

d) $\widehat{Index\ 2013} = 191.6 - 0.683\ Index\ 2007$

e) Moscow was predicted to have an index of 191.6 − .683(134.4) = 99.80, but the 2013 index was only 81.58, so the residual is 81.58 − 99.80 = −18.22%.

45. a)

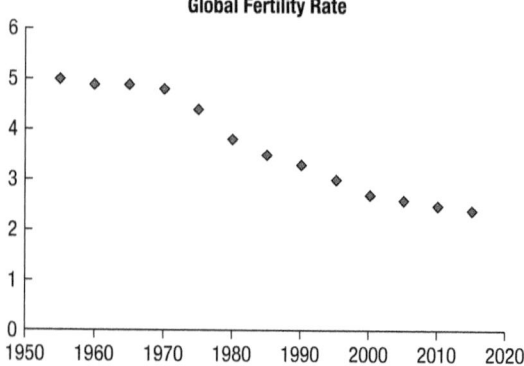

b) Linear regression should not be used directly as the data are not linear.

The data would not become linear using logarithms, squares, or square roots. Therefore, linear regression cannot be used on data transformed in these ways, either.

c)

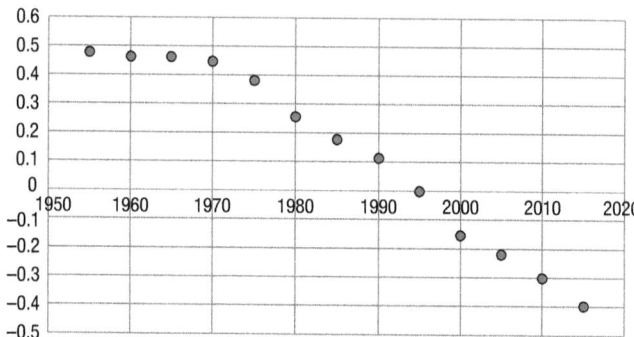

The variables (year and fertility rate) are quantitative. The scatterplot is linear from 1970 onwards after doing the transformation. There are no outliers. The spread is uniform. The residuals show no pattern.

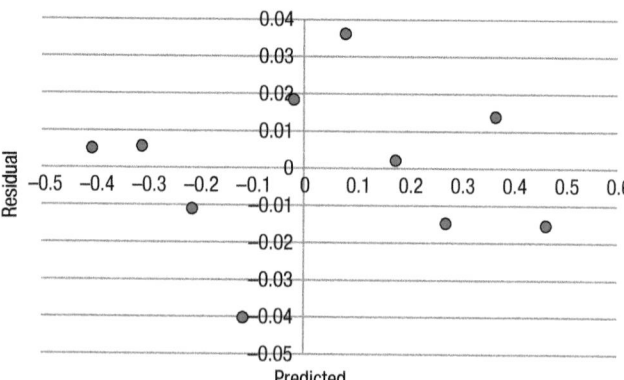

The regression is $\overline{\log 10(fertility - 2)} = 38.35 - 0.0192*year$.

The forecast for 2020 is $\overline{\log(fertility - 2)} = 38.35 - 0.0192*2020 = -0.499$.

The forecast for 2020 is $\widehat{fertility} = 2 + 10^{(-0.499)} = 2.32$.

The original data look as though it trends toward 2 and will not go lower.

Hence we subtract 2 from the data to get a number that will trend toward 0, which is the minimum for taking logarithms.

The data are linear after 1970 but not if we include the period 1955–65.

47. a)

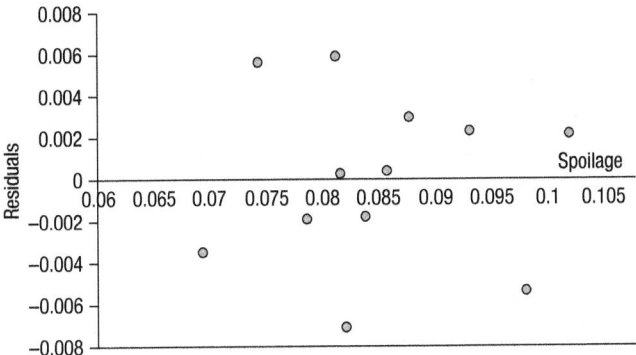

The variables are quantitative. The scatterplot is linear. There are no outliers. The spread is fairly uniform. The linear model is $\widehat{\text{spoilage}} = 0.144 - 0.0215*\text{volume}$.

The residuals show no pattern.

b) $\widehat{\text{Spoilage}} = 0.144 - 0.0215*4 = 5.84\%$

c) The variables are quantitative. The scatterplot is linear. There are no outliers. The spread is fairly uniform. The linear model is $\widehat{\text{volume}} = 6.09 - 39.1*\text{spoilage}$.

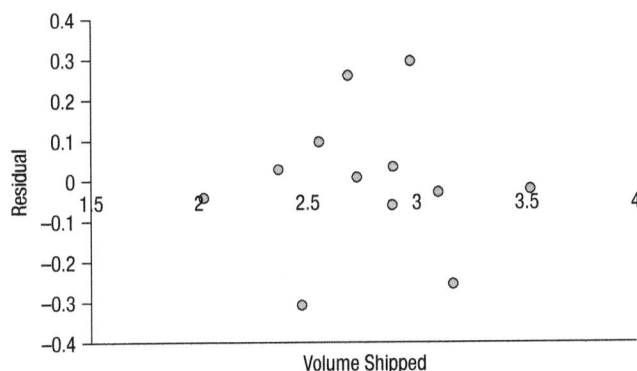

The residuals show no pattern.

d) Volume = $6.09 - 39.1*0.05 = 4.13$ tonnes

e) R-squared is the same for each model = 0.84. R-squared is the square of the correlation coefficient. There is only one correlation coefficient. Therefore the R-squared must be the same for each model

f) For every additional tonne shipped, we estimate a reduction of 2.15% in spoilage. For every percentage reduction in spoilage, we estimate an increase of 0.391 tonnes of volume.

49.

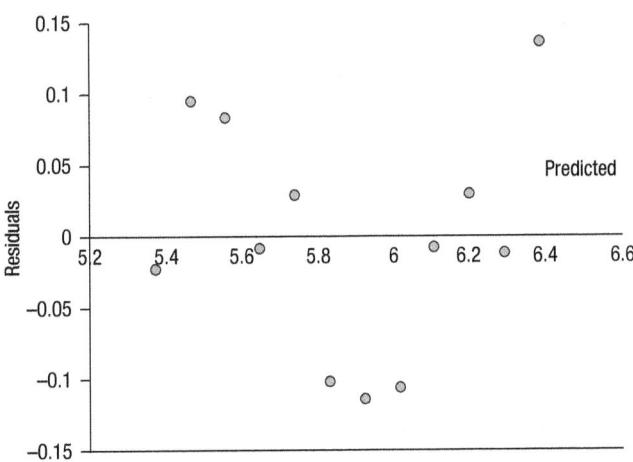

a)

	Quantitative variables	Linear trend	Outliers	Spread
BC	Yes	Yes	No	Uniform
Ontario	Yes	No	No	Uniform
Quebec	Yes	No	Yes	Uniform

b) A linear model can be used for British Columbia. The residuals show no pattern.

$\widehat{\text{Sales}} = 5.28 + 0.0919*\text{Month}$

c) The expected increase in sales is 0.0191 $m per month. This is consistent in the sense that the linear model fits the data throughout the whole year. The *R*-squared is 0.944, showing that the model explains 94.4% of the data variability.

d) $\overline{\text{British Columbia amount}} = 0.0919*0.5 = 0.0459$ $m

51.

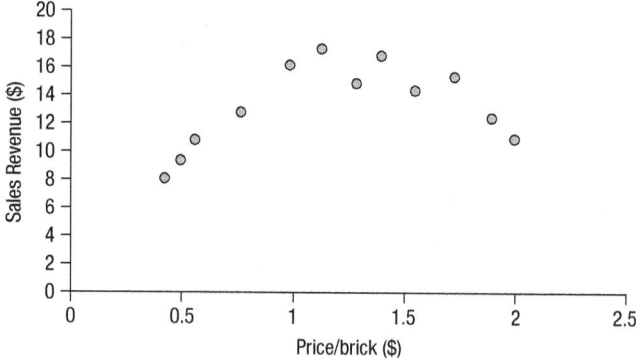

The data provided shows a nonlinear trend, with sales rising to a peak and declining at the higher prices. We do not have a simple way to transform the variables to deal with this shape.

Although some students may have additional knowledge beyond this introductory chapter on linear regression and may be able to fit a quadratic model to these data, the key to the exercise is a careful reading of the question.

The question specifically asks for a linear model, and it also ask us to estimate the *number of bricks*, not the sales revenue. We should therefore use data on the number of bricks, which can easily be calculated from the sales revenue and the price of the bricks. We obtain:

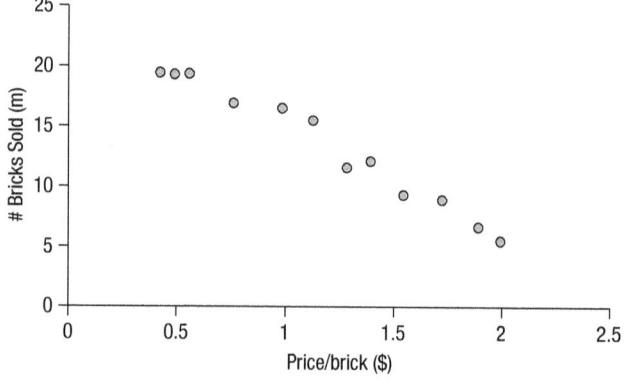

Checking the conditions for linear regression:
- Data are quantitative.
- Trend is linear.
- No outliers.
- Uniform spread throughout the data.

The linear model is: $\overline{\text{Number of bricks}} = 24.1 - 9.13*\text{price}$

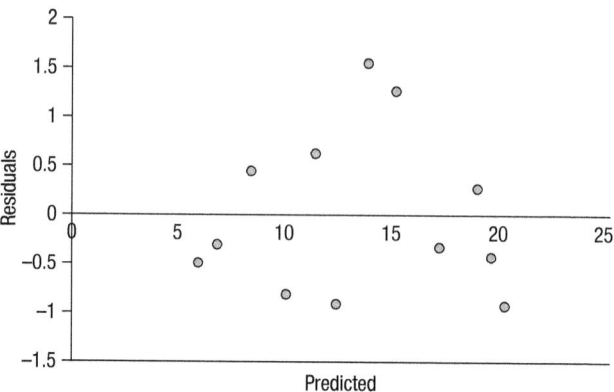

The residuals show no pattern. The numbers of bricks the company could forecast to sell are:
18.0m at $0.67/brick
16.2m at $0.87/brick

53. From the graph of sales, we can see that Larry did not have enough production capacity in quarters 2, 4, 7, and 10. We need to remove these data points from our forecast of demand, since we don't know how much higher demand was than sales during those quarters.

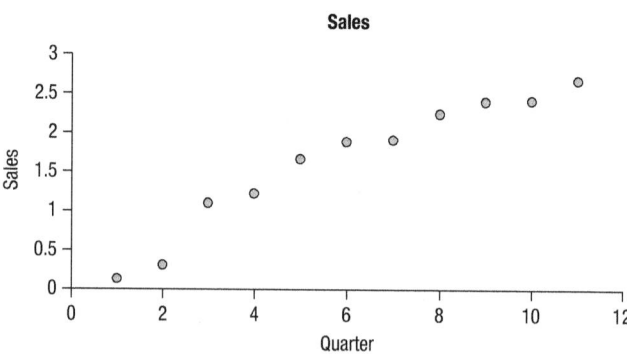

a)

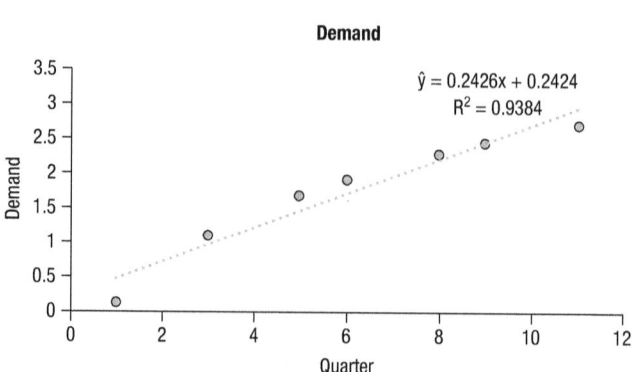

b)

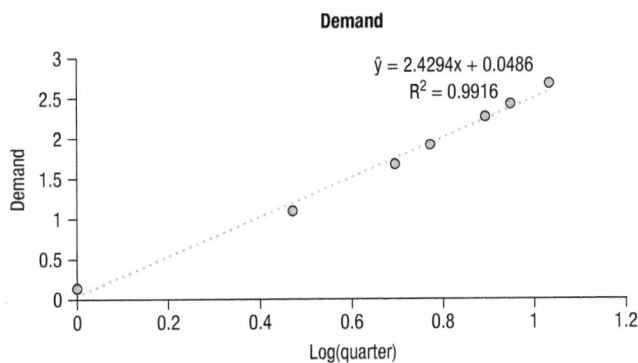

c) The regression in b) is preferable for two reasons. (i) The *R*-squared is higher, indicating that the regression explains more of the variability in the data. (ii) The residuals are negative at the start and at the end and are positive in the middle in a). This indicates that the trend line is curved and is better represented by the log transformation in b).

CHAPTER 7 JUST CHECKING ANSWERS

1. For each additional employee, sales are expected to increase by $122.74 (thousands of dollars).

2. *Sales* per *employee*

3. $1227.40 (thousands of dollars)

4. For each additional employee, monthly sales are expected to increase, on average, $122,740.

5. About 0.85 SDs.

6. About 1.7 SDs below the mean sales.

7. Differences in the number of employees account for about 72.2% of the variation in the monthly sales.

8. It's positive, because the slope (1122.74) in the regression equation is positive.

9. R^2, no. Slope, yes.

CHAPTER 8

SECTION EXERCISE ANSWERS

1. a) Independent (unless a large group of one gender comes to the ATM machine together).
   b) Independent. The last digit of one student's social insurance number provides no information about another.
   c) Not independent. How you perform on one test provides information about other tests.

3. a) It won't work, but it won't hurt, either. Each number drawn is equally likely and independent of the others, so this set of numbers is just as likely as any other in the next drawing.
   b) It won't work, but it won't hurt. Each number drawn is equally likely and independent of the others, so randomly generated numbers are just as likely as any others in the next drawing.

5. a) Subjective, since the probability is based on expertise and opinion.
   b) Empirical, since the probability is based on data.
   c) Theoretical, since the probability is based on the theoretical behaviour of dice.

7. a) 0.75
   b) 0.25
   c) $0.75^2 = 0.5625$
   d) $0.75 + 0.75 - (0.5625) = 0.9375$ or $1 - (0.25^2) = 0.9375$

9. a) $760/1200 = 0.63$
   b) Marginal.
   c) $210/1200 = 0.175$
   d) Joint.

11. a) $210/500 = 0.42$
    b) $210/760 = 0.2763$
    c) $440/500 = 0.88$

13. a) $100\% - 30\% = 70\%$
    b) Joint.
    c)

		Online Banking		
		Yes	No	
Age	Under 50	0.25	0.15	0.40
	50 or Older	0.05	0.55	0.60
		0.30	0.70	1.00

    d) $0.25/0.40 = 0.625$
    e) No, because the conditional probability of banking online for those under 50 is 0.625. The probability of banking online is 0.30, which is not the same.

15. a)

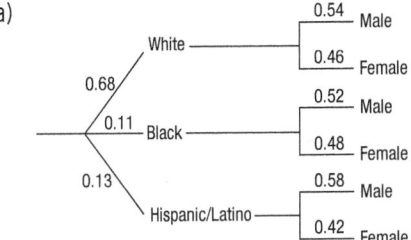

    b) 0.0546
    c) 0.46

17. 0.744

CHAPTER EXERCISE ANSWERS

19. a) Outcomes are equally likely and independent.
   b) Most likely a personal probability expressing his degree of belief that there will be a rate cut.

21. a) The overall probability of an airplane crash does not change as a result of recent crashes.
   b) The overall probability of a crash does not change as a result of a period in which there were no crashes.

23. a) Yes (the sum of the probabilities $= 1$, and each probability is between 0 and 1).
   b) Yes (the sum of the probabilities $= 1$, and each probability is between 0 and 1).
   c) No (the sum of the probabilities > 1).
   d) Yes (the sum of the probabilities $= 1$, and each probability is between 0 and 1).
   e) No (the sum of the probabilities $\neq 1$ and one value is negative).

25. 0.078

27. a) $1 - (0.17 + 0.07 + 0.04) = 0.72$
   b) $1 - (0.07 + 0.04) = 0.89$
   c) $0.17 + 0.07 + 0.04 = 0.28$

29. a) $0.72*0.72 = 0.5184$
   b) $0.28*0.28 = 0.0784$
   c) $1 - 0.5184 = 0.4816$

31. a) The repair needs for the two cars must be independent of each other.
   b) This may not be reasonable. An owner may treat the two cars similarly, taking good (or poor) care of both. This may decrease (or increase) the likelihood that each needs to be repaired.

33. a) $0.64 + 0.21 - 0.17 = 0.68$
   b) $1 - 0.68 = 0.32$
   c) $0.21 - 0.7 = 0.04$

35. a) 0.340
   b) 0.080

37. a) $0.76*(1 - 0.38) = 0.4712$
   b) $(1 - 0.76) + 0.76*(1 - 0.38) = 0.7112$
   c) $1 - 0.76*0.38 = 0.7112$

39. a) Since all of the events are disjoint (a person cannot have more than one blood type!), use the Addition Rule where applicable.
   i) P(Type AB) = 1 − P(not Type AB) = 1 − P(Type O or Type A or Type B) = 1 − (0.46 + 0.42 + 0.09) = 0.03
   ii) P(Type A or Type B) = 0.42 + 0.09 = 0.51
   iii) P(not Type O) = 1 − P(Type O) = 1 − 0.46 = 0.54

   b) Since all of the events are independent (one person's blood type doesn't affect the blood type of the next), the Multiplication Rule may be used.
   i) P(all four are Type O) = (0.46)(0.46)(0.46)(0.46) ≈ 0.045
   ii) P(no one is Type AB) = P(not AB and not AB and not AB and not AB) = (0.97)(0.97)(0.97)(0.97) ≈ 0.885
   iii) P(they are not all Type A) = 1 − P(all Type A) = 1 − (0.42)(0.42)(0.42)(0.42) = 0.969
   iv) P(at least one person is Type B) = 1 − P(no one is Type B) = 1 − (0.91)(0.91)(0.91)(0.91) ≈ 0.314

41. a) $0.4/0.5 = 0.8$
   b) i) P(Zn AND Cu) = 0.4, which is not zero. Zn and Cu are not mutually exclusive.
   ii) Zn and Cu are independent if P(Cu) = P(Cu|Zn). P(Cu) = 0.6: P(Cu|Zn) ≈ 0.8. They are not independent.
   c) P(Cu or Zn) = 0.6 + 0.5 − 0.4 = 0.7 for one sample. For 5 samples $P = 0.7^5 = 0.168$.

43. a) 0.550
   b) 0.792
   c) 0.424
   d) 0.918

45. a) 0.333
   b) 0.429
   c) 0.667

47. a) 0.11
   b) 0.27
   c) 0.407
   d) 0.344

49. No. 28.8% of men with normal blood pressure have high cholesterol, but 40.7% with men with high blood pressure have high cholesterol.

51. a) 0.086
   b) 0.437
   c) 0.156
   d) 0.174
   e) 0.177
   f) No.

53. a) 0.47
   b) 0.266
   c) No, since P(Pool|Garage) = 0.266, which is not equal to P(Pool) = 0.21.
   d) Having a garage and a pool are not mutually exclusive events. P(Pool and Garage) = 0.17, not 0.

55. No, since P(American|Student) = 0.549, which is not equal to P(American) = 0.591.

57. a)

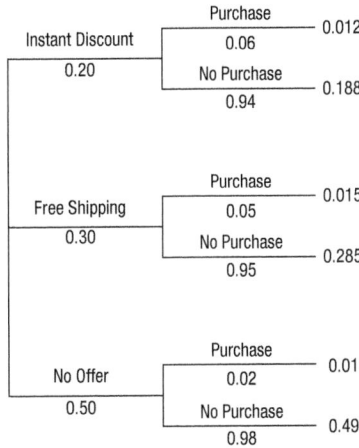

b) 3.7%

c) 0.015/(0.012 + 0.015 + 0.01) = 0.405

59. a)

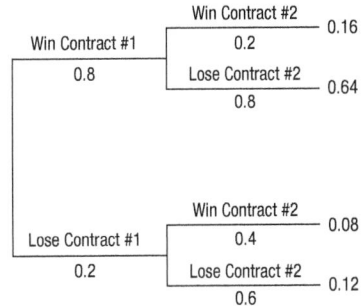

b) 0.8*0.2 = 0.16

c) 0.16/(0.16 + 0.08) = 0.667

61. a)

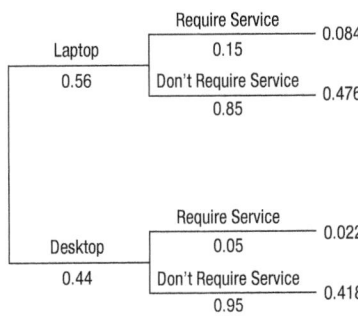

b) 10.6%

c) 0.084/(0.084 + 0.022) = 0.792

63. a) $0.3^3 = 0.027$

b) $(0.4 + 0.1)^3 = 0.125$

c) $0.1^3 = 0.001$

d) $(1 - 0.1)^3 = 0.729$

e) $1 - (1 - 0.4)^3 = 0.784$

65. P(acceptable temperature and gravity) = 0.02*0.09 = 0.0018

P(unacceptable temperature and gravity) = 0.98*0.91 = 0.8918

		Surface temperature		
		Acceptable	**Unacceptable**	
Surface gravity	**Acceptable**	0.0018	0.0882	**0.09**
	Unacceptable	0.0182	0.8918	**0.91**
		0.02	**0.98**	**1.00**

67. a) Empirical.

b) Not independent.

c) If the events were independent, the probability of them both happening is 0.27*0.34 = 0.091. Since they are not independent, we should use a conditional probability in the calculation, which is always larger than the regular probability. Hence the result will be greater than 0.091.

69. Subjective.

71. a) Empirical probability assessment since it is stated that it was based on "experience over the past five years."

b) Subjective probability assessment since it is for a new program for which no data exists.

c) P(admitted | offer accepted after four weeks) P(arrive | admitted)

d) There are two ways an applicant can be admitted: acceptance of offer within four weeks; or acceptance of offer after four weeks and subsequently being admitted. The probability of one or the other of these happening is:

P(admitted) = P(accept ≤ 4 weeks) + P(accept > 4 weeks)*P(admitted | accept > 4 weeks) = 0.61 + 0.12*0.5 = 0.67

P(arrive) = P(admitted)*P(arrive | admitted) = 0.67*0.92 = 0.616

e) Similarly, P(arrive) = (0.8 + 0.1*0.5)*0.95 = 0.807

73. a) (i) CEO: subjective; (ii) stockbroker: empirical

b) P = 0.9*0.8 = 0.72 if the two groups of shareholders behave independently. This is a reasonable assumption since their interests are from the perspectives of different companies.

75. a)

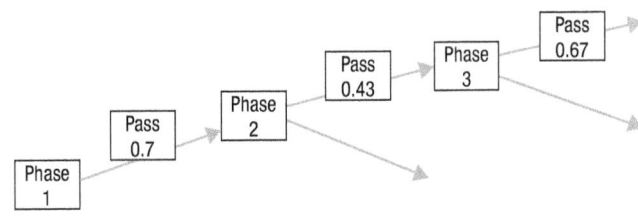

b) Empirical
c) 0.43, 0.67
d) P(Pass all 3 phases) = 0.7*0.43*0.67 = 0.20

77. a) Overconfidence bias may result from the fact that the company believes its equipment to be so good and because it is making profits.
b) Sunk cost bias may result from the fact that they have just put in the effort to submit a detailed bid.
c) Recency bias may result from the fact that the last eight quarters have shown increasing profits, but we are not told about previous performance.

79. We need the probability that all the panels are over 250 watts (=2000/8 watts). Assuming each panel's power is independent of the power of each other panel, the probability is $(0.5)^8 = 0.0039$

CHAPTER 8 JUST CHECKING ANSWERS

1. The probability of going up on the next day is not affected by the previous day's outcome.

2. a) 0.30
   b) 0.30(0.30) = 0.09
   c) $(1 - 0.30)^2 (0.30) = 0.147$
   d) $1 - (1 - 0.30)^5 = 0.832$

3. a)

		Weekday		
		Yes	No	Total
Before 5:00 P.M.	Yes	0.07	0.41	0.48
	No	0.20	0.32	0.52
	Total	0.27	0.73	1.00

b) P(WD | B5) = P(WD and B5) / P(B5)
   = 0.07/0.48
   = 0.146
c) No, shoppers can do both (and 7% do).
d) To be independent, we'd need P(WD | B5) = P(WD). P(WD | B5) = 0.146, but P(WD) = 0.27. Since these aren't equal, the two events "before 5 p.m." and "weekday" are not independent.

4. The biosketch is neutral and gives no information as to whether the person is an engineer or librarian. P(engineer | biosketch) = P(engineer) = 0.86 = the prior probability, given that there are six times as many engineers as librarians in Canada.

5. Since the initial (prior) probability of being an engineer is P(engineer) = 0.86, we have:
   P(engineer | female) = 0.2*0.86/(0.2*0.86 + 0.75*0.14) = 0.62
   There is more chance that this woman is an engineer than a librarian since there are many more engineers in total than librarians in total.

CHAPTER 9

SECTION EXERCISE ANSWERS

1. a) Discrete.
   b) Yes/no.

3. 1.2

5. 0.748

7. a) $19
   b) $7

9. a) $\mu = 30; \sigma = 6$
   b) $\mu = 26; \sigma = 5$
   c) $\mu = 30; \sigma = 5.39$
   d) $\mu = -10; \sigma = 5.39$

11. a) $110 and $12.
    b) $450 and $40.
    c) $190 and $14.422.
    d) X and Y are independent for the SD calculation, but not necessarily for the sum.

13. Yes.

15. Geometric, $p = 0.26$.

17. a) $e^{(-0.6)} \times \dfrac{0.6^0}{0!} = 0.5488$
    b) 0.4512

19. a) Yes. The time of delivery is uniformly distributed over the next three weeks.
    b) No. A discrete uniform distribution could be used for the number of the solar panel that fails, but not a continuous one.

21. In economics the student scored 1.25 standard deviations above the mean. On the math exam, she scored 1.50 standard deviations above the mean, so she did "better" on the math exam.

23. You scored 2.2 standard deviations above the mean.

25. a) According to the 68–95–99.7 Rule, only 5% of the distribution is beyond two standard deviations from the mean, so only 2.5% is more than two standard deviations above the mean. Less than 3% of the distribution is above a z-score of 2.20. You qualify.
    b) You need to assume that the distribution is unimodal and symmetric for the 68–95–99.7 Rule to apply.

27. a)

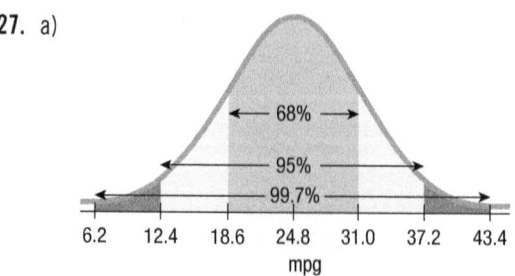

b) 18.6 to 31.0 mpg
c) 16%
d) 13.5%
e) Less than 12.4 mpg

29. Yes. The histogram is unimodal and symmetric and the Normal probability plot is straight.

31. a) $\sigma = 3.48$; $z = 0.934$; $P = 0.175$.
b) Answers may vary. That's a fairly high proportion, but the decision depends on the relative costs of not selling seats and bumping passengers.

33. $\lambda = 1/5850 = 0.000171$.
P(failure time < 1000) $= 1 - e^{-1000\lambda} = 0.157$.

CHAPTER EXERCISE ANSWERS

35. a) 1, 2, 3, . . ., n
b) Discrete.

37. a) 0, 1, 2, 3, 4
b) Discrete.
c) No, the outcomes are not equally likely.

39. a) The mean for the relay team's total time in this event is $\mu = 50.72 + 55.51 + 49.43 + 44.91 = 200.57$ seconds.
The standard deviation for the relay team's total time in this event is
$$\sigma = \sqrt{0.24^2 + 0.22^2 + 0.25^2 + 0.21^2}$$
$$= \sqrt{0.2126 \text{ seconds}^2} \approx 0.46 \text{ seconds}$$
b) Find the probability that the relay team's total time in this event is less than 199.48 seconds. Since each swimmer's times follow a Normal mode and we know the expected value and standard deviation of the relay team's total time, we can convert 199.48 seconds to its corresponding z score as follows:
$$z = \frac{199.48 - 200.57}{0.46} = -2.37;$$
find $P(z < -2.37) = 0.0089$

41. a) 2.25
b) 1.26

43. $\mu = 74.0$ seconds.
$\sigma = 20.57$ seconds.

45. a) Profits on insurance are highly variable. Although there will be many small gains, there will occasionally be large losses when the company has to pay a claim.
b) $\mu = \$300$
$\sigma = \$8485.28$
c) $\mu = \$150,000$
$\sigma = \$189,736.66$

d) A flood that affects multiple homes in a given area. A forest fire that destroys many homes in the same rural community.

47. a) B = # of basic models; D = # of deluxe models; Net profit = $120B + $150D − $200
b) $\mu = \$928$.
c) $\sigma = \$187.45$.
d) Mean − no; SD − yes (sales are independent).

49. a) Let X_i = price of ith Hulk figure sold; Y_i = price of ith Iron Man figure sold; Insertion Fee = $0.55; T = Closing Fee = $0.0875(X_1 + X_2 + \cdots + X_{19} + Y_1 + \cdots + Y_{13})$
Net Income = $(X_1 + X_2 + \cdots + X_{19} + Y_1 + \cdots + Y_{13})$ $- 32(0.55) - 0.0875(X_1 + X_2 + \ldots + X_{19} + Y_1 + \cdots + Y_{13})$.
b) $(1 - 0.0875)*(19*\$12.11 + 13*\$10.19) - 32*\$0.55 = \$313.24$
c) Variance = $(1 - 0.0875)^2*(19*1.38^2 + 13*0.77^2) = 36.55$. SD = $6.05.
d) Yes, to compute the standard deviation.

51. a) No, not Bernoulli trials. Possible outcomes are 1, 2, 3, 4, 5, and 6. There are more than two outcomes.
b) Yes, it may be considered a Bernoulli trial. Only two possible outcomes: Type A and not Type A. Assuming that the 120 donors are representative of the population, the probability of having Type A blood is 43%. The trials are not independent because the population is finite, but the 120 donors represent less than 10% of all possible donors.
c) No, not Bernoulli trials. The probability of choosing a man changes after each promotion and the 10% Condition is violated.
d) No, not Bernoulli trials. We would be sampling without replacement, so the trials are not independent. Samples without replacement may be considered Bernoulli trials if the sample size is less than 10% of the population, but 500 is more than 10% of 3000.
e) Yes, it may be considered a Bernoulli trial. Only two possible outcomes: sealed properly and not sealed properly. Probability that a package is unsealed is constant as long as the packages checked are a representative sample of all. Also, the 24 packages are less than 10% of the population.

53. a) 0.0819
b) 0.0064
c) 0.16
d) 0.992

55. 14.28, or about 15 patients.

57. a) 0.0783 pixels.
b) 0.280
c) $1 - \dfrac{e^{-0.047}0.047^0}{0!} = 0.0459$
d) $1 - 0.954087 - 0.044842 - 0.001054 = 0.000017$

59. a) $\dfrac{e^{-1.2273}1.2273^0}{0!} = 0.293$

b) $\dfrac{e^{-1.2273}1.2273^1}{1!} = 0.3597$

c) $1 - 0.293 - 0.3597 = 0.347$

61. a) $0.67^6 = 0.0905$

b) $0.67^4 \times 0.33^2 \times \dfrac{6!}{(4!2!)} = 0.329$

c) $P(4) + P(5) + P(6) = 0.3291 + 0.2673 + 0.0905 = 0.687$

63. a) 0.239

b) Nova Scotia is typical of Canada with respect to the occurrence of this type of traffic accident.

c) We have no reason to think last week in Nova Scotia was exceptional since the probability of this many accidents on roads is quite high at 0.239.

65. a) $\mu = 53.6$ serves; $\sigma = 4.2$ serves.

b) $np = 80 \times 0.67 = 53.6 \geq 10$; $n = 80 \times 0.33 = 26.4 \geq 10$; serves assumed to be independent.

c) 0.0034 (0.0048 with continuity correction).

67. a) 16%

b) 50%

c) 95%

d) 0.15%

69. a) 2.4%

b) 8.0%

c) −8.8%

d) $-3.2\% < x < 8.0\%$

71. a) 0.50

b) 0.16

c) 0.025

d) More than 1.298 is more unusual.

73. a) One standard deviation above the mean = 1.19 + 0.043 = 1.233

b) Mean = 1.19

c) Two standard deviations on either side of the mean = $1.19 \pm 2*0.043 = (1.104, 1.276)$

d) Two standard deviations below the mean = $1.19 - 2*0.043 = 1.104$

75. a) Quarterly return > 8.50%

b) Quarterly return < 4.69%

c) 5.26% < quarterly return < 7.14%

d) Quarterly return > 4.69%

77. a) About 16%.

b) Using data, one standard deviation below the mean is $3.66 - 4.93 = -1.27$ hours, which is impossible.

c) Since the standard deviation is larger than the mean, the distribution is strongly skewed to the right and not symmetric.

79. a) The Normal model.

b) 30.85%

c) 17.00%

d) Using P = 0.75, Q3 = 204.19. Similarly Q1 = 171.81. IQR = 32.38 mg/dL

e) z = 1.036. Top 15% are above 188 + 1.036*24 = 212.9 mg/dL.

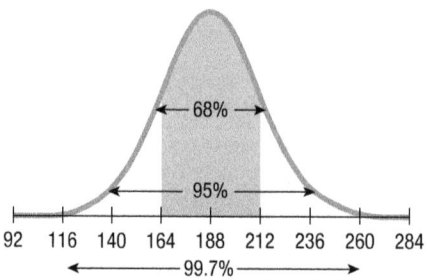

81. a) 5.3 grams.

b) 6.4 grams.

c) Younger hens lay eggs that have more consistent weights than the eggs laid by the older hens. The standard deviation of the weights of eggs laid by the younger hens is lower than the standard deviation of the weights of eggs laid by the older hens.

d) According to the Normal model, the mean weight is 62.7 grams, with a standard deviation of 6.2 grams.

83. a) Poisson model, since it is a good model to use when the data consist of counts of occurrences. The events must be independent and the mean number of occurrences stays constant.

b) 0.1353

c) 0.3233

85. a) Since we are told the average rate per year, and assuming that each of these accidents occurs independently of others, we use a Poisson distribution.

b) $1 - P(0) - P(1) - P(2) = 1 - 0.00029 - 0.00235 - 0.00959 = 0.988$

c) Last week was exceptional compared to the recent year, since the probability of getting this few accidents of this type is very low: 0.0122.

87. a) The exponential model can be used to model the time between events, especially when the number of arrivals of those events can be modelled by a Poisson model.

b) 0.8647

c) 1/2 day.

89. Poisson distribution with average rate = $\lambda = 4.1$

$$P(x \text{ accidents}) = \dfrac{e^{-\lambda}\lambda^x}{x!}$$

a) $P(0) = 0.01657$
$P(1) = 0.06795$
$P(2) = 0.1393$
$P(2 \text{ or fewer}) = 0.224$

b) There is no evidence that the government's measures were or were not effective, since having 2 accidents or fewer has a probability of 0.22 even without any government action.

91. Poisson distribution with average rate $= \lambda = 4.2$.

$$P(x \text{ accidents}) = \frac{e^{-\lambda}\lambda^x}{x!}$$

a) $P(6) = 0.11$
b) $P(0) = 0.0150$
   $P(1) = 0.0630$
   $P(2) = 0.1323$
   $P(3) = 0.1852$
   $P(\text{less than } 4) = 0.40$
c) We are assuming thunderstorms occur at random, independently of each other.

93. Normal approximation to the binomial

N	308
P	0.0074
Np	2.2792 not >10
Nq	305.7208 >10
Sqrt(npq)	1.504106
X	7
Z	3.471033
P	0.999741

We cannot tell whether Aboriginals are better represented than previously since a key assumption (below) is not true.
We are assuming the MPs are randomly selected from the Canadian population. This may or may not be true.
We are assuming the Canadian population is more than 3080, which is true.
We are assuming $np > 10$, which is not true, and $nq > 10$, which is true.

95. a) Expected cost $= \$0.39\text{bn}$.
b) Since successful drilling is dependent on geology and the different revenues are dependent on future prices, they are independent and we can multiply the probabilities.
   Expected revenue $= \$0.565\text{bn}$.
   Expected profit $= 0.565 - 0.065 - 0.39 = \$0.11\text{bn}$.

97. $\$1.9\text{bn}$.

99.

Revenue			mean		
Sales	50	300	175		
Svc contract	2	5	3.5		
Profit			mean	z	SD
Sales (X)	5	30	17.5	1.644854	7.59946
Svc contract (Y)	0.6	1.5	1.05	1.644854	0.273581

a) Expected total revenue $= 175*15000 + 3.5*12000 = \$2667\text{m}$

b) Expected total profit $= 17.5*15000 + 1.05*12000 = \$275.1\text{m}$
c) $\text{Var}(15000*X + 12000*Y) = 225000000 \text{ Var}(X) + 144000000 \text{ Var}(Y) = 13004931171$
   SD of total profits $= \text{sqrt(Variance)} = 114039.2 \$K$
   To calculate the 90% range, we use $z = 1.645$.
   The range is the mean $= \$275.1\text{m}$ plus/minus $1.645*\$114.0392\text{m}$.

	Lower	Upper
Range of total profits	$87.5m	$462.6m

101. Let O be the Osaka price, T be the Toronto price, and F be the Frankfurt price.
$P(O < T) = P(O - T < 0)$
We calculate the mean and SD for $O - T$ and $F - T$ and then the corresponding z and P values.

Region	Purchasing Office City	Estimated Price	Standard Deviation		z	P
Asia	Osaka	7.8	2.3			
N.America	Toronto	6.1	1.2			
EU	Frankfurt	7.1	0.6			
$O - T$		1.7	2.594224		−0.6553	0.256137
$F - T$		1	1.341641		−0.74536	0.228028

a) We should issue an RFP in Osaka because there is a probability of 0.256 that the price there will be lower than in Toronto
b) We should not issue an RFP in Frankfurt because there is a probability of 0.228 that the price there will be lower than in Toronto
c) Although the estimated price in Osaka is highest of all three locations, the uncertainty in that price is also high, resulting in a good chance that the price will be lower than in Toronto.

103. Answers will vary.

105. Supernova occurrence follows a Poisson distribution.
a) $\lambda = 0.2$ per 100 million years. $P(>0) = 1 - P(0) = 1 - \exp(-0.2) = 0.18$
b) $\lambda = 2$ per 100 million years. $P(0) = \exp(-2) = 0.14$

107. Purchases follow a Poisson distribution with mean 4.5 per month, assuming customers arrive at random.
$P(n) = \exp(-4.5)*4.5^n / n!$
$P(>6) = 1 - P(0) - P(1) - P(2) - P(3) - P(4) - P(5) - P(6) = 1 - 0.831 = 0.169$

CHAPTER 9 JUST CHECKING ANSWERS

1. a) $[100 + 100 = 200]$ seconds
b) $\sqrt{50^2 + 50^2} = 70.7$ seconds
c) The times for the two customers are independent.

2. There are two outcomes (contact, no contact); the probability of contact stays constant at 0.76, and random calls should be independent.

3. Binomial (or Normal approximation).

4. Geometric.

5. a) On the first test, the mean is 88 and the SD is 4, so $z = (90 - 88)/4 = 0.5$. On the second test, the mean is 75 and the SD is 5, so $z = (80 - 75)/5 = 1.0$. The first test has the lower z-score, so it is the one that will be dropped.
   b) The second test is 1 standard deviation above the mean, farther away than the first test, so it's the better score relative to the class, and it is, therefore, fair to retain this mark.

6. The mean is 184 centimetres, with a standard deviation of 8 centimetres. Two metres are 200 centimetres, which is 2 standard deviations above the mean. We expect 2.28% of the men to be above 2 metres.

7. a) We know that 68% of the time we'll be within 1 standard deviation (2 min) of 20. So 32% of the time we'll arrive in less than 18 or more than 22 minutes. Half of those times (16%) will be greater than 22 minutes, so 84% will be less than 22 minutes.
   b) 24 minutes is 2 standard deviations above the mean. From Table Z we find that 2.28% of the times will be more than 24 minutes.
   c) Traffic incidents may occasionally increase the time it takes to get to school, so the driving times may be skewed to the right, and there may be outliers.
   d) If so, the Normal model would not be appropriate and the percentages we predict would not be accurate.

8. When passengers arrive as a group, the Poisson distribution cannot be used. Passengers arriving by metro and by bus definitely arrive in groups. Sometimes people on foot or in taxis do too. It is only for people arriving individually on foot or by taxi that we can use the Poisson distribution.

9. The number of passengers arriving in a given time interval is Poisson. The time interval between passengers is Exponential.

10. Poisson, only.

11. Exponential or Poisson.

CHAPTER 10

SECTION EXERCISE ANSWERS

1. a) Normal.
   b) 0.36
   c) They wouldn't change. The shape is still approximately Normal and the mean is still the true proportion.

3. a) 0.0339
   b) 0.5
   c) 0.842 (0.843 using a rounded answer from part a)
   d) 0.0091
   e) 0.0384

5. Yes. Assuming the survey is random, they should be independent. We don't know the true proportion, so we can't check np and nq, but we have observed 10 successes, which is sufficient.

7. a) Prices cannot be less than 0, but there is nothing to prevent some from being expensive, so they are likely to be skewed to the high end.
   b) It should resemble the population distribution and be skewed to the right.
   c) Nearly Normal. The Central Limit Theorem tells us this.

9. a) Normal.
   b) 215mg/dl.
   c) $30/\sqrt{42} = 4.63$ mg/dl.
   d) Only c would change, to $30/\sqrt{100} = 3.0$ mg/dl.

11. a) 0.0357
    b) 400

CHAPTER EXERCISE ANSWERS

13. All the histograms are centred near 0.05. As n gets larger, the histograms approach the Normal shape, and the variability in the sample proportions decreases.

15. a) Symmetric, because probabilities of success and failure are equal.
    b) 0.5
    c) 0.125
    d) $np = 8 < 10$

17. a) About 68% should have proportions between 0.4 and 0.6, about 95% between 0.3 and 0.7, and about 99.7% between 0.2 and 0.8.
    b) $np = 12.5$, $nq = 12.5$; both are ≥ 10.
    c)

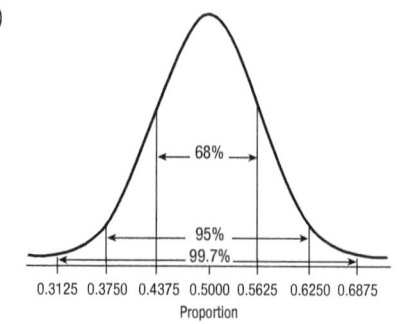

$np = nq = 32$; both are ≥ 10.
    d) Becomes narrower (less spread around 0.5).

19. a) This is a fairly unusual result: about 2.26 SDs above the mean.

b) The probability of that is about 0.012. So, in a class of 100, this is certainly a reasonable possibility.

21. a)

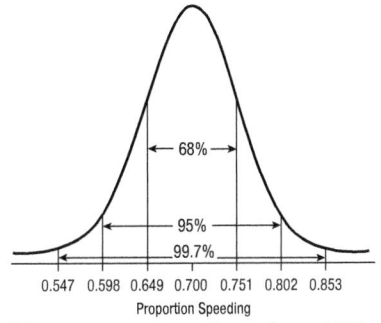

Proportion Speeding

b) 80 cars represent less than 10% of all cars. Both $np = 56$ and $nq = 24 \geq 10$. Drivers *may* be independent of each other, but if the flow of traffic is very fast, they may not be. Or weather conditions may affect all drivers; in these cases they may get more or fewer speeders than they expect.

23. a) Assume that these children are typical of the population. They represent fewer than 10% of all children. We expect 20.4 nearsighted and 149.6 not; both are at least 10.

b)

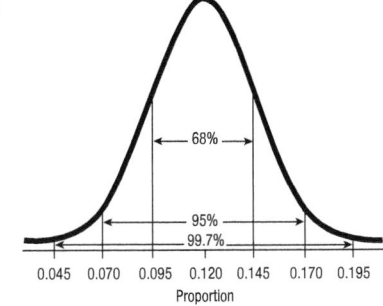

Proportion

c) There is a 0.95 probability of getting between 12 and 29.

25.

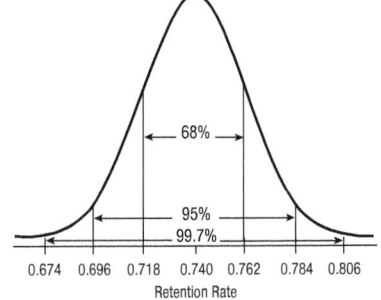

Retention Rate

These are not random samples, and not all colleges may be typical (representative); $np = 296$, $nq = 104$ are large enough. 400 students is less than 10% of all college students.

27. 0.212. It is reasonable to think that those polled are independent of each other and represent less than

10% of all potential voters. We assume the sample was selected at random. The Success/Failure Condition is met: $np = 208$, $nq = 192$. Both ≥ 10.

29. 0.088 using a sampling distribution with a mean of 0.08 and a standard deviation of 0.022.

31. a) Normal, centre at μ, standard deviation $\sigma/\sqrt{n}$.

b) Standard deviation will be smaller. Centre will remain the same.

33. a) The histogram is unimodal and slightly skewed to the right, and centred at 36 inches with a standard deviation near four inches.

b) All the histograms are centred near 36 inches. As n gets larger, the histograms approach the Normal shape and the variability in the sample means decreases. The histograms are fairly Normal by the time the sample reaches size five.

35. a)

n	Observed mean	Theoretical mean	Observed st.dev.	Theoretical st.dev.
2	36.314	36.33	2.855	2.842
5	36.314	36.33	1.805	1.797
10	36.341	36.33	1.276	1.271
20	36.339	36.33	0.895	0.899

b) They are all very close to what we would expect.

c) For samples as small as five, the sampling distribution of sample means is unimodal and very symmetric.

d) The distribution of the original data is nearly unimodal and symmetric, so it doesn't take a very large sample size for the distribution of sample means to be approximately Normal.

37.

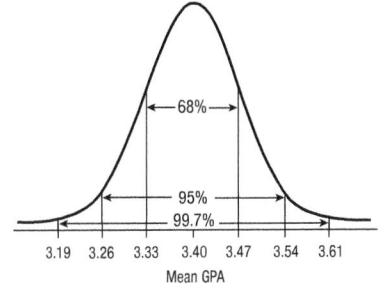

Mean GPA

Normal, $\mu = 3.4, \sigma = 0.07$. We assume that the students are randomly assigned to the seminars and represent less than 10% of all possible students, and that individual GPAs are independent of one another.

39. The standard deviation of the sampling distribution model for the mean is $\dfrac{\sigma}{\sqrt{n}}$. So cities in which the average is based on a smaller number of drivers will have greater variation in their averages and will be more likely to be both safest and least safe.

41. Assume for (a) and (b) the % is the same in Montreal and Quebec.
   a) $SD = \sqrt{0.29*0.71/100} = 0.0454$; $z = (0.3 - 0.29)/0.454 = 0.220$; $P = 0.413$.
   b) With n = 400 we need 25% common law. $SD = 0.0227$; $z = (0.25 - 0.29)/0.0227 = -1.76$; $P = 0.961$. There is a probability of 0.961 of getting at least 100 common law couples.

43. a) 0.884
   b) 0.984
   c) A sample size of 20 is too small to perform the required calculations, since the values of np would be 20×0.38 and 20×0.11, which are both less than 10.

45. a) $SD = 1/\sqrt{(52)} = 0.139$ months; $z = (25.6 - 26)/0.139 = -2.88$; $P = 0.00196$.
   b) $SD = 0.38/\sqrt{(52)} = 0.0527$ Kg; $z = (3.9 - 3.75)/0.0527 = 2.846$; $P = 0.00221$.
   c) First calculate P(> 4.25). $z = (4.25 - 3.75)/0.38 = 1.316$; $P = 0.0941$.
   $SD = \sqrt{(0.0941(1 - 0.0941)/250)} = 0.0185$; $z = (20/250 - 0.0941)/0.0185 = -0.765$; $P = 0.778$.

47. a) Some people work much longer than the mean plus two or three standard deviations. Also, many people stay a short time before moving on. Finally, the left tail cannot be very long, because a person cannot work at a job for fewer than zero years (or work fewer than zero hours).
   b) The Central Limit Theorem guarantees that the distribution of the mean time is Normally distributed for large sample sizes, as long as the assumptions and conditions are satisfied. The CLT doesn't help us with the distribution of individual times.

49. a) 0.0478
   b) 0.863
   c) $SD = 0.12/\sqrt{3} = 0.069$; $z = (10 - 10.2)/0.069 = -2.90$; $P = 0.0019$
   d) $SD = 0.12/\sqrt{24} = 0.024$; $z = (10 - 10.2)/0.024 = -8.33$; P is essentially zero.

51. a) Mean = $(100*0 + 600*1 + 200*2 + 100*3)/1000 = 1.3$
   b) 1.3 assuming it is a random sample
   c) $s = \sqrt{((100*(0 - 1.3)^2 + \ldots + 100*(3 - 1.3)^2)/1000)} = 0.781$
   d) $SE = 0.781/\sqrt{(1000)} = 0.0247$
   e) (i) no, because the survey question does not have a YES/NO answer; (ii) yes, since the survey question has a quantitative answer.

53. n = 1023; sample proportion = 0.54; population proportions = 0.48.

$$SD\,(\text{sample proportion}) = \sqrt{\frac{0.48 * 0.52}{1023}} = 0.01562$$

$$z = \frac{0.52 - 0.48}{0.01562} = 3.841$$

P = 0.00006122

55. a) Same as in the population: 145,010/1,066,610 = 0.1360
   b) np and nq are both greater than or equal to 10 and the sample is less than 10% of the population. Target proportion = 300/2000 = 0.15. $SD = \sqrt{(0.136*0.864/2000)} = 0.0108$.
   $z = (0.15 - 0.136)/0.0108 = 1.296$; $P = 1 - 0.9025 = 0.0975$.
   c) # couple families = 1,066,610 − 145,010 = 921,610; # of people in couple families = 1,066,610*2.969033 − 145,010*2.61644 = 2,787,390
   Same as in the population: 2,787,390/921,610 = 3.024
   d) Need the SD of the number of people per couple family in order to answer this question.
   e) The median for couple families in the population cannot be deduced from the median for total families and lone-parent families since medians cannot be added/subtracted.
   f) Cannot answer this question for the reason given in (e) and also because the Central Limit Theorem applies to means, not to medians.

57. a) Expected number that have hepatitis C = 2500*0.03 = 75; np and nq are both greater than or equal to 10 and the sample is less than 10% of the population of BC; $SD = \sqrt{(0.03*0.97/2500)} = 0.003412$; $z = (0.02 - 0.03)/0.003412 = -2.931$; $P = 0.00169$
   b) $SE = 12.5/\sqrt{(2500)} = 0.25$
   c) $np = 76$ but $nq = 4$, which is too low. The calculation cannot be performed.
   d) Part c) cannot be answered because the sample size is too small. We need at a minimum $nq = 10$, i.e., $n = 10/0.05 = 200$ people in the sample with hepatitis C.

59. a) Sample size and standard deviation of the sample for Ontario.
   b) Sample size and standard deviation of the population for Alberta.

61. a) $np = 325 > 10$; $nq = 675 > 10$; $SE = \sqrt{(0.325*0.675/1000)} = 0.0148$
   b) $SE = s/\sqrt{(1000)}$
   $s = \sqrt{(((1 - 0.325)^2*325 + (0 - 0.325)^2*675)/1000)} = 0.468$
   $SE = 0.468/\sqrt{(1000)} = 0.0148$
   c) Parts a) and b) address the same issue using different approaches. Part a) uses the sampling distribution of a proportion; b) uses the sampling distribution of a mean.

CHAPTER 10 JUST CHECKING ANSWERS

1. A Normal model (approximately).

2. At the actual proportion of all customers who like the new location.

3. $SD(\hat{p}) = \sqrt{\dfrac{(0.5)(0.5)}{100}} = 0.05.$

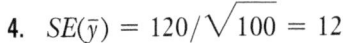

4. $SE(\bar{y}) = 120/\sqrt{100} = 12$.

5. Decreases according to $1/\sqrt{sample\ size}$.

6. The standard error decreases to $1/\sqrt{2} = 70.7\%$ of the original value.

CHAPTER 11

SECTION EXERCISE ANSWERS

1. a) p is the proportion of all backpacks entering the stadium that contain alcoholic beverages; $\hat{p}$ is the proportion in the sample $\hat{p} = 17/130 = 0.131$. Yes. This seems to be a random sample.

   b) p is the proportion of all visitors to the website who approve of recent "bossnapping." $\hat{p}$ is the proportion in the sample $\hat{p} = 0.492$. No. This is a volunteer sample and may be biased.

   c) This question is about the mean weight, not a proportion. The methods of this chapter are not appropriate, see Chapter 13.

3. a) 0.35
   b) 0.034
   c) (0.282,0.418) or without rounding (0.283,0.417)

5. a) False. Doesn't make sense. Workers are not proportions.
   b) True.
   c) False. Our best guess is 0.48, not 0.95.
   d) False. Our best guess is 0.48, but we're not sure that's correct.
   e) False. The statement should be about the true proportion, not future samples.

7. a) Narrower. (0.295, 0.405) (using 1.645 standard errors on each side)
   b) Narrower. (0.296, 0.404)
   c) Wider. (0.263, 0.437) (using 2.576 standard errors on each side)
   d) 4 times as large: 800 students.

9. a) *Population*—all customers who recently bought new cars; *sample*—167 people surveyed about their experience; *p*—proportion of all new car buyers who are dissatisfied with the salesperson; $\hat{p}$—proportion of new car buyers surveyed who are dissatisfied with the salesperson (0.03). We can't use the methods of Chapter 11 because only five people were dissatisfied. Also, the sample may not be representative.

   b) *Population*—all college students; *sample*—2883 who were asked about their cell phones at the football stadium; *p*—proportion of all college students with cell phones; $\hat{p}$—proportion of college students at the football stadium with cell phones (0.778). We should be cautious—students entering the football stadium may not represent all students. Sample may be biased.

11. a) About 2401 (using 1.96 standard errors).
    b) About 4148 (using 2.576 standard errors).
    c) About 385 (using 1.96 standard errors).

13. a) 141
    b) 318
    c) 564

15. $SE(\hat{p}_1 - \hat{p}_2) = \sqrt{\dfrac{\hat{p}_1\hat{q}_1}{n_1} + \dfrac{\hat{p}_2\hat{q}_2}{n_2}}$

    $= \sqrt{\dfrac{0.154*0.846}{195} + \dfrac{0.094*0.906}{256}} = 0.03164$

    The critical value for a 99% confidence interval: $z^* = 2.576$. The confidence interval for the difference between two proportions is:

    $(\hat{p}_1 - \hat{p}_2) \pm z^* SE(\hat{p}_1 - \hat{p}_2) = 0.154 - 0.094 \pm$

    $2.576*0.03164 = 0.06 \pm 0.0815$

    i.e., between –0.0215 and 0.1415.

17. The true percentage of employees with a certain opinion is within 4% of the executive's estimate with some degree of confidence.

19. a) *Population*—all cars in the local area; *sample*—134 cars stopped; *p*—proportion of all cars with safety problems; $\hat{p}$—proportion of cars in sample that have safety problems (10.4%).
    All conditions are met, so a one-proportion z-interval can be calculated.

    b) *Population*—the general public; *sample*—602 viewers who logged on to the website; *p*—proportion of the general public who think corporate corruption is "worse"; $\hat{p}$—proportion of viewers who logged on to the website and voted that corporate corruption is "worse" (81.1%).
    Sample is not random. No confidence interval can be calculated.

21. If repeated samples of the same sample size were taken and confidence intervals constructed (according to the formula given in the text), in the long run 95% of these intervals would contain the true on-time arrival rate.

    a) Not correct. This is not the meaning of a confidence interval.
    b) Not correct. Different samples will give different results. Most likely, none of the samples will have *exactly* 88% on-time orders.
    c) Not correct. A confidence interval says something about the unknown population proportion, not the sample proportion in different samples.
    d) Not correct. In this sample we *know* that 88% arrived on time. There is no need to make an interval for the sample proportion.
    e) Not correct. The interval is about the proportion of on-time orders, not about the days.

23. a) False. We are less sure of falling in a smaller interval.
   b) True.
   c) False. The margin of error decreases as the square root of the sample size increases. We need a sample 4 times as large.

25. We are 90% confident that between 29.9% and 47.0% of Canadian cars are made in Japan.

27. a) $1.645*\sqrt{0.38*0.62/1012} = 2.5\%$
   b) Pollsters are 90% confident that the true proportion of adults who do not use email is within 2.5% of the estimated 38%.
   c) A 99% confidence interval requires a larger margin of error. In order to increase confidence, the interval must be wider.
   d) 3.9%
   e) Smaller margins of error will give us less confidence in the interval.

29. a) (12.7%, 18.6%)
   b) We are 95% confident that between 12.7% and 18.6% of all accidents involve teenagers.
   c) About 95% of random samples of size 582 will produce intervals that contain the true proportion of accidents involving teenagers.
   d) The confidence interval contradicts the assertion of the politician. The figure quoted by the politician—one out of every five, or 20%—is outside the interval.

31. The grocer can't conclude anything about the opinions of all his customers from the survey. The Randomization Condition is not met.

33. (15.2%, 20.8%); however, this kind of survey probably underestimates the true proportion

35. a) 0.7
   b) $0.7 \pm 1.96*\sqrt{0.7*0.3/550} = (0.662, 0.738)$. The proportion of companies certified in the U.S. is less than in Canada.

37. a) There may be response bias based on the wording of the question.
   b) (0.455, 0.515)
   c) Smaller, since the sample size is larger.

39. a) Sample is not large enough.
   b) Since the conditions are not met, a confidence interval cannot be calculated.

41. a) This was a random sample of less than 10% of all self-employed taxpayers; there were 20 successes and 206 failures, both at least 10.
   b) (0.051, 0.126)
   c) 95% confident that between 5.1% and 12.6% of all self-employed individuals had their tax returns audited in the past year.
   d) If we select repeated samples of 226 individuals, then we can expect about 95% of the confidence intervals created to contain the true proportion of all self-employed individuals who were audited.

43. a) The confidence interval for the true proportion of all 18- to 29-year olds who believe the U.S. is ready for a woman president will be about twice as wide as the confidence interval for the true proportion of all U.S. adults, since it is based on a sample about one-fourth as large (assuming approximately equal proportions).
   b) (0.56, 0.68)

45. $0.02 = 1.96*\sqrt{0.25*0.75/n}$; n = 1801

47. $9/60 = 0.15$; $0.03 = 1.645*\sqrt{0.15*0.85/n}$; n = 384

49. $0.025 = z*\sqrt{0.65*0.35/972}$; $z = 1.634$ corresponding to a 90% confidence level.

51. In the data set 67 customers qualified. $67/500 = 0.134$; $1.96*\sqrt{0.134*0.866/500} = 0.030$; CI = $0.134 \pm 0.030 = (0.104, 0.164)$

53. We are 95% confident that between 40% and 46% of Canadian adults think that the health care system should fund abortions whenever they are requested. We are 95% confident that between 38% and 44% of Canadian adults think that the health care system should only fund abortions in the event of medical emergencies.

55. a) $\sqrt{(0.247*0.753/1005)} = 0.01360$; $z = 1.96$; CI = $0.247 \pm 1.96*0.01360 = (0.220, 0.274)$
   We are 95% confident that the proportion of adult Canadians buying something during the Black Friday sales promotions in 2014 was between 0.220 and 0.274.
   b) The width of the confidence interval is proportional to $1/\sqrt{}$(sample size), so to halve the width we need 4 times the sample size. $1005*4 = 4020$
   c) Ratio of widths = ratio of z values = $2.576/1.96 = 1.314$
   d) $\sqrt{(0.272*0.728/1010)} = 0.01400$
   For the difference in the proportions, the standard error is $\sqrt{(0.0136^2 + 0.014^2)} = 0.01952$.
   The 95% confidence interval for the difference in the proportions is between –0.0133 and 0.0633.
   We are 95% confident that the difference in the proportion of adult Canadians buying something during the Black Friday sales between 2013 and 2014 was between –0.0133 and 0.0633.
   Since this interval includes zero, we are not 95% confident that the proportion declined from 2013 to 2014.

57. a) $SE(\hat{p}) = \sqrt{\dfrac{\hat{p}\hat{q}}{n}} = \sqrt{\dfrac{0.34*0.66}{1000}} = 0.01498$
   The critical value for a 95% confidence interval: $z* = 1.96$.

The confidence interval is:

$\hat{p} \pm z*SE(\hat{p}) = 0.34 \pm 1.96*0.01498$

$= 0.34 \pm 0.0294$

i.e., between 0.31 and 0.37.

b) "34% of adult Canadians support abolishing the Senate. This result is accurate to plus or minus 2.9% 19 times out of 20."

59.

$$SE(\hat{p}_1 - \hat{p}_2) = \sqrt{\frac{\hat{p}_1 \hat{q}_1}{n_1} + \frac{\hat{p}_2 \hat{q}_2}{n_2}}$$

$$= \sqrt{\frac{0.32*0.68}{384} + \frac{0.43*0.57}{236}}$$

$$= 0.04006$$

The critical value for a 90% confidence interval: $z* = 1.645$. The confidence interval for the difference between two proportions is:

$(\hat{p}_1 - \hat{p}_2) \pm z*SE(\hat{p}_1 - \hat{p}_2) = 0.32 - 0.43 +$ $1.645*0.04006$

$= -0.11 \pm 0.0660$

i.e., between −0.18 and −0.04.

61. a) The 95% confidence interval for a sample of 1006 adults is at most

$$\pm 1.96*\sqrt{\frac{0.5*0.5}{1006}} = 0.031$$

The statement "plus or minus 3.1% 19 times out of 20" is correct for the result for the whole country. However, the sample size for the different age groups is smaller than 1006 and the confidence intervals for those groups are therefore wider than $\pm 3.1\%$.

The statement is non-professional and infringes on Item A of the ASA Ethical Guidelines

b) No. The width of the confidence interval is dependent on the sample size and is not affected by the population size. If we survey 3 times as many people in Ontario, the confidence interval for Ontario will be 1/sqrt(3) = 0.577 times as large as the one for BC. To get confidence intervals of similar widths we should interview similar numbers of people in the two provinces.

63. We need a 90% confidence interval for the difference between the proportions of positive outcomes from the two methods that does not include zero. That is, ME = 0.55 − 0.3 = 0.25.

For a 90% confidence interval, we have $z* = 1.645$.

$n = (0.55*0.45 + 0.3*0.7)*1.645^2/0.25^2 = 19.8$

This indicates that we need a sample size of 20 patients for each treatment. However, we also need to check the assumptions and conditions. The smallest probability is $p_1 = 0.3$, for which $np_1 = 6 < 10$. We therefore need to increase n to 34 so that $np_1 = 10.2$.

The sample size required = 34 for each treatment.

CHAPTER 11 JUST CHECKING ANSWERS

1. Wider. More certainty implies less precision.

2. Lower. More precision implies less certainty

3. Smaller. A larger sample size improves precision.

CHAPTER 12

SECTION EXERCISE ANSWERS

1. a) H_0: $p = 0.40$ vs. H_A: $p \neq 0.40$. Two-sided.
   b) H_0: $p = 0.42$ vs. H_A: $p > 0.42$. One-sided.
   c) H_0: $p = 0.50$ vs. H_A: $p > 0.50$. One-sided.

3. a) False. A high P-value shows that the data are consistent with the null hypothesis, but provides no evidence for rejecting the null hypothesis.
   b) False. It results in rejecting the null hypothesis, but does not prove that it is false.
   c) False. A high P-value shows that the data are consistent with the null hypothesis, but does not prove that the null hypothesis is true.
   d) False. Whether a P-value provides enough evidence to reject the null hypothesis depends on the risk of a Type I error that one is willing to assume (the α level).

5. a) True.
   b) False. The alpha level is set independently and does not depend on the sample size.
   c) False. The P-value would have to be less than 0.01 to reject the null hypothesis.
   d) False. It simply means we do not have enough evidence at that alpha level to reject the null hypothesis.

7. Step 1. H_0: $p = 0.35$; H_A: $p > 0.35$
   Step 2. $\alpha = 0.01$
   Step 3. We assume this was a professionally conducted survey with randomization and independently chosen employees. We assume the company has more than 3000 employees so that the sample is less than 10% of the population. We verify $300*0.35 > 10$ and $300*0.65 > 10$.
   Step 4. $n = 300$; $\hat{p} = 0.46$
   Step 5. $SE(\hat{p}) = \sqrt{(0.35*0.65 / 300)} = 0.0275$
   $z = (0.46 - 0.35)/0.0275 = 4.00$
   $P < 0.0001$
   Step 6. The survey result is statistically significant,
   Step 7. We reject the hypothesis that the proportion of employees that would take advantage of the credit union is less than or equal to 0.35.
   Step 8. We are 99% confident that the proportion of employees taking advantage of the credit union will be greater than 0.35.
   All eight steps are relevant.

9. a) $z = \pm 1.96$
   b) $z = 1.645$
   c) $z = 2.33$; n is not relevant for critical values for z.

11. a) (0.196, 0.304)
   b) No, because 0.20 is a plausible value.
   c) The SE is based on

$$\hat{p}: SE(\hat{p}) = \sqrt{\frac{\hat{p}\hat{q}}{n}} = \sqrt{\frac{(0.25)(0.75)}{250}} = 0.0274.$$

The SD is based on the hypothesized value 0.20, so

$$SD(\hat{p}) = \sqrt{\frac{p_0 q_0}{n}} = \sqrt{\frac{(0.20)(0.80)}{250}} = 0.0253.$$

   d) The SE, since it is sample based.

13. $H_0: p_1 = p_2$
    $H_A: p_1 < p_2$

Pooled estimate, $\bar{p} = \dfrac{x_1 + x_2}{n_1 + n_2} = \dfrac{0.13*1003 + 0.15*1980}{1003 + 1980}$

$= 0.1433.$

$$SD(\hat{p}_1 - \hat{p}_2) = \sqrt{\bar{p}\,\bar{q}\left(\frac{1}{n_1} + \frac{1}{n_2}\right)}$$

$$= \sqrt{0.1433*0.8567\left(\frac{1}{1003} + \frac{1}{1980}\right)} = 0.01358$$

$$z = \frac{\hat{p}_1 - \hat{p}_2}{SD(\hat{p}_1 - \hat{p}_2)} = -1.473$$

P = 0.0704, which is not less than 0.05, so we cannot conclude any difference at the 95% level.

15. a) Type I error. The actual value is not greater than 0.3, but they rejected the null hypothesis.
   b) No error. The actual value is 0.50, which was not rejected.
   c) Type II error. The actual value was 55.3 points, which is greater than 52.5.
   d) Type II error. The null hypothesis was not rejected, but it was false. The true relief rate was greater than 0.25.

17. a) $H_0: p = 0.56$, $H_A: p > 0.56$, $p_0 = 0.56$

   b) $SD(\hat{p}) = \sqrt{\dfrac{0.56*0.44}{100}} = 0.0496$

For a significance level of $\alpha = 0.01$ with a one-sided test, the critical z value is 2.33 from the Normal distribution.
$p^* = 0.56 + 2.33 \times 0.0496 = 0.676$
Now moving to the lower graph in **Figure 12.10**, we can calculate the power of the test:
$z = (0.676 - 0.70)/0.0496 = -0.490$
From the Normal distribution, we find the power of the test is $1 - 0.312 = 0.688$.
The probability of correctly identifying an increased percentage of "very satisfied" guests is 0.181.
   c) The power is not affected by the result of the survey. It is only dependent on the design of the test itself.

d) If the significance level is higher we are placing less importance on Type I errors, p^* is lower, and hence there is more importance placed on Type II errors. If the probability of Type II errors is smaller, then the power is higher.

CHAPTER EXERCISE ANSWERS

19. a) $H_0: p = 0.90$
       $H_A: p > 0.90$
   b) $H_0: p = 0.50$
       $H_A: p > 0.50$
   c) $H_0: p = 0.02$
       $H_A: p < 0.02$

21. Statement d) is the correct interpretation of the P-value.

23. If the rate of seatbelt usage after the campaign is the same as the rate of seatbelt usage before the campaign, there is a 17% chance of observing a rate of seatbelt usage this large or larger after the campaign in a sample of the same size by natural sampling variation alone.

25. Statement e) is the correct interpretation of the P-value.

27. It is not reasonable to conclude that the new formula and the old one are equally effective. Also, the inability to make that conclusion has nothing to do with the P-value. The company cannot prove the null hypothesis (that the new formula and the old formula are equally effective), but can only fail to find evidence that would cause us to reject it.

29. a) $2336*0.24 > 10$; $2336*0.76 > 10$; $SE = \sqrt{0.24*0.76/2336} = 0.008366$; $0.24 \pm 1.96*0.008366 = (0.223, 0.257)$.
   b) There is evidence that these reports are significantly different because 0.28 is not within the confidence interval.
   c) The significance level is $\alpha = 0.05$; it is a two-tailed test based on a 95% confidence interval.

31. a) Less likely, because 5% is less than 7.2%. Lowering α decreases the chance of rejecting the null hypothesis.
   b) Alpha levels must be chosen *before* examining the data. Otherwise, the alpha level could always be selected at a value that would reject the null hypothesis.

33. Null and alternative hypotheses should involve p, not $\hat{p}$.
The question is about *failing* to meet the goal. H_A should be $p < 0.96$.
The student failed to check $nq = (200)(0.04) = 8$. Since $nq < 10$, the Success/Failure Condition is violated. Similarly, the 10% Condition is not verified.

$$SD(\hat{p}) = \sqrt{\frac{pq}{n}} = \sqrt{\frac{(0.96)(0.04)}{200}} \approx 0.014.$$

The student used $\hat{p}$ and $\hat{q}$.

Value of z is incorrect. The correct value is

$$z = \frac{0.94 - 0.96}{0.014} \approx -1.43.$$

P-value is incorrect. P $= z < -1.43) = 0.076$
For the P-value given, an incorrect conclusion is drawn. A P-value of 0.12 provides no evidence that the new system has failed to meet the goal.

35. a) H_0: $p = 0.05$

H_A: $p > 0.05$

b) The study doesn't state whether the sample is an SRS, so we have to assume that the sample is representative of the population. 384 children $< 10\%$ of all children; $np = (384)(0.05) = 19.2$, which is > 10, and $nq = (384)(0.95) = 364.8 > 10$.

c) $SD = \sqrt{0.05*0.95/384} = 0.0111$; $z = (46/384 - 0.05)/0.0111 = 6.31$; P-value < 0.0001

d) If 5% of children have genetic abnormalities, the chance of observing 46 or more children with genetic abnormalities in a random sample of 384 children is essentially zero.

e) We have enough evidence to reject the null hypothesis H_0. There is strong evidence that more than 5% of children have genetic abnormalities.

f) We don't know that environmental chemicals cause genetic abnormalities, only that the rate is higher now than in the past. We cannot show causation.

37. a) H_0: $p = 0.34$

H_A: $p < 0.34$

b) **Plausible Independence Condition:** It is reasonable to think that the students' attendance records are independent of one another.
Randomization Condition: Although not specifically stated, we can assume that the National Center for Educational Statistics used random sampling.
10% Condition: The 8302 students are less than 10% of all students.
Success/Failure Condition: $np = (8302)(0.34) = 2822.68$ and $n = (8302)(0.66) = 5479.32$ are both greater than 10, so the sample is large enough.

c) P-value $= 0.0272$

d) The null hypothesis H_0 is rejected at $\alpha = 0.05$.

e) Result is statistically significant at $\alpha = 0.05$, but it is not clear that it has practical significance. The percentage dropped only from 34% to 33%.

39. H_0: $p = 0.02$

H_A: $p > 0.02$

Two conditions are not satisfied. 22 is greater than 10% of the population of 150 cars, and $np = 4.4$, which is not greater than 10. It is not a good idea to proceed with a hypothesis test.

41. H_0: $p = 0.03$

H_A: $p \neq 0.03$

$np = 14.07 > 10$; $nq = 454.93 > 10$.
$SD = \sqrt{0.03*0.97/469} = 0.007877$;
$z = (7/469 - 0.03)/0.007877 = -1.91$; P $= 2*0.028 = 0.056 > 0.05$. No evidence that $p \neq 0.03$.

For the confidence interval:

$np = 7 < 10$
The hypothesis test cannot be performed. The confidence interval cannot be calculated.

43. H_0: $p = 0.25$

H_A: $p > 0.25$

The conditions are satisfied.
$z = (137/500 - 0.25)/\sqrt{(0.25*0.75/500)} = 1.24$
P $= 0.1076 > 0.1$
There is no evidence that the magazine should publish an online edition.
For $\alpha = 0.1$ with a one-sided test, the critical z value is 1.28.
$p* = 0.25 + 1.28*0.0194 = 0.275$
$z = (0.275 - 0.27)/0.0194 = 0.247$
The power of the test is P $= 1 - 0.597 = 0.402$.
The probability of correctly identifying a proportion of readers over 25% interested in an online edition is 0.402.

45. H_0: $p = 0.40$

H_A: $p < 0.40$

$43*0.4 > 10$; $43*0.6 > 10$; assume the company has $> 43*10$ potential executives; assume executives are representative of employees even though not chose randomly.
$SD = \sqrt{0.4*0.6/43} = 0.0747$; $z = (13/43 - 0.4)/0.0747 = -1.31$; P $= 0.0955 > 0.05$. No evidence that $p \neq 0.4$.

47. H_0: $p = 0.109$

H_A: $p < 0.109$

$1782*0.109 > 10$; $1782*0.891 > 10$; $1782 < 10\%$ of all high school students; assume students in this school district are representative of students nationally.
$SD = \sqrt{0.103 * 0.897/1782} = 0.0072$; $z = (175/1782 - 0.109)/0.0072 = -1.463$; P $= 0.072 > 0.05$. No evidence that drop out rate decreased.

49. H_0: $p = 0.90$

H_A: $p < 0.90$

$122*0.9 > 10$; $122*0.1 > 10$; $122 < 10\%$ of all travellers who lost luggage; assume these travellers are representative of travellers who lost luggage.
$SD = \sqrt{0.9 * 0.1/122} = 0.0272$; $z = (103/122 - 0.9)/0.0272 = -2.05$; P $= 0.0201 < 0.05$. There is evidence that the proportion of travellers having luggage delivered is < 0.9.

51. H_0: $p = 0.30$

H_A: $p \neq 0.30$

$120*0.3 > 10$; $120*0.7 > 10$; $120 < 10\%$ of all recent graduates; assume these are representative of all recent graduates.
$SD = \sqrt{0.3*0.7/120} = 0.04183$; $z = (0.27 - 0.3)/0.04183 = -0.717$; $P = 0.473 > 0.05$. There is no evidence that the proportion of graduates encountering unethical practices is different from 0.3.

53. a) H_0: The repair shop is following standards
H_A: The repair shop is not following standards

b) A Type I error is concluding that the shop is not meeting standards when it actually is. A Type II error is when the regulators certify the shop when it is not meeting the standards.

c) The shop's owner would consider a Type 1 error to be more serious because that error would state that the shop is not meeting standards when it actually is, which would result in the shop's license being revoked.

d) Environmentalists would consider a Type II error to be more serious because that error would state that the shop is meeting standards when it actually is not and could be polluting.

55. a) Probability of detecting that the shop is not meeting standards when it is not.

b) 40 cars produces a higher power value because n is larger.

c) If we use a 10% level of significance, then we have a greater chance to reject the null hypothesis.

d) If the repair shop's inspectors are a lot out of compliance, the power will be greater, since larger problems are easier to detect.

57. a) One-tailed; we are testing to see if a decrease in the dropout rate is associated with the software.

b) H_0: $p = 0.13$; H_A: $p < 0.13$

c) The professor buys the software when the dropout rate has not actually decreased.

d) The professor doesn't buy the software when the dropout rate has actually decreased.

e) The probability of buying the software when the dropout rate has actually decreased.

59. H_0: $p = 0.11$

H_A: $p > 0.11$

$500*0.11 > 10$; $500*0.89 > 10$; $500 < 10\%$ of all customers spending $> \$1000$; the sample is randomly chosen and therefore representative of all customers.
$SD = \sqrt{0.11*0.89/500} = 0.0140$; $z = (67/500 - 0.11)/0.0140 = 1.715$; $P = 0.043 < 0.05$. There is evidence that the proportion of customers is higher than the historical figure of 0.11.

61. H_0: $p = 0.5$

H_A: $p > 0.5$

This is a professionally conducted survey by Angus Reid. We can be confident that these conditions are met. $SD = \sqrt{0.5*0.5/411} = 0.02466$; $z = (0.59 - 0.5)/0.02466 = 3.649$; $P = 0.000132$. The null hypothesis can be rejected. We can be 99.99% confident that scrapping the marijuana decriminalization legislation has the support of over 50% of Conservative voters.

63. a) H_0: $p = 0.43$
H_A: $p < 0.43$
The conditions are satisfied.
$SD(\hat{p}) = \sqrt{(0.43*0.57/1005)} = 0.01562$
$z = (0.40 - 0.43)/0.01562 = -1.921$
$P = 0.0274 > 0.01$
The null hypothesis cannot be rejected at the 1% significance level.
We have insufficient information to conclude whether less than 43% of Canadians prefer an elected head of state in 2013.

b) $\alpha = 0.01$, and this is a one-sided test. Therefore z^* is 2.33 from the Normal distribution.
$p^* = p_0 - z^* \times SD(\hat{p}) = 0.43 - 2.33*0.01562 = 0.3936$
$z = (p^* - p)/SD(\hat{p}) = (0.3936 - 0.41)/0.01562 = -1.049$
From the Normal distribution we get $\beta = 0.853$, so that the Power $= 1 - \beta = 0.147$.
This is not a very powerful test since (i) 0.41 and 0.43 are very close and therefore tough to distinguish, and (ii) a low significance level 0.01 has been chosen.

c) H_0: $p_1 - p_2 = 0.05 = K$
H_A: $p_1 - p_2 > 0.05$
The conditions are satisfied as in part a).

$$SE(\hat{p}_1 - \hat{p}_2) = \sqrt{\frac{\hat{p}_1\hat{q}_1}{n_1} + \frac{\hat{p}_2\hat{q}_2}{n_2}} = 0.0212$$

$$z = \frac{\hat{p}_1 - \hat{p}_2 - K}{SE(\hat{p}_1 - \hat{p}_2)} = 2.363$$

$P = 0.00907 < 0.05$
In 2013, support for an elected head of state was more than 5% higher than it had been in 2010.

65. Assumption: The Canadian Parliament is a random selection of the Canadian population.
$p_0 = 0.039$; $7/308 = 0.02273 = \hat{p}$; $N = 308$
$np_0 = 12.0 > 10$
$nq_0 = 296 > 10$
H_0: $p = p_0$
H_A: $p \neq p_0$
$$z = \frac{\hat{p} - p_0}{\sqrt{\frac{p_0 q_0}{n}}} = -1.475$$
$p = 0.070$

Underrepresentation is not significant at the 95% level. However, it is significant at the 90% level.

67. a) $p_0 = 0.70$; $\hat{p} = 0.72$; $N = 1000$
$np_0 = 700 > 10$

$nq_0 = 300 > 10$

$H_0: p = p_0$

$H_A: p > p_0$

$z = \dfrac{\hat{p} - p_0}{\sqrt{\dfrac{p_0 q_0}{n}}} = 1.38$

$P = 0.916 < 0.95$

We cannot reject the null hypothesis that less than or equal to 70% of Canadians support direct election of senators at the 95% level.

b) $p_0 = 0.70; \hat{p} = 0.71; N = 1000$

$np_0 = 700 > 10$

$nq_0 = 300 > 10$

$H_0: p = p_0$

$H_A: p > p_0$

$z = \dfrac{\hat{p} - p_0}{\sqrt{\dfrac{p_0 q_0}{n}}} = 0.69$

$P = 0.755 < 0.90$

We cannot reject the null hypothesis that less than or equal to 70% of Canadians supporting a referendum on Senate reform at the 90% level.

c) This statement is unethical according to Item A of the ASA Ethical Guidelines, since it is inaccurate. It is not true at normally acceptable significance levels. It is misleading to state that 70% of Canadians hold both these views. Since the statement was made to the press, it also infringes Item C on publications.

69. a) $p_0 = 0.50; \hat{p} = 0.54; N = 1025$

$np_0 = 512 > 10$

$nq_0 = 512 > 10$

$H_0: p = p_0$

$H_A: p > p_0$

$z = \dfrac{\hat{p} - p_0}{\sqrt{\dfrac{p_0 q_0}{n}}} = 2.56$

$p = 0.995$

At the 99.5% significance level, we can say that more than 50% of the British Columbia population supported the carbon tax.

b) The statement is ethical, since it is true at a very high level of statistical significance. The statement could be improved by stating the significance level.

c) Test comparing two proportions. Average $p = 0.536$; $SE = 0.0352$; $z = 0.569$; P-value $= 0.285 > 0.10$. We cannot conclude that support for the tax has gone down.

71. $H_0: p_1 = p_2$

$H_A: p_1 < p_2$

Since the null hypothesis asserts that the two proportions are the same, we use a pooled estimate of the proportion, or

$$\bar{p} = \frac{x_1 + x_2}{n_1 + n_2} = \frac{0.62*1016*0.133 + 0.55*1016*0.388}{1016*(0.133 + 0.388)}$$

$$= 0.5679.$$

$$SD(\hat{p}_1 - \hat{p}_2) = \sqrt{\bar{p}\,\bar{q}\left(\frac{1}{n_1} + \frac{1}{n_2}\right)}$$

$$= \sqrt{05679*0.4321\left(\frac{1}{1016*0.133} + \frac{1}{1016*0.388}\right)}$$

$$= 0.01358$$

$$z = \frac{\hat{p}_1 - \hat{p}_2}{SD(\hat{p}_1 - \hat{p}_2)} = -1.418$$

$P = 0.078 > 0.05$. We cannot conclude a greater percentage in Quebec at the 95% level.

73. $H_0: p_1 = p_2$

$H_A: p_1 < p_2$

Since the null hypothesis asserts that the two proportions are the same, we use a pooled estimate of the proportion, or

$$\bar{p} = \frac{x_1 + x_2}{n_1 + n_2} = \frac{0.32*1000*0.384 + 0.43*1000*0.236}{1000*(0.384 + 0.236)}$$

$$= 0.3619$$

$$SD(\hat{p}_1 - \hat{p}_2) = \sqrt{\bar{p}\,\bar{q}\left(\frac{1}{n_1} + \frac{1}{n_2}\right)}$$

$$= \sqrt{0.3619*0.6381\left(\frac{1}{384} + \frac{1}{236}\right)} = 0.03975$$

$$z = \frac{\hat{p}_1 - \hat{p}_2}{SD(\hat{p}_1 - \hat{p}_2)} = -2.767$$

The significance level is $P = 0.997 > 0.99$. More people in Quebec support abolishing the Senate than in Ontario at the 99% significance level.

75. $H_0: p_1 = p_2$

$H_A: p_1 \neq p_2$

Since the null hypothesis asserts that the two proportions are the same, we use a pooled estimate of the proportion, or

$$\bar{p} = \frac{x_1 + x_2}{n_1 + n_2} = \frac{0.614*1000 + 0.653*1000}{2000} = 0.6335$$

$$SD(\hat{p}_1 - \hat{p}_2) = \sqrt{\bar{p}\,\bar{q}\left(\frac{1}{n_1} + \frac{1}{n_2}\right)}$$

$$= \sqrt{0.6335*0.3665 \left(\frac{2}{1000} \right)} = 0.02055$$

$$z = \frac{\hat{p}_1 - \hat{p}_2}{SD(\hat{p}_1 - \hat{p}_2)} = -1.898$$

$p = 0.0288$. Since this is a two-tailed test, p is doubled to give 0.0577, so there is not a significant difference at the 95% level.

77. p_1 is the proportion of men preferring an elected head of state and p_2 is the proportion of women preferring an elected head of state.

H_0: $p_1 - p_2 = 0.10 = K$

H_A: $p_1 - p_2 > 0.10$

Since this is a professionally conducted survey, the conditions are met.

$$SE(\hat{p}_1 - \hat{p}_2) = \sqrt{\frac{\hat{p}_1\hat{q}_1}{n_1} + \frac{\hat{p}_2\hat{q}_2}{n_2}} = 0.03052$$

$$z = \frac{\hat{p}_1 - \hat{p}_2 - K}{SD(\hat{p}_1 - \hat{p}_2)} = 3.604$$

$P = 0.000157 < 0.01$. We can therefore reject the null hypothesis.

In 2013, support for an elected head of state was more than 10% higher for men than for women at the 1% significance level.

79. Test comparing two proportions:

p_1 is the proportion of men

p_2 is the proportion of women

H_0: $p_1 = p_2$

H_A: $p_1 \neq p_2$

The conditions are satisfied since this is a professionally conducted survey and covers less than 10% of the population.

$$\bar{p} = \frac{x_1 + x_2}{n_1 + n_2} = 0.889$$

$$SE(\hat{p}_1 - \hat{p}_2) = \sqrt{\bar{p}\,\bar{q}\left(\frac{1}{n_1} + \frac{1}{n_2}\right)} = 0.01986$$

$$z = \frac{\hat{p}_1 - \hat{p}_2}{SE(\hat{p}_1 - \hat{p}_2)} = -1.611$$

The corresponding P from the Normal distribution is 0.0536. Since this is a two-sided test, the P-value is 0.107, which is not significant at the 1% level. We cannot conclude that there is a difference between men and women on this issue.

81. a) The P-value should be interpreted to say that we have insufficient evidence to demonstrate that more than 0.2% are cracked.
b) This lack of evidence may be due to not having a large enough sample for testing.

83. a) $230/265 = 86.8\%$, so January this year is certainly a lower proportion. However, January is far from being a random sample of this year's fatal accidents. Winter driving conditions may cause many non–driver-related accidents in January that are not typical of the rest of the year. We have insufficient information to comment about this year as a whole. Secondly, although we are not told n, the number of accidents in January, it is likely to be slightly higher than $265/12$. Therefore, nq is probably less than 10. We need to know n to check this condition.
b) 82% is less than 86.8% in 2014, but we cannot apply hypothesis testing since the sample is 50% of the population (half the year) and therefore violates the 10% Condition.

CHAPTER 12 JUST CHECKING ANSWERS

1. a) H_0: $p = 0.5$; H_A: $p \neq 0.5$
b) H_0: $p = 0.92$; H_A: $p > 0.92$
c) H_0: $p = 0.17$; H_A: $p < 0.17$

2. You can't conclude that the null hypothesis is true. You can conclude only that the experiment was unable to reject the null hypothesis. They were unable, on the basis of 12 patients, to show that aspirin was effective.

3. The null hypothesis is H_0: $p = 0.75$.

4. $$SD(\hat{p}) = \sqrt{\frac{0.75*0.25}{2500}} = 0.00866. \quad z = \frac{x - \mu}{\sigma}$$

$$= \frac{0.78 - 0.75}{0.00866} = 3.46.$$ The alternative hypothesis is

H_A: $p > 0.77$ so we need a one-sided test. From Table Z, the probability is 0.9997, so that the P-value is $1 - 0.9997 = 0.0003$, a very small value. We can reject the null hypothesis and conclude that the new drug provides relief to more than 75% of patients.

5. 1) We want to investigate whether the proportion, p, of cracks detected is greater than the baseline proportion $p_0 = 0.92$, therefore our hypotheses are: H_0: $p = 0.92$; H_A: $p > 0.92$.
2) Since this is a situation where we have quantitative data that is accurate, we choose $\alpha = 0.01$.
3) Cracked cylinder blocks were chosen at random. This should make them independent of each other. $n = 500$ and we assume the company manufactures more than 5000 cylinder blocks. $np_0 = 460 > 10$. $n(1 - p_0) = 40 > 10$.
4) We tested 500 cracked cylinder blocks and found a proportion $\hat{p} = 0.94$ of cracks were detected.
5) $$SD(\hat{p}) = \sqrt{\frac{0.92*(1 - 0.92)}{500}} = 0.0121$$

$$z = \frac{0.94 - 0.92}{0.0121} = 1.65$$

From the table in **Appendix B**, $P_{Tab} = 0.9505$, so the probability of getting 0.94 cracks detected or a higher value is a P-value of $1 - 0.9505 = 0.0496$.

6) Our P-value = 0.0496 is not less than our $\alpha = 0.01$. We therefore have a result that is not statistically significant at the 1% level.

7) We cannot therefore reject the null hypothesis that $p = 0.92$.

8) We have no evidence that the ultrasound-based test is an improvement on our existing test at the 1% significance level. However. our P-value is 0.0496 so that it would be significant at the 5% level. The manufacturer should not go ahead with the new test if it requires a 1% significance level. If it accepts a 5% significance level, it should assess the cost of the new test compared to the costs of replacing faulty cylinder heads under warranty before deciding whether the new test will improve profitability.

6. $SE(\hat{p}) = \sqrt{\dfrac{0.25*(1 - 0.25)}{300}} = 0.025$. The critical value from **Table 12.2** is 1.645, since this is a one-sided test. The confidence interval is $(0.25 - 1.645*0.025, \infty)$ $= (0.209, \infty)$.

7. $H_0: p = 0.21; H_A: p > 0.21$. $SD(\hat{p}) = \sqrt{\dfrac{0.21*(1 - 0.21)}{300}}$

$= 0.0235$. $z = \dfrac{0.25 - 0.21}{0.0235} = 1.70$. P-value = 0.0445.

8. There is a difference between $SD(\hat{p})$ and $SE(\hat{p})$ due to the SE being based on $\hat{p}$ and the SD being based on p.

9. Since last year's proportion 0.21 is contained in the confidence interval, we cannot reject the null hypothesis that $p = 0.21$. We have insufficient evidence to claim the proportion has increased this year. However, 0.21 is only just inside the confidence interval.

Since the P-value is less than our 5% significance level, we can conclude that the proportion has increased this year. However, our P-value is only just less than 5%.

This is an example where the conclusion from the confidence interval is different from the conclusion from the P-value. This is because those conclusions are "only just" true and because of the difference between the SE and SD.

10. Increase the sample size.

11. The power of the test is lower if the true percentage is 27% than if it is 29% since the power of the test depends on the *effect size*, that is, the difference between last year's 21% and this year's percentage.

12. For a one-sided 10% significance test, $z = 1.28$ (from Table Z in **Appendix B**, or from **Table 12.2**).

$SE(\hat{p}) = \sqrt{\dfrac{0.21*0.79}{300}} = 0.0235$

So the critical value is $p* = 0.21 + 1.28*0.0235 = 0.241$.

13. The power of the test is calculated from

$$z = \frac{(0.241 - 0.28)}{0.0235} = -1.697.$$

The corresponding probability from Table Z, **Appendix B**, is $\beta = 0.0449$, so the power of the test is 0.955.

14. The power is unaffected by the result, $\hat{p}$, of the test.

15. Yes. The power is increased if the sample size is higher.

16 No. If the significance level is reduced, $p*$ moves to the right in **Figure 12.10** so that the power is reduced.

CHAPTER 13

SECTION EXERCISE ANSWERS

1. a) $9.84/\sqrt{25} = 1.968$ years
   b) $9.84/\sqrt{100} = 0.984$ years (half as large)

3. a) $n - 1 = 24$
   b) $n - 1 = 99$

5. a) $31.84 \pm 2.064*9.84/\sqrt{25} = (27.78, 35.90)$ years
   b) $2.064*9.84/\sqrt{25} = 4.06$ years
   c) $31.84 \pm 1.96*10/\sqrt{25} = (27.92, 35.76)$ years. Slightly narrower.

7. Independence: The data were from a random survey and should be independent.
   Randomization: The data were selected randomly.
   10% Condition: These customers are fewer than 10% of the customer population.
   Nearly Normal: The histogram is unimodal and symmetric, which is sufficient.

9. a) Not correct. A confidence interval addresses the mean weight gain of the population of all cows. It says nothing about individual cows.
   b) Not correct. A confidence interval addresses the mean weight gain of the population of all cows. It says nothing about individual cows.
   c) Not correct. We are certain the mean weight gain of the cows in the study is 56 pounds.
   d) Not correct. The statement implies that the average weight gain varies, which it doesn't.
   e) Not correct. This interval is actually one of many that could have been generated, depending on the cows chosen for the sample.

11. a) $H_0: \mu = 25$
    b) Two-sided: $\mu \neq 25$
    c) $(31.84 - 25)/(9.84/\sqrt{25}) = 3.476$
    d) < 0.001
    e) Reject H_0. There is strong evidence that the mean age is not 25.
    f) Because the 95% confidence interval does not contain 25, we can reject H_0 at $\alpha = 0.05$.

13. a) Four times as big, or $n = 100$.
    b) 100 times a big, or $n = 2500$.

CHAPTER EXERCISE ANSWERS

15. a) 1.74
   b) 2.37
   c) 0.0524
   d) 0.0889 (Absolute value makes this two-sided)

17. The width of a 95% confidence interval increases, assuming the sample size remains the same.

19. a) $1.49 \pm 2.045*0.18/\sqrt{30} = (\$1.42, \$1.56)$
   b) $1.49 \pm 1.7*0.18/\sqrt{30} = (\$1.43, \$1.55)$
   c) $1.49 \pm 2.045*0.18/\sqrt{60} = (\$1.44, \$1.54)$

21. Assumptions and conditions for a t-interval are not satisfied. For a sample size of only 20, the distribution is clearly skewed to the right. There is a large outlier pulling the mean to a higher value.

23. a) The data are a random sample of all days. In addition, the distribution should be unimodal and symmetric with no outliers.
   b) $12600 \pm 1.68*1500/\sqrt{44} = (\$12,220, \$12,980)$
   c) 90% confident that the interval ($12,220, $12,980) contains the true mean daily income.
   d) 90% of all random sample of size 44 will produce intervals that contain the true mean daily income of the parking garage.
   e) $12,800 is within the interval. It is a plausible value.

25. a) 95% confidence level gives us increased confidence that the mean is contained with the interval.
   b) It widens the confidence interval due to higher error. The resulting interval is wider than before.
   c) By collecting a larger sample, they can decrease the error and, therefore, decrease the margin of error and the resulting confidence interval.

27. a) $2350 \pm 2.009*425/\sqrt{51} = (\$2230.44, \$2469.56)$
   b) Independence—probably okay; randomization not specified, and sample probably not more than 10% of population. Normal Population Assumption—check by looking at a histogram of the data. With a sample size of 51, the t procedures should be acceptable to use us long as the distribution is at least somewhat symmetric and unimodal.
   c) 95% confident that the interval $2227.93 to $2472.07 contains the true mean increase in sales tax revenue.

29. If the mean monthly sales due to online purchases have not changed, there is a 1% chance that mean sales at least as high as those observed would occur. This is rare and considered to be a significant value.

31. a) $H_0: \mu = 23.3$ years; $H_A: \mu > 23.3$ years.
   b) Randomization: 40 online shoppers were selected randomly. Normality: sample of 40 shoppers is large enough that it should be safe to proceed.

c) $t = (24.2 - 23.3)/(5.3/\sqrt{40} = 1.074$, corresponding to $P = 0.145$
   d) If the mean age of shoppers remains at 23.3 years, there is a 14.5% chance of getting a sample mean of 24.2 years or older simply from natural sampling variation.
   e) Not enough evidence to suggest that the mean age of online shoppers has increased from the menu.

33. a) Independence Assumption: The 16 bags were selected randomly and we can assume that they are independent and representative of all bags. Nearly Normal Condition: The histogram of actual data appears roughly unimodal and fairly symmetric with no outliers.
   b) $1238.19 \pm 2.13145*94.282/\sqrt{16} = 1238.19 \pm 2.13145*94.282/\sqrt{16} = (1187.95, 1288.4)$
   c) To claim that *every* bag contained at least 1000 chips would be false. The average number of chips is > 1000.

35. Independence Assumption: We assume that these mutual funds were selected at random and that 35 funds are less than 10% of all mutual funds. Nearly Normal Condition: A histogram or boxplot could be created from the given data. The boxplot shows a symmetric distribution.

Test: $H_0: \mu = 8$; $H_A: \mu > 8$. $t = (8.418 - 8)/0.493 = 0.848$. P-value $= 0.20$. This value fails to reject the null hypothesis. There is insufficient evidence that the mean five-year return was greater than 8%.

37. Cannot reject the null hypothesis of a mean $200 collection. The value $200 is within the 90% confidence interval, so it cannot be rejected at the $\alpha = 0.05$ level.

39. Yes, there is definite potential for collecting more money. A larger trial would narrow the confidence interval (n larger) and make the decision clearer.

41. a) $H_0: \mu = 100$; $H_A: \mu < 100$.
   b) Different samples have different means. The sample size is fairly small. Differences in means could be due to natural sampling variation. A statistical analysis is required to make sound decisions.
   c) Batteries selected are representative of all batteries. The sample represents fewer than 10% of the company's batteries and the lifetime data are approximately Normal without outliers.
   d) $t = (97 - 100)/(12/\sqrt{16}) = -1.0$ resulting in a P-value of 0.167. We cannot reject the null hypothesis at the 5% level, so we conclude that there is insufficient evidence to suggest that the mean is significantly less than the advertised value of 100.
   e) Type II error would have occurred (the null hypothesis is not rejected when it is actually false).

43. a) 95% confidence interval is 0.0834 to 0.0992 ppm. Cutoff value for acceptable levels is 0.08, which is lower than the lowest value in the confidence interval. At $\alpha = 0.025$, the null hypothesis is rejected and it can be concluded that the average levels are greater than 0.08 ppm.

b) Boycott resulting from Type I error might harm the salmon producers needlessly. Boycott from Type II error would not take place but the public would be exposed to the risk of eating salmon with elevated contamination levels.

45. a) The air samples were selected randomly and there is no bias present in the sample.

b) The histogram of air samples is not exactly Normal, but the sample size is large, so inference is okay.

47. a) $14.9 - 11.6 = 3.3$ km/hr.

b) $1.96*8/\sqrt{n} = 2$. Therefore, $n = 62$. With this value of n, the value of t is 2.00, not 1.96. Repeating the calculation with $t = 2.00$, we get $n = 64$. We should use a sample size of 64.

49. a) $680 \pm 2.04*75/\sqrt{32} = (\$653, \$707)$

b) Test: $H_0: \mu = 650$; $H_A: \mu \neq 650. t = (680-650)/(75/\sqrt{32}) = 2.26$. P-value of 0.031. Can reject null hypothesis. Evidence that the mean audit cost is different from $650.

c) Confidence interval does not contain $650. This provides evidence that the current year's mean audit cost is significantly different from $650.

51. a) Timeplot shows no pattern, which means that the measurements are independent from each other. Since an entire year is measured, it is likely that we have representative values. Sample is fewer than 10% of all possible wind readings. The histogram indicates that the distribution is near Normality. We can proceed with the inference procedures.

b) Test: $H_0: \mu = 8$; $H_A: \mu > 8$ km/hr. $t = 0.1663$; $df = 1113$; P-value $= 0.434$. This value is not significant and we should not recommend building the turbine at this site.

53. a) $t = (\text{score}-501)/SE. t^* = 2.576$. Switzerland, Austria, and Belgium are not significantly above 501.

b) score $\pm 1.96*SE = (517, 533)$

c) $t = (\text{score}-550)/SE = 0.968$. P-value $= 0.167 > 0.05$. Not significant.

55. H_0: Average number of hours per year $= 1765$

H_A: Average number hours per year < 1765

$$t = \frac{1710 - 1765}{\frac{486}{\sqrt{1000}}} = -3.58$$

A one-tailed t-test gives $P = 0.0002$.
We assume the people surveyed are independent of each other. This is true, since the people were randomly selected.

The sample size of 1000 is certainly less than 10% of the Canadian working population.
We are not given the distribution of our sample, so we cannot check whether the data are unimodal and symmetric. The sample standard deviation is small compared to the sample mean, giving no evidence that the sample is skewed. We assume this condition is satisfied.

57. a) H_0: Average house price $= \$339,100$

H_A: Average house price $> \$339,100$

$n = 54$
Sample mean: $\bar{y} = 418\,200$
Sample standard deviation: $s = 194\,300$
Degrees of freedom: $df = 53$

$$t = \frac{418\,200 - 339\,100}{\frac{194\,300}{\sqrt{54}}} = 2.992$$

A one-tailed t-test gives $P = 0.0021$.
Assumptions and conditions: We assume the houses surveyed are independent of each other. This is true since the houses were randomly selected.
The sample size of 54 is certainly less than 10% of the number of houses in Canada.
We are not given the distribution of our sample and so cannot check whether the data are unimodal and symmetric. The standard deviation of the sample is less than half the mean, giving no evidence of a skewed distribution. We assume this condition is satisfied.
House prices have increased, on average, at the 99% significance level, assuming the sample is unimodal and symmetric.

b) $n = 54$
Sample mean: $\bar{y} = 418\,200$
Sample standard deviation: $s = 194\,300$
Degrees of freedom: $df = 53$ giving a t-value of 2.006 for a 95% significance level.

$$SE = \frac{194,300}{\sqrt{54}} = 26,441$$

The confidence interval is $418,200 \pm 2.032*26,441 = (365,166, 471,234)$.
The confidence interval is valid, assuming the sample is unimodal and symmetric. This assumption is probably true.

c) The consumer group did not provide each of the 54 house prices, so it is not possible to check whether the distribution is unimodal and symmetric. It claims that prices have increased by over 20%, which would bring prices to $406,920. However, it really means *average* prices and should include the confidence interval, which encompasses a range less than $406,920. Item A for lack of professionalism and Item C for publishing imprecise results are violated.

59. a) Standard error $= 75/\sqrt{(2.6)} = 0.300$
For a 99% confidence level and 74 degrees of freedom, $t^* = 2.64$.
The confidence interval is (5.71, 7.29).

b) We cannot be 99% certain that the score is different from last year.

c) $n = \left(\dfrac{t^*_{n-1}s}{ME}\right)^2$. For our first iteration, we approximate t^* by $z^* = 2.576$. We have $s = 2.6$ and ME $= 0.5$. Therefore, $n = 180$.
For our second iteration, we look up t^* in Table T, **Appendix B**, with a 99% confidence level and df $= n - 1 = 179$ to get $t^* = 2.60$. Using the formula again gives $n = 184$. A third iteration gives the same result. We should survey 184 nurses.

CHAPTER 13 JUST CHECKING ANSWERS

1. For a census, means or proportions *are* the true population values. When we estimate parameters from a sample, we use a confidence interval to take sample-to-sample variability into account.

2. They don't know the population standard deviation, so they must use the sample *SD* as an estimate. The additional uncertainty is taken into account by *t*-models.

3. The margin of error for a confidence interval for a mean depends, in part, on the standard error:

$$SE(\bar{y}) = \frac{s}{\sqrt{n}}$$

Since *n* is in the denominator, smaller sample sizes generally lead to larger *SE*s and correspondingly wider intervals.

4. The critical values for *t* with fewer degrees of freedom would be slightly larger. The $\sqrt{n}$ part of the standard error changes a lot, making the *SE* much larger. Both would increase the margin of error. The smaller sample is one-fourth as large, so the confidence interval would be roughly twice as wide.

5. We expect 95% of such intervals to cover the true value, so 5 of the 100 intervals might be expected to miss.

6. The standard error would be likely to decrease if we had a larger sample size.

7. $n = \left(\dfrac{t^*_{n-1}s}{ME}\right)^2$. For our first iteration we approximate t^* by $z^* = 1.96$. We have $s = 0.25$ and $ME = 0.125$. Therefore, $n = 15.4$. To be on the safe side we round up to $n = 16$.
For our second iteration we look up t* in Table T, Appendix C, with a 95% confidence level and $df = n - 1 = 15$ to get $t^* = 2.13$. Using the formula again gives $n = 18.2$ which we round up to a sample size of 19.

CHAPTER 14

SECTION EXERCISE ANSWERS

1. a) 9.6 years.

b) $\sqrt{\dfrac{7.51^2}{30} + \dfrac{7.85^2}{35}} = 1.91$ years.

c) $9.6/1.91 = 5.03$

3. a) <0.001

b) <0.001

c) In both cases, reject H_0. There is very strong evidence to suggest that there is a difference in the mean ages of houses in the two neighborhoods.

5. a) (5.77, 13.43) years.

b) The sample sizes are larger.

c) No.

d) It suggests that we should reject H_0, since 0 is not a plausible value for the true mean difference.

7. a) $S_{pooled} = 7.695$;

$SE_{pooled} = 7.695 \sqrt{\dfrac{1}{30} + \dfrac{1}{35}} = 1.914$;

$t = 5.01$; P-value < 0.001. Reject H_0. There is strong evidence to reject the hypothesis that the means are equal.

b) $(57.2 - 47.6) \pm 2.000*1.914 = (5.77, 13.43)$ years.

c) Very close. When the standard deviations are close these two methods give similar results.

9. a) Paired. Each pair consists of a volunteer using each chair.

b) Not paired. The samples are random within each neighbourhood.

c) Paired. Each pair consists of an hour in which the productivity of the two workers is compared.

11. a) Yes, each pair is a store for which the customers with and without the program are compared.

b) 3 customers.

c) 4.52 customers.

d) $4.52/\sqrt{10} = 1.43$ customers.

e) $3/1.43 = 2.098$

f) 9

g) One-sided. They want to know if traffic increased.

h) 0.0327

i) We can reject the null hypothesis. There is evidence of an increase in traffic.

13. $3 \pm 1.833*1.43 = (0.379, 5.621)$ customers.

CHAPTER EXERCISE ANSWERS

15. The data are independent (not paired) since different truckers drove different routes.

a) $SE = \sqrt{\dfrac{3^2}{20} + \dfrac{2^2}{20}} = 0.806$; $df = 33.1$;

$t = 2.0345$; CI $= 3 \pm 2.0345*0.806 = (1.36, 4.64)$

b) Confidence interval does not contain the value zero (no difference value). Yes, Route A is faster, on average.

17. a) $H_0: \mu_C - \mu_A = 0; H_A: \mu_C - \mu_A > 0.$

b) Independent Group Assumption: The percentage of sugar in the children's cereals is unrelated to the percentage of sugar in adults' cereals. Randomization Condition: It is reasonable to assume that the cereals are representative of all children's and adults' cereals in regard to sugar content. Nearly Normal Condition: The histogram of adults' cereal sugar content is skewed to the right, but the sample sizes are of reasonable size. The Central Limit Theorem allows us to proceed.

c) $SE = \sqrt{\dfrac{6.418^2}{19} + \dfrac{7.6124^2}{28}} = 2.0585; df = 42.78;$
$t = 1.682; CI = 36.65 \pm 2.0585*1.682 = (33.19, 40.11)$

d) 95% confidence interval does not contain zero, so we can conclude that the mean sugar content of children's cereals is significantly higher than for adults' cereals.

19. The hypotheses are $H_0: \mu_{After} - \mu_{Before} = 0; H_A: \mu_{After} - \mu_{Before} > 0$. Independence Assumption: Sales should be independent but they are not randomly chosen. Nearly Normal Condition: The stem plots of the scores show the distributions as unimodal and approximately symmetric. $\bar{y}_{After} = 53.67, \bar{y}_{Before} = 38.79,$ $s_{After} = 9.356, s_{Control} = 7.929,$ yielding $t = 5.942$. The P-value is obtained through technology methods. The $t^* = 2.015$ for $df = 4.79$ yields a P-value for a one-sided test as 0.0000002. This value is less than 5% and rejects the null hypothesis. There is evidence that the sales were better after the change was made in product placement.

21. a)

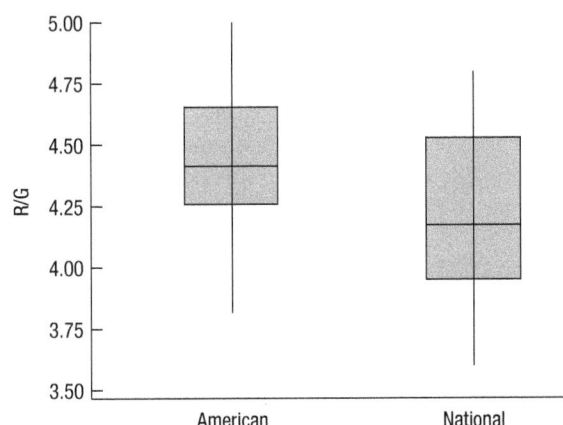

b) $4.45 \pm 2.16*0.0843 = (4.27, 4.63)$ runs.

c) $4.22 \ 2.16*0.0919 = (4.02, 4.41)$ runs.

d) Each individual confidence interval is based on the standard error for a single mean but to compare means we need the standard error for the difference in sample means. An appropriate way to compare the two leagues would be with a two sample difference of means confidence interval.

23. a) For the males, substituting into the equation $SE = \dfrac{s}{\sqrt{n}} = \dfrac{352}{\sqrt{45}} = 14.16$ the 95% CI for the male applicants becomes $\$352 \pm 2.015*14.16 = \$352 \pm 28.54 = (\$323.46, \$380.54)$. For the females, the corresponding 95% CI for the female applicants has a standard $SE = \dfrac{s}{\sqrt{n}} = \dfrac{80}{\sqrt{45}} = 11.93,$ yielding $\$310 \pm 2.015*11.93 = \$310 \pm 24.03 = (\$285.96, \$334.04)$.

b) The overlap suggests that there may be no difference in the means; however, this should be investigated by calculating a two-sample t-interval.

c) Calculate the observed difference in the two means: $\bar{y}_M - \bar{y}_F = \$352 - \$310 = \$42. \ SE(\bar{y}_M - \bar{y}_F)$
$= \sqrt{\dfrac{(95)^2}{45} + \dfrac{(80)^2}{45}} = 18.51$

From technology, the degrees of freedom are 85.5. The critical t-value for df of 85.5 is 1.988 (manually calculate or from technology). The 95% confidence interval is $\$42 \pm 1.988*18.51 = \$42 \pm 36.81 = (\$5.19, \$78.81)$. The mean monthly expenditures are higher for males by $\$5.19$ to $\$78.81$.

d) The two-sample method is correct mathematically. The problem cannot be solved correctly using two separate confidence intervals because we would be adding standard deviations rather than variances. The two-sample difference of means method takes this into account.

25. $H_0: \mu_J - \mu_A = 0; H_A: \mu_J - \mu_A \neq 0$. P-value $= 0.274 > 5\%$ and we fail to reject the null hypothesis. Although the mean delivery time during August is higher, the difference in delivery time from June is not significant.

27. a) Randomly assign half of the volunteers to see the ads without sexual images, recording how many products they remember. The other half of the volunteers see the ads with sexual images, recording how many products they remember. The groups are then switched and the same measurement is carried out.

b) Randomly divide volunteers into two groups. Show one group ads with sexual images and the other group ads without. Compare how many products each group remembers.

29. a) $H_0: \mu_W - \mu_S = 0; H_A: \mu_W - \mu_S > 0.$

b) P-value $= 0.002$; this value is $<5\%$ and we reject the null hypothesis. Mean weekly sales in winter months are greater than in summer months.

c) Other factors that could influence pizza sales would be weather and other sporting events.

31. a) Test: $H_0: \mu_R - \mu_N = 0$; $H_A: \mu_R - \mu_N < 0$. P-value $= 0.0944$. Support the null hypothesis. There is insufficient evidence to believe that the mean number of objects remembered by those who listen to rap music is lower than the mean number of objects remembered by those who listen to no music.

b) No difference was detected in part a).

33. a) Independent Groups Assumption: The samples are not related. Randomization Condition: The sample was taken randomly. Nearly Normal Condition: The distributions are approximately symmetric. The sample size is large enough that we can safely use the two-sample t-procedures.

b) $H_0: \mu_1 - \mu_2 = 0$; $H_A: \mu_1 - \mu_2 \neq 0$.

c) $t = -0.277$; $df = 38.8$; $P = 0.783 > 0.05$

d) We cannot conclude that the mean prices of single-family homes in these two towns are significantly different.

35. a) Paired t-test is appropriate. We have pairs of Fridays in five different months. They can be considered similar pairs as they are adjacent Fridays, as opposed to randomly chosen Fridays.

b) P-value $= 0.0212$. Mean number of cars on the M25 motorway on Friday the 13th is less than the mean number of cars on the previous Friday.

c) Don't know if the Friday pairs were selected at random. If they were not chosen randomly, that could affect our conclusion. The sample of five pairs is considered to be very small. The Nearly Normal Condition appears to be met by the differences (large difference might be suspicious).

37. Adding variances requires that the variables are independent. The price quotes are for the same cars, so they are paired, that is, not independent.

39. a) Histogram. It's compiled from data of *Local − Online*. Zero represents no difference and positive values represent a positive difference of *Local − Online*. The bigger the difference, the lower the online price.

b) Drivers are likely to get similar quotes both locally and online, making the differences and the spread or standard deviation smaller as well.

c) Price quotes are paired. Random sample consisted of fewer than 10% of the agent's customers. The histogram of differences is approximately Normal.

41. Test: $H_0: \mu(Local - Online) = 0$; $H_A: \mu (Local - Online) > 0$. $t = 0.826$; $df = 9$; $P = 0.215 > 5\%$. These data do not provide evidence that online premiums are lower, on average.

43. a) The individual times may show a trend of improving speed over time but the differences may be independent of each other. The data are subject to random year-to-year fluctuations, and these data can be assumed to be representative of similar races. We don't have any information to check the Nearly Normal Condition.

b) $-2.12097 \pm 2.042 \times (33.434/\sqrt{31}) = (-14.4, 10.1)$.

c) No, the 95% confidence interval contains 0. There is no evidence of a difference between men's and women's finishing times. The data does not allow us to conclude whether the men's winner on foot is faster or slower than the women's wheelchair winner.

45. a) $H_0: \mu_{Diff} = 0$; $H_A: \mu_{Diff} \neq 0$.

b) $t = 22.7/(113.6/\sqrt{145}) = 2.406$; $P = 0.017$

c) $22.7 \pm 1.977 \times 113.6/\sqrt{145} = (4.05, 41.35)$

47. a) $H_0: \mu_{Diff} = 0$; $H_A: \mu_{Diff} > 0$.
$t = 47.5/(122.8/\sqrt{23}) = 1.855$
$P = 0.038 < 0.05$.
The program increases productivity.

b) The increase in keystrokes per hour is
$$47.5 \pm 2.074 \times \frac{122.8}{\sqrt{23}} = (-5.61, 100.61)$$

c) The confidence interval in (b) does contain zero, so it looks as though we cannot reject the null hypothesis. However we rejected it in (a). The difference is that in (a) we rejected the null hypothesis at the 95% significance level. In (b) there is 95% probability of being within the confidence interval, i.e. 2.5% probability of being either side. There is therefore a 97.5% probability of being above the lower limit (−5.61) of the confidence interval. We are therefore 95% sure that there is a productivity improvement, from part (a), but we are not 97.5% sure.

49. Productivity, part 2.   The Independent groups assumption: the employees are from different companies, independent from each other. Randomization condition: the sample is stated as random and we can assume that the employees are representative of their companies. 10% condition: number of employees is less than 10% of all employees. The samples are large so we can proceed with the t-procedures because of the Central Limit Theorem.

$$t = \frac{13 - 7}{\sqrt{\dfrac{7.9^2}{30} + \dfrac{6.2^2}{48}}} = 3.535$$

$P = 0.000445$

There is strong evidence that the mean increase of the fitness program firm is significantly greater than the mean increase of this company.

51. a) Independent Groups Assumption: The same cows were used before and after injection as pairs; the cows should be representative of others of their breed. Randomization Condition: The sample is not stated as random, but the cows should be representative of their breed. 10% Condition: Fewer than 10% of all cows. Nearly Normal Condition: We don't have data to check for a Normal distribution of differences.

b) $14 \pm 2.001*5.2/\sqrt{60} = (12.66, 15.34)$.

c) Based on this sample, we are 95% confident that the average increase in milk production for Ayrshire cows given BST is between 12.66 and 15.34 pounds per day.

d) Farmer should use the BST for increased milk production.

53. Paired Data Assumption: The data are paired by city. Randomization Condition: It is not stated that these cities were chosen randomly, and these cities might not be representative of all European cities. Results should be interpreted cautiously and any generalizations may be suspect. 10% Condition: 12 cities are less than 10% of all European cities. Nearly Normal Condition: The histogram of the temperature difference is roughly symmetric and unimodal. 90% confident that the average high temperature in European cities in July is an average of 32.3°F to 41.3°F higher than in January.

55. a) Paired Data Assumption: The data are before and after job satisfaction ratings for the same workers. Randomization Condition: The workers were randomly selected to participate. 10% Condition: Assume that 10 workers are less than 10% of the workers at the company. Nearly Normal Condition: The boxplot of the distribution of the differences in job satisfaction are approximately symmetric and unimodal.

b) Test: $H_0: \mu_{Diff} = 0$; $H_A: \mu_{Diff} > 0$. $t = 3.60$; $df = 9$; P = 0.0029. Reject the null hypothesis. There is evidence that the mean job satisfaction rating has increased since the exercise program was implemented.

57. a) Test: $H_0: \mu_{Diff} = 0$; $H_A: \mu_{Diff} > 0$. $t = 4.47$; $df = 9$; P = 0.0008. Reject the null hypothesis. There is strong evidence of a mean increase in gas mileage between regular and premium gas.

b) 90% confident that the mean increase in gas mileage when using premium rather than regular gasoline is between 1.18 and 2.82 miles per gallon.

c) Premium gas costs more than regular gasoline. The increase in price might outweigh the increase in mileage.

d) $t = 1.74$; $df = 17.9$; P = 0.1148. We would have failed to reject the null hypothesis and concluded that there was no evidence of a mean difference in mileage. The variation in performance of individual cars is greater than the variation related to the type of gasoline. Also, the two-sample test is not appropriate because we don't have independent samples. The advantage of the matched pairs test is that variation is reduced by using each car twice.

59. a) Test: $H_0: \mu_A = 30$; $H_A: \mu_A > 30$. $t = 6.06$; $df = 19$; P < 0.0001. Reject the null hypothesis. Strong evidence that the mean number of strikes that Little Leaguers can throw after the training is more than 30.

b) Test: $H_0: \mu_D = 0$; $H_A: \mu_D > 0$. $t = 0.135$; $df = 19$; P = 0.4472. Fail to reject the null hypothesis. The training does not appear to be effective.

61. Test: $H_0: \mu_D = 0$; $H_A: \mu_D \neq 0$. Data are paired by brand; brands are independent of each other. The boxplot of differences shows an outlier (100) for Great Value. With the outlier, the $t = 1.332$; $df = 11$; P = 0.2098. Without the outlier, the $t = 0.833$; $df = 10$; P = 0.4241. Do not reject H_0. Conclude that data do not provide evidence of a difference in mean.

63. H_0: The number of rooms per person is the same.

H_A: The number of rooms per person is higher in Canada than in USA.

a) The standard error is $\sqrt{\dfrac{0.875^2}{1000} + \dfrac{0.805^2}{1000}} = 0.03760$.

Degrees of freedom =

$$\frac{0.03760^4}{(0.000766^2 + 0.000648^2)/999} = 1984.$$

$t = \dfrac{2.5-2.3}{0.0376} = 5.319$; P = 6*10^{-8} which is certainly significant at the 0.05 level. The null hypothesis is therefore rejected.

b) The square of the pooled standard deviation is: $999*(0.875^2 + 0.805^2)/(2*999) = 0.7068$.

The standard error is $\sqrt{0.7068 * \left(\dfrac{2}{1000}\right)}$

= 0.03760. The number of degrees of freedom is 2*999 = 1998.

$t = \dfrac{2.5 - 2.3}{0.03760} = 5.319$ as in part (a). The null hypothesis is therefore rejected.

c) We have one sample in Canada and the other in USA. It is not a single sample surveyed twice.

d) Repeating the calculation for surveys of 100 homes, we obtain P-values of (a) 0.0471 and (b) 0.0471. We would not reject the null hypothesis at the 0.01 significance level.

65 a) *SE of difference in means =* $\sqrt{(0.001109 + 0.002134)} = 0.05695$

$t = 0.1/0.05695 = 1.756$

Degrees of freedom = 3155
From the t-table, P is between 0.05 and 0.1.
The difference is not significant at the 95% level.

b) SE of difference in means =
$$\sqrt{(0.003929 + 0.001278)} = 0.07216$$
$t = 0.4/0.07216 = 5.54$
Degrees of freedom = 2293
From the t-table, P is less than 0.01.
The difference is significant at the 99% level.

67 a) You need the standard deviations of the math scores, the number of students tested in each country, and how the students were selected (in particular, whether the selection was randomized).

b) H_0: Math score in Germany = Math score in Canada
H_A: Math score in Germany ≠ Math score in Canada
H_0: Math score in Japan = Math score in Canada
H_A: Math score in Japan ≠ Math score in Canada

c) This is not a case of paired samples since different people were tested in each country.

69. a)   Comparing steep/shallow slopes in January

   i)   In January there are 31 days with about 7 hours of sunshine. The installer is interested in long-term profitability, so we can take the average "effectiveness" over about $7 \times 31 = 217$ hours and a maximum of 4 years (some projects may have been installed within the 4-year period of data availability). Our data sample is therefore 30 measures of average effectiveness for steep slope and 30 for shallow slope.

   ii) H_0: Average effectiveness with steep slope = Average effectiveness with shallow slope
   H_A: Average effectiveness with steep slope > Average effectiveness with shallow slope

   iii)   We should use the one-sided two sample t-test, since we are comparing independent groups.

   iv)   Since we have only 30 data points, we should test the data for Normality using a Normal probability plot and a histogram to check whether the distribution is skewed. Outliers should be investigated as to whether there is something exceptional about the installation.

b)   Comparing 3 days before/after first major snowfall

   i)   Around the first major snowfall, there are about 7 hours of sunshine per day. The installer is interested in long-term profitability, so we can take the average "effectiveness" over about $7 \times 3 = 21$ hours and a maximum of 4 years (some projects may have been installed within the 4-year period of data availability). Our data sample is therefore 30 measures of average effectiveness before/after the first major snowfall (A) for steep slope and (B) another 30 for shallow slope.

   ii)   We need two sets of hypotheses since the installer is interested in the effect of slope.
   (A) for steep slope
   H_0: Average effectiveness before first major snowfall = Average effectiveness after first major snowfall
   H_A: Average effectiveness before first major snowfall ≠ Average effectiveness after first major snowfall
   (B) for shallow slope
   H_0: Average effectiveness before first major snowfall = Average effectiveness after first major snowfall
   H_A: Average effectiveness before first major snowfall ≠ Average effectiveness after first major snowfall

   iii)   We should use the two-sided paired sample t-test, since we are comparing the same customers before and after the snowfall.

   iv)   Since we have only 30 data points for each test, we should test the data for Normality using a Normal probability plot and a histogram to check whether the distribution is skewed. Outliers should be investigated as to whether there is something exceptional about the installation.

CHAPTER 14 JUST CHECKING ANSWERS

1. $H_0: \mu_{eyes} - \mu_{flowers} = 0$

2.   **Independence Assumption:** The amount paid by one person should be independent of the amount paid by others.
   Randomization Condition: This study was observational. Treatments alternated a week at a time and were applied to the same group of office workers. There was no randomization.
   Nearly Normal Condition: We don't have the data to check, but it seems unlikely there would be outliers in either group.
   Independent Groups Assumption: The same workers were recorded each week, but week-to week independence is plausible.

3. $H_A: \mu_{eyes} - \mu_{flowers} \neq 0$.

4.   The average amount of money that office workers left to pay for food at an office coffee station was different when a picture of eyes was placed behind the "honesty box" than when the picture was one of flowers.

5.   These are independent groups sampled at random, so use a two-sample t-confidence interval to estimate the size of the difference.

6.   Since the same random sample of students was sampled both in the first year and again in the fourth year of their university experience, this is a paired t-test.

7. A male and a female are selected from each work group. The question calls for a paired *t*-test.

8. Since the sample of companies is different in each of the industries, this would be a two-sample test. There is no "pairing."

9. Since the same 50 companies are surveyed twice to examine a change in variables over time, this would be a paired *t*-test.

CHAPTER 15

SECTION EXERCISE ANSWERS

1. a) Retrospective.
   b) Prospective.

3. Experimental units: cookies
   Treatments: chocolate chip choice (milk, dark, semi-sweet)
   Response: Rating by trained testers
   Randomization: random presentation to the tasters

5. Control: All other aspects of the recipes were kept the same.
   Randomization: Cookies were presented to tasters in random order.
   Replication: 10 tasters did the rating.

7.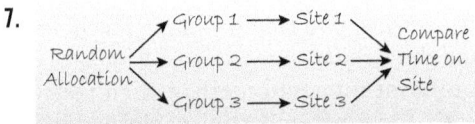

9. Single-blind. Customers were blind to treatments, but the kitchen staff knew.

11. a) 3, 36, and 39
    b) $1177.97 - 856.07 = 321.90$
    c) $856.07/3 = 285.36$
    d) $321.90/36 = 8.94$

13. a) H_0: The number of salmon attacked by sea lice per cubic metre is not affected by pesticide treatment. H_A: At least one of the pesticide treatments affects the number of salmon attacked by sea lice per cubic metre differently than the others.
    b)

Source of Variation	SS	df	MS	F	P-value	F crit
Farms	2.161667	2	1.080833	6.495826	0.031533	5.143253
Pesticides	2.509167	3	0.836389	5.026711	0.044707	4.757063
Error	0.998333	6	0.166389			
Total	5.669167	11				

   c) The number of salmon attacked by sea lice per cubic metre is affected by pesticide treatment and also

depends on the farm. Further analysis is required to determine the best pesticide treatment to use.

15. a) Chips (milk, dark, semi) and oil (butter, margarine).
    b) Six treatments: milk/butter, dark/butter, semi/butter, milk/margarine, dark/margarine, semi/margarine.
    c) For example: The relative ratings of the chips were different for cookies baked with butter than for cookies made with margarine.

CHAPTER EXERCISE ANSWERS

17. a) Temperature, washing time, and detergent.
    b) Temperature (hot, cold), washing time (short, long), detergent (standard, new).
    c) Level of whiteness as measured by an optical scanner.

19. a) Both detergents should be tested under the same conditions to ensure that the results can be compared directly.
    b) If cold-water washing is eliminated, the results will not be able to be generalized to cold-water washing.
    c) Treatments should be administered in random order to ensure that no other unforeseen influences could affect the response in a systematic way.

21. a) Difference between the Mozart and the quiet groups was more than would have been expected from ordinary sampling variation.
    b)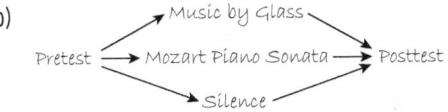
    c) Mozart group shows the smallest median difference and the least improvement. All of the boxes overlap and there does not appear to be a significant difference.
    d) No. Difference does not seem significant compared with the usual variation. All boxes overlap.

23. a) Observational; randomly select a group of children aged 10 to 13, have them taste the cereal, and ask them if they like the cereal.
    b) Randomly assign children to 2 groups that eat the old/new flavours and ask them to rate the flavour.
    c) Block the groups in b) according to whether they watch the show.

25. a) Students were not randomly assigned. Those who signed up for the prep course may be a special group whose scores would have improved anyway.
    b) Test a group of students. Randomly assign students to be tutored or not. Then retest.
    c) After the SAT exam, separate volunteers by blocks of low, average, and high scores. Randomly assign half of each block to the tutoring and half to the no-tutoring groups. Then retest.

27. a) H_0: The mean number of Executive seats sold is the same for the different periods.
H_A: The mean number of Executive seats sold is not the same for the different periods.
b) Conditions are not met. Randomization not specified; inference not clear. Spreads of the three groups look very different. Boxplots do not appear symmetric. Histograms should be used to check the Nearly Normal Condition.

29. a) H_0: The mean cell phone adoption rates are equal in the three regions.
H_A: The mean cell phone adoption rates are not equal in the three regions.
b) No. Countries selected randomly; Randomization Condition is met. Boxplots suggest spreads are quite different and show several outliers. Use other plots to check the Nearly Normal Condition.

31. a) H_0: $\mu_1 = \mu_2 = \mu_3 = \mu_4 = \mu_5 = \mu_6$ (the mean time it takes to serve a customer is the same for each teller).
H_A: the mean time it takes to serve a customer are not all equal.
b) P-value of 0.19. Cannot reject the null hypothesis.

33. a) Observational study. The factor was not deliberately manipulated.
b) Retrospective because it uses previously collected data.
c) H_0: Mean responses to the e-security questions are all equal for three communities.
H_A: Mean responses to the e-security questions are not all equal for three communities.
d) MST = 6.615/2 = 3.3075; MSE = 96.998/183 = 0.5300; F = 3.3075/0.5300 = 6.24
e) P-value is 0.002. Can reject null hypothesis. A causal link cannot be established because this is an observational study.

35. a) This was an experiment. Factors are deliberately manipulated to specify treatments, and the subjects are assigned to the treatments randomly.
b) Website trustworthiness.
c) Two: website configuration with respect to assurance and type of product purchased.
d) Nine: three types of websites and three types of purchases.
e) H_0: The mean *trustworthiness* ratings of websites are the same for those with a third-party assurance seal, a self-proclaimed assurance displayed, and no assurance seal.
H_0: The mean *trustworthiness* ratings of websites is the same for online purchases of books, cameras, and insurance.
H_0: There is no interaction effect—the effect of each factor is the same at all levels of the other factor.

37. a) Observational study
b) H_0: The mean DJIA closing is the same each day of the week.
H_0: The mean DJIA closing is the same each month.
H_0: Differences in days are no different from month to month.
c) There is no apparent difference in DJIA according to day of the week.
d) There does appear to be a difference from month to month.
e) There is no interaction between day of the week and month.

39. a) Observational study. Factors are not deliberately manipulated to specific treatments.
b) Boxplots indicate roughly equal variance and fairly symmetric distributions. However, other plots should be used to check the Nearly Normal Condition. The companies were randomly selected.
c) There is no significant interaction effect and no evidence that mean wages are different across three regions, but there is a difference between sales and advertising managers.
d) Yes, because the interaction effect is not significant.

41. a) Experiment. The machine setting factor was deliberately manipulated. Shift is a blocking factor.
b) The difference between the length and specifications.
c) Nine treatments, two factors—three machine settings and three shifts.
d) No significant interaction effect. Can conclude that both the shift and the machine settings appear to have a significant effect. From the table alone, we cannot determine which effect is more important.

43. a) MST = 17.3/2 = 8.65; MSE = 0.460/6 = 0.0767
b) 8.65/0.0767 = 112.78.
c) Data provide very strong evidence that the means are not equal.
d) Experimental runs were performed in random order, the variances of the treatment groups are similar, and the residuals are nearly Normal.
e) A boxplot of the *Stores* by *Method*, a plot of residuals vs. predicted values, a Normal probability plot, and a histogram of the residuals.
f) 0.277

45. a) Observational study.
b) H_0: The mean *Sugar Content* is the same for the cereals on each *Shelf*. H_A: The mean *Sugar Content* for the cereals is not equal.
c) P-value provides strong evidence that the mean *Sugar Content* is not the same for each *Shelf*.
d) No. Can conclude only that the means are not all equal.

47. a) H_0: Head injuries are, on average, about the same regardless of the size of the car.
H_0: Which seat you sit in doesn't affect the degree of head injury.

b) Yes, they appear to be met.

c) No significant interaction. P-values for both *Seat* and *Size* are <0.0001. Thus, we reject both of the null hypotheses.

49. a) This is a trial in which new varieties are tested and is therefore a statistical experiment. The missing information is that the placement of the different varieties at each site should be done randomly.

b) A randomized block analysis gives:

Source of Variation	SS	df	MS	F	P-value	F crit
Sites	103.805	2	51.9025	59.2607	0.000112	5.143253
Varieties	25.9025	3	8.634167	9.85823	0.009807	4.757063
Error	5.255	6	0.875833			
Total	134.9625	11				

c) The yield of the four varieties of canola is significantly influenced by the site used for the trial (P-value = 0.0001). There is also a significant difference in yield among the four varieties tested (P-value = 0.0098). Further testing would be necessary to determine which of these four varieties is significantly higher yielding than the others.

51. a) This is a randomized block design with the four different environments as the blocks.

b)

Source of Variation	SS	df	MS	F	P-value	F crit
Environment	0.466875	3	0.155625	6.81155	0.010821	3.862548
Design	0.391875	3	0.130625	5.717325	0.018031	3.862548
Error	0.205625	9	0.022847			
Total	1.064375	15				

c) The environment has a statistically significant impact on annual electricity generation, with a P-value of 0.011. The optical design also has a statistically significant impact on annual electricity generation, with a P-value of 0.018. Further testing would be necessary to determine which of these four designs results in significantly higher electricity generation than the others.

CHAPTER 15 JUST CHECKING ANSWERS

1. Gather reports from veterinarians and pet hospitals. Look into the histories of sick animals. This would be a retrospective observational study.

2. Treatment: Feed the new food and a standard food to pets. Response: Judge the health of the animals, possibly by having a veterinarian examine them before and after the feeding trials.

3. Control by choosing similar animals. Perhaps choose just one breed and test animals of the same age and health. Treat them otherwise the same in terms of exercise, attention, and so on.
Randomize by assigning animals to treatments at random.
Replicate by having more than one animal fed each formulation.

4. A control group could be fed a standard laboratory food, if we have one known to be safe. Otherwise we could prepare a special food in our test kitchens to be certain of its safety.

5. The veterinarian evaluating the animals should be blind to the treatments. For double-blinding, all technicians handling the animals should also be blinded. That would require making the control food look as much like the test food as possible.

6. Yes. Test dogs and cats separately.

7. No. We've failed to reject the hypothesis of a difference, but that's all we can conclude. There is insufficient evidence to discern any difference. But that should be sufficient for the company's purposes.

CHAPTER 16

SECTION EXERCISE ANSWERS

1. a) (30, 30, 30, 30), 30 for each season

b) $(25 - 30)^2/30 + \ldots = 1.933$

c) 3

3. a) Mean = df = 3

b) No, it's smaller than the mean.

c) It would say that there is no evidence to reject the null hypothesis that births are distributed uniformly across the seasons.

d) 7.815 using Table X in Appendix B

e) Do not reject the null hypothesis. As in part c), there is no evidence to suggest that births are not distributed uniformly across the seasons.

5. a) (−0.913, 0.913, 0.365, −0.365)

b) No, they are quite small for z-values.

c) Because we did not reject the null hypothesis, we shouldn't expect any of the standardized residuals to be large.

7. a) The age distribution of customers at the two branches are the same.

b) A chi-square test of homogeneity (independence).

c)

	Age			
	Less than 30	30–55	56 or older	Total
In-town branch	25	45	30	100
Mall branch	25	45	30	100
Total	50	90	60	200

d) 9.778
e) $df = (R-1)*(C-1) = (2-1)*(3-1) = 2$
f) 5.991
g) Reject H_0 and conclude that the age distributions at the two branches are not the same.

CHAPTER EXERCISE ANSWERS

9. a) Chi-square test of homogeneity (independence).
   b) Some other statistical test. Account size is not a count.
   c) Chi-square test of homogeneity (independence).

11. a) 10 times.
    b) Use a chi-square test for goodness-of-fit.
    c) H_0: The die is fair (all faces have the same probability of coming up).
       H_A: The die is not fair (some faces are more or less likely to come up than others).
    d) **Counted Data Condition:** We are counting the number of times each face comes up.
       Randomization Condition: Die rolls are random and independent of each other.
       Expected Cell Frequency Condition: We expect each face to come up 10 times, and $10 > 5$.
    e) 5
    f) $(11-10)^2/10 + \ldots = 5.6, P = 0.3471$
    g) Fail to reject the null hypothesis. There is no evidence that the die is unfair.

13. a) Use a chi-square test for goodness-of-fit.
    b) **Counted Data Condition:** Counts are actual lottery counts.
       Randomization Condition: The lottery mechanism uses randomization and guarantees independence.
       Expected Cell Frequency Condition: The expected counts are all greater than five.
    c) H_0: The likelihood of drawing each numeral is equal.
       H_A: The likelihood of drawing each numeral is *not* equal.
    d) $\chi^2 = 6.46$. P-value is 0.693 and too large to reject the null hypothesis H_0.
    e) The P-value says that if the drawings were fair, an observed chi-square value of 6.46 or higher would occur about 69% of the time. This is not unusual at all, so we don't reject the null hypothesis that the values are uniformly distributed.

15. a) 0.402
    b) 0.081
    c) 0.622
    d) 285.48
    e) H_0: Survival was independent of status on the ship.
       H_A: Survival depended on status on the ship.
    f) 3
    g) P-value is essentially 0, so we reject the null hypothesis. There is strong evidence that survival depended on status.

17. a) This is a chi-square test for homogeneity (independence).
    b) H_0: Major enrollment is independent of birth order.
       H_A: There is an association between major enrollment and birth order.
    c) **Counted Data Condition:** The data are counts.
       Randomization Condition: This is not a random sample of students, but there is no reason to think that this group of students isn't representative, at least of students in a Statistics class.
       Expected Cell Frequency Condition: The expected counts are low for the Social Science and Professional majors for both third and fourth or higher birth order. We'll keep an eye on these when we calculate the standardized residuals.
    d) $(4-1)*(4-1) = 9$
    e) P-value is low. Reject the null hypothesis. There is some evidence of an association between birth order and college enrollment.
    f) Unfortunately, three of the four largest standardized residuals are in cells with expected counts less than five. We should be very wary of drawing conclusions from this test.

19. a) Use a chi-square test for homogeneity (independence).
    b) **Counted Data Condition:** The data are counts.
       Randomization Condition: Although not specifically stated, we will assume that the women were randomly assigned to treatments.
       Expected Cell Frequency Condition: The expected frequencies are all greater than five.
    c) H_0: The proportion of urinary tract infections is the same for each group.
       H_A: The proportion of urinary tract infections is different among the groups.
    d) $\chi^2 = 7.776$; $df = 2$. P-value = 0.020. Reject the null.
    e) There is strong evidence of a difference in the proportion of urinary tract infections for cranberry juice drinkers, lactobacillus drinkers, and women that drink neither of the two beverages.
    f) There is evidence that women who drink cranberry juice are less likely to develop urinary tract infections, and women who drank lactobacillus are more likely to develop urinary tract infections.

21. a) Homogeneity (independence).
    b) H_0: Age is independent of frequency of shopping at this department store.
       H_A: Age is not independent of frequency of shopping at this department store.
    c) **Counted Data Condition:** The counts are recorded from a survey.
       Randomization Condition: Assume the survey was conducted randomly (not specifically stated).
       Expected Cell Frequency Condition: The expected frequencies are all greater than five.
    d) P-value is low. We reject the null hypothesis. There is evidence of an association between age and frequency of shopping at this department store.
    e) Negative residuals for low frequency categories among the older women and positive residuals for higher frequency categories among the older women. We can conclude that older women in the survey shop more frequently at this department store than expected.

23. $\chi^2 = 0.782$; $df = 1$. P-value is 0.377 and too large to reject the null hypothesis H_0 that gender and buying books online are not related.
    There is not enough evidence to conclude that either men or women are more likely to make online purchases of books.

25. $\chi^2 = 18.95$; $df = 1$. P-value is essentially zero and small enough to reject the null hypothesis H_0. There is evidence to conclude that the proportions are not equal.

27. Test: H_0: Marital status is independent of frequency of shopping. H_A: Marital status is not independent of frequency of shopping. $\chi^2 = 23.858$; $df = 8$. P-value is 0.001. Reject the null hypothesis H_0. There is strong evidence of an association between marital status and frequency of shopping at this department store. Based on the residuals, married customers shopped at this store with more frequency than expected, and more single women shopped never/hardly ever compared to what was expected.

29. a) Chi-square test of homogeneity (independence).
    b) **Counted Data Condition:** The counts are recorded from a survey.
       Randomization Condition: Assume the survey was conducted randomly (not specifically stated).
       Expected Cell Frequency Condition: The expected counts are all greater than five.
    c) H_0: The emphasis on quality is independent of frequency of shopping.
       H_A: The emphasis on quality is not independent of frequency of shopping.
    d) $\chi^2 = 30.007$; $df = 6$. P-value is essentially zero ($p < 0.001$). Reject the null hypothesis.
    e) There is evidence of an association between the emphasis on quality and frequency of shopping at this department store.

31. a) Expected counts:

Perceived Value	Men	Women
Excellent	6.67	5.33
Good	12.78	10.22
Average	12.22	9.78
Below Average	8.33	6.67

   A chi-test is appropriate because all of the counts are greater than five. In addition, these executives are representative of all executives who completed the program.
    b) 3
    c) $\chi^2 = 9.306$. P-value is 0.0255. Reject the null hypothesis. There is evidence that the distribution of responses about the value of the program for men and women executives are different.

33. a) Chi-square test of homogeneity (independence).
    b) **Counted Data Condition:** The counts are recorded from a survey.
       Randomization Condition: Assume the sample was taken randomly (not specifically stated).
       Expected Cell Frequency Condition: The expected counts are all greater than five.
    c) H_0: Outsourcing is independent of industry sector. H_A: There is an association between outsourcing and industry sector.
    d) $\chi^2 = 2815.97$; $df = 9$. P-value is essentially zero. Reject the null.
    e) There is strong evidence of an association between outsourcing and industry sector.

35. a) Chi-square test for homogeneity (independence).
    b) Count data; assume that the sample was taken randomly; expected counts are all greater than 5
    c) H_0: The distribution of employee job satisfaction level attained is the same for different management styles.
       H_A: The distribution of employee job satisfaction level attained is different for different management styles.
    d) $\chi^2 = 178.453$; df = 12; P-value is essentially 0
    e) Since the P-value is so low, we reject the null hypothesis. There is strong evidence that the distribution of employee job satisfaction level attained is different across management styles. Generally, exploitative authoritarian management is more likely to have lower levels of employee job satisfaction than consultative or participative styles.

37. Test: H_0: Reading online journals or blogs is independent of generation.
    H_A: There is an association between reading online journals or blogs and generation.

$\chi^2 = 48.408$; $df = 8$. P-value is essentially zero. Reject the null hypothesis and conclude that reading online journals or blogs is not independent of generational age.

39. Use a chi-square test of homogeneity (independence). Test: H_0: Systems used have same distribution for both types of industry. H_A: Distribution of type of system differs in the two industries.
$\chi^2 = 157.256$; $df = 3$. P-value is essentially zero. Reject the null hypothesis and conclude that the type of ERP system used differs across industry type. Those in manufacturing appear to use more inventory management and ROI systems.

41. Since this is a professionally conducted survey by Angus Reid, we can be confident the sample was selected so that the conditions are met.
The expected number in each cell is greater than 5 if we remove the "Not Sure" response.
The number of respondents in each cell is calculated from the percentage of the population in that province; e.g., for BC/Preventing Crime: 0.13*0.49*1013 = 64.52, rounding off to 65.

We now calculate the expected number of respondents in each cell; e.g., for the top left cell, 503*128/960 = 67.07. We next calculate (Observed − Expected)² / Expected. We total all these values to get the chi-square.
Chi square = 3.601214
Critical value for 95% significance level = 11.1
$df = 1*5 = 5$
P-value = 0.608131
There is no evidence of significant difference among provinces since the P-value is much higher than 0.05 or Chi Sq < Critical Value.

43. Since this is a professionally conducted survey by Angus Reid, we can be confident the sample was selected so that the conditions are met.
a) Chi square = 33.12878
   $df = 1*2 = 2$
   Critical value = 5.99
   P-value = 6.4E − 08
   There is a significant difference among men and women since P is much less than 5% or Chi Sq > Critical value.
b) Chi square = 23.60698
   $df = 2*2 = 4$
   Critical value = 9.49
   P-value = 9.57E − 05
   There is a significant difference among the three countries since P is much less than 5% or Chi Sq > Critical value.

45. *Independence and randomization conditions.* We are told this is a random selection of oncologists at a conference.

It does not represent oncologists who were not at the conference.

Expected			
Very useful	77.22384	38.85174	48.9244186
Acceptable	51.01453	25.6657	32.31976744
Too costly	32.76163	16.48256	20.75581395

Expected cell frequency condition. The expected number in each cell is > 5.

Chi Sq	8.742172
Df	4
Critical value	9.49
P-value	0.067877

There is no significant difference among the oncologists since P > 0.05 or Chi Sq < Critical Value.

CHAPTER 16 JUST CHECKING ANSWERS

1. This is a test of homogeneity (independence). The clue is that the question asks whether the distributions are alike.

2. This is a test of goodness-of-fit. We want to test the model of equal assignment to all lots against what actually happened.

3. This is a test of homogeneity (independence). We have responses on two variables and we're asked whether there's any dependence between them.

CHAPTER 17

SECTION EXERCISE ANSWERS

1. a) Ranks.
   b) Ranks.
   c) Not ranks—data are quantitative.

3. a) Two products are being compared and the same panel of consumers rates both the new product and its competitor product.

5. b) The ratings on sweetness are being compared for two independent groups (a panel of teenagers and a panel of adults).

7. The drinks rated most and least sweet must be in different groups.

9. d) The ratings of a new course are being compared among four independent groups.

11. c) It involves determining the presence of a consistent (or monotone) trend of water heights with changing moon phases. e) is an alternate answer for estimating whether there is a relationship between these variables.

13. e) We need to measure the association between two variables (home value and age). c) is an alternate answer if we are interested in monotonicity.

CHAPTER EXERCISE ANSWERS

15. a) Test: H_0: The two groups are the same—there is no difference between reading comprehension scores associated with the new and old reading activities.

H_A: One of the samples is shifted higher or lower than the other. Using the CLT, $E(T_{new}) = 369$; $E(T_{control}) = 451$; $SD = 36.332$; $z = 2.615$; $P \approx 0.009$, and therefore we can reject the null hypothesis at a level of $\alpha = 0.01$. In other words, there is a difference between reading comprehension associated with the new and old reading activities.

b) A better test might be designed with the intent of pairing; in this case by having reading comprehension assessed on the same students but using the different methods at different times (similar to the example in section 17.5). This research design would rely upon a Wilcoxon signed-rank test.

17. a) Hypotheses:

H_0: The distribution of sugar content in children's and adults' cereals have the same centre.

H_A: They have different centres.

b) Assumptions and conditions:
   i. Randomization Condition. Unfortunately, the method of data collection is not specifically stated and we will have to proceed with the analysis assuming that it was adhered to.
   ii. Independent Groups Assumption. The groups are independent of each other as they are stated to be predefined children's and adults' cereal groupings.

c) Using the Wilcoxon Rank Sum Test, with the Central Limit Theorem, we have the lower rank sum for the childrens cereals: $E(T) = 456$; $Var(T) = 2128$; $z = 5.77$. The P-value associated with the two-sided results is close to approaching 0, and therefore we can reject the null hypothesis. In other words, there is a difference between sugar content in children's and adults' cereals (from observation, the lowest sugar content in children's cereal exceeds the sugar content in any of the adults' cereals).

d) Based on the histograms that follow, the underlying distribution for the adults' cereal data appears non-Normal, and to assess the data without worrying about the non-Normality of the distribution it is necessary to evaluate the information based on a non-parametric test. However, if the data distributions were both Normal, it would be preferable to run the two-sample t-test as it provides more power than the nonparametric Wilcoxon test.

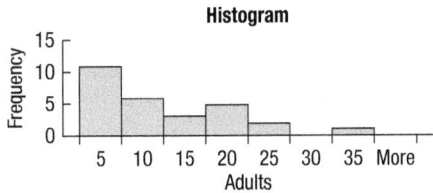

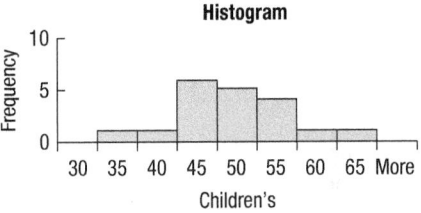

19. Use a Mann-Whitney test

Variable	n	median
size 19th	5	27.00
size 20th	9	15.50
W = 54.5		
Test of medians equal Reject the null at $\alpha = 0.10$		vs. medians not equal is significant at 0.0278.

21. a) Hypotheses:
   H_0: There is no change in average weight during the 12 weeks.
   H_A: There is a change in average weight during the 12 weeks.
   Assumptions and conditions:
   i. Randomly selected. Students were recruited but appeared to match the rest of the freshman class—satisfied.
   ii. Naturally paired. The students provided weights for before and after measurements.
   z-stat $= -5.562$ and, as a result, the null hypothesis can be rejected. In other words, there was a change in the weights of students.

b) The paired t-test would provide more power than the nonparametric statistic. However, if the distribution of the population is unknown or non-Normal, the nonparametric statistics would be preferred.

23. $N = 7$; $W = 2.5$. For a one-tailed test, Table W2 in Appendix B shows the P-Value to be between 0.025 and 0.05.

Reject the null hypothesis. ERP appears to be effective.

25. Wilcoxon signed-rank test

$N = 5$; $W = 15$. For a two-tailed test, Table W2 in Appendix B shows the P-Value to be above 0.05.

Do not reject the null hypothesis.

27.

Factor	N	Median	Avg Rank	Z
Robin	15	22.45	18.3	−1.26
Sparrow	13	23.05	24.7	1.13
Wagtail	14	22.85	22.0	0.17
Overall	42	21.5	21.5	

$H = 1.92$ $DF = 2$ $P = 0.383$
$H = 1.96$ $DF = 2$ $P = 0.376$ (adjusted for ties)
Do not reject the null hypothesis.

29. a) The relationship is negative and strongly monotonic.

b) There is a strong association between GDP and Crowdedness.

c) The non-linearity.

31. a) Kendall's tau would be a more appropriate measure to use if we are more concerned with the direction of the association between housing starts and Home Depot sales. This is especially useful since the relationship does not appear to be linear.

b) Kendall's tau allows the analyst to measure the monotonicity of the relationship (consistency of the relationship). Negative monotonicity will imply a discordant relationship and a positive value will imply a concordant relationship.

33. Neither the correlation coefficient nor Kendall's tau implies causality. The correlation coefficient assumes a linear structure and implies that there is a positive linear relationship between the two variables. Kendall's tau implies a concordant relationship but the relationship is weaker than the correlation coefficient. There are a number of situations that show that a higher median income might be related to a lower housing cost index.

35. a) Item H, since it is pressuring the statistician to support a result that it prefers.

b) Item A, since the data are paired and therefore the Wilcoxon signed-rank test should have been used.

CHAPTER 18

SECTION EXERCISE ANSWERS

1. People in this community spend about $17.28 plus 0.354 on eating out each week for each $1000 of household income.

3. a) Linearity: The plot appears linear.

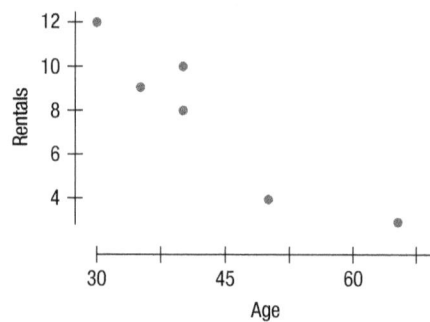

b) Independence: It is likely that the customers are independent. It is likely that errors made by the regression will be independent.

c) Equal Spread: The plot appears to have a consistent spread.

d) Normality: We can't tell from what we know.

5. a) 9.8, 8.5, 5.9, 2.0, 8.5, 11.1

b) −0.8, −0.5, −1.9, 1.0, 1.5, 0.9

c) $\sqrt{((-0.8)^2 + \cdots + (0.9)^2)/(6 - 2)} = 1.46$

7. $s_x = 12.5167$, $s_e = 1.46$, $n = 6$, $SE(b_1) = 0.052$

9. a) $0.265/0.0454 = 5.837$

b) 3

c) 0.01

d) Yes, the P-value is smaller than 0.05.

11. a) $H_0: \rho = 0$

$H_A: \rho \neq 0$

b) $t_{96} = 0.20\sqrt{(98 - 2)/(1 - 0.20^2)} = 2.0$

c) The t-statistic is just barely larger than the critical value. We can reject the null hypothesis.

13. a) 19.07 ($1000)

b) $SE = \sqrt{0.0873^2 * (12 - 10.4)^2 + 1.477^2/10}$ = 0.488. $19.07 \pm 2.306*0.488 = (17.94, 20.19)$ in $1000s

c) $SE = \sqrt{0.0873^2*(12 - 10.4)^2 + \dfrac{1.477^2}{10} + 1.477^2}$ = 1.553 $19.07 \pm 2.306*1.553 = (15.48, 22.66)$ in $1000s

15. a) 90% of customers 10 minutes before show time spend between $4.60 and $9.30 at the concession stand.

b) We can be 90% confident that the mean amount spent by customers at the concession stand 10 minutes before the movie begins is between $6.65 and $7.25.

c) The concessions manager is probably more interested in estimating the mean sales. As an individual moviegoer, you are probably more interested in the typical size of a sale (perhaps to check that you don't spend too much).

CHAPTER EXERCISE ANSWERS

17. a) $\widehat{Temp} = 16.43 + 0.0405\ CO_2$.

b) $R = 0.508$. Test: $H_0: \rho = 0$; $H_A: \rho \neq 0$. $t = 0.508\sqrt{35/(1 - 0.258)} = 3.49$; $P = 0.0013$. Null hypothesis is rejected. There is strong evidence that there is an association between temperature and CO_2 levels.

c) $H_0: \beta_1 = 0$; $H_A: \beta_1 \neq 0$. $t = 0.0405/0.0116 = 3.49$, P-value = 0.0013. Null hypothesis is rejected. There is strong evidence that there is an association between temperature and CO_2 levels. Years with higher CO_2 levels tend to be warmer on average.

d) Predictions will have a lot of error associated with them. R^2 value of 25.8% means that only 25.8% of the variability in temperature can be explained by the CO_2 concentration levels.

19. a) $\widehat{Price} = -312 + 94.5\ Size$. The model suggests that for every square foot increase in size, the houses increase in cost by $94.5, or houses cost about $94.5 per square foot.

b) Negative intercept makes no physical sense in this case. P-value for the intercept is 0.51, which indicates that we can't discern a difference between the intercept value and zero. It makes sense to say that a house of zero size has a value of $0.

c) It is the residual standard deviation, indicating that the amounts by which house prices differ from predictions made by this model vary with a standard deviation of about $54,000.

d) $2.39 per square foot.

e) For other models on a different sample of houses, we'd expect the slopes of the regression line to vary, with a standard deviation of about $2.39 per square foot.

21. a) The scatterplot looks reasonably straight; the residuals look random and nearly Normal; and the residuals don't display any clear change in variability.

b) 95% confident that Saratoga housing costs increase at a rate of between $89.76 and $99.2 per square foot.

23. a) From technology, the regression equation is $\overline{2010Unemp} = 3.06 + 0.826 \times 2007Unemp$

b) There are several possible outliers (Lithuania, Latvia, Spain, and Estonia) and two high-leverage cases (South Africa and Macedonia). This regression should be interpreted with care.

Residual Plots for 2010

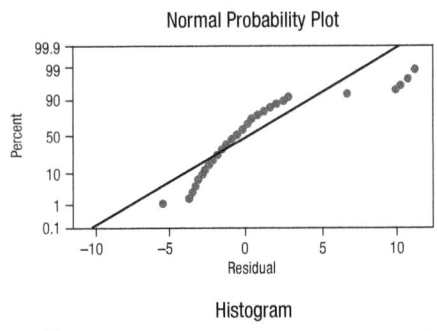

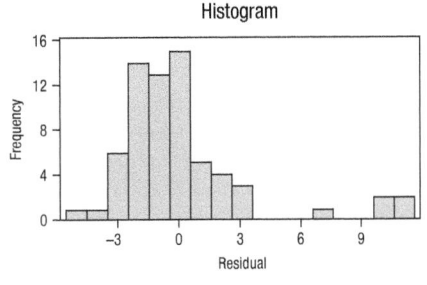

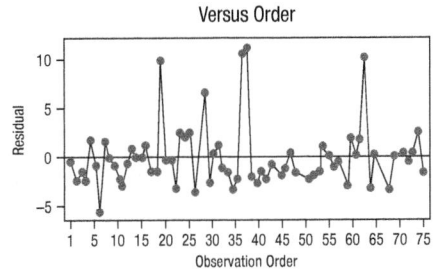

Predictor	Coef	SE Coef	T	P
Constant	3.0614	0.7275	4.21	0.000
2007	0.82627	0.8396	9.84	0.000

$S = 3.29472$
$R\text{-Sq} = 59.8\%\ R\text{-Sq(adj)} = 59.2\%$
Analysis of Variance

Source	DF	SS	MS	F	P
Regression	1	1051.4	1051.4	96.86	0.000
Residual Error	65	705.6	10.9		
Total	65	1757.0			

c) The P-value for the slope is <0.0001. Clearly this is a non-zero slope.

d) This model explains 59.8% of the variability in male unemployment rate in 2010 (represented by $R^2 = 0.598$).

25. a) Conditions are satisfied. The scatterplot is sufficiently straight enough to at least try linear regression. The residual plots show no pattern and the spread of the residuals is consistent. The Normal probability plot is fairly straight.

b) Test: H_0: There is no linear relationship between the size of a home and its assessed value. ($\beta_1 = 0$). H_A: There is a linear relationship between the size of a home and its assessed value. ($\beta_1 \neq 0$). Regression equation:

$\widehat{Assessed\ Value} = 37,108.8 + 11.90 \times (SqFt)$.

$t = 2.77$; $df = 16$; $P = 0.0136$; reject the null hypothesis. Larger homes have higher assessed values.

c) This model explains 32.5% of the variability in assessed house value (represented by $R^2 = 0.325$).

d) $11.90 \pm 1.7259*4.29 = (4.41, 19.39)$.

e) No, we can show an association, but we cannot show cause and effect.

f) Expected assessment $= 37108.8 + 11.8987*2100 = \$62,096.07$. 95% prediction interval $= 62096.07 \pm$

$$2.120\sqrt{4.290^2*(2100 - 2003.39)^2 + \frac{4682^2}{18} + 4682^2}$$

$= (\$51,860, \$72,332)$. There is no evidence that this home has an assessment that is too high. The assessed value of $70,200 falls within the prediction interval.

The homeowner might calculate the 95% confidence interval by dropping the last term under the square root above: ($59,597, $64,595). The assessment is outside this range but for an individual home the prediction interval should be used.

27. The residuals increase with the predicted values. Inference cannot be performed and a confidence interval cannot be calculated.

29. a) 33

b) Conditions:
Linearity Condition: The scatterplot shown is fairly straight.
Independence Assumption: The residuals plot is not curved.
Equal Spread Condition: The residuals show a fairly equal spread.
Nearly Normal Condition: The histogram of the residuals is fairly symmetric. Normal probability plot seems to be at least slightly curved upward.

c) Test: H_0: There is no linear relationship between cost and power. ($\beta_1 = 0$). H_A: There is a positive linear relationship between cost and power. ($\beta_1 \neq 0$).

$t = 3.23$; $P = 0.0029$. The null hypothesis should be rejected. There is strong evidence of a positive linear relationship between cost and power. Batteries that cost more tend to have more power.

d) $R^2 = 25.2\%$, indicating a fairly weak positive association.

e) $\widehat{Power} = 384.594 + 4.146 \times Cost$ with *Power* measured in cold cranking amps and *Cost* in dollars.

f) $4.146 \pm 1.6955*1.282 = (1.97, 6.32)$

g) We are 90% confident that the mean power increases by between 1.97 and 6.32 cold cranking amps for each additional dollar in cost.

31. a) The first scatterplot shows a somewhat curved relationship. If we use Hours per Output as the response variable, the relationship seems more linear.

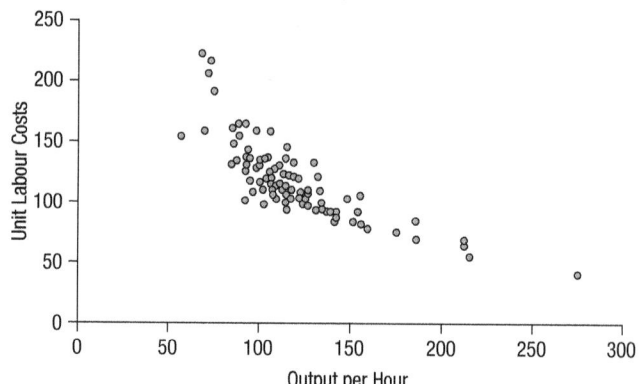

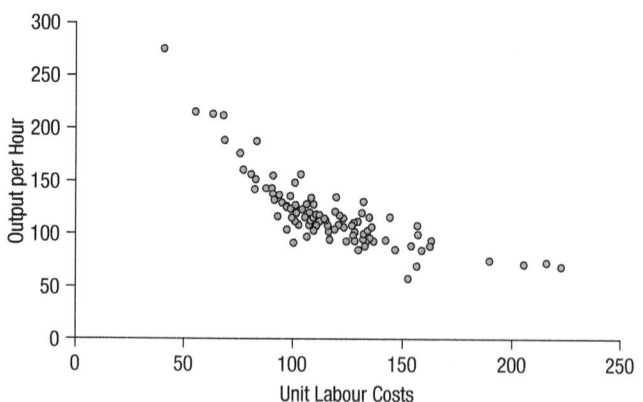

b) H_0: There is no linear relationship between productivity and unit labour cost. ($\beta_1 = 0$). H_A: There is a linear relationship between productivity and unit labour cost. ($\beta_1 \neq 0$). Regression Analysis: Reciprocal of Output versus Unit.labour.costs

Predictor	Coef	SE Coef	T	P
Constant	0.0017753	0.0004156	4.27	0.000
Unit.labour.costs	0.00006170	0.00000348	17.73	0.000

$S = 0.00106736$

$R\text{-Sq} = 72.0\%$

$R\text{-Sq(adj)} = 71.8\%$

The t-value shown is 17.73 with a P-value <0.0001. The null hypothesis should be rejected. There is strong evidence of a negative linear relationship between productivity and unit labour cost indexes. Higher productivity indices are associated with lower unit labour cost indices across industries.

33. a) H_0: There has been no change in the percentage of people responding with "no opinion." ($\beta_1 = 0$).
H_A: There has been a change in the percentage of people responding with "no opinion." ($\beta_1 \neq 0$).

b) $t = -1.21$; P $= 0.246$. We fail to reject the null hypothesis. There is insufficient evidence that the percentage of people responding with "no opinion" has changed.

c) There are two outliers. A regression model is not appropriate.

35. a) $0.675 \pm 1.6544 * 0.057 = (0.581, 0.769)$

b) 90% confident that the Math SAT scores increase by between 0.581 and 0.769 points for each additional point scored on the Verbal test.

37. a) H_0: There is no linear association between the average hourly wages of sales managers and advertising managers. ($\beta_1 = 0$).
H_A: There is a linear relationship between the average hourly wages of sales managers and advertising managers. ($\beta_1 \neq 0$).

b) $t = 5.76$; P < 0.001. We reject the null hypothesis. There is strong evidence of a linear relationship between the average hourly wages of sales managers and advertising managers.

c) We conclude that there is strong evidence of a linear relationship between the average hourly wages of sales managers and advertising managers.

39. a) The hypotheses to test the association between the two variables:
H_0: There is no linear association between Job Growth in 2010 and 2012. ($\beta_1 = 0$).
H_A: There is no linear relationship between Job Growth in 2010 and 2012. ($\beta_1 \neq 0$).

b) The P-value of 0.0498 is less than the conventional α of 0.05 but just barely so. We reject the null hypothesis but using caution.

c) Only $R^2 = 5.7\%$ of the variance in 2012 job growth can be explained by the linear regression on 2010 job growth.

d) The data do not provide an indication that job growth has been consistent in these companies. Those that had supported large job growth in 2010 did not necessarily do so in 2012.

41. Test: H_0: There is not a linear relationship between the effectiveness of the video and the player's initial ability. ($\beta_1 = 0$).
H_A: There is a linear relationship between the effectiveness of the video and the player's initial ability. ($\beta_1 \neq 0$).
$t = 0.112$. P $= 0.9118$ means that the association we see in the data is quite likely to occur by chance. We fail to reject the null hypothesis. Effectiveness of the program does not appear to depend on the initial ability of the player.

43. a) Zappos had a negative job growth—it lost jobs in 2010. In 2011, it appears to have expanded rapidly.

b) If the outlier were left in place, the regression line might have a negative slope even though the trend for the other companies is slightly positive.

c) The regression equation without the outlier is
$\overline{2012\ Job\ Growth} = 0.0628 + 0.200\ 2010\ Job\ growth$

Predictor	Coef	SE Coef	T	P
Constant	0.062826	0.008976	7.00	0.000
2012 Job Growth	0.2003	0.1002	2.00	0.050

$S = 0.0738042$

$R\text{-Sq} = 5.7\%$

$R\text{-Sq(adj)} = 4.38\%$

$\overline{2012\ Job\ Growth} = 0.0704 - 0.033\ 2010\ Job\ growth$

45. a) $(-4.988, 5.285)$

b) Yes, it will probably be accurate, but not very useful since most of the pitchers fall into this range.

47. a) Test: H_A: There is no linear association between $Log\ Assets$ and $Log Sales$. ($\beta_1 = 0$).
H_A: There is a linear relationship between $Log Assets$ and $Log Sales$. ($\beta_1 \neq 0$).
P-value < 0.0001; reject the null hypothesis. There is strong evidence of a linear relationship between $Log Assets$ and $Log Sales$. Companies with more assets tend to have higher sales.

b) $R^2 = 33.9\%$, so 33.9% of the variability in $Log Sales$ can be accounted for by $Log Assets$.

49. a) Conditions:
Linearity Condition: The scatterplot is straight enough to try linear regression.
Independence Assumption: One cardholder's spending should not affect another's spending. The residuals plot shows no pattern. These 99 cardholders are a random sample of cardholders.
Equal Spread Condition: The residuals plot shows some increased spread for larger values of December charges.
Nearly Normal Condition: The histogram of residuals is unimodal and symmetric with two high outliers.

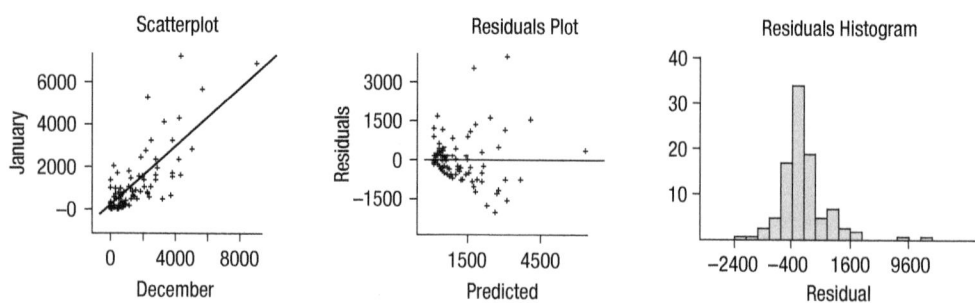

We should proceed cautiously. There are some issues with the conditions for regression.

The regression model is $\widehat{January} = 120.73 + 0.6995(December)$

b) The regression equation predicts that cardholders who charged $2000 in December will charge $120.73 + 0.6995(2000) = \$1519.73$ in January, on average.

c) Cardholders charged an average of $1336.03 in December.

$$\hat{y}_v \pm t^*_{n-2}\sqrt{SE^2(b_1) \cdot (x_v - \bar{x})^2 + \frac{s_e^2}{n}}$$

$$= 1519.73 \pm (1.9847)\sqrt{0.0562^2 \cdot (2000 - 1336.03)^2 + \frac{874.5^2}{99}} = (1330.24, 1709.24)$$

We are 95% confident that the average January charges for a cardholder who charged $2000 in December will be between $1330.24 and $1709.24.

d) We are 95% confident that a cardholder who charged $2000 in December charged between $290.76 and $669.76 less than $2000 in January, on average.

e) The residuals show increasing spread, so the confidence intervals may not be valid. We should be very cautious when attempting to interpret them too literally.

51. a) The relationship seems linear with uniform scatter, but there is not enough data to check for Normality.

b) There is probably a linear association.

c) Estimated attendance $= -120,463 + 5305.56*$ PitchAge. For each coefficient, $P < 0.01$. Teams with pitchers one year older have 5305 more fans on average at each game.

53. a) The trends might not be linear. The data are a time series that are probably correlated. The spread/variance might not be uniform. The residuals might not be Normally distributed.

b)

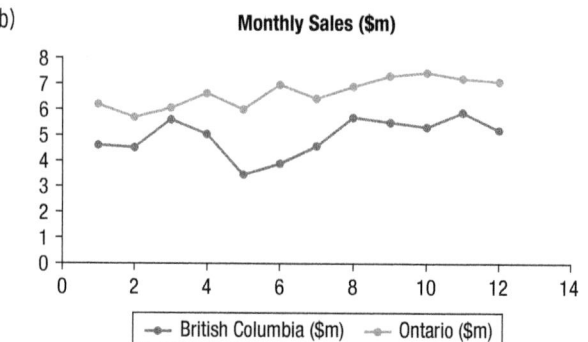

For British Columbia, the linear regression is:

	Coefficients	Standard Error	t Stat	P-value
Intercept	4.334545	0.43298	10.01097	1.57E-06
Month	0.093531	0.05883	1.589851	0.142952

Sales $= 4.33 + 0.0588*$Month

The P-value for the slope is 0.143.

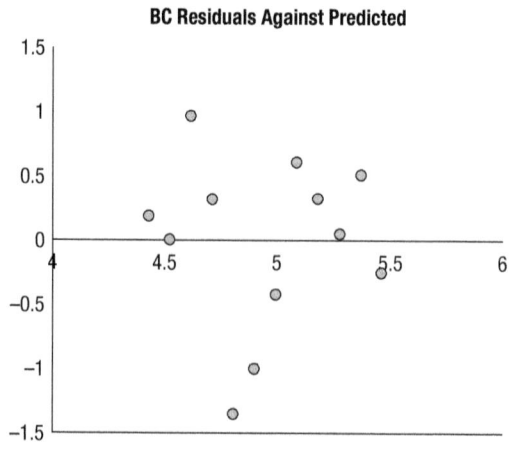

The trend is linear. The spread is uniform. The residuals are random with no evidence of non-Normality. However, there is clearly correlation between the data points since the data are a time series.

For Ontario, the linear regression is:

	Coefficients	Standard Error	t Stat	P-value
Intercept	5.776667	0.196371	29.41718	4.81E-11
Month	0.134615	0.026682	5.04527	0.000503

Sales = 5.78 + 0.135*Month

The P-value for the slope is 0.000503

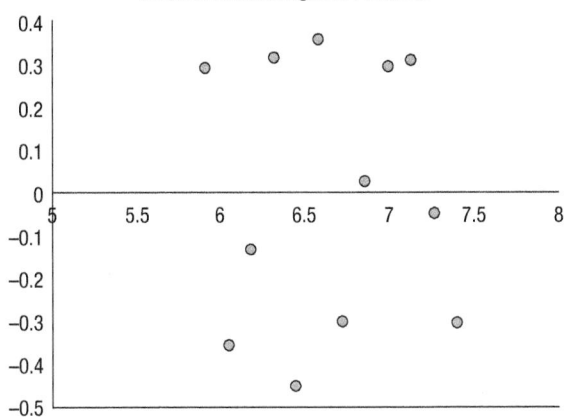

Ontario Residuals Against Predicted

The trend is linear. The spread is uniform. The residuals are random with no evidence of non-Normality. However, there is clearly correlation between the data points since the data are a time series.

Ontario has the higher sales growth per month of 0.135 $m/month and receives bonus (i).

Ontario has the more significant sales growth per month with P = 0.000503 and receives bonus (ii).

c) To compare the two provinces, we calculate the difference between their sales and regress that against month.

Difference ($m)
1.59
1.16
0.46
1.59
2.56
3.04
1.85
1.18
1.77
2.11
1.32
1.88

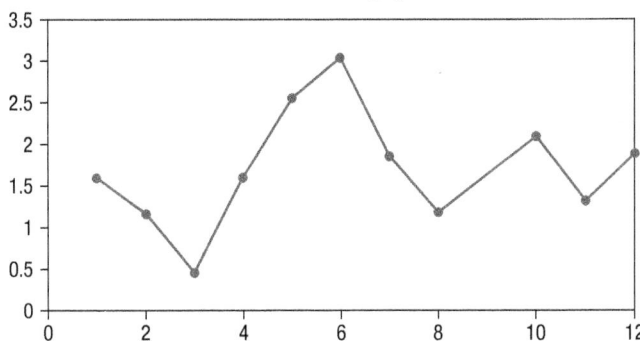

Difference ($m)

The regression is:

	Coefficients	Standard Error	t Stat	P-value
Intercept	1.442121	0.425909	3.385983	0.006933
Month	0.041084	0.05787	0.709939	0.493964

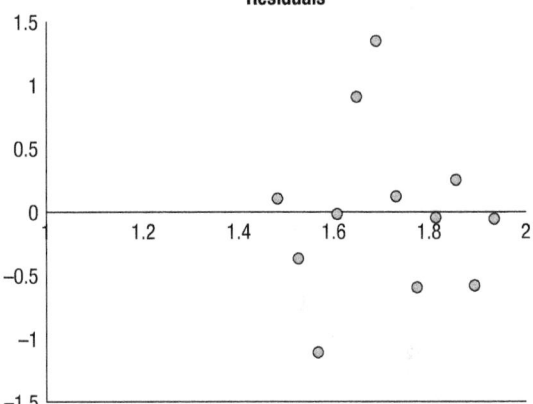

Residuals

The trend is linear. The spread is uniform. The residuals are random with no evidence of non-Normality. However, there is clearly correlation between the data points since the data are a time series.

The P-value is very high at 0.494, indicating no significant difference in slope between the provinces.

55. (i) Alice talks about high earnings bringing about high share prices. Regression cannot establish causality.
   (ii) Alice wants to extrapolate outside the range of the data when the regression has been done, without acknowledging the limitations on doing this.
   (iii) Both Alice and Bob assume that regression is possible without acknowledging the conditions that must be satisfied.
   (iv) Bob thinks his regression will explain more of the variability. This is measured by R^2. However R^2 is just the square of the correlation coefficient which is the same for each regression.

CHAPTER 18 JUST CHECKING ANSWERS

1. I would need to see a scatterplot to check if the Linearity Assumption is reasonable and to make sure that there are no outliers, and a residual plot to check the Equal Spread Condition. I'd also like to see a histogram or Normal probability plot of the residuals to make sure the Nearly Normal Condition is satisfied. Finally, I'd like to see the residuals plotted in time to check whether the residuals appear independent. Without verifying these conditions, I wouldn't know whether my analysis is valid.

2. The 95% CI for the slope is $1133.8 \pm 2.052(513.1)$, or $(80.9, 2186.7)$.

3. H_0: The slope $\beta_1 = 0$. H_A: The slope $\beta_1 \neq 0$. Since the P-value $= 0.036$, we reject the null hypothesis (at $\alpha = 0.05$) and conclude that there is a linear relationship between enrollment and unemployment.

4. Strength is a judgment call, but I'd be hesitant to call a relationship with an R^2 value of only 15% strong.

5. Approximately 15% of the variation in enrollment at the University of New Mexico is accounted for by variation in the unemployment rate in New Mexico.

6. The test says that we can reject the hypothesis that the correlation is 0 (at $\alpha = 0.05$) and conclude that there is a linear relationship between enrollment and unemployment. This is exactly what the test of the slope in question 3 told us. The correlation is zero if and only if the slope is zero. There is no new information here.

CHAPTER 19

SECTION EXERCISE ANSWERS

1. The different segments are not scattered at random throughout the residuals plot. Each segment may have a different relationship.

3. Yes, it is clear that the relationship between January and December spending is not the same for all five segments. Using one overall model to predict January spending would be very misleading.

5. a) 464.6 ($000)
   b) No. Extrapolating what their sales might be with 500 employees based on data with between 2 and 20 employees working is likely to be very wrong.

7. a) $354,472
   b) An extrapolation this far from the data is unreliable.

9. a) $\widehat{Sales} = 14.32 + 0.297\ Number\ of\ SalesPeople\ Working$
   b) The intercept is higher and the slope is much lower.
   c) High leverage and influential.
   d) Not really. The line is so influenced by the new point that it passes close to it.

11. a)

Quarter	Sales($M)	Predicted	Residual
1	12	19.02	−7.02
2	41	23.89	17.11
3	15	28.76	−13.76
4	48	33.63	14.37
5	25	38.5	−13.76
6	55	43.37	11.63
7	23	48.24	−25.24
8	69	53.11	15.89
9	51	57.98	−6.98
10	80	65.85	17.15
11	54	67.72	−13.72
12	87	72.59	14.41
13	64	77.46	−13.46
14	94	82.33	11.67
15	62	87.2	−25.2
16	108	92.07	15.93

b)

Sales alternate above and below the trend line from one quarter to the next quarter.

c) $D = [(17.11 + 7.02)^2 + \cdots + (15.93 + 25.2)^2]/[(7.02)^2 + \cdots + (15.93)^2] = 3.62$

d) From the table in Appendix B for n = 16, k = 1, we get 1.10 and 1.37.

e) No. $D > 1.37$

f) Yes. $D > 4 - 1.10$

13. a) $d_L = 1.48$, $d_U = 1.57$. The observed value is less than d_L, so we can reject the null hypothesis of no autocorrelation.
   b) The statistic tests for time-related correlation. We can conclude that there is evidence of positive autocorrelation.

15. No. The scatterplot shows a linear relationship and the residuals plot has no obvious pattern. No transformation is suggested.

17. A re-expression is called for. Taking the log or reciprocal of *Cost per Unit* would probably improve the linearity.

19. a) Log
   b) 0

CHAPTER EXERCISE ANSWERS

21. a) There is a clear pattern between the two variables. The trend is increasing but is not linear throughout. There is a linear portion from 1 to 11 years of schooling and another from 15 to 19.

b) The association is strong with little variability from the general trend.

c) Not appropriate for the whole data set but could be used on the portions given in a).

d) Positive at each end and negative in the centre.

e) Logarithm.

23. a) Fitting a linear model to the association between the number of cell phones and HDI would be misleading, since the relationship is not straight.

b) The residuals plot will be curved downward.

25. a) Appropriate. Low R^2 simply means that the model is not accurate. If the residuals plot shows no pattern, this model may be appropriate.

b) No, not likely to be accurate, but they may be the best that the intern can get. Two variables that are being studied by the intern have a weak association.

27. a) The slopes of the regression lines are approximately the same, so the earnings increase at about the same rate as the movies get longer.

b) Although the costs per minute are about the same, it costs about $50 million less to make a comedy than an adventure movie, on average, with the same running time.

c) Omitting *Harry Potter* would make the slope for the dramas less steep. We would conclude that there is little relationship between gross receipts and run time for dramas.

29. a) According to the linear model, tracking errors averaged about 294 nautical miles in 1970 and have decreased an average of 5.39 nautical miles per year since then.

b) Residuals based on this model have a standard deviation of 39.10 nautical miles.

c) The linear model for the trend in predicting error is
$$\widehat{Error} = 294.138 - 5.392(2015 - 1970) = 51.5$$
The model predicts an error of only 51.5 nautical miles in 2015. Based on this prediction, the Center may not achieve its goal.

d) From technology the Durbin-Watson statistic = 19.24 with a P-Value > 0.1. There is no evidence of autocorrelation.

e) We should be cautious in assuming that the improvements in prediction will continue at the same rate.

31. a) 1) The point has high leverage and makes the large residual a bit smaller.

2) The point is influential. It is well away from the mean of the explanatory variable and has enough leverage to change the slope of the regression line.

3) If the point were removed, the correlation would become stronger. Without the point, the positive association would be reinforced.

4) The slope would increase, becoming steeper after the removal of the point. The regression line would follow the general cloud of points more closely.

b) 1) The point has high leverage and a small residual.

2) The point is influential. The point alone gives the scatterplot the appearance of an overall positive direction, when the points are actually fairly scattered.

3) If the point were removed, the correlation would become weaker. Without the point, there would be very little evidence of linear association.

4) The slope would decrease, from a positive slope to a slope near zero. Without the point, the slope of the regression line would be nearly flat.

c) 1) The point has little leverage and a large residual.

2) The point is not influential. It is very close to the mean of the explanatory variable, and the regression line is anchored at the point (x, y), and would only pivot if it were possible to minimize the sum of the squared residuals. No amount of pivoting will reduce the residual for the stray point, so the slope would not change.

3) If the point were removed, the correlation would become slightly stronger. The point detracts from the overall pattern, and its removal would reinforce the association.

4) The slope would remain roughly the same. Since the point is not influential, its removal would not affect the slope.

d) 1) The point has high leverage and a small residual.

2) The point is not influential. It has the potential to be influential, because its position far from the mean of the explanatory variable gives it high leverage. However, the point is not exerting much influence because it reinforces the association.

3) If the point were removed, the correlation would become weaker. The point heavily reinforces the association. Removing it would weaken the association.

4) The slope would remain roughly the same since the point is not influential.

33. 1) Point d is influential. Its addition will pull the slope of the regression line toward point d, resulting in the steepest negative slope, a slope of –0.45.

2) Point e is very influential, but since it is far away from the group of points, its addition will only pull the slope down slightly. The slope is –0.30.

3) Point c is directly below the middle of the group of points. Its position is directly below the mean of the explanatory variable. It has no influence. Its addition will leave the slope the same, 0.

4) Point b is almost in the centre of the group of points, but not quite. It has very little influence, but what influence it has is positive. The slope will increase very slightly with its addition, to 0.05.

5) Point a is very influential, Its addition will pull the regression line up to its steepest positive slope, 0.85.

35. a) As speed increases by one mile per hour, fuel economy is expected to decrease by 0.1 miles per gallon.

b) It is the predicted mileage at a speed of zero miles per hour. It's not possible to get 32 miles per gallon if you aren't moving.

c) Residuals are negative for higher gas mileages. Model is predicting higher than the actual mileage.

d) When a car is driven at 50 miles per hour, the model predicts mileage of 27 miles per gallon.

e) When a car is driven at 45 miles per hour, the model predicts mileage of 27.5 miles per gallon. From the graph, the residual at 27.5 mpg is +1. The actual gas mileage is $27.5 + 1 = 28.5$ mpg.

f) The association between fuel economy and speed is probably quite strong, but not linear.

g) Not an appropriate model for the association between fuel economy and speed. The residuals plot has a clear pattern. If the linear model were appropriate, we would expect scatter in the residuals plot.
    Infringes item A of the ASA Ethical Guidelines on professionalism.

37. a) The data from the late 1800s to 1950 are high leverage points. Since they generally follow the same linear trend as the 1975–2011 data, those data points increase the correlation and the R^2 value.

b) The residuals plot shows a slight bend, so the linear model is probably appropriate, but we should proceed with caution.

c) For every 10 years that pass, the model predicts a decrease of approximately 0.20 years in average age difference at first marriage (drops about 0.02 per year).

d) These data begin with $x = 1975$. The y-intercept is the predicted difference in age at the year $x = 0$, which is almost 2000 years ago; an extrapolation that far into the past is not meaningful. The earliest year for which we have data is 1975.

39. a) No re-expression needed.

b) Re-express to straighten the relationship.

c) Re-express to equalize the spread.

41. a) $\hat{y} = 1.2 + 0.8(2) = 2.8$

b) $\ln \hat{y} = 1.2 + 0.8(2) = 2.8$ so $\hat{y} = 16.44$
   $(\hat{y} = e^{2.8})$

c) $\sqrt{\hat{y}} = 1.2 + 0.8(2) = 2.8$ so $\hat{y} = 2.8^2 = 7.84$

d) $\dfrac{1}{\hat{y}} = 1.2 + 0.8(2) = 2.8$ so $\hat{y} = \dfrac{1}{2.8} = 0.36$

e) $\hat{y} = 1.2(2)^{0.8} = 2.09$

43. a) $\hat{y} = 2 + 0.8(\ln 10) = 3.84$

b) $\log \hat{y} = 5 - 0.23(10) = 2.7$
   so $\hat{y} = 10^{2.7} = 501.19$

c) $\dfrac{1}{\sqrt{\hat{y}}} = 17.1 - 1.66(10) = 0.5$ so $\hat{y} =$
   $\left(\dfrac{1}{0.5}\right)^2 = 4$

45. a) Linearity Condition violated. Possibly increased variation at higher values. Independence may be in doubt since this is a time series.

b) This plot looks both straighter and more consistent in variation.

c) The residuals show a pattern, but it tracks up and down and could not be improved by an alternative transformation.

47. a) About $672,000,000

b) *logValue* grows at 0.0001915 per licensed *Fisher*. Possibly more fishers cause a more valuable harvest, but greater value would likely attract more fishers, so the causation might run the other way. Or improving technology could both lead to more value and attract more fishers.

49. a)

	Coefficients	Standard Error	t Stat	P-value
Intercept	515.5517017	3.253418147	158.4646	2.13E-80
Quarter	8.10237506	0.089802873	90.22401	8.75E-66

$R^2 = 0.9927$

b) Each quarter the GDP increases by $8.102bn on average. The P-value is extremely small, indicating this to be highly statistically significant. The regression accounts for 99.27% of the variability in the data.

51. a) $\overline{\sqrt{BoardFeet}} = -4 + Diameter$

b) 36

c) 1024

53. The histogram is much more unimodal and symmetric after we take logs.

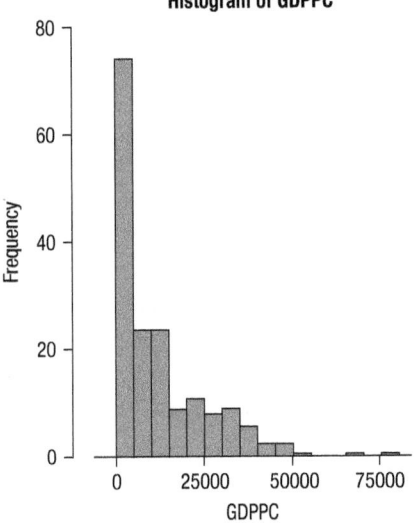

Histogram of GDPPC

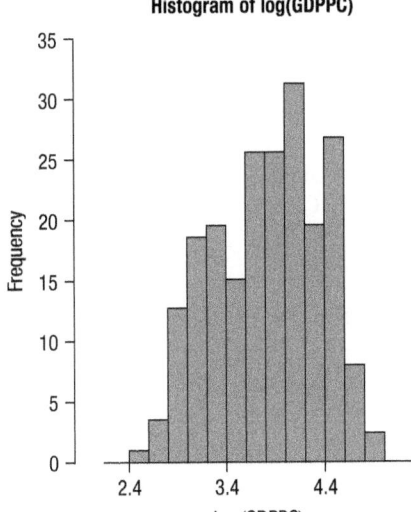

Histogram of log(GDPPC)

55. The plot cannot be straightened by a transformation because it is not a simple monotonically increasing or decreasing shape; rather, it oscillates up and down.

57. a)

	Coefficients	Standard Error	t Stat	P-value
Intercept	−0.02511617	0.302749233	−0.0829603	0.9353735
NRP	1.679994764	0.092054539	18.2499938	1.424E-09

$R^2 = 0.968$
$\widehat{RP} = -0.0251 + 1.68 \text{ NRP}$

b) $t = 18.25$, which is very significant since the corresponding P-value is about 10^{-9} (extremely small),

c) Ontario is an outlier.

d) Ontario has high leverage since it is very far from the mean of the data.

e)

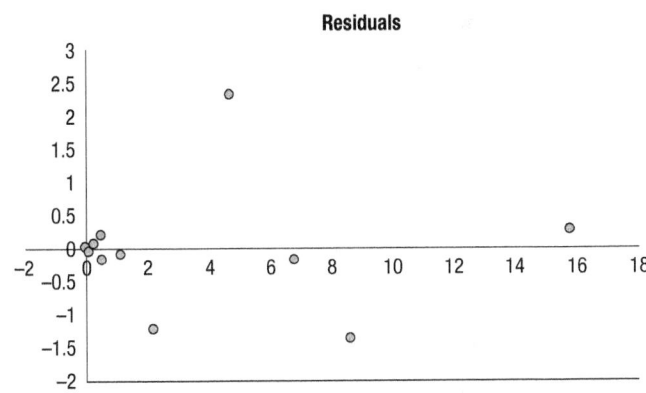

	Coefficients	Standard Error	t Stat	P-value
Intercept	0.034126562	0.332805128	0.10254218	0.9203535
NRP	1.613107299	0.158757623	10.1608179	1.373E-06

$R^2 = 0.912$
$\widehat{RP} = 0.0341 + 1.613 \text{ NRP}$

f) The slope coefficient changes from 1.680 to 1.613 and originally had a standard error of 0.0921. The change is therefore $(1.680 - 1.613)/0.0921 = 0.727$ standard errors. Ontario is not influential.

g) The provinces and territories could have been sequenced in any way, so there is no rationale for expecting autocorrelation in this data. There is therefore no reason to calculate a DW statistic.

h) The scatterplot of the data is linear and the residuals are random, so there is no reason to transform the data.

Residuals

CHAPTER 19 JUST CHECKING ANSWERS

1. Not high leverage, not influential, large residual

2. High leverage, not influential, small residual

3. High leverage, influential, not large residual

4. None

5. Logarithm

CHAPTER 20

SECTION EXERCISE ANSWERS

1. a) $99,859.89
   b) $35,140.11
   c) The house sold for about $35,100 more than our estimate.

3. a) $\widehat{USGross} = -222.9898 + 1.13442 \, Budget + 24.9724 \, Stars - 0.40329 \, RunTime$
   b) After allowing for the effects of *RunTime* and *Stars*, each million dollars spent making a film yields about $1.13 million in gross revenue.

5. a) Linearity: The plot is reasonably linear with no bends.

b) Equal Spread: The plot fails the Equal Spread Condition. It is much more spread out to the right than the left.

c) Normality: A scatterplot of two of the variables doesn't tell us anything about the distribution of the residuals.

7. a) $H_0: \beta_{Stars} = 0$

b) $t = 24.9724/5.884 = 4.24$

c) $P \leq 0.0001$

d) Reject the null hypothesis and conclude that the coefficient of *Stars* is not zero.

9. a) $R^2 = 0.474$ or 47.4%

About 47.4% of the variation in *USGross* is accounted for by the least squares regression on *Budget*, *RunTime*, and *Stars*.

b) Adjusted R^2 accounts for the number of predictors, so it differs from R^2, which does not.

CHAPTER EXERCISE ANSWERS

11. a) Linearity: The scatterplots show little pattern, but are not nonlinear. Independence: States are not a random sample, but they may be independent of each other. Equal Variance: The scatterplots do not appear to have a changing spread. Normality: To check the Nearly Normal Condition, we'll need to look at the residuals; we can't check it with these plots.

b) 0.26%

13. a) $\widehat{Violent\ Crime} = 1370.22 + 0.795\ Police\ Officer\ Wage - 12.641\ Graduation\ Rate$

b) After allowing for the effects of graduation rate (or, alternatively, among states with similar graduation rates), states with higher police officer wages have more crime at the rate of 0.7953 crimes per 100,000 for each dollar per hour of average wage.

c) 501.244 crimes per 100,000

15. a) $0.221 = \dfrac{0.7949}{3.598}$

b) 50 states. There are 47 degrees of freedom and that's equal to $n - k - 1$. With two predictors, $50 - 2 - 1 = 47$.

c) The t-ratio is negative because the coefficient is negative.

17. a) $H_0: \beta_{Officer\ Wage} = 0;\ H_A: \beta_{Officer\ Wage} \neq 0$

b) $P = 0.8262$; that's not small enough to reject the null hypothesis at $\alpha = 0.05$ and conclude that the coefficient is discernibly different from zero.

19. This is a causal interpretation, which is not supported by regression. For example, among states with high graduation rates, it may be that those with higher violent crime rates choose (or are obliged) to spend more to hire police officers, or that states with higher costs of living must pay more to attract qualified police officers but also have higher crime rates. Moreover, the coefficient of *Police Wage* cannot be distinguished from 0.

21. Constant Variance Condition: may be met by the residuals vs. predicted plot (but some may judge otherwise). Nearly Normal condition: met by the Normal probability plot.

23. a) Incorrect: Doesn't mention other predictors. Suggests direct relationship between only two variables: *Age* and *Price*.

b) Correct.

c) Incorrect: Can't predict x from y.

d) Incorrect interpretation of R^2 (this model accounts for 92% of the variability in *Price*).

25. a) Incorrect: This is likely to be extrapolation since it is unlikely that they observed any data points with no advertising of any kind.

b) Incorrect: Suggests a perfect relationship.

c) Incorrect: Can't predict one explanatory variable (x) from another.

d) Correct.

27. a) F-ratio has a very low P-value; the regression is significant.

b) Need to check the scatterplot of residuals against predicted values and the histogram of residuals.

c) Salary is not a significant contributor to CSR Rating at the 90% level, since the P-value of its coefficient is > 0.1. Options are a significant contributor to CSR rating at the 95% level, since the P-value of its coefficient is < 0.05.

d) No interpretation for the coefficient since it is not significantly different from zero.

e) They could expect the CSR rating to increase by 0.08 standard deviations.

29. a) $\widehat{Price} = -152,037 + 9530\ Baths + 139.87\ Area$

b) 71.1%

c) For houses with the same number of bathrooms, each square foot of area is associated with an increase of $139.87 in the price of the house, on average.

d) Regression model says that for houses of same size, there is no evidence that those with more bathrooms are priced higher since the corresponding P-value is very large.

31. a) $\widehat{Salary} = 9.788 + 0.110\ Service + 0.05\ Education + 0.071\ Test\ Score + 0.004\ Typing\ wpm + 0.065\ Dictation\ wpm$

b) $\widehat{Salary} = 9.788 + 0.110 \times 120 + 0.053 \times 9 + 0.071 \times 50 + 0.004 \times 60 + 0.065 \times 30 = 29.205$ or \$29,205.

c) The t-value is 0.013 with 24 < df and a P-value = 0.9897 (two-tailed), which is not significant.

d) Could take out the explanatory variable X4 (*typing speed*), since it is not significant.

e) *Age* is likely to be collinear with several of the other predictors already in the model.

33. a) This model explains less than 4% of the variation in *GDP per Capita*. The P-value is not particularly low.

b) Because more education is generally associated with a higher standard of living, it is not surprising that the simple association between *Primary Completion Rate* and GDP is positive.

c) The coefficient now is measuring the association between *GDP/Capita* and *Primary Completion Rate* after accounting for the two other predictors.

35. a) $\widehat{PBE} = 87.0 - 0.345 \, CPI + 0.000011 \, Personal \, Consumption + 0.0001 \, Retail \, Sales.$

b) $R^2 = 66.7\%$ and all t-ratios are significant. It looks like these variables can account for much of the variation in Walmart revenue.

37. a) $\widehat{Logit \, (Drop)} = 0.4419 + 0.0379 \, Age - 0.0468 \, HDRS$

b) $0.4419 + 0.0379 \,(30) - 0.0468(30) = 0.1749$

c) $1/(1 + e^{-0.1749}) = 0.544$

d) 2.342

e) 0.912

39. *Displacement* and *Bore* would be good predictors. Relationship with *Wheelbase* isn't linear.

41. a) Yes, an $R^2 = 90.9\%$ says that most of the variability of *MSRP* is accounted for by this model.

b) No, in a regression model, you can't predict an explanatory variable from the response variable.

43. a) The F-ratio has a very low P-value, which implies that the regression is significant overall.

b) EL, EX, EX^2, and ED, since the P-values of their coefficients are < 0.05.

c) EL is related to earnings (w) at the 95% level, since the P-value of its coefficient is < 0.05. The relation between EL and w is not linear but the relation between ln(EL) and ln(w) is linear.

d) The low P-values associated with the coefficients for ED and EL.

e) Many other factors might contribute to weekly earnings, such as gender, disability, etc.

CHAPTER 20 JUST CHECKING ANSWERS

1. 58.4% of the variation in *Percent Body Fat* can be accounted for by the multiple regression model using *Height*, *Age*, and *Weight* as predictors.

2. For a given *Height* and *Weight*, an increase of one year in *Age* is associated with an increase of 0.137% in *Body Fat* on average. For a given *Age* and *Weight*, an increase of 1 cm in *Height* is associated with a decrease of 0.50164% in *Body Fat* on average. Taller people have less body fat on average.

3. The multiple regression coefficient is interpreted for *given* values of the other variables. That is, for people of the same *Weight* and *Age*, an increase of one centimetre of *Height* is associated with, on average, a decrease of 0.502% in *Body Fat*. The same cannot be said when looking at people of all *Weights* and *Ages*.

4. Histograms are used to examine the shapes of distributions of individual variables. We check especially for multiple modes, outliers, and skewness. They are also used to check the shape of the distribution of the residuals for the Nearly Normal Condition.

5. Scatterplots are used to check the Linearity Condition in plots of *y* vs. any of the *x*-values. They are used to check plots of the residuals or Studentized residuals against the predicted values, against any of the predictors, or against *Time* to check for patterns.

6. The Normal model is needed only when we use inference; it isn't needed for computing a regression model. We check the Nearly Normal Condition on the residuals.

CHAPTER 21

SECTION EXERCISE ANSWERS

1. a) Unionized = 1, No Union = 0 (or the reverse).
   b) Female = 1, Male = 0 (or the reverse).
   c) Paid on time = 1, Past due = 0 (or the reverse).
   d) Three variables. Liberal = 1, not = 0; Conservative = 1, not = 0; NDP = 1, not = 0.

3. a) To make two different intercepts for the two types of movies.
   b) If *R* then 1; If *PG* then 0.

5. (One possible answer for each: other equivalent codings are possible.)
   a) Three variables: One variable that is 1 for Apartment, 0 otherwise. One that is 1 for Condo, 0 otherwise. One that is 1 for Townhouse, 0 otherwise.
   b) Two variables: One that is 1 for Full-time, 0 otherwise. One that is 1 for Part-time, 0 otherwise.

7. a) If *PG-13* then 0; If *R* then 1.
   b) The interaction term is the product of the indicator variable and the *Budget* variable.

9. \$0.219m. This is a fundamental property of leverage.

11. Because of the high correlation between several of the predictor variables, a stepwise search might find a very different model from the best of the "all subsets" model.

13. $1/(1 - 0.9875) = 80.00$

CHAPTER EXERCISE ANSWERS

15. a) Cheese pizzas (Type 1) scored about 15.6 points higher, after allowing for the effects of *calories* and *fat*. Cheese pizzas can be expected to sell better.
    b) Check scatterplots of the data to check for linearity. Check the plot of the residuals against predicted values or against each predictor, looking for patterns or outliers. Should also check for evidence that the residuals are nearly Normal with a Normal probability plot or histogram.

17. a) Both Reggio's and Michelina's pizzas are predicted to have high scores, but both received lower scores (more than 30 points lower) than we would otherwise have predicted from the model.
    b) Yes, their unusually large predicted values indicate that they must be different from the other pizzas in some ways, and their large (negative) residuals indicate that they would be influential and affect the regression by "pulling" the regression line downward. Large negative residual values will make the regression line less positive. Could calculate the *t*-ratio for the two types of pizzas. If *t*-values are large, we can reject the null hypothesis that either pizza fits the regression model and determine that either value is an outlier. Other supporting calculations would be the leverage values and Cook's Distances.

19. a) Indicator or "dummy" variable.
    b) Sales are about $10.5 billion higher in December, after accounting for the CPI.
    c) Assume that the slope is the same for the December points as for the others. That appears to be true in the scatterplot.

21. a) There are different slopes for the two types.
    b) Cheese pizzas (Type 1) have scores that grow less rapidly with calories (a slope 0.46 smaller) than do pepperoni pizzas. The slope of taste score on calories is estimated to be 1.92 points per gram for pepperoni pizzas and $1.92 - 0.4615 = 1.45$ points per gram for cheese pizzas.
    c) Adjusted R^2 is higher than adjusted R^2 for the previous model. Also, the *t*-ratios are larger. Overall, it looks like a more successful model. There is a consistent difference between pepperoni and cheese pizzas incorporated into the model.
    All coefficients are significantly different from zero.

23. a) Large Cook's Distance suggests that Alaska is influential. Its leverage is high, and its residual is one of the lowest.

b) After allowing for the other predictors, Alaska's life expectancy is 2.23 years lower than expected. The P-value of 0.02 says that Alaska is an outlier.
   c) The model where Alaska is removed and replaced with a dummy variable model is a better choice because of a higher adjusted R^2 and smaller standard deviation of residuals.

25. a) $\widehat{\text{Exch Rt}} = 0.6585 + 0.0000262*\text{M\&M} + 0.000385*\text{Gold} + 0.000584*\text{Energy}$. The P-value for the M&M coefficient is 0.644, making it not significantly different from zero. The model explains 65.0% of the variation in the exchange rate (as given by the adjusted R-squared) and the standard error is 0.0459.
    b) Predicted exchange rate for July 2011 is 1.0208 and the associated error is 0.02545.
    c) After increasing data for July 2011 by 1, the predicted value = 1.0981. The leverage of July 2011 is $(1.0981 - 1.0208) = 0.0773$.
    d) Cook's Distance
    $= e^2*h/(k*s^2*(1 - h)^2)$
    $= 0.02545*0.02545*0.0773/(3*0.0459*0.0459*(1 - 0.0773)*(1 - 0.0773))$
    $= 0.0.009304$

27. a) Adjusted R^2 accounts for the number of predictors. If removing a predictor causes it to increase, then that predictor contributed little to the model. *Primary Education* can be omitted.
    b) *t*-ratio of less than 0.05 or greater than 0.05 depends on including *Primary Education* in the model. It is suspicious that the author, in his desire to claim that regulation harms *GDP/Capita*, has found an irrelevant predictor that has the effect of nudging the P-value just below 0.05.

29. a) P-value of 0.686. Would not conclude that the true coefficient is not zero. It cannot be interpreted.
    b) R^2 of the second regression shows that *Diverted* is linearly related to other predictors and thus suffers from collinearity.
    c) The same answer as b).
    d) $1/(1 - 0.856) = 6.94$

31. a) Points may be influential. They have unusually low predicted values and large residuals, so this seems likely.
    b) Two of the coefficients have not changed very much, but the coefficient of *Number of Shows* has changed from negative but not significant to positive and strongly significant.
    c) The second model. The first regression was influenced by the two possibly influential points, which turned out not to be representative weeks on Broadway due to the strike. This relates to Item A of the ASA Ethical Guidelines on professionalism.

33. The two countries with the largest leverage values are Chad (0.3624) and Luxembourg (0.2708). Chad also has an extremely high Cook's Distance value. Chad, with a very low HDI score, has very low life expectancy, high maternal mortality, low schooling, and very few cell phone users. Luxembourg is nearly the opposite, with the highest *GDP per capita* of any country in the data set.

35. a) $\widehat{\text{Exch Rt}} = 0.6142 + 0.001229*\text{Energy};\ R^2 = 0.4526$
$\widehat{\text{Exch Rt}} = 0.7869 + 0.000578*\text{Gold};\ R^2 = 0.5715$
$\widehat{\text{Exch Rt}} = 0.7376 + 0.000222*\text{M\&M};\ R^2 = 0.5906$
The M&M index explains more of the variability in the exchange rate than the other indices.

b) $\widehat{\text{Exch Rt}} = 0.7433 + 0.000131*\text{M\&M} + 0.00029*\text{Gold};\ \text{Adj } R^2 = 0.6251$
$\widehat{\text{Exch Rt}} = 0.7001 + 0.000189*\text{M\&M} + 0.000253*\text{Energy};\ \text{Adj } R^2 = 0.5852$
The R^2 is improved by adding Gold as a second index. Both Gold and M&M have significant coefficients. We should therefore include both of these indices as explanatory variables.

CHAPTER 21 JUST CHECKING ANSWERS

1. The predictors would be *Years Experience + Gender + Years Experience*Gender*. The last term will account for possible different slopes.

2. There would need to be two *Education* indicator variables to account for the three levels.

3. It is not surprising that *Age* and *Years Experience* are correlated, leading to the collinearity. One of them should be removed, or they should somehow be combined into one variable.

CHAPTER 22

SECTION EXERCISE ANSWERS

1. a) Yes.
   b) No, not vs. time.
   c) No, for each worker, not over time.
   d) Yes.

3. a)

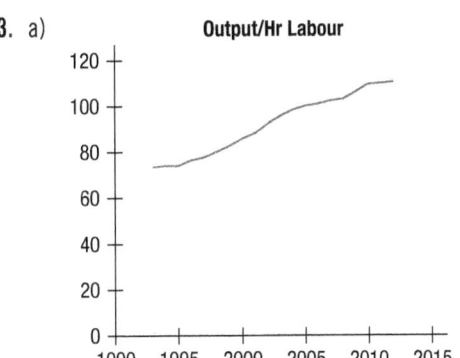

Output/Hr Labour

b) Trend: positive, slightly curved, strong.
c) No evidence of a seasonal component.

5. a) For example, for February we have $(0.963 + 0.977)/2 = 0.97$
   0.97
   0.9560
   0.9465
   0.9895
   1.0370
   1.0995
   1.1905
   1.2455
   1.1970
   1.1135
   1.0580
   b) 1.058

7. 2.32% (If your value was negative, you forgot the absolute value.)

9. *
   0.963
   0.977
   0.935
   0.958
   1.021
   1.053
   1.146
   1.235
   1.256
   1.138
   1.089

11. $0.3277 + 1.328*1.027 - 0.6341*1.089 = 1.001$

13. a) Dummy or indicator variable.
    b) A set of indicator variables must omit one to avoid collinearity.
    c) No.

CHAPTER EXERCISE ANSWERS

15. a) 200-day—the moving average with the longer length is smoother.
    b) SES model using $\alpha = 0.10$—the smoothing coefficient closer to zero is smoother.
    c) Most recent data point is weighted more heavily; model responds more quickly; not as smooth.

17. a) Naive forecast. Another possibility is the AR(1) model.
    b) Exponential model.
    c) Seasonal dummy variable model, or an AR model that uses sales from the same season in prior years (lag4).

19. a) 22,988 $M
    b) 0.2: 22,394 $M

21. a) 475.88 $/tonne
    b) 486.23$/tonne
    c) a): 17.53%; b): 15.73%.

23. a) Irregular
b) Second graph

25. a) The green graph is the MA-4, since it is not as smooth as the other graph.
b) The purple graph is the MA-7, since it is more smooth than the other graph.
c) The MA-4 needs four data values before it starts. The MA-7 needs seven data values before it starts.

27. a) $\hat{y} = b_0 = b_{lag1} = 0.100 - 1.12 \times 2.3 = \$2.676$ B
b) APE for Q4: 7.72%; (underforecast).
c) 2.6%; (overforecast).

29. a) $= 6.7532 + 0.83834*136.1 + 0.11313*135.85 = 136.22$
b) 1.94%
c) 135.97; the AR model prediction is closer.

31. a) 112 (years since the start of the 20th century: 2012 $- 1900 = 112$).
b) $\overline{\%Responding\ Yes} = 5.58 + 0.999 \times Year = 5.58 - 0.999 \times 112 = 117.47\%$; forecast $> 100\%$, not possible.

33. a) Estimate of retail sales in September 2006.
b) Rate of increase or retail sales per month.
c) Forecast $= 33448518381 + 38 \times 55724727.16 = 35570000000$
d) Residuals are seasonal with dips in January and February.
e) Probably low because it does not take into account the seasonality in the data.

35. a) $\hat{y} = 1.1 - 0.2t = 1.1 + 0.2 \times 1 = \$1.3$ million
b) Q3, because it has the lowest coefficient.
c) Q4, because it has the highest coefficient.
d) Sales on average are $0.5 million greater in Q4 than in Q1.

37. a) The P-value indicates that the slope of the time trend is significantly different from zero.
b) The coefficient for November is not significantly different from zero, so it should not be interpreted.
c) Yes. Many of the month indicators are highly significant.
d) $302,921.34 + 2,197.59*63 + 29,403.22 = 470,773$

39. a) Log of the number of passengers grew at 0.0249 per month.
b) In January 1990, there were about $10^{5.64949} = 446,159$ passengers.
c) January and February.
d) Trend, seasonal, and possibly an eight-year cyclic component.

41. Single exponential smoothing is pulled down by an outlier. Moving average spreads out the effect of the outlier across several months. Seasonal regression is not noticeably affected.

43. a) $\overline{E\text{-}commerce\ sales\ (\$m)} = 2022.8 + 900.138\ Time - 486.223Q2 - 709.611Q3 + 3288.03Q4$
b) $\overline{log(E\text{-}commerce\ sales)} = 3.73222 + 0.024502\ Time - 0.00263785\ Q2 - 0.00543049\ Q3 + 0.072158\ Q4$
c) The multiplicative model.

45. a) The AR(2) model involves Y(t-2) and can therefore be calculated from June 2006 to March 2009.
$\hat{y} = 842.3 + 0.8536 \times y_{lag1} - 0.2059 \times y_{lag2}$
The forecast for April 2009 = 2009.6 Sm.
b) The MA-4 for March 2008 is 2875.7.
The MA-4 for March 2009 is 2124.2.
The forecast for April 2009 is 2124.2.
c) May 2006 is 2135.3.
March 2009 is 2250.6.
The forecast for June 2009 is 2250.6.

47. a) $\overline{Crude\ Price\ (\$Bar)} = 12.82 + 0.6417 \times Time$
b) $\overline{Log\ (Crude\ Price\ (\$Bar))} = 1.2437 + 0.00767 \times Time$
c) $12.82 + 0.6417*75 = 60.95$; $10^{1.81895} = 65.94$
d) The linear fit seems to fit the best because the APE % is the lowest.

49. a) Analysis of P-values indicate that the only significant predictor is $OPEC\_Prod_{Lag1}$.
The resulting regression equation is:
$\overline{OPEC\_Prod} = 1145 + 0.963\ OPEC\_Prod_{Lag1}$
b) 31,258.06
c)

Model	Forecast (thousand barrels/day)	Actual	APE(%)
MA (6)	31,689.8	31,286.5	1.29
MA (12)	31,937.5	31,286.5	2.08
SES ($\alpha = 0.9$)	31,299.4	31,286.5	0.04
AR (1)	31,258.06	31,286.5	0.09

d) The single exponential model seems to fit the best because the APE is the lowest.

51.

	Short-term forecasts	Long-term forecasts	Type of data
Exponential smoothing	Yes, with a high value of the smoothing parameter	Yes, with a low value of the smoothing parameter	Data without trends
Additive regression	Yes	Yes	Data with a linear trend and constant amplitude seasonality
Multiplicative regression	Yes	Yes	Data with a linear trend and increasing amplitude seasonality

CHAPTER 22 JUST CHECKING ANSWERS

1. Trend and seasonal.

2. The value is the mean of the final four values, about 557. It might be a bit low as a prediction.

3. $(550 + 642.9)/2 = 596.45$

4. Four terms because there is a strong seasonal component with period 4.

5. 10.0017. Revenue grew at about $10 million per quarter.

6. Dummy variables require that we leave one out.

7. Higher. The four quarterly effects have to sum to zero and the others are all negative.

CHAPTER 23

SECTION EXERCISE ANSWERS

1. a) State of nature.
   b) Action.
   c) Action.

3.

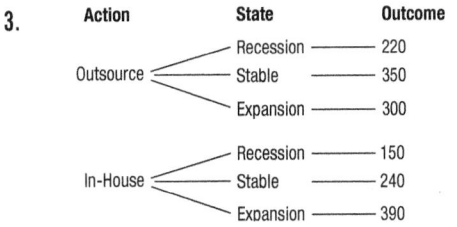

5. a) Outsource.
   b) In-house.

7. a) EV(Out source) = 294, EV(In-house) = 312.
   b) Outsource.

9. SD(Outsource) = 41.76, CV(Outsource) = 0.14, SD(In-house) = 99.68, CV(In-house) = 0.32

CHAPTER EXERCISE ANSWERS

11.

		Stay for Interview	
		No	Yes
Action	Fully Changeable Fare	$750	$750
	Nonrefundable Fare	$650	$800

13.

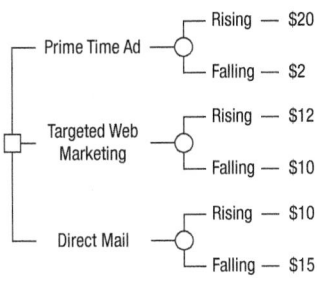

15.

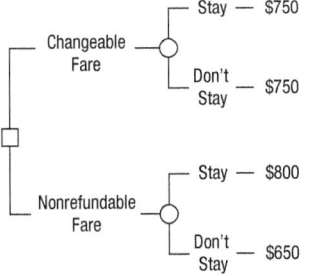

17. EV (Fully Changeable Fare) = $750.
EV (Nonrefundable Fare) = $695. Better to choose the nonrefundable fare.

19. EV (Fully Changeable Fare) = $750.
EV (Not changeable) = $755, so the changeable fare is a slightly better choice.

21. a) If P (rising confidence) = 0.70, EV (Prime Time) = $14.60.
E (Targeted Web Marketing) = $11.40.
EV(Direct Mail) = $11.50.
Choose prime time, since the expected payoff is highest.
   b) If P (rising confidence) = 0.10, EV (Prime Time) = $9.20.
F (Targeted Web Marketing) = $10.80.
EV (Direct Mail) = $13.00.
Choose direct mail in this case, since the expected payoff is highest.

23. a) $EV_\mu PI = 0.7*\$20 + 0.30*\$15 = \$18.50$
$EVPI = |EV_\mu PI - EV| = |\$18.50 - \$14.60|$
$= \$3.90$
   b) $EV_\mu PI = 0.4*\$20 + 0.60*\$15 = \$17.00$
$EVPI = |EV_\mu PI - EV| = |\$17.00 - \$13.00|$
$= \$4.00$

25. a)

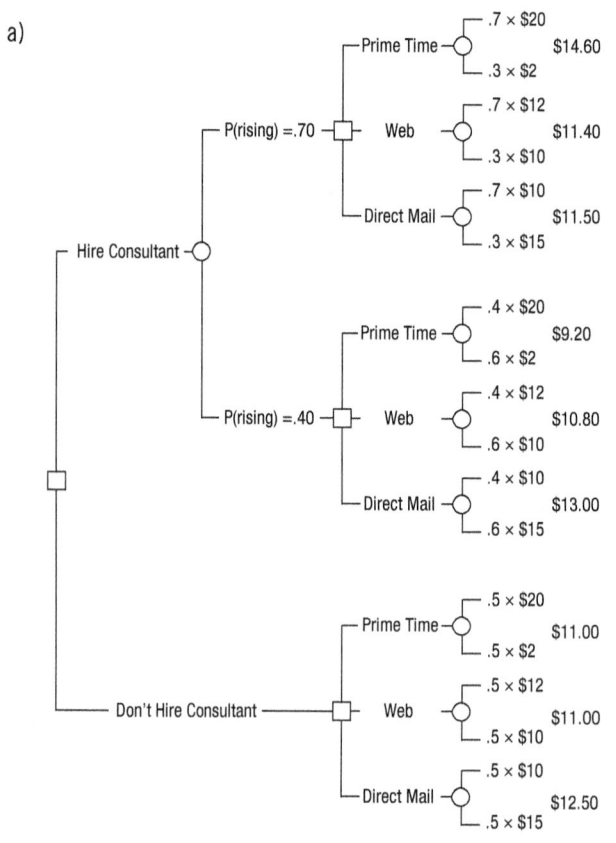

b) Yes, both alternatives with information have a better return: $1.36.

c) Compare 50–50: 0.5*$11.40 + 0.5*$9.20 = $10.30; 70–40: 0.7*$11.40 + 0.4*$9.20 = $11.66: Difference = $11.66 − $10.30 = $1.36.

27.

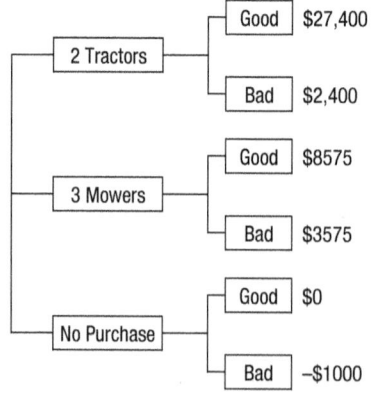

| | | Growing Season | |
		Good	Bad
Purchase Decision	Two Tractors	$27,400	$2,400
	Three Mowers	$8375	$3575
	No Purchase	$0	−$1000

29. Akbar: Tractors, with a positive gain of $27,400. Lance: Mowers, with the worst result being $3575.

31.

		EV	SD	RRR
Purchase Decision	Two Tractors	$19,900.00	11,456.44	1.737
	Three Mowers	$7075	2291.28	3.088
	No Purchase	−$300.00	458.26	−0.655

33. a)

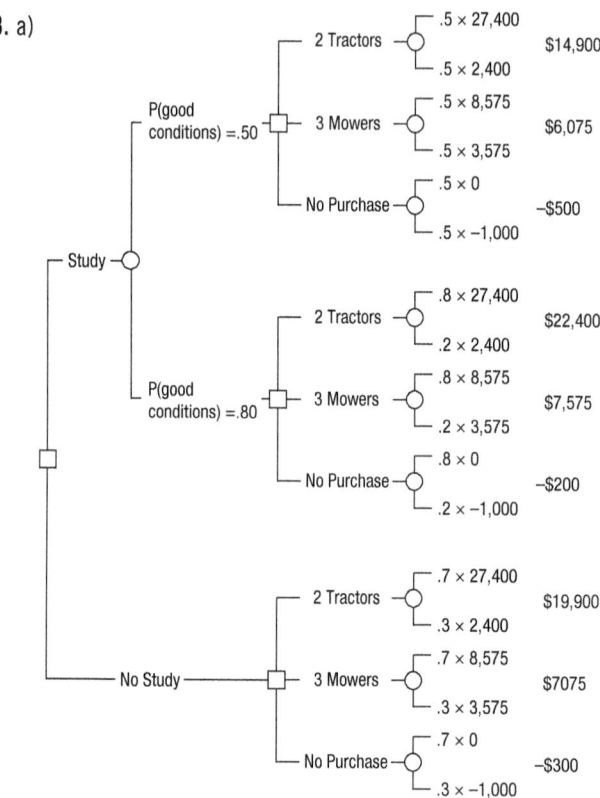

b) EVwST = $17,900

c) No. In all scenarios, the Tractor investment seems the best course to take.

35. a) EV(Stock A) = $800;
EV(Stock B) = $2300

b) SD(Stock A) = $2749.55;
SD (Stock B) = $1833.03

c) CV(Stock A) = 3.437;
CV (Stock B) = 0.797
RRR (Stock A) = 0.291;
RRR (Stock B) = 1.255

d) Stock B; it has a higher expected value and a lower SD. Its RRR is much higher.

37. a) EV (High-End Bike) = $4465;
EV (Moderately Priced Bike) = $2650

b) SD (High-End Bike) = $1995;
SD (Moderately Priced Bike) = $1050

c) CV (High-End Bike) = 0.447;
CV (Moderately Priced Bike) = 0.396
RRR (High-End Bike) = 2.238;
RRR (Moderately Priced Bike) = 2.524

d) Answers may vary. Decision will depend on store owner's acceptance of risk.

39. The stockbroker's advice contains three errors:
- The option of not buying is not considered.
- The underwriters buying and early investors selling are assumed to be independent. However, they may well be dependent.
- The probabilities that the stockbroker quotes are approximate. It is necessary to do a sensitivity analysis to check out the effect of different values for those probabilities.

The broker's advice therefore infringes Item A of the ASA Ethical Guidelines for lack of professionalism.

41. First well
Expected profit –0.12
Second well
Expected profit 0.111
Total expected profit from drilling –0.009
Cost of not drilling 0.375

a) The decision is to drill.
b) If the revenue from one well is $1.5bn or less, the decision would be not to drill.
c) The variance of profits should also be taken into account.

CHAPTER 24

SECTION EXERCISE ANSWERS

1. a)

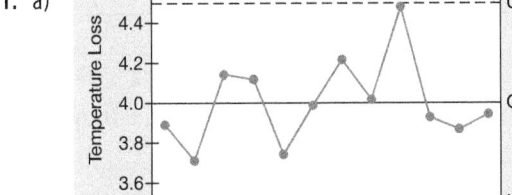

b) Yes, but one container was quite close to the upper limit.
c) $(4.5 - 3.5)/(6*0.2) = 0.833$
d) They need to decrease the process standard deviation. There is too great a chance that a container will fall outside the specification limits.

3. a) $1\sigma: 4 \pm 1*0.2 = (3.8, 4.2)$
$2\sigma: 4 \pm 2*0.2 = (3.6, 4.4)$
$3\sigma: 4 \pm 1*0.2 = (3.4, 4.6) = (LCL, UCL)$

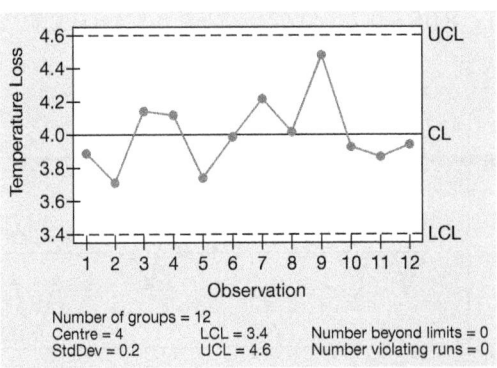

b) No.
c) No.
d) No.
e) No.
f) No.
g) No.
h) The process seems to be in control.

5. a) $0.01/\sqrt{5} = 0.00447$ m (or 0.447 cm)
b) Outside $91.4 \pm 3*0.00447 = (91.387, 91.413)$ m
c) $SD(\overline{X}) = 0.00316$m; Outside (91.391, 91.409) m

7. a) $\sqrt{(0.02 * 0.98/50)} = 0.0198$
b) $0.02 \pm 3*0.0198 = (0, 0.0794)$
c) $0.0794*50 = 4$ (round up 3.97)

CHAPTER EXERCISE ANSWERS

Note: For questions 9–14, answers were based on the conditions mentioned within the textbook.

9. Constructing control limits. This can be stated, since the manufacturer is basing the limits on the data itself and the data being used for comparison has being collected when the process is in control. Note that specification limits are not implied because no external requirement is mentioned.

11. Specification limits; NHSF is external to the manufacturers.

13. Specification requirement imposed by the Gemini observatories.

15. Common-cause variation. The lack of a pattern implies that the process is random.

17. 0.0027. Assuming that the process was in control when the control limits were set and that the distribution is Normal (based on the Central Limit Theorem).

19. a) $8.05 \pm 0.729 \times 0.67 = (7.58, 8.52) = (LCL, UCL)$

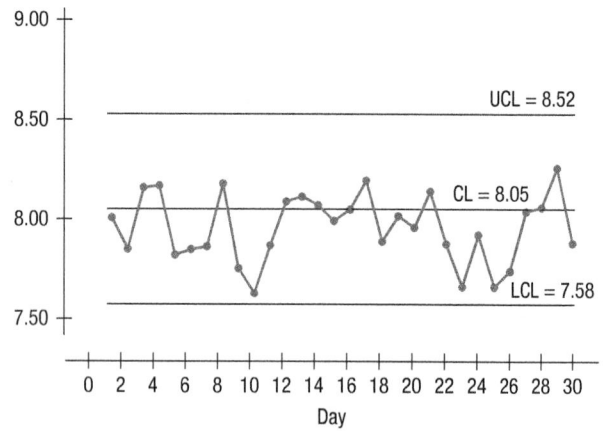

b) $UCL = 2.282 \times 0.67; \ LCL = 0 \times 0.67$

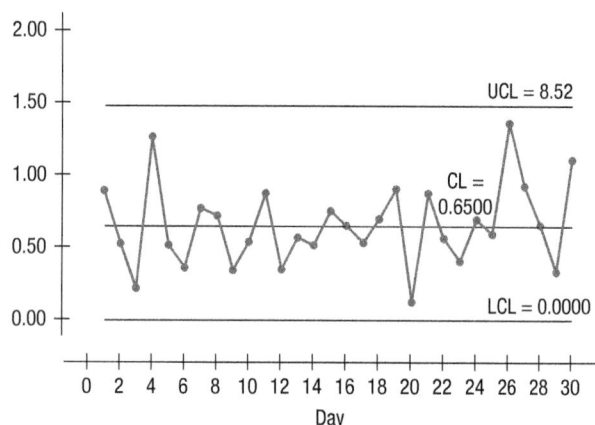

c) Process would be considered in control.

21. a) $(LCL, UCL) = 21.20 \pm 3 \times 0.29/\sqrt{3} = (20.70, 21.70)$

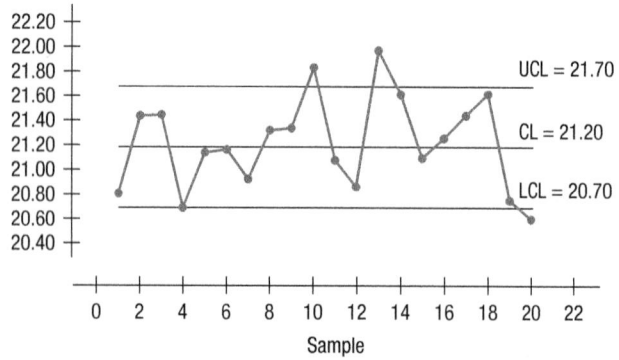

b) $R = d_2\sigma = 1.693 \times 0.29 = 0.491$
    $UCL = 1.26$
    $LCL = -0.28$, round to 0.

c) Yes, it is out of control. The x-bar chart shows four violations: samples 10 and 13 exceed the UCL and samples 4 and 20 fall below the LCL.

d) Referring now to the *specification* of between 20.2 and 22.2 for each roll, and the data on individual rolls in the question, Lane 1 Sample 13 does not meet the specification.

23. a) $(LCL, UCL) = 17.70 \pm 3 \times \sqrt{17.7} = (0.079, 30.321)$

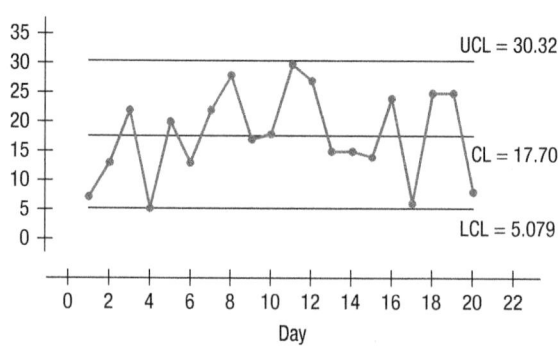

b) Not in control as the observation on day four falls below the LCL.

25. a) 4.57
b) $4.57 + 3 \times \sqrt{4.57} = 10.98$
c) $4.57 - 3 \times \sqrt{4.57} = -1.84$. LCL cannot be a negative number and is therefore rounded to a value of zero (0).

d)
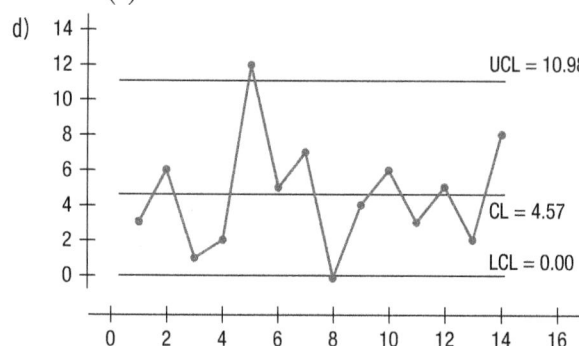

e) Out of control, as observation 5 exceeds the UCL.

27. a)

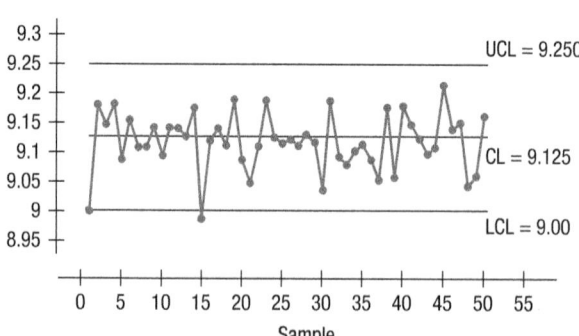

b) Not in control.
c) Two: samples 1 and 15.
d) Immediately as the first baseball was too small.

29. There are six points decreasing in a row, starting with sample 1 and continuing to sample 7. The consultant should have asked for an inspection between sample 6 and sample 7, in addition to sample 13.
This shows a lack of professionalism and therefore infringes the ASA Ethical Guidelines Item A.

Statistical Tables, Formulas, and Excel/XLStat

Row	Table of Random Digits									
1	96299	07196	98642	20639	23185	56282	69929	14125	38872	94168
2	71622	35940	81807	59225	18192	08710	80777	84395	69563	86280
3	03272	41230	81739	74797	70406	18564	69273	72532	78340	36699
4	46376	58596	14365	63685	56555	42974	72944	96463	63533	24152
5	47352	42853	42903	97504	56655	70355	88606	61406	38757	70657
6	20064	04266	74017	79319	70170	96572	08523	56025	89077	57678
7	73184	95907	05179	51002	83374	52297	07769	99792	78365	93487
8	72753	36216	07230	35793	71907	65571	66784	25548	91861	15725
9	03939	30763	06138	80062	02537	23561	93136	61260	77935	93159
10	75998	37203	07959	38264	78120	77525	86481	54986	33042	70648
11	94435	97441	90998	25104	49761	14967	70724	67030	53887	81293
12	04362	40989	69167	38894	00172	02999	97377	33305	60782	29810
13	89059	43528	10547	40115	82234	86902	04121	83889	76208	31076
14	87736	04666	75145	49175	76754	07884	92564	80793	22573	67902
15	76488	88899	15860	07370	13431	84041	69202	18912	83173	11983
16	36460	53772	66634	25045	79007	78518	73580	14191	50353	32064
17	13205	69237	21820	20952	16635	58867	97650	82983	64865	93298
18	51242	12215	90739	36812	00436	31609	80333	96606	30430	31803
19	67819	00354	91439	91073	49258	15992	41277	75111	67496	68430
20	09875	08990	27656	15871	23637	00952	97818	64234	50199	05715
21	18192	95308	72975	01191	29958	09275	89141	19558	50524	32041
22	02763	33701	66188	50226	35813	72951	11638	01876	93664	37001
23	13349	46328	01856	29935	80563	03742	49470	67749	08578	21956
24	69238	92878	80067	80807	45096	22936	64325	19265	37755	69794
25	92207	63527	59398	29818	24789	94309	88380	57000	50171	17891
26	66679	99100	37072	30593	29665	84286	44458	60180	81451	58273
27	31087	42430	60322	34765	15757	53300	97392	98035	05228	68970
28	84432	04916	52949	78533	31666	62350	20584	56367	19701	60584
29	72042	12287	21081	48426	44321	58765	41760	43304	13399	02043
30	94534	73559	82135	70260	87936	85162	11937	18263	54138	69564
31	63971	97198	40974	45301	60177	35604	21580	68107	25184	42810
32	11227	58474	17272	37619	69517	62964	67962	34510	12607	52255
33	28541	02029	08068	96656	17795	21484	57722	76511	27849	61738
34	11282	43632	49531	78981	81980	08530	08629	32279	29478	50228
35	42907	15137	21918	13248	39129	49559	94540	24070	88151	36782
36	47119	7665 L	21732	32364	58545	50277	57558	30390	18771	72703
37	11232	99884	05087	76839	65142	19994	91397	29350	83852	04905
38	64725	06719	86262	53356	57999	50193	79936	97230	52073	94467
39	77007	26962	55466	12521	48125	12280	54985	26239	76044	54398
40	18375	19310	59796	89832	59417	18553	17238	05474	33259	50595

Table Z: The Normal Distribution

Areas under the standard Normal curve. Find the row corresponding to your value of z to one decimal position. Find the column corresponding to the second decimal position of z. The probability of being less than z is given in the cell for that row and column.

				Second decimal place in z						
0.09	0.08	0.07	0.06	0.05	0.04	0.03	0.02	0.01	0.00	z
									0.0000†	−3.9
0.0001	0.0001	0.0001	0.0001	0.0001	0.0001	0.0001	0.0001	0.0001	0.0001	−3.8
0.0001	0.0001	0.0001	0.0001	0.0001	0.0001	0.0001	0.0001	0.0001	0.0001	−3.7
0.0001	0.0001	0.0001	0.0001	0.0001	0.0001	0.0001	0.0001	0.0002	0.0002	−3.6
0.0002	0.0002	0.0002	0.0002	0.0002	0.0002	0.0002	0.0002	0.0002	0.0002	−3.5
0.0002	0.0003	0.0003	0.0003	0.0003	0.0003	0.0003	0.0003	0.0003	0.0003	−3.4
0.0003	0.0004	0.0004	0.0004	0.0004	0.0004	0.0004	0.0005	0.0005	0.0005	−3.3
0.0005	0.0005	0.0005	0.0006	0.0006	0.0006	0.0006	0.0006	0.0007	0.0007	−3.2
0.0007	0.0007	0.0008	0.0008	0.0008	0.0008	0.0009	0.0009	0.0009	0.0010	−3.1
0.0010	0.0010	0.0011	0.0011	0.0011	0.0012	0.0012	0.0013	0.0013	0.0013	−3.0
0.0014	0.0014	0.0015	0.0015	0.0016	0.0016	0.0017	0.0018	0.0018	0.0019	−2.9
0.0019	0.0020	0.0021	0.0021	0.0022	0.0023	0.0023	0.0024	0.0025	0.0026	−2.8
0.0026	0.0027	0.0028	0.0029	0.0030	0.0031	0.0032	0.0033	0.0034	0.0035	−2.7
0.0036	0.0037	0.0038	0.0039	0.0040	0.0041	0.0043	0.0044	0.0045	0.0047	−2.6
0.0048	0.0049	0.0051	0.0052	0.0054	0.0055	0.0057	0.0059	0.0060	0.0062	−2.5
0.0064	0.0066	0.0068	0.0069	0.0071	00073	0.0075	0.0078	0.0080	0.0082	−2.4
0.0084	0.0087	0.0089	0.0091	0.0094	0.0096	0.0099	0.0102	0.0104	0.0107	−2.3
0.0110	0.0113	0.0116	0.0119	0.0122	0.0125	0.0129	0.0132	0.0136	0.0139	−2.2
0.0143	0.0146	0.0150	0.0154	0.0158	0.0162	0.0166	0.0170	0.0174	0.0179	−2.1
0.0183	0.0188	0.0192	0.0197	0.0202	0.0207	0.0212	0.0217	0.0222	0.0228	−2.0
0.0233	0.0239	0.0244	0.0250	0.0256	0.0262	0.0268	0.0274	0.0281	0.0287	−1.9
0.0294	0.0301	0.0307	0.0314	0.0322	0.0329	0.0336	0.0344	0.0351	0.0359	−1.8
0.0367	0.0375	0.0384	0.0392	0.0401	0.0409	0.0418	0.0427	0.0436	0.0446	−1.7
0.0455	0.0465	0.0475	0.0485	0.0495	0.0505	0.0516	0.0526	0.0537	0.0548	−1.6
0.0559	0.0571	0.0582	0.0594	0.0606	0.0618	0.0630	0.0643	0.0655	0.0668	−1.5
0.0681	0.0694	0.0708	0.0721	0.07.35	0.0749	0.0764	0.0778	0.0793	0.0808	−1.4
0.0823	0.0838	0.0853	0.0869	0.0885	0.0901	0.0918	0.0934	0.0951	0.0968	−1.3
0.0985	0.1003	0.1020	0.1038	0.1056	0.1075	0.1093	0.1112	0.1131	0,1151	−1.2
0.1170	0.1190	0.1210	0.1230	0.1251	0.1271	0.1292	0.1314	0.1335	0.1357	−1.1
0.1379	0.1401	0.1423	0.1446	0.1469	0.1492	0.1515	0.1539	0.1562	0.1587	−1.0
0.1611	0.1635	0.1660	0.1685	0.1711	0.1736	0.1762	0.1788	0.1814	0.1841	−0.9
0.1867	0.1894	0.1922	0.1949	0.1977	0.2005	0.2033	0.2061	0.2090	0.2119	−0.8
0.2148	0.2177	0.2206	0.2236	0.2266	0.2296	0.2327	0.2358	0.2389	0.2420	−0.7
0.2451	0.2483	0.2514	0.2546	0.2578	0.2611	0.2643	0.2676	0.2709	0.2743	−0.6
0.2776	0.2810	0.2843	0.2877	0.2912	0.2946	0.2981	0.3015	0.3050	0.3085	−0.5
0.3121	0.3156	0.3192	0.3228	0.3264	0.3300	0.3336	0.3372	0.3409	0.3446	−0.4
03483	0.3520	0.3557	0.3594	0.3632	0.3669	0.3707	0.3745	0.3783	0.3821	−0.3
0.3859	0.3897	0.3936	0.3974	0.4013	0.4052	0.4090	0.4129	0.4168	0.4207	−0.2
0.4247	0.4286	0.4325	0.4364	0.4404	0.4443	0.4483	0.4522	0.4562	0.4602	−0.1
0.4641	0.4681	0.4721	0.4761	0.4801	0.4840	0.4880	0.4920	0.4960	0.5000	−0.0

†For $z \leq -3.90$, the areas are 0.0000 to four decimal places.

Table Z (cont.)
Areas under the standard Normal curve

		Second decimal place in z								
z	0.00	0.01	0.02	0.03	0.04	0.05	0.06	0.07	0.08	0.09
0.0	0.5000	0.5040	0.5080	0.5120	0.5160	0.5199	0.5239	0.5279	0.5319	0.5359
0.1	0.5398	0.5438	0.5478	0.5517	0.5557	0.5596	0.5636	0.5675	0.5714	0.5753
0.2	0.5793	0.5832	0.5871	0.5910	0.5948	0.5987	0.6026	0.6064	0.6703	0.6141
0.3	0.6179	0.6217	0.6255	0.6293	0.6331	0.6368	0.6406	0.6443	0.6480	0.6517
0.4	0.6554	0.6591	0.6628	0.6664	0.6700	0.6736	0.6772	0.6808	0.6844	0.6879
0.5	0.6915	0.6950	0.6985	0.7019	0.7054	0.7088	0.7123	0.7157	0.7190	0.7224
0.6	0.7257	0.7291	0.7324	0.7357	0.7389	0.7422	0.7454	0.7486	0.7517	0.7549
0.7	0.7580	0.7611	0.7642	0.7673	0.7704	0.7734	0.7764	0.7794	0.7823	0.7852
0.8	0.7881	0.7910	0.7939	0.7967	0.7995	0.8023	0.8051	0.8078	0.8106	0.8133
0.9	0.8159	0.8186	0.8212	0.8238	0.8264	0.8289	0.8315	0.8340	0.8365	0.8389
1.0	0.8413	0.8438	0.8461	0.8485	0.8508	0.8531	0.8554	0.8577	0.8599	0.8621
1.1	0.8643	0.8665	0.8686	0.8708	0.8729	0.8749	0.8770	0.8790	0.8810	0.8830
1.2	0.8849	0.8869	0.8888	0.8907	0.8925	0.8944	0.8962	0.8980	0.8997	0.9015
1.3	0.9032	0.9049	0.9066	0.9082	0.9099	0.9115	0.9131	0.9147	0.9162	0.9177
1.4	0.9192	0.9207	0.9222	0.9236	0.9251	0.9265	0.9279	0.9292	0.9306	0.9319
1.5	0.9332	0.9345	0.9357	0.9370	0.9382	0.9394	0.9406	0.9418	0.9429	0.9441
1.6	0.9452	0.9463	0.9474	0.9484	0.9495	0.9505	0.9515	0.9525	0.9535	0.9545
1.7	0.9554	0.9564	0.9573	0.9582	0.9591	0.9599	0.9608	0.9616	0.9625	0.9633
1.8	0.9641	0.9649	0.9656	0.9664	0.9671	0.9678	0.9686	0.9693	0.9699	0.9706
1.9	0.9713	0.9719	0.9726	0.9732	0.9738	0.9744	0.9750	0.9756	0.9761	0.9767
2.0	0.9772	0.9778	0.9783	0.9788	0.9793	0.9798	0.9803	0.9808	0.9812	0.9817
2.1	0.9821	0.9826	0.9830	0.9834	0.9838	0.9842	0.9846	0.9850	0.9854	0.9857
2.2	0.9861	0.9864	0.9868	0.9871	0.9875	0.9878	0.9881	0.9884	0.9887	0.9890
2.3	0.9893	0.9896	0.9898	0.9901	0.9904	0.9906	0.9909	0.9911	0.9913	0.9916
2.4	0.9918	0.9920	0.9922	0.9925	0.9927	0.9929	0.9931	0.9932	0.9934	0.9936
2.5	0.9938	0.9940	0.9941	0.9943	0.9945	0.9946	0.9948	0.9949	0.9951	0.9952
2.6	0.9953	0.9955	0.9956	0.9957	0.9959	0.9960	0.9961	0.9962	0.9963	0.9964
2.7	0.9965	0.9966	0.9967	0.9968	0.9969	0.9970	0.9971	0.9972	0.9973	0.9974
2.8	0.9974	0.9975	0.9976	0.9977	0.9977	0.9978	0.9979	0.9979	0.9980	0.9981
2.9	0.9981	0.9982	0.9982	0.9983	0.9984	0.9984	0.9985	0.9985	0.9986	0.9986
3.0	0.9987	0.9987	0.9987	0.9988	0.9988	0.9989	0.9989	0.9989	0.9990	0.9990
3.1	0.9990	0.9991	0.9991	0.9991	0.9992	0.9992	0.9992	0.9992	0.9993	0.9993
3.2	0.9993	0.9993	0.9994	0.9994	0.9994	0.9994	0.9994	0.9995	0.9995	0.9995
3.3	0.9995	0.9995	0.9995	0.9996	0.9996	0.9996	0.9996	0.9996	0.9996	0.9997
3.4	0.9997	0.9997	0.9997	0.9997	0.9997	0.9997	0.9997	0.9997	0.9997	0.9998
3.5	0.9998	0.9998	0.9998	0.9998	0.9998	0.9998	0.9998	0.9998	0.9998	0.9998
3.6	0.9998	0.9998	0.9999	0.9999	0.9999	0.9999	0.9999	0.9999	0.9999	0.9999
3.7	0.9999	0.9999	0.9999	0.9999	0.9999	0.9999	0.9999	0.9999	0.9999	0.9999
3.8	0.9999	0.9999	0.9999	0.9999	0.9999	0.9999	0.9999	0.9999	0.9999	0.9999
3.9	1.0000[†]									

[†]For $z \geq 3.90$, the areas are 1.0000 to four decimal places.

Table T: The t Distribution

Values of t_α. Choose a row for the degrees of freedom, df, and find your t-value in that row. The corresponding probability (as demonstrated in the graphs to the left) is given at the top of the table.

	Two-tail probability	0.20	0.10	0.05	0.02	0.01	
	One-tail probability	0.10	0.05	0.025	0.01	0.005	
	df						df
	1	3.078	6.314	12.706	31.821	63.657	1
	2	1.886	2.920	4.303	6.965	9.925	2
	3	1.638	2.353	3.182	4.541	5.841	3
	4	1.533	2.132	2.776	3.747	4.604	4
	5	1.476	2.015	2.571	3.365	4.032	5
	6	1.440	1.943	2.447	3.143	3.707	6
	7	1.415	1.895	2.365	2.998	3.499	7
	8	1.397	1.860	2.306	2.896	3.355	8
	9	1.383	1.833	2.262	2.821	3.250	9
	10	1.372	1.812	2.228	2.764	3.169	10
	11	1.363	1.796	2.201	2.718	3.106	11
	12	1.356	1.782	2.179	2.681	3.055	12
	13	1.350	1.771	2.160	2.650	3.012	13
	14	1.345	1.761	2.145	2.624	2.977	14
	15	1.341	1.753	2.131	2.602	2.947	15
	16	1.337	1.746	2.120	2.583	2.921	16
	17	1.333	1.740	2.110	2.567	2.898	17
	18	1.330	1.734	2.101	2.552	2.878	18
	19	1.328	1.729	2.093	2.539	2.861	19
	20	1.325	1.725	2.086	2.528	2.845	20
	21	1.323	1.721	2.080	2.518	2.831	21
	22	1.321	1.717	2.074	2.508	2.819	22
	23	1.319	1.714	2.069	2.500	2.807	23
	24	1.318	1.711	2.064	2.492	2.797	24
	25	1.316	1.708	2.060	2.485	2.787	25
	26	1.315	1.706	2.056	2.479	2.779	26
	27	1.314	1.703	2.052	2.473	2.771	27
	28	1.313	1.701	2.048	2.467	2.763	28
	29	1.311	1.699	2.045	2.462	2.756	29
	30	1.310	1.697	2.042	2.457	2.750	30
	32	1.309	1.694	2.037	2.449	2.738	32
	35	1.306	1.690	2.030	2.438	2.725	35
	40	1.303	1.684	2.021	2.423	2.704	40
	45	1.301	1.679	2.014	2.412	2.690	45
	50	1.299	3.676	2.009	2.403	2.678	50
	60	1.296	1.671	2.000	2.390	2.660	60
	75	1.293	1.665	1.992	2.377	2.643	75
	100	1.290	1.660	1.984	2.364	2.626	100
	120	1.289	1.658	1.980	2.358	2.617	120
	140	1.288	1.656	1.977	2.353	2.611	140
	180	1.286	1.653	1.973	2.347	2.603	180
	250	1.285	1.651	1.969	2.341	2.596	250
	400	1.284	1.649	1.966	2.336	2.588	400
	1000	1.282	1.646	1.962	2.330	2.581	1000
	∞	1.282	1.645	1.960	2.326	2.576	∞
	Confidence level	80%	90%	95%	98%	99%	

Two tails

$-t_{\alpha/2}$ 0 $t_{\alpha/2}$

One tail

0   t_α

Table X: **The Chi Squared Distribution, see Chapter 16.**

Values of χ_α^2. Choose a row for the degrees of freedom, df, and find your chi-squared-value in that row. The corresponding probability is given at the top of the table.

Right-tail probability, α	0.10	0.05	0.025	0.01	0.005
df					
1	2.706	3.841	5.024	6.635	7.879
2	4.605	5.991	7.378	9.210	10.597
3	6.251	7.815	9.348	11.345	12.838
4	7.779	9.488	11.143	13.277	14.860
5	9.236	11.070	12.833	15.086	16.750
6	10.645	12.592	14.449	16.812	18.548
7	12.017	14.067	16.013	18.475	20.278
8	13.362	15.507	17.535	20.090	21.955
9	14.684	16.919	19.023	21.666	23.589
10	15.987	18.307	20.483	23.209	25.188
11	17.275	19.675	21.920	24.725	26.757
12	18.549	21.026	23.337	26.217	28.300
13	19.812	22.362	24.736	27.688	29.819
14	21.064	23.685	26.119	29.141	31.319
15	22.307	24.996	27.488	30.578	32.801
16	23.542	26.296	28.845	32.000	34.267
17	24.769	27.587	30.191	33.409	35.718
18	25.989	28.869	31.526	34.805	37.156
19	27.204	30.143	32.852	36.191	38.582
20	28.412	31.410	34.170	37.566	39.997
21	29.615	32.671	35.479	38.932	41.401
22	30.813	33.924	36.781	40.290	42.796
23	32.007	35.172	38.076	41.638	44.181
24	33.196	36.415	39.364	42.980	45.559
25	34.382	37.653	40.647	44.314	46.928
26	35.563	38.885	41.923	45.642	48.290
27	36.741	40.113	43.195	46.963	49.645
28	37.916	41.337	44.461	48.278	50.994
29	39.087	42.557	45.722	59.588	52.336
30	40.256	43.773	46.979	50.892	53.672
40	51.805	55.759	59.342	63.691	66.767
50	63.167	67.505	71.420	76.154	79.490
60	74.397	79,082	83.298	88.381	91.955
70	85.527	90.531	95.023	100.424	104.213
80	96.578	101.879	106.628	112.328	116.320
90	107.565	113.145	118.135	124.115	128.296
100	118.499	124.343	129.563	135.811	140.177

Table F: The F Distribution, see Chapter 15, Section 7 and Chapter 20, Section 5.   Numerator df

α = 0.01 Denominator df	1	2	3	4	5	6	7	8	9	10	11	12	13	14	15	16	17	18	19	20	21	22
1	4052.2	4999.3	5403.5	5624.3	5764.0	5859.0	5928.3	5981.0	6022.4	6055.9	6083.4	6106.7	6125.8	6143.0	6157.0	6170.0	6181.2	6191.4	6200.7	6208.7	6216.1	6223.1
2	98.50	99.00	99.16	99.25	99.30	99.33	99.36	99.38	99.39	99.40	99.41	99.42	99.42	99.43	99.43	99.44	99.44	99.44	99.45	99.45	99.45	99.46
3	34.12	30.82	29.46	28.71	28.24	27.91	27.67	27.49	27.34	27.23	27.13	27.05	26.98	26.92	26.87	26.83	26.79	26.75	26.72	26.69	26.66	26.64
4	21.20	18.00	16.69	15.98	15.52	15.21	14.98	14.80	14.66	14.55	14.45	14.37	14.31	14.25	14.20	14.15	14.11	14.08	14.05	14.02	13.99	13.97
5	16.26	1327	12.06	11.39	10.97	10.67	10.46	1029	10.16	10.05	9.96	9.89	9.82	9.77	9.72	9.68	9.64	9.61	9.58	9.55	9.53	9.51
6	13.75	10.92	9.78	9.15	8.75	8.47	8.26	8.10	7.98	7.87	7.79	7.72	7.66	7.60	7.56	7.52	7.48	7.45	7.42	7.40	7.37	7.35
7	12.25	9.55	8.45	7.85	7.46	7.19	6.99	6.84	6.72	6.62	6.54	6.47	6.41	636	6.31	6.28	6.24	6.21	6.18	6.16	6.13	6.11
8	11.26	8.65	7.59	7.01	6.63	6.37	0.18	6.03	5.91	5.81	5.73	5.67	5.61	556	5.52	5.48	5.44	5.41	5.38	5.36	5.34	5.32
9	10.56	8.02	6.99	6.42	6.06	5.80	5.61	5.47	5.35	526	5.18	5.11	5.05	5.01	4.96	4.92	4.89	4.86	4.83	4.81	4.79	4.77
10	10.04	7.56	6.55	5.99	5.64	5.39	5.20	5.06	4.94	4.85	4.77	4.71	4.65	4.60	4.56	4.52	4.49	4.46	4.43	4.41	4.38	4.36
11	9.65	7.21	6.22	5.67	5.32	5.07	4.89	4.74	4.63	4.54	4.46	4.40	4.34	4.29	4.25	4.21	4.18	4.15	4.12	4.10	4.08	4.06
12	9.33	6.93	5.95	5.41	5.06	4.82	4.64	4.50	4.39	4.30	4.22	4.16	4.10	4.05	4.01	3.97	3.94	3.91	3.88	3.86	3.84	3.82
13	9.07	6.70	5.74	5.21	4.86	4.62	4.44	4.30	4.19	4.10	4.02	3.96	3.91	3.86	3.82	3.78	3.75	3.72	3.69	3.66	3.64	3.62
14	8.86	6.51	5.56	5.04	4.69	4.46	4.28	4.14	4.03	3.94	3.86	3.80	3.75	3.70	3.66	3.62	3.59	3.56	3.53	3.51	3.48	3.46
15	8.68	6.36	5.42	4.89	4.56	4.32	4.14	4.00	3.89	3.80	3.73	3.67	3.61	3.56	3.52	3.49	3.45	3.42	3.40	3.37	3.35	3.33
16	8.53	6.23	5.29	4.77	4.44	4.20	4.03	3.89	3.78	3.69	3.62	3.55	3.50	3.45	3.41	3.37	3.34	3.31	3.28	3.26	324	3.22
17	8.40	6.11	5.19	4.67	4.34	4.10	3.93	3.79	3.68	3.59	3.52	3.46	3.40	3.35	3.31	3.27	3.24	3.21	3.19	3.16	3.14	3.12
18	8.29	6.01	5.09	4.58	4.25	4.01	3.84	3.71	3.60	3.51	3.43	3.37	3.32	3.27	3.23	3.19	3.16	3.13	3.10	3.08	3.05	3.03
19	8.18	5.93	5.01	4.50	4.17	3.94	3.77	3.63	3.52	3.43	3.36	3.30	3.24	3.19	3.15	3.12	3.08	3.05	3.03	3.00	2.98	2.96
20	8.10	5.85	4.94	4.43	4.10	3.87	3.70	3.56	3.46	3.37	3.29	3.23	3.18	3.13	3.09	3.05	3.02	2.99	2.96	2.94	2.92	2.90
21	8.02	5.78	4.87	4.37	4.04	3.81	3.64	3.51	3.40	3.31	3.24	3.17	3.12	3.07	3.03	2.99	2.96	2.93	2.90	2.88	2.86	2.84
22	7.95	5.72	4.82	4.31	3.99	3.76	3.59	3.45	3.35	3.26	3.18	3.12	3.07	3.02	2.98	2.94	2.91	2.88	2.85	2.83	2.81	2.78
23	7.88	5.66	4.76	4.26	3.94	3.71	3.54	3.41	3.30	3.21	3.14	3.07	3.02	2.97	2.93	2.89	2.86	2.83	2.80	2.78	2.76	2.74
24	7.82	5.61	4.72	4.22	3.90	3.67	3.50	3.36	3.26	3.17	3.09	3.03	2.98	2.93	2.89	2.85	2.82	2.79	2.76	2.74	2.72	2.70
25	7.77	5.57	4.68	4.18	3.85	3.63	3.46	3.32	3.22	3.13	3.06	2.99	2.94	2.89	2.85	2.81	2.78	2.75	2.72	2.70	2.68	2.66
26	7.72	5.53	4.64	4.14	3.82	3.59	3.42	3.29	3.18	3.09	3.02	2.96	2.90	2.86	2.81	2.78	2.75	2.72	2.69	2.66	2.64	2.62
27	7.68	5.49	4.60	4.11	3.78	3.56	3.39	3.26	3.15	3.06	2.99	2.93	2.87	2.82	2.78	2.75	2.71	2.68	2.66	2.63	2.61	2.59
28	7.64	5.45	4.57	4.07	3.75	3.53	3.36	3.23	3.12	3.03	2.96	2.90	2.84	2.79	2.75	2.72	2.68	2.65	2.63	2.60	2.58	2.56
29	7.60	5.42	4.54	4.04	3.73	3.50	3.33	3.20	3.09	3.00	2.93	2.87	2.81	2.77	2.73	2.69	2.66	2.63	2.60	2.57	2.55	2.53
30	7.56	5.39	4.51	4.02	3.70	3.47	3.30	3.17	3.07	2.98	2.91	2.84	2.79	2.74	2.70	2.66	2.63	2.60	2.57	2.55	2.53	2.51
32	7.50	5.34	4.46	3.97	3.65	3.43	3.26	3.13	3.02	2.93	2.86	2.80	2.74	2.70	2.65	2.62	2.58	2.55	2.53	2.50	2.48	2.46
35	7.42	5.27	4.40	3.91	3.59	3.37	3.20	3.07	2.96	2.88	2.80	2.74	2.69	2.64	2.60	2.56	2.53	2.50	2.47	2.44	2.42	2.40
40	7.31	5.18	4.31	3.83	3.51	3.29	3.12	2.99	2.89	2.80	2.73	2.66	2.61	2.56	2.52	2.48	2.45	2.42	2.39	2.37	2.35	2.33
45	7.23	5.11	4.25	3.77	3.45	3.23	3.07	2.94	2.83	2.74	2.67	2.61	2.55	2.51	2.46	2.43	2.39	2.36	2.34	2.31	2.29	2.27
50	7.17	5.06	4.20	3.72	3.41	3.19	3.02	2.89	2.78	2.70	2.63	2.56	2.51	2.46	2.42	2.36	2.35	2.32	2.29	2.27	2.24	2.22
60	7.08	4.98	4.13	3.65	3.34	3.12	2.95	2.82	2.72	2.63	2.56	2.50	2.44	2.39	2.35	2.31	2.28	2.25	2.22	2.20	2.17	2.15
75	6.99	4.90	4.05	3.58	3.27	3.05	2.89	2.76	2.65	2.57	2.49	2.43	2.38	2.33	2.29	2.25	2.22	2.18	2.16	2.13	2.11	2.09
100	6.90	4.82	3.98	3.51	3.21	2.99	2.82	2.69	2.59	2.50	2.43	2.37	2.31	2.27	2.22	2.19	2.15	2.12	2.09	2.07	2.04	2.02
120	6.85	4.79	3.95	3.48	3.17	2.96	2.79	2.66	2.56	2.47	2.40	2.34	2.28	2.23	2.19	2.15	2.12	2.09	2.06	2.03	2.01	1.99
140	6.82	4.76	3.92	3.46	3.15	2.93	2.77	2.64	2.54	2.45	2.38	2.31	2.26	2.21	2.17	2.13	2.10	2.07	2.04	2.01	1.99	1.97
180	6.78	4.73	3.89	3.43	3.12	2.90	2.74	2.61	2.51	2.42	2.35	2.28	223	2.18	2.14	2.10	2.07	2.04	2.01	1.98	1.96	1.94
250	6.74	4.69	3.86	3.40	3.09	2.87	2.71	2.58	2.48	2.39	2.32	2.26	2.20	2.15	2.11	2.07	2.04	2.01	1.98	1.95	1.93	1.91
400	6.70	4.66	3.83	3.37	3.06	2.85	2.68	2.56	2.45	2.37	2.29	2.23	2.17	2.13	2.08	2.05	2.01	1.98	1.95	1.92	1.90	1.88
1000	6.66	4.63	3.80	3.34	3.04	2.82	2.66	2.53	2.43	2.34	2.27	2.20	2.15	2.10	2.06	2.02	1.98	1.95	1.92	1.90	1.87	1.85

Table F (cont.)

Numerator df

α = 0.01	23	24	25	26	27	28	29	30	32	35	40	45	50	60	75	100	120	140	180	250	400	1000
1	6228.7	6234.3	6239.9	6244.5	6249.3	6252.9	6257.1	6260.4	6266.9	6275.3	6286.4	6295.7	6302.3	6313.0	6323.7	6333.9	6339.5	6343.2	6347.9	6353.5	6358.1	6362.8
2	99.46	99.46	99.46	99.46	99.46	99.46	99.46	99.47	99.47	99.47	99.48	99.48	99.48	99.48	99.48	99.49	99.49	99.49	99.49	99.50	99.50	99.50
3	26.62	26.60	2658	26.56	26.55	26.53	26.52	26.50	26.48	26.45	26.41	26.38	26.35	26.32	26.28	26.24	26.22	26.21	26.19	26.17	26.15	26.14
4	13.95	13.93	13.91	13.89	13.88	13.86	13.85	13.84	13.81	13.79	13.75	13.71	13.69	13.65	13.61	13.58	13.56	13.54	13.53	1351	13.49	13.47
5	9.49	9.47	9.45	9.43	9.42	9.40	9.39	9.38	9.36	9.33	9.29	9.26	9.24	9.20	9.17	9.13	9.11	9.10	9.08	9.06	9.05	9.03
6	7.33	7.31	7.30	7.28	7.27	7.25	7.24	7.23	7.21	7.18	7.14	7.11	7.09	7.06	7.02	6.99	6.97	6.96	6.94	6.92	6.91	6.89
7	6.09	6.07	6.06	6.04	6.03	6.02	6.00	5.99	5.97	5.94	5.91	5.88	5.86	5.82	5.79	5.75	5.74	5.72	5.71	5.69	5.68	5.66
8	5.30	5.28	5.26	5.25	5.23	5.22	5.21	5.20	5.18	5.15	5.12	5.09	5.07	5.03	5.00	4.96	4.95	4.93	4.92	4.90	4.89	4.87
9	4.75	4.73	4.71	4.70	4.68	4.67	4.66	4.65	4.63	4.60	4.57	4.54	4.52	4.48	4.45	4.41	4.40	4.39	4.37	4.35	4.34	4.32
10	4.34	4.33	4.31	4.30	4.28	4.27	4.26	4.25	4.23	4.20	4.17	4.14	4.12	4.08	4.05	4.01	4.00	3.98	3.97	3.95	3.94	3.92
11	4.04	4.02	4.01	3.99	3.98	3.96	3.95	3.94	3.92	3.89	3.86	3.83	3.81	3.78	3.74	3.71	3.69	3.68	3.66	3.64	3.63	3.61
12	3.80	3.78	3.76	3.75	3.74	3.72	3.71	3.70	3.68	3.65	3.62	3.59	3.57	3.54	3.50	3.47	3.45	3.44	3.42	3.40	3.39	3.37
13	3.60	3.59	3.57	3.56	3.54	3.53	3.52	3.51	3.49	3.46	3.43	3.40	3.38	3.34	3.31	3.27	3.25	3.24	3.23	3.21	3.19	3.18
14	3.44	3.43	3.41	3.40	3.38	3.37	3.36	3.35	3.33	3.30	3.27	3.24	3.22	3.18	3.15	3.11	3.09	3.08	3.06	3.05	3.03	3.02
15	3.31	3.29	3.28	326	3.25	324	3.23	3.21	3.19	3.17	3.13	3.10	3.08	3.05	3.01	2.98	2.96	2.95	2.93	2.91	2.90	2.88
16	3.20	3.18	3.16	3.15	3.14	3.12	3.11	3.10	3.08	3.05	3.02	2.99	2.97	2.93	2.90	2.86	2.84	2.83	2.81	2.80	2.78	2.76
17	3.10	3.08	3.07	3.05	3.04	3.03	3.01	3.00	2.98	2.96	2.92	2.89	2.87	2.83	2.80	2.76	2.75	2.73	2.72	2.70	2.68	2.66
18	3.02	3.00	2.98	2.97	2.95	2.94	2.93	2.92	2.90	2.87	2.84	2.81	2.78	2.75	2.71	2.68	2.66	2.65	2.63	2.61	2.59	2.58
19	2.94	2.92	2.91	2.89	2.88	2.87	2.86	2.84	2.82	2.80	2.76	2.73	2.71	2.67	2.64	2.60	2.58	2.57	2.55	2.54	2.52	2.50
20	2.88	2.86	2.84	2.83	2.81	2.80	2.79	2.78	2.76	2.73	2.69	2.67	2.64	2.61	2.57	2.54	252	2.50	2.49	2.47	2.45	2.43
21	2.82	2.80	2.79	2.77	2.76	2.74	2.73	2.72	2.70	2.67	2.64	2.61	2.58	2.55	2.51	2.48	2.46	2.44	2.43	2.41	2.39	2.37
22	2.77	2.75	2.73	2.72	2.70	2.69	2.68	2.67	2.65	2.62	2.58	2.55	2.53	2.50	2.46	2.42	2.40	2.39	2.37	2.35	2.34	2.32
23	2.72	2.70	2.69	2.67	2.66	2.64	2.63	2.62	2.60	2.57	2.54	2.51	2.48	2.45	2.41	2.37	2.35	2.34	2.32	2.30	2.29	2.27
24	2.68	2.66	2.64	2.63	2.61	2.60	259	2.58	2.56	2.53	2.49	2.46	2.44	2.40	2.37	2.33	2.31	2.30	2.28	2.26	2.24	2.22
25	2.64	2.62	2.60	2.59	2.58	2.56	2.55	2.54	2.52	2.49	2.45	2.42	2.40	2.36	2.33	2.29	2.27	2.26	2.24	2.22	2.20	2.18
26	2.60	2.58	2.57	2.55	2.54	2.53	2.51	2.50	2.48	2.45	2.42	2.39	2.36	2.33	2.29	2.25	2.23	2.22	2.20	2.18	2.16	2.14
27	2.57	2.55	2.54	2.52	2.51	2.49	2.48	2.47	2.45	2.42	2.38	2.35	2.33	2.29	2.26	2.22	2.20	2.18	2.17	2.15	2.13	2.11
28	2.54	2.52	2.51	2.49	2.48	2.46	2.45	2.44	2.42	2.39	2.35	2.32	2.30	2.26	2.23	2.19	2.17	2.15	2.13	2.11	2.10	2.08
29	2.51	2.49	2.48	2.46	2.45	2.44	2.42	2.41	2.39	2.36	2.33	2.30	2.27	2.23	2.20	2.16	2.14	2.12	2.10	2.08	2.07	2.05
30	2.49	2.47	2.45	2.44	2.42	2.41	2.40	2.39	236	2.34	2.30	2.27	2.25	2.21	2.17	2.13	2.11	2.10	2.08	2.06	2.04	2.02
32	2.44	2.42	2.41	2.39	2.38	2.36	2.35	2.34	2.32	2.29	2.25	2.22	2.20	2.16	2.12	2.08	2.06	2.05	2.03	2.01	1.99	1.97
35	2.38	2.36	2.35	2.33	2.32	2.30	2.29	2.28	2.26	2.23	2.19	2.16	2.14	2.10	2.06	2.02	2.00	1.98	1.96	1.94	1.92	1.90
40	2.31	2.29	2.27	2.26	2.24	2.23	2.22	2.20	2.18	2.15	2.11	2.08	2.06	2.02	1.98	1.94	1.92	1.90	1.88	1.86	1.84	1.82
45	2.25	2.23	2.21	2.20	2.18	2.17	2.16	2.14	2.12	2.09	2.05	2.02	2.00	1.96	1.92	1.88	1.85	1.84	1.82	1.79	1.77	1.75
50	2.20	2.18	2.17	2.15	2.14	2.12	2.11	2.10	2.08	2.05	2.01	1.97	1.95	1.91	1.87	1.82	1.80	1.79	1.76	1.74	1.72	1.70
60	2.13	2.12	2.10	2.08	2.07	2.05	2.04	2.03	2.01	1.98	1.94	1.90	1.88	1.84	1.79	1.75	1.73	1.71	1.69	1.66	1.64	1.62
75	2.07	2.05	2.03	2.02	2.00	1.99	1.97	1.96	1.94	1.91	1.87	1.83	1.81	1.76	1.72	1.67	1.65	1.63	1.61	1.58	1.56	1.53
100	2.00	1.98	1.97	1.95	1.93	1.92	1.91	1.89	1.87	1.84	1.80	1.76	1.74	1.69	1.65	1.60	1.57	1.55	1.53	1.50	1.47	1.45
120	1.97	1.95	1.93	1.92	1.90	1.89	1.87	1.86	1.84	1.81	1.76	1.73	1.70	1.66	1.61	1.56	1.53	1.51	1.49	1.46	1.43	1.40
140	1.95	1.93	1.91	1.89	1.88	1.86	1.85	1.84	1.81	1.78	1.74	1.70	1.67	1.63	1.58	1.53	1.50	1.48	1.46	1.43	1.40	1.37
180	1.92	1.90	1.88	1.86	1.85	1.83	1.82	1.81	1.78	1.75	1.71	1.67	1.64	1.60	1.55	1.49	1.47	1.45	1.42	1.39	1.36	1.32
250	1.89	1.87	1.85	1.83	1.82	1.80	1.79	1.77	1.75	1.72	1.67	1.64	1.61	1.56	1.51	1.46	1.43	1.41	1.38	1.34	1.31	1.27
400	1.86	1.84	1.82	1.80	1.79	1.77	1.76	1.75	1.72	1.69	1.64	1.61	1.58	1.53	1.48	1.42	1.39	1.37	1.33	1.30	1.26	1.22
1000	1.83	1.81	1.79	1.77	1.76	1.74	1.73	1.72	1.69	1.66	1.61	1.58	1.54	1.50	1.44	1.38	1.35	1.33	1.29	1.25	1.21	1.16

Denominator df

Table F (cont.)

Numerator df

α = 0.05

Denominator df	1	2	3	4	5	6	7	8	9	10	11	12	13	14	15	16	17	18	19	20	21	22
1	161.4	199.5	215.7	224.6	230.2	234.0	236.8	238.9	240.5	241.9	243.0	243.9	244.7	245.4	245.9	246.5	246.9	247.3	247.7	248.0	248.3	248.6
2	18.51	19.00	19.16	19.25	19.30	19.33	19.35	19.37	19.38	19.40	19.40	19.41	19.42	19.42	19.43	19.43	19.44	19.44	19.44	19.45	19.45	19.45
3	10.13	9.55	9.28	9.12	9.01	8.94	8.89	8.85	8.81	8.79	8.76	8.74	8.73	8.71	8.70	8.69	8.68	8.67	8.67	8.66	8.65	8.65
4	7.71	6.94	6.59	6.39	6.26	6.16	6.09	6.04	6.00	5.96	5.94	5.91	5.89	5.87	5.86	5.84	5.83	5.82	5.81	5.80	5.79	5.79
5	6.61	5.79	5.41	5.19	5.05	4.95	4.88	4.82	4.77	4.74	4.70	4.68	4.66	4.64	4.62	4.60	4.59	4.58	4.57	4.56	4.55	4.54
6	5.99	5.14	4.76	4.53	4.39	4.28	4.21	4.15	4.10	4.06	4.03	4.00	3.98	3.96	3.94	3.92	3.91	3.90	3.88	3.87	3.86	3.86
7	5.59	4.74	4.35	4.12	3.97	3.87	3.79	3.73	3.68	3.64	3.60	3.57	3.55	3.53	3.51	3.49	3.48	3.47	3.46	3.44	3.43	3.43
8	5.32	4.46	4.07	3.84	3.69	3.58	3.50	3.44	3.39	3.35	3.31	3.28	3.26	3.24	3.22	3.20	3.19	3.17	3.16	3.15	3.14	3.13
9	5.12	4.26	3.86	3.63	3.48	3.37	3.29	3.23	3.18	3.14	3.10	3.07	3.05	3.03	3.01	2.99	2.97	2.96	2.95	2.94	2.93	2.92
10	4.96	4.10	3.71	3.48	3.33	3.22	3.14	3.07	3.02	2.98	2.94	2.91	2.89	2.86	2.85	2.83	2.81	2.80	2.79	2.77	2.76	2.75
11	4.84	3.98	3.59	3.36	3.20	3.09	3.01	2.95	2.90	2.85	2.82	2.79	2.76	2.74	2.72	2.70	2.69	2.67	2.66	2.65	2.64	2.63
12	4.75	3.89	3.49	3.26	3.11	3.00	2.91	2.85	2.80	2.75	2.72	2.69	2.66	2.64	2.62	2.60	2.58	2.57	2.56	2.54	2.53	2.52
13	4.67	3.81	3.41	3.18	3.03	2.92	2.83	2.77	2.71	2.67	2.63	2.60	2.58	2.55	2.53	2.51	2.50	2.48	2.47	2.46	2.45	2.44
14	4.60	3.74	3.34	3.11	2.96	2.85	2.76	2.70	2.65	2.60	2.57	2.53	2.51	2.48	2.46	2.44	2.43	2.41	2.40	2.39	2.38	2.37
15	4.54	3.68	3.29	3.06	2.90	2.79	2.71	2.64	2.59	2.54	2.51	2.48	2.45	2.42	2.40	2.38	2.37	2.35	2.34	2.33	2.32	2.31
16	4.49	3.63	3.24	3.01	2.85	2.74	2.66	2.59	2.54	2.49	2.46	2.42	2.40	2.37	2.35	2.33	2.32	2.30	2.29	2.28	2.26	2.25
17	4.45	3.59	3.20	2.96	2.81	2.70	2.61	2.55	2.49	2.45	2.41	2.38	2.35	2.33	2.31	2.29	2.27	2.26	2.24	2.23	2.22	2.21
18	4.41	3.55	3.16	2.93	2.77	2.66	2.58	2.51	2.46	2.41	2.37	2.34	2.31	2.29	2.27	2.25	2.23	2.22	2.20	2.19	2.18	2.17
19	4.38	3.52	3.13	2.90	2.74	2.63	2.54	2.48	2.42	2.38	2.34	2.31	2.28	2.26	2.23	2.21	2.20	2.18	2.17	2.16	2.14	2.13
20	4.35	3.49	3.10	2.87	2.71	2.60	2.51	2.45	2.39	2.35	2.31	2.28	2.25	2.22	2.20	2.18	2.17	2.15	2.14	2.12	2.11	2.10
21	4.32	3.47	3.07	2.84	2.68	2.57	2.49	2.42	2.37	2.32	2.28	2.25	2.22	2.20	2.18	2.16	2.14	2.12	2.11	2.10	2.08	2.07
22	4.30	3.44	3.05	2.82	2.66	2.55	2.46	2.40	2.34	2.30	2.26	2.23	2.20	2.17	2.15	2.13	2.11	2.10	2.08	2.07	2.06	2.05
23	4.28	3.42	3.03	2.80	2.64	2.53	2.44	2.37	2.32	2.27	2.24	2.20	2.18	2.15	2.13	2.11	2.09	2.08	2.06	2.05	2.04	2.02
24	4.26	3.40	3.01	2.78	2.62	2.51	2.42	2.36	2.30	2.25	2.22	2.18	2.15	2.13	2.11	2.09	2.07	2.05	2.04	2.03	2.01	2.00
25	4.24	3.39	2.99	2.76	2.60	2.49	2.40	2.34	2.28	2.24	2.20	2.16	2.14	2.11	2.09	2.07	2.05	2.04	2.02	2.01	2.00	1.98
26	4.23	3.37	2.98	2.74	2.59	2.47	2.39	2.32	2.27	2.22	2.18	2.15	2.12	2.09	2.07	2.05	2.03	2.02	2.00	1.99	1.98	1.97
27	4.21	3.35	2.96	2.73	2.57	2.46	2.37	2.31	2.25	2.20	2.17	2.13	2.10	2.08	2.06	2.04	2.02	2.00	1.99	1.97	1.96	1.95
28	4.20	3.34	2.95	2.71	2.56	2.45	2.36	2.29	2.24	2.19	2.15	2.12	2.09	2.06	2.04	2.02	2.00	1.99	1.97	1.96	1.95	1.93
29	4.18	3.33	2.93	2.70	2.55	2.43	2.35	2.28	2.22	2.18	2.14	2.10	2.08	2.05	2.03	2.01	1.99	1.97	1.96	1.94	1.93	1.92
30	4.17	3.32	2.92	2.69	2.53	2.42	2.33	2.27	2.21	2.16	2.13	2.09	2.06	2.04	2.01	1.99	1.98	1.96	1.95	1.93	1.92	1.91
32	4.15	3.29	2.90	2.67	2.51	2.40	2.31	2.24	2.19	2.14	2.10	2.07	2.04	2.01	1.99	1.97	1.95	1.94	1.92	1.91	1.90	1.88
35	4.12	3.27	2.87	2.64	2.49	2.37	2.29	2.22	2.16	2.11	2.07	2.04	2.01	1.99	1.96	1.94	1.92	1.91	1.89	1.88	1.87	1.85
40	4.08	3.23	2.84	2.61	2.45	2.34	2.25	2.18	2.12	2.08	2.04	2.00	1.97	1.95	1.92	1.90	1.89	1.87	1.85	1.84	1.83	1.81
45	4.06	3.20	2.81	2.58	2.42	2.31	2.22	2.15	2.10	2.05	2.01	1.97	1.94	1.92	1.89	1.87	1.86	1.84	1.82	1.81	1.80	1.78
50	4.03	3.18	2.79	2.56	2.40	2.29	2.20	2.13	2.07	2.03	1.99	1.95	1.92	1.89	1.87	1.85	1.83	1.81	1.80	1.78	1.77	1.76
60	4.00	3.15	2.76	2.53	2.37	2.25	2.17	2.10	2.04	1.99	1.95	1.92	1.89	1.86	1.84	1.82	1.80	1.78	1.76	1.75	1.73	1.72
75	3.97	3.12	2.73	2.49	2.34	2.22	2.13	2.06	2.01	1.96	1.92	1.88	1.85	1.83	1.80	1.78	1.76	1.74	1.73	1.71	1.70	1.69
100	3.94	3.09	2.70	2.46	2.31	2.19	2.10	2.03	1.97	1.93	1.89	1.85	1.82	1.79	1.77	1.75	1.73	1.71	1.69	1.68	1.66	1.65
120	3.92	3.07	2.68	2.45	2.29	2.18	2.09	2.02	1.96	1.91	1.87	1.83	1.80	1.78	1.75	1.73	1.71	1.69	1.67	1.66	1.64	1.63
140	3.91	3.06	2.67	2.44	2.28	2.16	2.08	2.01	1.95	1.90	1.86	1.82	1.79	1.76	1.74	1.72	1.70	1.68	1.66	1.65	1.63	1.62
180	3.89	3.05	2.65	2.42	2.26	2.15	2.06	1.99	1.93	1.88	1.84	1.81	1.77	1.75	1.72	1.70	1.68	1.66	1.64	1.63	1.61	1.60
250	3.88	3.03	2.64	2.41	2.25	2.13	2.05	1.98	1.92	1.87	1.83	1.79	1.76	1.73	1.71	1.68	1.66	1.65	1.63	1.61	1.60	1.58
400	3.86	3.02	2.63	2.39	2.24	2.12	2.03	1.96	1.90	1.85	1.81	1.78	1.74	1.72	1.69	1.67	1.65	1.63	1.61	1.60	1.58	1.57
1000	3.85	3.00	2.61	2.38	2.22	2.11	2.02	1.95	1.89	1.84	1.80	1.76	1.73	1.70	1.68	1.65	1.63	1.61	1.60	1.58	1.57	1.55

Table F (cont.)

Numerator df

$\alpha = 0.05$	23	24	25	26	27	28	29	30	32	35	40	45	50	60	75	100	120	140	180	250	400	1000
1	248.8	249.1	249.3	249.5	249.6	249.8	250.0	250.1	250.4	250.7	251.1	251.5	251.8	252.2	252.6	253.0	253.3	253.4	253.6	253.8	254.0	254.2
2	19.45	19.45	19.46	19.46	19.46	19.46	19.46	19.46	19.46	19.47	19.47	19.47	19.48	19.48	19.48	19.49	19.49	19.49	19.49	19.49	19.49	19.49
3	8.64	8.64	8.63	8.63	8.63	8.62	8.62	8.62	8.61	8.60	8.59	8.59	8.58	8.57	8.56	8.55	8.55	8.55	8.54	8.54	8.53	8.53
4	5.78	5.77	5.77	5.76	5.76	5.75	5.75	5.75	5.74	5.73	5.72	5.71	5.70	5.69	5.68	5.66	5.66	5.65	5.65	5.64	5.64	5.63
5	4.53	4.53	4.52	4.52	4.51	4.50	4.50	4.50	4.49	4.48	4.46	4.45	4.44	4.43	4.42	4.41	4.40	4.39	4.39	4.38	4.38	4.37
6	3.85	3.84	3.83	3.83	3.82	3.82	3.81	3.81	3.80	3.79	3.77	3.76	3.75	3.74	3.73	3.71	3.70	3.70	3.69	3.69	3.68	3.67
7	3.42	3.41	3.40	3.40	3.39	3.39	3.38	3.38	3.37	3.36	3.34	3.33	3.32	3.30	3.29	3.27	3.27	3.26	3.25	3.25	3.24	3.23
8	3.12	3.12	3.11	3.10	3.10	3.09	3.08	3.08	3.07	3.06	3.04	3.03	3.02	3.01	2.99	2.97	2.97	2.96	2.95	2.95	2.94	2.93
9	2.91	2.90	2.89	2.89	2.88	2.87	2.87	2.86	2.85	2.84	2.83	2.81	2.80	2.79	2.77	2.76	2.75	2.74	2.73	2.73	2.72	2.71
10	2.75	2.74	2.73	2.72	2.72	2.71	2.70	2.70	2.69	2.68	2.66	2.65	2.64	2.62	2.60	2.59	2.58	2.57	2.57	2.56	2.55	2.54
11	2.62	2.61	2.60	2.59	2.59	2.58	2.58	2.57	2.56	2.55	2.53	2.52	2.51	2.49	2.47	2.46	2.45	2.44	2.43	2.43	2.42	2.41
12	2.51	2.51	2.50	2.49	2.48	2.48	2.47	2.47	2.46	2.44	2.43	2.41	2.40	2.38	2.37	2.35	2.34	2.33	2.33	2.32	2.31	2.30
13	2.43	2.42	2.41	2.41	2.40	2.39	2.39	2.38	2.37	2.36	2.34	2.33	2.31	2.30	2.28	2.26	2.25	2.25	2.24	2.23	2.22	2.21
14	2.36	2.35	2.34	2.33	2.33	2.32	2.31	2.31	2.30	2.28	2.27	2.25	2.24	2.22	2.21	2.19	2.18	2.17	2.16	2.15	2.15	2.14
15	2.30	2.29	2.28	2.27	2.27	2.26	2.25	2.25	2.24	2.22	2.20	2.19	2.18	2.16	2.14	2.12	2.11	2.11	2.10	2.09	2.08	2.07
16	2.24	2.24	2.23	2.22	2.21	2.21	2.20	2.19	2.18	2.17	2.15	2.14	2.12	2.11	2.09	2.07	2.06	2.05	2.04	2.03	2.02	2.02
17	2.20	2.19	2.18	2.17	2.17	2.16	2.15	2.15	2.14	2.12	2.10	2.09	2.08	2.06	2.04	2.02	2.01	2.00	1.99	1.98	1.98	1.97
18	2.16	2.15	2.14	2.13	2.13	2.12	2.11	2.11	2.10	2.08	2.06	2.05	2.04	2.02	2.00	1.98	1.97	1.96	1.95	1.94	1.93	1.92
19	2.12	2.11	2.11	2.10	2.09	2.08	2.08	2.07	2.06	2.05	2.03	2.01	2.00	1.98	1.96	1.94	1.93	1.92	1.91	1.90	1.89	1.88
213	2.09	2.08	2.07	2.07	2.06	2.05	2.05	2.04	2.03	2.01	1.99	1.98	1.97	1.95	1.93	1.91	1.90	1.89	1.88	1.87	1.86	1.85
21	2.06	2.05	2.05	2.04	2.03	2.02	2.02	2.01	2.00	1.98	1.96	1.95	1.94	1.92	1.90	1.88	1.87	1.86	1.85	1.84	1.83	1.82
22	2.04	2.03	2.02	2.01	2.00	2.00	1.99	1.98	1.97	1.96	1.94	1.92	1.91	1.89	1.87	1.85	1.84	1.83	1.82	1.81	1.80	1.79
23	2.01	2.01	2.00	1.99	1.98	1.97	1.97	1.96	1.95	1.93	1.91	1.90	1.88	1.86	1.84	1.82	1.81	1.81	1.79	1.78	1.77	1.76
24	1.99	1.98	1.97	1.97	1.96	1.95	1.95	1.94	1.93	1.91	1.89	1.88	1.86	1.84	1.82	1.80	1.79	1.78	1.77	1.76	1.75	1.74
25	1.07	1.96	1.96	1.95	1.94	1.93	1.93	1.92	1.91	1.89	1.87	1.86	1.84	1.82	1.80	1.78	1.77	1.76	1.75	1.74	1.73	1.72
26	1.96	1.95	1.94	1.93	1.92	1.91	1.91	1.90	1.89	1.87	1.85	1.84	1.82	1.80	1.78	1.76	1.75	1.74	1.73	1.72	1.71	1.70
27	1.94	1.93	1.92	1.91	1.90	1.90	1.89	1.88	1.87	1.86	1.84	1.82	1.81	1.79	1.76	1.74	1.73	1.72	1.71	1.70	1.69	1.68
28	1.92	1.9]	1.91	1.90	1.89	1.88	1.88	1.87	1.86	1.84	1.82	1.80	1.79	1.77	1.75	1.73	1.71	1.71	1.69	1.68	1.67	1.66
29	1.91	1.90	1.89	1.88	1.88	1.87	1.86	1.85	1.84	1.83	1.81	1.79	1.77	1.75	1.73	1.71	1.70	1.69	1.68	1.67	1.66	1.65
30	1.90	1.89	1.88	1.87	1.86	1.85	1.85	1.84	1.83	1.81	1.79	1.77	1.76	1.74	1.72	1.70	1.68	1.68	1.66	1.65	1.64	1.63
32	1.87	1.86	1.85	1.85	1.84	1.83	1.82	1.82	1.80	1.79	1.77	1.75	1.74	1.71	1.69	1.67	1.66	1.65	1.64	1.63	1.61	1.60
35	1.84	1.83	1.82	1.82	1.81	1.80	1.79	1.79	1.77	1.76	1.74	1.72	1.70	1.68	1.66	1.63	1.62	1.61	1.60	1.59	1.58	1.57
40	1.80	1.79	1.78	1.77	1.77	1.76	1.75	1.74	1.73	1.72	1.69	1.67	1.66	1.64	1.61	1.59	1.58	1.57	1.55	1.54	1.53	1.52
45	1.77	1.76	3.75	1.74	1.73	1.73	1.72	1.71	1.70	1.68	1.66	1.64	1.63	1.60	1.58	1.55	1.54	1.53	1.52	1.51	1.49	1.48
50	1.75	1.74	1.73	1.72	1.71	1.70	1.69	1.69	1.67	1.66	1.63	1.61	1.60	1.58	1.55	1.52	1.51	1.50	1.49	1.47	1.46	1.45
60	1.7	1.70	1.69	1.68	1.67	1.66	1.66	1.65	1.64	1.62	1.59	1.57	1.56	1.53	1.51	1.48	1.47	1.46	1.44	1.43	1.41	1.40
75	1.67	1.66	1.65	1.64	1.63	1.63	1.62	1.61	1.60	1.58	1.55	1.53	1.52	1.49	1.47	1.44	1.42	1.41	1.40	1.38	1.37	1.35
100	1.64	1.63	1.62	1.61	1.60	1.59	1.58	1.57	1.56	1.54	1.52	1.49	1.48	1.45	1.42	1.39	1.38	1.36	1.35	1.33	1.31	1.30
120	1.62	1.61	1.60	1.59	1.58	1.57	1.56	1.55	1.54	1.52	1.50	1.47	1.46	1.43	1.40	1.37	1.35	1.34	1.32	1.30	1.29	1.27
140	1.61	1.60	1.59	1.57	1.57	1.56	1.55	1.54	1.53	1.51	1.48	1.46	1.44	1.41	1.38	1.35	1.33	1.32	1.30	1.29	1.27	1.25
180	1.59	1.58	1.57	1.56	1.55	1.54	1.53	1.52	1.51	1.49	1.46	1.44	1.42	1.39	1.36	1.33	1.31	1.30	1.28	1.26	1.24	1.22
250	1.57	1.56	1.55	1.54	1.53	1.52	1.51	1.50	1.49	1.47	1.44	1.42	1.40	1.37	1.34	1.31	129	1.27	1.25	1.23	1.21	1.18
400	1.56	1.54	1.53	1.52	1.51	1.50	1.50	1.49	1.47	1.45	1.42	1.40	1.38	1.35	1.32	128	1.26	125	1.23	1.20	1.18	1.15
1000	1.54	1.53	1.52	1.51	1.50	1.49	1.48	1.47	1.46	1.43	1.41	1.38	1.36	1.33	130	1.26	1.24	1.22	120	1.17	1.14	1.11

Denominator df

Table F (cont.)

Numerator df

$\alpha = 0.1$	1	2	3	4	5	6	7	8	9	10	11	12	13	14	15	16	17	18	19	20	21	22
1	39.9	49.5	53.6	55.8	57.2	58.2	58.9	59.4	59.9	60.2	60.5	60.7	60.9	61.1	61.2	61.3	61.5	61.6	61.7	61.7	61.8	61.9
2	8.53	9.00	9.16	9.24	9.29	9.33	935	9.37	9.38	9.39	9.40	9.41	9.41	9.42	9.42	9.43	9.43	9.44	9.44	9.44	9.44	9.45
3	5.54	5.46	5.39	5.34	531	5.28	5.27	5.25	5.24	5.23	5.22	5.22	5.21	5.20	5.20	5.20	5.19	5.19	5.19	5.18	5.18	5.18
4	4.54	4.32	4.19	4.11	4.05	4.01	3.98	3.95	3.94	3.92	3.91	3.90	3.89	3.88	3.87	3.86	3.86	3.85	3.85	3.84	3.84	3.84
5	4.06	3.78	3.62	3.52	3.45	3.40	3.37	3.34	3.32	3.30	3.28	3.27	3.26	325	3.24	3.23	3.22	3.22	3.21	3.21	3.20	3.20
6	3.78	3.46	3.29	3.18	3.11	3.05	3.01	2.98	2.96	2.94	2.92	2.90	2.89	2.88	2.87	2.86	2.85	2.85	2.84	2.84	2.83	2.83
7	3.59	3.26	3.07	2.96	2.88	2.83	2.78	2.75	2.72	2.70	2.68	2.67	2.65	2.64	2.63	2.62	2.61	2.61	2.60	2.59	2.59	2.58
8	3.46	3.11	2.92	2.81	2.73	2.67	2.62	2.59	2.56	2.54	2.52	2.50	2.49	2.48	2.46	2.45	2.45	2.44	2.43	2.42	2.42	2.41
9	3.36	3.01	2.81	2.69	2.61	2.55	2.51	2.47	2.44	2.42	2.40	2.38	2.36	2.35	2.34	2.33	2.32	2.31	2.30	2.30	2.29	2.29
10	3.29	2.92	2.73	2.61	2.52	2.46	2.41	2.38	2.35	2.32	2.30	2.28	2.27	2.26	2.24	2.23	2.22	2.22	2.21	2.20	2.19	2.19
11	3.23	2.86	2.66	2.54	2.45	2.39	2.34	2.30	2.27	2.25	2.23	2.21	2.19	2.18	2.17	2.16	2.15	2.14	2.13	2.12	2.12	2.11
12	3.18	2.81	2.61	2.48	2.39	2.33	2.28	2.24	2.21	2.19	2.17	2.15	2.13	2.12	2.10	2.09	2.08	2.08	2.07	2.06	2.05	2.05
13	3.14	2.76	2.56	2.43	2.35	2.28	2.23	2.20	2.16	2.14	2.12	2.10	2.08	2.07	2.05	2.04	2.03	2.02	2.01	2.01	2.00	1.99
14	3.10	2.73	2.52	2.39	2.31	2.24	2.19	2.15	2.12	2.10	2.07	2.05	2.04	2.02	2.01	2.00	1.99	1.98	1.97	1.96	1.96	1.95
15	3.07	2.70	2.49	2.36	2.27	2.21	2.16	2.12	2.09	2.06	2.04	2.02	2.00	1.99	1.97	1.96	1.95	1.94	1.93	1.92	1.92	1.91
16	3.05	2.67	2.46	2.33	2.24	2.18	2.13	2.09	2.06	2.03	2.01	1.99	1.97	1.95	1.94	1.93	1.92	1.91	1.90	1.89	1.88	1.88
17	3.03	2.64	2.44	2.31	2.22	2.15	2.10	2.06	2.03	2.00	1.98	1.96	1.94	1.93	1.91	1.90	1.89	1.88	1.87	1.86	1.86	1.85
18	3.01	2.62	2.42	2.29	2.20	2.13	2.08	2.04	2.00	1.98	1.95	1.93	1.92	1.90	1.89	1.87	1.86	1.85	1.84	1.84	1.83	1.82
19	2.99	2.61	2.40	2.27	2.18	2.11	2.06	2.02	1.98	1.96	1.93	1.91	1.89	1.88	1.86	1.85	1.84	1.83	1.82	1.81	1.81	1.80
20	2.97	2.59	2.38	2.25	2.16	2.09	2.04	2.00	1.96	1.94	1.91	1.89	1.87	1.86	1.84	1.83	1.82	1.81	1.80	1.79	1.79	1.78
21	2.96	2.57	2.36	2.23	2.14	2.08	2.02	1.98	1.95	1.92	1.90	1.87	1.86	1.84	1.83	1.81	1.80	1.79	1.78	1.78	1.77	1.76
22	2.95	2.56	2.35	2.22	2.13	2.06	2.01	1.97	1.93	1.90	1.88	1.86	1.84	1.83	1.81	1.80	1.79	1.78	1.77	1.76	1.75	1.74
23	2.94	2.55	2.34	2.21	2.11	2.05	1.99	1.95	1.92	1.89	1.87	1.84	1.83	1.81	1.80	1.78	1.77	1.76	1.75	1.74	1.74	1.73
24	2.93	2.54	2.33	2.19	2.10	2.04	1.98	1.94	1.91	1.88	1.85	1.83	1.81	1.80	1.78	1.77	1.76	1.75	1.74	1.73	1.72	1.71
25	2.92	2.53	2.32	2.18	2.09	2.02	1.97	1.93	1.89	1.87	1.84	1.82	1.80	1.79	1.77	1.76	1.75	1.74	1.73	1.72	1.71	1.70
26	2.91	2.52	2.31	2.17	2.08	2.01	1.96	1.92	1.88	1.86	1.83	1.81	1.79	1.77	1.76	1.75	1.73	1.72	1.71	1.71	1.70	1.69
27	2.90	2.51	2.30	2.17	2.07	2.00	1.95	1.91	1.87	1.85	1.82	1.80	1.78	1.76	1.75	1.74	1.72	1.71	1.70	1.70	1.69	1.68
28	2.89	2.50	2.29	2.16	2.06	2.00	1.94	1.90	1.87	1.84	1.81	1.79	1.77	1.75	1.74	1.73	1.71	1.70	1.69	1.69	1.68	1.67
29	2.89	250	2.28	2.15	2.06	1.99	1.93	1.89	1.86	1.83	1.80	1.78	1.7o	1.75	1.73	1.72	1.71	1.69	1.68	1.68	1.67	1.66
30	2.88	2.49	228	2.14	2.05	1.98	1.93	1.88	1.85	1.82	1.79	1.77	1.75	1.74	1.72	1.71	1.70	1.69	1.68	1.67	1.66	1.65
32	2.87	2.48	2.26	2.13	2.04	1.97	1.91	1.87	1.83	1.81	1.78	1.76	1.74	1.72	1.71	1.69	1.68	1.67	1.66	1.65	1.64	1.64
35	2.85	2.46	2.25	2.11	2.02	1.95	1.90	1.85	1.82	1.79	1.76	1.74	1.72	1.70	1.69	1.67	1.66	1.65	1.64	1.63	1.62	1.62
40	2.84	2.44	2.23	2.09	2.00	1.93	1.87	1.83	1.79	1.76	1.74	1.71	1.70	1.68	1.66	1.65	1.64	1.62	1.61	1.61	1.60	1.59
45	2.82	2.42	2.21	2.07	1.98	1.91	1.85	1.81	1.77	1.74	1.72	1.70	1.68	1.66	1.64	1.63	1.62	1.60	1.59	1.58	1.58	1.57
50	2.81	2.41	2.20	2.06	1.97	1.90	1.84	1.80	1.76	1.73	1.70	1.68	1.6ft	1.64	1.63	1.61	1.60	1.59	1.58	1.57	1.56	1.55
60	2.79	2.39	2.18	2.04	1.95	1.87	1.82	1.77	1.74	1.71	1.68	1.66	1.64	1.62	1.60	1.59	1.58	1.56	1.55	1.54	1.53	1.53
75	2.77	2.37	2.16	2.02	1.93	1.85	1.80	1.75	1.72	1.69	1.66	1.63	1.61	1.60	1.58	1.57	1.55	1.54	1.53	1.52	1.51	1.50
100	2.76	2.36	2.14	2.00	1.91	1.83	1.78	1.73	1.69	1.66	1.64	1.61	1.59	1.57	1.56	1.54	1.53	1.52	1.50	1.49	1.48	1.48
120	2.75	2.35	2.13	1.99	1.90	1.82	1.77	1.72	1.68	1.65	1.63	1.60	1.58	1.56	1.55	1.53	1.52	1.50	1.49	1.48	1.47	1.46
140	2.74	2.34	2.12	1.99	1.89	1.82	1.76	1.71	1.68	1.64	1.62	1.59	1.57	155	1.54	1.52	1.51	1.50	1.48	1.47	1.46	1.45
180	2.73	2.33	2.11	1.98	1.88	1.81	1.75	1.70	1.67	1.63	1.61	1.58	1.56	1.54	1.53	1.51	1.50	1.48	1.47	1.46	1.45	1.44
250	2.73	2.32	2.11	1.97	1.87	1.80	1.74	1.69	1.66	1.62	1.60	1.57	1.55	1.53	1.51	1.50	1.49	1.47	1.46	1.45	1.44	1.43
400	2.72	2.32	2.30	1.96	1.86	1.79	1.73	1.69	1.65	1.61	1.59	1.56	1.54	1.52	1.50	1.49	1.47	1.46	1.45	1.44	1.43	1.42
1000	2.71	2.31	2.09	1.95	1.85	1.78	1.72	1.68	1.64	1.61	1.58	1.55	1.53	1.51	1.49	1.48	1.46	1.45	1.44	1.43	1.42	

Denominator df

Table F (cont.)

Numerator df

$\alpha = 0.1$ Denominator df	23	24	25	26	27	28	29	30	32	35	40	45	50	60	75	100	120	140	180	250	400	1000
1	61.9	62.0	62.1	62.1	62.1	62.2	62.2	62.3	62.3	62.4	62.5	62.6	62.7	62.8	62.9	63.0	63.1	63.1	63.1	63.2	63.2	63.3
2	9.45	9.45	9.45	9.45	9.45	9.46	9.46	9.46	9.46	9.46	9.47	9.47	9.47	9.47	9.48	9.48	9.48	9.48	9.49	9.49	9.49	9.49
3	5.18	5.18	5.17	5.17	5.17	5.17	5.17	5.17	5.17	5.16	5.16	5.16	5.15	5.15	5.15	5.14	5.14	5.14	5.14	5.14	5.14	5.1
4	3.83	3.83	3.83	3.83	3.82	3.82	3.82	3.82	3.81	3.81	3.80	3.80	3.80	3.79	3.78	3.78	3.78	3.77	3.77	3.77	3.77	3.76
5	3.19	3.19	3.19	3.18	3.18	3.18	3.18	3.17	3.17	3.16	3.16	3.15	3.15	3.14	3.13	3.13	3.12	3.12	3.12	3.11	3.11	3.11
6	2.82	2.82	2.81	2.81	2.81	2.81	2.80	2.80	2.80	2.79	2.78	2.77	2.77	2.76	2.75	2.75	2.74	2.74	2.74	2.73	2.73	2.72
7	2.58	2.58	2.57	2.57	2.56	2.56	2.56	2.56	2.55	2.54	2.54	2.53	2.52	2.51	2.51	2.50	2.49	2.49	2.49	2.48	2.48	2.47
8	2.41	2.40	2.40	2.40	2.39	2.39	2.39	2.38	2.38	2.37	2.36	2.35	2.35	2.34	2.33	2.32	2.32	2.31	2.31	2.30	2.30	2.30
9	2.28	2.28	2.27	2.27	2.26	2.26	2.26	2.25	2.25	2.24	2.23	2.22	2.22	2.21	2.20	2.19	2.18	2.18	2.18	2.17	2.17	2.16
10	2.18	2.18	2.17	2.17	2.17	2.16	2.16	2.16	2.15	2.14	2.13	2.12	2.12	2.11	2.10	2.09	2.08	2.08	2.07	2.07	2.06	2.06
11	2.11	2.10	2.10	2.09	2.09	2.08	2.08	2.08	2.07	2.06	2.05	2.04	2.04	2.03	2.02	2.01	2.00	2.00	1.99	1.99	1.98	1.98
12	2.04	2.04	2.03	2.03	2.02	2.02	2.01	2.01	2.01	2.00	1.99	1.98	1.97	1.96	1.95	1.94	1.93	1.93	1.92	1.92	1.91	1.91
13	1.99	1.98	1.98	1.97	1.97	1.96	1.96	1.96	1.95	1.94	1.93	1.92	1.92	1.90	1.89	1.88	1.88	1.87	1.87	1.86	1.86	1.85
14	1.94	1.94	1.93	1.93	1.92	1.92	1.92	1.91	1.91	1.90	1.89	1.88	1.87	1.86	1.85	1.83	1.83	1.82	1.82	1.81	1.81	1.80
15	1.90	1.90	1.89	1.89	1.88	1.88	1.88	1.87	1.87	1.86	1.85	1.84	1.83	1.82	1.80	1.79	1.79	1.78	1.78	1.77	1.76	1.76
16	1.87	1.87	1.86	1.86	1.85	1.85	1.84	1.84	1.83	1.82	1.81	1.80	1.79	1.78	1.77	1.76	1.75	1.75	1.74	1.73	1.73	1.72
17	1.84	1.84	1.83	1.83	1.82	1.82	1.81	1.81	1.80	1.79	1.78	1.77	1.76	1.75	1.74	1.73	1.72	1.71	1.71	1.70	1.70	1.69
18	1.82	1.81	1.80	1.80	1.80	1.79	1.79	1.78	1.78	1.77	1.75	1.74	1.74	1.72	1.71	1.70	1.69	1.69	1.68	1.67	1.67	1.66
19	1.79	1.79	1.78	1.78	1.77	1.77	1.76	1.76	1.75	1.74	1.73	1.72	1.71	1.70	1.69	1.67	1.67	1.66	1.65	1.65	1.64	1.64
20	1.77	1.77	1.76	1.76	1.75	1.75	1.74	1.74	1.73	1.72	1.71	1.70	1.69	1.68	1.66	1.65	1.64	1.64	1.63	1.62	1.62	1.61
21	1.75	1.75	1.74	1.74	1.73	1.73	1.72	1.72	1.71	1.70	1.69	1.68	1.67	1.66	1.64	1.63	1.62	1.62	1.61	1.60	1.60	1.59
22	1.74	1.73	1.73	1.72	1.72	1.71	1.71	1.70	1.69	1.68	1.67	1.66	1.65	1.64	1.63	1.61	1.60	1.60	1.59	1.59	1.58	1.57
23	1.72	1.72	1.71	1.70	1.70	1.69	1.69	1.69	1.68	1.67	1.66	1.64	1.64	1.62	1.61	1.59	1.59	1.58	1.57	1.57	1.56	1.55
24	1.71	1.70	1.70	1.69	1.69	1.68	1.68	1.67	1.66	1.65	1.64	1.63	1.62	1.61	1.59	1.58	1.57	1.57	1.56	1.55	1.54	1.54
25	1.70	1.69	1.68	1.68	1.67	1.67	1.66	1.66	1.65	1.64	1.63	1.62	1.61	1.59	1.58	1.56	1.56	1.55	1.54	1.54	1.53	1.52
26	1.68	1.68	1.67	1.67	1.66	1.66	1.65	1.65	1.64	1.63	1.61	1.60	1.59	1.58	1.57	1.55	1.54	1.54	1.53	1.52	1.52	1.51
27	1.67	1.67	1.66	1.65	1.65	1.64	1.64	1.64	1.63	1.62	1.60	1.59	1.58	1.57	1.55	1.54	1.53	1.53	1.52	1.51	1.50	1.50
28	1.66	1.66	1.65	1.64	1.64	1.63	1.63	1.63	1.62	1.61	1.59	1.58	1.57	1.56	1.54	1.53	1.52	1.51	1.51	1.50	1.49	1.48
29	1.65	1.65	1.64	1.63	1.63	1.62	1.62	1.62	1.61	1.60	1.58	1.57	1.56	1.55	1.53	1.52	1.51	1.50	1.50	1.49	1.48	1.47
30	1.64	1.64	1.63	1.63	1.62	1.62	1.61	1.61	1.60	1.59	1.57	1.56	1.55	1.54	1.52	1.51	1.50	1.49	1.49	1.48	1.47	1.46
32	1.63	1.62	1.62	1.61	1.60	1.60	1.59	1.59	1.58	1.57	1.56	1.54	1.53	1.52	1.50	1.49	1.48	1.47	1.47	1.46	1.45	1.44
35	1.61	1.60	1.60	1.59	1.58	1.58	1.57	1.57	1.56	1.55	1.53	1.52	1.51	1.50	1.48	1.47	1.46	1.45	1.44	1.43	1.43	1.42
40	1.58	1.57	1.57	1.56	1.56	1.55	1.55	1.54	1.53	1.52	1.51	1.49	1.48	1.47	1.45	1.43	1.42	1.42	1.41	1.40	1.39	1.38
45	1.56	1.55	1.55	1.54	1.53	1.53	1.52	1.52	1.51	1.50	1.48	1.47	1.46	1.44	1.43	1.41	1.40	1.39	1.38	1.37	1.37	1.36
50	1.54	1.54	1.53	1.52	1.52	1.51	1.51	1.50	1.49	1.48	1.46	1.45	1.44	1.42	1.41	1.39	1.38	1.37	1.36	1.35	1.34	1.33
60	1.52	1.51	1.50	1.50	1.49	1.49	1.48	1.48	1.47	1.45	1.44	1.42	1.41	1.40	1.38	1.36	1.35	1.34	1.33	1.32	1.31	1.30
75	1.49	1.49	1.48	1.47	1.47	1.46	1.45	1.45	1.44	1.43	1.41	1.40	1.38	1.37	1.35	1.33	1.32	1.31	1.30	1.29	1.27	1.26
100	1.47	1.46	1.45	1.45	1.44	1.43	1.43	1.42	1.41	1.40	1.38	1.37	1.35	1.34	1.32	1.29	1.28	1.27	1.26	1.25	1.24	1.22
120	1.46	1.45	1.44	1.43	1.43	1.42	1.41	1.41	1.40	1.39	1.37	1.35	1.34	1.32	1.30	1.28	1.26	1.26	1.24	1.23	1.22	1.20
140	1.45	1.44	1.43	1.42	1.42	1.41	1.41	1.40	1.39	1.38	1.36	1.34	1.33	1.31	1.29	1.26	1.25	1.24	1.23	1.22	1.20	1.19
180	1.43	1.43	1.42	1.41	1.40	1.40	1.39	1.39	1.38	1.36	1.34	1.33	1.32	1.29	1.27	1.25	1.23	1.22	1.21	1.20	1.18	1.16
250	1.42	1.41	1.41	1.40	1.39	1.39	1.38	1.37	1.36	1.35	1.33	1.31	1.30	1.28	1.26	1.23	1.22	1.21	1.19	1.18	1.16	1.14
400	1.41	1.40	1.39	1.39	1.38	1.37	1.37	1.36	1.35	1.34	1.32	1.30	1.29	1.26	1.24	1.21	1.20	1.19	1.17	1.16	1.14	1.12
1000	1.40	1.39	1.38	1.38	1.37	1.36	1.36	1.35	1.34	1.32	1.30	1.29	1.27	1.25	1.23	1.20	1.18	1.17	1.15	1.13	1.11	1.08

Table D

Critical Values d_L and d_U of the Durbin-Watson Statistic D (Critical Values Are One-Sided)[‡] *(see Section 19.5)*

α = 0.05

n	$k=1$ d_L	$k=1$ d_U	$k=2$ d_L	$k=2$ d_U	$k=3$ d_L	$k=3$ d_U	$k=4$ d_L	$k=4$ d_U	$k=5$ d_L	$k=5$ d_U
15	1.08	1.36	0.95	1.54	0.82	1.75	0.69	1.97	0.56	2.21
16	1.10	1.37	0.98	1.54	0.86	1.73	0.74	1.93	0.62	2.15
17	1.13	1.38	1.02	1.54	0.90	1.71	0.78	1.90	0.67	2.10
18	1.16	1.39	1.05	1.53	0.93	1.69	0.82	1.87	0.71	2.06
19	1.18	1.40	1.08	1.53	0.97	1.68	0.86	1.85	0.75	2.02
20	1.20	1.41	1.10	1.54	1.00	1.68	0.90	1.83	0.79	1.99
21	1.22	1.42	1.13	1.54	1.03	1.67	0.93	1.81	0.83	1.96
22	1.24	1.43	1.15	1.54	1.05	1.66	0.96	1.80	0.86	1.94
23	1.26	1.44	1.17	1.54	1.08	1.66	0.99	1.79	0.90	1.92
24	1.27	1.45	1.19	1.55	1.10	1.66	1.01	1.78	0.93	1.90
25	1.29	1.45	1.21	1.55	1.12	1.66	1.04	1.77	0.95	1.89
26	1.30	1.46	1.22	1.55	1.14	1.65	1.06	1.76	0.98	1.88
27	1.32	1.47	1.24	1.56	1.16	1.65	1.08	1.76	1.01	1.86
28	1.33	1.48	1.26	1.56	1.18	1.65	1.10	1.75	1.03	1.85
29	1.34	1.48	1.27	1.56	1.20	1.65	1.12	1.74	1.05	1.84
30	1.35	1.49	1.28	1.57	1.21	1.65	1.14	1.74	1.07	1.83
31	1.36	1.50	1.30	1.57	1.23	1.65	1.16	1.74	1.09	1.83
32	1.37	1.50	1.31	1.57	1.24	1.65	1.18	1.73	1.11	1.82
33	1.38	1.51	1.32	1.58	1.26	1.65	1.19	1.73	1.13	1.81
34	1.39	1.51	1.33	1.58	1.27	1.65	1.21	1.73	1.15	1.81
35	1.40	1.52	1.34	1.58	1.28	1.65	1.22	1.73	1.16	1.80
36	1.41	1.52	1.35	1.59	1.29	1.65	1.24	1.73	1.18	1.80
37	1.42	1.53	1.36	1.59	1.31	1.66	1.25	1.72	1.19	1.80
38	1.43	1.54	1.37	1.59	1.32	1.66	1.26	1.72	1.21	1.79
39	1.43	1.54	1.38	1.60	1.33	1.66	1.27	1.72	1.22	1.79
40	1.44	1.54	1.39	1.60	1.34	1.66	1.29	1.72	1.23	1.79
45	1.48	1.57	1.43	1.62	1.38	1.67	1.34	1.72	1.29	1.78
50	1.50	1.59	1.46	1.63	1.42	1.67	1.38	1.72	1.34	1.77
55	1.53	1.60	1.49	1.64	1.45	1.68	1.41	1.72	1.38	1.77
60	1.55	1.62	1.51	1.65	1.48	1.69	1.44	1.73	1.41	1.77
65	1.57	1.63	1.54	1.66	1.50	1.70	1.47	1.73	1.44	1.77
70	1.58	1.64	1.55	1.67	1.52	1.70	1.49	1.74	1.46	1.77
75	1.60	1.65	1.57	1.68	1.54	1.71	1.51	1.74	1.49	1.77
80	1.61	1.66	1.59	1.69	1.56	1.72	1.53	1.74	1.51	1.77
85	1.62	1.67	1.60	1.70	1.57	1.72	1.55	1.75	1.52	1.77
90	1.63	1.68	1.61	1.70	1.59	1.73	1.57	1.75	1.54	1.78
95	1.64	1.69	1.62	1.71	1.60	1.73	1.58	1.75	1.56	1.78
100	1.65	1.69	1.63	1.72	1.61	1.74	1.59	1.76	1.57	1.78

α = 0.01

n	$k=1$ d_L	$k=1$ d_U	$k=2$ d_L	$k=2$ d_U	$k=3$ d_L	$k=3$ d_U	$k=4$ d_L	$k=4$ d_U	$k=5$ d_L	$k=5$ d_U
15	0.81	1.07	0.70	1.25	0.59	1.46	0.49	1.70	0.39	1.96
16	0.84	1.09	0.74	1.25	0.63	1.44	0.53	1.66	0.44	1.90
17	0.87	1.10	0.77	1.25	0.67	1.43	0.57	1.63	0.48	1.85
18	0.90	1.12	0.80	1.26	0.71	1.42	0.61	1.60	0.52	1.80
19	0.93	1.13	0.83	1.26	0.74	1.41	0.65	1.58	0.56	1.77
20	0.95	1.15	0.86	1.27	0.77	1.41	0.68	1.57	0.60	1.74
21	0.97	1.16	0.89	1.27	0.80	1.41	0.72	1.55	0.63	1.71
22	1.00	1.17	0.91	1.28	0.83	1.40	0.75	1.54	0.66	1.69
23	1.02	1.19	0.94	1.29	0.86	1.40	0.77	1.53	0.70	1.67
24	1.04	1.20	0.96	1.30	0.88	1.41	0.80	1.53	0.72	1.66
25	1.05	1.21	0.98	1.30	0.90	1.41	0.83	1.52	0.75	1.65
26	1.07	1.22	1.00	1.31	0.93	1.41	0.85	1.52	0.78	1.64
27	1.09	1.23	1.02	1.32	0.95	1.41	0.88	1.51	0.81	1.63
28	1.10	1.24	1.04	1.32	0.97	1.41	0.90	1.51	0.83	1.62
29	1.12	1.25	1.05	1.33	0.99	1.42	0.92	1.51	0.85	1.61
30	1.13	1.26	1.07	1.34	1.01	1.42	0.94	1.51	0.88	1.61
31	1.15	1.27	1.08	1.34	1.02	1.42	0.96	1.51	0.90	1.60
32	1.16	1.28	1.10	1.35	1.04	1.43	0.98	1.51	0.92	1.60
33	1.17	1.29	1.11	1.36	1.05	1.43	1.00	1.51	0.94	1.59
34	1.18	1.30	1.13	1.36	1.07	1.43	1.01	1.51	0.95	1.59
35	1.19	1.31	1.14	1.37	1.08	1.44	1.03	1.51	0.97	1.59
36	1.21	1.32	1.15	1.38	1.10	1.44	1.04	1.51	0.99	1.59
37	1.22	1.32	1.16	1.38	1.11	1.45	1.06	1.51	1.00	1.59
38	1.23	1.33	1.18	1.39	1.12	1.45	1.07	1.52	1.02	1.58
39	1.24	1.34	1.19	1.39	1.14	1.45	1.09	1.52	1.03	1.58
40	1.25	1.34	1.20	1.40	1.15	1.46	1.10	1.52	1.05	1.58
45	1.29	1.38	1.24	1.42	1.20	1.48	1.16	1.53	1.11	1.58
50	1.32	1.40	1.28	1.45	1.24	1.49	1.20	1.54	1.16	1.59
55	1.36	1.43	1.32	1.47	1.28	1.51	1.25	1.55	1.21	1.59
60	1.38	1.45	1.35	1.48	1.32	1.52	1.28	1.56	1.25	1.60
65	1.41	1.47	1.38	1.50	1.35	1.53	1.31	1.57	1.28	1.61
70	1.43	1.49	1.40	1.52	1.37	1.55	1.34	1.58	1.31	1.61
75	1.45	1.50	1.42	1.53	1.39	1.56	1.37	1.59	1.34	1.62
80	1.47	1.52	1.44	1.54	1.42	1.57	1.39	1.60	1.36	1.62
85	1.48	1.53	1.46	1.55	1.43	1.58	1.41	1.60	1.39	1.63
90	1.50	1.54	1.47	1.56	1.45	1.59	1.43	1.61	1.41	1.64
95	1.51	1.55	1.49	1.57	1.47	1.60	1.45	1.62	1.42	1.64
100	1.52	1.56	1.50	1.58	1.48	1.60	1.46	1.63	1.44	1.65

[†]n = number of observations; k = number of independent variables.

Table R

Shewhart Factors for Quality Control Using Samples of Size n, see Chapter 24

n	A_2	A_3	B_1	B_2	d_2	d_3	D_3	D_4
2	1.880	2.659	0	3.27	1.128	0.852	0	3 267
3	1.023	1.954	0	2.57	1.693	0.888	0	2.574
4	0.729	1.628	0	2.27	2.059	0.880	0	2 282
5	0.577	1.427	0	2.09	2.326	0.864	0	2.114
6	0.483	1.287	0.030	1.97	2.534	0.848	0	2.004
7	0.419	1.182	0.118	1.88	2.704	0.833	0.076	1.924
8	0.372	1.099	0.185	1.82	2.847	0.820	0.136	1.864
9	0.337	1.032	0.239	1.76	2.970	0.808	0.184	1.816
10	0.308	0.975	0.284	1.72	3 078	0.797	0 223	1.777
11	0.285	0.928	0.321	1.68	3.173	0.787	0.256	1.744
12	0.266	0.886	0.354	1.65	3.258	0.779	0.283	1.717
13	0.249	0.850	0.382	1.62	3.336	0.771	0.307	1.693
14	0.235	0.817	0.406	1.59	3.407	0.763	0.328	1.672
15	0.224	0.789	0.428	1.57	3.472	0.756	0.347	1.653
16	0.212	0.763	0.448	1.55	3.532	0.750	0.363	1.637
17	0.203	0.739	0.466	1.53	3.588	0.744	0.378	1.622
18	0.194	0.718	0.482	1.52	3.640	0.738	0.391	1.608
19	0.187	0.698	0.497	1.50	3.689	0.734	0.403	1.597
20	0.180	0.680	0.510	1.49	3.735	0.728	0.415	1.585
21	0.173	0.663	0 523	1.48	3.778	0.724	0.425	1.575
22	0.167	0.647	0.534	1.47	3.819	0.721	0.434	1.566
23	0.162	0.633	0.545	1.46	3.858	0.716	0.443	1 557
24	0.157	0.619	0.555	1.45	3.895	0.711	0.451	1.548
25	0.153	0.606	0.565	1.43	3.931	0.709	0.459	1.541

Table W1

Critical Values of T_L and T_U for Wilcoxon Rank-Sum Test: Independent Samples, see Chapter 17, Section 4.

Test statistic is the rank sum associated with the smaller sample (if equal sample sizes, either rank sum can be used). Reject the null hypothesis at the indicated α level if the test statistic falls below the lower bound, T_L, or above the upper bound, T_U. For groups larger than 10, use the Normal approximation given in the text.

a. $\alpha = 0.025$ **one-tailed;** $\alpha = 0.05$ **two-tailed**

n_1 / n_2	3		4		5		6		7		8		9		10	
	T_L	T_U	T_L	T_U	T_L	T_U	T_L	T_U	T_L	T_U	T_L	T_U	T_L	T_U	T_L	T_U
3	5	16	6	18	6	21	7	23	7	26	8	28	8	31	9	33
4	6	18	11	25	12	28	12	32	13	35	14	38	15	41	16	44
5	6	21	12	28	18	37	19	41	20	45	21	49	22	53	24	56
6	7	23	12	32	19	41	26	52	28	56	29	61	31	65	32	70
7	7	26	13	35	20	45	28	56	37	68	39	73	41	78	43	83
8	8	28	14	38	21	49	29	61	39	73	49	87	51	93	54	98
9	8	31	15	41	22	53	31	65	41	78	51	93	63	108	66	114
10	9	33	16	44	24	56	32	70	43	83	54	98	66	114	79	131

b. $\alpha = 0.05$ **one-tailed;** $\alpha = 0.10$ **two-tailed**

n_1 / n_2	3		4		5		6		7		8		9		10	
	T_L	T_U	T_L	T_U	T_L	T_U	T_L	T_U	T_L	T_U	T_L	T_U	T_L	T_U	T_L	T_U
3	6	15	7	17	7	20	8	22	9	24	9	27	10	29	11	31
4	7	17	12	24	13	27	14	30	15	33	16	36	17	39	18	42
5	7	20	13	27	19	36	20	40	22	43	24	46	25	50	26	54
6	8	22	14	30	20	40	28	50	30	54	32	58	33	63	35	67
7	9	24	15	33	22	43	30	54	39	66	41	71	43	76	46	80
8	9	27	16	36	24	46	32	58	41	71	52	84	54	90	57	95
9	10	29	17	39	25	50	33	63	43	76	54	90	66	105	69	111
10	11	31	18	42	26	54	35	67	46	80	57	95	69	111	83	127

Source: From Wilcoxon, F., & Wilcox, R. A. (1964). *Some rapid approximate statistical procedures.* Copyright © 1964 by BASF Corporation.

Table W2

Critical Values of T_0 in the Wilcoxon Paired Difference Signed-Rank Test, see Chapter 17 Section 2.
Reject the null hypothesis at the indicated α level if the test statistic is smaller than the corresponding critical value.

One-Tailed	Two-Tailed	n = 5	n = 6	n = 7	n = 8	n = 9	n = 10
$\alpha = 0.05$	$\alpha = 0.10$	1	2	4	6	8	11
$\alpha = 0.025$	$\alpha = 0.05$		1	2	4	6	8
$\alpha = 0.01$	$\alpha = 0.02$			0	2	3	5
$\alpha = 0.005$	$\alpha = 0.01$				0	2	3
		n = 11	**n = 12**	**n = 13**	**n = 14**	**n = 15**	**n = 16**
$\alpha = 0.05$	$\alpha = 0.10$	14	17	21	26	30	36
$\alpha = 0.025$	$\alpha = 0.05$	11	14	17	21	25	30
$\alpha = 0.01$	$\alpha = 0.02$	7	10	13	16	20	24
$\alpha = 0.005$	$\alpha = 0.01$	5	7	10	13	16	19
		n = 17	**n = 18**	**n = 19**	**n = 20**	**n = 21**	**n = 22**
$\alpha = 0.05$	$\alpha = 0.10$	41	47	54	60	68	75
$\alpha = 0.025$	$\alpha = 0.05$	35	40	46	52	59	66
$\alpha = 0.01$	$\alpha = 0.02$	28	33	38	43	49	56
$\alpha = 0.005$	$\alpha = 0.01$	23	28	32	37	43	49
		n = 23	**n = 24**	**n = 25**	**n = 26**	**n = 27**	**n = 28**
$\alpha = 0.05$	$\alpha = 0.10$	83	92	101	110	120	130
$\alpha = 0.025$	$\alpha = 0.05$	73	81	90	98	107	117
$\alpha = 0.01$	$\alpha = 0.02$	62	69	77	85	93	102
$\alpha = 0.005$	$\alpha = 0.01$	55	61	68	76	84	92
		n = 29	**n = 30**	**n = 31**	**n = 32**	**n = 33**	**n = 34**
$\alpha = 0.05$	$\alpha = 0.10$	141	152	163	175	188	201
$\alpha = 0.025$	$\alpha = 0.05$	127	137	148	159	171	183
$\alpha = 0.01$	$\alpha = 0.02$	111	120	130	141	151	162
$\alpha = 0.005$	$\alpha = 0.01$	100	109	118	128	138	149
		n = 35	**n = 36**	**n = 37**	**n = 38**	**n = 39**	
$\alpha = 0.05$	$\alpha = 0.10$	214	228	242	256	271	
$\alpha = 0.025$	$\alpha = 0.05$	195	208	222	235	250	
$\alpha = 0.01$	$\alpha = 0.02$	174	186	198	211	224	
$\alpha = 0.005$	$\alpha = 0.01$	160	171	183	195	208	
		n = 40	**n = 41**	**n = 42**	**n = 43**	**n = 44**	**n = 45**
$\alpha = 0.05$	$\alpha = 0.10$	287	303	319	336	353	371
$\alpha = 0.025$	$\alpha = 0.05$	264	279	295	311	327	344
$\alpha = 0.01$	$\alpha = 0.02$	238	252	267	281	297	313
$\alpha = 0.005$	$\alpha = 0.01$	221	234	248	262	277	292
		n = 46	**n = 47**	**n = 48**	**n = 49**	**n = 50**	
$\alpha = 0.05$	$\alpha = 0.10$	389	408	427	446	466	
$\alpha = 0.025$	$\alpha = 0.05$	361	379	379	415	434	
$\alpha = 0.01$	$\alpha = 0.02$	329	345	362	380	398	
$\alpha = 0.005$	$\alpha = 0.01$	307	323	339	356	373	

Source: From Wilcoxon, F., & Wilcox, R. A. (1964). *Some rapid approximate statistical procedures.* Copyright © 1964 by BASF Corporation.

Selected Formulae

$Range = Max - Min$

$IQR = Q3 - Q1$

Outlier Rule-of-Thumb: $y < Q1 - 1.5 \times IQR$ or $y > Q3 + 1.5 \times IQR$

$$\bar{y} = \frac{\sum y}{n}$$

$$s = \sqrt{\frac{\sum (y - \bar{y})^2}{n - 1}}$$

$z = \dfrac{y - \mu}{\sigma}$ (model based) $z = \dfrac{y - \bar{y}}{s}$ (data based)

$$r = \frac{\sum z_x z_y}{n - 1}$$

$\hat{y} = b_0 + b_1 x$ where $b_1 = r\dfrac{s_y}{s_x}$ and $b_0 = \bar{y} - b_1 \bar{x}$

$P(\mathbf{A}) = 1 - P(\mathbf{A}^C)$

$P(\mathbf{A} \text{ or } \mathbf{B}) = P(\mathbf{A}) + P(\mathbf{B}) - P(\mathbf{A} \text{ and } \mathbf{B})$

$P(\mathbf{A} \text{ and } \mathbf{B}) = P(\mathbf{A}) \times P(\mathbf{B}|\mathbf{A})$

$$P(\mathbf{B}|\mathbf{A}) = \frac{P(\mathbf{A} \text{ and } \mathbf{B})}{P(\mathbf{A})}$$

If $\mathbf{A}$ and $\mathbf{B}$ are independent, $P(\mathbf{B}|\mathbf{A}) - P(\mathbf{B})$

$E(X) = \mu = \sum x P(x)$ $Var(X) = \sigma^2 = \sum (x - \mu)^2 P(x)$

$E(X \pm c) = E(X) \pm c$ $Var(X \pm c) = Var(X)$

$E(aX) = aE(X)$ $Var(aX) = a^2 Var(X)$

$E(X \pm Y) = E(X) \pm E(Y)$ $Var(X \pm Y) = Var(X) + Var(Y)$

          if X and Y are independent

Geometric: $P(X = x) = q^{x-1} p$ $\mu = \dfrac{1}{p}$ $\sigma = \sqrt{\dfrac{q}{p^2}}$

Binomial: $P(X = x) = {}_nC_x p^x q^{n-x}$ $\mu = np$ $\sigma = \sqrt{npq}$

Poisson: $P(X = x) = \dfrac{e^{-\lambda} \lambda^x}{x!}$ $\mu = \lambda$ $\sigma = \sqrt{\lambda}$

Sampling distribution of a proportion, $\hat{p} = \dfrac{x}{n}$, is Normally distributed with $\mu(\hat{p}) = p$

and $SD(\hat{p}) = \sqrt{\dfrac{pq}{n}}$

Sampling distribution of a mean, $\bar{y}$:

(CLT) As n grows, the sampling distribution approaches the Normal model with

$$\mu(\bar{y}) = \mu_y \quad SD(\bar{y}) = \frac{\sigma}{\sqrt{n}}$$

Inference

Confidence interval for parameter $= \mathbf{statistic \pm critical\ value \times SE(statistic)}$

$$\text{Test statistic} = \frac{statistic - parameter}{SD(statistic)}$$

Parameter	Statistic	SD(statistic)	SE(statistic)
p	$\hat{p}$	$\sqrt{\dfrac{pq}{n}}$	$\sqrt{\dfrac{\hat{p}\hat{q}}{n}}$
μ	$\bar{y}$	$\dfrac{\sigma}{\sqrt{n}}$	$\dfrac{s}{\sqrt{n}}$
$\mu_1 - \mu_2$	$\bar{y}_1 - \bar{y}_2$	$\sqrt{\dfrac{\sigma_1^2}{n_1} + \dfrac{\sigma_2^2}{n_2}}$	$\sqrt{\dfrac{s_1^2}{n_1} + \dfrac{s_2^2}{n_2}}$
μ_d	d	$\dfrac{\sigma_d}{\sqrt{n}}$	$\dfrac{s_d}{\sqrt{n}}$
σ_ε	$s_e = \sqrt{\dfrac{\sum(y - \hat{y})^2}{n - 2}}$	(divide by $n - k - 1$ in multiple regression)	
β_1	b_1	(in simple regression)	$\dfrac{s_e}{s_x\sqrt{n - 1}}$
μ_v	$\hat{y}_v$	(in simple regression)	$\sqrt{SE^2(b_1) \cdot (x_v - \bar{x})^2 + \dfrac{s_e^2}{n}}$
y_v	$\hat{y}_v$	(in simple regression)	$\sqrt{SE^2(b_1) \cdot (x_v - \bar{x})^2 + \dfrac{s_e^2}{n} + s_e^2}$

Pooling: For testing difference between proportions: $\hat{P}_{pooled} = \dfrac{y_1 + y_2}{n_1 + n_2}$

For testing difference between means: $s_p = \sqrt{\dfrac{(n_1 - 1)s_1^2 + (n_2 - 1)s_2^2}{n_1 + n_2 - 2}}$

Substitute these pooled estimates in the respective SE formulas for both groups when assumptions and conditions are met.

Chi-square: $\chi^2 = \sum \dfrac{(Obs - Exp)^2}{Exp}$

Assumptions for Inference	And the Conditions That Support or Override Them

Proportions (*z*)

- **One sample**
  1. Individuals are independent.
  2. Sample is sufficiently large.

      1. A random sample with size $n < 10\%$ of the population.
      2. Expected successes and failures: $np \geq 10$ and $nq \geq 10$.

Means (*t*)

- **One Sample** ($df = n - 1$)
  1. Individuals are independent.
  2. Population has a Normal model.

      1. A random sample with size $n < 10\%$ of the population.
      2. Histogram is unimodal and symmetric.*

- **Matched pairs** ($df = n - 1$)
  1. Data are matched.
  2. Individuals are independent.
  3. Population of differences is Normal.

      1. (Think about the design.)
      2. Random samples with size $n < 10\%$ of the population.
      3. Histogram of differences is umimodal and symmetric.*

- **Two independent samples** (df from technology)
  1. Groups are independent.
  2. Data in each group are independent.
  3. Both populations are Normal.

      1. (Think about the design.)
      2. Random sample with size $n < 10\%$ of the population.
      3. Both histograms are unimodal and symmetric.*

Distributions/Association (x^2)

- **Goodness of fit** (df = # of cells $- 1$; one variable, one sample compared with population model)

  1. Data are counts.
  2. Data in sample are independent.
  3. Sample is sufficiently large.

      1. (Are they?)
      2. Random samples with size $n < 10\%$ of the population.
      3. All expected counts ≥ 5.

- **Homogeneity (Independence)** [df = $(r - 1)(c - 1)$; sample from one population classified on two variables]

  1. Data are counts.
  2. Data are independent.
  3. Sample is sufficiently large.

      1. (Are they?)
      2. Random samples with size $n < 10\%$ of the population.
      3. All expected counts ≥ 5.

Regression with *k* predictors (*t*, df = $n - k - 1$)

- **Association** of each quantitative predictor with the response variable

  1. Form of relationship is linear.

  2. Errors are independent.
  3. Variability of errors is constant.

  4. Errors follow a Normal model.

      1. Scatterplots of *y* against each *x* are straight enough. Scatterplot of residuals against predicted values shows no special structure.
      2. No apparent pattern in plot of residuals against predicted values.
      3. Plot of residuals against predicted values has constant spread, doesn't "thicken."
      4. Histogram of residuals is approximately unimodal and symmetric, or Normal probability plot is reasonably straight.*

Analysis of variance (*F*, df depends on number of factors and number of levels in each)

- **Equality** of the mean response across levels of categorical predictors

  1. Additive Model (if there are 2 factors with no interaction term).
  2. Independent errors.
  3. Equal variance across treatment levels.

  4. Errors follow a Normal model.

      1. Interaction plot shows parallel lines (otherwise include an interaction term if possible).
      2. Randomized experiment or other suitable randomization.
      3. Plot of residuals against predicted values has constant spread. Boxplots (partial boxplots for 2 factors) show similar spreads.
      4. Histogram of residuals is unimodal and approximately symmetric, or Normal probability plot is reasonably straight.

(*Less critical as *n* increases)

Quick Guide to Inference

Inference about?	One group or two?	Procedure	Model	Parameter	Estimate	SE	Chapter
Proportions	One sample	1-proportion z-interval	z	p	$\hat{p}$	$\sqrt{\dfrac{\hat{p}\hat{q}}{n}}$	11
		1-proportion z-test				$\sqrt{\dfrac{p_0 q_0}{n}}$	12
Means	One sample	t-interval t-test	t $df = n - 1$	μ	$\bar{y}$	$\dfrac{s}{\sqrt{n}}$	13
	Two independent groups	2-sample t-test 2-sample t-interval	t df from technology	$\mu_1 - \mu_2$	$\bar{y}_1 - \bar{y}_2$	$\sqrt{\dfrac{s_1^2}{n_1} + \dfrac{s_2^2}{n_2}}$	14
	Matched pairs	paired t-test paired t-interval	t $df = n - 1$	μ_d	$\bar{d}$	$\dfrac{s_d}{\sqrt{n}}$	
Association (one quantitative and two or more categorical variables)	Two or more samples	ANOVA	F $df = k - 1$ and $N - k$			MST/MSE	15
Distributions (one or two categorical variables)	One sample	goodness-of-fit	χ^2 $df = \#$ of cells $- 1$			$\sum \dfrac{(Obs - Exp)^2}{Exp}$	16
	One or two samples	homogeneity (independence) χ^2 test	χ^2 $df = (r - 1)(c - 1)$				
Association (one quantitative variable modelled by one quantitative variable)	One sample	linear regression t-test or confidence interval for β	t $df = n - 2$	β_1	b_1	$\dfrac{s_e}{s_x\sqrt{n - 1}}$ (compute with technology)	18, 19
		confidence interval for μ_ν		μ_ν	$\hat{y}_\nu$	$\sqrt{SE^2(b_1) \cdot (x_\nu - \bar{x})^2 + \dfrac{s_e^2}{n}}$	
		prediction interval for y_ν		y_ν	$\hat{y}_\nu$	$\sqrt{SE^2(b_1) \cdot (x_\nu - \bar{x})^2 + \dfrac{s_e^2}{n} + s_e^2}$	
Association (one quantitative variable modelled by k quantitative variables)	One sample	multiple regression t-test or confidence interval for each β_j	t $df = n - (k + 1)$	β_j	b_j	(from technology)	20, 21
		F-test for regression model	F $df = k$ and $n - (k + 1)$			MSR/MSE	

Technology Help: Excel with XLStat

To ensure that XLStat recognizes different symbols for missing data, click **Options** on the right of the XLStat ribbon. Then click the **Missing data** tab and check the buttons next to **Consider empty cells as missing data** and **Consider also the following values as missing data**. Under the latter, select all options. Click **Save**.

CHAPTER 3

To use a specific sampling scheme to sample from data:

- Choose the **XLStat tab** at the top of the Excel ribbon.
- On the far left of the ribbon, click **Preparing data**.
- Choose the **Data sampling** option.

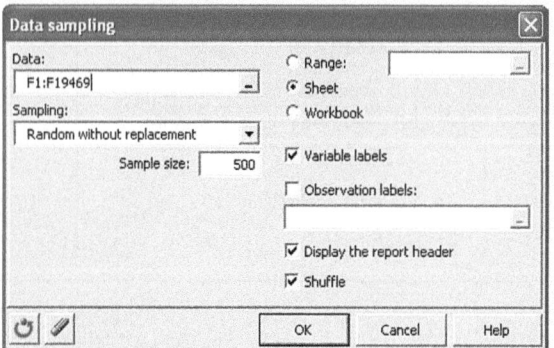

- Enter the cell range of your data.
- Choose the type of sampling from the drop-down list. The sampling types available in XLStat are described in the XLStat help manual.

CHAPTER 4

To create a contingency table from unsummarized data:

- On the XLStat tab, choose **Preparing data**.
- From the menu, choose **Create a contingency table**.
- In the dialogue box, enter your data range on the General tab. Your data should be in two columns, one of which is the row variable and the other is the column variable.

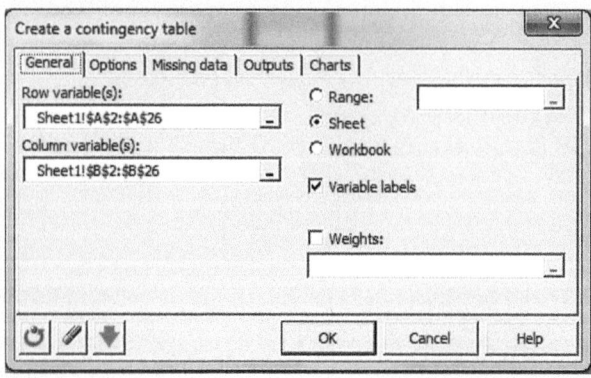

- On the Outputs tab, check the box next to **Contingency table** and optionally choose **Percentages/Row** or **Column** to see the conditional distributions.

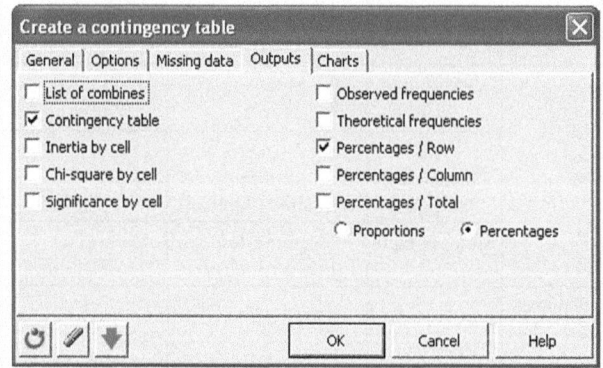

To make a bar chart or pie chart:

- Choose **Visualizing data**, and then select **Univariate plots**.
- For quantitative data, enter the cell range of your data in the **Quantitative data** field.
- Select the type of chart on the **Charts (1)** tab.

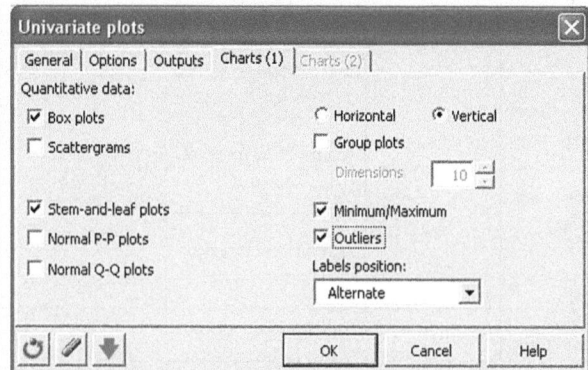

- For qualitative data, enter the cell range of your data in the **Qualitative data** field.
- Select the type of chart on the **Charts (2)** tab

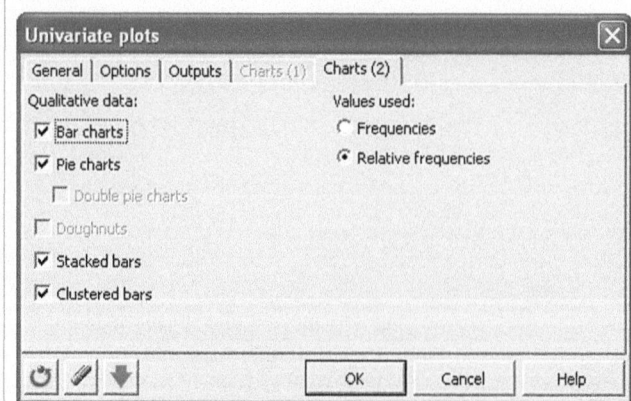

- To make a segmented or side-by-side bar chart, enter the column variable in the **Qualitative variable** field and the row variable in the **Subsamples** field; choose **Stacked bars** and **Cluster bars** on the **Charts (2)** tab.

CHAPTER 5

To make a histogram:

- Choose **Visualizing data** from the XLStat ribbon tab, and then choose **Histograms.**
- Enter the cell range of your data in the **Data** field.

Note: You can either choose the number of bins or choose specific bin ranges on the **Options** tab. If you specify your own bins, XLStat requires that the bin data contain the lower bound of the first bin, and then each successive upper bound of the bins, as in the image below.

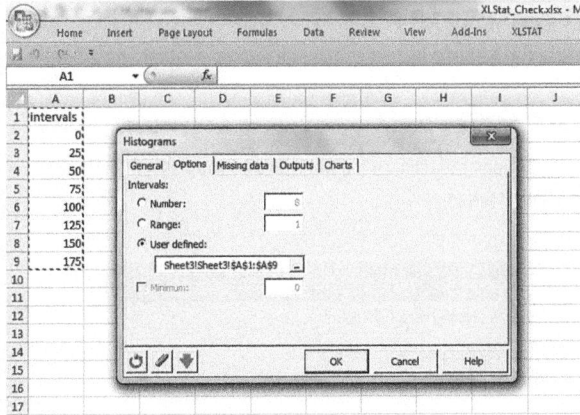

The Histogram command also reports the summary statistics; specify which statistics are reported on the **Outputs** tab in the dialogue box.

Boxplots and stem-and-leaf plots can be made by choosing **Visualizing data** and then **Univariate plots.**

CHAPTER 7

To analyze regression statistics and plots:

- Select **Modeling data,** and then choose **Linear regression.**
- Enter the cell range of the dependent variable in the **Quantitative** field.
- If the explanatory variable is quantitative, check the quantitative box. Otherwise, be sure to check the qualitative box.
- Enter the cell range of the explanatory variable in the appropriate field.

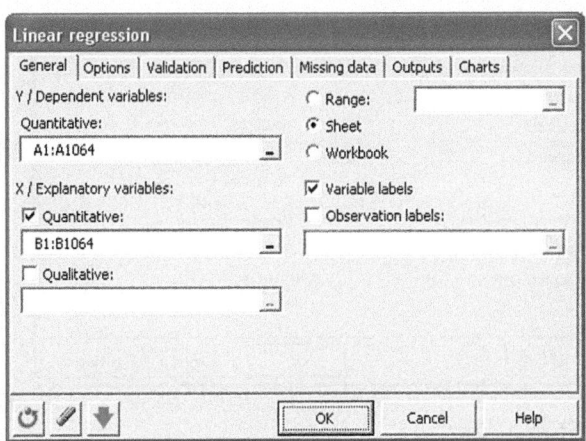

- To plot the scatterplot and residual plot, in the Linear Regression dialogue box, select the **Charts** tab.

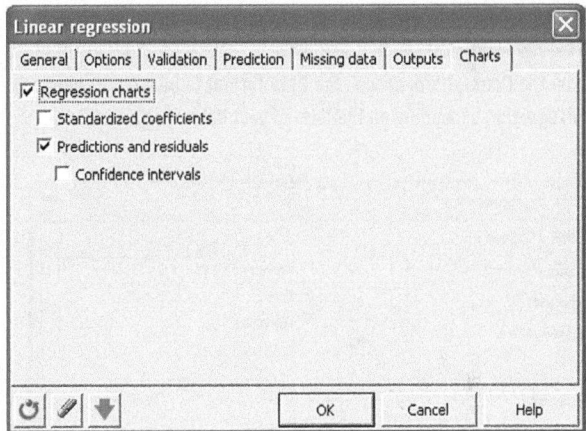

- Select **Regression charts** and **Predictions and residuals.** These plots appear at the bottom of the worksheet report that's produced. The regression statistics and linear model are near the top of the report.

CHAPTER 9

XLStat will not calculate Normal distribution probabilities, but it will make Normal probability plots (XLStat calls these Q-Q plots):

- Select **Visualizing data,** and then **Univariate plots.**
- On the General tab, click the Quantitative data box and then select the data on your worksheet.
- Note that under the **Charts (1)** tab, **Normal Q-Q plots** is checked.

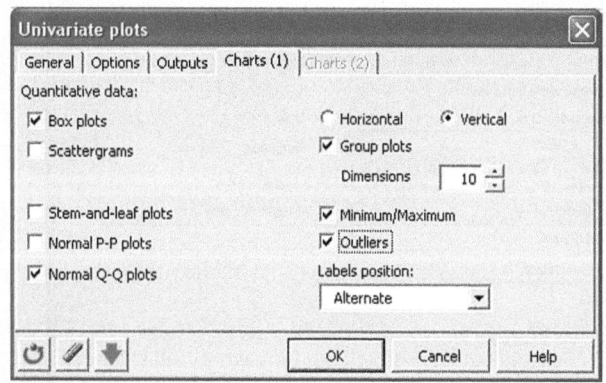

- Click **OK**.
- If prompted, click **Continue**.

CHAPTER 11

To find a one-proportion z-interval:

- Select **Parametric Tests**, and then choose **Tests for one proportion**.
- Under the **General** tab, choose the **Data format** to be either **Frequency** or **Proportion** depending on the form of your data.

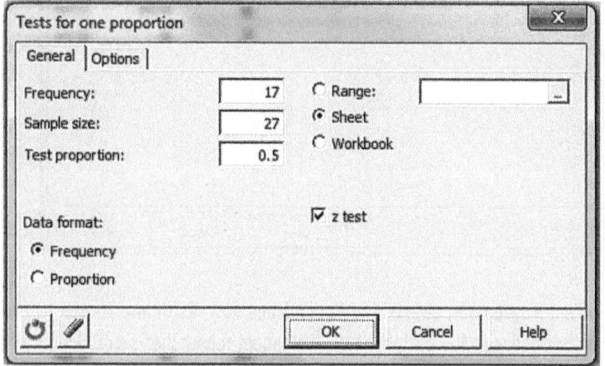

- Enter the **frequency** of your variable (or **proportion**) and the **sample** size.
- Enter the **test proportion**.

Under **Data format**, choose the appropriate button.

- Under the **Options** tab, choose the **Alternative hypothesis** of **Proportion — Test proportion ≠ D**. Enter **0** for the **Hypothesized difference (D)**.
- Enter 5 under **Significance Level**. The output will show the 95% confidence interval.
- Choose the radial button for **Sample** under **Variance**.
- Choose the **Wald confidence interval**.

CHAPTER 12

To find a one-proportion z-interval:

- Select **Parametric Tests**, and then choose **Tests for one proportion**.
- Under the **General** tab, choose the **Data format** to be either **Frequency** or **Proportion** depending on the form of your data.
- Enter the **frequency** of your variable (or **proportion**) and the **sample size**.
- Enter the **test proportion**.

Under **Data format** choose the appropriate button.

- Under the **Options** tab choose the **Alternative hypothesis** of **Proportion — Test proportion ≠ D**. Enter 0 for the **Hypothesized difference (D)**.
- Enter 5 under **Significance Level**. The output will show the 95% confidence interval.

CHAPTER 13

To find a one-sample z-interval or a one-sample t-interval:

- Choose **Parametric Tests**, and then **One-sample t-test and z-test**.
- Under the **General** tab, enter your data cell range and choose either z-**test** or **Student's t test**.
- On the **Options** tab, choose the **Alternative hypothesis** of **Mean 1 ≠ Theoretical mean**.

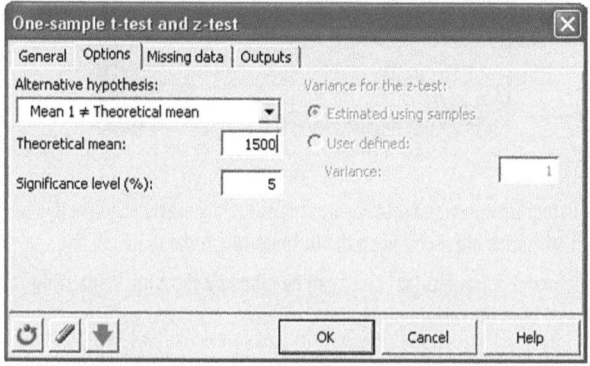

- For calculating just a confidence interval, you can leave the **Theoretical mean** field blank. If you're also conducting a hypothesis test, enter the theoretical mean here.
- Under **Significance Level**, enter the desired level of significance. The output will yield the $(1 - \alpha)$ 100% confidence level.

To conduct a one-mean z-test or a one-mean t-test:

- Choose **Parametric Tests**, and then **One-sample t-test and z-test**.
- Complete the dialogue box as you did for a confidence interval.
- Fill in the field for **Theoretical mean** with the population mean from your null hypothesis.

CHAPTER 14

To conduct a *t*-test for the difference between two means:

- Choose **Parametric tests,** and then **Two-sample *t*-test and *z*-test.**

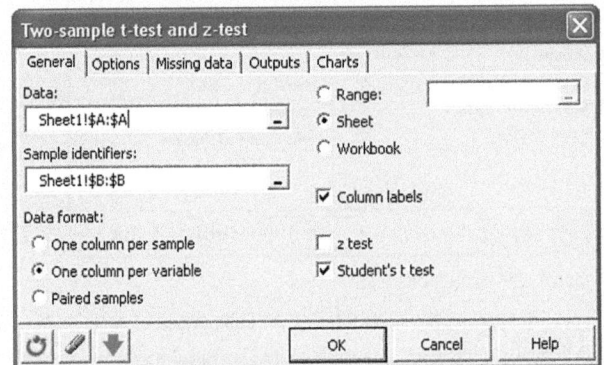

- If the two samples are in two separate columns in your workbook, choose the option **One column per sample.**

- If your data are *stacked* (one column lists the data, and the other the group identifier), choose the option **One column per variable.**

- If the data are paired, choose the option **Paired samples.**

- Enter the range of cell data.

- On the **Options** tab, for a test that's not pooled, uncheck the box next to **Assume equality.**

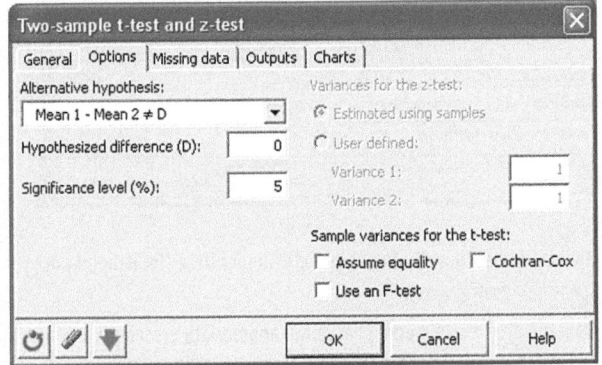

The output yields the results of a hypothesis test and a confidence interval for the difference between means.

CHAPTER 15

To perform a one-way ANOVA:

- Select **Modeling data,** and then select **ANOVA.** Note that XLStat requires stacked data.

- Enter the quantitative response variable cell range in the **Y/Dependent variables** field.

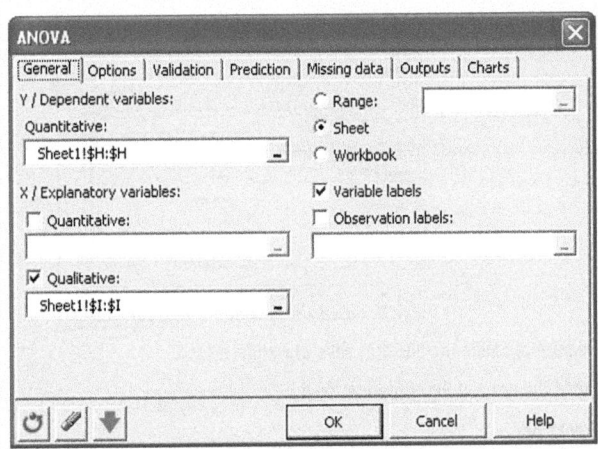

- Enter the group variable in the **Qualitative** field under **X/Explanatory variables.**

To do a multiple comparison procedure:

- Select an appropriate procedure on the **Outputs** tab.

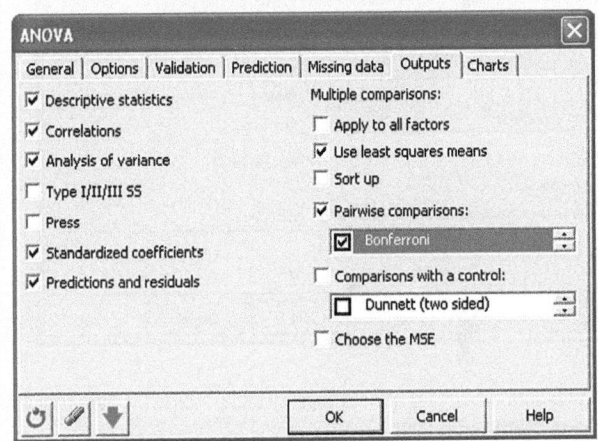

- Select the box for **Pairwise comparisons** and scroll to see several options.

CHAPTER 16

To perform a chi-square goodness-of-fit test:

- Choose **Parametric Tests,** and then select **Multinomial goodness of fit test.**

- In one column you should have the observed frequencies of the categories of the variable. Enter this under **Frequencies.**

- In another column you should have either the expected frequencies or the proportions. Enter this under **Expected frequencies** (or expected proportions) and choose the appropriate **data format.**

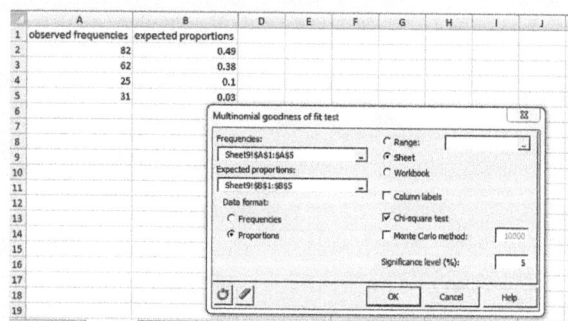

- Be sure to check the box that says **Chi-square test.**
- Enter the desired **Significance level.**
- Select **OK.**
- Select **Continue** (if prompted).

To perform a chi-square test for homogeneity:

- Choose **Correlation/Association tests,** and then select **Tests on contingency tables.**

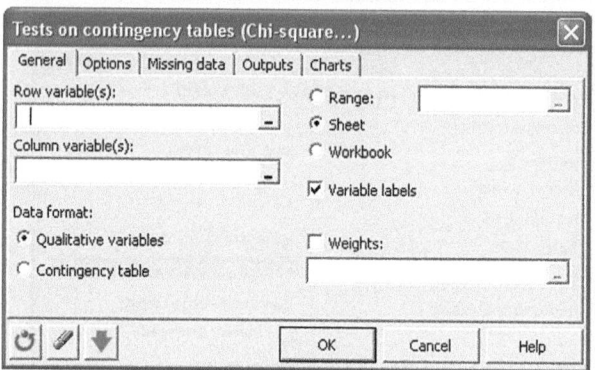

- If your data are already in a contingency table, choose the **Data format** option **Contingency table.**
- If your data are not in a contingency table, choose **Qualitative variables.**
- Enter the cell range of your data.
- On the **Options** tab, check **Chi-square test.**
- On the **Outputs** tab, choose **Proportions/Row** or **Proportions/Column** if you wish to see the conditional distributions.

CHAPTER 17

To conduct the Wilcoxon rank-sum/Mann-Whitney test or the Wilcoxon signed-rank test for two samples:

- Choose **Nonparametric tests,** and then select **Comparison of two samples.**
- Choose the **Mann-Whitney test** option on the **General** tab for the Wilcoxon rank-sum test.

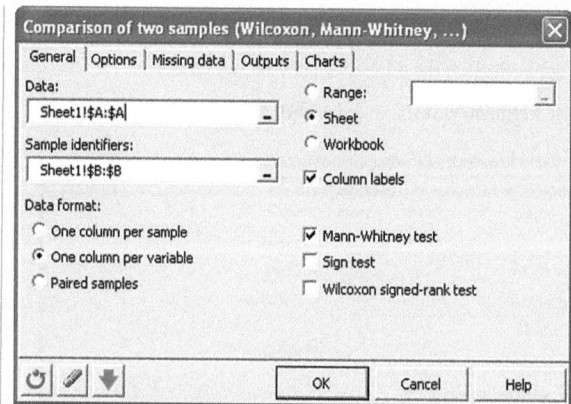

To conduct a Kruskal-Wallis test:

- Choose **Nonparametric tests,** then select **Comparison of samples** for the Kruskal-Wallis test.
- If the data are unstacked and the samples are of unequal sizes, choose the option **Remove the observations** from the **Missing data** tab.

To find Kendall and Spearman coefficients:

- Choose **Similarity/Dissimilarity matrices** from the **Describing data** tab.

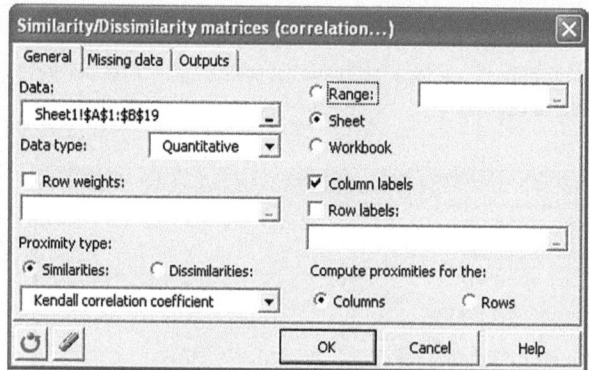

- Make sure that **Quantitative** is selected under Data (for Kendall and Spearman coefficients).
- From the drop-down menu, choose the appropriate procedure.

CHAPTERS 18 AND 19

To analyze regression statistics and plots:

- Choose the **Modeling data** menu, then select **Linear regression.**
- On the **Charts** tab, select **Regression charts** and **Predictions and residuals** to plot the scatterplot and residual plot. These plots appear at the bottom of the worksheet report. The regression statistics and linear model appear near the top of the report.

To form prediction intervals:

- Type the *x*-values into a cell in the workbook.

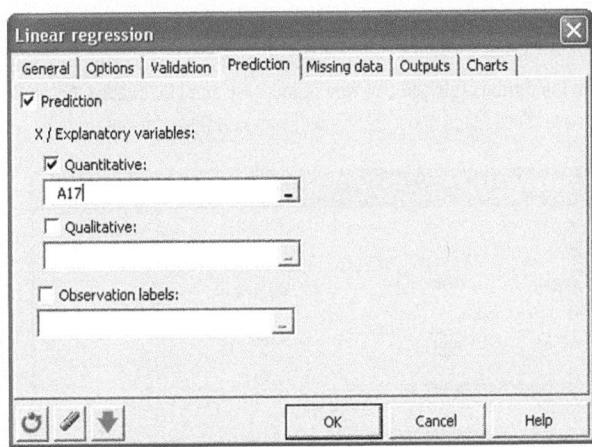

- On the **Prediction** tab, enter that cell in the **Quantitative** field. The prediction interval will be found at the end of the generated report.

To make a scatterplot by groups:

- Choose **Visualizing data**, then select **Scatter plots.**

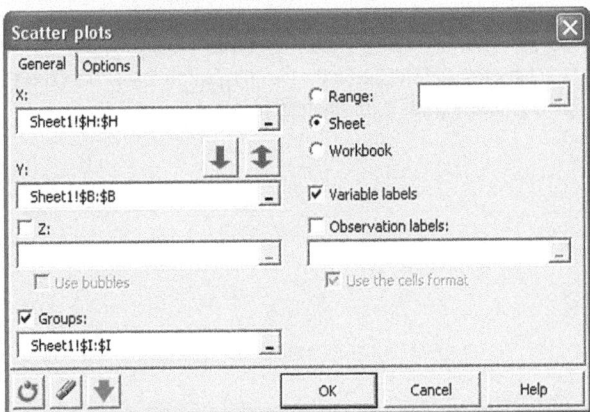

- Enter the explanatory, response, and group variable cell ranges.
- In the resulting plot, click anywhere on the plot to access the **Chart Tools Layout** tab.
- Select the **Trendline** button to add a trendline for each group.
- Click on each trendline to change its colour in the **Format trendline** menu.
- The Durbin-Watson statistic is calculated in the results for **Linear regression** from the **Modeling data** button. It's reported as **DW** in the Goodness-of-fit statistics section of the report.

To save residuals using XLStat:

- Choose the **Modeling data** menu, and then select **Linear regression.**
- On the **Charts** tab select **residuals.**

To create transformed variables using XLStat:

- Choose the **Preparing data** menu, and then select **Variables transformation.**
- Select variable name and location.
- Select **other** under transformation, and select desired transformation from the **transformations tab**.
- Transformed variables can also be created using Excel's built-in functions.

CHAPTER 20

Building a multiple regression model in XLStat is the same as building a simple linear one:

- Choose **Modeling data,** and then select **Linear regression.**

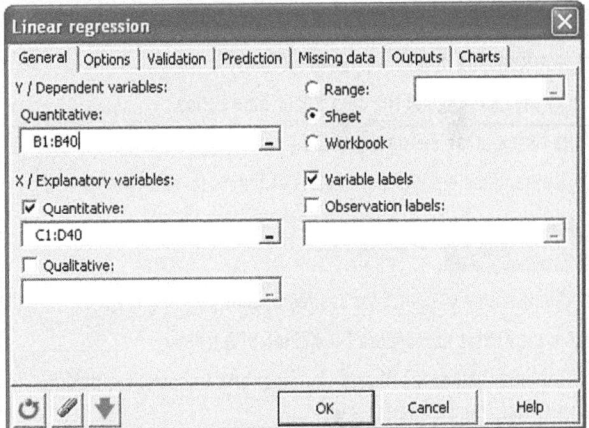

- In the **X/Explanatory variable** field, enter the cell range of all columns of explanatory variable data.

Note: The Pearson version of XLStat does not do logistic regression.

CHAPTER 21

XLStat can handle both qualitative (indicator) and quantitative (explanatory) variables. To build a "best" model:

- Choose **Modeling data.**
- Select all desired explanatory variables in the dialogue box for **Linear regression.**
- On the **Options** tab, XLStat gives you options for building a **Best model** using various criteria that you can select, or building a model based on significance in a **stepwise** or **forward** or **backward** direction.

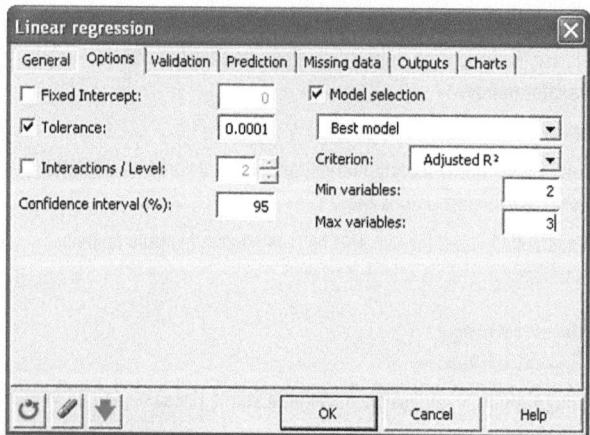

CHAPTER 22

To construct an autoregressive moving average (ARMA(p, q)) model:

- Select **Modeling data**, then select **ARMA**.
- Enter the cell range of the data under **Time series**.
- Note that you can centre the data by selecting the appropriate box.
- XLStat requires input of parameters of the model such that $p + q > 0$.

CHAPTER 24

To implement control charts for desired bounds:

- From the XLStat tab, choose the **XLStat-SPC** toolbar.
- Select either **Subgroup charts** (for x-bar and R charts) or **Attribute charts** (for p and c charts).
- Select the desired chart from the **Mode** tab in the dialogue box.
- Under the General tab, type the data range into the **Data field**.

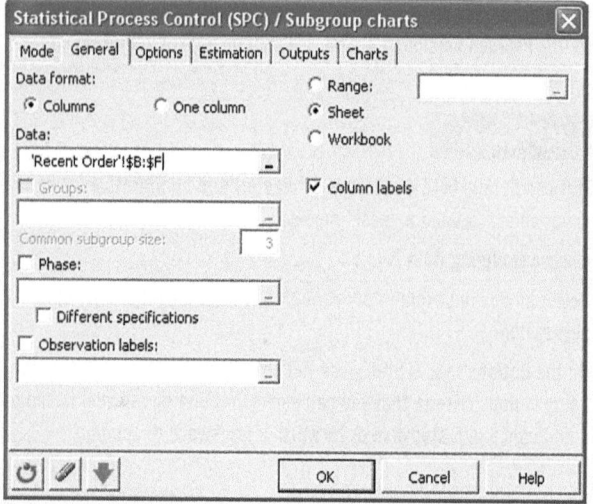

- If your data have sampled values in rows for each sample, choose the **Data Format Columns.**
- In the **Options** tab, you can type in your UCL and LCL directly, but if you leave these fields blank, XLStat will compute these for you.

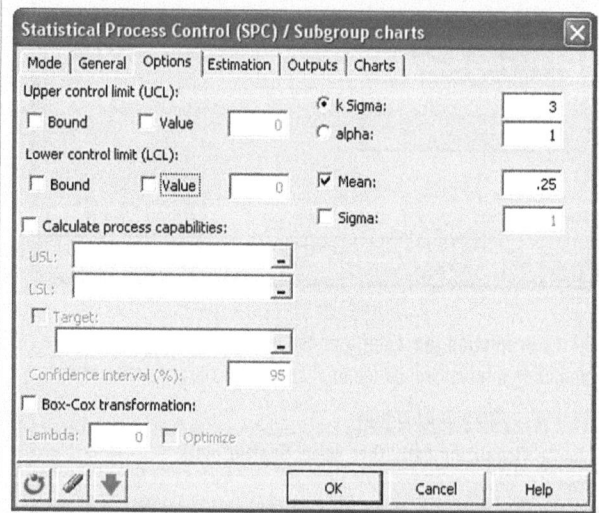

- If you have a specific value for the mean, type it in. Under the **Estimation** tab, choose **R bar** as the **method for sigma**.

Ethical Guidelines for Statistical Practice

Prepared by the Committee on Professional Ethics of the ASA: American Statistical Association

This appendix contains an extract of those ASA Ethical Guidelines that are used in this book, focusing on Items A, C, and H.

The **Ethical Guidelines** address eight general topic areas and specify important ethical considerations under each topic.

A. *Professionalism* points out the need for competence, judgment, diligence, self-respect, and worthiness of the respect of other people.

B. *Responsibilities to Funders, Clients, and Employers* discusses the practitioner's responsibility for assuring that statistical work is suitable to the needs and resources of those who are paying for it, that funders understand the capabilities and limitations of statistics in addressing their problem, and that the funder's confidential information is protected.

C. *Responsibilities in Publications and Testimony* addresses the need to report sufficient information to give readers, including other practitioners, a clear understanding of the intent of the work, how and by whom it was performed, and any limitations on its validity.

D. *Responsibilities to Research Subjects* describes requirements for protecting the interests of human and animal subjects of research—not only during data collection but also in the analysis, interpretation, and publication of the resulting findings.

E. *Responsibilities to Research Team Colleagues* addresses the mutual responsibilities of professionals participating in multidisciplinary research teams.

F. *Responsibilities to Other Statisticians or Statistical Practitioners* notes the interdependence of professionals doing similar work, whether in the same or different organizations. Basically, they must contribute to the strength of their professions overall by sharing nonproprietary data and methods, participating in peer review, and respecting differing professional opinions.

G. *Responsibilities Regarding Allegations of Misconduct* addresses the sometimes painful process of investigating potential ethical violations and treating those involved with both justice and respect.

H. *Responsibilities of Employers, Including Organizations, Individuals, Attorneys, or Other Clients Employing Statistical Practitioners* encourages employers and clients to recognize the highly interdependent nature of statistical ethics and statistical validity. Employers and clients must not pressure practitioners to produce a particular "result," regardless of its statistical validity. They must avoid the potential social harm that can result from the dissemination of false or misleading statistical work.

ETHICAL GUIDELINES USED IN THIS TEXT

Out of these eight guidelines, we will be focusing on just three: A, C, and H.

A. Professionalism

1. Strive for relevance in statistical analyses. Typically, each study should be based on a competent understanding of the subject-matter issues, statistical protocols that are clearly defined for the stage (exploratory, intermediate, or final) of analysis before looking at those data that will be decisive for that stage, and technical criteria to justify both the practical relevance of the study and the amount of data to be used.

2. Guard against the possibility that a predisposition by investigators or data providers might predetermine the analytic result. Employ data selection or sampling methods and analytic approaches that are designed to ensure valid analyses in either frequentist or Bayesian approaches.

3. Remain current in dynamically evolving statistical methodology; yesterday's preferred methods may be barely acceptable today and totally obsolete tomorrow.

4. Ensure that adequate statistical and subject-matter expertise is both applied to any planned study. If this criterion is not met initially, it is important to add the missing expertise before completing the study design.

5. Use only statistical methodologies suitable to the data and to obtaining valid results. For example, address the multiple potentially confounding factors in observational studies and use due caution in drawing causal inferences.

6. Do not join a research project unless you can expect to achieve valid results and you are confident that your name will not be associated with the project or resulting publications without your explicit consent.

7. The fact that a procedure is automated does not ensure its correctness or appropriateness; it is also necessary to understand the theory, data, and methods used in each statistical study. This goal is served best when a competent statistical practitioner is included early in the research design, preferably in the planning stage.

8. Recognize that any frequentist statistical test has a random chance of indicating significance when it is not really present. Running multiple tests on the same data set at the same stage of an analysis increases the chance of obtaining at least one invalid result. Selecting the one "significant" result from a multiplicity of parallel tests poses a grave risk of an incorrect conclusion. Failure to disclose the full extent of tests and their results in such a case would be highly misleading.

9. Respect and acknowledge the contributions and intellectual property of others.

10. Disclose conflicts of interest, financial and otherwise, and resolve them. This may sometimes require divestiture of the conflicting personal interest or withdrawal from the professional activity. Examples where conflict of interest may be problematic include grant reviews, other peer reviews, and tensions between scholarship and personal or family financial interests.

11. Provide only such expert testimony as you would be willing to have peer reviewed.

C. Responsibilities in Publications and Testimony

1. Maintain personal responsibility for all work bearing your name; avoid undertaking work or coauthoring publications for which you would not want to acknowledge responsibility. Conversely, accept (or insist upon) appropriate authorship or acknowledgment for professional statistical contributions to research and the resulting publications or testimony.

2. Report statistical and substantive assumptions made in the study.

3. In publications or testimony, identify who is responsible for the statistical work if it would not otherwise be apparent.

4. Make clear the basis for authorship order, if determined on grounds other than intellectual contribution. Preferably, authorship order in statistical publications should be by degree of intellectual contribution to the study and material to be published, to the extent that such ordering can feasibly be determined. When some other rule of authorship order is used in a statistical publication, the rule should be disclosed in a footnote or endnote. (Where authorship order by contribution is assumed by those making decisions about hiring, promotion, or tenure, for example, failure to disclose an alternative rule may improperly damage or advance careers.)

5. Account for all data considered in a study and explain the sample(s) actually used.

6. Report the sources and assessed adequacy of the data.

7. Report the data cleaning and screening procedures used, including any imputation.

8. Clearly and fully report the steps taken to guard validity. Address the suitability of the analytic methods and their inherent assumptions relative to the circumstances of the specific study. Identify the computer routines used to implement the analytic methods.

9. Where appropriate, address potential confounding variables not included in the study.

10. In publications or testimony, identify the ultimate financial sponsor of the study, the stated purpose, and the intended use of the study results.

11. When reporting analyses of volunteer data or other data not representative of a defined population, include appropriate disclaimers.

12. Report the limits of statistical inference of the study and possible sources of error. For example, disclose any significant failure to follow through fully on an agreed sampling or analytic plan and explain any resulting adverse consequences.

13. Share data used in published studies to aid peer review and replication, but exercise due caution to protect proprietary and confidential data, including all data that might inappropriately reveal respondent identities.

14. As appropriate, promptly and publicly correct any errors discovered after publication.

15. Write with consideration of the intended audience. (For the general public, convey the scope, relevance, and conclusions of a study without technical distractions. For the professional literature, strive to answer the questions likely to occur to your peers.)

H. Responsibilities of Employers, Including Organizations, Individuals, Attorneys, or Other Clients Employing Statistical Practitioners

1. Recognize that the results of valid statistical studies cannot be guaranteed to conform to the expectations or desires of those commissioning the study or the statistical practitioner(s). Any measures taken to ensure a particular outcome will lessen the validity of the analysis.

2. Valid findings result from competent work in a moral environment. Pressure on a statistical practitioner to deviate from these guidelines is likely to damage both the validity of study results and the professional credibility of the practitioner.

3. Make new statistical knowledge widely available in order to benefit society at large. (Those who have funded the development of statistical innovations are entitled to monetary and other rewards for their resulting products, software, or research results.)

4. Support sound statistical analysis and expose incompetent or corrupt statistical practice. In cases of conflict, statistical practitioners and those employing them are encouraged to resolve issues of ethical practice privately. If private resolution is not possible, recognize that statistical practitioners have an ethical obligation to expose incompetent or corrupt practice before it can cause harm to research subjects or society at large.

5. Recognize that within organizations and within professions using statistical methods generally, statistics practitioners with greater prestige, power, or status have a responsibility to protect the professional freedom and responsibility of more subordinate statistical practitioners who comply with these guidelines.

6. Do not include statistical practitioners in authorship or acknowledge their contributions to projects or publications without their explicit permission.

Index

Note: Page numbers in *f* indicates a figure, *n* indicates a footnote, *t* indicates a table, and *W* indicates online chapter pages.

Note: Page numbers in *f* indicates a figure, *n* indicates a footnote, *t* indicates a table, and *W* indicates online chapter pages.

Note: Page numbers in *f* indicates a figure, *n* indicates a footnote, *t* indicates a table, and *W* indicates online chapter pages.

Note: Page numbers in *f* indicates a figure, *n* indicates a footnote, *t* indicates a table, and *W* indicates online chapter pages.

Note: Page numbers in *f* indicates a figure, *n* indicates a footnote, *t* indicates a table, and *W* indicates online chapter pages.

Note: Page numbers in *f* indicates a figure, *n* indicates a footnote, *t* indicates a table, and *W* indicates online chapter pages.

Note: Page numbers in *f* indicates a figure, *n* indicates a footnote, *t* indicates a table, and *W* indicates online chapter pages.

Note: Page numbers in *f* indicates a figure, *n* indicates a footnote, *t* indicates a table, and *W* indicates online chapter pages.

Note: Page numbers in *f* indicates a figure, *n* indicates a footnote, *t* indicates a table, and *W* indicates online chapter pages.

Note: Page numbers in *f* indicates a figure, *n* indicates a footnote, *t* indicates a table, and *W* indicates online chapter pages.

Note: Page numbers in *f* indicates a figure, *n* indicates a footnote, *t* indicates a table, and *W* indicates online chapter pages.

Note: Page numbers in *f* indicates a figure, *n* indicates a footnote, *t* indicates a table, and *W* indicates online chapter pages.

Note: Page numbers in *f* indicates a figure, *n* indicates a footnote, *t* indicates a table, and *W* indicates online chapter pages.

Note: Page numbers in *f* indicates a figure, *n* indicates a footnote, *t* indicates a table, and *W* indicates online chapter pages.

Note: Page numbers in *f* indicates a figure, *n* indicates a footnote, *t* indicates a table, and *W* indicates online chapter pages.

Note: Page numbers in *f* indicates a figure, *n* indicates a footnote, *t* indicates a table, and *W* indicates online chapter pages.

Note: Page numbers in *f* indicates a figure, *n* indicates a footnote, *t* indicates a table, and *W* indicates online chapter pages.

Note: Page numbers in *f* indicates a figure, *n* indicates a footnote, *t* indicates a table, and *W* indicates online chapter pages.

Note: Page numbers in *f* indicates a figure, *n* indicates a footnote, *t* indicates a table, and *W* indicates online chapter pages.